dictionary of weapons
and military terms

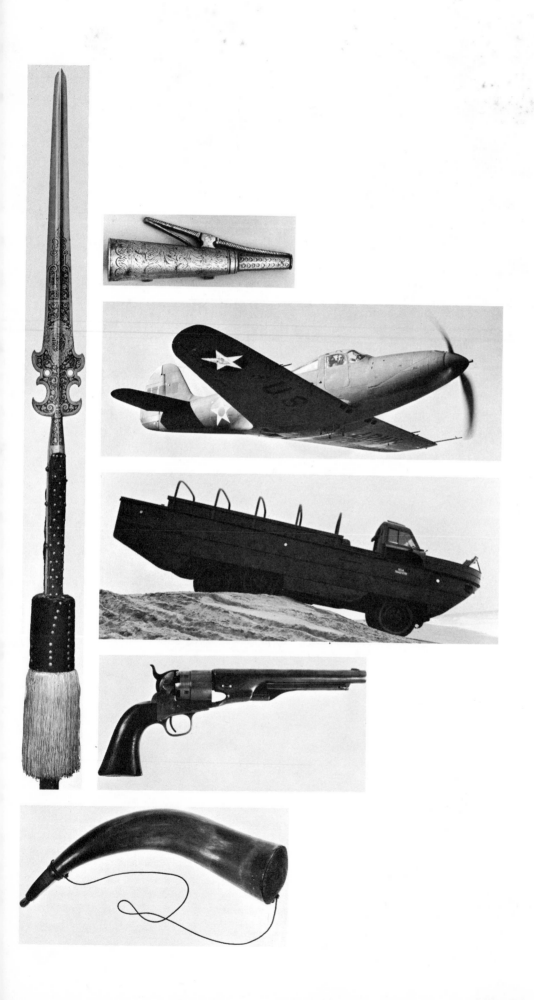

John Quick, Ph.D.
Consultant, Arthur D. Little, Inc.

dictionary of weapons
and military terms

new york   st. louis   **McGRAW-HILL BOOK COMPANY**
san francisco   düsseldorf   johannesburg   kuala lumpur
london   mexico   montreal   new delhi   panama
rio de janeiro   singapore   sydney   toronto

Library of Congress Cataloging in Publication Data

Quick, John, date.
    Dictionary of weapons and military terms.

    Bibliography: p.
    1. Military art and science—Dictionaries.
I. Title.
U24.Q5   623'.03   73-8757

1 2 3 4 5 6 7 8 9 0   HDBP   7 6 5 4 3

The editors for this book were Harold B. Crawford and
Stanley E. Redka, the designer was Naomi Auerbach, and its
production was supervised by George E. Oechsner. It was set
in Laurel by York Graphic Services, Inc.

It was printed by Halliday Lithographic Corporation
and bound by The Book Press.

This book is dedicated to my son, Jim.

contents

foreword

It is difficult to estimate the amount of time and energy that man has spent as a weapons builder—and impossible to measure the attendant hardship, misery, and loss from the use of these weapons. Still, there is a fascination in the subject of the hardware, the systems, the counter-systems, and all aspects of the power that an individual or a nation can wield.

National power has been a matter of concern to me for many years. Indeed, it was disagreement on the application of power that caused me to leave the Department of Defense in 1958. War plans in existence in the mid-1950s would have reflected deaths on a scale approaching 1 billion human beings—with hundreds of millions of others seriously affected by a poisoned atmosphere and other bomb effects.

It seemed to me at the time that man had reached the point where the mere possession of weapons no longer solved national defense problems—that indeed it caused *more* problems. For many years the thinking of our generals and our statesmen has reflected the Clausewitzian orthodoxy: "War is a continuation of politics by other means." The "other means," of course, are weapons; hence resort to weapons has been equated with solving problems that otherwise are beyond solution. In Orwellian simplicity, "Weapons equal solutions." No longer is this true. In fact, "weapons equal problems." Since Hiroshima, other nations have joined the nuclear club; as a result, if nuclear weapons were to be employed today, the potential damage to the human race would far exceed 1 billion casualties.

While considering this subject in the late 1950s, I came to the conclusion that mere possession of high-explosive weapons—nuclear weapons—no longer is a valid measure of a nation's strength. In fact, I concluded that measuring a nation's strength in terms of the size of its army, navy, and air force is grossly inadequate if one is searching for a measure of national power. If men and conventional weapons were to be employed against each other, then such a quantitative comparison would have meaning, but because the destruction wrought by the total inventories of weapons would be so great, we must search for other parameters that have meaning. In other words, for man, his problems, and his resources of today, strategy has assumed a completely new dimension because the earth—from the military man's point of view—has become one small tactical theater. In the global village in which we live, all weapons of war—from rifles to ballistic missiles—have become tactical.

The first object of strategy in employing national power should be to achieve our national goals without the need to employ tactical forces. Thus the measure of success of a strategy in the employment of national power is the degree to which battle becomes unnecessary.

This dictionary provides a comprehensive record of the significant weapons and weapon systems developed over the centuries. As such it will be invaluable to students and professional military men. Beyond that, however, it provides, through an examination of artifacts, a glimpse of man's attitude toward ever-improving systems for waging wars. Only by understanding those attitudes that have led to wars in the past can we begin to devise strategies to avoid wars in the future.

(James M. Gavin is chairman of the board and chief executive officer of Arthur D. Little, Inc. He joined the company following his retirement from the U.S. Army after 33 years of service. At the time of his retirement, he was chief of research and development of the Department of the Army. General Gavin served as U.S. Ambassador to France from early 1961 until the fall of 1962.)

Lieut. Gen. James M. Gavin
U.S. Army, Ret.

acknowledgments

My first thanks clearly go to a board of review, the members of which have provided me with invaluable guidance, assistance, and advice since the beginning of this project several years ago. Members of this board included Mr. James W. Cheevers, Curator of the U.S. Naval Academy Museum at Annapolis; Mr. David Eggenberger, formerly Editor in Chief for Multivolume Encyclopedias at McGraw-Hill and author of *Dictionary of Battles;* and Mr. Harold L. Peterson, Chief Curator of the National Park Service and of U.S. Historical Sites and the author of some 20 books, including the *Encyclopedia of Firearms.*

I am also indebted to Lieut. Gen. James M. Gavin; Mr. Merrill Lindsay; Dr. Helmut Nickel, of the Metropolitan Museum of Art; Mr. Craddock Goins, of the Smithsonian Institution; and Mr. Karl Kempf, formerly Curator of the Museum at the Aberdeen Proving Grounds. Special thanks must also go to my friend Tom LaBau, for the long-term use of a large number of his reference books, and to my wife, Hope, for her efforts in research, translation, filing, and typing.

A great number of other people and organizations have provided invaluable suggestions and help in the accumulation of information and photographs for this dictionary. I am particularly indebted to the following.

Dr. Allmayer-Beck, Heeresgeschichtliches Museum, Vienna; Mr. N. J. Anthong, Associate Editor, *Army* magazine; Mr. D. W. Bainbridge, Hawker Siddeley Aviation Ltd.; Office of the Belgian General Staff; Mr. C. Blair, Victoria and Albert Museum; Brig. Gen. L. A. Bourgeois, Canadian Department of National Defence, Ottawa; Mr. M. Brennan, The Imperial War Museum; Mr. M. V. Brown, Hawker Siddeley Aviation Ltd.; Mr. Harry Burns, Grumman Aerospace Corporation; Mr. Martin Caidin; Mr. Peter Callahan, Defense Marketing Systems (a McGraw-Hill company); Mr. Robert A. Carlisle, Still Photo Branch, Office of Information, U.S. Navy; Mr. C. F. Coady, Editor, *Army Journal* (Australia); Dr. Nando

Cucciniello, Siai-Marchetti, Milan; Mr. B. Deshayes, Swedish Defense Staff, Stockholm; Mr. Dan DeVito, Sikorsky Aircraft; Sir Harold Evans, Vickers Ltd., London; Mr. Francis S. Fox, Raytheon Company; The Defense Ministry of France; Mr. A. Gerli, Rinaldo Piaggio Aircraft, Genoa; Gen. R. T. Goncalves, Brazilian Defense Department, Rio de Janeiro; Mr. Leslie Goodier, Arthur D. Little, Inc.; Mr. H. B. Greenwood, U.S. Navy Department Library; Mr. K. Halsne, Norwegian Defense Department, Oslo; Mr. Gunnar Hamra, A. B. Bofors, Sweden; Miss Elizabeth R. Harrington, Director Research Library, Arthur D. Little, Inc.; Mr. Larry M. Hayes, Bell Helicopter Company; Mr. D. Heller, British Aircraft Corporation Ltd.; Mr. Thomas Hohmann, Modern Military Record Service, The National Archive; Mr. Hiroshi Inoue, Shin Meiwa Industry Co. Ltd., Aerospace Division, Tokyo; Mr. Francis E. Knapper, Washington National Record Center; Mr. F. Robert Kniffin, General Dynamics; Mr. W. Krämer, Steyr-Daimler-Puch Aktiengesellschaft, Vienna; Dr. H. R. Kurz, Swiss Military Department, Bern; Mr. R. W. Larson, Lockheed Aircraft Corporation; Mr. N. Gordon Le Bert, McDonnell Douglas Corporation; Mrs. Frances Lewis, Aerospace Audio-Visual Service, U.S. Air Force; Mr. R. E. Lewis, Editor, *Ordnance* magazine; Lieut. Cmdr. D. H. Mackay, Editor, *The Canadian Military Journal;* Brig. Gen. L. Malatto, Ministry of Defense, Buenos Aires, Argentina; Mr. Ralph H. McClarren, Aviation/Space Writers Association; Mr. W. D. McBride, Martin Marietta Aerospace Group; Mr. H. J. Meier, Vereinigte Flugtechnische Werke—Fokker, Bremen; The Military Historical Institute, Prague, Czechoslovakia; Miss Carolyn B. Musselman, Engineering Library, Arthur D. Little, Inc.; Mr. Y. Nada, Kawasaki Heavy Industries, Ltd., Tokyo; Oberstleutnant Nitz, Ministry of Defense, Federal Republic of Germany, Bonn; Mr. Geoffrey Norris, British Aircraft Corporation Ltd.; Mr. Donald J. Norton, Bell Aerospace Company; Colonel H. Nowaczyk, Military, Air and Navy Attaché, Embassy of the Polish People's Republic, Washington; Mr. Leslie Sanson, Photographic Department, Vickers Ltd., London; Lieut. Orit Sarig, Israel Defence Forces, Tel-Aviv; Mr. Arthur L. Schoeni, Vought Aeronautics Company; Mr. Stephan A. Schwartz, Associate Editor, *Navy* magazine; Mr. Lyle Schwilling, Goodyear Aerospace; Mrs. Ruth Seely, U.S. Army Photographic Agency; Mr. Richard H. Shearin, Vought Missiles and Space Company; Adm. Giovanni Sleiter, Italian Ministry of Defense, Rome; The Swedish Air Force; Col. Frantisek Sykora, Military and Air Attaché, Embassy of the Czechoslovak Socialist Republic, Washington; Mr. J. White, Short Brothers & Harland, Belfast; Mr. G. H. Wiltsher, Alvis Limited, Coventry; Mr. A. L. Whitsenhuysen, Australian Department of Supply, Canberra; and Mr. William H. Varley, Arthur D. Little, Inc.

John Quick

A-1 See **Skyraider.**

A-3 See **Skywarrior.**

A-4 See **Skyhawk.**

A-5 See **Vigilante.**

A-6 See **Intruder.**

A-7 See **Corsair II.**

A-20 See **Havoc.**

A-24 See **Dauntless.**

A-25 See **Helldiver.**

A-26 See **Invader.**

A-29 See **Hudson.**

A-34 See **Buccaneer.**

A-35 See **Vengeance.**

A-37 A light two-place twin-turbojet attack aircraft developed by Cessna and first flown in 1963. Used by the forces of the United States and South Vietnam, it has a speed of 476 mph, and carries a 7.62mm Minigun and other weapons. See **Dragonfly.**

AA See **antiaircraft.**

AAA See **antiaircraft artillery.**

AAC Alaskan Air Command.

AACLC Amphibious air-cushioned landing craft.

AACOMS Army Area Communications System. An integrated communications system, including shelters, to provide secure multichannel communications for U.S. Army tactical field units.

AAF Army Air Force.

AALC Amphibious assault landing craft.

AAM Air-to-air missile.

AAT machine gun See **French 7.5mm machine gun model 52 (AAT).**

AAV Airborne assault vehicle.

AAW Antiair warfare. A generic term to describe any weaponry designed to be employed against airborne weapons systems.

AAWS Aerial Artillery Weapons System.

AB **1.** A U.S. Navy crane ship. **2.** Able seaman.

A/B Afterburner.

abab An obsolete term for a Turkish sailor.

aback A term applied to a sailing vessel with yards so trimmed that the wind is on the forward side, thus tending to drive the ship astern.

abaft Toward the stern of a ship.

abandon To relinquish a military position or district.

abandon ship To leave a ship in an emergency, for example, in the event of sinking.

abated arms Blunt-edged weapons such as those used in tournaments.

abatis A system of defense in which trees

A-37. (*Cessna Aircraft Corporation.*)

are chopped down and the branches pointed toward the enemy. The projecting limbs are often sharpened to a point.

abbasai talwar A Punjabi saber with a slightly curved blade.

abbasi A Rajput sword with a straight blade.

abblast See **arbalest.**

Abbot A British 105mm self-propelled gun with a crew of four and a weight of 36,500 lb. The gun has a range of 17,000 meters and can fire at a sustained rate of 12 rounds per minute. The weight of the projectile is 35 lb 6 oz.

ABC-M7A2/3 and M25A1/2 U.S. riot-control grenades.

ABD A U.S. Navy advance-base dock.

abeam The direction at right angles to the line of the keel of a ship or the centerline of an aircraft.

Abercrombie A class of British monitors of about 7,900 tons standard displacement completed in 1941–1943. They had a length of 373 ft, a speed of 12 knots, and main armament of two 15-in. guns.

Able See **Weapon Alpha.**

able-bodied A term applied to one who is physically capable of military service.

Able (code) A word formerly authorized for the letter A in transmitting messages when a possibility of a misunderstanding existed. See also **Alpha (code).** The following are the formerly authorized code words (now replaced by Alpha): Able, Baker, Charlie, Dog, Easy, Fox, George, How, Item, Jig, King, Love, Mike, Nan, Oboe, Peter, Queen, Roger, Sugar, Tare, Uncle, Victor, William, X-ray, Yoke, and Zebra.

ablecti In the Roman Army, a body of men serving as bodyguard to the commanding general. The guard consisted of 40 mounted and 160 dismounted men.

ABLES Airborne Battlefield Light Equipment System. A U.S. Army system weighing 800 lb and mounted on helicopters. It illuminates a 300-meter area from an altitude of 1,500 ft.

Abbot. (*Vickers Ltd.*)

ABSD. (*U.S. Navy.*)

aboard On or in a vessel.

abort Failure to accomplish a mission for any reason other than enemy action. It may occur at any point from initiation of operation to destination.

aborted firing A firing which is cut off either manually or automatically after the firing command has been given, but before ignition has been initiated.

about A word used to express the movement of troops or artillery as it changes front.

abreast A naval expression meaning "side by side" or "by the side of."

ABSD A U.S. Navy advance-base section dock.

absent without leave (AWOL) The offense of unpermitted absence from a ship or a command.

absolute deviation The distance between the center of the target and the point where the projectile hits or bursts.

abutment A block or framework at the rear of a cannon. It receives the rearward thrust when the cannon is fired.

AC 1. The U.S. military designation for the war gas **hydrogen cyanide,** which see. **2.** A U.S. Navy collier.

ACB An amphibious construction battalion.

accelerator A cannon in which several charges are fired in succession to increase the velocity of the projectile in the bore.

acceptance trials Trials carried out by the eventual military users of a weapon or equipment to determine whether the specified performance and characteristics have been met.

access The ability and opportunity of an individual to gain knowledge or possession of classified material.

accessible Said of a place or position that can be easily approached.

access road A public road permitting access to a military or naval installation.

ACCHEAN The NATO abbreviation for Allied Command Channel.

accintus The complete accouterments of a soldier in ancient times.

accommodation ladder A flight of steps leading down a ship's side by which small boats may be entered or the vessel boarded.

accouterments The equipment and trappings of a soldier, other than dress or arms.

accuracy of fire The precision of fire expressed by the closeness of a grouping of shots around the center of the target.

ace A term that originated in France during World War I and was in common usage by 1916. It describes an airman with a confirmed record of shooting down five enemy aircraft. The first aces emerged in 1915 after the development of synchronizing systems that enabled a machine gun to be fired through the spinning propeller of an airplane.

ACE The NATO abbreviation for Allied Command Europe.

Ace High A communications network in operation between Turkey and Arctic Norway to provide secure communications for NATO commanders in Europe.

achico A bola with three balls.

acies A Roman word for the steel edge of an iron weapon.

acinaces A short, edged weapon used by the ancient Persians.

ack-ack A term originated by British signalers to describe an antiaircraft gun or its fire.

acknowledge To inform the originator of a message that his communication has been understood.

ACLANT The NATO abbreviation for Allied Command Atlantic.

A Class A class of British patrol submarines of 1,385 tons standard surface displacement completed in 1945–1948. They have a length of 283 ft, a beam of 22 ft, a speed of 8 knots submerged, and a complement of 60 to 68 men. They are armed with six 21-in. torpedo tubes. (They were originally designed with ten 21-in. torpedo tubes and one 4-in. deck gun.)

aclides In ancient Roman use, a weapon with a line attached so that after it was thrown, it could be drawn back and reused.

aclys A small Roman missile weapon, such as a dart.

ACM A U.S. Navy auxiliary minelayer.

acontium A kind of dart or javelin used by the ancient Greeks.

acoubuoys Acoustic listening devices used in Southeast Asia. Dropped by aircraft, these units have sensors which pick up enemy movements and transmit to receivers which tape the data for later analysis and transmission to land stations or orbiting aircraft.

acoustic jamming The deliberate radiation or reradiation of mechanical or electroacoustic signals to prevent clear reception by the enemy and to deter enemy weapon systems.

acoustic mine A mine that is designed to be actuated by the sounds emitted by its target, such as the sound waves from a ship's propellers, engines, or the like.

acoustic torpedo A torpedo that is guided by sound. Some (passive types) home on sounds emanating from the target; others (active types) generate sounds and home on the echoes. An example is **U.S. torpedo Mark 44,** which see.

ACP The Abbreviation for "automatic Colt pistol."

acquereaux A stone-throwing device used in the Middle Ages.

acquinite The French designation for **chloropicrin** (which see), a World War I gas.

acquire With acquisition radar systems, the process of detecting the presence and location of a target in sufficient detail to permit identification. With tracking radar systems, the process of positioning a radar beam so that a target is in that beam, thus permitting the effective employment of weapons.

ACR A U.S. Navy armored cruiser.

acronym A word formed from the first letters or syllables of the successive parts of a compound term. An example is the word "radar," which was derived from "*ra*dio *d*etection *a*nd *r*anging." Acronyms are frequently used in naming military systems.

acrostolium The ornament on the prow of an ancient vessel; the origin of the later figurehead.

action **1.** The mechanism of a gun, usually breechloading, by which it is loaded, fired, and unloaded. **2.** Combat in war, such as engagements on both land and water.

action deferred A term indicating that tactical action of a specific kind is being withheld for better tactical advantage; that weapons are available and commitment is pending.

action port (action starboard) A command to gun crews to indicate the direction of an enemy attack.

action report A detailed report of combat with the enemy.

activate **1.** To put into existence by official order a unit, post, camp, station, base, or shore activity which has previously been constituted and designated by name or number, or both, so that it can be organized to function in its assigned capacity. **2.** To prepare for active service a naval ship or craft which has been in an inactive or reserve status. **3.** To initiate the action of a fuze or other detonating system that requires a positive act to set it in motion or make it sensitive.

active acoustic torpedo A torpedo which homes on reflected sound which it emits.

active aircraft Aircraft which are currently and actively engaged in supporting flying missions.

active air defense Direct defensive action taken to destroy or reduce the effectiveness of an enemy air attack. It includes such measures as the use of aircraft, antiaircraft artillery, electronic countermeasures, and surface-to-air guided missiles.

active defense The employment of limited offensive action and counterattacks to deny a contested area or position to the enemy. See also **passive defense.**

active duty Full-time service as distinct from inactive, retired, or reserve duty. Also called "active service."

active electronic countermeasures The major subdivision of electronic countermeasures concerning electronic jamming and electronic deceptions.

active homing guidance A system of homing guidance wherein both the source for illuminating the target and the receiver are carried within the missile.

active hostility A term in international law that once referred to any proceeding that could be considered an adequate cause for war.

active jamming The deliberate radiation or reradiation of electromagnetic energy to impair the use of certain frequencies.

active list A list of all the officers in the military services.

active material Material, such as plutonium and certain isotopes of uranium, which is capable of supporting a fission chain reaction.

active sonar Equipment which provides information on distant underwater objects by evaluating the reflections of its own sound emissions.

acton A stuffed jacket worn under the mail in medieval armor. Later the term was used to describe a jacket plated with steel.

ACM, the U.S.S. *Barricade* ACM-3. (*U.S. Navy.*)

actual ground zero (AGZ) The point on the surface of land or water at, or vertically below or above, the center of an actual nuclear detonation.

actual range In bombing, the horizontal distance a bomb travels from the moment it is released until the moment it hits.

actuator A trigger mechanism that slides forward and back on some kinds of automatic weapons and prepares each round to be fired.

ACV 1. Armored command vehicle. **2.** A U.S. Navy auxiliary aircraft carrier. **3.** Air-cushion vehicle. A vehicle that rides on a layer of air generated by its own fans and trapped underneath by contoured skirts. Such vehicles need no direct contact with the surface, but depend on the surface to trap the air underneath.

AD 1. See **Skyraider. 2.** A U.S. Navy destroyer tender; a ship that repairs destroyers.

adage, adarge A shield of Arabic origin used by the Moors and later by the Spanish (and later still by Spanish colonists in Mexico and the American Southwest well into the nineteenth century). It was usually in the form of two ellipses with their longer sides overlapping and could be made of leather, wood, or iron.

adamsite (DM) Diphenylaminechlorarsine chloride. This war gas (also a mob- and riot-control gas) has a very rapid rate of action. Only about 1 minute is required for temporary incapacitation. It causes the same symptoms as diphenylchloroarsine (DA), but the effects develop more slowly. Also called a "sternutator" or "sneeze gas," it was developed at the end of World War I (by Roger Adams, an American).

adapter A part or piece designed to permit parts of different sizes or shapes to be fitted together. In weapons use, for example, there are adapters that permit the use of ammunition other than that designed for a particular piece.

adarga A light leather shield used by the Moors and later by the Spaniards.

add A fire-correction term used by observers in adjusting fire to indicate that an increase in range (so many yards or meters) will follow and is desired.

ADG A U.S. Navy degaussing ship.

adit A passage undergound used by miners to reach the point they intend to sap.

ADIZ Air-defense identification zone.

adjust To correct the elevation and deflection of a weapon so as to place the center of impact on the target.

adjusted elevation The corrected elevation of a gun. The adjustment, made after observing the gun's fire, ensures that its projectile will hit the target.

adjusted range The corrected range of a gun. The adjustment, made after observing the gun's fire, ensures that succeeding rounds will hit the target.

adjustment The process used in artillery and naval gunfire to obtain correct direction, range, and height of burst (if time fuzes are used) when engaging a target by observed fire.

adjutant A staff officer that is responsible to his commander for all official correspondence (except combat orders) such as personnel and other records, the distribution of orders, and so forth.

ADM-20 See **Quail.**

administration The management of all phases of military operations not directly concerned with strategy or tactics.

administrative command Command that is without operational functions and is concerned only with logistics, maintenance, and the like.

administrative movement A movement in which troops and vehicles are arranged to expedite their movement and conserve time and energy when no enemy interference, except by air, is anticipated. It is also called an "administrative march."

Admirable A class of U.S. fleet minesweepers (AM) of 650 tons standard displacement completed in 1942–1944. They had a speed of 15 knots and a complement of 104 men and were armed with one 3-in. gun and four 40mm antiaircraft guns.

admiral A naval officer of the highest rank. In the U.S. Navy there are four grades: fleet admiral, admiral, vice admiral, and rear admiral. The equivalent ranks in the U.S. Army are general of the army, general,

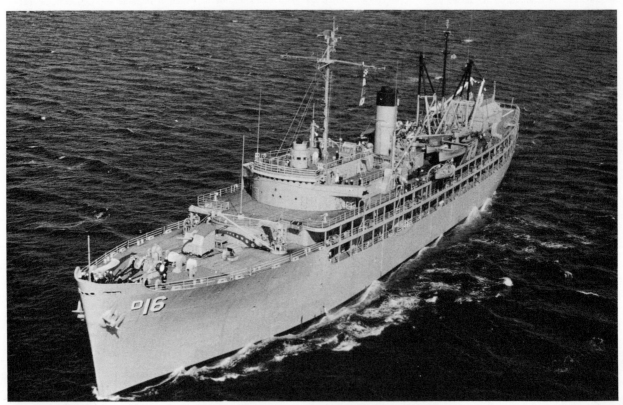

AD, the destroyer tender U.S.S. *Cascade.* (*U.S. Navy.*)

Admiral Graf Spee. (*The Imperial War Museum.*)

lieutenant general, and major general. The term originates in the Near East, where a sea lord was known as an *amir-al-bahr*. Adopted by the seafaring peoples of the Mediterranean, the word became the Spanish *almirante* and the French *amiral*.

Admiral Graf Spee A German armored cruiser (often referred to as a "pocket battleship") launched in 1934. It had two sister ships, *Admiral Scheer* and *Lützow* (ex-*Deutschland*). They had a displacement of 12,100 tons, a length of 609 ft, a beam of 70 ft, a speed of 26 knots, and a complement of 1,150 men. They were armed with six 11-in., eight 5.9-in., six 4.1-in., eight 37mm, and twenty-eight 20mm guns; eight 21-in. torpedo tubes; and two aircraft. After sinking nine ships in the South Atlantic and Indian Oceans, *Admiral Graf Spee* was damaged on December 13, 1939, in the Battle of the Plate River (by the British cruisers *Achilles*, *Ajax*, and *Exeter*). It was scuttled outside Montevideo four days later.

Admiral Hipper One of five German heavy cruisers of 13,900 tons displacement built between 1937 and 1939. Sister ships included *Blücher*, *Lützow*, *Prinz Eugen*, and *Seydlitz*. They had a length of about 650 ft, a beam of 70 ft, a speed of 32 knots, and a complement of 1,600 men. They were armed with eight 8-in., twelve 4.1-in., twelve 37mm, and twenty-eight 20mm guns, plus twelve 21-in. torpedo tubes and three aircraft. *Admiral Hipper* was bombed in Kiel and scuttled in May 1945.

Admiral Makarov See **Nürnberg.**

Admiral of the Navy A special U.S. Navy rank created for George Dewey after the Spanish-American War.

Admiral Scheer A German armored cruiser launched in 1933 and a sister ship of the **Admiral Graf Spee,** which see. After

considerable action in the early stages of World War II (including raiding activity in the Atlantic and Indian Oceans during which it destroyed 17 ships), it was capsized in Kiel after an RAF bombing raid on April 9, 1945.

Admiral's March The ceremonial band music that is played for flag officers and officials of equivalent rank.

Admiralty A British term that derives from the Lord High Admiral of England, or the commissioners for executing his office, commonly called the "Board of Admiralty." The institution dates from 1512, when a board of commissioners was appointed by Henry VIII to examine and report upon the state of the navy.

adscriptii In the Roman light infantry, one of the divisions consisting of irregular troops.

ADSID Air-delivered seismic intrusion detector. An aerially emplaced sensor dropped to detect and radio back the sounds of moving equipment or men.

advanced base A base located in or near a theater of operations whose primary mission is to support military operations.

advanced covered way In fortifications, the terreplein on the exterior of the advanced ditch, similar to the first covered way.

advanced ditch In fortifications, an excavation beyond the glacis of the *enceinte*. Since its surface is a prolongation of the slope, the ditch provides no shelter for the enemy.

advanced fleet anchorage A secure anchorage for a large number of naval ships, mobile support units, and auxiliaries, located in or near a theater of operations.

advanced guard The leading element of an advancing force. Its primary mission is to ensure the uninterrupted advance of the

main body. It has the following functions: to find and exploit gaps in the enemy's defensive system; to prevent the main body of the advancing force from running blindly into enemy opposition; and to clear away minor opposition or, if major opposition is met, to cover the deployment of the main body.

advanced lunettes In fortifications, works that resemble ravelins or bastions and have faces or flanks. They are formed atop, or beyond, the glacis.

Advanced Terrier A ship-to-air missile developed in the late 1950s to replace Terrier aboard U.S. Navy ships. It has an overall length of 27 ft, a launching weight of 3,000 lb, and a range of over 20 mi. The Navy designation is RIM-2.

advanced works In fortifications, positions built beyond the covered way and glacis, but within range of the main works.

advance force (amphibious) A temporary organization within the amphibious task force which precedes the main body to the objective point. Its function is to participate in preparing the objective for the main assault by such operations as reconnaissance, seizure of supporting positions, minesweeping, preliminary bombardment, underwater demolitions, and air support.

adversary The enemy generally. Specifically, an opponent in hand-to-hand combat.

AE A U.S. Navy ammunition ship. (Picture, next page.)

AEC Atomic Energy Commission. This is the U.S. agency in charge of efforts in the field of atomic energy.

AEF American Expeditionary Forces, 1917–1918.

A.E.G. C and J types German (Allgemeine Elektrizitats Gesellschaft) two-place single-engine reconnaissance biplanes introduced in 1915 (C type) and 1917 (J type). They

AE, ammunition ship U.S.S. *Wrangell.* (*U.S. Navy.*)

A.E.G. G.III. (*The Smithsonian Institution, National Air Museum.*)

aeneatores Military musicians of ancient times. They sounded trumpets and horns.

aerial barrage Formerly, a defense against air attack. It consisted of a barrier of barrage balloons.

aerial bomb A bomb designed to be dropped from an airplane and carrying a high explosive, incendiary, or other agent. Aerial bombs are detonated either on contact or by a timing device.

aerial cannon A cannon designed or modified for use on aircraft.

aerial dart A metal dart designed to be dropped from an aircraft. Aerial darts were used in World War I against targets such as zeppelins. See also **fléchette.**

aerial gunnery The use of guns, especially flexible guns, from aircraft.

aerial mine **1.** A mine designed to be dropped from an airplane, especially into water. **2.** A light-case bomb developed during the early stages of World War II. It was the predecessor of the blockbuster and was normally dropped by parachute.

aerial observation Observation from an aircraft, particularly the observation of artillery fire.

aerial pickets Aircraft disposed around a position, area, or formation, primarily to detect, report, and track approaching enemy aircraft.

aerial supply The act or process by which aerial delivery of supplies is made to ground units.

aerial torpedo A torpedo designed or adapted to be launched from a low-flying aircraft into water. It is also a term that once applied to the explosive projectile thrown by a trench mortar and designed so as to fall point down.

Aermacchi M.B. 326 An Italian two-seat jet basic-trainer, tactical ground-attack, and counterinsurgency aircraft in service with the Italian forces and with several other countries. It is made under license in South Africa and Australia. It was first flown in 1960, has a speed of 539 mph, and is armed with 4,000 lb of assorted arma-

had a speed of 98 mph. The C.IV was armed with a Parabellum gun for the observer and a forward-firing synchronized Spandau machine gun. It could also carry 198 lb of bombs. J types had twin Spandaus mounted in the floor of the rear cockpit to fire forward and downward at an angle of about 45°.

A.E.G. G types German three- and four-place twin-engine bombers produced between 1915 and 1918. The G.I was not built in significant numbers. The G.II, intro-

duced in July 1915, carried two or three defensive machine guns and a 441-lb bombload. The G.III appeared at the end of 1915 and carried a 661-lb bombload. The most widely built type was the G.IV, which appeared in late 1916. It carried a crew of three or four, was armed with a Parabellum gun in the front and rear cockpits, and carried a 772-lb bombload. The G.V was produced too late in the war to see combat. It carried a 1,323-lb bombload and had an endurance of 6 hours.

aerial bomb. (*U.S. Marine Corps.*)

Aermacchi M.B. 326 in Australian markings. (*Australian Department of Supply.*)

Aero A-100/101. (*Military Historical Institute, Prague.*)

AFDB. The AFDB-7 is shown here with the fleet ballistic-missile submarine *Abraham Lincoln*, an SSBN of the *George Washington* class. (*U.S. Navy.*)

Afghan stock. (*The Metropolitan Museum of Art, bequest of George C. Stone, 1936.*)

ment on under-wing attachments (rockets, gun pods, etc.).

aero A basket used by Roman soldiers to carry earth during the construction of fortifications.

Aero A-100/101 A single-engine light tactical-reconnaissance biplane bomber first flown in 1933 and the standard light bomber of Czechoslovakia until the beginning of World War II.

AERO-7/B and 27/A U.S. bomb-rack designations.

aerodynamic missile A missile which uses aerodynamic forces to maintain its flight path, generally employing propulsion, guidance, and a winged configuration.

aerographer An enlisted man in the aviation branch of the U.S. Navy. His duties include weather observation and the preparation of weather forecasts, particularly regarding flying conditions.

aeromedical evacuation system A system which provides control of patient movement by air transport, specialized medical attendants and equipment for in-flight medical care, facilities for the limited medical care of in-transit patients, and communication with medical facilities regarding patient airlift movements.

aero squadron Particularly during World War I, a unit charged with carrying out air operations. The U.S. Army's First Aero Squadron carried out operations on the Mexican border with General Pershing in 1916.

aerostat Any aircraft that derives its buoyancy or lift from a lighter-than-air gas contained within its envelope or one of its compartments. Airships and balloons are examples of aerostats.

aerumnula A wooden pole or fork carried by Roman soldiers when on the march. Attached to it were such things as tools, equipment, food, and baggage.

AEW Airborne early warning. The term is applied to systems which by means of radar or other devices make it possible to detect the approach of enemy aircraft or missiles.

AEWS Advanced Earth Satellite Weapon System. One of the weapons developed for the U.S. Air Force by General Electric.

AF 1. Air Force. 2. A U.S. Navy store ship.

AF-1 See **Fury.**

AFCENT The NATO abbreviation for Allied Forces Central Europe.

AFD A U.S. Navy auxiliary floating dock.

AFDB A U.S. Navy large auxiliary floating dry dock, non-self-propelled.

AFDL A U.S. Navy small auxiliary floating dry dock, non-self-propelled.

AFDM A U.S. Navy medium auxiliary floating dry dock, non-self-propelled.

affirmative Communications term meaning "yes," "permission granted," "authorized," "approved," "recommended approve," etc.

afforciament An old term meaning "fortress" or "stronghold."

affût A French term for a gun carriage or a portion of the carriage in more complex forms.

Afghan stock A stock produced in Afghanistan for crude muzzle-loading guns. It has a pronounced curve behind the lock and then sweeps into a wide end.

AFNORTH The NATO abbreviation for Allied Forces Northern Europe.

Afrika Korps A German force that operated in North Africa from 1940 to 1943. It consisted of panzer divisions supported by strong Luftwaffe elements and was under the command of Field Marshal Erwin Rommel (nicknamed "The Desert Fox"). By June 1942, this force had driven the British across the desert to El Alamein, the last strongpoint before the Suez Canal. The Battle of El Alamein (October 24 to November 5, 1942) was a decisive setback for the Germans and marked the beginning of their retreat out of Egypt back into Libya and Tunisia (where they surrendered in May 1943).

AFS A U.S. Navy combat store ship.

AFSOUTH The NATO abbreviation for Allied Forces Southern Europe.

aft (after) Toward the stern of a ship or the tail of an aircraft.

AGEH, the *Plainview* (AGEH-1). (*U.S. Navy.*)

afterbody The section of a ship's hull or a torpedo body to the rear of the centerline.

afterburner An auxiliary combustion chamber within, or attached to, the tailpipe of certain jet engines in which hot unused oxygen of exhaust gases from fuel already burned is used to burn a second fuel and thus augment the temperature and density of the exhaust gases as they leave the tailpipe, with consequent increase in thrust. An afterburner is useful on takeoff and in combat situations where additional thrust may be required to maneuver.

afterburning **1.** The process of fuel injection and combustion in the exhaust jet of a turbojet engine. **2.** The irregular burning of some rocket motors for a period of time after the main burning and thrust have ceased.

afut An ancient term for a gun carriage.

AFV A British abbreviation for armored fighting vehicle.

AG A U.S. Navy miscellaneous auxiliary (vessel).

Agano A class of Japanese 6,650-ton light cruisers completed between 1941 and 1944. They had a speed of 35 knots and main armament consisting of six 6.1-in. and four 3-in. guns, two torpedo tubes, and two aircraft.

AGB A U.S. Navy icebreaker.

AGC A U.S. Navy amphibious command ship or flagship.

AGD A U.S. Navy seagoing dredge.

AGDE A U.S. Navy escort research ship.

AGEH A U.S. Navy open-ocean antisubmarine-warfare hydrofoil research ship.

agent In intelligence usage, one who is authorized or instructed to obtain or to assist in obtaining information for intelligence or counterintelligence purposes.

Ager "coffee-mill" gun See **coffee-mill gun.**

agger **1.** Mounds of earth raised in front of positions under attack. The system was developed by the Romans to provide commanding locations for their catapults and to afford shelter for troops massing for an attack. **2.** The middle part of a military road, raised so as to provide a runoff for water and to keep the road dry.

aggression An attack or act of hostility, often the first act leading to a war or a controversy.

agiem-clich A saber once used in Persia and Turkey. It featured a very crooked blade that was rounded near the point.

AGIL Airborne general illuminating light. A U.S. development that casts a cone of light four times as bright as the moon over an area 2 mi in diameter from a distance of 12,000 ft.

Agile A class of U.S. wooden minesweepers of 750 tons standard displacement completed in the 1950s. They had a speed of 15.5 knots, a complement of 72 men, and a length of 165 ft.

AGL A U.S. Navy lighthouse tender.

AGM **1.** Air-to-ground missile. **2.** A U.S. Navy missile-range instrumentation ship.

AGM-12 See **Bullpup.**

AGM-15 See **Shrike.**

AGM-22 See **Nord 5210 (SS.11 and AS.11).**

AGM-28 See **Hound Dog.**

AGM-45 See **Shrike.**

agmen The Roman name for an army on the march.

agminalis An ancient word for a horse which carried equipment and baggage; a packhorse.

AGMR A U.S. Navy major communications relay ship.

agny astra An early Hindu fire-tipped dart or rocket that was discharged horizontally from a bamboo tube. It was used against cavalry.

Ago C.II A German single-engine (pusher) two-seat biplane introduced in 1915. It had a speed of 85 mph and was armed with one free-firing Parabellum machine gun for use by the observer.

Ago C.IV A German single-engine (tractor) two-seat biplane of 1917. It was equipped with a forward-firing Spandau gun for the pilot and a ring-mounted Parabellum gun for the observer.

AGOR A U.S. Navy oceanographic research ship.

AGM, the U.S.N.S. *Longview*. (*U.S. Navy.*)

AGP A U.S. Navy motor torpedo-boat tender.

AGR A U.S. Navy ocean radar-station picket ship.

agrapes Hooks and eyes used with both ordinary dress and armor.

agreed point A predetermined point on the ground, identifiable from the air and used when aircraft assist in fire adjustment.

aground Said of a ship that is fast to the bottom. A ship runs aground or goes aground.

AGS A U.S. Navy surveying ship.

AGSC A U.S. Navy coastal surveying ship.

AGSL A U.S. Navy satellite-launching ship.

AGSS A U.S. Navy high-speed target submarine.

AGTR A U.S. Navy technical research ship.

Agusta A 101G An Italian three-engine helicopter for freight, rescue, and antisubmarine duties, first flown in 1964. It can carry 35 passengers and has a speed of 140 mph.

Agusta-Bell 204B An Italian medium-size utility helicopter similar to the Bell UH-1B Iroquois. It is used by the armed forces of several countries.

Agusta-Bell 205 An Italian multipurpose utility helicopter corresponding to the UH-1D and UH-1H versions adopted by the U.S. armed forces.

AGZ Actual ground zero, which see.

AH A U.S. Navy hospital ship. (Picture, next page.)

Ago C.II. (*The Smithsonian Institution, National Air Museum.*)

ahead-thrown weapon A missile projected by rocket power ahead of a ship and used in ASW.

AHP A U.S. Navy evacuation hospital ship.

Aichi D3A2 Type 99 See **Val.**

Aichi D4Y3 Suisei See **Judy.**

Aichi E11A1 See **Laura.**

Aichi E13A1 See **Jake.**

Aichi E16A1 Zui-un See **Paul.**

Aichi H9A1 A Japanese twin-engine flying boat of World War II.

Aichi M6A1 Seiran A Japanese floatplane of World War II.

Aida A code name used by the Germans in World War II to describe their offensive operation against British forces in Libya and Egypt. The offensive began on May 26, 1942.

aide-de-camp An officer selected by a general to assist him in his duties, carry orders, and represent him in correspondence.

aigremore Charcoal specially prepared for making gunpowder.

aiguillettes 1. The ornamental cords, tags, or loops sometimes attached to military and naval uniforms and worn by attachés and aides. **2.** The points or laces used to attach arm defenses in suits of armor. (Picture, next page.)

aigunia Machines or engines of war.

aile A wing or flank of an army or fortification.

aileron A hinged or pivoted item forming a horizontal control surface, usually a portion of the trailing edge of a wing. Its primary function is to control the roll movement of an airplane or glider about its longitudinal axis.

ailette In medieval armor, an iron or steel

AGSS, the U.S.S. *Dolphin.* (*U.S. Navy.*)

AH, the hospital ship U.S.S. *Repose*. (*U.S. Navy.*)

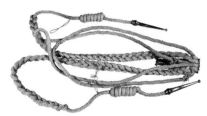

aiguillette. (*The Smithsonian Institution.*)

plate worn over the coat of mail to protect the shoulder.

aim To point a weapon or align the sights of a weapon toward a target.

AIM Area interdiction mine. A land mine developed for the U.S. Air Force by Explosives Corp. of America. It uses a liquid explosive called "Astrolite G."

AIM-4A, B, C, D, and E See **Falcon.**

AIM-4F and G See **Super Falcon.**

AIM-7 See **Sparrow.**

AIM-9 See **Sidewinder.**

AIM-26A See **Nuclear Falcon.**

aimable cluster A cluster of bombs, especially fragmentation or incendiary bombs, held together in such a way that they can be aimed and dropped by ordinary bombing methods.

aimable-cluster adapter An adapter with efficient ballistic characteristics used to hold bombs together in an outer case.

aim-frontlet A piece of wood formerly used by gunners to level and direct their pieces. It was hollowed out to fit the middle of the gun and was of a height equal to that of the breech.

aiming circle An instrument used in artillery and machine-gun fire for measuring horizontal and vertical angles.

aiming error Any error that results from a miscalculation of latitude, longitude, distance, speed, etc.

aiming point The point at which the line of sight is directed when the gun is being laid for direction.

aiming post In mortar firing, a wooden or metal post having contrasting painted transverse bands and a metal point or stake for driving into the ground. It is used as a sighting point in direct fire.

air In artillery, a statement by an observer to indicate a burst above the level of the base of the target; airburst.

AIR-2 See **Genie.**

Airabonita Unsuccessful aircraft-carrier version of the Bell P-39 Airacobra.

Airacobra The Bell P-39 Airacobra was a single-seat single-engine fighter-bomber flown for the first time in April 1939. It was unique in that the engine was located behind the pilot, the propeller being turned by a 10-ft extension shaft. Of the 9,558 aircraft produced, 4,758 were allocated to the Soviet Union. The later versions of the airplane were provided with 1,325-hp engines and flew at speeds of 376 mph. Armament consisted of one 37mm cannon M9, two .50 cal. machine guns, and four .30 cal. machine guns.

Airacomet The Bell P-59 Airacomet was a single-seat jet interceptor fighter and fighter-bomber and the first turbojet-powered aircraft to be flown by the United States. In its first flight on October 2, 1942, it achieved a speed of 404 mph. Although it never saw service as a warplane, it provided valuable experience as a jet trainer. It was powered by two turbojet engines of 2,000-lb thrust each and was armed with one 37mm cannon and three .50 cal. machine guns, plus two 1,000-lb bombs or eight 60-lb rockets. Top speed was 413 mph.

air alert The operational status of aircraft in the air that are ready for the immediate accomplishment of a mission.

air-alert mission Aircraft airborne in the battle area to answer calls for immediate air support from the ground forces.

air and naval gunfire liaison company An organization composed of Marine and Navy personnel specially qualified for shore control of naval gunfire and close air support. Also known as **ANGLICO,** which see.

air arm A British term referring to the system of national defense that utilizes aircraft.

air attack Attack from the air. Attack by aircraft, especially against surface targets. There are three major classifications: (1) A

Airacobra. (*Bell Aerospace Company.*)

coordinated air attack may utilize a combination of two or more types of attack (such as dive, glide, low-level) in one strike, using one or more types of aircraft. (2) A *deferred* air attack is a procedure in which attack groups rendezvous as a single unit. It is used when attack groups are launched from more than one station, with their departure on the mission being delayed pending further orders. (3) A *divided* air attack is a method of delivering a coordinated air attack which consists of holding the units in close tactical concentration up to a point and then splitting them to attack an objective from different directions.

air barrage   A barrage of exploding bombs dropped from aircraft. Also, an antiaircraft barrage.

air base   An establishment, comprising an airfield and its installations, facilities, personnel, and activities, for the flight operation, maintenance, and supply of aircraft and air organizations.

air battle   A battle in the air between two or more aircraft. Also, a battle for air superiority involving strikes on airfields, aircraft factories, and so forth.

air blockade   The isolation, or the denial of an enemy's use, of a place, harbor, route, or the like by air action.

airborne   As applied to personnel, equipment, etc., the term means "transported by air." It also applies to material being or designed to be transported by aircraft, as distinguished from weapons and equipment installed in, and remaining a part of, the aircraft. It also applies to an aircraft from the instant it becomes entirely sustained by air until it ceases to be so sustained.

airborne alert   A state of aircraft readiness wherein combat-equipped aircraft are airborne and ready for immediate action. It is designed to reduce reaction time and to increase the survivability factor.

airborne assault weapon   An unarmored, mobile, full-tracked gun providing a mobile antitank capability for airborne troops. It can be airdropped.

airborne command post   A suitably equipped aircraft used by the commander for the control of his forces.

airborne early warning   The detection of enemy air or surface units by radar or other equipment carried in an airborne vehicle and the transmitting of a warning to friendly units.

airborne early warning and control   Air surveillance and control provided by airborne early-warning vehicles which are equipped with search and height-finding radar and communications equipment for controlling weapons.

airborne forces   Forces composed primarily of ground and air units organized, equipped, and trained for airborne operations.

airborne infantry   Infantry organized and trained to be carried by air to a battle area and landed by transport aircraft, as distinguished especially from parachute infantry or troops. Also called "air infantry."

airborne operation   An operation involving the movement and delivery by air, into an objective area, of combat forces and their logistic support for execution of a tactical or a strategic mission. The means employed may be any combination of airborne units, air-transportable units, and types of transport aircraft, depending on the mission and the overall situation.

airborne troops   Ground units whose primary mission is to make assault landings from the air. In some contexts, "airborne troops" refers specifically to troops landed by aircraft, as distinguished from parachute troops. Some other special contexts restrict the term to include only those troops landed by parachute or glider, as distinguished from those landed in powered aircraft.

airborne unit   A ground unit organized, trained, and equipped for airborne assault.

air-breathing engine   An engine that uses or takes in air from the outside to oxidize its fuel, as distinguished especially from a rocket motor or rocket engine.

air-breathing missile   A missile engine that requires air intake for combustion of its fuel, such as a ramjet or turbojet. Such a missile cannot operate beyond the atmosphere.

airburst   An explosion of a bomb or projectile above the surface, as distinguished from an explosion on contact with the surface or after penetration. It also refers to the explosion of a nuclear weapon in the air, above land or water, at a height greater than the maximum radius of the fireball.

air chief marshal   A commissioned rank in the RAF and the RCAF. It corresponds to the rank of general in the USAF.

air command   A major subdivision of the Air Force; for operational purposes it normally consists of two or more air forces.

air commodore   A commissioned rank in the RAF and the RCAF. It corresponds to the rank of brigadier general in the USAF.

air-control center   An area set aside in a submarine for the control of aircraft. It is the equivalent of a combat information center on an aircraft or a ship.

air controller   An individual especially trained for, and assigned the duty of, the control (by use of radio, radar, or other means) of such aircraft as may be allotted to him for operation within his area.

air-control ship   A ship detailed the responsibility for air defense.

air-cooled   A term used in reference to engines or machine guns that are cooled by air.

Air Corps   The former aviation orga-

airborne operation. (*U.S. Army.*)

nization of the U.S. Army, broken down into brigades, wings, groups, and flights. It was commanded by a general known as the "Chief of the Air Corps."

air corridors   Restricted air routes of travel specified for use by friendly aircraft and established for the purpose of preventing friendly aircraft from being fired on by friendly forces.

air cover   The protection against attack, especially air attack, given by airplanes to surface or airborne forces. The term also refers to the airplanes giving, or designated to give, this protection.

aircraft   In the broadest sense, any machine or craft designed for navigation of the air and given lift by its own buoyance, by the dynamic reaction of air particles against its surfaces, or by its reaction to a jet stream. Broadly speaking, this term may be applied to rigid and nonrigid airships, airplanes, helicopters, kites, kite balloons, winged missiles, ballistic missiles, gliders, orthopters, and so forth. The term is usually applied to airplanes or aerostats.

aircraft ammunition Ammunition designed to be shot, launched, or dropped from aircraft. Ammunition such as smallarms or artillery ammunition, torpedoes, etc., adapted to, but not specifically designed for, aircraft use is *not* designated "aircraft ammunition."

aircraft antisubmarine attack The conditions under which a submarine is observed by an aircraft are described in the following ways, with time marked from the time ordnance is launched. *Early:* when the submarine is surfaced or diving with parts still exposed. *Visible:* when the submarine is submerged but still visible. *Tardy:* when the submarine has been in a dive for less than 10 seconds. *Blind:* when the submarine is fully submerged and not visible. *Late:* when the submarine has been submerged from 10 to 20 minutes.

aircraft carrier A major offensive ship of the fleet whose chief weapon is its aircraft. The U.S. Navy designations are CV, CVA, CVAN, etc.

aircraft commander The pilot designated

pilot in command of a given aircraft. He is responsible for its safe operation and is in command of all personnel on board during flight.

aircraft control and warning system A system established to control and report the movement of aircraft. It consists of observation facilities (radar, passive electronic, visual, or other means), control centers, and necessary communications.

aircraft depth bomb Bombs of this type are used primarily against underwater targets, but can also be used as general-purpose bombs. They are designed with a flat nose to minimize ricochet when they are dropped into the water from low altitudes. Approximately 70 percent of their complete weight consists of explosive material, and they are equipped with a hydrostatic tail fuze that functions at predetermined depths rather than on impact.

aircraft dispersal area An area on a military installation designed primarily for the dispersal of parked aircraft, the purpose of which is to make such aircraft less vulnerable in the event of an enemy air raid.

aircraft division Two sections of aircraft of the same type. See **aircraft section.**

aircraft machine-gun turret An armored enclosure installed in an aircraft for housing the armament and related accessories. It is designed to rotate about one or more axes,

thus permitting positioning and firing of the machine gun(s) in a number of directions or angles.

aircraft pylon A suspension device externally installed under the wing or fuselage of an aircraft. It is aerodynamically designed to fit the configuration of specific aircraft so as to create the least amount of drag. It provides a means of attaching fuel tanks, bombs, rockets, torpedoes, rocket motors, or machine-gun pods.

aircraft rocket A rocket missile designed to be fired from an airplane or helicopter.

aircraft scrambling Directing the immediate takeoff of aircraft from a ground-alert condition of readiness.

aircraft section A basic tactical unit consisting of two aircraft of the same type.

aircraftsman A British term for an airplane mechanic. He is a noncommissioned member of a ground crew.

aircraft squadron Two or more divisions of aircraft. See **aircraft division.**

aircraft system Any aircraft, including its airframe, propulsion machinery, and electrical, electronic, and mechanical equipment.

aircraft vectoring The directional control of in-flight aircraft through transmission of azimuth headings.

aircrew The crew of an aircraft.

aircrewman A member of the crew of an

aircraft carrier, the U.S.S. *Saratoga* of the Forrestal class. (*U.S. Navy.*)

aircraft, often as distinguished from the pilot or the officers.

air defense   All measures designed to reduce or nullify the effectiveness of hostile acts by vehicles (including missiles) in the earth's envelope of atmosphere.

air-defense area   With regard to an overseas situation, a specifically defined airspace for which air defense must be planned and provided. With regard to the United States, airspace of defined dimensions, designated by the appropriate agency, within which ready control is required in the interest of national security during an air-defense emergency.

air-defense artillery   Weapons and equipment for actively combating air targets from the ground. Weapons are classed as light (20 to 57mm), medium (58 to 99mm), and heavy (100mm or greater).

air-defense battle zone   A volume of airspace surrounding an air-defense fire unit or defended area, extending to a specified altitude and range, in which the fire-unit commander will engage and destroy targets not identified as friendly.

air-defense control center   The principal information, communications, and operations center from which all aircraft, antiaircraft operations, air-defense artillery, guided missiles, and air-warning functions of a specific area of air-defense responsibility are supervised and coordinated.

air-defense early warning   Early notification of the approach of enemy airborne weapons or weapons carriers obtained by electronic or visual means.

air-defense emergency   An emergency condition, declared or confirmed by the commander in chief, North American Air Defense Command; the commander in chief, Continental Air Defense Command; or higher authority, which exists when attack upon the continental United States, Alaska, Canada, or U.S. installations in Greenland by hostile aircraft or missiles is considered probable, is imminent, or is taking place.

air-defense interceptor zone (ADIZ)   The airspace above a specified area in which ready recognition and control of aircraft are required.

air-defense readiness   An operational status requiring air-defense forces to maintain higher-than-ordinary preparedness for short periods of time.

air-defense warning conditions   Degrees of air-raid probability indicated according to the following code: *Air-defense warning yellow:* attack by hostile aircraft or missiles is probable. *Air-defense warning red:* attack by hostile aircraft or missiles is imminent or is in progress. *Air-defense warning white:* attack by hostile aircraft or missiles is improbable.

airdrop   The unloading of personnel or materiel from aircraft in flight, as in an airborne assault or air-supply operation. (Picture, next page.)

airedale   A slang term for a naval aviator.

air evacuation   Evacuation by aircraft of personnel and cargo.

airfield   An area prepared for the accommodation (including any buildings, installations, and equipment), landing, and takeoff of aircraft.

air fleet   **1.** A large group of military aircraft under a common command.   **2.** All of a country's military aircraft.

airfoil   A surface or body, such as a wing, propeller, blade, rudder, or the like, especially designed to obtain a reaction, such as lift or thrust, from the air through which it moves.

air force   The military organization of a country charged with the responsibility for air warfare.

air force base   In the United States, an air base for the support of Air Force units consisting of landing strips and all components or related facilities for which the Air Force has operating responsibility, together with interior lines of communications and the minimum surrounding area required for local security (normally not greater than an area of 20 sq mi).

aircraft machine-gun turret. Unmanned twin .50 cal. turret guns aboard a B-36 bomber. (*U.S. Air Force.*)

aircraft rocket. A Sparrow III launched from a Phantom II. (*U.S. Navy.*)

airframe   The structural components of an airplane or missile including the framework and skin of such parts as the fuselage, empennage, wings, landing gear (minus tires), and engine mounts.

air group   The aircraft of a carrier, made up of squadrons.

airgun   A rifle or gun operated by compressed air rather than a powder charge. It was invented in Germany, and the first examples date from the late sixteenth century. (Picture, next page.)

airhead   A designated geographic area in an area of operations used as a base of supply and evacuation by air. The term may also refer to an area in a hostile or threatened territory which, when seized and held, ensures the continuous air landing of troops and materiel and provides maneuver space necessary for projected operations. Normally, it is the area seized in the assault phase of an airborne operation.

air intelligence   The activity formerly

airdrop. Supply drop from Air Force C-119 aircraft. (*U.S. Army.*)

known as "air combat intelligence." It deals with the intelligence aspects of naval air operations in the U.S. Navy.

air intercept Visual or radar contact made by a friendly aircraft with another aircraft. Normally the air intercept is conducted in the following five phases: (1) *Climb phase:* airborne to cruising altitude. (2) *Maneuver phase:* receipt of initial vector to target until beginning transition to attack speed and altitude. (3) *Transition phase:* increase or decrease of speed and altitude required for the attack. (4) *Attack phase:* turn to attack heading, acquisition of target, completion of attack, and turn to breakaway heading. (5) *Recovery phase:* breakaway to landing.

air-intercept zone A subdivided part of the destruction area in which it is planned to destroy or defeat the enemy airborne threat with interceptor aircraft.

air interdiction Air operations conducted to destroy, neutralize, or delay the enemy's military potential before it can be brought to bear effectively against friendly forces, at such distance from friendly forces that detailed integration of each air mission with the fire and movement of friendly forces is not required.

air-launched ballistic missile A ballistic missile launched from an airborne vehicle.

air liaison officer An officer (aviator-pilot) attached to a ground unit who functions as the primary adviser to the ground commander on air-operation matters.

airlift To transport passengers and cargo by use of aircraft. Also, the total weight of personnel and cargo that is, or can be, carried by air.

Airlight A U.S. Air Force illumination system that puts out 600,000 lumens over 40° beam spread and is used for battlefield illumination, interdiction lighting, and perimeter-defense lighting.

air logistic support Support by air landing or airdrop including air supply, movement of personnel, evacuation of casualties and prisoners of war, and recovery of equipment and vehicles.

airman An enlisted man engaged in the operation or maintenance of an aircraft. Specifically, an enlisted man or woman in the U.S. Air Force.

air marshal A commissioned rank in the RAF and the RCAF. It corresponds to the rank of lieutenant general in the USAF.

Air Medal A U.S. decoration first established in 1942 and awarded to any person serving in any capacity who distinguishes himself by meritorious achievement while participating in aerial flight. It is often awarded for flying a certain number of combat missions.

Air Ministry A department of the British ministry that is concerned with military and civil aviation. It was formed on January 2, 1918.

airmobile operations Operations in which combat forces and their equipment move about the battlefield in air vehicles under the control of a ground-force commander to engage in ground combat.

air observer An individual whose primary mission is to observe or take photographs from an aircraft in order to adjust artillery fire or obtain military information.

air offensive Sustained operations by strategic or tactical air weapon systems against hostile air forces of surface targets.

Airone The Italian C.R.D.A. Cant Z.506B Airone (Heron) was a trimotor five-seat reconnaissance-bomber and torpedo twin-float seaplane first flown in 1936. It saw considerable service during World War II. It flew at speeds of 217 mph and was armed with one 12.7mm machine gun and three 7.7mm machine guns; it carried a bomb-load of 2,645 lb.

air park Formerly in the Air Service of the AEF, an installation near an airdrome used for the salvage, supply, and maintenance of aircraft.

air photoreconnaissance The obtaining of information by air photography. There are three types: (1) strategic photoreconnaissance, (2) tactical photoreconnaissance, and (3) survey-cartographic photoreconnaissance.

air pickets Airborne early-warning aircraft disposed around a position, area, or formation primarily to detect, report, and track approaching enemy aircraft and to control intercepts.

airplane A heavier-than-air aircraft supported by the dynamic reaction of air against its wings. It may be driven by a propeller or a high-velocity jet. The class, however, includes gliders, helicopters, gyroplanes, and winged guided missiles. A monoplane has one wing; a biplane, a triplane, quadraplane, or multiplane has two, three, four, or more wings, respectively, placed one above the other.

airplane flare A flare, often magnesium, that is dropped from an airplane to illuminate a ground area. A small parachute decreases the rate of descent.

airport A place where aircraft can land to receive and discharge passengers and cargo. There are normally facilities for fueling and repairs.

air raid An attack of a place by aircraft. It may consist of a bombing or strafing attack against a position or a city.

air reconnaissance The acquisition of intelligence information employing visual observation or sensors in air vehicles.

air rifle A rifle that utilizes compressed air to propel a projectile.

air scoop An air duct on an aircraft that directs a part of the airstream to a power plant or a ventilating system.

airscrew The British word for an airplane propeller.

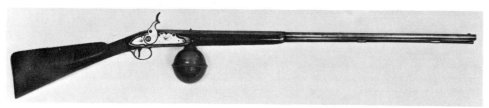

airgun. (*The Smithsonian Institution, H. May Collection.*)

airship. The *Macon* over Berkeley, Calif., 1932. (*U.S. Air Force.*)

Air Search Attack Team (ASAT) The U.S. Navy designation for an aircraft ASW team consisting of both search and attack aircraft.

Air Search Attack Unit (ASAU) The U.S. Navy designation for the ASW aircraft assigned to locate and destroy submarines.

air service The part of a country's military or naval services charged with the operation and maintenance of aircraft.

airship An aerostat provided with a propelling system and a means of controlling the direction of motion. Airships are of three types: (1) *Rigid:* the form is maintained by a rigid structure. (2) *Semirigid:* the form is maintained by means of a rigid or jointed keel and the pressure of the gas contained within an envelope. (3) *Nonrigid (or flexible):* the form is maintained strictly by the pressure of the gas contained within an envelope.

airspeed The speed of an aircraft relative to its surrounding air mass. The unqualified term "airspeed" can refer to any of the following: *Calibrated airspeed:* the indicated airspeed corrected for instrument installation error. *Equivalent airspeed:* the calibrated airspeed corrected for compressibility error. *Indicated airspeed:* the airspeed shown by an airspeed indicator. *True airspeed:* the equivalent airspeed corrected for error due to air density (altitude and temperature).

air stabilizer A parachute-type device attached to the tail of an aerial torpedo for the purpose of slowing it down before impact with the water.

air station A place for receiving and servicing aircraft.

air strike An attack on specific objectives by fighter, bomber, or attack aircraft on an offensive mission. It may consist of several air organizations under a single command in the air.

airstrip An unimproved surface which has been adapted for takeoff or landing of aircraft, usually having minimum facilities.

air superiority In an air battle of one force over another, that degree of dominance which permits the conduct of operations by the former and its related land, sea, and air forces at a given time and place without prohibitive interference by the opposing force.

air supply The delivery of cargo by airdrop or air landing.

air support See **close air support.**

air supremacy The degree of air superiority that renders the opposing air force incapable of effective interference.

air surveillance The systematic observation of airspace by electronic, visual, or other means primarily for the purpose of identifying and determining the movements of aircraft and missiles, friendly and

airstrip. P-39 Airacobras on a strip at Bougainville, Solomon Islands, December 1943. (*U.S. Air Force.*)

AKA, the attack cargo ship U.S.S. *Seminole.* (*U.S. Navy.*)

enemy, in the airspace under observation.

Air Systems Command In the U.S. Navy a functional command replacing the Bureau of Naval Weapons in a 1966 Navy Department reorganization.

air-to-air bombing The action of dropping bombs upon flying aircraft.

air-to-air missile (AAM) A missile designed to be launched from an airborne carrier at a target above the surface.

air-to-surface missile (ASM) A missile designed to be launched from an airborne carrier to a surface target.

air-to-underwater missile (AUM) A missile designed to be launched from an airborne carrier to an underwater target.

air transport group An organization of transport aircraft used to carry amphibious troops to the objective area.

air umbrella Airborne aircraft that provide protective cover above other aircraft or over a ground force or position.

air vice marshal A commissioned rank in the RAF and the RCAF. It corresponds to the rank of major general in the USAF.

AK U.S. Navy cargo ship.

AKA U.S. Navy attack cargo ship.

Akagi A Japanese aircraft carrier similar to the *Kaga* and sunk during the Battle of Midway in 1942.

AKD A U.S. Navy dock cargo ship.

aketon See **gambeson.**

Akikaze A class of Japanese destroyers of about 1,270 tons standard displacement built in the early 1920s and used during World War II. They had a length of 336 ft, a beam of 29 ft, a speed of about 30 knots, and a complement of 190 men. They were armed with four 4.7-in. guns and six 21-in. torpedo tubes.

Akitsuki A class of Japanese 2,700-ton destroyers completed between 1942 and 1945.

They had a speed of 33 knots and original armament of eight 3.9-in. and four 25mm guns, four 24-in. torpedo tubes, and six depth-charge throwers (and 73 depth charges). Of the 12 produced, half were lost in action during World War II.

AKL A U.S. Navy light cargo ship.

AKN A U.S. Navy net cargo ship.

AKR A U.S. Navy vehicle cargo ship.

AKROLL I A U.S. 2-ton amphibious jeep using huge low-pressure tires.

Akron A large, rigid airship built by Goodyear and commissioned by the U.S. Navy in 1931. It carried a trapeze for the landing of airplanes (the F9C single-seat fighter) and had hangar facilities for five of them. The airship displaced 6,500,000 cu ft and was 785 ft long and 133 ft in diameter. It set a world's record in November 1931 by making a 10-hour flight with 207 persons aboard. It crashed off the New Jersey coast on April 4, 1933, after some 1,500 hours of service. It had one sister ship, the *Macon.*

AKS A U.S. Navy stores-issue ship.

AKSS A U.S. Navy cargo submarine.

AKV A U.S. Navy cargo ship and aircraft ferry.

AL A U.S. Navy lightship.

Alabama Two battleships were named for the state of Alabama. The first *Alabama* was launched in 1898, one of three sister ships that included *Alabama, Illinois,* and *Wisconsin.* It had a length of 374 ft, a beam of 72 ft, a speed of 16 knots, and a complement of 535 men. It was armed with four 13-in. guns, fourteen 6-in. guns, sixteen six-pounders, six one-pounders, and four 18-in. torpedo tubes. The second *Alabama* was commissioned in 1942 and is of the **Indiana** class, which see. It was active in the Pacific theater during World War II and is now preserved as a memorial in Mobile, Ala.

alai A regiment in the Turkish Army.

alala A war cry of the ancient Greeks.

Akron, shown at its mooring mast at Sunnyvale, Calif., 1932. (*U.S. Navy.*)

AKV. (*U.S. Navy.*)

alamani An Indian saber resembling the German hussar sword.

Alamogordo bomb Also called the "Trinity bomb," the first atomic bomb detonated on July 16, 1945, at Alamogordo, N.Mex.

à la poulaine solerets Foot guards with long, pointed toes that were worn with Gothic armor in the fifteenth century.

alares In Roman times, the troops stationed on the wing of an army.

alarm The sudden apprehension of being attacked by surprise.

alarm gun A gun fired to give an alarm.

alarm post A place where troops go during an alarm.

Alaska A class of U.S. large cruisers of 27,500 tons standard displacement completed in 1944. The class consisted of *Alaska* and *Guam*. They had a length of 808 ft, a beam of 91 ft, a speed of 33 knots, and a complement of 1,900 men. They were armed with nine 12-in. and twelve 5-in. guns, plus fifty-six 40mm and thirty-four 20mm antiaircraft guns. Four aircraft were carried. (Picture, next page.)

Albacore A pre-World War II Fairey-built biplane used by the British Fleet Air Arm.

Albany A class of U.S. guided-missile cruisers (CG) converted from heavy cruisers in 1962–1964. The class includes *Albany, Chicago,* and *Columbus.* They have a standard displacement of 13,700 tons, a length of 673 ft, a beam of 70 ft, a speed of 33 knots, and a complement of 1,000 men. They are armed with two 5-in. guns, two twin Talos surface-to-air launchers, and two twin Tartar surface-to-air launchers. (Picture, next page.)

Albatros B types German two-place single-engine reconnaissance and observation biplanes designed by Ernst Heinkel and first flown in 1914. They flew at speeds up to 65 mph and were used as observation aircraft until 1915 and as trainers after that.

Albatros C.I A German two-place single-engine reconnaissance and observation biplane introduced in the spring of 1915. It had a speed of 87 mph and a ring-mounted Parabellum gun in the rear cockpit, and it carried 154 lb of bombs. It was used in substantial numbers in Russia and on the Western front.

Albatros C.III A German two-place single-engine reconnaissance biplane that went into service late in 1915. The most widely produced Albatros C type, this aircraft was used for visual and photographic recon-

Alabama. (*U.S. Navy.*)

Alaska. (*U.S. Navy.*)

Albatros D.V. (*The Smithsonian Institution, National Air Museum.*)

Albany. (*U.S. Navy.*)

naissance in Macedonia, Russia, and the Western front until early 1917. It could also be used for light bombing duties since it could carry 198 lb of bombs. It was armed with a Parabellum gun for the observer and a synchronized forward-firing Spandau machine gun. It had a maximum speed of 87 mph.

Albatros C.V, C.VII, C.X, and C.XII German two-place single-engine reconnaissance and observation biplanes that first appeared in 1916. Four hundred and twenty-four C.V's were built, but had problems with engine crankcase failures. The C.VII was in service from late 1916 to late 1917, and the C.X appeared in mid-1917, staying in service for about a year. The C.XII was in service from early 1918 until the Armistice. It flew at speeds of 108.7 mph and was armed with a forward-firing Spandau machine gun and a ring-mounted Parabellum gun in the observer's cockpit.

Albatros D.I and D.II German single-seat single-engine biplane fighters that first appeared in August 1916. They were the first German fighters to mount twin 7.92mm Spandau machine guns. They had a speed of 108 mph, and both versions entered service in late 1916.

Albatros D.III A German single-seat single-engine biplane fighter with the basic fuselage of the D.II but with various other modifications, including new wing design. The best of the Albatros fighters, it entered service at the beginning of 1917. It had a speed of about 108 mph, but was more maneuverable than the D.II. It was followed by other types, particularly the D.V and D.Va, but they improved very little on the D.III.

Albatros W.4 A German single-place single-engine biplane seaplane based on the Albatros D.I landplane and first delivered in September 1916. It had a speed of about 100 mph.

albesia A kind of ancient shield. Also called "decumana."

alblast See **arbalest.**

ALBM An air-launched ballistic missile.

alborium An eleventh-century bow made of hazel.

Albrighton A class of British frigates (ex-escort destroyers) of 1,087 tons standard displacement completed in 1942–1943. They had a speed of 26 knots, a complement of 168 men, and armament consisting of four 4-in. guns, four two-pounder pom-poms, two 20mm (or 40mm) antiaircraft guns, and two 21-in. torpedo tubes.

alcaide A Spanish, Protuguese, or Moorish commander of a castle or fortress.

Alcatel acoustic torpedoes A series of French torpedoes of which the E14 is typical. It has a length of 168 in., a diameter of 21 in., a speed of 25 knots, and a weight of 1,980 lb (of which 440 lb is the explosive charge).

alcazar The Spanish name for a fortress.

Alcione The Cant Z.1007 Alcione (King-fisher) was a three-engine bomber used by the Italians during World War II. It had a top speed of 280 mph, a range of 800 mi with a 2,600-lb bombload, and armament consisting of two 12.7mm and two 7.7mm machine guns.

Alder Tag (German for "Eagle Day") The German code name for the beginning of the all-out air offensive against the RAF, set for August 10, 1940. Germany expected to defeat the RAF Fighter Command in four days and to destroy the remainder of British airpower within 30 days, setting the stage for a planned invasion of England on September 15.

Aldis lamp A portable signal light used aboard ships and aircraft. Dots and dashes are transmitted by rotating a mirror at whose focus the light is located. It is visible only from the point at which it is directed.

Aldis sight A World War I telescopic gunsight developed for fighter planes and mounted through the windshield.

alee Away from the direction of the wind, generally referring to the helm of a ship.

alert 1. Readiness for action, defense, or protection. **2.** A warning signal of a real or threatened danger, such as an air attack. **3.** The period of time during which troops stand by in response to an alarm. **4.** To forewarn; to prepare for action.

alert, dusk or dawn Special precautions (normally all hands to battle stations) at times when an attack is likely, such as just prior to first light or at sunset.

Alf The code name used by the Allies in World War II to describe the Kawanishi E7K1/2. This Japanese three-seat single-engine biplane shipboard reconnaissance

Alfa machine gun. (*Spanish Ministry of Defense.*)

Alize. (*U.S. Air Force.*)

twin-float seaplane was first flown in 1933. It was used as a catapult aircraft on warships and also operated from shore stations. Armed with three 7.7mm machine guns, this aircraft had a speed of 171 mph.

Alfa machine guns Machine guns of Spanish manufacture. The Alfa Model 1944 is a 7.92mm machine gun that resembles the Breda Model 1937 in some respects. It is a gas-operated weapon with selective fire, a cyclic rate of fire of 780 rounds per minute, a length of about 57 in., a barrel length of 29.53 in., and a weight of 59.5 lb. It has a muzzle velocity of 2,493 fps, and is fed from a 100-round metallic link belt loaded in a drum. The Alfa Model 55 is a later version that fires the 7.62mm NATO cartridge, is shorter, and has a ribbed barrel and a lighter tripod.

Algerine A class of British minesweepers of 950 to 1,040 tons standard displacement completed in 1942–1945. They had a speed of 16.5 knots, a complement of 104 to 138 men, and armament consisting of one 4-in. gun, four to six 40mm or 20mm antiaircraft guns, and depth-charge throwers.

align To bring into line, such as the front and rear sights of a gun.

ALIRT Adaptive Long Range Infrared Tracker. A U.S. Raytheon-developed optical tracking system that identifies missile warheads from decoys against an infrared background of clouds and solar radiation.

Alize A French Breguet Br 1050 three-seat single-engine (turboprop) carrier-borne antisubmarine aircraft that was first flown in 1956. It has a speed of 292 mph.

Alkali The NATO code name for the Soviet air-to-air missile carried by the MiG-17 and MiG-19. It has a range of 3 to 4 mi.

Alkartasuna .32 ACP automatic pistol A Spanish automatic designed on the lines of the Colt .32 automatic. It has a magazine capacity of nine cartridges, an overall length of $6\frac{3}{8}$ in., a barrel length of $3\frac{5}{8}$ in., and a weight of about 34 oz. Under the name "Ruby automatic pistol," a weapon of this design was used by the French Army at the beginning of World War II. (Picture, next page.)

all-around fire A weapon or mount that is capable of firing in any direction is said to have all-around fire.

all available A command or request to obtain the fire of all artillery able to deliver effective fire on a given target.

all clear A signal that enemy aircraft are retiring.

allecret Light body armor used by cavalry and infantry in the sixteenth century. It probably consisted of a breastplate with gussets and a backplate.

Allen M. Sumner A class of U.S. destroyers (DD) of about 2,200 tons standard displacement produced between 1944 and 1945. A large number have been modernized since

Alkartasuna .32 ACP automatic pistol. (*The Smithsonian Institution, Ravenscroft Collection.*)

that time. They have a length of 376.5 ft, a beam of 40.9 ft, a speed of 34 knots, and a complement of 274 men. Original armament consisted of six 5-in. and four 3-in. guns, plus hedgehogs, depth charges, and torpedoes. Modernized versions carry six 5-in. guns, two triple torpedo launchers, two fixed torpedo tubes, and two drone antisubmarine helicopters (DASH).

all hands The entire company of a ship.

Alligator A nickname for U.S. LVT's (landing vehicle, tracked) during World War II.

allocation The designation of specific numbers and types of aircraft sorties for use during a specified time period or for carrying out an assigned task.

allotment A portion of a serviceman's pay that is paid, at his request, to a designated party or to a bank.

allumelle A thin, slender sword used in the Middle Ages, particularly for piercing the joints or weak parts of armor.

all-weather fighter A fighter aircraft equipped with radar devices and other special equipment which enables it to intercept its target in the dark or in daylight weather conditions which do not permit visual interception. It is usually a multiplace airplane.

ally Any nation united with another under

a treaty that may be offensive, defensive, or both. In World War II the Allies (or Allied Nations) were aligned against the Axis Powers (Italy, Germany, and Japan).

Almain rivets A kind of flexible, light armor made of overlapping plates which were designed to slide on rivets. It is of German origin.

almogávar A lightly armed Spanish foot soldier of medieval times.

aloft Above the decks of a ship; overhead.

Alouette III The French Sud-Aviation SE 3160 general-purpose armed reconnaissance and antitank helicopter first flown in 1959. With a speed of 131 mph, it is armed with a number of alternative systems, including missiles, 20mm cannons, rockets, and torpedoes.

Alpha (code) An authorized word for the letter A, used in transmitting messages when a possibility of a misunderstanding exists. It supersedes the old **Able** code, which see. The following are authorized code words: Alpha, Bravo, Charlie, Delta, Echo, Foxtrot, Golf, Hotel, India, Juliet, Kilo, Lima, Mike, November, Oscar, Papa, Quebec, Romeo, Sierra, Tango, Uniform, Victor, Whisky, X-ray, Yankee, and Zulu.

ALPHA A U.S. Navy rocket-boosted depth charge, formerly called "Able." For details, see **Weapon Alpha.**

Alpino A class of Italian frigates of 2,700 tons standard displacement completed in 1968. They have a speed of 28 knots, a complement of 254 men, and armament consisting of six 3-in. guns, one single-barreled depth-charge mortar, two triple torpedo tubes, and two ASW helicopters.

Alsos Mission A mission named after Major General L. R. Groves, who was head of the Manhattan District during World War II (*alsos* is Greek for "grove"). The Alsos Mission was composed of American military men and scientists and was established for the purpose of determining Ger-

many's progress in the field of nuclear physics. It lasted from the fall of 1943 to the fall of 1945.

alternate command post Any location designated by a commander to assume command-post functions in the event that the command post becomes inoperative. It may be partially or fully equipped and manned, or it may be the command post of a subordinate unit.

alternate water terminal A water terminal with facilities for berthing from two to five ships simultaneously at wharves or working anchorages, located within sheltered coastal waters and adjacent to reliable highway or rail transportation nets. It covers a relatively small area and is located away from population centers. The scope of operation is such that it is not designated a probable nuclear target.

alternative airfield An airfield with minimum essential facilities for use as an emergency landing ground, when main or redeployment airfields are out of action, or as required for tactical flexibility.

AM A U.S. Navy minesweeper.

amatol A high explosive made of a mixture of ammonium nitrate and trinitrotoluene (TNT). There are two main types, classified according to the percentage ratio of ammonium nitrate to TNT: 50:50 amatol, which is capable of being melt-loaded or cast, and 80:20 amatol, which must be consolidated by pressing or extruding. This explosive has approximately the same force as TNT and has been used as the bursting charge for projectiles and bombs when toluene, used in the manufacture of TNT, was in short supply.

Amatsukaze A Japanese guided-missile destroyer of 3,050 tons standard displacement completed in 1965, the largest naval vessel built in Japan after World War II. It has a length of 429 ft, a beam of 44 ft, a speed of 33 knots, and a complement of

Allen M. Sumner. (*U.S. Navy.*)

290 men. It is armed with a Tartar launcher, four 3-in. guns, two hedgehogs, and torpedo-dropping gear.

AMB A U.S. Navy minesweeper, harbor.

ambuscade A surprise attack upon an enemy; an ambush.

ambush A place of concealment from which a surprise attack can be made upon an enemy; a trap

amentum A leather strap used by the Romans and Greeks to throw lances. It was attached to the middle of the shaft.

Americal Division The name of the U.S. Army's only unnumbered division. It was formed from a task force sent to New Caledonia at the beginning of World War II, and the name is derived from a combination of "America" and "New Caledonia."

American Campaign Medal A U.S. military decoration awarded persons under certain specified conditions for service within the American theater between December 7, 1941, and March 2, 1946.

American Defense Service Medal A U.S. military decoration awarded persons who entered military service under orders to active duty for a period of 12 months or more between September 8, 1939, and December 7, 1941.

American Expeditionary Force (AEF) The American armed forces sent to Europe and other fronts in World War I.

American Volunteer Group (AVG) A volunteer air force aiding the Nationalist Chinese against the Japanese between the summer of 1941 and the spring of 1942. It consisted of Americans under the command of Claire Chennault. After the American entry into World War II, Chennault rose to the rank of major general and became the commanding general of the Fourteenth Air Force in China. The AVG was popularly called the "Flying Tigers."

AMGOT An acronym for Allied Military Government.

amidships Midway between the bow and stern of a ship.

Amiot 143 A French five-seat twin-engine night-bomber and reconnaissance aircraft first flown in 1934 and used operationally in the early part of World War II. It was armed with four 7.5mm machine guns and carried a bombload of about 3,200 lb. (Picture, next page.)

Amiot 350 A series of four-seat twin-engine medium-range bombers developed by France in the late 1930s and used in the early days of World War II. It was armed with one 20mm cannon and two 7.5mm machine guns and carried a bombload of approximately 2,500 lb.

AML 245 A light armored car developed for the French Army and first delivered in 1961. This system has a crew of three, a weight between 4.7 and 5.4 tons (depending on turret design), a road speed of 56

AM. (*U.S. Navy.*)

mph, and armament consisting of one 60mm mortar (with a range of 1,800 meters) and a choice of one or two 7.5mm, 7.62mm, 12.7mm, or 20mm machine guns.

ammo A slang term for ammunition.

ammo plus, ammo minus, ammo zero Terms indicating the amount of ammunition left. *Ammo plus:* I have more than half my ammunition left. *Ammo minus:* I have less than half my ammunition left. *Ammo zero:* I have no ammunition left.

ammonal A high-explosive mixture made of ammonium nitrate, TNT, and flaked or powdered aluminum. When used as a bursting charge in projectiles, it produces high temperature and a bright flash on detonation. It was a widely used shell filler in World War I.

ammonium picrate See **explosive D.**

ammonpulver A flashless and smokeless propellant powder used by Germany and Austria in World War I. It was a mixture of 80 to 90 percent ammonium nitrate and 10 to 20 percent charcoal, with or without the addition of potassium nitrate.

ammunition A generic term which includes all manner of missiles to be thrown against an enemy, such as bullets, projectiles, rockets, grenades, torpedoes, bombs, and guided missiles with their necessary propellants, primers, fuzes, detonators, and charges of conventional explosives, nuclear explosives, and chemical and other materials.

ammunition belt A fabric or metal band with loops for carrying cartridges that are fed from it into a machine gun or other automatic weapon; a feed belt. The term may also refer to a belt with loops or pockets for carrying cartridges or clips of cartridges, although this is usually called a "cartridge belt." (Picture, next page.)

ammunition box A box in which linked ammunition is folded and from which it can be fed into a machine gun.

ammunition carrier A vehicle that accompanies guns and carries ammunition for them. Also, a member of a gun or mortar squad who carries ammunition and helps load in actual firing.

Amatsukaze. (*Japan Defense Agency.*)

Amiot 143. (*The Imperial War Museum.*)

ammunition chest A receptacle, as on a caisson, limber, or gun carriage, in which ammunition is kept.

ammunition data card A card put into a box of ammunition to identify it by type or composition. It may also provide instructions for handling the ammunition.

ammunition dump A temporary storage place for military ammunition.

ammunition handler 1. One whose primary duty is the handling and servicing of ammunition. **2.** A soldier who prepares ammunition for firing and who, as a member of a weapons crew, assists in the final delivery of ammunition to the loader.

ammunition identification Identification of ammunition by type, size, and manufacturer's symbol, lot number, and grade.

ammunition pit A hole or trench in the ground in which ammunition is stored temporarily. An ammunition pit is usually placed near the gun from which the ammunition is to be fired.

ammunition shoes A British term for the soft, metal-free shoes worn by soldiers and sailors in a magazine.

ammunition train An organization consisting of personnel and vehicles for transporting ammunition. The term is synony-

ammunition belt. (*U.S. Army.*)

mous with "truck convoy" if the vehicles are loaded with ammunition.

amorce 1. An old term for the fine-grained powder once used for priming guns. **2.** A portfire or quick match.

amorcoir An instrument that was used for priming a musket; a powder flask. Also the name of the small copper box that held percussion caps.

amorcoir. (*The Metropolitan Museum of Art, gift of William H. Riggs, 1913.*)

amphibian An airplane that can operate from either land or water. Also a term referring to flat-bottomed tracked vehicles that are used on land or water and employed in landing or evacuating troops and equipment.

amphibious Capable of operating on land and sea.

amphibious assault ship A ship designed to transport and land troops, equipment, and supplies by means of embarked helicopters. Designated as LPH, some of these ships were formerly CVA's or CVS's.

amphibious cargo carrier A track-propelled carrier designed to carry a small number of troops or a small amount of cargo across calm waters, principally rivers and swamps. It may also be used as a prime mover.

amphibious command ship A naval ship from which a commander exercises control in amphibious operations.

amphibious control group The personnel, ships, and craft designated to control the

water-borne ship-to-shore movement in an amphibious operation.

amphibious force Naval, landing, and supporting forces that are trained, organized, and equipped for amphibious operations.

amphibious group The command within the amphibious force, consisting of the commander and his staff. It is designed to control the various units in a division-size amphibious operation.

amphibious lift The total capacity of assault shipping utilized in an amphibious operation.

amphibious mine A mine designed especially to hinder beach landings and river-crossing operations by damaging or destroying landing craft, small boats, water-fording vehicles, and floating bridges. It may be of various types, such as contact, controlled, drifting, etc.

amphibious operation An attack which is launched from the sea by naval and landing forces embarked in ships or craft and which involves a landing on a hostile shore. The amphibious operation includes the following phases: planning, embarkation, rehearsal, movement, and assault.

amphibious raid A landing from the sea on a hostile shore involving swift incursion into, or a temporary occupancy of, an objective, followed by a planned withdrawal.

amphibious squadron A tactical and administrative organization composed of amphibious assault shipping to transport troops and equipment for an amphibious assault operation.

amphibious tank A vehicle mounting a howitzer or cannon, capable of delivering direct fire from the water as well as ashore, and used in providing early artillery support in amphibious operations.

amphibious tractor (AMTRAC) A vehicle used for the movement of troops and cargo from ship to shore in the assault phase of amphibious operations or for limited movement of troops and cargo over land or water. See **AMTRAC.**

amphibious transport dock (LPD) A U.S. Navy ship designed to transport and land troops, equipment, and supplies by means of embarked landing craft, amphibious vehicles, and helicopters.

amphibious troops Troop components, ground and airborne, assigned to land in an amphibious operation.

amphibious vehicle A wheeled or tracked vehicle capable of operating on both land and water.

amphibious vessel A ship used to make assault landings. U.S. Navy types are flagship, AGC; attack cargo ship, AKA; attack transport, APA; and helicopter transport, LPH.

AMS A U.S. Navy motor minesweeper. Also, the U.S. Army Map Service.

amphibious assault ship, the U.S.S. *Guam* (LPH-9) of the Iwo Jima class. (*U.S. Navy.*)

AMTRAC A 9-ton personnel landing vehicle used by the U.S. Army and the U.S. Marine Corps. It is amphibious and operates at speeds of 30 mph on land and 6 mph on water. It has a range of 190 mi and is manufactured by Borg Warner. See also **amphibious tractor.**

amusette A swivel gun or wall gun shaped like a musket; an early breechloading brass gun, mounted like a cannon but fired like a musket. There were many sizes of amusettes.

AMX 13 A French light tank first produced in 1950. It has a crew of three, a weight of 15 tons, a road speed of 37 mph, and main armament consisting of a 75mm, 90mm, or 120mm gun and one 7.5mm or 7.62mm machine gun. It may also be equipped with four SS11 antitank missiles mounted externally on the turret roof. These may be of 75, 90, or 105mm. A total of 17 vehicles are based on the same chassis design of the AMX 13. They include a mortar carrier, a 105mm howitzer, a 30mm antiaircraft gun, a recovery tank, etc. (Picture, next page.)

AMX 30 A French main battle tank first produced in 1962. It has a crew of four, a weight of 35.5 tons, a speed of 40 mph, and armament consisting of one 105mm QF gun (with a maximum antitank range of 2,000 meters), one coaxial 12.7mm machine gun, and one 7.62mm machine gun. (Picture, next page.)

AMX-VTP M-56 A French armored personnel carrier developed during the mid-

amphibious command ship, the U.S.S. *Pocono* (AGC-16) of the *Mount McKinley* class. (*U.S. Navy.*)

amphibious transport dock, the U.S.S. *Duluth* (LPD-6). (*U.S. Navy.*)

AMX 13. *(French Ministry of Defense.)*

AMX 30. *(French Ministry of Defense.)*

AN. *(U.S. Navy.)*

1950s and based on a lengthened AMX 13 tank chassis. It carries the commander, a driver, and 11 infantrymen. It has a weight of 14 tons, a road speed of 37 mph, and armament consisting of a turret-mounted 7.62mm or 12.5mm machine gun.

AN A U.S. Navy net-laying ship.

An A designation for Soviet aircraft designed by Oleg Konstantinovich Antonov.

An-2 See **Colt.**

An-3 See **Camp.**

An-10 See **Cat.**

An-12 See **Cub.**

An-14 See **Clod.**

An-22 See **Cock.**

An-24 See **Coke.**

Anab The NATO code name for the air-to-air missile that is now a standard weapon in the Soviet Air Force. It has a length of about 13 ft and either infrared or semiactive radar homing guidance systems. They were first seen in 1961.

Anatra D and DS Russian two-place single-engine reconnaissance biplanes. The Anatra D was in service from mid-1916 until the end of 1917. The DS was introduced in mid-1917 and continued to be produced until the November Revolution. Both were armed with forward-firing and rear-mounted machine guns. They had a speed of about 89 mph.

anchor A device of iron so shaped as to grip the bottom and hold a vessel by the chain or rope attached.

anchorage An area set apart for anchored vessels; a suitable place for anchoring.

anchor deck A very short forecastle for the stowing of the anchor.

anchor's aweigh Said of an anchor when it is off the bottom.

anchor watch A detail of the crew keeping watch while a vessel is at anchor.

ANCOVS Active Night Covert Vision System. A U.S. Air Force development for gunships to permit airborne night viewing, target acquisition, and gunfire direction. It consists of a stabilized image intensifier and a laser illuminator.

Andover The British Hawker Siddeley, a twin-engine (turboprop) military transport in service with the RAF. It has a speed of 265 mph and carries up to 58 troops. It was first flown in 1963.

Andrea Doria A class of Italian guided-missile escort cruisers of 6,500 tons displacement completed in 1964. They have a speed of 30 knots, a complement of 478 men, and armament consisting of a Terrier twin launcher, eight 3-in. antiaircraft guns, and two triple torpedo tubes.

anelace A short English sword of the fourteenth century.

angels Radar reflection of short duration observed at low atmospheric altitudes (usually below 3,000 ft) and believed to be caused by birds or insects.

angel shot A kind of chain shot that consists of sections of a hollow ball chained to a central disk.

angle of approach In gunnery, the angle between the line along which a moving target is traveling and the line along which the gun is pointed. The angle of approach is never greater than 90°.

angle of clearance The angle between the line along which a gun or launcher is pointed at the target and the line along which the weapon must be pointed in order that a projectile or missile fired from it will clear any obstruction between the weapon and the target.

angle of defense In fortifications, the exterior angle between the line of defense and the line of the flank of an adjacent bastion.

angle of deflection In gunnery, the horizontal angle between the line of sight and the axis of the bore of the gun.

angle of departure The vertical angle between the line from the muzzle of the gun to the target and a line (line of site) along which the gun is pointed at the instant the projectile leaves the muzzle.

angle of depression The angle between the horizontal and the line along which the gun is pointed when aimed below the horizontal.

angle of elevation Also called simply "elevation," this is the angle which the axis of the barrel makes with the horizontal line.

angle of fall The angle at which a projectile falls. It is the angle made at the point of fall by the tangent to the trajectory with a horizontal line in the plane of fire.

angle of impact The acute angle between the tangent to the trajectory (at the point of impact of a projectile) and the plane tangent to the surface of the ground at the point of impact.

angle of position See **angle of site.**

angle of safety The minimum permissible angular clearance, at the gun, of the path of a projectile above the friendly troops. It is the angle of clearance corrected to ensure the safety of the troops.

angle of site The vertical angle between the line of site, or position, and the horizontal.

angle of traverse The horizontal angle through which a gun can be turned on its mount.

angle on the bow In firing a torpedo, the angle between the fore and aft axis of the target and the line of sight, measured from the target's bow to port or to starboard.

ANGLICO See **air and naval gunfire liaison company.**

Anglo-Saxon sword The Anglo-Saxon swords of the fifth to the seventh centuries were usually long (on the order of 3 ft), straight, double-edged, and rounded at the point.

angon A barbed javelin used in the seventh century by the Franks. It had an iron head and could be used for either throwing or stabbing.

anime A kind of ancient cuirass made of horizontal plates, usually overlapping upward.

anippus Grecian light cavalry.

anisocycle An ancient spiral-shaped spring used for throwing arrows a great distance.

ANL A U.S. Navy net-laying ship.

ANMCC Alternate National Military Command Center. A U.S. hardened site for backup support in case of national emergency. It is a portion of the National Military Command System (chief subsystem of the World Wide Military Command and

Andover. (*Hawker Siddeley Aviation, Ltd.*)

Ansaldo S.V.A. (*The Smithsonian Institution, National Air Museum.*)

Control System). The personnel of the NMCS Support Center would be rapidly evacuated to the ANMCC in the event of war. It is continually manned.

AN-M1A2, M1A3, M1A4, and M4A2 Designations for U.S. 100-lb fragmentation-bomb clusters.

AN-M2 and M3 U.S. .50 cal. aircraft machine guns.

AN-M8 **1.** A U.S. grenade. **2.** A U.S. pyrotechnic pistol.

AN-M14 TH3 A U.S. incendiary grenade.

AN-M30A1 A U.S. 100-lb general-purpose bomb.

AN-M41A1 A U.S. 20-lb fragmentation bomb.

AN-M-46 A U.S. 100-lb photoflash bomb.

AN-M47A2 and M47A4 U.S. 100-lb incendiary bombs.

AN-M50A2, M50A3, M50T-A2, and M50T-X-A3 U.S. 4-lb incendiary bombs.

AN-M56A2 A U.S. 4,000-lb light-case bomb.

AN-M57A1 A U.S. 250-lb general-purpose bomb.

AN-M59A1 A U.S. 1,000-lb semi-armor-piercing bomb.

AN-M64A1 A U.S. 500-lb general-purpose bomb.

AN-M65A1 A U.S. 1,000-lb general-purpose bomb.

AN-M66A2 A U.S. 2,000-lb general-purpose bomb.

AN-M69A1 A U.S. 6-lb incendiary bomb.

AN-M76 A U.S. 500-lb incendiary bomb.

AN-M78 A U.S. 500-lb nonpersistent gas bomb.

AN-M79 A U.S. 1,000-lb nonpersistent gas bomb.

AN-M81 A U.S. 260-lb fragmentation bomb.

AN-M88 A U.S. 220-lb fragmentation bomb.

AN-MK-1 Models 1, 2, and 3 U.S. 1,000-lb armor-piercing bombs.

AN-MK-47A1 A U.S. 100-lb depth bomb.

AN-MK-54 A U.S. 300-lb depth bomb.

annunciator In naval terminology, an engine-order telegraph.

anoxia Oxygen deficiency experienced by fliers at altitudes in excess of 15,000 ft if unprotected by oxygen masks or pressurized cabins. The symptoms are failure of reflexes and coordination and diminution of hearing and vision.

Ansaldo A.I Balilla (Hunter) An Italian single-place single-engine biplane fighter first flown in the latter part of 1917. It was armed with twin Vickers machine guns synchronized to fire forward between the propeller blades and had a speed of nearly 140 mph. It saw only limited production and operational use.

Ansaldo S.V.A. series Italian single-seat single-engine reconnaissance and light bomber biplanes first flown in March 1917. Various types, from S.V.A.4 to S.V.A.10, were produced during the war. The major version was the S.V.A.5. It had a speed of 142.9 mph and was armed with two forward-firing Vickers machine guns. It was used for bombing raids across the Alps to Germany and Austria and along the length of the Adriatic.

anse des pièces   See **dolphins.**

antecessores   Light Roman cavalry, the advance guard of an army on the march.

Antelope   The code name for a project in which Lockheed used a Polaris A-3 in tests of a number of advanced maneuverable warheads and decoy systems.

antemural   An ancient fortifications term for outworks.

antepilani   Soldiers in the Roman heavy infantry who formed the first two ranks in the line of battle. The first rank was called "hastati," and the second "principes."

antesignani   Soldiers of the Roman light infantry who protected the colors.

antestature   An old French fortifications term for a small trench or work formed of palisades or sacks of earth.

antiairborne minefield   A minefield laid primarily for protection against airborne attack.

antiaircraft   Said of systems, such as surface guns or missile launchers, used for defense against aircraft. Antiaircraft include fire, projectiles, guided missiles, etc., directed from the surface to airborne targets.

antiaircraft artillery (AAA)   Projectile weapons and related equipment such as searchlights, radar, etc., employed on the ground or on ships to strike at airborne aircraft (including ballistic and guided missiles).

antiaircraft barrage   A barrage of antiair-

craft fire through which enemy aircraft are expected to fly; sometimes called a "predicted barrage." In a less precise definition, any concentration of antiaircraft fire.

antiaircraft bomb   During World War II the United States developed a 5.5-lb bomb intended to be dropped from fighter planes in order to break up tight enemy bomber formations prior to closing in for close-range attack.

antiaircraft defense   The total defense on the ground or on ship employed against aircraft (including ballistic and guided missiles).

antiaircraft gun   A gun designed especially for use against aircraft, easily shifted in direction and elevation, having great range, and capable of firing at high angles of elevation.

antiaircraft missile   A guided missile intended to be launched from the surface against an airborne target. See **guided missile.**

antiaircraft projectile   A general term applied to projectiles for antiaircraft ammunition.

antiamphibious minefield   A minefield laid primarily for protection against amphibious attack.

anticrop agent   A living organism or chemical used to cause disease or damage to selected food or industrial crops.

antidisturbance fuze   A fuze designed to become armed after impact or after being emplaced so that any further movement or disturbance will result in detonation.

antilift device   A device arranged to detonate the mine to which it is attached, or to detonate another mine or charge nearby, if the mine is disturbed.

antimateriel agent   A living organism or chemical used to cause deterioration of, or damage to, selected materiel.

antimechanized defense   Antitank defense. All means used for defense against armored combat vehicles. It may include such means as armored units, antitank weapons and grenades, field artillery, antiaircraft artillery, ditches, traps, minefields, and any other means available.

antimissile missile   A defensive missile designed to intercept and destroy another missile in flight.

antipersonnel   Said of projectiles, bombs, mines, grenades, or the like that are designed to kill, wound, or obstruct personnel.

antipersonnel grenade   A general term for any hand grenade or rifle grenade designed primarily for casualty effect against personnel. It usually refers to a fragmentation grenade.

antipersonnel mine   A land mine, for use against personnel, consisting of a small amount of high explosive, generally less than 1 lb, in a metallic or nonmetallic container fitted with a detonating fuze. It

is actuated by pressure or release of pressure by pull on a trip wire. Two types are available: the blast type, which explodes in place, and the bounding type, which projects a fragmenting body into the air, where it explodes and scatters fragments over a wide area.

antipersonnel minefield   A minefield laid primarily for protection against infantry attack.

antirecovery device   A device incorporated into a naval mine to explode it if disturbed.

antiremoval device   A device attached to a land mine to protect it against removal. Usually attached to the mine either on the bottom or on the side, it is designed to function when a pull is exerted on the mine at the time of removal or when pressure is released from the device when the mine is lifted from its position.

antiricochet device   A device attached to bombs to prevent ricochet and possible danger to the dropping plane. The device usually consists of a parachute unit, fuze adapter, and fuze, and is attached to the tail end of the bomb. The bomb is slowed by the parachute, enabling the dropping aircraft to pass beyond the danger area before the bomb is detonated.

antisubmarine   Said of equipment, mines, or missiles that are designed to attack or destroy submarines.

antisubmarine action   An operation by one or more antisubmarine ships or aircraft, or a combination of the two, against a particular enemy submarine. It begins when contact has been gained by any ship or aircraft of the unit. Any number of antisubmarine attacks may be carried out as part of the action. The action ends when the submarine has been destroyed or when contact has been lost and cannot be regained.

antisubmarine barrier   The line formed by a series of static devices or mobile units arranged for the purpose of detecting, denying passage to, or destroying hostile submarines.

antisubmarine patrol   The systematic and continuing investigation of an area or along a line to detect or hamper submarines, used when the direction of submarine movement can be established.

antisubmarine rocket   See **Asroc.**

antisubmarine support aircraft carrier (CVS)   A U.S. Navy ship designed primarily to support and operate aircraft and for sustained antisubmarine warfare and escort convoys. It also may be used to provide close air support.

antisubmarine torpedo   See **ASTOR.**

antisubmarine warfare   Operations conducted against submarines, their supporting forces, and their operating bases. It includes the location, classification, tracking,

antiaircraft artillery. A U.S. radar-controlled 90mm antiaircraft gun. (*U.S. Army.*)

and destruction of submarines by other submarines or by surface craft, aircraft, or land-based installations.

antitank   Said of systems or devices designed to destroy or to be used against tanks.

antitank defense   See **antimechanized defense.**

antitank ditch   A deep ditch prepared as an obstacle to enemy tanks. It is also called a "tank ditch."

antitank grenade   A rifle grenade designed to be used against tanks or other armored vehicles.

antitank grenade. A Russian-made grenade of the Korean conflict. (*U.S. Army.*)

antitank guided missile   An antitank missile whose flight path is controlled by a combination of optical sighting and command signals from an automatic computer through multiple wire command links. It may also contain an infrared homing device for final range correction. It is designed to be launched from any type of vehicle or ground emplacement. This definition excludes items whose trajectory cannot be altered in flight.

antitank gun   A gun designed or suitable for use against tanks or other armored vehicles.

antitank mine   A mine designed to immobilize or destroy a tank.

antitank minefield   An area in which a pattern of antitank mines is planted to stop or slow down enemy tanks or other armored vehicles.

antitank obstacle   A tank obstacle. A natural or man-made obstruction or barrier which will stop or slow down tanks or other armored vehicles or cause them to maneuver or change direction. Antitank obstacles include ditches, wire rolls, concrete pillars, and blocks.

antitank weapon   Any weapon designed or suitable for use against tanks or other armored vehicles. Antitank rockets, antitank grenades, and antitank guns are exam-

antitank weapon. The U.S. Dragon medium antitank weapon system. (*U.S. Army.*)

ples of antitank weapons.

antiwithdrawal device   A device intended to detonate an item of ammunition if an attempt is made to remove the ammunitions fuze. It may be an integral part of the fuze or a separate unit.

Antonov A-7 glider   A troop transport glider developed by the Soviet Union and used during World War II. It had a wingspan of about 62 ft and a length of about 38 ft.

anvil   **1.** A rigid metal part of a primer assembly. The explosive primer mixture is compressed against it by the action of the firing pin against the primer cap.   **2.** An archaic term for the handle of a sword.

3. A small, narrow flag at the end of a lance.

Anzac   An acronym formed from the initials of Australian and New Zealand Army Corps.

Anzio   A class of U.S. escort aircraft carriers (CVE) of about 7,800 tons standard displacement commissioned in 1943–1944. They had a speed of 19.5 knots and a wartime complement of over 800 men, and they carried 30 aircraft. They had a length of 512 ft and an extreme width of 108 ft.

Anzio Annie (Annies)   Railroad guns were little used in World War II. Notable exceptions were two German 280mm K-5E railroad guns used after the Anzio landings.

Anzio Annie. (*U.S. Army.*)

APD, the U.S.S. *William J. Pattison* (APD-104). (*U.S. Navy.*)

They weighed 240 tons and fired 550-lb shells at the advancing Allies. These guns, known as "Anzio Annies," were finally surrounded and captured.

AO   A U.S. Navy oiler or tanker. Also, aviation ordnanceman.

Aoba   A class of 9,000-ton Japanese cruisers built in 1926. Both (*Aoba* and *Kinugasa*) were lost to U.S. carrier planes during World War II. They had a speed of 33 knots, a complement of 773 men, and main armament consisting of six 8-in. and four 4.7-in. guns, four torpedo tubes, and two aircraft.

AOE   A U.S. Navy fast combat support ship capable of carrying petroleum products and explosives.

AOG   A U.S. Navy gasoline tanker.

AOL   Absent over leave. See **absent without leave (AWOL)**.

AOR   A U.S. Navy replenishment tanker, specially equipped for refueling ships underway at sea.

AOSS   A U.S. Navy submarine fitted as a tanker.

AP   **1.** A U.S. Navy transport; a passenger-carrying ship. **2.** Short for "armor piercing" and, in some references, "automatic pistol." **3.** Antipersonnel.

APA   A U.S. Navy attack transport.

APAM   Antipersonnel-antimateriel. A generic term applied to munitions having the dual role of destroying personnel and materiel.

aparejo   A kind of pack saddle once used in the U.S. military service.

APB   A U.S. Navy self-propelled barracks ship.

APC   **1.** Armored personnel carrier. A U.S. Army full-tracked, lightweight, air-transportable, amphibious multipurpose vehicle

designed primarily for the mobility and protection of ground troops. Synonymous with M113 vehicles (see **U.S. armored personnel carrier M113**). **2.** An ammunition term meaning "armor-piercing-capped." **3.** A U.S. Navy designation for a small coastal transport.

APD   A U.S. Navy high-speed transport. See also **amphibious vessel**.

APDS   An armor-piercing discarding-sabot artillery projectile.

APDS-T   An armor-piercing discarding-sabot artillery projectile with tracer.

APERS   Antipersonnel.

aperture sight   An irregularly shaped adjustable mechanical item usually integral to a rear sight. It functions as a peephole through which the sight at the opposite end of a gun is brought into view in aiming at a target or object.

Apex Boats   Part of a U.S. Navy system used during landing operations in World War II. One landing craft (the apex boat) towed two others (drones) loaded with explosives to the landing site, released them, and directed them by radio control into obstructions that were to be blown up.

APF   A U.S. Navy administrative flagship.

APG   A U.S. Navy supporting gunnery ship.

APH   A U.S. Navy transport fitted to evacuate the wounded.

aphracti   Open vessels used in ancient times. They were built without decks or hatches and were furnished at head and stern with crossplanks, where the men stood to fight.

Aphrodite   A German radar decoy used during World War II. It consisted of a submarine-launched balloon that trailed plates covered with metal foil.

API   See **armor-piercing incendiary**.

APIT   See **armor-piercing incendiary tracer**.

APL   A U.S. Navy barracks craft (non-self-propelled).

APM   A U.S. Navy mechanized artillery transport.

APN   A U.S. Navy nonmechanized artillery transport.

apobates   Ancient warriors who fought mounted on chariots. They were also called "anabates" or "paraebates." Their equipment consisted of helmet, breast armor, lance, javelin, sword, and shield. They sometimes alighted from their chariots to attack adversaries on foot.

APP   A U.S. Navy troop barge, Class A.

apparatus   Ammunition and equipage for war.

apparatus belli   Munitions of war.

appareilles   In fortifications, the slopes leading to the platform of the bastion.

appease   To make political or economic concessions to a threatening potential aggressor, such as those made to Nazi Germany in 1938.

approach   The route by which attackers can gain access to a fortified place or military position. It may include works, trenches, or covered roads.

approach trench   A communication or fire trench providing protected contact between front and rear elements of a defensive position.

APR   A U.S. Navy rescue transport.

apron   **1.** A paved, surfaced, or prepared area where aircraft stand for purposes of loading or unloading passengers or cargo, refueling, parking, or servicing. **2.** In fortifications, that portion of a superior slope of a parapet or the interior slope of a pit designed to protect the slopes against blast. **3.** A square piece of sheet lead used to cover the vent of a cannon to keep it clean and also to keep the charge dry. **4.** An area of a pier or wharf upon which cargo is unloaded.

apron of mail   A skirt of mail that hung from the waist and was used to fill the space between the tassets (defenses for the upper thighs).

apron shield   A steel shield attached to an artillery piece to protect the gunners.

APS   **1.** A U.S. Navy minelaying submarine. **2. Armor-piercing sabot**, which see.

APSS   A U.S. Navy submarine transport.

AP-T, APT   See **armor-piercing tracer**.

APT   A U.S. Navy troop barge, Class B.

APV   A U.S. Navy transport and aircraft ferry.

APY   A U.S. Navy giant Y boat.

Aquaskit   A device used during World War II by the Allies to deceive the enemy during battle. It was dropped by air and, on striking water, fired Very lights.

AR   **1.** An automatic rifle. **2.** A U.S. Navy repair ship.

AR-15   See **M-16A1**.

ARAAV   Armored reconnaissance–airborne

assault vehicle. The U.S. Army lightweight air-droppable assault vehicle utilizing a 152mm gun-launcher capable of firing a conventional round or the Shillelagh missile. See also **General Sheridan.**

Arado Ar 196 A German two-seat single-engine shipboard reconnaissance and coastal patrol twin-float seaplane first flown in 1938. It was introduced in 1939 and used on the catapults of the principal German warships (*Scharnhorst, Gneisenau, Admiral Graf Spee, Lützow, Prinz Eugen,* etc.). It was armed with two 20mm cannons and three 7.9mm machine guns and carried two 110-lb bombs. Its maximum speed was 193 mph.

Arado Ar 234 See **Blitz.**

Arado AR 240 A German twin-engine two-place high-altitude fighter and reconnaissance aircraft used in World War II. They had a speed of 330 mph and were armed with six MG-151 20mm cannons.

ARB A U.S. Navy battle-damage repair ship.

arbalest A crossbow consisting of a wood, compound, or steel bow mounted in a wooden shaft. It was equipped with a string and a trigger and usually had a mechanical device for bending the bow. An arbalest could be used to throw arrows, bullets, and darts; larger ones were capable of shooting stones. Most often a short, stout arrow, called a "quarrel," was used in the arbalest; usually these arrows had a three- or four-sided head. Arbalests were much in use in the post-Roman period. In England during the fourteenth century they gave way to the longbow, which was more convenient to use in battle, but they remained the predominant projectile weapon in continental Europe until the ascendancy of firearms.

arbalestina A small window or cross-

apron, showing a row of U.S. Air Force F-104 aircraft. (*U.S. Air Force.*)

shaped opening in a wall from which crossbows were shot.

arbalist A crossbowman.

arbor, depth charge A device for holding a depth charge on its projector. See **K-gun.**

arbrier The stock of a crossbow.

arc See **elevating arc.**

ARC A U.S. Navy cable-repairing or cable-laying ship.

arc à jalet A small crossbow used to throw bullets.

archer A bowman. A person skilled in the use of bow and arrow.

archer's stakes Pointed wooden stakes about 6 ft long. They were carried by fifteenth-century archers to plant in the ground as a defense against cavalry.

archery The use of bow and arrows in battle or hunting or as a sport.

arch-gaye, lance-gaye A lance consisting of a sharp-pointed piece of iron attached to a light wooden handle. It was used by the Gauls and Franks.

archie A World War I slang term for antiaircraft artillery.

architonnerre A machine invented by Archimedes to throw iron bullets with great force.

arçon The front part of the saddle; the bow.

ARD A U.S. Navy auxiliary floating dry dock. (Picture, next page.)

ARDC A U.S. Navy auxiliary floating dry dock, concrete,

ARDM A U.S. Navy medium auxiliary repair dry dock.

area The territory allocated to an army or a portion of an army for military operations.

area bombing Bombing a general area. Area bombing differs from precision bombing, which is bombing at a specific target, and from pattern bombing, which is sys-

Arado Ar 196. (*The Smithsonian Institution, National Air Museum.*)

tematic covering of a target according to a plan.

area defense A defense against air attack organized to protect an area, as distinguished from a point defense or line defense.

area evacuation The movement of merchant ships, under naval control, from a threatened general area to safer localities.

area fire Fire delivered on a prescribed area. The term is applicable regardless of the tactical purpose of the fire, but area fire is generally neutralization fire.

area, forward The combat zone.

area of operations That portion of an area of conflict necessary for military operations, either offensive or defensive, pursuant to an assigned mission, and for the administration incident to such military operations.

area of war That area of land, sea, and air which is, or may become, involved directly in the operations of war.

area target A target consisting of an area such as an entire munitions factory, rather than a single building or similar point target.

arbalest. (*The Smithsonian Institution, R. G. Packard Collection.*)

ARD. (*U.S. Navy.*)

Argus. (*Canadian Armed Forces photograph.*)

Arethusa A class of British light cruisers of 5,270 tons standard displacement produced in 1935–1937. They had a speed of 32 knots, a complement of 500 men, and main armament consisting of six 6-in. and eight 4-in. guns, six 21-in. torpedo tubes, and one aircraft.

Arethuse A class of French hunter-killer submarines of 400 tons standard surface displacement completed in 1958–1960. They have a speed (submerged) of 18 knots, a complement of 45 men, and armament consisting of four 21.7-in. torpedo tubes.

ARG A U.S. Navy internal-combustion-engine repair ship.

Argentine 7.65mm Madsen machine guns Argentina used six models of the Madsen machine gun, from Model 1910 to Model 1935. See **Madsen machine guns.**

Argentine .45 cal. ACP Halcón Model 1946 submachine gun See **Halcón .45 cal. submachine guns Models 1943 and 1946.**

Argentine .45 cal. Model 1916 and Model

Arizona. (*U.S. Navy.*)

1927 automatic pistols Copies of the Colt M1911 and M1911A1 automatic pistols. Some were produced by Colt, but the majority by an Argentine government arsenal at Rosario, the Fabrica Militar de Armes Portatiles "Domingo Mathieu."

Argentine 9mm Parabellum Halcón Model M.L. 57 submachine gun See **Halcón 9mm submachine gun M.L. 57.**

Argentine Mauser 7.65mm rifle Model 1891 This bolt-action rifle is similar to the 7.65mm M1890 Turkish Mauser and has an overall length of 48.6 in. and a barrel length of 29.1 in. It has an empty weight of 8.58 lb, a five-round magazine, and a muzzle velocity of 2,755 fps.

Argentine Mauser 7.65mm rifle Model 1909 This weapon is a slight modification of the German Gewehr 98 (rifle 98). It is a bolt-action rifle with an overall length of 49 in. and a barrel length of 29.1 in. It has a staggered-row box magazine with a capacity of five cartridges and an empty weight of 9.2 lb. The muzzle velocity is 2,755 fps.

Argentine 9mm Parabellum P.A.M. 1 submachine gun This weapon is a modification of the U.S. M3A1. It varies in that it is manufactured exclusively to fire the 9mm Parabellum cartridge. The overall length has been shortened by about 1 in., the weight has been reduced by over 1 lb, and the rear sights are an open flip type set for either 100 or 200 meters. A fixed aperture is standard on the U.S. M3A1. This weapon has been the standard of the Argentine Army since the late 1940s. A newer model, the P.A.M. 2, has provision for selective semiautomatic fire.

Argument Operation Argument was a concentrated air attack mounted during World War II against German aircraft production facilities. During a 6-day period (also called popularly "The Big Week") that began on February 19, 1944, some 3,800 sorties were flown by all available USAAF and RAF bombers.

Argus The Canadair CP-107 Argus is a Canadian four-engine (piston) reconnaissance aircraft that was first flown in 1957. It has a speed of 315 mph and can carry 4,000 lb of stores internally and two 3,800-lb missiles under the wings.

ARH A U.S. Navy heavy-hull repair ship.

aries An ancient battering ram, named after the Greek god of war.

Ariete The Reggiane Re.2002 Ariete (Ram) was a single-seat single-engine fighter-bomber that was derived from the Italian Falco I and Falco II fighters. First operational in 1942, it flew at speeds of 329 mph and was armed with two 12.7mm Breda-SAFAT machine guns and two 7.7mm Breda-SAFAT machine guns.

Arisaka The popular designation for the 6.5mm (later 7.7mm) rifle of the Japanese Army, its official rifle from 1906 to 1945. A carbine was also known by that name.

Arisaka rifles, carbines See **Japanese 6.5mm rifle Type 30, Japanese 6.5mm rifle Type 38,** and **Japanese 6.5mm rifile Type 97.**

Arizona A U.S. battleship of the Pennsylvania class, commissioned in 1916. It was sunk at Pearl Harbor on December 7, 1941. It sank so rapidly that of the 1,400 men on board, 1,103 were lost (over half the total casualties suffered by the entire fleet at Pearl Harbor). Now enshrined as a memorial, with her crew considered buried at sea, the *Arizona* remains in commission as the senior ship of the U.S. Pacific Fleet.

Arkansas A class of U.S. battleships with a standard displacement of 26,100 tons. There were two ships in the class, *Arkansas* and *Wyoming*, both commissioned in 1912. They had a length of 562 ft, a beam of 106 ft, a speed of 19 knots, and a complement of 1,300 men. The *Arkansas*, in later years, was armed with twelve 12-in. and sixteen 5-in. guns, plus eight 3-in. antiaircraft guns. Three aircraft were carried. It was used during the invasions of Normandy and Southern France, and later during the operations at Iwo Jima and Okinawa.

Ark Royal A British aircraft carrier (ex-*Irresistible*) of 43,000 tons standard displacement completed in 1955. It has a length of 845 ft, a width of 166 ft, a speed of 31.5 knots, and a complement of 2,620 men. It carries thirty aircraft and eight helicopters and is armed with four quadruple Seacat surface-to-air systems. (*Ark Royal* was also the name of an earlier British aircraft carrier completed in 1938. It had a length of 800 ft, a speed of 31 knots, and a complement of 1,575 men; it carried 60 aircraft.)

ARL A U.S. Navy landing-craft repair ship.

arm **1.** A combat branch of a military force. Specifically, a branch of the army, such as the infantry, armored cavalry, or artillery, the primary function of which is combat. **2.** A weapon for use in war (usually "arms"). **3.** To supply with arms, weapons, or means of attack. **4.** To make ammunition ready for detonation, as by removal of safety devices or alignment of the explosive elements in the explosive train of the fuze. **5.** To prepare a nation for war by training troops and producing weapons.

ARM **1.** Antiradiation missile. A term applied to a missile which has as its mission the defeat of surface-to-air missiles (SAM) by destroying the radar sites that guide them through sensing and homing in on the signals produced by the radar. Efforts include **Standard ARM** and **Shrike,** which see. **2.** A U.S. Navy heavy-machinery repair ship.

ARM 1 An antiradiation missile which homes on radar.

armada A fleet or squadron of armed ships.

Ark Royal, under attack by Italian aircraft in the Mediterranean during World War II. (*The Imperial War Museum.*)

armament 1. The weapons of an airplane, tank, ship, or the like; the weapons of a unit or organized force. **2.** *pl.* War equipment, weapons, and supplies.

armatae Ancient ships which were fitted with both sails and oars, but which fought under oars only.

armed Equipped with weapons of offense or defense.

armed forces The military and naval forces of a nation or a group of nations.

armed forces of the United States A collective term for all the components of the U.S. Army, Navy, Air Force, and Coast Guard.

armed guard Naval gun crews on merchant ships during wartime.

armed merchantman An armed merchant ship of a neutral state. Under international law, a vessel may be armed without prejudice to its status as a merchant ship.

armed neutrality A condition in which a country is neutral to powers at war with each other, but armed to protect itself from aggression on the part of either belligerent.

armed peace Peace secured by maintaining a military establishment.

armed reconnaissance A mission with the primary purpose of locating and attacking targets of opportunity, i.e., enemy materiel, personnel, and facilities, in assigned general areas or along assigned ground communications routes, and not for the purpose of attacking specific briefed targets.

armes blanches A French term used by students and collectors to include cutting and thrusting weapons as well as armor.

armet A closed helmet that first appeared in the fifteenth century and was used to protect the head and neck. It became widely popular during the sixteenth century.

armet. (*The Metropolitan Museum of Art, Bashford Dean Memorial Collection, gift of Edward S. Harkness, 1929.*)

armored car. A French armored vehicle of World War II. (*U.S. Army.*)

arming As applied to fuzes, the changing from a safe condition to a state of readiness for functioning. Generally a fuze is caused to arm by such means as acceleration, rotation, clock mechanism, chemical action, electrical action, or air travel or by a combination of these.

arming doublet A close-fitting garment worn under the armor and equipped with padding, mail gussets in the armpits, and laces (points) for attaching pauldrons and vambraces.

arming crew Men who service weapons and supply ammunition to aircraft aboard aircraft carriers.

arming points In armor, the cords attached to the arming doublet or hose and used for tying on various portions of armor. The cords are threaded through holes in the vambrace, cuisses, sabbatons, etc.

arming range The distance from a weapon or launching point at which a fuze is expected to become armed.

arming sword A knight's fighting sword, used for cutting and thrusting.

armins Velvet or cloth coverings placed on the shafts of pikes, halbards, etc.

armistice A truce or suspension of hostilities.

armlet A piece of armor that protects the arm from the bowstring.

armor 1. Any physical protective covering, such as metal, used on tanks, airplanes, etc., or on persons, against projectiles or fragments. **2.** Armored units or forces such as tanks, antitank guns, and mechanized artillery. **3.** In a weapon system, that component which gives protection to the vehicle or the weapon on its way to the target.

armored car A wheeled motor vehicle with protective armor plate designed for combat use and usually equipped with armament.

armored cavalry Units organized and equipped to perform missions requiring great mobility, fire power, and shock action. In modern practice, the combat personnel are mounted in organic armed and armored vehicles such as tanks, self-propelled weapons, and personnel carriers.

Armored Commando V-100 Another name for the U.S. armored car M706. This wheeled, armored, and armed amphibious vehicle is the only armored car presently in the U.S. inventory. It has a weight of 13,500 lb and a maximum speed of 62 mph and is designed to carry either 12 troops (in the fixed-turret version) or 9 men (rotating-turret) on reconnaissance and escort missions. It is armed with either twin .30 cal. or one .30 and one .50 cal. machine gun.

armored infantry A field army unit designed to close and destroy the enemy by fire and maneuver, to repel hostile assault in close combat, and to provide support for tanks.

armored personnel carrier An armored vehicle which provides protection from small-arms fire and shell fragments; it is used to transport personnel both on and off the battlefield. The APC shown (designated *Schützenpanzer* in German) is built by the Austrian firm of Steyr-Daimler-Puch and is armed with a 20mm cannon.

armored reconnaissance airborne assault vehicle A lightly armored, mobile, full-tracked vehicle serving as the main reconnaissance vehicle in infantry and airborne operations and as the principal assault weapon of airborne troops.

armored vehicle A wheeled or track-laying vehicle mounting armor plate, used for combat security or cargo. Armored vehicles include tanks, personnel carriers, armored cars, self-propelled artillery, and various special-purpose vehicles.

armorer Originally, the craftsman who forged the various parts of a suit of armor from steel plates and riveted them together.

armored personnel carrier. (*Steyr-Daimler-Puch.*)

Later, a person who made, modified, cleaned, or repaired arms. Currently defined as a person, particularly a ground-crew member, who repairs, loads, and services aircraft armament and bombs.

armor garniture This consists of armor and its "double pieces," the reinforcing plates used to adapt the basic unit for various uses in the field and several forms of military sport.

armor-piercing (AP) Said of ammunition, bombs, bullets, projectiles, and the like; designed to penetrate armor and other resistant targets.

armor-piercing bomb A missile, designed for dropping from aircraft, which is capable of penetrating the heaviest deck armor without breaking up. Also effective against reinforced-concrete structures, it usually contains an explosive charge of explosive D, making up about 15 percent of the total weight of the bomb.

armor-piercing bullet A bullet having a hard metal core, a soft metal envelope, and a bullet jacket. When the bullet strikes armor, the envelope and jacket are stopped, but the armor-piercing core continues forward and penetrates the armor.

armor-piercing incendiary (API) Armor-piercing projectiles specially designed to set fires after piercing armor.

armor-piercing incendiary tracer An armor-piercing projectile designed to set fires after piercing armor, and also fitted with a tracer for spotting.

armor-piercing sabot (APS) A type of projectile which is armor-piercing and which incorporates a sabot.

armor-piercing tracer (AP-T, APT) An armor-piercing projectile fitted with a tracer for spotting.

armor plate A plate of armor. The French made practical use of naval armor during the Crimean War of 1855. It was made of iron. By 1876 iron gave way to plates of

steel or of steel-faced iron.

armory 1. A place or building where arms are stored or where drills and reviews are held. **2.** Aboard ship, a compartment where small arms and light machine guns are stowed and serviced. **3.** Formerly, a place or building where arms were manufactured.

arms Weapons of offense or defense. Generally speaking, objects of any kind that may be used as weapons.

arms chest A box or case used as a portable locker for holding or transporting small firearms.

arms control 1. Any plan, arrangement, or process, resting upon explicit or implicit international agreement and governing any aspect of the following: the numbers, types, and performance characteristics of weapon systems (including their command and control, logistics, support arrangements, and any related intelligence-gathering mechanisms) and the numerical strength, organization, equipment, deployment, or employment of the armed forces retained by the parties. (It encompasses "disarmament,") **2.** On some occasions, those measures taken for the purpose of reducing instability in the military environment.

arms locker A chest or cabinet in which small arms are stored or displayed.

arms rack A frame or fitting, usually vertical, for storing arms.

Armstrong gun A cannon developed by Sir W. G. Armstrong in England in about 1850. It consisted of multiple tubes of wrought iron shrunk around one another. Smaller calibers were normally breechloaders; larger ones loaded from the muzzle.

army The land military forces of a nation. Also, a unit of the U.S. Army made up of two or more army corps.

army base A base or group of installations for which a local commander is responsible, consisting of facilities necessary for support

of army activities. It includes the security, internal lines of communications, utilities, plants and systems, and real property for which the army has operating responsibility.

army corps A tactical unit larger than a division and smaller than a field army. A corps usually consists of two or more divisions together with auxiliary arms and services.

army group Several field armies under a designated commander.

Army List An officially published list of the commissioned officers in an army.

army of occupation A military government operated by an army in territory formerly held by a defeated enemy.

Army of Occupation Medal A U.S. military decoration awarded persons who have served with U.S. occupation forces under certain conditions since World War II.

Army Register In the United States, a War Department annual register that contains the names of army officers and a brief summary of their service.

arquebus See **harquebus.**

arquebusier See **harqebusier.**

array 1. A naval term describing two or more hydrophones feeding into a common

arresting gear. A U.S. Navy Crusader fighter landing aboard the U.S.S. *Midway* (CVA-41). (*U.S. Navy.*)

receiver. **2.** Order or disposition in regular lines for battle.

arresting gear A system of wires on an aircraft-carrier deck that are designed to stop an airplane after its tail hook has engaged it.

arrière-garde In the fourteenth century an army was divided into three parts: the *avant-garde*, the *bataille*, and the *arrière-garde*. The *avant-garde* was closest to the line of battle, and the *arrière-garde* was the farthest away. It thus constituted the reserve.

arrow 1. A missile weapon made to be

arrow. (*The Smithsonian Institution.*)

ARS, the U.S.S. *Current.* (*U.S. Navy.*)

shot from a bow. It consists of a straight wooden shaft with a sharp head of stone or metal and is fitted with feathers to improve its flight characteristics. **2.** In fortifications terminology, a work placed at the salient angle of the glacis. It communicated with the covered way.

arrowhead The striking end of an arrow. It may consist of a thin stone or metal wedge with or without a barb or barbs.

arrow projectile A relatively long projectile which is designed to be fired from a gun of a caliber considerably larger than the diameter of the projectile body. It is stabilized by fins having a span approximately that of the caliber of the gun. This design

is made for the purposes of increasing the velocity, of decreasing the time of flight, and/or of increasing the striking energy of the projectile.

ARS A U.S. Navy salvage ship.

ARSD A U.S. Navy salvage-lifting ship.

arsenal A place where arms or ammunition is produced and where materiel is stoned, repaired, and issued.

arshin A Russian unit of measure equal to a pace and equivalent to .78 yd. All Russian rifles manufactured before 1930 had sights graduated in arshins.

arsine (SA) This war gas is a blood agent and has a delayed-action casualty effect. Effects are delayed from 2 hours to as much as 11 days. SA interferes with the functioning of the blood and damages the liver and kidneys. Slight exposure causes headache and uneasiness. Increased exposure causes chills, nausea, and vomiting. Severe exposure damages the blood, causing anemia. See **blood agents.**

ARST A U.S. Navy salvage-craft tender.

ARSV Armored reconnaissance scout vehicle. Also known as "Scout," the U.S. Army's XM800 is a lightweight, aluminum-armored, highly mobile vehicle with an amphibious capability providing mobility for scout elements.

Artemis The program name for active sonar systems which are part of the Trident program of coastal submarine surveillance and detection.

artificer A term once in common use to describe one who works in an arsenal or laboratory on shells, fuzes, grenades, artillery, and so forth.

artificial moonlight A World War II designation to describe illumination from searchlights used during combat.

artillator A fourteenth-century maker of bows, arrows, darts, and other military stores.

artillery Complete projectile-firing weapons consisting of cannon or missile launch-

ers on suitable carriages or mounts. Modern field-artillery cannons are classified according to caliber: *Light:* 120mm and less. *Medium:* 121mm to 160mm. *Heavy:* 161mm to 210mm. *Very heavy:* greater than 210mm. In the beginning, cannons were given names such as "falcon," "minion," "saker," etc. By the early eighteenth century, they were classified by the weight of their solid shot: four-pounder, six-pounder, twelve-pounder, and so forth.

artillery ammunition Ammunition for cannons above 30mm (1.181 in.) in caliber.

artillery bogie The portion of an artillery weapon, consisting of wheels, axles, and various supporting appurtenances, which is the principal weight-bearing unit when the weapon is being transported.

artillery cart A trailer that carries equipment used by artillery units for fire control, communications, and mapping. It is attached to a field gun for traveling.

artillery cleaning staff A round wooden or metal staff with or without a metal handle and with a head unit designed for holding a piece of fabric or cotton for swabbing the bore of a mortar or a short-barrel cannon.

artilleryman One who manages or serves a piece of artillery.

artillery park The camp of one or more field batteries.

artillery preparation Heavy artillery fire delivered before an attack to disrupt communications and disorganize the enemy's defense.

artillery sled A flat-bottomed steel item usually curved up at one end. It usually has wheel welds and attaching facilities for fastening the wheels of artillery mounts. It is used primarily to transport weapons over snow, ice, swamps, or rough terrain.

artillery train A number of pieces of ordnance mounted on traveling carriages.

ARV **1.** Armored recovery vehicle. The U.S. Army's M578 ARV is used to recover vehicles and self-propelled artillery in the 15- to 30-ton class. It uses the same body, suspension, and power train components as the 175mm field-artillery gun (M107) and 8-in. howitzer (M11). **2.** A U.S. Navy aircraft repair ship.

ARVA A U.S. Navy aircraft repair ship, aircraft.

ARVE A U.S. Navy aircraft repair ship, engine.

ARVH A U.S. Navy aircraft repair ship, helicopter.

arx An obsolete term for a fort or castle.

AS A U.S. Navy submarine tender.

AS-1 A Soviet air-to-surface missile. See **Kennel.**

AS-2 A Soviet air-to-surface missile. See **Kipper.**

AS-3 A Soviet air-to-surface missile. See **Kangaroo.**

artillery bogie, showing a U.S. 40mm antiaircraft gun (Bofors) of 1941.

AS-4 A Soviet air-to-surface missile. See **Kitchen.**

AS-5 A Soviet air-to-surface missile. See **Kelt.**

AS-30 A French Air Force and Navy supersonic air-to-surface missile with a range of almost 9 mi. The prime contractor is Nord Aviation.

Asashio A class of Japanese 1,960-ton destroyers built in the late 1930s. They had a speed of 35 knots, a complement of 200 men, and armament consisting of five 6-in. and four 25mm guns and eight 24-in. torpedo tubes. All 10 ships of this class were lost during World War II.

ASAT Air search attack team.

ASAU Air search attack unit.

ASDIC Echo-ranging equipment. An acronym formed from Anti-Submarine Detection Investigation Committee. It was the British equivalent of **sonar,** which see.

Ash The NATO code name for a large Soviet air-to-air missile, four of which are carried by the Tupolev Tu-28 (Fiddler). It has a length of about 20 ft and a diameter of 8 in.

ASH A type of submarine-exhaust detection device.

ashcan A depth charge.

ashore Said of a ship on the bottom or on the shore; aground.

Asiatic-Pacific Campaign Medal A U.S. military decoration awarded persons for service of a specified kind within the Asiatic-Pacific theater of war between December 7, 1941, and March 2, 1946.

askar A native infantry soldier in the army of an Arabic-speaking country.

askari Formerly on the east coast of Africa, a native soldier in the service of a European power.

ASM Air-to-surface missile.

ASP Antisubmarine patrol.

ASPB Assault support patrol boat. A U.S. shallow-water gunboat capable of patrolling hostile rivers and shorelines and featuring high speed, shallow draft, armor, firepower, troop space, mine protection, and mine countermeasures.

ASPECT A short-pulse ASW classification device designed for destroyer use but then used in helicopters.

aspect angle The angle between the longitudinal axis of the target (projected rearward) and the line of sight to the interceptor measured from the tail of the target.

aspic A light French cannon of the Renaissance.

Aspidistra A large medium-wave radio transmitter used during World War II to broadcast secretly from England to Germany. It was capable of changing its wavelength very quickly and was used to interrupt German military communications and sometimes to take over frequencies of German home stations.

ASR, the U.S.S. *Chanticleer* (ASR-7). (*U.S. Navy.*)

aspis A large Greek round or oblong shield frequently made of bronze.

ASR 1. A U.S. Navy submarine rescue vessel. **2.** Air-sea rescue.

Asroc A rocket-assisted antisubmarine ballistic weapon developed by Honeywell for the U.S. Navy and operational in 1961. It is a ballistic rocket carrying as payload an Mk 44 Model 0 high-speed acoustic homing torpedo. The length of the weapon is 15 ft, the firing weight is 1,000 lb, and the range is from 1 to 6 mi. The Navy designation is RUR-5A.

ASSA A U.S. Navy cargo submarine.

assagai A slender hardwood spear or light javelin used by certain tribes in South Africa. It is usually tipped with iron.

assault 1. The climax of an attack; closing with the enemy in hand-to-hand fighting. **2.** In an amphibious operation, the period cf time from the crossing of the line of departure by the first scheduled wave to the seizure of the initial objectives. **3.** To make a short, violent, but well-ordered attack against a local objective, such as a gun emplacement, a fort, or a machine-gun nest. **4.** A phase of an airborne operation beginning with delivery by air of the assault echelon of the force into the objective area and extending through attack of assault

Asroc. (*U.S. Navy.*)

assault waves, showing U.S. Marine Corps LVTP tracked personnel landing vehicles. (*U.S. Navy.*)

objectives and consolidation of the initial airhead.

assault aircraft Powered aircraft, including helicopters, which move assault troops and cargo into an objective area and which provide for their resupply.

assault boat A square-ended or round-ended watercraft constructed of rigid materials and designed for landing troops upon a bridgehead. It is unframed except on the bottom and has a handrail-type gunwale for facility in carrying the craft. It is commonly paddled. It may be designed for attaching at the stern to another, similar craft.

assault craft Landing craft used in amphibious operations.

assault gun Any of various sizes and types of guns that are self-propelled or mounted on tanks and are used for direct fire from close range against point targets.

assault line The line of combat units committed to the attack and intended to execute the assault.

assault shipping Amphibious vessels carrying assault troops and equipment for a landing operation.

assault waves Scheduled, leading waves of boats and amphibious vehicles of an amphibious landing.

assembly A drumbeat or bugle call used as a signal for troops to assemble.

asser A weapon used on Roman warships. It consisted of an iron-headed, heavy pole and was used to batter enemy ships.

ASSP A U.S. Navy transport submarine.

astern Toward the back or after end of a ship or formation.

ASTOR Antisubmarine *tor*pedo. For details of this submarine-launched nuclear-warhead torpedo, see **U.S. torpedo Mark 45.**

Astra 9mm (Largo) automatic pistol Model 1921 This pistol was adopted by Spain in 1921. It is unusual in that it will chamber and fire the following cartridges: 9mm Largo (Bergmann Bayard), 9mm Browning Long, 9mm Parabellum, 9mm Steyr, and the .38 cal. super automatic. It has an overall length of 8.7 in., a 5.9-in. barrel, and

a weight of 2.1 lb. It has a muzzle velocity (9mm Largo) of about 1,210 fps and uses a detachable box magazine with a capacity of eight cartridges.

astragal In gunnery, the narrow, rounded molding, usually flanked by fillets, used as decoration on muzzle-loading cannon tubes.

ASW 1. Antisubmarine warfare. A generic term applied to any method or equipment (such as detection, surveillance, or destruc-

Astra 9mm (Largo) automatic pistol Model 1921. (*Spanish Ministry of Defense.*)

tion) used for the defeat of enemy submarine operations employing a ground-, air-, sea-, or satellite-based system. **2.** A U.S. Navy antisubmarine warfare or support aircraft carrier.

asymmetry factor The ratio of length to width of a sea target.

as you were A command meaning "resume former activity or formation."

AT A U.S. Navy oceangoing tug.

ATA A U.S. Navy auxiliary oceangoing tug.

atash bazi Eighteenth-century fire-throwing machines used in India.

ATC A U.S. Navy armored troop carrier.

ategar An old English hand dart. It is so called from the Saxon *aeton*, "to fling," and *gar*, "a weapon."

ATF U.S. Navy fleet ocean tug.

athanati A 1,000-man corps in the ancient Persian Army. They were called "The Immortals" because as one of the members died, another was put in his place.

Atherstone A class of British frigates (ex-escort destroyers) of 1,000 tons standard displacement completed in 1940–1941. They had a speed of 25 knots, a complement of 146 men, and armament consisting of four 4-in. guns and two 20mm antiaircraft guns.

athwartships Said of anything that extends or moves from side to side in a ship or aircraft; in a direction at right angles to fore and aft.

ATL A U.S. Navy tank landing craft.

Atlanta 1. A class of U.S. light cruisers (CL) converted to Juneau class antiaircraft cruisers (CLAA). See **Juneau. 2.** A class of U.S. 6,000-ton light cruisers completed in 1942. There were four ships in the class: *Atlanta, Juneau, San Diego,* and *San Juan.* They had a length of 541 ft, a beam of 52

AT. (*U.S. Navy.*)

Atlanta. (*U.S. Navy.*)

ft, and a speed of 38 knots. They were armed with twelve 5-in. guns, twelve smaller antiaircraft guns, six 21-in. torpedo tubes, and two airplanes. *Atlanta* and *Juneau* were sunk by the Japanese at the Battle of Guadalcanal in November 1942.

Atlantic The French Breguet Br 1150 twin-engine (turboprop) long-range maritime reconnaissance aircraft was first flown in 1961 and has a crew of 12. It has a speed of 380 mph and may be armed variously with bombs, depth charges, rockets, and torpedoes. It is in service with the French, German, and Netherlands forces.

Atlantic Charter A declaration of eight major principles in the national policies of the United States and Great Britain, including disavowal of territorial aggrandizement, restoration of sovereign rights, self-government, access on equal terms to raw materials, freedom of the seas, and the disarmament of aggressor nations. The declaration was made at a meeting in the North Atlantic by President Roosevelt and Prime Minister Churchill on August 14, 1941.

Atlantis The most successful German raider cruiser of World War II. See **raider cruisers.**

Atlas ICBM A liquid-propellant, one-and-a-half stage, rocket-powered intercontinental ballistic missile equipped with a nuclear warhead; designated as CGM-16. The CGM-16D is equipped with radio-inertial guidance and dispersed by complexes. The CGM-16E and HGM-16F are equipped with all-inertial guidance and deployed in a hardened and dispersed configuration. The Atlas ICBM has a speed of 15,000 mph, a range of 6,300 mi, and a weight of 260,000 lb. The prime contractor is General Dynamics/Astronautics.

atlatl A Mexican spear-thrower.

at my command The command used when it is desired to control the exact time of delivery of fire.

ATO A U.S. Navy ocean tug, old.

Atoll The NATO code name for a Soviet air-to-air missile similar in many respects to the U.S. Sidewinder. It has infrared guidance, a single-stage solid-propellant engine, a length of 110 in., and a diameter of 4.75 in. It is carried by the MiG-21 (Fishbed) fighter.

atomic age A period of history marked by the first utilization of atomic energy. It can be considered to have begun on August 6, 1945 (when the first atomic bomb was used in warfare at Hiroshima, Japan); on July 16, 1945 (the date of the explosion of the first experimental atomic bomb at Alamogordo, N.Mex.); or on December 2, 1942 (the date of the first successful operation of a uranium pile in Chicago, Ill.).

atomic bomb A bomb whose explosive power derives from the sudden release of atomic energy. The release is the function of splitting, or fission, of the heavy nuclei of uranium or plutonium atoms by bombardment with neutrons. The atomic bomb dropped on Hiroshima on August 6, 1945, was nicknamed "Little Boy." It weighed 9,700 lb and had the explosive power of 20,000 tons of TNT. It was 129 in. long and 31.5 in. in diameter. It devastated four sq mi in the heart of Hiroshima, killing 66,000 and injuring 69,000. Sixty-seven percent of the city's structures were destroyed or se-

Atlas ICBM. (*U.S. Air Force.*)

atomic bomb. Nuclear weapon of the "Little Boy" type, the kind detonated over Hiroshima, Japan, in World War II. (*U.S. Air Force.*)

attack aircraft carrier, the U.S.S. *John F. Kennedy* (CVA-67) of the Kitty Hawk class. (*U.S. Navy.*)

Audaz. (*Spanish Ministry of Defense.*)

Auk. (*U.S. Navy.*)

verely damaged. The bomb dropped on Nagasaki on August 9, 1945, was a 2-kiloton bomb nicknamed "Fat Man." It killed 39,000, injured 25,000, and destroyed or severely damaged 40 percent of Nagasaki's structures.

atomic cannon The popular name for the **U.S. 280mm gun cannon M-66,** which see.

atomic demolition munition A nuclear device designed or adapted for use as a demolition munition.

atomic warfare Nuclear warfare.

atomic warhead A warhead designed to

produce nuclear fission or fusion to destroy a target area.

atomic weapon A bomb, shell, guided missile, or the like in which the warhead consists of nuclear-fissionable radioactive material such as uranium 235 or plutonium 239 as the explosive charge.

ATR A U.S. Navy ocean tug, rescue.

ATS A U.S. Navy salvage tug.

ATSS A U.S. Navy auxiliary training submarine.

attached artillery Artillery attached temporarily to a subordinate infantry unit.

attack To assault or to fall upon with force.

attack aircraft carrier (CVA, CVAN) A warship designed to support and operate aircraft, engage in attacks on targets afloat or ashore, and engage in sustained operations in support of other forces. In the U.S. Navy they are designated as CVA and CVAN. CVAN is nuclear-powered.

attack bomber A light or medium bomber designed or modified for low-flying bombing or strafing attacks.

attack cargo ship (AKA) A naval ship designed or converted to transport combat-loaded cargo in an assault landing. Landing-craft carrying capability, speed of ship, armament, and size of hatches and booms are greater than those of comparable cargo-ship types.

attack carrier striking forces Naval forces, the primary offensive weapon of which is carrier-based aircraft. Ships, other than carriers, act primarily to support and screen against submarine and air threat and secondarily against surface threat.

attack director The computing element of an ASW fire-control system.

attack force All ships, troops, and aircraft used in the assault phase of an amphibious operation.

attack group A subordinate task organization of the Navy forces of an amphibious task force. It is composed of assault shipping and supporting naval units designated to transport, protect, land, and initially support a landing group.

attack heading 1. The interceptor heading during the attack phase which will achieve the desired track-crossing angle. **2.** The assigned magnetic-compass heading to be flown by aircraft during the delivery phase of an air strike.

attack plane A multiweapon carrier aircraft which can carry bombs, torpedoes, and rockets.

attack transport (APA) A naval ship designed for combat-loading a battalion landing team with its equipment and supplies and having the facilities, including landing craft, for landing them on a hostile beach.

attend the side A naval term to call personnel to the quarterdeck to meet important persons.

attention The attitude of readiness for action on receiving orders which is assumed in response to the command of "attention."

attrition The reduction of the effectiveness of a force caused by loss of personnel and materiel.

attrition minefields Minefields intended primarily to cause damage to enemy ships.

attrition minesweeping Minesweeping designed to minimize the number of live mines at any one time in a channel or area being subjected to heavy, continuous mining attack when clearance sweeping is impossible and port closure unacceptable.

attrition rate A rate, usually expressed as a percentage, reflecting the loss of personnel or equipment due to defined causes in a given period of time.

Atwell shelter A prefabricated half-cylindrical hut of wood, fiber glass, and canvas, used especially in cold-weather areas for personnel shelter or storage.

Audaz A class of Spanish antisubmarine destroyers of 1,227 tons standard displacement completed in 1953–1964. They have a length of 308 ft, a beam of 30.5 ft, a speed of 31.6 knots, and a complement of 191 men. They are armed with two 3-in. guns,

Australia. (*Royal Australian Navy.*)

two 40mm guns, and two side-launching racks for antisubmarine torpedoes.

Augusta A class of U.S. heavy cruisers (CA) of about 9,050 tons standard displacement completed in 1930–1931. There were six ships in the class. They had a length of 570 ft, a beam of 66 ft, and a speed of 33 knots. Main armament consisted of nine 8-in. and four 5-in. guns. Four aircraft were carried.

Auk A class of U.S. ocean minesweepers (AM) of 890 tons standard displacement completed in 1942–1945. They had a length of 215 ft, a beam of 32 ft, a speed of 18 knots, and a wartime complement of 105 men. They were armed with one 3-in. gun and two or four 40mm antiaircraft guns.

AUM An air-to-underwater missile.

Austen Mk I submachine gun The *Australian Sten* submachine gun incorporates design elements of the English Mk II Sten and the German MP-40 submachine guns. It is designed to fire the 9mm Parabellum cartridge and has a muzzle velocity of 1,280 fps. Operating on the blowback principle, it has selective full-automatic and semiautomatic fire and a cyclic rate of fire of 500 to 550 rounds per minute. With stock retracted, it is 21.75 in. long and has a barrel length of 7.80 in. With a 28-round magazine, the weight of the weapon is 10.25 lb. The rear sight is a fixed aperture set for 100 yd. Production from 1942 to 1945 was about 20,000 weapons.

Australia An Australian heavy cruiser of 10,000 tons standard displacement completed in 1929 and originally a sister ship of *Cumberland* in the Royal Navy. Another sister ship, *Canberra*, was torpedoed in the Battle of Savo Island and subsequently sank

on August 9, 1942. *Australia* had a length of 630 ft, a beam of 68 ft, a speed of 31.5 knots, and a complement of 679 men. It was armed with six 8-in. guns, eight 4-in. guns, twenty 40mm guns, and sixteen two-pounders.

Australian 9mm Parabellum submachine gun Model F1 Of Australian design and manufacture, this weapon is of blowback operation and capable of automatic fire only. The overall length is 28.12 in., and the weight, with bayonet, is 9.88 lb. It has a cyclic rate of fire of 600 rounds per minute and a muzzle velocity of about 1,300 fps. It utilizes a 34-round magazine. (Picture, next page.)

Australian 9mm Parabellum submachine gun Model X3 A blowback-operated submachine gun designed with many of the desirable characteristics of the Owen submachine gun, the standard weapon of the Australian Army from 1941 to 1962. Officially adopted in 1962, it uses 9mm Parabellum cartridges and has selective full automatic and semiautomatic fire. It has a cyclic rate of fire of 600 rounds per minute and, with a standard 34-round magazine, weighs 8.80 lb. The length is 28.12 in., and the barrel length is about 8 in. The muzzle velocity is approximately 1,200 fps. (Picture, next page.)

Austrian 8mm machine guns (Maxim) The Models 1889 and '89/04 were weapons of the Maxim machine-gun type. See **Maxim machine gun.**

Austrian 9mm Parabellum submachine gun MP 34 See **Steyr-Solothurn 9mm Mauser submachine gun MP 34.**

Austrian 105mm self-propelled gun,

Australian 9mm Parabellum submachine gun Model F1. (*Australian Department of Supply.*)

Panzerjager K See **PANZERJAGER K.**

Austrian Solothurn Model 30 machine gun See **Solothurn 8mm machine gun Model 30S.**

Austro-Hungarian 80mm gun, Model 1914 A World War I weapon that fired a 14.7-lb projectile and had a range of 9,514 yards.

Austro-Hungarian 100mm light howitzer, Model 1914 A Skoda-produced World War I weapon that fired a 35-lb projectile and had a range of 8,748 yards.

Austro-Hungarian 150mm howitzer, Model 1916 A Skoda-produced World War I weapon that fired a 96-lb projectile and had a range of 12,029 yards.

authentication Communication security measure designed to prevent fraudulent transmissions.

authentic document A document bearing a signature or seal attesting that it is genuine and official. If it is an enemy document, it may have been prepared for purposes of deception, and the accuracy of such a document, even though authenticated, must be confirmed by other information, e.g., conditions of capture.

auto cat An airplane that is used to relay radio messages automatically.

autoloading Self-loading. An autoloading gun fires, extracts, ejects, and reloads once with each action of the firing mechanism.

Automat See **Federov 6.5mm semiautomatic rifle Automat.**

automatic Said of a firearm that employs either gas pressure or force of recoil and mechanical spring action for ejecting the empty cartridge case after the first shot and loading the next cartridge from the magazine.

automatic feed mechanism A mechanism in an automatic gun that puts fresh cartridges into the chamber, ready for firing.

automatic fire Continuous fire from an automatic gun, lasting until the pressure on the trigger is released. Automatic fire differs from semiautomatic fire of automatic weapons and from single-shot fire of hand-loaded weapons, in both of which a separate trigger pull is required for each shot fired.

automatic gun charger A gun charger that includes a mechanism for the clearance of gun stoppages and the retention of the breech mechanism to the rear of the gun receiver.

automatic pilot An automatic control mechanism for keeping an aircraft in level flight and on a set course. Sometimes called "gyro pilot," "mechanical pilot," or "robot pilot."

automatic pistol A pistol capable of automatic or, more commonly, semiautomatic fire.

automatic rifle A rifle capable commonly of either semiautomatic or full automatic fire.

automatic sight A gunsight, especially a telescopic sight, by means of which the alignment of the laying points or telescope on the object to be hit brings the gun into the proper position as to elevation and direction.

automatic weapon Specifically, as used in reference to antiaircraft artillery, any weapon of 75mm or smaller.

auxiliary landing field (ALF) A landing facility normally used for special purposes or emergencies, but normally regarded as a part of an air-station complex.

AV A U.S. Navy seaplane tender.

Avalanche The World War II code name for the Allied amphibious assault on Salerno, Italy, the objective of which was to capture Naples and nearby airfields. It took place on September 9, 1943, and involved the first landing of U.S. forces on the European continent in the war.

avast In naval parlance, an order to stop, to cease hauling.

AVB A U.S. Navy advance aviation base ship.

AVC A U.S. Navy large catapult lighter.

AVD A U.S. Navy seaplane tender (destroyer).

Avenger The Grumman TBF-1 single-engine carrier-based torpedo bomber developed for the U.S. Navy and used during World War II. It had a speed of 271 mph, a range of 1,215 mi with one torpedo, and armament consisting of one .50 cal. and one .30 cal. machine gun.

aventail A synonym for **camail,** which see.

AVG A U.S. Navy aircraft escort vessel.

AVH A U.S. Navy aircraft rescue boat.

aviation badge See **wings.**

Avia B-534 One of the few biplanes in service at the beginning of World War II, this single-seat enclosed-cockpit airplane was used by the Czech Army Air Force. After Germany occupied Czechoslovakia, the Luftwaffe used them as fighter-trainers and as tugs. After the Slovak Air Force was formed, these airplanes saw service on the Russian front. They had a speed of 245 mph and were armed with four 7.7mm machine guns. (Picture, p. 42.)

Aviatik B.II and B.III Austro-Hungarian two-place single-engine biplane reconnaissance aircraft first flown in 1915. The B.II

Australian 9mm Parabellum submachine gun Model X3. (*Australian Department of Supply.*)

had a speed of 67 mph and carried two 22-lb bombs for nuisance raids. The B.III was armed with a Schwarzlose machine gun on a flexible mounting in the rear. By 1916 they had been withdrawn from the front line and were being used as trainers.

Aviatik D.I An Austro-Hungarian single-seat single-engine biplane fighter first flown early in 1917. It had a speed of 115 mph and was armed with two forward-firing 8mm Schwarzlose machine guns. It served until the Armistice on the Balkan, Italian, and Russian fronts.

Aviere A class of Italian destroyers of 1,620 tons standard displacement produced in the

ning of World War II. It had a speed of up to 105 mph. (Picture, next page.)

AVS A U.S. Navy aviation supply ship.

AVT A U.S. Navy auxiliary aircraft transport.

AW A U.S. Navy distilling ship.

awash Said of a ship or other vessel that is so low that water washes over it.

aweigh The position of an anchor which has been broken out and is off the bottom.

Awl The NATO code name for the Soviet missile carried by the MiG Flipper aircraft. It has a length of about 16 ft and a configuration similar to that of the U.S. Sparrow IIIB.

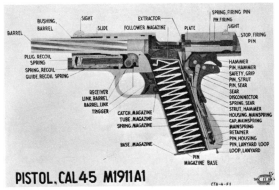

automatic pistol, the U.S. M1911A1. (*U.S. Army.*)

AV, the U.S.S. *Currituck* (AV-7). (*U.S. Navy.*)

late 1930s. They had a speed of 39 knots, a complement of 165 men, and main armament consisting of four 4.7-in. guns and six 21-in. torpedo tubes.

AVLB Armored vehicle launched bridge. This system, constructed of lightweight aluminum alloy, is hydraulically operated and is mounted on a Chrysler Corp. M60 tank chassis. It provides a 60-ft span capable of withstanding weights up to 60 tons. (Picture, next page.)

AVLM Antivehicle land mine.

AVM A U.S. Navy guided-missile ship.

AVP A U.S. Navy small seaplane tender.

AVR A U.S. Navy aircraft rescue vessel.

Avro 504 A British two-place single-engine biplane first flown in July 1913. It was used during World War I in a number of roles: as a reconnaissance plane, as a bomber, as an antizeppelin fighter, and as a trainer. Numerous armament systems were employed, often with a forward-firing machine gun and another weapon for the observer. It was produced for more than 10 years, and more than 10,000 were built, a number of which were still in service at the begin-

Avenger. (*U.S. Navy.*)

Avia B-534. (*Military Historical Institute, Prague.*)

AVLB. (*U.S. Army.*)

Avro 504. (*The Smithsonian Institution, National Air Museum.*)

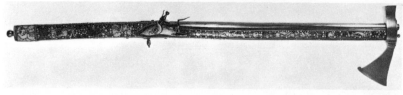

ax pistol. (*The Smithsonian Institution, G. Kennan Collection.*)

awl pike A staff weapon used for thrusting. It had a long, spiked blade, usually quadrangular in section and fitted with a disk at the base.

AWS Aircraft weaponization systems. A U.S. Army designation applying to armament systems for rotary-wing aircraft and including gun pods, mounts, launchers, ammunition, and fire-control equipment.

axial mining Continuous or intermittent nuisance mining in great depth along the axes of enemy advance.

axis An alliance entered into by two or more major powers to demonstrate their solidarity. During World War II, the term "Axis" referred to Germany, Italy, Japan, and the puppet governments of Croatia, Slovakia, and Romania.

Axis Sally The popular name for the American woman (Mildred E. Gillars) who broadcast Nazi propaganda to Allied troops during World War II. She was convicted of treason by a U.S. jury in 1949, but was released in 1961.

ax pistol A combination weapon consisting of a pistol with an ax blade attached.

AZ A U.S. Navy airship tender.

azimuth A direction expressed as a horizontal angle usually in degrees or mils and measured clockwise from north. Thus azimuth will be true azimuth, grid azimuth, or magnetic azimuth, depending upon which north is used.

azimuth circle An instrument for measuring azimuths. It is a graduated circle and may be mounted on a sight or a gun carriage.

azon (*azimuth only*) A kind of bomb used in World War II that had movable control surfaces in the tail adjusted by radio signals to control the bomb in azimuth only. Hence the terms "azon bomb" and "azon missile." Bombs of this type were employed in the CBI (China-Burma-India) theater of operations.

B-2   See **Condor**.

B-3, 4, 5, and 6   See **Panther**.

B-17   See **Flying Fortress**.

B-18   See **Bolo**.

B-24   See **Liberator**.

B-25   See **Mitchell**.

B-26   The designation of the Martin **Marauder**, which see. It may also refer to the Douglas **Invader**, which see, which was originally designated the A-26.

B-29   See **Superfortress**.

B-32   See **Dominator**.

B-34 and B-37   See **Ventura**.

B-36   The Convair B-36 bomber was developed for the USAAF and was first flown in 1946. It was the largest and heaviest warplane ever built. It was equipped with six pusher (piston) engines, and later models were modified to accept an additional four jet engines. This brought the top speed of the aircraft to 439 mph. The B-36 had a crew of 16, a range of 7,500 mi with a 10,000-lb bombload, and armament consisting of eight remotely controlled turrets, each of which contained two 20mm cannons. It was retired in 1958.

B-45   See **Tornado**.

B-47   See **Stratojet**.

B-50   An improved version of the B-29 Superfortress, this Boeing-built aircraft first flew in June 1947. It had a speed of 385 mph and could carry a bombload of 28,000 lb. It was the first aircraft to fly nonstop

B-36. (*U.S. Air Force.*)

B-50. (*U.S. Air Force.*)

around the world, this event taking place in March 1950. Aerial tankers refueled the airplane four times.

B-52 See **Stratofortress.**

B-57 See **Canberra.**

B-58 See **Hustler.**

B-66 See **Destroyer.**

BA See **bromacetone.**

baby incendiary bomb A small British incendiary bomb of World War I.

Baby Nambu 7mm automatic pistol See **Nambu 8mm automatic pistol Model 1904.**

BAC 167 A light attack jet aircraft developed from the Jet Provost and now in service with the air forces of several countries. Built by British Aircraft Corporation, the prototype of this airplane was first flown in 1967. It has a speed of 470 mph and is armed with two 7.62mm machine guns and under-wing loads of rockets, napalm, and bombs.

bacchi The name of two ancient weapons. One resembled a battering ram, and the other cast out fire.

Bachem BA 349A Natter See **Natter.**

backblast A blast of gases to the rear of recoilless weapons, rocket launchers, and rocket-assisted takeoff units. The backblast area is dangerous to personnel.

backfire The rearward escape of gases or cartridge fragments that occurs when a firearm or gun is fired.

background noise Any noise which limits echo detection. At sea, this noise can interfere with sonar and may be caused by sea life, sea action, or the system itself.

Back Net The NATO code name for a type of Soviet E-band early-warning and surveillance radar.

back plate A plate at the rear of the breech mechanism of certain automatic guns. In small arms, it is the plate which closes the rear of the receiver group.

backplate A piece of armor used to cover the back.

Back Porch The code name for a tropo-

spheric scatter communications system installed in Vietnam and linked with U.S. forces in Thailand. It became operational in 1964.

back step In marching, the retrograde movement of a body of men without a change in front.

back strap A band of metal along the back of a revolver or pistol grip or on the grip of a sword.

backsword A sword with a single-edged cutting blade having a flat back. The term is normally applied to seventeenth- and eighteenth-century swords.

back to battery The return of a gun, after recoil, to its firing position.

bacteriological warfare Warfare conducted with bacteriological weapons such as bombs filled with bacteria. See **biological warfare.**

badelaire A short cutting sword with a broad falchion-shaped blade. It dates from the sixteenth century.

badge An award for proficiency or qualification, as in marksmanship.

Badger 1. The NATO code name for the Tupolev Tu-16 swept-back twin-jet medium bomber in service with the Soviet Air Force and Naval Air Force and first seen in 1954. It has a range of 3,975 mi and a speed of 587 mph and is armed with seven 23mm cannons and up to 9 tons of bombs. Badger B carries two Kennel air-to-surface anti-shipping missiles. Badger C carries one Kipper air-to-surface missile. **2.** A weapon developed by the Canadians during World War II. It consisted of a large flame-thrower fitted to a personnel carrier.

Baedeker raid (from the Baedeker guide) In World War II, an air raid upon a historically important English or European city, usually conducted for reprisal rather than against military or industrial installations.

baffle painting Camouflaging a ship with a pattern that gives it a deceptive appear-

ance as to size, form, course, or speed.

bag 1. To "bag" an airplane or other aircraft is to shoot it down or destroy it in a given action. **2.** The envelope or gas chamber of a balloon or other aerostat. **3.** Short for **propellant bag,** which see.

baiky The enclosed ground of an ancient fort.

bailey The court, or courts, of a castle in the Middle Ages.

bail out To jump or eject from an aircraft.

Bainbridge 1. A U.S. nuclear-powered guided-missile frigate (DLGN) of 7,600 tons standard displacement completed in 1962. It has a length of 565 ft, a beam of 57.9 ft, a speed of +30 knots, and a complement of about 450 men. It is armed with four 3-in. guns, two twin Terrier surface-to-air launchers, one ASROC eight-tube launcher, and two triple torpedo launchers. **2.** The name of the U.S. Navy's first destroyer, commissioned in 1902. It had a length of 250 ft, a beam of 23.5 ft, a speed of 29 knots, and a complement of 75 men. It was armed with two 3-in. guns and two 18-in. torpedo tubes.

Baiter A German tank destroyer first introduced in 1944 and built by Skoda. It consisted of a 75mm Pak, caliber length 48, mounted on a Czech 38 tank chassis. It had a crew of four and was also armed with a 7.9mm machine gun. It was deployed with tank destroyer battalions in infantry divisions.

baiting A tactic in which the personnel of a submarine are lulled into a false sense of security. The object is to induce them to take action that makes the submarine liable to detection.

Baka bomb A Japanese rocket-propelled manned suicide bomb with a length of 19 ft 10 in., a wingspan of 16 ft 5 in., and a high-explosive warhead weight of 2,640 lb. In operation the bomb is carried aloft by a Betty bomber and launched at an altitude of 27,000 ft. The system was designed for

Bainbridge. (*U.S. Navy.*)

level flight at a speed of 535 mph and a speed in the final dive of 620 mph. (*Baka* means "foolish," and this is a slang reference to the system. The Japanese called it *Jinrai Butai*, which means "divine thunderbolt.")

bake off   To fire unintentionally. It refers to the fact that an automatic or semiautomatic weapon gets very hot when it is fired. If a cartridge remains in the chamber, the heat of the metal can cause it to fire. The bolt of the weapon should be cleared to avoid this problem. "Cook off" has the same meaning.

Baker rifle   A short military muzzle-loading flintlock rifle of .625 cal. designed by Ezekiel Baker, a London gunsmith. It was adopted in 1800 as the first official British service rifle. It was manufactured until 1838, when it was superseded by the Brunswick rifle.

balance of power   Among nations an equilibrium in the ability to wage war.

balance step   A goose step.

Balao   A class of U.S. fleet submarines of 1,450 tons standard displacement commissioned between 1943 and 1948. One hundred and twenty-two were produced, and most were operational during World War II. They had a length of 312 ft, a beam of 27.2 ft, a speed of 20 knots on the surface (10 knots submerged), and a complement of about 85 men. They were armed with ten 21-in. torpedo tubes, one 5-in. gun, a 40mm antiaircraft gun, 20mm guns, and .50 cal. machine guns. On November 29, 1944, the *Archerfish* of this class sank the Japanese supercarrier *Shinano* (64,800 tons), the largest ship ever sunk by a submarine. The *Shinano* had been in commission for only 10 days.

balarao   A long, wide two-edged dagger.

baldric   A shoulder belt for a sword or hunting horn.

ball   **1.** A bullet for general use, as distinguished from bullets for special uses such as armor-piercing bullets, incendiary bullets, high-explosive bullets, etc.   **2.** A small-arms propellant which is oblate spheroidal in shape, generally a double-base propellant. The word "ball" is a carryover from a time when most projectiles were spherical in shape.

ball ammunition   Non-armor-piercing small-arms ammunition in which the projectile is solid. It is intended for use against personnel or light material targets or for training purposes.

ball butt   A spherical form of butt found on some wheel-lock pistols, Cossack pistols, etc.

ball cartridge   A term used in the military service applied to a round of small-arms ammunition consisting of a cartridge case, a primer, powder, and a solid bullet.

Ballester Molina .45 cal. ACP automatic

Balao. (*U.S. Navy.*)

ballista. (*The Metropolitan Museum of Art, bequest of Alan Rutherford Stuyvesant, 1954.*)

pistol   A slightly modified copy of the Colt 45 cal. M1911A1 made in Argentina by the firm of Hafdasa. Large numbers were made during World War II. This recoil-operated weapon has an overall length of 8.5 in. and a barrel length of 5 in. and an empty weight of 2.25 lb. The magazine has a capacity of seven cartridges, and the muzzle velocity is 830 fps.

ball gunner   Short for "ball-turret gunner."

ballista   An ancient military engine, often in the form of a crossbow, used for hurling large missiles. Ballistas could propel a 10- or 12-ft javelin or a 5-lb missile to a range of 500 yd. Sometimes the ancients made a missile of pebbles in a matrix of baked clay. Such missiles shattered when they struck and could not be fired back by the enemy. Small ballistas could throw a 1-lb rock to a range of 300 to 350 yd.

ballistic   Pertaining to ballistics or the motion of missiles.

ballistic cap   A hollow metal cap placed over an armor-piercing cap to continue the ogival curve of the head of the projectile and reduce air resistance.

ballistic correction   A correction in aiming a gun, necessary because of variation in powder temperature, gun erosion, or the motion of the target, the wind, or the gun itself.

ballistic curve   The actual path of a projectile under the influence of the resistance of the air, as distinguished from the pa-

rabola it would trace if acted on by gravity alone.

ballistic missile   Any missile which does not rely upon aerodynamic surfaces to produce lift and consequently follows a ballistic trajectory when thrust is terminated.

ballistic-missile early-warning system   An electronic system for providing detection and early warning of attack by enemy intercontinental ballistic missiles.

ballistics   The science or art that deals with the motion, behavior, appearance, or modification of missiles or other vehicles acted upon by propellants, wind, gravity, temperature, or any other modifying substance, condition, or force. The study is divided into **external ballistics** and **internal ballistics,** which see.

ballistics of bombs   The science of the motion of bombs dropped from aircraft.

ballistic table   A table of figures regarding the flight of a given projectile, such as range, angle of departure, time of flight, angle of fall, muzzle velocity, and so forth.

ballistic test   A trial of ordnance, projectiles, armor, or powder to determine suitability for acceptance. It is also called a "proof test."

ballistic trajectory   The trajectory traced by a bomb, shell, rocket, or other missile after the propulsive force is terminated and the body is acted upon only by gravity and aerodynamic drag.

balloon barrage. (*U.S. Army.*)

ball turret, atop a Focke Wulf Condor. (*Vereinigte Flugtechnische Werke—Fokker.*)

ballistite One of the first military smokeless powders. It was invented by Nobel and consisted of 59 percent nitrocellulose and 41 percent nitroglycerine. It is still used in some rocket, mortar, and small-arms ammunition.

ballock dagger See **kidney dagger.**

ballonet A gastight fabric compartment within an airship.

balloon An aerostat without a propelling system. It consists of a bag, usually spherical, of silk or other tough, light material that is made nonporous and filled with heated air or a gas lighter than air.

balloon apron An antiaircraft device consisting of cables hanging perpendicularly from other cables extending between two or more balloons.

balloon barrage An antiaircraft defense normally consisting of a number of balloons, usually together and equipped with balloon aprons, held captive by steel cables, and strategically moored near vital areas or installations. The cables or aprons force attacking planes to fly at higher altitudes, thus impeding attack. Sometimes called "balloon curtain" or "balloon apron."

Balloon Corps An unofficial title given to a small number of balloonists who engaged in tactical observation for the Union Army between June 1861 and July 1863.

balloon gun An early antiaircraft gun developed for use against balloons.

balloting The bounding of a spherical projectile in a smoothbore gun due to space between the bore and projectile.

ball powder A powder with a minimum corrosive effect on gun barrels. It is produced by forming nitrocellulose into small balls.

ball screw A screw that could be attached to the end of the ramrod. It was used to remove lead balls from a muzzle-loading gun.

ball seater A tool to fit a cartridge projectile in line with the axis of the shell.

ball turret A turret in the shape of a ball. It is designed to project or to be let down from the belly of an airplane and to house the gunner. It rotates as the gunner brings his guns to bear.

balta A Turkish battle-ax.

Baltimore **1.** A class of U.S. heavy cruisers (CA) of about 13,600 tons standard displacement completed between 1943 and 1945. There were 14 ships in the class. They had a length of 673 ft, a beam of 71 ft, a speed of 34 knots, and a wartime complement of 1,700 men. They were armed with nine 8-in. and twelve 5-in. guns, plus fifty-two 40mm antiaircraft guns. One helicopter was carried. **2.** A twin-engine bomber developed by Martin for the RAF and used in World War II.

bancal A type of curved eighteenth-century French saber.

banded mail A term resulting from a misconception of early representations of mail that were thought to show a kind of armor consisting of alternate rows of leather or cotton and single chain mail.

banderole A small streamer attached to the head of a lance. In the Middle Ages it was often called a "pencil."

bandhook A rifle. A British soldiers' slang term for **bundook,** which see.

bandit A term used to describe enemy aircraft.

band of fire Extremely dense fire from one or more automatic weapons.

bandoleer In modern parlance, a closed loop of fabric containing pockets designed to accommodate small-arms ammunition. It is used by individual soldiers for carrying ammunition; one or more bandoleers are suspended over the shoulders. In the seventeenth century the term referred to a belt holding separate charges of powder in wooden or metal containers.

bands The strips of metal that encircle the barrel and stock of a gun to hold them together.

Bangalore torpedo A metal tube or pipe that is packed with a high-explosive charge. A Bangalore torpedo is used chiefly to cut a path through barbed wire or to detonate buried mines.

banquette The step of earth within the parapet, sufficiently high to enable standing defenders to fire over the crest of the parapet with ease.

Banshee A U.S. McDonnell-built single-seat twin-jet fighter developed for the U.S. Navy and first flown in 1947. Later versions had a speed of 610 mph.

Bantam A small Swedish wire-guided anti-tank missile designed to be used by an individual soldier and also suitable for mounting on vehicles. Launching weight of the missile is 16.5 lb (including a warhead weight of 4.2 lb); the range is 300 to 2,000 meters. (Picture, next page.)

banzai attack (charge) A reckless massed frontal assault so called because of the shouts with which Japanese soldiers in World War II accompanied such attacks. "Banzai" means "10,000 years," "forever."

BAR Browning automatic rifle.

BARB British angular rate bombsight.

barbacan, barbican An outwork covering the approach to the drawbridge or gateway of a fortress or castle.

Barbarossa Literally, "red beard." A surname of Frederick I (1123–1190), Holy Roman Emperor, who is represented in legend not as dead, but as sleeping in a mountain cave in Thuringia until he comes forth to rescue Germany and make her chief of nations. Operation Barbarossa was the code name for the German invasion of Russia in World War II.

barbed wire A wire, or strand of twisted wires, armed with barbs or sharp points.

barbette A mound of earth, platform, support, or carriage upon which guns are mounted to fire over a wall or parapet, rather than through a port or opening. On warships, the armor protecting the rotating part of a ship's turret below the gunhouse.

barbette carriage A gun carriage that elevates the gun sufficiently to fire over a parapet. (Picture, next page.)

barbole A heavy battle-ax.

barbuta A fifteenth-century Italian helmet.

BARC A U.S. Army 100-ton amphibious

Baltimore. (*U.S. Navy.*)

resupply cargo barge. It has four 165-hp engines. Built by Western Gear, it is a large version of the LARC. (Picture, next page.)

barca A term once used in Spain and the Philippine Islands for a small gunboat. (Picture, next page.)

barce A small gun, shorter and thicker than a falconet, once used aboard ships.

bard A protective covering, of mail or plate, for a horse.

bardiche A polearm with a long, curved ax blade, often crescent-shaped.

barge **1.** A boat for the personal use of a flag officer. **2.** A vessel, usually towed, that carries liquids (e.g., a fuel barge).

Barham A British battleship of the **Queen Elizabeth** class, which see.

Bark See **IL-2.**

barkers An obsolete naval term for lower-deck guns and pistols.

barking irons Large dueling pistols.

Bar Lock The NATO code name for a type of Soviet F-band early-warning and surveillance radar.

bandoleer. (*The Smithsonian Institution.*)

barong A Moro knife or sword with a thick back and a thin edge.

barracks Originally a temporary hut made from branches or trees for sheltering soldiers. Later, the term referred to temporary structures for short occupancy, as during a siege. It now means a building or set of buildings for lodging soldiers.

Barracuda A British Fairey-built three-place naval torpedo bomber used during World War II. It had a speed of 228 mph

Banshee. (*McDonnell Douglas.*)

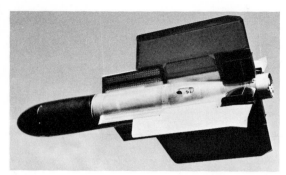

Bantam. (*A. B. Bofors.*)

barbette carriage. (*U.S. Army.*)

BARC. (*U.S. Army.*)

bardiche. (*The Metropolitan Museum of Art, John Stoneacre Ellis Collection, gift of Augustus Van Horne Ellis, 1926.*)

and a range of 1,150 mi and carried six 250-lb bombs.

barrage **1.** A prearranged barrier of fire, except that delivered by small arms, designed to protect friendly troops and installations by impeding enemy movements across defensive lines or areas. **2.** A protective screen of balloons that are moored to the ground and kept at given heights to prevent or hinder operations by enemy aircraft. Also called "balloon barrage." **3.** A type of electronic countermeasure intended for simultaneous jamming over a wide area of frequency spectrum.

barrage balloon A balloon restrained from free flight by means of a cable attaching it to the earth. It is used to support wires or nets as protection against air attacks. See **balloon barrage.**

barrage fire Antiaircraft fire placed as a curtain or barrier across the probable course of enemy airplanes.

barrage jamming The simultaneous jamming of a number of adjacent channels or frequencies (radio or radar).

barrage rocket A combined blast and

fragmentation weapon designed for firing from ship to shore in an amphibious attack.

barrel A metal tube fastened to the action of a weapon. The barrel may be rifled, or it may have a smooth interior surface (bore).

barrel assembly The barrel of a gun with the parts necessary to attach it to the rest of the gun.

barrel helm The barrel-shaped helmet of the thirteenth century. It was flat on top and completely enclosed the head.

barrel life As applied to small-arms and automatic weapons, the number of rounds which may be fired through a barrel at a particular firing schedule before the barrel becomes unserviceable. Barrel life varies with the firing schedule.

barrel shank The threaded portion of a barrel encircled by the receiver.

barricade **1.** A fortification, often in a street. It is made in haste of trees, earth, overturned vehicles, or anything else that will obstruct an enemy. **2.** The aircraft barrier on the flight deck of an aircraft carrier.

barrier **1.** A fence or other obstacle made to stop an enemy. **2.** The collapsible fences on an aircraft-carrier flight deck to stop airplanes which miss the arresting gear. **3.** A fortress or fortified town on a country's frontier.

Barrier A U.S. Navy passive acoustic detection system for antisubmarine warfare. Hydrophones, strung along the ocean floor, listen for sound signatures of submarines passing overhead or nearby. These signals are transmitted by undersea cable to nearby data handling and display centers. Barrier is believed to involve adaptations provided friendly nations for surveillance and tracing of their own. It is related to **Caesar** and **SOSUS,** which see.

barrier gate In fortifications, a gate through a barrier.

barrier minefield (land-mine warfare) A minefield laid to block enemy attack formations in selected areas, especially to the flanks, and to deflect his approach into selected battle areas.

barrier patrol A ship or aircraft patrol designed to detect passage of submarines through a particular ocean area.

bar shot A rodlike projectile for cannons, often confused with crossbar shot. It is a projectile consisting of two spheres, hemispheres, or cylinders connected by a bar of iron. It was once used primarily to destroy masts or rigging in naval combat.

bar sight The rear sight of a firearm. It consists of a movable bar with a notch or peep.

bartizan An overhanging structure for lookout or defense, usually projecting at an angle of a building or near an entrance gateway.

barrel assembly. (*U.S. Army.*)

BARV Beach armored recovery vehicle.

bascinet See **basinet**.

bascule bridge A kind of drawbridge with a counterweight swinging up and down.

base 1. A locality from which operations are projected or supported. 2. An area or locality containing installations which provide logistic or other support. 3. A home airfield or home carrier. 4. In fortifications, the imaginary line connecting the salient angles of a bastioned front. 5. In armor, a quilted defense for the upper legs. 6. In artillery, an iron breechloading swivel gun of the sixteenth and seventeenth centuries. 7. An old boat gun; a wall-piece on the musketoon principle, carrying a 5-oz ball.

base altitude In air operations, an altitude maintained during a given mission, especially on the flight to the target, rendezvous, or the like.

base command An area containing a military base or a group of such bases organized under one commander.

base-ejection shell A type of shell which ejects its load from its base.

base fuze A fuze located in the base of a projectile or bomb.

baselard A fourteenth- and fifteenth-century dagger or short sword with a pommel in the form of a crossbar. The design originated in Basel, Switzerland.

base line In gunnery, the measured line used to obtain ranges by triangulation.

base of operations An area or facility from which a military force begins its offensive operations, to which it falls back in case of

bar shot. (*The Smithsonian Institution, National Museum Collection.*)

reverse, and in which supply facilities are organized.

base of the breech The rear surface of the breech of an old-time cannon. Also called the "breech face."

base piece A directing piece.

base point In gunnery, a well-defined point on the terrain which is used as an origin for direction.

base ring 1. A metal ring which is bolted to the concrete of the emplacement and which supports the weight of a gun or mortar carriage. 2. A ring on the breech of a cannon dividing the base from the first reinforcing ring.

bases Knee-length pleated fabric skirts commonly worn with armor in the early seventeenth century.

base spray Fragments of a bursting projectile that are thrown to the rear in the line of flight (in contrast with "nose spray," the fragments thrown to the front, and "side spray," the fragments thrown to the side).

base unit A unit or organization in a tactical operation around which a movement or maneuver is planned and performed.

base wallah A British soldiers' slang term for a soldier permanently stationed at a base.

bashi-bazouk Formerly, a soldier belonging to irregular Turkish troops.

basic data In gunnery, the essential facts needed to place fire on a target—the location of the target relative to the battery in terms of direction, or deflection; distance, or range; and difference in altitude, or site.

basic intelligence General intelligence concerning the capabilities, vulnerabilities, and intentions of foreign nations; used as a base for a variety of intelligence products for the support of planning, policy making, and military operations.

basic load (ammunition) That quantity of nonnuclear ammunition which is authorized and required by each service to be on hand within a unit or formation at all times.

It is expressed in rounds, units, or units of weight as appropriate.

basilisk An ancient piece of brass ordnance, 10 ft long and weighing 7,200 lb, which is said to have thrown stoneshot weighing 200 lb.

basinet A light helmet, often pointed, which evolved in the fourteenth century. It was so called because it resembled a basin. At first it was open and worn under the battle helmet, but later it was made with a visor. (Picture, next page.)

basket A structure within a tank turret that carries the men who operate the turret. It rotates as the turret rotates.

basket hilt A basketlike guard over the handle of a weapon such as a sword or foil to protect the hand. A series of connecting bars completely covers the hand.

basket mast A type of mast once used on battleships. It was made of straight pieces

baselard. (*The Metropolitan Museum of Art, gift of Jean Jacques Reubell, 1926.*)

of steel tubing interwoven to resemble a basket or cage. (Picture, next page.)

baslard A corruption of "baselard" or "basilard"; a dagger or short sword of the fifteenth century.

bassinet A French term for the pan of a musket.

bastard A term applied to guns of an unusual make or proportion, whether longer or shorter or having a smaller diameter of bore, such as bastard culverin, bastard cannon, etc.

bastard sword See **Hand-and-a-half sword**.

bastide A small fort, blockhouse, or fortified house or tower.

bastille, bastile Originally, a movable wooden tower used in warfare. In feudal fortifications, a tower or elevated work used in the defense of a fortified place.

bastion In fortifications, a structure projecting from the main enclosure of a fortification. It consists of two faces meeting in a salient angle that commands the fore-

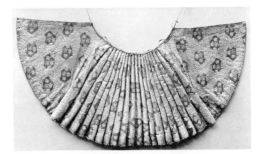

bases. (*The Metropolitan Museum of Art, Rogers Fund, 1921.*)

basinet. (*The Metropolitan Museum of Art, Bashford Dean Memorial Collection, 1929.*)

Bat. (*U.S. Army.*)

ground and outworks. It also has two flanks, each able to defend by a flanking fire the face of the adjacent bastion and the adjacent curtain (the wall joining the flank of one bastion with the adjacent flank of another).

bastionet A small bastion flanking a ditch.

baston A corruption of "baton," a staff or mace.

Bat 1. A U.S. Army recoilless rifle for antitank use. **2.** A U.S. Navy glide bomb carrying a high-explosive payload of 1,000 lb. A winged weapon, it employed active radar homing and had a range of 15 to 20 mi. They were used in the Pacific theater in 1945 and launched by privateer patrol bombers. In one action, a Bat sank a Japanese destroyer at maximum range.

BAT Battalion antitank.

bataille The main division of an army in the fourteenth century.

batardeau 1. A wall built across the ditch of a fortification. It was equipped with a sluice gate to regulate the height of water. **2.** A small sixteenth-century knife carried

in a pocket of the sword sheath.

bateau A lightweight flat-bottomed boat for use on rivers or inland waters.

bathorse A horse that carried baggage during a campaign.

baticole Steel breeches worn under lamboys.

batman In the British Army, the personal military servant of an officer.

baton A kind of club, cudgel, or staff. Later it became the symbol of a leader, and finally the peculiar distinction of the field marshal.

BAT rifle The term commonly applied to the 106mm battalion antitank (BAT) rifle. Also called "BAT weapon."

BAT spotting rifle The term commonly applied to the .50 cal. spotting rifle mounted on the 106mm battalion antitank (BAT) rifle mount.

battalion A body of troops, usually a tac-

tical unit composed of a headquarters and two or more companies or batteries.

battalion landing team In an amphibious operation, an infantry battalion normally reinforced by necessary combat and service elements; the basic unit for planning an assault landing.

Battalion of Death A fighting unit, composed of women, organized in Russia in 1917. It became a part of the Russian Army and saw action in several engagements.

batter An old ordnance term meaning to direct the massed fire of many cannons against any fortress or works.

batterie, battery On the snaphaunce or flintlock, an upright metal striking plate upon which the pyrites or flint falls, causing sparks which ignite the priming powder.

battering charge Formerly in naval gunnery, a charge of powder heavier than the ordinary charge and used against ironclads

basket mast, aboard the U.S.S. *Delaware.* (*U.S. Navy.*)

or masonry at short range for a limited number of shots.

battering ram An ancient device used to beat down the walls or gates of a besieged place. It consisted of a large beam with an iron head, the latter very often in the shape of a ram's head (hence the name). Battering rams were mounted in several ways: on the arms and shoulder of numerous men, suspended from an overhead frame so as to swing back and forth, and mounted on wheels. Some rams were 120 ft in length. They continued in use until cannons became powerful enough to be more effective.

battering train A train of artillery used for siege operations.

battery **1.** A tactical and administrative unit corresponding to a company or similar unit in other branches of the Army. **2.** A group of guns or other weapons, such as mortars, machine guns, artillery pieces, or searchlights, set up under one tactical commander in a certain area. **3.** All guns, torpedo tubes, searchlights, or missile launchers of the same size or caliber or used for the same purpose, either installed in one ship or otherwise operating as an entity. **4.** A tube (barrel) in battery is a gun tube fully returned from recoil upon its cradle. A tube out of battery is a tube not fully returned from recoil. **5.** A variant of **batterie,** which see.

battery chart A chart on which a battery's firing data are tabulated.

battery control The direction of use of all a ship's mounts or turrets of a similar caliber or purpose. The standard types of control include collective, dispersed, divided, and sector.

battery d'enfilade A battery that enfilades a work or a line of troops.

battery dress Flash- and splinter-protective clothing worn in battle by navy men on surface ships.

battery wagon A wagon once used to transport the tools and materials for repair of a battery's carriages.

battle "Battle" usually refers to a general, prolonged fight. It contrasts with "engagement" (which can be an encounter between two armies, smaller subdivisions of armies, etc.) and "action" (which is usually a sharp but brief offensive or defensive operation).

Battle A class of British destroyers of 2,315 tons standard displacement completed in 1945–1947. They had a length of 379 ft, a beam of 40 ft, a speed of 32 knots, and a complement of 337 men (wartime). Armament consisted of four 4.5-in. guns, ten 40mm antiaircraft guns, two depth-charge throwers, and ten 21-in. torpedo tubes. Twenty-four ships of this class were completed.

battle-area control unit (BACU) In World War II, a radar control unit that was set up in a forward area for the purpose of directing aircraft to targets.

battle-ax A form of ax once used as an offensive weapon.

battle-ax pistol A combination of wheellock or flintlock pistol and battle-ax, the butt of the pistol being the handle of the battle-ax.

battle bill A list of battle assignments based on a ship's armament and complement.

battle casualty Any person who is lost to his organization by reason of having been declared dead, wounded, missing, captured, or interned, providing such loss is incurred in action.

battle cruiser A warship used for high-speed, cruising, scouting, and long-range fighting. It has the size and armament of a battleship, but lacks the heavy armor protection of a battleship.

battlefield illumination The lighting of the zone of action of ground combat and combat support troops by artificial means other than invisible rays.

battlefield recovery The removal of disabled or abandoned materiel, either enemy or friendly, from the battlefield and its movement to a recovery collecting point or to a maintenance or supply establishment.

battlefield surveillance The continuous (all weather, day and night), systematic watch over the battle area to provide timely information for combat intelligence.

battle fleet A naval force consisting of all types of warships.

battle gaff A gaff, with battle flag attached, sometimes hoisted on a military mast.

battleground The ground or place where a battle has taken place.

battle lantern Battery-powered electric lanterns for emergency use aboard warships.

battle lights Aboard warships, dim red lights belowdecks for minimum illumination.

battle line A line along which a battle is waged. In naval terminology, a unit composed mainly of battleships and cruisers.

battlements Indentations, consisting of alternate solid parts and open spaces, along the tops of old castles or fortified walls. This arrangement afforded some protection to the defenders.

battleplane An armed military airplane.

battle police A military force detailed to prevent straggling during battle.

battle position A place in which the main effort of the defense is concentrated.

battle quoit See **chakra.**

battle range The range at which a military weapon's sights are adjusted when the weapon is in the normal or carrying position.

battle reserves Reserve supplies accumulated by an army, detached corps, or detached division in the vicinity of the battlefield, in addition to unit and individual reserves.

battleship (BB) A modern battleship is

battle-ax. (The Metropolitan Museum of Art, gift of William H. Riggs, 1913.)

heavily armed and armored. It is a vessel usually displacing 45,000 tons or more, equipped with 16-in. guns, and capable of speeds of 30 knots. (Picture, next page.)

battle sight A predetermined sight setting that, carried on a weapon, will enable the firer to engage targets effectively at battle ranges when conditions do not permit exact sight settings.

battle star A small metal star affixed to a campaign ribbon to denote participation in a battle in that theater of operations.

battle wagon A slang term for a battleship.

bay **1.** A bomb-storage section in the fuselage of an airplane. **2.** The portion of a ship used as a hospital usually in the forward part between decks. **3.** In the construction of military pontoon bridges, the length of bridges between the centers of adjacent pontoons. **4.** In fortifications, a section of trench that lies between two adjacent traverses.

Bay A class of British frigates of 1,580 tons standard displacement completed in 1945–1946. They had a speed of 19.5 knots, a complement of 157 men, and armament consisting of four 4-in. guns, six 40mm and two 20mm antiaircraft guns, one hedgehog, and four depth-charge throwers.

bayonet An edged steel weapon with a tapered point and a formed handle designed to be attached to the muzzle end of a rifle, shotgun, or the like. Bayonets were first introduced in Bayonne, France, in the seventeenth century, and the earlier forms were made to be fitted into the bore of a musket or rifle. (Picture, next page.)

bayonet knife An edged steel weapon with a tapered point and a formed handle for overhand or underhand gripping. It is designed for use as a hand weapon, for general-purpose use in the field, or as a bayonet when attached to the muzzle end of a carbine, rifle, or the like. The blade is less than twice the length of the handle, and it is usually without a blood groove. (Picture, next page.)

bayonet lug A projection on a military weapon for engaging a slot on a bayonet.

bayonet scabbard A leather or metal case for carrying a bayonet.

bazooka The popular name applied to the 2.36-in. rocket launcher used by the United

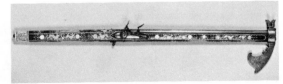

battle-ax pistol. (The Metropolitan Museum of Art, gift of Mrs. George S. Amory, 1964.)

battleship, the U.S.S. *New Jersey* of the *Iowa* class. (*U.S. Navy.*)

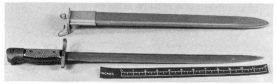

bayonet. (*U.S. Army.*)

bayonet knife, showing the U.S. Army M3A1 (top) and a Russian knife. (*U.S. Army.*)

States in World War II. The later-model 3.5-in. rocket launcher was termed the "super bazooka." The original 2.36-in. model fired a projectile weighing about $3\frac{1}{2}$ lb and had a range of 400 yd. It was 54 in. in length, was breechloading, and weighed about 12 lb. It was so called because of its resemblance to a sound contraption used by Bob Burns, an American comedian.

Bazooka pants A World War II nickname for the additional armor used to protect tank tracks from antitank fire.

BB A short-range bomber (*Blizhnii bombovos*) used in the names of Russian aircraft from 1925 to 1945, as in BB-I, BB-22, etc.

BB A U.S. Navy battleship.

BBC The U.S. military designation for the war gas **bromobenzylcyanide,** which see.

BBG A U.S. Navy guided-missile capital ship.

B Class A class of U.S. submarines commissioned in 1924–1926. They were armed with six 21-in. torpedo tubes and one 3-in. deck gun. They had a submerged speed of 8 knots.

BDL A U.S. Army 600-ton beach discharge lighter.

Be A designation for Soviet aircraft designed by Georgi Mikhailovich Beriev.

Be-6 See **Madge.**

Be-10 See **Mallow.**

Be-12 See **Mail.**

B.E. In a designation system adopted by the British Royal Aircraft Factory in 1911, B.E. signified *Blériot Expérimental.* This merely identified general-purpose two-place tractor biplanes and had no design or other connection with Blériot aircraft.

B.E.1, B.E.2, B.E.2a, and B.E.2b British two-place single-engine observation and bombing biplanes designed by Geoffrey de Havilland and F. M. Green. The B.E.1 was first flown on January 1, 1912. The B.E.2 appeared in February 1912, and 2a's and 2b's followed by 1914. A B.E.2a was the first British aircraft to land in France after the outbreak of World War I. They had a speed of 70 mph and could carry one 100-lb bomb. Their only armament was a rifle or pistol carried by the observer. They were obsolete by late 1915.

B.E.2c and B.E.2d The B.E.2c, a continuation of the B.E. series, was first flown in mid-1914. It could carry two 112-lb bombs and was armed with a free-firing Lewis gun in the rear cockpit. It sometimes carried an upward-firing Lewis gun above the top wing. 2d's entered service in the spring of 1916. These aircraft suffered from the fact that they were too stable to outmaneuver an enemy and too slow to run away. About 1,300 of the two types are estimated to have been produced.

B.E.2e This was the final production model of the B.E. series and represented no real improvement over the performance of earlier types. It has been estimated that upward of 1,800 were built. They had a maximum speed of about 82 mph and served in Macedonia and India as well as on the Western front.

B.E.12 A variation of the B.E.2c, this single-seat single-engine biplane was produced as a fighter, entering production in the late spring of 1916. It had a speed of 97 mph and was armed with twin Lewis guns. Because of its lack of maneuverability, it was reclassified as a light bomber and could carry sixteen 16-lb or two 112-lb bombs.

beach **1.** The area extending from the shoreline inland to a marked change in physiographic form or material or to the line of permanent vegetation (coastline). **2.** In amphibious operations, that portion of the shoreline designated for landing of a tactical organization.

beach capacity An estimate, expressed in

bazooka. An early version of the U.S. 2.36-in. rocket launcher of World War II. (*U.S. Army.*)

B Class, the U.S.S. *Bass.* (*U.S. Navy.*)

terms of measurement tons, or weight tons, of cargo that may be unloaded over a designated strip of shore per day.

beach dump A temporary storage for supplies landed in an amphibious operation.

beach group, naval A naval unit to provide personnel, boats, and equipment to supplement the shore party of the landing force in an amphibious operation.

beachhead A designated area on a hostile shore which, when seized and held, ensures the continuous landing of troops and materiel and provides maneuver space requisite for subsequent projected operations ashore. It is the physical objective of an amphibious operation.

beaching gear A wheeled dolly used for moving a seaplane or flying boat on shore.

beach marker A colored panel or other device used to mark the limits of specific

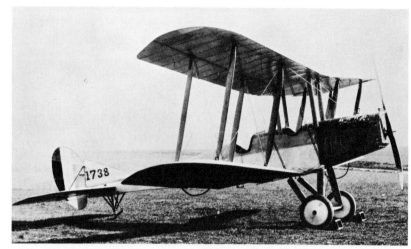

B.E.2C. (*The Smithsonian Institution, National Air Museum.*)

beachhead, showing U.S. LST's unloading men and materiel during the invasion of Leyte Island during World War II. (*U.S. Navy.*)

Bear. (*U.S. Air Force.*)

Bearcat. (*U.S. Navy.*)

Beardmore-Farquhar .303 cal. aircraft machine gun. (*The Smithsonian Institution, Treasury Department Collection.*)

landing beaches for assault craft in an amphibious landing.

beachmaster The naval officer in command of the beachmaster unit of the naval beach group.

beachmaster unit A commissioned naval unit of the naval beach group designed to provide to the shore party a naval compo-nent known as a "beach party" which is capable of supporting the amphibious land-ing of one division (reinforced).

beach matting Steel netting or mesh laid on the soft sand of a beach to improve the traction of vehicles.

beach obstacle An artificial obstacle that is placed on possible landing beaches be-tween the high-water line and the vegeta-tion and is intended for use against person-nel or vehicles.

beach party The naval component of the shore party.

beach reserves In amphibious operations, an accumulation of supplies of all classes established in dumps in beachhead areas.

beach support area The area to the rear of a landing force or elements thereof, estab-lished and operated by shore party units, which contains the facilities for the unload-ing of troops and materiel and the support of the forces ashore; it includes facilities for the evacuation of wounded, prisoners of war, and captured materiel.

beacon **1.** A light or electronic source which emits a distinctive or characteristic signal used for the determination of bear-ings, courses, or location. **2.** Formerly a signal fire on a pole, building, or other height to signal the approach of an enemy.

bead The string of a longbow had a bead tied to the center at the place where the arrow was nocked. When the archer drew the bead, he made ready to shoot. The expression "to draw a bead on somebody" can thus be traced to the days of chivalry.

bead, bead sight The name given the small knob mounted at the muzzle end of the barrel of a firearm to serve as a front sight.

Beagle The NATO code name for the Ilyushin IL-28 four-seat twin-jet tactical bomber in service with the Soviet Air Force and used by several other countries. It first appeared in numbers in 1950 and has a range of 1,500 mi, a speed of 580 mph, and armament consisting of twin 23mm cannon in nose and tail turrets and a bombload of about 4,500 lb.

beak A heavy beam that projected from the prow of an ancient galley. It was com-monly tipped with metal and used to pierce the hull of an enemy vessel.

beaked ax A bill with a hook or beak on the back.

beam The breadth of a vessel at the widest part.

beam attack An attack directed against the side of an aircraft, tank, or ship.

beam rider A missile guided by a radar or radio beam to the target.

bear The bearing or direction of a gun or a ship.

Bear The NATO code name for the Tupo-lev Tu-20 four-engine (turboprop) long-range and maritime reconnaissance bomber in service with the Soviet Air Force and Naval Air Force and first seen in 1955. It has a speed of 500 mph, a range of 7,800 mi, and armament consisting of 20mm or 23mm cannon. Bear A carries up to 25,000 lb of bombs in an internal bay. Bear B carries a Kangaroo air-to-surface missile under the fuselage. Bear C is much the same as Bear B.

Bearcat The Grumman F8F single-seat single-engine shipboard interceptor and fighter-bomber was developed for the U.S. Navy and first flown in August 1944. It was introduced too late in World War II to see combat, but this airplane had exceptional performance and, for a period of time, held the world record for the fastest climb to 10,000 ft. It had a speed of 421 mph and was armed with four .50 cal. machine guns plus two 1,000-lb bombs or four 5-in. rockets.

Beardmore-Farquhar .303 cal. aircraft machine gun A British machine gun of World War I, this weapon was gas- and spring-actuated and air-cooled and had a rate of fire of 450 to 550 rounds per minute. It weighed 16.25 lb (making it one of the lightest machine guns ever constructed) and was fed from a 77-round drum magazine.

bearing The horizontal angle at a given point measured clockwise from a specific reference datum to a second point. It is expressed in three figures from 000 to 360°. True bearing is measured from the north. Relative bearing is measured from the bow of a ship or aircraft.

bearing arrow A military arrow.

bearing bow A military bow.

Beast The NATO code name for the Soviet Ilyushin IL-2 or IL-10 Shturmovik (Stormovik) single-engine two-seat close-support and reconnaissance monoplane of World War II. It was armed with two 23mm cannons and two 7.62mm machine guns in the wings and a 12.7mm machine gun in a rear cockpit. It could carry two 1,100-lb bombs.

beat To give a signal by beating a drum or other instrument.

beat a retreat To retreat or retire from battle. The term comes from the military drum signal to retreat.

beat of drum A certain tempo or pattern of drumbeats which varies according to the command to be imparted, e.g., a call to arms, a call to quarters, and attack.

Beaufighter A British fighter variant of the Type 152 Bristol Beaufort general reconnaissance and torpedo bomber, this two-seat twin-engine night fighter was first flown on July 17, 1939. With the aid of radar this airplane was largely accountable for the defeat of the Luftwaffe's night offensive against Britain in 1940–1941. Later versions of the Beaufighter were used as long-range antishipping strike fighters. They flew at speeds of 333 mph and were armed with four 20mm Hispano cannons and six .303 cal. Browning machine guns.

Beaufort A British Bristol-built aircraft of World War II, the Beaufort could be used as a medium bomber, a torpedo carrier, or a general reconnaissance aircraft. It had a crew of four, a speed of 270 mph, and armament consisting of four .303 cal. machine guns. It could carry a 1,500-lb bomb

Beaufighter. (*British Aircraft Corporation Ltd.*)

Beaumont-Vitali 11mm rifle Model 71/88. (*The Smithsonian Institution, L. Carmichael Collection.*)

Beaver. (*U.S. Air Force.*)

or torpedo load. The torpedo version of this aircraft was called "Torbeau."

Beaufort Scale A system for indicating the velocity of wind. The force is indicated numerically as follows:

Force of wind	Approximate velocity in nautical miles per hour
0. Calm	0–3
1. Light air	7
2. Light breeze	11
3. Gentle breeze	15
4. Moderate breeze	20
5. Fresh breeze	25
6. Strong breeze	30
7. Moderate gale	35
8. Fresh gale	42
9. Strong gale	50
10. Whole gale	56
11. Storm	65
12. Hurricane	78 or over

Beaumont 11mm rifle Model 1871 A single-shot rifle adopted by the Netherlands in 1871. It had an overall length of 52 in., a barrel length of 32.8 in., and a weight of 9.6 lb. It was invented by the Dutch engineer Beaumont in 1870.

Beaumont-Vitali 11mm rifle Model 71/88 The Beaumont Model 1871 rifle modified to a repeating rifle by the addition, in 1888, of a Vitali box-magazine modification.

beaver Originally, the armor which protected the lower part of the face.

Beaver The de Havilland (Canada) Beaver is a single-engine five- to seven-passenger utility aircraft with a speed of 163 mph. When used by American forces, it is designated U-6A.

beavertail A wide, thick fore-end on a

bec-de-corbin. (*The Metropolitan Museum of Art, gift of William H. Riggs, 1913.*)

Belfast. (*Short Brothers & Harland Ltd.*)

Belgian 7.65mm Mauser rifle M1889. (*Belgian Ministry of Defense.*)

tion difficult, and their slow speed complicated interception.

Beehive U.S. Army fléchette-loaded fragmentation shells used with 90mm, 105mm, and 106mm weapons for antipersonnel operations.

Beep See **Dodge weapons carrier.**

beetle A large wooden hammer used for driving in palisades.

Beetles An Allied World War II nickname for concrete and steel pontoons on which rested pier roadways. See **Whales.**

BEF See **British Expeditionary Force.**

beffroi See **belfrey.**

Beholla .32 ACP automatic pistol A German weapon manufactured by Becker & Hollander and widely used in World War I

shotgun or a rifle.

bebra An ancient German javelin, an imitation of the Roman pilum.

bec-de-corbin A fifteenth-century war hammer with a curved point resembling a crow's beak.

bec-de-faucon The fluke of an ax or hammer that is curved to a sharp point in the shape of a falcon's beak.

bed A mortar bed. A solid piece upon which a mortar is placed when fired. It serves the same purpose as a gun carriage.

bedaines Stone bullets of the Middle Ages. They were thrown from catapults.

Bedcheck Charlies The nickname for low-flying Communist aircraft used for making nuisance raids over Seoul or the Korean front lines during the Korean conflict. The wood and fabric construction of these small, antique airplanes made radar detec-

and to some extent in World War II. It has a magazine capacity of seven cartridges, an overall length of 5.51 in., a barrel length of 2.92 in., and a weight of 22.14 oz.

beleaguer To surround with an army as in a siege operation or a blockade.

belemnon An ancient Greek dart.

Belfast **1.** A British four-engine heavy strategic transport built by the firm of Short and first flown in 1964. It carries 200 troops or 78,000 lb of freight, including the largest guns and vehicles used by the British forces. It has a speed of 352 mph. **2.** A British cruiser of improved *Liverpool* type and at one time the largest cruiser in the Royal Navy. (Two ships of this type were completed, the *Edinburgh* having been lost in action in 1942.) *Belfast* had a length of 613 ft, a beam of 66 ft, a speed of 32.5 knots, and a complement of 847 men. Armament

consisted of twelve 6-in. and eight 4-in. guns, plus thirty-four two-pounder pom-poms, seven 40mm and two 20mm antiaircraft guns, and six 21-in. torpedo tubes. It was completed in 1939, but was reconstructed during World War II and again in 1956–1959.

belfrey A movable tower used to a considerable extent in the twelfth and thirteenth centuries. It consisted of wooden frameworks many stories high. The lower part was often occupied by a ram, and the upper parts by armed archers and crossbowmen. Belfreys were equipped with bridges over which the attackers could enter a fortified place.

Belgian 7.65mm machine gun Model 1906–1912 A machine gun of Hotchkiss design. See **Hotchkiss machine guns.**

Belgian 7.65mm machine guns (Maxim) Weapons of the Maxim machine-gun type. Belgian models included the 1908, the '08/15, and the 1911. See **Maxim machine gun.**

Belgian 7.65mm Mauser rifle M1889 The Belgian organization of Fabrique Nationale d'Armes de Guerre was originally founded to make this rifle. The weapon was also made by Fabrique d'Armes de l'État and, during World War I, by the American firm of Hopkins and Allen of Norwich, Conn. This bolt-action weapon has an overall length of 50.13 in. and a barrel length of 30.69 in. The weight is 8.88 lb, and the muzzle velocity 2,034 fps. It contains a five-round box magazine. The carbine form of this weapon differs from the rifle only in lower weight and shorter length; there are no mechanical differences.

Belgian 7.65mm Mauser rifle M1935 This rifle has the Mauser Model 98 bolt system and flush magazine and has a weight of 9 lb, an overall length of 43.6 in., a barrel length of 23.5 in., and a muzzle velocity of 2,755 fps. It has a magazine with a capacity of five cartridges.

Belgian 7.65mm Mauser rifle M1936 Also called the "Model 89/36" because it was converted from the M1889 rifle. It is about 43 in. long and has a barrel length of 23.7 in. The weight is 8.7 lb, and the muzzle velocity is about 2,375 fps. The magazine has a capacity of five rounds.

Belgian 9mm submachine gun Model 34 This weapon was the standard submachine gun of the Belgian Army from 1934 to 1939. It is identical in design and function to the German Schmeisser MP-28II and was manufactured in Belgium by Anciens Établissements Pieper. The weapon may sometimes be referred to as the "Mi 34 Schmeisser-Bayard."

Belgian 9mm Parabellum submachine gun M.I. 53 A submachine gun that is nothing more than a modified Mk II Sten.

Belgian 9mm Parabellum Vigneron sub-

Belknap. (*U.S. Navy.*)

machine gun M2 See **Vigneron 9mm Parabellum submachine gun M2.**

Belgian .303 cal. machine gun Model 1914 B.S.A. A Belgian-produced **Lewis Machine Gun,** which see. It was nicknamed the "Belgian Rattlesnake" by the Germans. Other Lewis types in Belgian service included the Mark VII and Mark VIII.

Belgian Rattlesnake A World War I German nickname for the Lewis gun as produced for Belgian forces (the Belgian .303 cal. machine gun Model 1914 B.S.A.).

belier An ancient battering ram.

Belknap A class of U.S. guided-missile frigates (DLG) of about 6,570 tons standard displacement completed between 1964 and 1967. They have a length of 547 ft, a beam of 54.8 ft, a speed of 34 knots, and a complement of 418 men. They are armed with one 5-in. and two 3-in. guns, one twin Terrier launcher (which can also launch Asroc rockets), and two triple torpedo launchers. There are nine ships in this class.

bell **1.** The bell-shaped muzzle end of the barrel of an antique gun. **2.** In naval usage, a bell represents the time so indicated. On board a ship, four, eight, and twelve o'clock are marked by eight bells; 4:30, 8:30, and 12:30 are marked by one bell; five, nine, and one o'clock are marked by two bells; and so on, until eight bells is reached again. Eight bells marks the end of an ordinary watch.

belligerent When some faction within a country engages in war against the general government of that country, it has no standing under international law until it is recognized as belligerent by neutral powers. Recognition comes only when it is noted that the faction is maintaining an independent de facto government. This recognition then protects the faction and subjects it to the laws of war.

Bellona The Roman goddess of war.

belly tank, aboard a U.S. Douglas Skyraider. (*U.S. Marine Corps.*)

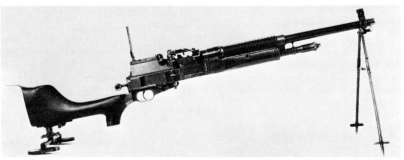

Benét-Mercié 8mm machine gun Model 1909. (*The Smithsonian Institution, Treasury Department Collection.*)

bells of arms Small tents used to protect muskets in the eighteenth century.

belly-land To land an airplane on its belly, without the benefit of its landing gear.

belly tank A detachable auxiliary gas tank used to increase the range of an aircraft. It is usually carried under the fuselage.

belted ammunition Cartridge ammunition arranged in a belt for use in a machine gun.

belted ball A bullet with a raised band or belt around it. It was used in a rifle that had rifling consisting of two wide grooves.

belted case A cartridge case with a band or belt just ahead of its extractor groove. It is used to seat the cartridge in the chamber.

belt-fed The term describing an automatic weapon that is supplied by cartridges from a feed belt.

Benét-Mercié 8mm machine gun Model 1909 A French gas-operated air-cooled automatic weapon with a rate of fire of 650 rounds per minute. It weighed 27 lb and was fed by a 24- to 30-round strip. It was

Berdan II .42 cal. rifle Model 1870. (*The Smithsonian Institution, War Department Collection.*)

used for infantry and aircraft purposes and it was adopted by the French and American Armies in 1910. The French used the 8mm Lebel cartridge, and the United States specified .30/06. The Model 1909 was the standard United States automatic machine gun until 1917, seeing limited service in the landings at Vera Cruz in 1913 and against the Mexican bandit Pancho Villa in 1916.

Benson-Mayo A class of United States destroyers (DD) of 1,620 tons standard displacement produced in the period 1940–1943. Thirty were completed and saw extensive service during World War II, during which time three were lost to enemy action. They had a length of 347.7 ft, a beam of 36 ft, a speed of 37.6 knots, and a complement of 230 men. Armament included four 5-in. guns, four 40mm and seven 20mm antiaircraft guns, depth charges, and torpedo tubes.

benzyl chloride A colorless liquid made by brominating boiling toluene. It was used in World War I as a tear gas.

Berdan I .42 cal. rifle This American-designed rifle was adopted by imperial Russia in 1868. The block is hinged forward and is raised to extract and load, after the design of the single-shot Springfield. The hammer, however, resembles that of the French Chassepot in design. The rifle is about 53 in. long and weighs about 9.75 lb. It was replaced by the Berdan II.

Berdan II .42 cal. rifle Model 1870 This weapon is entirely different in design from the Berdan I. The Berdan II is a single-shot

bolt-action rifle with an overall length of 53 in., a barrel length of 32.8 in., and a weight of 9.8 lb. It was adopted in 1870.

Berdan, Hiram A United States Army Ordnance Department colonel who invented the Berdan primer in 1870.

Berdan primer A Berdan primer utilizes a boss in the cartridge-case head to serve as an anvil (in contrast with the Boxer primer, which contains its own anvil). This system was used for about 20 years in the United States and is still widely used in Europe.

berdiche See **bardiche.**

Beretta 7.62mm NATO rifle BM59 series After World War II, Beretta received contracts for the manufacture of the U.S. .30 cal. M1 rifle. These weapons were used by the Italian Army and were also made for Denmark and Indonesia. Later modifications were made for the 7.62mm NATO cartridge to provide selective fire and to modify the feed mechanism to accept a 20-round detachable magazine. There are numerous designations for the BM59 series. The BM59D has a straight-line stock with a pistol grip, bipod, and grenade launcher. The BM59GL has a grenade launcher and grenade-launcher sights attached. The BM59 is also made in Mark I, Mark II, Mark II (Modified), Mark III, Mark III (Modified), and Mark IV. The variations include various combinations of flash hiders, folding stocks, winter triggers, and so forth. The Mark IV has selective-fire capability, an overall length of 43.1 in., a barrel length of 19.3 in., a weight of 10.4 lb, a cyclic rate of fire of 750 rounds per minute, and a muzzle velocity of 2,700 fps. It uses a 20-round magazine.

Beretta 7.65mm automatic pistol Model 1915 The Model 1915 was the first Beretta automatic pistol introduced to Italian forces. This hammerless weapon is blowback-operated, has an overall length of 6 in., a barrel length of 3.4 in., and a weight of 1.25 lb. It features a detachable box magazine with a capacity of seven cartridges. The pistol has a muzzle velocity of about 960 fps. Another version of this pistol was also produced and designated the Model 1915. It is chambered for the 9mm Glisenti cartridge.

Beretta 7.65mm automatic pistol Model 1915/1919 This is a hammerless pistol with an overall length of 6 in., a barrel length of 3.4 in., and a weight of 1.31 lb.

The detachable box magazine has a capacity of 8 cartridges, and the weapon has a muzzle velocity of about 960 fps.

Beretta 7.65mm automatic pistol Model 1931 This Italian weapon was the official pistol of the Italian Navy. It has a magazine capacity of seven cartridges, an overall length of $5\frac{3}{4}$ in., a barrel length of $3\frac{5}{16}$ in., and a weight of approximately 22 oz. This pistol was originally issued in 1923, but was modified in 1931 and again in 1934. Except for dimensions, this pistol is identical to the .38 ACP pistol Model 1934.

Beretta 9mm automatic pistol Model 1934 This weapon has an overall length of 6 in. and a barrel length of $3\frac{1}{2}$ in. It weighs 1.25 lb and has a magazine with a capacity of seven cartridges and a muzzle velocity of 970 fps. This weapon was very popular with the Italian Army during World War II. It fired the 9mm Corto (.38 ACP) cartridge. The Italian Army issues were marked with "RE" (*Regio Esercito*), meaning "Royal Army." Those marked "PS" were issued to police, or *carabinieri.*

Beretta 9mm (Glisenti) automatic pistol Model 1923 This model was the first service Beretta to have an external hammer. In other respects it is the same as the Model 1915–1919. The Italian Army used this weapon in limited quantities.

Beretta 9mm (Glisenti) submachine gun Model 1918 This Italian submachine gun was introduced in 1918 and is a modified version of the original Villar Perosa submachine gun. It uses the action, barrel, receiver, and magazine-feed system of the Villar Perosa Weapon, and these components were used from existing weapons at the end of World War I. (Because of this conversion, there are relatively few twin-barrel Villar Perosa submachine guns in existence.) The weapon used a 9mm Parabellum cartridge and operated on a retarded blowback principle. It fired on full automatic only at a cyclic rate of 900 rounds per minute. The length of the weapon was 33.50 in., and it had a barrel length of 12.50 in. The weight, with a 25-round magazine, was 8.20 lb. The muzzle velocity was on the order of 1,250 fps. This weapon was used by Italian forces during a period that extended from the end of World War I through the end of World War II. It was one of the first submachine guns and may have been in use before the Schmeisser-designed MP 18,I was introduced by the Germans. This weapon was designed by Tullio Marengoni, as were all Beretta submachine guns until the late 1950s.

Beretta 9mm Parabellum automatic pistol Model 1951 A weapon with an overall length of 8 in. and a barrel length of 4.50 in. The magazine has a capacity of eight cartridges, and the total weight of the pistol

Beretta 9mm automatic pistol Model 1934. (*The Smithsonian Institution, Treasury Department Collection.*)

is 1.93 lb. The muzzle velocity is 1,182 fps. It is the current Italian service pistol and the standard handgun of the Israeli and Egyptian forces. It is also sold commercially as the "Brigadier."

Beretta 9mm Parabellum submachine gun Model 12 A weapon placed in production in 1959 and ordered by the Italian government in 1961. It utilizes the 9mm Parabellum cartridge and has a muzzle velocity of about 1,250 fps. It is blowback-operated and has a cyclic rate of fire of 550 rounds per minute. With folding stock retracted, the length is 16.43 in., and it has a barrel length of 7.90 in. Loaded with a 40-round magazine, the weapon weighs 8.30 lb. Twenty- and thirty-round magazines are also available. The rear sight is adjustable for 100 and 200 meters.

Beretta 9mm Parabellum submachine gun Model 1938A An Italian submachine gun placed in mass production in 1938 and produced in one form or another until 1950. It employed the 9mm Parabellum cartridge, as well as a special high-velocity 9mm Parabellum round. The weapon is blowback-operated and fires at a cyclic rate of 600 rounds per minute. The fire-selector system is controlled by two triggers. Depressing the forward trigger produces semiautomatic fire, while pressure on the rear trigger produces full automatic fire. The length without bayonet is 37.25 in., the barrel length is 12.4 in., and the weight, with a 40-round magazine, is 10.95 lb. It has a muzzle velocity of 1,378 fps and rear open "V" sights adjustable from 100 to 500 meters in increments of 100 meters. The weapon is extremely well made and is noteworthy for its accuracy, usually ranking far above most other submachine guns. It was used by both Italian and German troops during World War II, with other orders going to the Rumanian government in 1939 and the Argentine government in 1947.

Beretta 9mm Parabellum submachine gun Model 38/44 The Model 38/44 is a further development of the Model 38/42, the major difference being that the 38/44 incorporated a lighter and simpler bolt and main operating spring. The model went into production in 1945 and continued for several years. Postwar deliveries of the weapon went to Syria, Pakistan, Iraq, and Costa Rica.

Beretta 9mm submachine gun Model 38/42 The Model 38/42 was designed in 1942 and was a simplified version of the Model 1938A submachine gun with selected design elements of the Beretta Model 1, a weapon designed in 1941 but never produced in numbers. Full-scale production of the Model 38/42 began in 1943 and continued until 1945. In the last two years of World War II, production of this

Beretta 9mm submachine gun Model 38/42. (*The Smithsonian Institution, Treasury Department Collection.*)

weapon was estimated at 20,000 units per month. The submachine gun employs the 9mm Parabellum cartridge and has an approximate muzzle velocity of 1,250 fps. The twin-trigger arrangement provides for full automatic and semiautomatic fire. The cyclic rate of fire is 550 rounds per minute. The overall length of the weapon is 31.50 in., and it has a barrel length of 8.40 in. Loaded with a 40-round magazine, it weighs 8.90 lb. The rear sight is adjustable to 100 and 200 meters.

Beretta 9mm submachine gun Model 38/49 The Model 38/49 is a further development of the Model 38/44, the major difference being the addition of a crossbolt safety. It was produced with and without bayonet, and in 1951 a folding-stock version was developed that was referred to as the "Beretta Model 2." This model was purchased by a number of world powers, including West Germany for use by its Border Patrol. The official West German designation for this weapon is the MP 1.

Bergamini A class of Italian frigates of 1,650 tons standard displacement completed in 1961–1962. They have a speed of 26 knots, a complement of about 250 men, and armament consisting of three 3-in. guns, one single-barreled depth-charge mortar, two triple torpedo tubes, and one helicopter.

Bergmann Bayard 9mm automatic pistol Model 1910 A weapon first patented in 1903 by Theodore Bergmann and officially adopted as a side arm by the Danish government in 1910. It also saw military service in Spain and in Greece. The pistol has an overall length of 10 in. and a barrel length of 4 in. It weighs about 36 oz and has a detachable box magazine with a capacity of 6, 8, or 10 cartridges. It fires a special 9mm Bayard Long cartridge.

Bergmann 7.92mm aircraft machine gun Model 1915 A German recoil-operated air-cooled machine gun with a rate of fire of 750 to 800 rounds per minute. It weighed 34 lb and was fed from a 200-round fabric belt.

Bergmann 7.92mm machine gun Model 1910 A German recoil-operated water-cooled machine gun with a rate of fire of 480 to 550 rounds per minute. It weighed 36 lb and was fed from a 200-round fabric belt.

Bergmann 9mm Parabellum submachine gun Model 34 A German submachine gun weighing 10½ lb, with sling, and having a length of 33 in. It fires single-shot or automatic, and the magazine has a capacity of 32 rounds. It has open sights, with a range of adjustment from 50 to 1,000 meters.

Bergmann submachine gun MP 34/I and MP 35/I A weapon first introduced in 1934 and modified in mid-1935. These were selective-fire weapons with a cyclic rate of fire of 650 rounds per minute. They were manufactured for use with the following cartridges: 9mm Parabellum, 9mm Bergmann Bayard, 9mm Mauser, .45 cal. ACP, and 7.63mm Mauser. Some 40,000 were used by German SS units during World War II. The two models are unique in having magazines that feed from the right side.

Beriev KOR-1/2 A Soviet single-engine two-seat shipboard observation-scout float seaplane first flown in 1934 and used as catapult aircraft on cruisers and also on coastal bases. It had a speed of 193 mph and was armed with two 7.62mm machine guns plus two 110-lb bombs.

Beriev MBR-2 (Be-2) A Soviet single-engine four- or five-seat short-range reconnaissance flying boat first flown in 1931, but in production until 1942.

Beriev MDR-6 (Be-4) A Soviet twin-engine five-seat long-range reconnaissance-bomber

Bergmann submachine gun MP 34/I. (*The Smithsonian Institution, Department of Defense Collection.*)

Berthier 8mm carbine. (*The Smithsonian Institution.*)

flying boat first flown in 1934 and in operation well into the 1950s. It carried about 1,200 lb of bombs, depth charges, or torpedoes on under-wing racks and was armed with two 7.62mm machine guns.

Berlin airlift   An action to circumvent a Russian blockade against all surface traffic across the Russian zone into West Berlin between June 1948 and September 1949. The USAF and the RAF sustained the city by flying in food and supplies.

berm   In fortifications, a narrow path between the parapet and the ditch.

Bermuda   The World War II British designation of the **Buccaneer,** which see.

Bernhard   A German World War II operation in which more than 100 million lb of counterfeit British bank notes were produced. Although the quality of these fakes was sufficiently good so that they escaped detection by the Bank of England, the attempt to disrupt the British economy failed. The notes were then used for such purposes as paying secret agents and buying arms.

Bersagliere   Sharpshooters or riflemen in a certain infantry corps of the Italian Army. The corps was formed in about 1850 by Victor Emmanuel II.

bersis   A type of cannon that was once much used at sea.

berth   **1.** A place to sleep aboard ship. **2.** A place for a vessel to tie up or to anchor. **3.** A margin of safety in passing a dangerous obstruction, as to give a rock a "wide berth."

Bertha   Certain of the large German cannons of World War I were called "Berthas," which was an allusion to Berta Krupp von Hohlen und Halbach, who was then head of the Krupp steel works. Krupp made most of the large guns then used by the German Army.

Berthier 8mm carbine   A bolt-action magazine-fed French military weapon used from 1890 through World War I. Variations developed from 1907 onward were used in both world wars.

Berthier machine gun   See **Vickers-Berthier .303 cal. aircraft machine gun Mk 1, Vickers-Berthier .303 light machine gun,** and **Vickers-Berthier .303 machine gun Mark III.**

Berthier-Vickers .303 cal. aircraft machine gun Mk I   A British World War I gas-operated air-cooled machine gun with a rate of fire of 750 to 900 rounds per minute. It weighed 31.5 lb and was fed from a 97-round flat drum.

berthon boat   A type of collapsible lifeboat once used on destroyers and small craft.

Besa 7.92mm machine gun Mk I   A British gas-operated air-cooled machine gun with a rate of fire of 550 to 800 rounds per minute. It weighed 47 lb and was fed from a 200-round link belt.

Besa 7.92mm tank machine guns   These are weapons used by the British for tank armament. They were developed from the Czech ZB53 (Model 37) machine guns through a manufacturing agreement with the firm of Zbrojovka Brno. The ZB53 was modified considerably to meet the needs of mass production, and the final product was called the "Besa." B.S.A. (Birmingham Small Arms Company) was the manufacturer of this weapon, and four different models (Mark 1, 47 lb; Mark 2, 48 lb; Mark 3, 54 lb; and Mark 3*, 53.5 lb) were produced. The Mark 1 and Mark 2 have two rates of automatic fire, and the Mark 3 and Mark 3* have only one. (Mark 1 and Mark 2, 450 and 750 rounds per minute; Mark 3 and Mark 3*, 450 rounds per minute.) It has a muzzle velocity of 2,700 fps, an overall length of 43.5 in., and a barrel length of 29 in.

Besa 15mm machine gun Mark 1   This British weapon was a B.S.A. (Birmingham Small Arms Company) modification of the Czech 15mm ZB60 Model 38. It was used mainly for primary armament on certain British armored cars during World War II. Introduced in 1939, this weapon has an overall length of 80.75 in. and a barrel length of 57.6 in. It weighs 125.5 lb and has a muzzle velocity of about 2,685 fps and a cyclic rate of fire of 400 to 500 rounds

per minute. It can be used for full automatic and semiautomatic fire.

besagne   In armor, a round or oval plate used for the protection of a joint.

besiege   To lay siege to a fortified place.

betty   A petard used for forcing open gates or doors.

Betty   The Allied code name for the Mitsubishi G4M Type 1 seven-place twin-engine long-range bomber developed for the Japanese Naval Air Force and first flown in 1939. It had a speed of 272 mph, a range of 2,262 mi, and armament consisting of four 20mm cannons and one 7.7mm machine gun, plus a bombload of 2,200 lb. A total of 2,479 bombers of this type were produced between 1940 and 1945.

bevor   Armor to protect the lower part of the face and neck. It is a variant of "beaver."

BIB   Baby incendiary bomb.

Biber   (German for "beaver") A World War II German midget submarine that carried two torpedoes. It was first used in August 1944.

bible (beugle, bugle)   A twelfth-century engine used for throwing large stones.

bidenhander   (German for "with both hands") A two-handed sword.

biffa   A kind of trebuchet, or medieval missile-hurling engine, with a movable counterpoise.

Big Bear   The NATO code name for a type of Soviet E/F-band ground-controlled interception radar.

Big Bertha   See **Bertha.**

Big Hook   A German World War II device developed for use in retreats. It consisted of a hook carried on a flatcar and towed behind a train to tear up ties. TNT charges were also dropped to damage rails. Other names for this system were "Track Ripper" and "Rail Rooter."

Big Look   The designation of U.S. Navy EC-121 (**Super Constellation,** which see) aircraft used to monitor North Vietnamese surface-to-air missile activity.

Big Mesh   The NATO code name for a type of Soviet E/F-band ground-controlled interception radar.

Big Stick   A U.S. Navy bomb-carrying canister for use on the A-4, A-6, and A-7 attack aircraft.

Big Week   See **Argument,** a World War II operation in which German aircraft production facilities were the targets of concentrated allied air attacks.

Big-wheel Ferret   A four-wheel British vehicle that is a follow-on to the Ferret scout car. The Big-wheel Ferret Mark 4 has a crew of two and a speed of 50 mph and is armed with one 7.62mm machine gun and two multibarreled smoke dischargers. The Mark 5 carries one 7.62mm machine gun and four Swingfire long-range antitank missiles.

Betty. (*U.S. Air Force.*)

Big Willie The collective name given by the Allies in World War II to the 340mm naval guns taken from the French battleship *Provence* and mounted in turrets of a fortress on the Island of Saint Mandrier in the harbor of Toulon, France.

Bikini A United States Marine Corps short-range propeller-driven radio-controlled photoreconnaissance drone system designed to gather intelligence for combat battalion or brigade units in forward areas. The entire system, consisting of two drones, a launcher, radio control equipment, and photographic equipment, is carried in a jeep-drawn trailer.

Bikini bomb Any of the test atomic bombs exploded near the island of Bikini in the Pacific Ocean.

bilbo Seventeenth- and eighteenth-century Spanish cup-hilted swords, often with double-edged blades.

bilboquet An 8-in. mortar that threw a shell weighing 60 lb about 700 yd.

bill An infantry weapon with a broad blade having a hooked cutting edge and usually spikes on the back and tip. It was mounted on a long shaft. First used as a weapon in the fourteenth and fifteenth centuries, it continued in use as late as the seventeenth century. Black bills and brown bills were so called because they were colored with paint or varnish.

billet **1.** Shelter for troops. **2.** To quarter troops. **3.** A personnel position or assignment which may be filled by one person.

bill hook A small brush hook once used for cutting wood for fascines and other military purposes.

Billinghurst volley gun A weapon used in the American Civil War. It consisted of an assemblage of 25 barrels that fired metallic cartridges. It used a primer train as a means of ignition.

billman One who is armed with a bill.

bingo When originated by a controlling activity, this term means "proceed to an alternate airfield or carrier as specified." When originated by a pilot, it means "I have reached minimum fuel for safe return to base or to a designated alternate."

binnacle A box or nonmagnetic metallic container for the compass, often fitted with lights for night work.

biological agent A microorganism which causes disease in man, plants, or animals or the deterioration of materiel.

biological operations The employment of biological agents to produce casualties in man or animals and damage to plants or materiel; also, the defense against such employment.

biological warfare The employment of living organisms, toxic biological products, and plant growth regulators to produce death or casualties in man, animals, or plants; also, the defense against such employment.

biological-warfare agents Although biological weapons have never been significant weapons of war, there is factual evidence that they have been used in some form since early times. In the Middle Ages, warring tribes dropped plague-ridden corpses into the wells of their enemies. This type of maneuver was practiced particularly in desert warfare, where wells were of strategic importance and were easily contaminated. During the French and Indian War in 1763, the British infected the Indians with smallpox by giving them blankets taken from infected patients. About 95 percent of the Indians who were exposed died of the disease. In World War I, German agents used the organism that produces glanders to inoculate horses being shipped from the United States to the Rumanian Cavalry. In 1940, the Chinese claimed that Japanese planes dropped plague-infected fleas mixed with grain in bags. Presumably, their purpose was to initiate an epidemic of plague by utilizing natural vectors. In the past, widespread natural disease epidemics have decimated the populations of various areas. The Black Death, or plague, caused a pandemic in Europe from 1347 to 1352, during which time it was estimated to have killed approximately one-fourth (25 million) of Europe's population. Potential biological antipersonnel agents might be found among the bacteria, rickettsiae, viruses, fungi, and toxins. Naturally occurring bacteria are responsible for many serious human diseases such as scarlet fever, meningococcal meningitis, gonorrhea, diphtheria, tuberculosis, anthrax, tetanus, certain pneumonias, typhoid and paratyphoid fevers, the bacillary dysenteries, meliodosis, plague, cholera, tularemia, brucellosis (undulant fever), glanders, syphilis, yaws, gas gangrene, and salmonella food poisoning. The rickettsiae cause Q fever, typhus fever, and the spotted fevers. The viruses cause influenza, poliomyelitis, rabies, smallpox, yellow fever, dengue fever, equine encephalomyelitis, psittacosis, infectious hepatitis, mumps, and measles. Fungi are responsible for coccidiodomycosis, histoplasmosis, and nacardiosis. The toxins include some of the most poisonous substances known, particularly those causing botulism, tetanus, diphtheria, and staphylococcus food poisoning. There are numerous other agents that could be used against animals and plants.

biological weapon An item of materiel which projects, disperses, or disseminates a biological agent including arthropod vectors.

bipennis A double-headed war ax.

biplane An airplane with two wings, usually one above the other. Most of the airplanes used in World War I were biplanes.

bipod An adjustable two-legged device attached to the muzzle end of a rifle or a

bilbo. (*The Smithsonian Institution, F. A. Ober Collection.*)

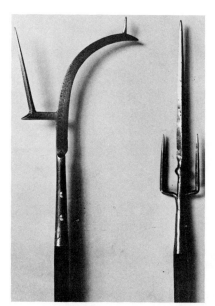

bill. (*The Metropolitan Museum of Art, gift of William H. Rights, 1913.*)

bipod, of Browning automatic rifle, Type D. (*Belgian Ministry of Defense.*)

Birddog. (*U.S. Army.*)

machine gun to serve as a support for the weapon during firing.

BIRDCAP See **Rescue Combat Air Patrol.**

Birddog A U.S. Cessna-built light observation aircraft that carries a pilot and observer and has a maximum speed of 115 mph. In use by the U.S. Army and Air Force, some 3,500 aircraft of this type have been built since their introduction in 1950.

bireme In classical antiquity, a galley with two tiers of rowers, the second tier occupying a raised deck.

biscaien, biscayan An old term for a type of long-barreled musket. It was also the name of a type of large lead canister shot.

Bishop's mantle A long cloak of mail, worn either alone or over armor. It dates from the latter part of the fifteenth century.

Bisley 1. A version of the British Bristol Blenheim, a light bomber of World War II. **2.** A target model of the Colt single-action revolver.

Bismark A German battleship of 41,700 tons displacement that was completed in 1939. It had a length of 792 ft, a beam of 118 ft, a speed of 30 knots, and a complement of 2,400 men. Armament consisted of eight 15-in., twelve 5.9-in., sixteen 4.1-in., sixteen 37mm, and fifty-eight 20mm guns; eight 21-in. torpedo tubes; and six aircraft. It had one sister ship, *Tirpitz*. The *Bismark* and *Prinz Eugen* sailed from Bergen and, in the Denmark Strait on May 24, 1941, sank the *Hood* and damaged the *Prince of Wales*. The *Bismark* was damaged by tor-

pedo planes from the *Victorious* and *Ark Royal* and by gunfire from *King George V* and *Rodney*. It was finally sunk by a British submarine on May 27, 1941.

Bison The NATO code name for the Myasishchev Mya-4 four-jet long-range reconnaissance bomber in service with the Soviet Air Force and Naval Air Force and first seen in the late 1950s. It has a range of 7,000 mi and a speed of 560 mph. It is armed with 23mm cannons and has an estimated bombload of 9,900 lb.

biting angle The smallest angle at which a projectile will penetrate armor.

bivouac 1. An assembly or encampment of troops on a piece of terrain, sometimes without shelter. **2.** To encamp for the night in the open air.

Black and Tan A member of the Royal Irish Constabulary in Ireland during the disturbances of 1919–1921. So called because members wore khaki uniforms and black hats and armbands.

black bill See **bill.**

black box On-board electronic equipment, so called because of the usual shape and color of the container. The term has come to mean electronic equipment in general.

Blackburn Kangaroo See **Kangaroo.**

Blackburn Ripon IIA A single-engine two-seat biplane shipboard torpedo-bomber and reconnaissance aircraft first flown in 1926. It entered the British service and was also sold to Finland. Later the aircraft was built under license in Finland, and aircraft

of this type fought in the war with the Soviet Union in 1939. It had a speed of 135 mph.

Black Cat A U.S. Navy nickname for the World War II PBY Catalina.

black flag A flag once flown in warfare to signal that no mercy would be shown the vanquished.

Black Fox A U.S. emergency airborne communications system for long-range link between defense centers. It operates with a 14,000-ft wire antenna trailed behind an EC-135 aircraft.

Black Maria A term that once applied to a heavy ordnance shell (also called "coal box" or "Jack Johnson"). It was loaded with TNT and created volumes of dense smoke when it exploded.

blackout A condition or period of darkness in a town, city, or military installation imposed as a precaution against air raids.

blackout light A lamp put on vehicles for use during blackouts; blackout lamp. It is used because it can be seen from the air only at very close range.

black powder Black powder, or gunpowder, is said to have been developed by the Chinese or Arabs in the thirteenth century. It is a mixture of about 75 parts powdered potassium nitrate or sodium nitrate, 15 parts charcoal, and 10 parts sulfur. It is now almost obsolete, its use being limited to certain types of primers, igniters, fuzes, and blank fire charges.

Black Saturday The name given to Saturday, June 13, 1942, by the Allies in World War II. On that date the British Eighth Army was forced by the German Afrika Korps to retreat after a tremendous tank battle.

Black Shirt A member of a fascistic organization, especially the Italian Fascisti or the German Schutzstaffel, so called because of the black shirts customarily worn by such groups.

Black Swan A class of British frigates (ex-sloops) of 1,470 tons standard displacement. They had a length of 299 ft, a beam of 27 ft, a speed of 18 knots, and a complement

Bismark. (*The Imperial War Museum.*)

of 180 men. They were armed with six 4-in. guns, four 40mm antiaircraft guns, and hedgehog A/S weapons.

Black Widow The Northrop P-61 (F-61) Black Widow is a two- or three-seat twin-engine night fighter and intruder developed for the USAAF and first flown in May 1942. It flew at speeds of 369 mph and was armed with four 20mm cannons, four .50 cal. machine guns in a remotely controlled turret, and two 1,000-lb bombs.

Blackwood A class of British antisubmarine frigates of 1,180 tons standard displacement completed in 1955–1958. They have a length of 310 ft, a beam of 33 ft, a speed of 27.8 knots, and a complement of 140 men. They are armed with two 40mm Bofors guns and two Limbo three-barreled mortars.

blade sight A type of thin front sight or post sight.

blank A wooden gunstock before it is cut to receive the metal parts.

blank ammunition A cartridge or shell loaded with powder but not with a bullet or projectile. It is used in training, in signaling, and in firing salutes. The powder charge is held in place by a wad crimped in the open end of the case. When a blank is fired, the wad can injure persons in front of the gun.

blanket **1.** A smoke concentration laid down over a friendly area to prevent enemy observation from the air. **2.** A term describing the process of stopping a ship's or a force's fire by interposing another of its vessels or a body of its own troops in the line of fire.

Blankney A class of British frigates (ex-escort destroyers) of 1,050 tons standard displacement completed in 1940–1942. They had a speed of 25 knots, a complement of 146 men, and armament of six 4-in. guns, four two-pounder pompoms, and two to four 40mm antiaircraft guns.

blast The brief and rapid movement of air vapor or fluid away from a center of outward pressure, as in an explosion or in the combustion of rocket fuel; the pressure accompanying this movement. This term is commonly used for "explosion," but the two terms may be distinguished.

blast, blast off To take off or to begin to travel, a term used particulary in connection with rocket-propelled missiles.

blast effect Destruction of, or damage to, structures and personnel by the force of an explosion on or above the surface of the ground. Blast effect may be contrasted with the cratering and ground-shock effects of a projectile or charge which goes off beneath the surface.

blast mark The worn area of ground in front of a gun, caused by the force of the blast of firing. Unconcealed, it may give away the position of the gun.

Bison. (*U.S. Air Force.*)

Black Widow. (*U.S. Air Force.*)

blast tube A tubular device surrounding the forward end of the barrel of aircraft guns. Because it extends beyond the barrel an effective distance, it restrains the blast until it is beyond adjacent aircraft structures which would otherwise be damaged. The blast tube is either attached to the gun or supported by the aircraft structure.

blazer An old naval term for a mortar vessel; so called because there was a great emission of flame when the mortar was fired.

Blenheim A British three-place twin-engine light bomber developed by Bristol and first flown in 1936. It had a speed of 266 mph, was armed with five .303 cal. Browning machine guns, and carried a bombload of about 1,000 lb. A later version of the Blenheim was referred to as the "Bisley." (Picture, next page.)

Blenheim IF and IVF This model of the British Bristol Blenheim (normally a three-seat light bomber) was used as a two-seat twin-engine night fighter until the introduction of the Bristol Beaufighter. Some 200 Blenheims were converted beginning in

1938. It was the first airplane to carry 1.5-meter interception radar, scoring its first success against the Luftwaffe with this equipment on July 22, 1940. This version was armed with four .303 cal. Browning machine guns firing from a ventral pack, one .303 cal. Browning in the wing, and one .303 cal. Vickers gun in a dorsal turret. It flew at speeds up to 260 mph.

Bleriot XI A French single-engine one- or two-place biplane introduced in 1910. It was used by the French, the Italians, and the British in the early part of World War I. It had a speed of about 66 mph. (Picture, next page.)

blimp A small nonrigid or semirigid airship. The U.S. Navy terminated airship operations in 1962. During World War II, however, they operated 134 K-class, 22 L-class, and 4 M-class airships, all of which were built by Goodyear.

Blind Bat Infrared-equipped AC-130 aircraft used by U.S. forces in Vietnam.

blind bombing Bombing a target that cannot be seen from the bombing plane. It implies the use of instruments like radar.

Blenheim. (*British Aircraft Corporation Ltd.*)

Bleriot XI. (*The Smithsonian Institution, National Air Museum.*)

blister, on a Douglas C-47 equipped for search and rescue missions. (*U.S. Air Force.*)

Blinder The NATO code name for the Tupolev Tu-22 twin-jet supersonic bomber in service with the Soviet Air Force and Naval Air Force and first seen in 1961. It reaches speeds up to Mach 1.5 and is armed with a radar-directed tail turret and a Kitchen air-to-surface missile. It has a crew of three.

blind shell A shell that bursts when it strikes, the bursting charge being ignited by the heat of impact.

blip A spot of light on a radarscope or an irregularity in the base line of a radarscope, especially such a spot or irregularity representing the relative position of a reflecting object such as an airplane. Also called "pip."

blister **1.** A dome-shaped (usually transparent) bulge in an airplane for use by an observer or for mounting a flexible gun. **2.** A naval term for a built-in bulge on a warship that protects the vessel against torpedoes and mines.

blistering agents War gases such as **distilled mustard (HD), ethyldichloroarsine (ED), lewisite (L), methyldichloroarsine (MD), mustard-lewisite (HL), nitrogen mustard (HN-1, HN-2, HN-3), phenyldichloroarsine (PD),** and **phosgene oxime (CX),** which see. They are employed for casualty effect; the use of ground may be restricted, movements slowed, and the use of materiel or installation hampered. These agents affect the eyes and lungs and blister the skin. During World War I mustard was the only blister agent in major use. Since then, blister agents have been developed which are odorless and which vary in duration of effectiveness. Most are insidious in action; there is little or no pain at the time of exposure except in the case of L and CX, which cause immediate pain on contact. The development of casualties is somewhat delayed. CX produces a wheal (similar to a beesting) rather than a water blister, which the other blister agents produce. Protection from blister agents is extremely difficult since they attack any part of the body which comes in contact with the liquid or vapor.

blistering gases See **Blistering agents.**

Blitz The German Arado Ar 234 Blitz was a single-seat reconnaissance bomber equipped with two turbojet engines. It was first flown on June 15, 1943, and later versions of the aircraft were equipped with pressurized cabins and ejection seats. The Blitz had a top speed of 461 mph and armament consisting of two 20mm cannons and a bombload of up to 3,300 lb.

blitz, blitzkreig A German expression meaning "lightning war" and used to describe the air raids and invasions by Germany in Europe in the late 1930s; hence a smashing, surprise assault with military forces, both ground and air.

Bloch 131 A French four-seat twin-engine bomber-reconnaissance aircraft developed in 1936. It was armed with three 7.5mm machine guns and carried approximately 1,600 lb of bombs.

Bloch 174 A French three-seat twin-engine reconnaissance and light bombing aircraft first flown in January 1939. It was armed with seven 7.5mm machine guns and carried eight 110-lb bombs. It had a speed of 329 mph.

Bloch 175 A French three-seat twin-engine light bomber and attack aircraft first flown in 1939 and manufactured until the German occupation. It had a speed of about 335 mph, was armed with seven 7.5mm machine guns, and carried a bombload of about 2,000 lb. Production resumed in 1945 and continued until 1950. Later models were armed with three 20mm cannons, eight 90mm rockets, and one 1,654-lb torpedo.

Bloch 210 This French five-seat twin-engine medium night bomber was first flown in 1934. It was armed with three 7.5mm machine guns and carried a total of 3,527 lb of bombs.

Bloch MB-151 and MB-152 Single-engine single-seat low-wing interceptor fighters developed in France in the late 1930s. They flew at a maximum speed of 320 mph and were armed with two 7.5mm machine guns and two 20mm Hispano-Suiza cannons.

block **1.** In firearms, the portion that locks the cartridge in the chamber. It may also be called the "breechblock," the "breech bolt," or the "bolt." **2.** An old gunnery term for a rectangular prism of wood used to raise and lower heavy cannons. According to their thickness, they were called "whole," "half," or "quarter" blocks.

blockade The shutting up of a particular area, usually a seaport, by means of troops or ships. The operation is designed to keep supplies from being brought in.

blockbuster A colloquial term for demolition bombs used during World War II. They ranged in weight from 2 to 11 tons and were considered powerful enough to destroy a city block. The first blockbuster was dropped on Berlin by the RAF on April 17, 1941. This bomb weighed 4,000 lb, of which 2,990 lb was explosive. Crews reported that the blast effect was so great that the shock could be felt in aircraft flying at altitudes of 14,000 ft.

blockhouse Originally, a small fort used to protect a bridge, a pass, or the like. Later the term referred to a structure of timbers or logs, often with an upper story that projected outward. This enabled the defenders to fire downward as well as in every direction. Currently the term refers to a small defensible structure made of wood, steel, or concrete used at isolated posts for the protection of troops.

blockship **1.** A ship sunk to block off a channel or harbor entrance. **2.** Formerly, a warship which is no longer employed for seagoing operations but which is used as a storeship or for the defense of a port.

Blohm und Voss BV 138 A German three-engine long-range maritime reconnaissance flying boat flown in 1937.

blood agents War gasses such as **arsine (SA), cyanogen chloride (CK),** and **hydrogen cyanide (AC),** which see. They are absorbed into the body primarily by breathing. They affect bodily functions through action on the enzyme cytochrome oxidase, thus preventing the normal transfer of oxygen from the blood to body tissue.

blood chit A small piece of cloth on which are printed an American flag and a statement in several languages to the effect that anyone assisting the bearer to safety will be rewarded.

blood gases See **blood agents.**

Bloodhound A surface-to-air guided-weapon system built by British Aircraft Corporation for the RAF and the forces of several other countries. It has ramjet engines, an overall length (with boosters) of 27.75 ft, and a range of more than 50 mi.

bloomer See **buckler,** sense 1.

blowback Escape, to the rear and under pressure, of gases formed during the firing of a gun. Blowback may be caused by a defective breech mechanism, a ruptured cartridge case, or a faulty primer.

blowback action An action in a weapon that utilizes the pressure of the propellant gases to force the bolt to the rear, independently of the barrel, which does not move relative to the receiver. The gases, produced by the propelling charge, act against the cartridge case, which in turn acts to force the bolt to the rear. A weapon which employs this method of operation is

Blitz. (*The Smithsonian Institution, National Air Museum.*)

Blohm und Voss BV 138. (*The Smithsonian Institution, National Air Museum.*)

characterized by the absence of any breech-lock or bolt-lock mechanism.

blow-forward action An action in a weapon that utilizes the pressure of the propellant gases to force the barrel forward from a standing breech to open the action and eject the fired case. A spring brings the barrel back to firing position and also reloads and cocks the gun. Typical of this action is that of the Borchardt pistol, the forerunner of the Luger.

blowing charge A small charge that blows the fuze plug out of a shell without rupturing the shell.

Blowpipe A British surface-to-air and surface-to-surface missile developed by the firm of Short. It has an overall length of 4.5 ft, a diameter of 3 in., and a launching weight of 28 lb. It has radio-command guidance and visual and TV tracking. (Picture, next page.)

BLT See **battalion landing team.**

BLU In U.S. Air Force usage, a bomb and mine unit.

BLU-1/B, 1B/B, and 1C/B U.S. 750-lb fire bombs.

BLU-7A/B and 7/B U.S. 750-lb antitank bombs.

BLU-10A/B and 10/B U.S. 250-lb fire bombs.

BLU-11/B A U.S. 500-lb fire bomb.

BLU-16/B and 17/B U.S. smoke bombs.

BLU-18/B A U.S. fragmentation bomb.

BLU-19, 20, 21, and 22 U.S. chemical bombs.

BLU-23/B A U.S. 500-lb fire bomb.

BLU-24/B and 24A/B U.S. fragmentation bombs.

BLU-25/B A U.S. antipersonnel bomblet.

BLU-26/B A U.S. fragmentation bomb.

BLU-27/B A U.S. 750-lb fire bomb.

BLU-28/B A U.S. biological-agent bomblet.

BLU-29/B A U.S. antipersonnel and anti-materiel bomb.

BLU-31/B A U.S. 800-lb demolition bomb.

BLU-32/B A U.S. 500-lb fire bomb.

BLU-32A/B A U.S. 595-lb fire bomb.

BLU-33/B A U.S. 1,500-lb general-purpose bomb.

BLU-34/B A U.S. 3,000-lb general-purpose bomb.

BLU-35/B A U.S. 250-lb fire bomb.

BLU-36/B, 40/B, and 41/B U.S. fragmentation bombs.

BLU-42/B, 43/B, and 44/B U.S. antipersonnel mines.

BLU-45/B A U.S. land mine.

BLU-46/B A U.S. antipersonnel bomb.

BLU-47/B A U.S. general-purpose bomb.

BLU-48/B and 49/B U.S. fragmentation bombs.

Blowpipe. (*Short Brothers & Harland Ltd.*)

Blue Steel. (*Hawker Siddeley Aviation, Ltd.*)

BLU-50/B and 52/B U.S. chemical bombs.

BLU-51/B and 53/B U.S. fire bombs.

BLU-54/B, 55/B, and 56/B U.S. antipersonnel bombs.

BLU-57/B A U.S. fragmentation bomb.

BLU-58/B A U.S. general-purpose bomb.

BLU-59/B, 60/B, 61/B, 62/B, and 63/B U.S. fragmentation bombs.

BLU-64/B A U.S. general-purpose bomb.

BLU-65/B A U.S. 820-lb fire bomb.

BLU-66/B A U.S. fragmentation bomb.

BLU-67/B A U.S. cratering bomb.

BLU-68/B, 69/B, and 70/B U.S. incendiary bombs.

BLU-71/B A U.S. land mine.

BLU-72/B and 76/B U.S. general-purpose bombs.

BLU-74/B and 75/B U.S. fire bombs.

bludgeon A short stick, with one thick, heavy, or loaded end, used as an offensive weapon; hence, any clublike weapon.

bludgeon pistol Historically, a weapon used as a firearm and a club. The barrel serves as a handle for the club-shaped butt.

Bluecher A German armored cruiser of 15,500 tons displacement completed in 1909. It had a speed of 26 knots, a complement of 847 men, and main armament consisting of twelve 8.2-in. and eight 6-in. guns. It was sunk by the British in the Battle of Dogger Bank in January 1914.

Blue Cross **diphenylchloroarsine (DA),** a German sneeze gas of World War I, which see.

bluejacket A Navy enlisted man below the rank of CPO (chief petty officer).

Blue Steel A rocket-powered standoff bomb with a thermonuclear warhead and a tail-first airplane configuration. Built by Hawker Siddeley Dynamics, it has a length of 35 ft and an estimated range of some 200 mi.

Blue Water A British Army surface-to-surface tactical missile with a range of about 80 to 100 mi. The prime contractor was English Electric Aviation Co., Ltd.

blunderbuss An obsolete short gun or firearm with a large, smooth bore and usually a bell muzzle. It was capable of holding a number of balls and was designed to shoot objects at close range without exact aim. Blunderbusses were introduced in the late part of the sixteenth century and were used until the first part of the nineteenth century. They were flintlock or wheel-lock (later percussion) guns, often equipped with bayonets which were hinged at the muzzle and folded back on the barrel when not in use.

blunt In fortifications, to replace a salient angle by a straight line of parapet: *pan coupé.*

blyde An ancient war machine similar to a catapult and used to throw stones.

Blyskawica A Polish destroyer of 2,144 tons standard displacement originally completed in 1937, but reconstructed in the late 1950s. It has a length of 374 ft, a beam of 37 ft, a speed of 39 knots, and a complement of 180 men. It is armed with eight 4-in. guns, ten 37mm antiaircraft guns, depth-charge throwers and racks, and three 21-in. torpedo tubes.

BM **1.** A U.S. Navy monitor. **2.** Boatswain's mate.

BMEWS Ballistic Missile Early Warning System. The U.S. Air Force 474L system which provides detection and location of missiles launched against Canada, England, and the United States. It is located at three sites with twelve primary detection-surveillance and tracking systems, two tropo-communications systems (BMEWS East and West), and one rearward communications system.

BO-4 A Swedish air-to-surface solid-propellant rocket missile with a speed of about 1,000 mph, a range of 50 mi, and infrared guidance.

boar A movable roof or shed used to protect the attackers of fortified places. See also **cat.**

BOAR A U.S. Navy air-to-surface rocket-boosted bomb.

board To come alongside a ship for the purpose of attacking it.

boarder One of a party detailed to go aboard an enemy vessel to capture or destroy it.

boarding nettings Nets formerly hoisted above the rails of a ship to hamper the enemy in reaching the decks.

boarding officer An officer who is detailed to go aboard a ship for the purpose of obtaining information about it. For an incoming warship he may go aboard to extend the usual naval courtesies.

boarding pike A pike used by sailors when attempting to board a vessel; also used to repel boarders.

boardwalk A military road of timber and brush over mud.

boar spear A spear having a transverse lug fitted below the broad blade. It was developed for hunting boar and other large animals and later became an insignia of rank.

boat A small vessel usually capable of being hoisted aboard a ship; also, the vernacular for "submarine."

boat deck The deck of a vessel upon which the lifeboats are secured.

boat group The basic organization of landing craft. One boat group is organized for each battalion landing team (or equivalent) to be landed in the first trip of landing craft or amphibious vehicles.

boat lanes Lanes, for amphibious assault landing craft, which extend seaward from the landing beaches to the line of departure. The width of the boat lanes is determined by the length of the corresponding beach.

boatswain (pronounced BO-sun) A warrant officer.

boatswain's call A whistle used by boatswains and boatswains' mates.

boatswain's mate (BM) A petty officer who supervises the deck force in seamanship duties. He is the assistant to the boatswain.

boatswain's pipe The whistled note or notes sounded on a boatswain's call as a signal and to give orders to winchmen and crane operators.

boattail The tapering rear section of certain bullets and shells.

Bob The NATO code name for a Soviet bomber. See **IL-4**.

boccacci An old Italian firearm, the muzzle of which was shaped like a trumpet.

Boche, boche A French slang term for a German or the Germans.

bodkin A small dagger or poniard.

body **1.** The principal part of any object. **2.** The tube of a built-up cannon. **3.** That part of a fuze which houses the working parts. **4.** The cylindrical portion of the projectile between the *bourrelet* and the rotating band. **5.** A force of men; a "body" of troops.

boedendag A weapon consisting of a long, heavy clublike shaft with a spike at its upper end. It could be used as a club or thrust like a spear.

Bofors (Bofors Armament Works, Sweden) A 40mm automatic cannon of a type developed in Sweden and adopted for manufacture and use by the United States and Britain in World War II. The Bofors

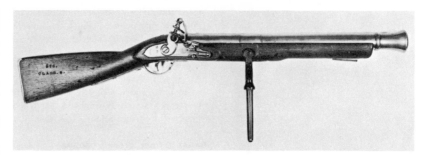

blunderbuss. (*The Smithsonian Institution, Navy Department Collection.*)

Blyskawica. (*Defense Ministry, Polish People's Republic.*)

boarding pike. (*The Metropolitan Museum of Art, gift of William H. Riggs, 1913.*)

boar spear. (*The Metropolitan Museum of Art, gift of George D. Pratt, 1929.*)

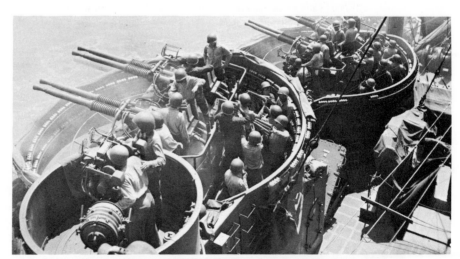

Bofors 40mm automatic cannon, aboard the U.S.S. *California.* (*U.S. Navy.*)

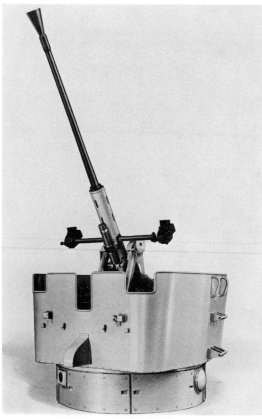

Bofors 40mm automatic gun L/70. (*A. B. Bofors.*)

normally serves as an antiaircraft weapon.

Bofors 20mm aircraft cannon A Swedish recoil-operated air-cooled cannon with a rate of fire of 650 to 700 rounds per minute. It weighed 84 lb and was fed by a 250-round link belt. It was developed in the 1930s.

Bofors 40mm automatic gun L/70 This weapon is the latest version of the Bofors 40mm light antiaircraft gun and has been in service since 1937. The first production models of this type were delivered in 1951. It has a total weight (including ground mount) of 12,560 lb and a maximum range of 3,000 meters. The gun is self-loading and is fed from clips of ammunition placed by the crew in guideways above the breech. This gun is in service with about 20 countries.

Bofors 40mm (twin) antiaircraft cannon A Swedish recoil-operated air-cooled weapon with a rate of fire of 260 to 300 rounds per minute. It weighed 2,300 lb and was fed by eight-round clips (one per barrel).

Bofors 57mm aircraft cannon A refinement of the antiaircraft guns, this aircraft cannon was a recoil-operated air-cooled weapon with a rate of fire of 100 rounds per minute. It was fed by a 25-round magazine.

Bofors Bantam A small wire-guided antitank missile in large-scale production for the Swedish and Swiss Armies. It has an overall length of 2.75 ft, a launching weight of 16.5 lb, a warhead weight of 4.1 lb, and a range of 6,600 ft.

bogey An air contact which is unidentified but assumed to be enemy.

bogie One of the weight-carrying wheels or rollers on the inside perimeter of the tread of a tank. The bogies serve to keep the treads in line.

Bogue A class of U.S. escort aircraft carriers (CVE) of about 9,800 tons standard displacement commissioned in 1942–1943. They had a speed of 18 knots and a complement of 800 men and carried 30 aircraft. They had a length of 496 ft and an extreme width of 112 ft.

bolade A mace.

Bolero The World War II code name for the buildup of U.S. troops and supplies in the United Kingdom in preparation for the cross-channel invasion of Europe.

Bolingbroke A World War II twin-engine bomber and general-purpose aircraft, similar to the Blenheim, flown by the RAF and the RCAF.

Bölkow Bö 810 Cobra See **Cobra**

bolo A heavy single-edged knife similar to a machete but usually shorter.

Bolo The Douglas B-18 was a twin-engine bomber developed in 1936 and used by the USAAF. Later versions were radar-equipped for antisubmarine duty. Only 217 were made.

bolster Formerly, a block of wood upon which a gun rested when it was moved from place to place. There were breech bolsters and muzzle bolsters.

bolt **1.** The sliding part in a breechloading weapon that pushes a cartridge into position and holds it there when the gun is fired. It may also be called the "breech-block." **2.** The short arrow shot from a crossbow. The tip was often made of steel and of square section, either pointed or blunt. (The terms *carreau* and "quarrel" mean the same thing and are derived from the French word *carré*, which means "square.") Most bolts had flights of wood or leather.

Bolt An acronym for *b*omb *l*aser *t*racking and applied to U.S. Air Force-guided bombs. As used in Southeast Asia, Air Force 750-, 2,000-, and 3,000-lb bombs were equipped with such guidance packages and were effective against bridges, interdiction points, and other pinpoint targets.

bolt action A rifle action in which a lever-operated bolt extends from the breech-block.

bolt mechanism The mechanical assembly in a bolt-action gun that includes the moving parts which insert, fire, and extract a round of ammunition.

Bomarc A U.S. Air Force long-range surface-to-air guided missile with a nuclear warhead for area air defense. It is powered by twin ramjet engines with either liquid or solid rocket boosters and is provided with terminal guidance. Designated as CIM-10, it has a weight of 16,000 lb and a range of about 440 mi. It was built by Boeing.

bomb **1.** In a broad sense, an explosive or other lethal agent, together with its container or holder, which is planted or thrown by hand, dropped from an aircraft, or projected by some other slow-speed device (as by lobbing it from a mortar) and is used to destroy, damage, injure, or kill.

Bofors Bantam. (*A. B. Bofors.*)

bogie. (*U.S. Army.*)

Bogue. (*U.S. Navy.*)

Bomarc. (*U.S. Air Force.*)

bomb. (*U.S. Army.*)

2. Anything similar to this object in appearance, operation, or effect, such as a leaflet bomb, a smoke bomb, a photoflash bomb, a bomblike container or chamber, etc. **3.** Specifically, an aerial bomb. The illustration shows a number of standard U.S. bombs used during World War II. They are, left to right: 20-lb fragmentation bomb M41; 23-lb fragmentation bomb M40; 100-lb demolition bomb M30; 300-lb bomb M31; 500-lb bomb M43; 1,000-lb bomb M44; 2,000-lb bomb M34; 500-lb bomb AN-M58; 1,000-lb bomb AN-M59; and 4,000-lb light-case demolition bomb M56.

bombard **1.** An ancient piece of ordnance that was very short and thick and had a wide bore. It was one of the earliest kinds of cannon and was used as long ago as the fourteenth century. It hurled stones and other missiles and was used in the attack and defense of fortified places. **2.** To hit a target such as a city or a fortification with bombs, shells, or grenades.

bombardelle A small bombard used in ancient times.

bombardier An aircrew member who operates the bombing equipment on a bomber.

bombardier-navigator A person who is both the bombardier and navigator aboard an airplane.

bombardment A sustained attack upon a city, military position, or other target with bombs, shells, rockets, or other explosive missiles.

bomb bay The compartment or bay in the fuselage of a bomber where the bombs are carried for release. (Picture, next page.)

bomb-bay doors The doors in the belly of an airplane, directly underneath the bomb bay.

bomb casing The container that holds the main explosive charge of a bomb.

bomb commander An officer responsible for an atomic bomb as it moves from the custody of the Atomic Energy Commission through various stages until it ultimately is released from the airplane.

bomb complete round A complete aerial bomb, including all the components, such as arming wires, fuzes, etc., necessary to attach the bomb to a release mechanism and to make it function after release.

bomb disposal A procedure for handling, disarming, or destroying unexploded bombs.

bomb-disposal unit See **explosive-ordnance-disposal unit.**

bolo. (*The Smithsonian Institution.*)

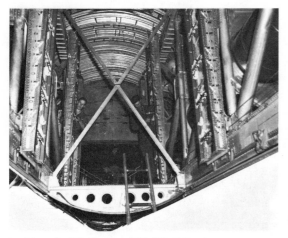

bomb bay, of a U.S. Air Force B-36. (*U.S. Air Force.*)

Boomerang. (*Australian Department of Supply.*)

bomber An airplane specifically designed to carry and drop bombs. A current definition includes the following types: (1) *Light:* a bomber designed for a tactical operating radius of under 1,000 nautical miles at design gross weight and design bombload. (2) *Medium:* a bomber designed for a tactical operating radius of between 1,000 and 2,500 nautical miles at design gross weight and design bombload. (3) *Heavy:* a bomber designed for a tactical operating radius over 2,500 nautical miles at design gross weight and design bombload.

bomber crew The aircrew that mans a bomber on a bombing mission. The crew was formerly composed of a pilot, a copilot, a navigator, a bombardier, a radio operator, gunners, and sometimes a flight engineer. The crews of modern bombers are far smaller.

bomber escort One or more fighters or bombers escorting friendly bombers.

bomb fin One of the airfoils attached to the rear of a bomb to provide directional stability.

bombing The action of dropping bombs from an aircraft with the purpose of hitting a target.

bombing errors (1) *Fifty percent circular error:* the radius of a circle, with the center at a desired mean point of impact, which contains half the missiles independently aimed to hit the desired mean point of impact. (2) *Fifty percent deflection error:* half the distance between two lines, drawn parallel to the aircraft's track and equidistant from the desired mean point of impact, which contains half the missiles independently aimed to hit the desired mean point of impact. (3) *Fifty percent range error:* half the distance between two lines, drawn perpendicular to the aircraft's track equidistant from the desired mean point of impact, which contains half the missiles independently aimed to hit the desired mean point of impact.

bombing height The distance above a target at the moment of bomb release, measured vertically from the target to the level of the bombing aircraft.

bombing table A table giving the bombsight settings required for dropping a particular type of bomb at various speeds and from various altitudes.

bombing types (1) *Glide bombing:* attack at angles of 30 to 55° without brakes or flaps. (2) *Dive bombing:* high-angle attack at 60 to 70° using dive brakes. (3) *Masthead* or *skip bombing:* level flight or shallow glide (under 30°). (4) *Horizontal bombing:* attack from steady, level flight at high or medium altitude. Other types or methods of bombing include area bombing, blind bombing, carpet bombing, density bombing, interdiction bombing, mass bombing, offset bombing, overcast bombing, pattern bombing, precision bombing, radar bombing, saturation bombing, shuttle bombing, toss bombing, and train bombing.

bomb line An imaginary line arranged, if possible, to follow well-defined geographic features, prescribed by the troop commander and coordinated with the air force commander, forward of which air forces are free to attack targets without danger to, or reference to, the ground forces. Behind this line all attacks must be coordinated with the appropriate troop commander.

bombproof A shelter, building, or other structure that is resistant or impervious to the effects of bombs or shells. It is usually partly or wholly underground.

bomb rack A suspension device permanently fixed to an aircraft. It is designed for attaching, arming, and releasing one or more bombs. It may also be utilized to accommodate other items such as mines, rockets, torpedoes, fuel tanks, rescue equipment, sonobuoys, flares, and the like.

bomb reconnaissance The act of reconnoitering to determine the presence of an unexploded missile; ascertain its nature; apply all practicable measures for the protection of personnel, installations, and equipment; and finally report essential information to the authority directing explosive-ordnance-disposal operations.

bomb-release circle In radar bombing, a circular track of light on the face of a plan-position indicator scope representing the desired dropping angle of a bomb. When the moving target spot on the PPI scope encounters the bomb-release circle, the proper dropping angle has been established and the bomb or bombs are dropped.

bomb-release line An imaginary line around a defended area or objective over which an aircraft should release its bomb in order to obtain a hit or hits on an area or objective.

bomb-release point The point in space at which bombs must be released to reach the desired point of detonation.

bomb run The flight course of a bombing airplane just before the release of bombs; bombing run.

bombs away Said by the bombardier the instant the bombs are released. It is a signal to the pilot and other aircrew members that the bombs have just been let go.

bomb shackle A suspension device installed in, but not permanently fixed to, an aircraft. It is designed for attaching, arming, and releasing a bomb. It may also be utilized to accommodate other items such as mines, rockets, torpedoes, fuel tanks, rescue equipment, sonobuoys, flares, and the like.

bombshell An old ordnance term for a hollow powder-filled globe of iron thrown from a mortar.

bombsight A device for determining the point in space at which a bomb or bombs must be released from an aircraft in order to hit a target.

bomb yoke A lever in the belly of a dive bomber which is used to swing a bomb clear of the propeller when released.

Bomine Bomb-mine. A U.S. development that is a combination of bomb and mine.

BOMROC A U.S. Navy shore bombardment rocket.

bone The white foam created at the bow of a vessel by its forward motion. A vessel is also said to carry a bone in her mouth or teeth.

bonnet In fortifications, a work consisting of two faces parallel to those of the ravelin and placed in front of the salient angle of the ravelin.

booby trap An explosive charge such as a mine, grenade, demolition block, shell, or bulk explosive fitted with a detonator and a firing device, all usually concealed and set to explode when an unsuspecting person touches off its firing mechanisms by stepping upon, lifting, or moving a harmless-looking object. Also often used as a verb.

booby-trapped mine A hidden mine arranged so that it will be detonated by the disturbance of an apparently harmless object.

Boomerang A single-engine one-place low-wing military airplane developed in Australia by the Commonwealth Aircraft Corporation and used during World War II as a fighter-bomber and a photoreconnaissance airplane. Also called the "CA-12," it was powered by a 1,200-hp engine and flew at speeds of 296 mph. It was armed with two 20mm Hispano cannons and four .303 cal. Browning machine guns.

boosted-rocket field-artillery weapon A helicopter-transportable direct-support artillery weapon employing the boosted-rocket principle. It is designated as the XM-70-115-mm.

booster 1. A high-explosive element sufficiently sensitive so as to be actuated by small explosive elements in a fuze or primer and powerful enough to cause detonation of the main explosive filling. 2. An auxiliary or inital propulsion system which travels with a missile or aircraft and which may or may not separate from the parent craft when its impulse has been delivered. A booster system may contain or consist of one or more units.

booster charge An explosive that sets off the main explosive charge. It is more sensitive to ignition than the main charge.

booster rocket A rocket that increases or helps increase the speed, range, or altitude of the airplane, rocket, or other vehicle to which it is attached.

boot A slang term for a newly enlisted recruit to the U.S. Navy or Marine Corps and presently in initial training.

boot camp A recruit training center for U.S. Navy and Marine Corps personnel.

boots A term that once meant the youngest officer in a regiment.

boots and saddle A cavalry bugle call for mounted formations.

booty The material or property seized on land by members of an armed force during a war. It contrasts with "prize," which is material or property captured on the high seas.

BOQ Bachelor officers' quarters.

Borchardt 7.65mm automatic pistol A weapon introduced in Germany in 1893 and the forerunner of the Luger. It was the first pistol to use the toggle-joint (blow-forward) locking system and also the first automatic pistol with a magazine that was removable from the grip. The pistol is named after Hugo Borchardt, an American who developed one of the earliest successful automatic pistols. He found it necessary to go to Germany to find a manufacturer to produce the pistol. George Luger, an engineer at Ludwig Loewe in Berlin, made improvements which resulted in the famous Luger pistol first introduced in 1900.

Borchardt-Luger pistol See **Luger automatic pistol.**

bord A round Anglo-Saxon shield made of wood and having a metal boss in the center.

bore The interior of a gun barrel or tube.

bore diameter In rifled barrels two diameters are involved: one measurement taken from the lands, and the other from the grooves. The land diameter is used to measure caliber in a rifled barrel.

bore-safe fuze A type of artillery fuze having an interrupter in the explosive train that prevents a projectile from exploding until after it has cleared the muzzle of the weapon.

boresight An instrument inserted in the bore of a gun to align its axis with its sights.

Borchardt 7.65mm automatic pistol. (*The Smithsonian Institution, Treasury Department Collection.*)

boresighting The process by which the axis of a gun bore and the line of sight of a gunsight are made parallel or are made to converge on a point. The term may be used in reference to any weapon and its sight.

boss A projection from a flat, or almost flat, surface. A boss is often found in the center of a shield.

Boston See **Havoc.**

Bostwick A class of U.S. escort ships (DE) of 1,240 tons standard displacement commissioned in the early 1940s. Sixteen are still in commission with the U.S. Navy, and fifty have been transferred to Allied navies. They have a length of 306 ft, a beam of 36.6 ft, a speed of 21 knots, and a complement of about 150 men. Armament consists of three 3-in. guns, two 40mm guns, depth charges, and hedgehogs.

Bosun The NATO code name for the Tupolev Tu-14 twin-jet attack bomber developed for the Soviet Naval Air Force and first seen in 1951.

Bostwick. (*U.S. Navy.*)

bottom turret, aboard a B-24 Liberator. *(U.S. Air Force.)*

bottleneck cartridge A cartridge case which tapers to a smaller diameter at the mouth.

bottom **1.** In ordnance, the plates used in grape or canister cartridges to separate layers of shot. **2.** In the construction of earthworks, a round disk in which holes have been drilled or punched. Rods are inserted in the holes to form a **gabion,** which see. **3.** In nautical terminology, the part of the ship that is ordinarily under water; hence the vessel itself; a ship.

bottom turret A turret in the bottom of an airplane fuselage.

bouche An early term for the mouth of a firearm. Also, the slit in the edge of a shield for a sword blade or the rounded opening for a lance. The slot or opening made it possible to use these weapons without exposing the arm or body.

bouchon A plug or stopper of the orifice in a grenade.

bouncer line In night UDU (**underwater demolition unit,** which see) operations, the point off the enemy beach at which the rubber boats are launched.

Bouncing Betty A nickname for the German antipersonnel S mine of World War II. When set off by trip wires, it would project into the air before exploding. It would detonate at 3 to 6 ft from the ground and scatter some 300 steel balls in all directions, to a range up to about 100 yd. The explosive charge weighed 1¼ lb.

bound **1.** A single movement, usually from cover to cover, made by troops often under artillery fire or small-arms fire. **2.** The distance covered in one movement by a unit which is advancing by bounds. **3.** An obsolete ordnance term meaning the path of a shot between two points of grazing.

Bounder The NATO code name for a Soviet aircraft with four turbojet engines of Myasischev design. It has a speed of about 700 mph and a service ceiling of 55,000 ft.

bounding mine A type of antipersonnel

bourlette. *(The Smithsonian Institution, Catholic University Collection.)*

mine, usually buried just below the surface of the ground. It has a small charge which throws the case up in the air. This explodes at a height of 3 or 4 ft, throwing shrapnel or fragments in all directions.

bounty The gift or extra allowance once used to induce men to enter military or naval service.

bounty jumper A person who enlisted in U.S. military service to get the bounty and then deserted. The term evolved during the latter part of the Civil War.

bourguignotte A burgonet, or open helmet with a caplike bill worn during the sixteenth and seventeenth centuries. It is believed to have been developed in Burgundy.

bourlette A mace studded with iron points.

bourrelet The bands around a projectile on which the projectile bears while in the bore of the weapon.

bow A projectile weapon made of a piece of wood or other material tapering in both directions from the middle and having the ends connected by a cord when this piece is bent. The side closest to the archer is called the "belly," and the side away from him is called the "back." The middle of the bow is called the "handle," and the ends, frequently tipped with horn, are called the "tips." There are notches for the string or cord in the tips, and these are called "nocks." It is used to propel arrows. See also **crossbow.**

bow The front or forward part of a ship.

bow chaser An old naval term for a gun placed in the bow to fire on a retreating vessel.

bow gun A gun mounted at the front of a ship or armored vehicle, especially a semifixed forward-firing gun in a tank.

bowie knife A single-edged utility and fighting knife named after Col. James Bowie (d. 1836), who made such knives popular.

bowman An archer.

bow-on Facing the firer. A bow-on target is a target that presents its narrower dimension exactly toward the gun firing at it. When an enemy tank is headed exactly at the gun firing at it, the tank is a bow-on target.

bowshot The distance traversed by an arrow shot from a bow. For example, the extreme range, or bowshot, of the old English longbow with flight arrows was about 400 yd.

bowstring The string of a bow.

bowyer The man who made or repaired military bows.

Box The NATO code name for the A-20 Havoc supplied to the Soviet Union under lend-lease.

box barrage A stationary artillery barrage on three sides of a given area. It is used to prevent the enemy's escape or reinforcement or to cover the front and flanks

of a friendly force. Also, in antiaircraft fire, a barrage delivered in a boxlike pattern by guns surrounding a defended target.

Boxer cartridge The first center-fire metallic cartridge to be used successfully. This cartridge, consisting of a coiled brass case with an iron head and an anvil primer and containing a roundnose lead bullet, was developed in the 1860s by Col. Edward M. Boxer, of England.

Boxer primer A primer in which the anvil is an integral part of the primer assembly. It is favored in the United States over the Berdan primer.

Boxers Members of a Chinese secret society called the "righteous, harmonious fists" or, in English, the Boxers. The group caused a rebellion in northern China in 1900.

boxlock A pistol or gun action in which the lock mechanism is contained within the frame.

box magazine A boxlike device that holds ammunition and feeds it into the receiver mechanism of weapons.

box respirator A gas mask having a mask that covers the face and a chemical-filled box that filters the air breathed by the user.

box-type bomb fin A bomb-fin assembly designed like a box and open at both ends.

boyau A winding zigzag trench made by besiegers to enable them to approach a position under cover. These trenches are also called "zigzags" or "approaches."

BPF British Pacific Fleet (World War II).

Brabanter A mercenary soldier of the Middle Ages, usually from the Belgian province of Brabant or from Germany.

bracelet Defensive armor for the arm.

bracer A device worn by archers to protect the left forearm from chafing caused by the bowstring.

bracket The distance between two strikes or series of strikes, one of which is over the target and the other of which is short of it or one of which is to the right of the target and the other of which is to the left of it.

bracketing A method of adjusting fire in which a bracket is established by obtaining an over and a short along the spotting line and then successively splitting the bracket in half until a target hit or desired bracket is obtained.

bracketing salvo A group of shots in which the number of shots going over the target equals the number falling short of it.

brackets The cheeks of a mortar's traveling carriage. The term may also refer to the part of the mortar bed that supports the trunnions.

braconnière In armor terminology a short skirt of narrow hoop-shaped plates of steel.

brainwash To manipulate various psychological and morale factors so as to induce a person to reveal confidential infor-

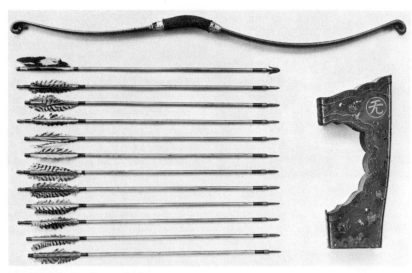

bow. (*The Metropolitan Museum of Art.*)

bowie knife. (*The Smithsonian Institution.*)

mation or to subscribe to false statements.

brake A weapon similar in design to the crossbow or the ballista.

branch **1.** A subdivision of any organization. **2.** A geographically separate unit of an activity which performs all or part of the primary functions of the parent activity on a smaller scale. Unlike an annex, a branch is not merely an overflow addition. **3.** An arm or service of the Army.

brandestoc A hatchet or war hammer, the handle of which conceals a long blade.

brandschwaermer A small rocket fired from a gun. It was formerly used to set fire to buildings thatched with straw.

braquemard A short double-edged broadsword of the sixteenth century.

brass **1.** A slang expression for persons of high rank or command. **2.** Expended brass cartridges.

brassard **1.** An armband, such as those worn by MPs or SPs. **2.** A term that once meant armor used for the protection of the arm.

brassart A portion of armor for the protection of the upper part of the arm, from the elbow to the shoulder.

brass hat A slang expression referring to the gold decoration on the cap visor of top-ranking officers. Hence, a person of high rank or command.

brattice In fortifications, an advanced temporary work, especially on a battlement.

Braunschweig A class of German 13,200-ton battleships completed in 1904–1906. It consisted of *Braunschweig, Elsass, Lothringen, Hessen,* and *Preussen.* They had a length of 410 ft, a speed of 18 knots, a complement of 691 men, and main armament consisting of four 11-in. and fourteen 6.7-in. guns, plus six 17.7-in. torpedo tubes.

bray A low wall built outside the ramparts. It was designed to prevent the enemy from approaching the ramparts.

brayette See **breech of mail**

Brazilian 7mm Madsen machine guns Brazil has used no fewer than 10 models of the Madsen machine gun, ranging from Model 1908 to Model 1946. See **Madsen machine guns.**

Brazilian 7mm Mauser rifle Model 1908 This weapon differs only slightly from the German Gew. and Kar. 98 series, the principal difference being the caliber.

Brazilian 114mm rocket A two-stage solid-propellant artillery rocket with a length of 6.5 ft and a range of 15 mi. It carries a conventional high-explosive warhead.

Brazilian Navy air-to-surface rocket FB.E.127 A spin-stabilized weapon intended for use from helicopters of the Brazilian Navy. It has a launching weight of 110 lb and a maximum range of 10.5 mi.

Brazilian Navy bombardment rocket R-115 A surface-to-surface rocket with a range of 4.6 mi, a total weight of 38.6 lb, and a warhead weight of 2.97 lb of high explosive.

breach An opening made in a fortification to facilitate an assault. The guns once used for this purpose were called "breaching batteries."

breaching The employment of any available means to secure a passage through an enemy minefield or fortification.

break To open a revolver or a shotgun.

breakthrough An offensive thrust that breaks through a defensive line.

breast That part of an arrow touching the bow when the arrow is in position for shooting. Also, a shortened term for a breastplate.

breastheight In fortifications, the interior slope of a parapet or trench.

breastplate A metal plate worn on the breast as defensive armor.

breastwork Earthwork which gives protection to defenders in a standing position, firing over the crest. Breastworks are constructed wholly or partly above the surface of the ground.

breath In armor, a hole or slit in the visor or beaver. It was used to provide ventilation.

Breda 6.5mm L.M.G. Model 30 An Italian light machine gun with a weight of 25½ lb and a length of 48½ in. It is recoil-operated and capable of automatic fire only. It has a rate of fire of 450 to 500 rounds per minute and is fed by a nondetachable magazine loaded with 20-round chargers. It has open sights (barleycorn and V) with a range of adjustment from 300 to 1,500 meters.

Breda 6.5mm machine gun Model 1924 An Italian recoil-operated machine gun

Breda 6.5mm L.M.G. Model 30. (*The Smithsonian Institution, Department of Defense Collection.*)

Breda 65. (*The Imperial War Museum.*)

with a rate of fire of 450 to 500 rounds per minute. This air-cooled weapon had a weight of 20 lb and was fed from a 20-round magazine.

Breda 6.5mm machine gun Model 1930 This was the standard Italian light machine gun in World War II. The weapon operates on a delayed blowback system and is capable of automatic fire only. It has an overall length of 48.5 in., a barrel length of 20.5 in., and a weight of 22.75 lb. The cyclic rate of fire is 450 to 500 rounds per minute, and the muzzle velocity is 2,063 fps. It operates from a 20-round nondetachable magazine that is fed by chargers.

Breda 7.35mm L.M.G. Model 38 This weapon has the same characteristics as the Breda 6.5mm L.M.G. Model 30. The only difference is the caliber.

Breda 7.35mm machine gun Model 38 This machine gun has the same characteristics as the Breda 6.5mm machine gun Model 1930.

Breda 7.7mm machine gun Model 1935 An Italian recoil- and blowback-operated air-cooled machine gun with a rate of fire of 600 to 650 rounds per minute. It had a weight of 27 lb and was fed from a 250-round link belt.

Breda 8mm machine gun Model 37 One of the best machine guns used by the Italians in World War II. This gas-operated weapon operates on full automatic fire only. It has an overall length of 50 in., a barrel length of about 25 in., and a weight of 42.8 lb. The tripod weighs 41.5 lb. The cyclic rate of fire is 450 rounds per minute, and the muzzle velocity is 2,600 fps. The weapon is fed from 20-round strips.

Breda 12.7mm aircraft machine gun Model 1937 An Italian gas-operated air-cooled machine gun with a rate of fire of 450 to 500 rounds per minute. It had a weight of 42.5 lb and was fed from a 20-round tray.

Breda 20mm cannon An Italian gas-operated air-cooled cannon with a rate of fire of 200 to 220 rounds per minute. It was introduced to the Italian Army in 1934 as an antitank gun and was mounted in a carriage similar to that of a field piece. In the late 1930s it was hastily modified for aircraft use (because the Italian Air Force realized that it needed greater firepower against large bombers).

Breda 65 An Italian fighter, bomber, and reconnaissance aircraft used in World War II. It had a speed of 267 mph and was armed with four 7.7mm machine guns, plus a 1,800-lb bombload.

Breda 88 See **Lince.**

Breda aircraft machine guns Prior to, and during, World War II a series of machine guns were made for aircraft use and developed in 7.7mm (.303 British), 7.92mm, and 12.7mm. The 7.7mm and 12.7mm guns were standard for the Italian forces.

Breda-Fiat 7.92mm machine gun Model 1930 An Italian recoil-operated air-cooled machine gun with a rate of fire of 350 to 500 rounds per minute. It weighed 20 lb and was fed from a 20-round magazine.

breech The rear part of the bore of a gun, especially the opening that permits the projectile to be inserted at the rear of the bore.

breech action The breech mechanism in breechloading small arms and guns. They can be variously classified as automatic,

bolt, falling-block, lever, and slide-action.

breechblock A movable iron or steel block in the mechanism of a breechloading gun or cannon that closes the breech opening of the barrel or tube during firing.

breech bolt A mechanism which closes the breech in a carbine, machine gun, and the like. It is designed to push a cartridge into the chamber of a gun by sliding action. It may contain the ejector, extractor, and/or firing pin.

breeching loop The loop of metal in (or in place of) the knob of a cascabel on some old muzzle-loading cannons.

breechloader A gun or other weapon that is loaded at the breech instead of at the muzzle. With the exception of mortars, nearly all modern guns are breechloading rather than muzzle-loading.

breechloading Receiving the charge at the breech instead of the muzzle.

breech mechanism A device for opening and closing the breech of a gun.

breech of mail A short sixteenth-century skirt of mail, sometimes called a "brayette."

breech piece The jacket of a heavy cannon.

breech pin See **breech plug.**

breech plug A removable screw-in plug that seals the breech end of a muzzle-loading gun barrel.

breech screw A type of breech plug used in muzzle-loading muskets and rifles to close the bottom of the bore.

breech sight A firearm's rear sight.

Breguet 4 and 5 French two-place single engine (pusher) biplane bombers introduced in 1916. They were armed with a single Hotchkiss or Lewis machine gun in the front cockpit and carried sixteen 16-lb bombs. They had a speed of about 85 mph.

Breguet 14 A French two-place single-engine biplane bomber that entered service in mid-1917. It was armed with one forward-firing synchronized Vickers machine gun and twin Lewis guns ring-mounted in the observer's cockpit. It could carry up to thirty-two 17.6-lb bombs. More than 8,000 of this basic type were produced between 1917 and 1926.

Breguet 521 Bizerte A French three-engine biplane long-range reconnaissance flying boat first flown in 1933.

Breguet 690 Series French two-seat twin-engine light attack bombers developed in the late 1930s. They were typically armed with one 20mm cannon and four 7.5mm machine guns, plus eight 110-lb bombs carried internally. Top speed was about 295 mph.

Breguet Atlantic See **Atlantic.**

Bren .303 cal. light machine gun This gas-operated aircooled weapon was developed from the Czech 7.92mm ZB26, and production commenced at Enfield in 1937.

breechblock, of a U.S. 105mm gun. (*U.S. Army.*)

The weapon was made in .303 cal. for British use and also in 7.92mm for the Chinese Nationalists. It was one of the best light machine guns of World War II, and is still in wide use around the world. The Bren was made in four basic models: the Mark 1, 2, 3, and 4. They varied slightly in butt assembly design and in other minor details. The Mark 4 is 42.9 in. long and has a barrel length of 22.25 in. The cyclic rate of fire is 520 rounds per minute, the muzzle velocity is about 2,400 fps, and the weight of the gun is 19.14 lb. The barrel weighs 5 lb. It is equipped with a 30-round box magazine. The Bren light machine gun L4A2 is a conversion of the later-model Brens to 7.62mm NATO.

Bren .303 cal. light machine gun. (*The Smithsonian Institution, Department of Defense Collection.*)

breteche A covered passage constructed on the top of a wall or tower. It was built out from the wall on projections (corbels) called "machicoulis." It was removed in peacetime.

brevet An honorary rank; it confers no right of command.

brevity code A code which provides no security but which has as its sole purpose the shortening of messages rather then the concealment of their content.

Brewer See **Firebar**.

bricole A fourteenth-century device for throwing stones. Also, a drag rope for hawling cannons by hand.

bridge The structure on a ship that contains control and communication facilities. It is topside and usually forward.

bridgehead An area of ground held or to be gained on the enemy's side of an obstacle. See also **airhead** and **beachhead**.

bridge train Formerly, the wagons, animals, personnel, and equipment in an army train necessary for the construction of bridges.

bridle The part in a gunlock that holds the tumbler and sear in place. The arm from the pan of a flintlock that provides a bearing for the frizzen screw.

bridle port A gunport forward on the gundeck of a warship.

bridoon The snaffle and rein of a military bridle.

briefing The act of giving in advance specific instructions or information.

brig A two-masted square-rigged sailing ship. Also, the jail aboard a ship.

brigade A unit usually smaller than a division to which are attached groups and/or battalions and smaller units tailored to meet anticipated requirements.

brigade major An officer on temporary duty to a brigade to assist the brigadier.

brigadier An officer in charge of a brigade; a brigadier general.

brigadier general An officer ranking next above a colonel and below a major general. In the U.S. service the insignia for this rank is a single silver star.

brigadine See **brigandine**.

Brigand A British twin-engine three-seat long-range attack aircraft developed by Bristol at the end of World War II.

brigandine A type of European armor used from the thirteenth to the sixteenth centuries. It consisted of overlapping metal scales or plates riveted to a canvas, cloth, or leather garment.

brigantine A two-masted sailing ship with the mainmast rigged with fore and aft sails and square-rigged foremast.

brisance The ability of an explosive to shatter the medium which confines it; the shattering effect of the explosive.

brise-mur A heavy piece of ordnance which was used during the fifteenth century to batter down walls, etc.

Bristol F.2A and F.2B British two-place single-engine biplane fighters introduced early in 1917. The F.2A was equipped with a 190-hp engine, and the F.2B with a more powerful engine and other modifications. The latter flew at speeds of 119 mph. Both were armed with a front-firing synchronized Vickers gun and a Lewis gun mounted on a Scarff ring in the rear cockpit. They were extremely efficient fighters, and more than 5,500 were ordered, a number of which remained in service with the RAF until 1932. (Picture, next page.)

Bristol M.IC A British single-place single-engine midwing monoplane that went into service in 1917. It was armed with one forward-firing Vickers machine gun and had a speed of about 132 mph. A limited number were built.

Bristol Scout A British single-place single-engine biplane fighter first flown in February 1914. It had a speed of 95 mph (very good for its day) and was armed with a single forward-firing machine gun.

brisure In fortifications, a rampart or parapet that deviates from the general direction.

Briteye A U.S. parachute flare that pro-

brigandine. (*The Metropolitan Museum of Art, gift of William H. Riggs, 1913.*)

Brigand. (*British Aircraft Corporation Ltd.*)

Bristol F. 2A. (*British Aircraft Corporation Ltd.*)

vides a 5,000-candlepower light output for 5 minutes.

British two-pounder antitank gun Mk 9 A World War II weapon with a weight of 1,757 lb and a projectile weight of 2.5 lb. It fired fixed ammunition and had a range of 8,000 yd.

British 3-in. antiaircraft gun A World War II weapon with a weight of 8.7 tons and a projectile weight of 16 lb. It fired fixed ammunition and had an effective ceiling of 20,000 ft.

British 3.45-in. recoilless rifle A World War II weapon with a weight of 55 lb and a projectile weight of 11 lb. It fired fixed ammunition and had a range of 1,000 yd.

British 3.7-in. antiaircraft gun Mk 1 A World War II weapon with a weight of 10.3 tons and a projectile weight of 27 lb. It fired fixed ammunition and had an effective ceiling of 32,000 ft.

British 4.5-in. antiaircraft gun. (*The Imperial War Museum.*)

British 3.7-in. antiaircraft gun Mk 6 A World War II weapon with a weight of 22.4 tons and a projectile weight of 28 lb. It fired fixed ammunition and had an effective ceiling of 45,000 ft.

British 3.7-in. howitzer A World War II weapon with a weight of 1,856 lb and a projectile weight of 20 lb. It fired fixed ammunition and had a range of 6,000 yd.

British 3.7-in. recoilless rifle A World War II weapon with a weight of 250 lb and a projectile weight of 22 lb. It fired fixed ammunition and had a range of 3,000 yd.

British 4.5-in. antiaircraft gun A World War II weapon with a weight of 16.5 tons and a projectile weight of 55 lb. It fired fixed ammunition and had an effective ceiling of 34,500 ft.

British 4.5-in. gun A World War II weapon with a weight of 6.3 tons and a projectile weight of 50 lb. It fired separate-loading ammunition and had a range of about 20,000 yd.

British 4.5-in. howitzer, Mark I A weapon that had a length of 70 in. and a weight of 3,010 lb; it could fire a 35-lb projectile to a range of 6,800 yd. It was used in World War I and, with a modern mount, in the Libyan campaigns of World War II.

British 5.25-in. twin antiaircraft gun A World War II weapon with a weight of 85.2 tons and a projectile weight of 80 lb. It fired fixed ammunition and had an effective ceiling of 43,000 ft.

British 5.5-in. gun A World War II weapon with a weight of 6.4 tons and a projectile weight of 100 lb. It fired separate-loading ammunition and had a range of 16,000 yd.

British 6-in. coast gun Mk 24 A World War II weapon with a weight of 41.4 tons and a projectile weight of 100 lb. It fired separate-loading ammunition and had a range of 21,700 yd.

British 6-in. howitzer, Mark I A Vickers-built weapon developed for use in World War I. It weighed 9,318 lb with carriage and could fire a 100-lb projectile 9,500 yd

or an 86-lb projectile 11,400 yd.

British six-pounder antitank gun Mk 2 A World War II weapon with a weight of 1.4 tons and a projectile weight of 6 lb. It fired fixed ammunition and had a range of 5,500 yd.

British six-pounder twin coast gun A World War II weapon with a weight of 11 tons and a projectile weight of 6.4 lb. It fired fixed ammunition and had a range of 5,150 yd.

British 7.2-in. howitzer Mk 6 A World War II weapon with a weight of 19.6 tons and a projectile weight of 200 lb. It fired separate-loading ammunition and had a range of 16,600 yd.

British 7.62mm machine gun L7A1 See **L7A1 7.62mm machine gun.**

British 7.69mm Madsen machine guns Great Britain has used five models of the Madsen machine gun, ranging from Model 1915 to Model 1939. See **Madsen machine guns.**

British 7.7mm aircraft machine gun Mark II A Browning machine gun.

British 9mm Parabellum submachine gun L2A3 See **Sterling 9mm Parabellum submachine gun L2A3.**

British 9mm Parabellum submachine gun (Sten) See **Sten 9mm Parabellum submachine gun.**

British 9.2-in. coast gun Mk 10 A World War II weapon with a weight of 156.8 tons and a projectile weight of 380 lb. It fired separate-loading ammunition and had a range of 31,600 yd.

British 9.2-in. heavy howitzer, Mark I and Mark II These Vickers-built weapons were used in both World Wars. The Mark I had a weight of 29,100 lb and could fire a 290-lb projectile a distance of 10,225 yd. The Mark II version was developed in 1918; it had a weight of 35,500 lb and a range of 13,080 yd.

British 15-in. coast gun Mk 1 A World War II weapon with a weight of 224 tons and a projectile weight of 1,920 lb. It fired separate-loading ammunition and had a range of 36,900 yd.

British 15mm Besa machine gun Originally a Czech design, this weapon was used as secondary armament on armored vehicles. See also **Besa 7.92mm machine gun Mk 1, Besa 7.92mm tank machine guns,** and **Besa 15mm machine gun Mark 1.**

British seventeen-pounder antitank gun M1 A World War II weapon with a weight of 2.3 tons and a projectile weight of 17 lb. It fired fixed ammunition and had a range of 10,000 yd.

British 18-in. coast gun Mk 1 A World War II weapon with a weight of 282.2 tons and a projectile weight of 2,500 lb. It fired separate-loading ammunition and had a range of 24,500 yd.

British twenty-five-pounder gun This

weapon was first designed in 1935 and was based on the eighteen-pounder gun used by the British Army in World War I. It was introduced in 1940, and the last significant modification was incorporated in 1943. Although it is no longer in use with field forces of the Royal Artillery, it is used by the forces of a number of other countries. It has an overall length of 15 ft 3 in. and a total weight of 3,840 lb and fires a 25-lb projectile to a maximum range of 13,400 yd.

British twenty-five-pounder gun-howitzer This 87.6mm weapon weighed 4,048 lb in firing position. It was capable of firing about four rounds per minute, each projectile having a weight of 25 lb and a range of 13,400 yd (about 7½ mi).

British 30mm cannon, Rarden See **Rarden 30mm cannon.**

British 30mm naval mounting A.32 See **Hispano-Suiza twin 30mm naval mounting A.32.**

British 40mm antiaircraft gun This Vickers-built weapon was designed in 1934 and had a weight of 2.6 tons and a projectile weight of 2 lb. It had an effective ceiling of 16,500 ft and a rate of fire of 200 rounds per minute (belt-fed, with 25 rounds in each belt).

British 47mm antitank gun A weapon developed by Vickers in the mid-1920s. It fired a high-explosive shell weighing 3.3 lb and had a range of about 2,850 meters.

British .50 cal. machine gun (Vickers) A large number of Maxim machine-gun types were employed by British forces as tank and aircraft armament. Marks I through V were used.

British 57mm antitank gun An antitank weapon with a range of 10,000 yd.

British 81mm medium mortar A weapon currently in use in the British Army. It has a weight of 78 lb, a barrel length of 50 in., and a range of 5,900 yd with a special charge. It can be fired at the rate of 15 rounds per minute. The HE round weighs 9 lb 13 oz.

British 95mm howitzer A World War II weapon with a weight of 1 ton and a projectile weight of 25 lb. It fired fixed ammunition and had a range of about 10,000 yd.

British 95mm recoilless rifle A World War II weapon with a weight of 1.2 tons and a projectile weight of 25 lb. It fired fixed ammunition and had a range of 10,800 yd.

British 105mm QF gun (L7A1) A gun with a range of 1,800 (APDS) to 5,500 meters (HESH). It is used as the main armament on the German Leopard main battle tank.

British 105mm self-propelled gun, Abbot See **Abbot.**

British .303 cal. Charger Loading Lee-Enfield Mark I This weapon was adopted

British 15-in. coast gun Mk 1. (*The Imperial War Museum.*)

British 40mm antiaircraft gun. (*Vickers Ltd.*)

British 47mm antitank gun. (*Vickers Ltd.*)

British .303 cal. Lee-Enfield carbine Mark I. (*The Smithsonian Institution, War Department Collection.*)

in July 1907 and is a conversion of the Long Lee-Enfield Marks I and I* to charger loading. The sights were also modified. Long Lee-Metford Marks II and II* were also converted at the same time and were at first called "Charger Loading Lee-Metfords," but later designated "Charger Loading Lee-Enfield Mark I*."

British .303 cal. Lee-Enfield carbine Mark I and Mark I* This weapon was adopted in August 1869 and is the same as the Lee-Metford Mark I carbine except for the type of rifling, the sights, and differences in sling attachments. It uses the same six-round magazine as the Lee-Metford carbine. The Mark I* differed from the Mark I only in that the cleaning rod was removed. It was adopted in May 1899.

British .303 cal. Lee-Enfield rifle Mark I This rifle was adopted in November 1895 and is the same as the Lee-Metford Mark II* except that deeper Enfield-type rifling was used (rather than the comparatively shallower Metford rifling).

British .303 cal. Lee-Enfield rifle Mark I* This rifle is the same as the Lee-Enfield Mark I except that the cleaning rod is eliminated. It was adopted in May 1899.

British .303 cal. Lee-Metford carbine Mark I This weapon was adopted in September 1894. It is 40 in. long and has a barrel length of 20.75 in. It weighs 7.43 lb, has a muzzle velocity of 1,940 fps, and utilizes a detachable six-round magazine. The bolt handle is bent to lie closer to the receiver.

British .303 cal. Lee-Metford rifle Mark I This bolt-action weapon was adopted in December 1888 and was first used with a black-powder cartridge with a muzzle velocity of 1,850 fps and a 215-grain bullet. The rifle utilizes an eight-round magazine.

British .303 cal. Lee-Metford rifle Mark I* This bolt-action rifle was adopted in January 1892 and differs from the Mark I in the design of its sights and the removal of the safety catch. The .303 cal. Cordite Mark I smokeless powder cartridge was

introduced shortly after this weapon appeared. The rifle has an overall length of 49.85 in. and a barrel length of 30.19 in. It weighs 10.43 lb, has a muzzle velocity of about 2,000 fps, and features an eight-round detachable box magazine.

British .303 cal. Lee-Metford rifle Mark II This rifle was adopted in 1892 and differs very slightly from the Lee-Metford Mark I*. The bolt and receiver are modified, and it has a lighter barrel and utilizes a 10-round magazine.

British .303 cal. Lee-Metford rifle Mark II* This rifle differs from the Mark II in having a safety catch added to the cocking piece. This required the alteration of the firing pin and bolt. It was adopted in 1895.

British .303 cal. light machine gun (Bren) See **Bren .303 cal. light machine gun.**

British .303 cal. light machine guns Mark I and Mark I* **Hotchkiss machine guns,** which see, in British service.

British .303 cal. light machine gun (Vickers-Berthier) See **Vickers-Berthier .303 cal. light machine gun.**

British .303 cal. machine gun (Lewis) For details of this weapon see **Lewis machine gun.** The British used four ground models of this weapon and three aircraft models.

British .303 cal. machine gun (Vickers) A large number of Maxim machine-gun types were employed by British forces as ground, tank, and aircraft armament. Marks I through VII were used.

British .303 cal. medium machine gun Mk I (Vickers) See **Vickers .303 cal. medium machine gun Mk I.**

British .303 cal. rifle No. 3 Mark I* (P-14) A bolt-action rifle made in the United States during World War I. When the United States entered the war, it was continued in U.S. .30 cal. and was called the "U.S. rifle .30 cal. M1917" and known commonly in the United States as the "Enfield." The British changed the nomenclature of the .303 version in 1926 from P-14 to rifle No. 3 Mark I*.

British .303 cal. rifle No. 4 Mark I This weapon was adopted in November 1939 and was the main British service rifle in World War II. It has an overall length of 44.5 in. and a barrel length of 25.2 in. It weighs 8.8 lb and has a muzzle velocity of 2,440 fps and a 10-round detachable box magazine.

British .303 cal. rifle No. 4 Mark I (T) This is the sniper version of the No. 4 Mark I and was adopted in February 1942. It is fitted with a No. 32 telescopic sight and a wooden cheekpiece.

British .303 cal. rifle No. 4 Mark I* This variation of the No. 4 Mark I was not adopted until November 1946. It was, however, in production in Canada from 1942 until 1945. It differs in some minor ways from the Mark I, principally in not having a bolt-head catch.

British .303 cal. rifle No. 4 Mark 2 This rifle was adopted in March 1949 and had much the same design as the No. 4 Mark I with modifications to the trigger and the fore-end.

British .303 cal. rifle No. 5 Mark 1 This weapon was adopted in September 1944 and represented a lightweight version of the No. 4. Sometimes called the "Jungle Carbine," this weapon has an overall length of 39.5 in., a barrel length of 18.7 in., and a weight of 7.15 lb. It has a muzzle velocity of 2,400 fps and a detachable box magazine with a capacity of 10 cartridges.

British .303 cal. S.M.L.E. rifle No. 1 Mark I This bolt-action rifle was adopted in December 1902 and was the first of the Short Magazine Lee-Enfields (S.M.L.E.) and the first British rifle to use a stripper-clip loading system. It has an overall length of 44.5 in. and a barrel length of 25.19 in. It weighs 8.12 lb and has a muzzle velocity of 2,060 fps and a 10-round detachable box magazine. It has a V-notch rear sight with windage adjustments and a barleycorn front sight.

British .303 cal. S.M.L.E. rifle No. 1 Mark I* A slightly modified S.M.L.E. rifle No. 1 Mark I. It was adopted in July 1906.

British .303 cal. S.M.L.E. rifle No. 1 Mark I** Adopted in 1908, this rifle was a conversion of the No. 1 Mark I done by the Royal Navy. The sights were changed, and a number of minor alterations were made.

British .303 cal. S.M.L.E. (converted) rifle No. 1 Mark II* This rifle represented a conversion of the Long Lee-Metford and Lee-Enfield rifles to the No. 1 Mark I*. It was adopted in July 1906.

British .303 cal. S.M.L.E. rifle No. 1 Mark III, Mark III* This rifle was adopted in January 1907 and was the basic British rifle used during World War I. It was also used to some extent in World War II. It has an overall length of 44.5 in. and a barrel length of 25.19 in. It weighs 8.62 lb, has a muzzle

British .303 cal. S.M.L.E. rifle No. 1 Mark III. (*The Smithsonian Institution, War Department Collection.*)

velocity of 2,060 fps, and utilizes a 10-round detachable box magazine. During World War I more than 3½ million of the Mark III and Mark III* were produced. The Mark III* has a muzzle velocity of 2,440 fps and differs only slightly from the Mark III.

British .303 cal. S.M.L.E. (converted) rifle No. 1 Mark IV This rifle represented a conversion of Long Lee-Enfields and Long Lee-Metfords to the same general design as the S.M.L.E. No. 1 Mark III. It was adopted in July 1907.

British .303 cal. S.M.L.E. rifle No. 1 Mark V This weapon was made in limited numbers in 1922 but was never adopted.

British .303 cal. S.M.L.E. rifle No. 1 Mark VI This weapon was the predecessor of the No. 4 rifle and was made in limited quantities between 1923 and 1926. It differs in quite a few details from earlier No. 1 rifles.

British .303 cal. Vickers machine gun This weapon weighed 33 lb with empty water jacket and 43 lb when full. It had a 24.5-in. barrel and a cyclic rate of 500 rounds per minute. Adopted in 1912 and based on an older U.S. Maxim, it was the standard British infantry and aircraft weapon during World War II.

British .380 cal. pistol No. 2 Mk I See **Webley .380 cal. pistol No. 2 Mk I.**

British .455 cal. revolvers (Webley) See **Webley .455 cal. revolvers.**

British .455 cal. self-loading pistol See **Webley .455 cal. self-loading pistol.**

British armored car, Daimler Mk II A World War II vehicle with a weight of about 8 tons, a crew of three, and a turret-mounted two-pounder gun. Production totaled 2,694.

British armored car, Saladin See **Saladin armored car.**

British armored car, Shorland See **Shorland armored car.**

British armored personnel carrier, Saracen See **Saracen armored personnel carrier.**

British Expeditionary Force The small regular army of Great Britain landed in France in August 1914 at the beginning of World War I.

British miniature submarine See **X-craft.**

British scout car, Ferret See **Ferret scout car.**

British tank, cruiser, Comet I See **Comet I.**

British tank, cruiser, Mk I This tank was built by Vickers-Armstrong and entered production in 1937. It had a crew of six and was armed with one two-pounder gun and three machine guns. Also designated A9, tanks of this type saw service in France and the Western Desert of Africa early in World War I.

British tank, cruiser, Mk VI, Crusader I See **Crusader I.**

British tank, cruiser, Mk VIII, Centaur I See **Centaur I.**

British .303 cal. Vickers machine gun. (*The Smithsonian Institution, Treasury Department Collection.*)

British tank, cruiser, Mk VIII, Cromwell IV See **Cromwell IV.**

British tank, heavy, Mk IV See **Churchill Mk III tank.**

British tank, infantry, Mk III, Valentine See **Valentine.**

British tank, infantry Mk IV, Churchill I See **Churchill I.**

British tank, infantry, Valentine See **Valentine.**

British tank, light, M3A1 (Stuart Mk IV) See **Honey.**

British tank, light, Mk I through VI The Vickers-Armstrong Mk I light tank entered service in 1930. It weighed 2.5 tons, had a crew of two, and was armed with one Vickers machine gun. The Mk II was used in Northern India in 1931–1935. The Mk III was used operationally in Palestine in 1936. The Mk IV fought in France and the Western Desert of Africa in 1939–1940 and was used in Greece, Crete, and Malta. The Mk V carried two machine guns, one .50 cal. and one .303 cal. The final version was the Mk VI, with an improved engine and armed with one 15mm and one 7.92mm machine gun. (Picture, next page.)

British tank, light, Mk VIA Built by Vickers Armstrong, this tank was introduced in 1938 for reconnaissance use and also for use in armored battalions. It carried a crew of three, was armed with two .303 Vickers machine guns, and weighed 5.8 tons. It was used in France in 1939–1940 and in the

early campaigns in the Western Desert of Africa.

British tank, light, Mk VIII See **Harry Hopkins tank.**

British tank, light, Scorpion See **Scorpion light tank.**

British tank, main battle, Vickers See **Vickers main battle tank.**

British tank, medium, "Fire Fly" See **Sherman V C (M4A4).**

British tank, medium, M3 See **Grant Mk I.**

British tank, medium, Mk A See **Whippet.**

British tank, medium, Mk II See **Matilda.**

British tank, medium, Mk IIA A tank built by Vickers Armstrong and introduced in about 1930. It was armed with one two-pounder QF gun, with two Vickers machine guns mounted in the hull sides. It was the first tank used by the Royal Tank Regiment to have all-round traverse (360°) and geared elevation for the gun. (Picture, next page.)

British tank, medium, Mk III See **Crusader,** sense 2.

British tank, Mk IV (female) This tank was built by William Foster and Company and was released in 1917 for use in battalions for infantry support. It carried a crew of eight and was armed with five .303 Lewis Model 1914 machine guns. (A "male" tank was armed with cannon and machine guns. A "female" tank was armed only with machine guns.) This tank had a weight of 30.2 tons.

British tank, cruiser, Mk I. (*Vickers Ltd.*)

British tank, light, Mk I. (*Vickers Ltd.*)

Brixia 6.5mm aircraft machine gun Model 1920 An Italian recoil-operated air-cooled machine gun with a rate of fire of 500 to 600 rounds per minute. It had a weight of 34 lb and was fed by a 50-round magazine.

broad arrow An arrow with a broad head. They were used from the fourteenth to the sixteenth centuries for hunting and in land warfare and at sea to cause damage to the sails and rigging of ships. It is also the mark used by British Ordnance to indicate government property.

broadside The simultaneous firing of all guns on one side of a warship.

broadsword A straight sword with a broad blade that was designed for cutting rather than stabbing. In the beginning it normally had a cross guard, but later it often had a cup or a basket hilt.

bromacetone A powerful lacrimator (tear gas) used in artillery shells and other weapons during World War I. It is called "BA" (British and American designation), *B Stoff* (German), or *Martonite* (French).

bromobenzylcyanide (BBC) A tear agent with an instantaneous irritating effect. It produces a burning sensation of the mucous membranes and severe irritation and lacrimation of the eyes with acute pain in the forehead. See **tear agents.** Called *Camite* by the French, it was first used by them in July 1918. It was the most powerful tear gas used in World War I.

Bronco The U.S. North American Rockwell-built OV-10 Bronco is a two-seat twin-engine armed reconnaissance STOL aircraft used for counterinsurgency operations. First flown in 1965, the aircraft is now used by the U.S. Air Force and Marine Corps. It has a speed of 280 mph, is armed with four 7.62mm machine guns, and can carry 4,600 lb of bombs. One version has rear deck space for six troops or 3,200 lb of cargo.

Bronstein A class of U.S. escort ship (DE) of 2,360 tons standard displacement built in 1963. They have an overall length of 371.5 ft, a beam of 40.5 ft, a speed of 26 knots, and a complement of 220 men. Armament consists of three 3-in. guns, one ASROC eight-tube launcher, two triple torpedo launchers, and two drone antisubmarine helicopters (DASH).

bronze oak-leaf cluster A decorative bronze device awarded in lieu of another decoration. It is affixed to the ribbon of the original decoration.

Bronze Star Medal A U.S. decoration established in 1944 and awarded for heroic or meritorious achievement or accomplishment in direct or indirect participation in operations against an enemy, except for aerial flights.

Brooke **1.** A class of U.S. guided-missile escort ships (DEG) having the same specifications as the Garcia class DE's, except that instead of carrying two 5-in. guns, they carry one 5-in. gun and a single Tartar surface-to-air missile. There are six ships in the class. **2.** A type of rifled cannon used in the American Civil War.

Brooklyn A class of U.S. light cruisers (CL) of about 9,475 tons standard displacement completed between 1937 and 1939. There were nine ships in the class. They had a length of 600 ft, a beam of 69 ft, a speed of 32.5 knots, and a wartime complement of 1,200 men. They were armed with fifteen 6-in. and eight 5-in. guns, plus twenty-eight 40mm and twenty-four 20mm antiaircraft guns. Four aircraft were carried.

Brown Bess A colloquial name for the British flintlock smoothbore musket adopted by the British Army in the early eighteenth century and in use until replaced by percussion-system weapons. The earliest types had barrels of 46 in. but by 1792 the barrels had decreased in length to 39 in. These muskets were equipped with a triangular-bladed socket bayonet. (Picture, p. 82.)

brown bill See **bill.**

Browning 7.65mm automatic pistol Models 1900 and 1903 This weapon was the first successful pistol invented by the American John M. Browning and was the first commercially successful blowback pistol. Produced by the Belgian manufacturers Fabrique Nationale, 1 million pistols of this design were in existence by July 1912. The magazine has a capacity of seven cartridges, and the pistol has an overall length of $6\frac{3}{4}$ in., a barrel length of 4 in., and a total weight of 22 oz. The 1903 model was developed for the 9mm Browning long cartridge and was a standard service pistol in Turkey, Denmark, the Netherlands,

British tank, medium, Mk IIA. (*Vickers Ltd.*)

Bronco. (*U.S. Navy.*)

broadsword. (*The Smithsonian Institution, R. G. Packard Collection.*)

Brooke. (*U.S. Navy.*)

Sweden, and Belgium.

Browning 7.65mm ACP automatic pistol Model 1910 An improved version of the Model 1903, this model has a magazine capacity of seven cartridges, an overall length of about 6 in., a barrel length of $3\frac{1}{2}$ in., and a weight of $20\frac{1}{2}$ oz. It was made for either the 7.65mm (.32 cal. ACP) or the 9mm Browning short (.380 cal. ACP) cartridge.

Browning 7.65mm ACP automatic pistol Model 1922 An enlarged version of the Model 1910, and sometimes called the "Model 10/22," this weapon features better balance, improved sighting, and a magazine capacity of nine cartridges. The overall length is 7 in., with a barrel length of $4\frac{1}{2}$ in. and an empty weight of 25 oz.

Browning 9mm Luger Hi-Power automatic pistol The last pistol designed by John M. Browning, this weapon has an overall length of 8 in., a barrel length of $4\frac{5}{8}$ in., and an empty weight of 32 oz. It features a double-line magazine that holds 13 cartridges. This pistol was used extensively by German SS troops in World War II. During the war it was manufactured in Canada for

Bronstein. (*U.S. Navy.*)

Brown Bess. (*The Smithsonian Institution.*)

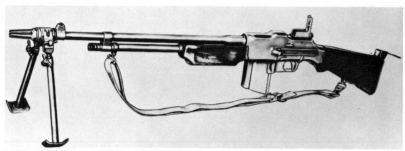

Browning automatic rifle Model 1918A2. (*U.S. Army.*)

use by Canadian, British, Greek, and Chinese troops. In 9mm Parabellum, this weapon is standard for the Belgian Army, the British Army, the Canadian armed forces, the Danish Army (where it is called the 9mm PM/46), and the Indonesian forces. It is also used in the Netherlands, Lithuania, and Rumania.

Browning .30 cal. aircraft machine guns Numerous Browning guns were used by the United States. They included the M1918, M1919, M1921, M1922, and M2. They were recoil-operated air-cooled machine guns with a rate of fire of 1,100 to 1,300 rounds per minute. The M1918 weighed 30.5 lb and was fed from a 250-round link belt.

Browning 37mm aircraft cannon M4 A weapon that was developed in the mid-1930s for the U.S. Army Air Corps. It was a recoil-operated air-cooled cannon with a rate of fire of 135 rounds per minute. It weighed 248 lb and was fed by a 30-round magazine.

Browning 37mm aircraft cannon M9 A follow-on to the 37mm M4, this weapon weighed 405 lb. It was little used by the United States, but was the principal aerial cannon employed by the Soviet Air Force (because they were using very large numbers of Bell Airacobra aircraft which were armed with M9 cannons firing through the propeller hub). The Russians used a high-velocity armor-piercing (HVAP) projectile which was particularly effective against tanks.

Browning .50 cal. aircraft machine gun M2 A U.S. recoil-operated air-cooled machine gun with a rate of fire of 780 to 850 rounds per minute. It had a weight of 61 lb and could fire several hundred link-belt rounds. It was the standard U.S. aircraft machine gun in World War II.

Browning automatic machine rifle A machine gun that is identical with the Browning automatic rifle, except that it has a water-cooled barrel and is provided with a tripod rest.

Browning automatic rifle Models 1918, 1918A1, and 1918A2 The Browning automatic rifle (BAR) was invented in 1917 by John Browning to meet the U.S. requirement for a World War I automatic rifle. The Model 1918 is a gas-operated selective-fire weapon with a cyclic rate of fire of 550 rounds per minute, a muzzle velocity or 2,805 fps, an overall length of 47 in., a barrel length of 24 in., and a weight of 16 lb. It utilizes a 20-round detachable box magazine. It has no bipod. The Model 1918A1 was adopted in 1937. It has the same characteristics as the 1918 but is equipped with a bipod and a shoulder-support plate that hinges up from the butt plate. Shortly before World War II, the

1918A2 was adopted. It features changes in the bipod, the forearm, and the buttstock, plus other minor changes. The model 1918A2 weighs 19.4 lb and was the standard squad automatic weapon used in World War II and Korea. BAR's have a maximum range of about 3,500 yd.

Browning machine guns See **U.S. .30 cal. aircraft machine gun M2 (Browning); U.S. .30 cal. Browning machine guns; U.S. .30 cal. machine gun M1917A1 (Browning); U.S. .30 cal. machine gun M1919A4 (Browning); U.S. .30 cal. machine gun M1919A6 (Browning); U.S. .30 cal. tank machine gun M37 (Browning); U.S. .50 cal. aircraft machine gun M2; U.S. .50 cal. aircraft machine gun M3; U.S. .50 cal. antiaircraft machine gun M2; U.S. .50 cal. antiaircraft machine gun M1921A1; U.S. .50 cal. heavy machine gun M2.**

Brownshirt A member of the German **Sturmabteilung (SA),** which see.

brown shoe A slang term for a U.S. naval aviator. They were so called because one of their uniforms called for brown shoes.

BRU-3/A A U.S. aircraft bomb-ejector rack.

Bruno See **German 240mm (24cm) railroad gun, Bruno.**

Brunswick rifle A British percussion service rifle designed by George Lovell and first made in 1837. It used a belted ball which followed the two deep semicircular grooves that constituted the rifling of the weapon.

B.S.A. .50 cal. aircraft machine gun Model 1924 A British recoil-operated air-cooled machine gun with a rate of fire of 400 to 500 rounds per minute. It had a weight of 46 lb and was fed from a 37-round flat drum.

B Stoff The German name for **bromacetone,** (which see), a powerful tear gas of World War I.

BT An abbreviation sometimes used to indicate boat-tail bullets.

BTO Bombing through overcast.

bubble canopy A cockpit canopy that has been molded in one piece.

Buccaneer **1.** The British Hawker Siddeley Buccaneer was originally developed by Blackburn and was first flown in 1958. It is a two-seat carrier-based low-level jet-strike aircraft. Later versions are armed with four under-wing pylons carrying Martel antiradar missiles. **2.** A U.S. Brewster-built single-engine two-seat scout dive bomber used in the early part of World War II by the U.S. Navy and by British forces (who called it the "Bermuda"). It had a speed of 284 mph and was armed with four .50 cal. machine guns and a 1,000-lb bombload.

buck To fly into, against, or through rough weather or gunfire. Also to "buck" for or try for a promotion.

buck and ball A cartridge containing a

bubble canopy, on a U.S. Lockheed T-33 jet trainer. (*U.S. Air Force.*)

spherical ball and three buckshot, formerly used in smoothbore muskets.

buckhorn sight A rear sight with a deep notch such as the one once used on the Springfield rifle.

Buckingham A British Bristol-built four-place twin-engine attack aircraft developed in 1943. It had a speed of 350 mph, a range of 2,300 mi, and armament consisting of nose-mounted and turret-mounted machine guns.

buckler 1. A flexible cover attached to the front armor plates of a gun turret to make it waterproof. The guns are free to train or elevate. The slang term is "bloomer." **2.** A small, round shield held in the left hand when fencing to stop or parry blows. It was used from the thirteenth to the seventeenth centuries.

Buckley A class of U.S. escort ships (DE) of 1,400 tons standard displacement commissioned in 1943–1944. They had a length of 306 ft, a beam of 37 ft, a speed of 23.5 knots, and a wartime complement of 212 men. The original armament consisted of three 3-in. guns, six 40mm and several 20mm antiaircraft guns, and three 21-in. torpedo tubes. Forty-six ships of this type were transferred to the Royal Navy, where they served as frigates. Fifty ships of this class were converted to high-speed transports (APD).

buckshot Small lead shot, once measured as being 165 to the pound, but made in various sizes.

budge barrel A barrel containing 40 to 60 lb of powder. One end is closed with a piece of leather that is drawn together with a cord, like a purse. It was used to carry powder from the magazine to the battery.

BuDocks The U.S. Navy Bureau of Yards and Docks.

Buffalo 1. The de Havilland (Canada) DHC-5 (U.S. C-8A) is a twin-engine turboprop assault transport first flown in April 1964. It has a three-man crew and can

Buccaneer. (*Hawker Siddeley Aviation, Ltd.*)

Buckingham. (*British Aircraft Corporation Ltd.*)

Buckley. (*U.S. Navy.*)

bulletproof vest. (*The Smithsonian Institution.*)

transport 42 troops. It is used by Canadian forces, the U.S. Army, and Brazilian forces. **2.** The Brewster F2A Buffalo was a single-seat single-engine interceptor and fighter-bomber developed for the U.S. Navy and first flown in January 1938. Under the designation B-339, numerous aircraft of this type were exported and used during World War II by Finland, the United Kingdom, the Netherlands, Australia, and New Zealand. The success of this airplane with the U.S. Navy and Marine Corps was minimal, particularly when pitted against a Japanese Zero. It had a speed of 321 mph and was armed with four .50 cal. machine guns and two 100-lb bombs.

Buffalo guns Allied nickname of the Korean conflict for the 14.5mm antitank rifles used by the North Koreans.

buff coat A heavy leather coat of the sixteenth and seventeenth centuries worn as armor. It was made of buffalo leather; hence its name.

Bug A biplane flying bomb of World War I. See **Liberty Eagle.**

builder's trials The trials conducted at sea or at a dock to prove the readiness of a ship for preliminary acceptance trials.

buildup The process of attaining prescribed strengths of units and prescribed levels of vehicles, equipment, stores, and supplies. The term also may be applied to the means of accomplishing this process.

built-up gun A gun that is composed of several parts formed separately and then united. A typical built-up gun consists of a steel tube wrapped with wire and reinforced with steel hoops.

bulge A structure added to the hull of a vessel to protect it against torpedoes, mines, and other explosives. It is also called a "blister."

bulkhead Watertight walls or partitions separating compartments within a ship.

Bull The NATO code name for the Soviet Tupolev Tu-4, a redesign of the B-29 Superfortress of World War II. A transport version of the same aircraft was designated the Tupolev Tu-70 (NATO code name Cart).

bulldog An obsolete term for a shipboard cannon or a short revolver.

Bulldog A modified U.S. Navy Bullpup missile using homing sensors and control mechanisms from the Sidewinder and Chaparral missiles.

bullet The projectile fired, or intended to be fired, from a small arm. The word derives from the French *boulette*, meaning a "small ball."

bullet crossbow See **prodd.**

bullet group The grouping of bullet holes in a target from one weapon fired from one place. Variations are due to improper aim or to ballistic differences.

bullet jacket A metal shell surrounding a metal core, the combination constituting a bullet for small arms. The jacket is either composed of, or coated with, a relatively soft metal such as gilding metal which engages the rifling in the bore, causing rotation of the bullet.

bullet mold An implement into which molten lead is poured to cast bullets.

bulletproof Resistant to bullets or rifle fire. Said of a bulletproof shelter or bulletproof glass.

bulletproof vest A vest made of steel chain, plates, or some other impenetrable material used to protect a man's torso from small-arms fire and shell fragments.

bullet shell An explosive bullet.

bullhorn An electric megaphone.

Bullpup An air-to-surface command-guided missile developed for the U.S. Navy by Martin Marietta and used operationally since April 1959. The first production version (AGM-12A) was essentially a standard 250-lb bomb powered by a solid-propellant rocket motor. AGM-12B is the current version in service with the U.S. Navy, Marine Corps, and Air Force. It has an improved high-explosive warhead and other refinements. AGM-12C has extended capabilities, and AGM-12D has interchangeable nuclear and conventional warheads. AGM-12B has a length of 10.5 ft, a firing weight of 571 lb, and a range of 7 mi. AGM-12C weighs 1,785 lb and has a range of 10 mi.

bulwark In fortifications, a rampart or wall thrown up for the defense of a place. It is usually low enough for the defenders to fire over.

Bumble Bee A German self-propelled 150mm howitzer on a Panzer IV chassis. It was built by Krupp-Alkett for use as a medium artillery weapon in armored divisions. Introduced in 1942, it had a crew of five, a weight of 25.4 tons, and armament consisting of a 150mm s.F.H. 18/1, caliber length 30; one 7.9mm MG 34; and two 9mm MP 38's.

Bumblebee The code name of a U.S. Navy program that dates back to 1944 and led to the development of surface-to-air missiles such as **Talos, Tartar,** and **Terrier,** which see.

bundook A variation of the Hindustani term *Bandūk,* which means a rifle or a musket. The term was employed by British soldiers in India.

bunker 1. A fortified structure for the protection of personnel, defended gun positions, or a defensive position. **2.** In naval usage, a storage space aboard ship for fuel oil or coal.

burg A house or a place having a protecting palisade or enclosure. It derives from the German word for "castle."

burgee A naval term for a swallow-tailed pennant or flag.

burgonet A type of French helmet used in the sixteenth and early seventeenth centuries by mounted officers, light horsemen, and infantry. Heavier types were used by siege troops.

Bullpup missiles, on the outboard pylons of a U.S. Navy Skyhawk aircraft. (*U.S. Air Force.*)

Bumble Bee. (*U.S. Army.*)

burgonet. (*The Metropolitan Museum of Art, Rogers Fund, 1904.*)

Burgund guidance A command guidance used by the Germans in World War II for guiding subsonic ground-to-air missiles. The commands were originated by simultaneous visual tracking of the target and missile, resulting in intersection of the two flight paths. The system used a joystick control (the Knuppel), a radio transmitter (the Kohl), and a radio receiver (the Strassburg), which were components common to all the radio-command systems.

burley The butt end of a lance.

Burmese 9mm Parabellum submachine gun Model BA-52 A slightly modified version of the Italian 9mm submachine gun Parabellum Model TZ-45.

burnout The point in time or in the missile trajectory when combustion of fuels in the rocket engine is terminated.

Burnside The name given the breechloading carbine invented by Union General A. G. Burnside. It used a tapered brass cartridge case.

burp gun A slang term for a submachine gun, deriving from the sound of a short burst fired from it. The nickname was originally given to the World War II German Schmeisser MP 40.

burr In gunnery, a round iron ring which serves to rivet the end of the bolt so as to form a round head.

burrel shot Formerly, a gunnery term referring to a type of case shot loaded with miscellaneous parts such as nails, stones, scraps of iron, and so forth.

burst The continuous series of shots fired from an automatic weapon by a single pressure on the trigger. Also, the explosion of a shell, as of an antiaircraft shell.

burster An explosive charge which bursts the container and spreads the contents of a chemical bomb, projectile, or mine.

bursting charge The main explosive charge in a mine, bomb, projectile, or the like that breaks the casing and produces fragmentation or demolition.

burst wave The damaging wave of compressed air caused by the bursting of a projectile or bomb.

busby A fur headdress or cap once worn in the British Army by hussars, artillerymen, and engineers.

Butcher The former NATO code name for the Ilyushin IL-28 now called **Beagle,** which see.

butt The rear end of a rifle stock or spear. It is also a term used to describe the mound of earth used as a backing for a target.

butterfield A confusion reflector made of wire mesh. See **confusion reflector.**

butterfly bomb A small fragmentation or antipersonnel bomb equipped with two folding wings which rotate and arm the fuze as the bomb descends. Designed to be dropped in clusters, they are frequently fitted with antidisturbance or delay fuzes. This type of bomb was developed by Germany and adopted for use by the United States.

button **1.** To button up, or to bring an action to completion, such as making an airplane ready for flight or a tank ready for action. **2.** The metal knob on the end of the breech of old-time cannons; the hindmost part of the cascabel.

butt plate A plate or pad used to cover and protect the heel of a gun butt.

buttress A sustaining or strengthening wall built at right angles to the main wall.

buttstock That section of the stock at the rear of the breech mechanism.

butt trap A compartment that has been hollowed out in the butt of a firearm and is used for carrying spare parts, cleaning implements, etc.

buzz To fly low and fast over an airfield or troops.

Buzzard The nickname of the Martinsyde F.4 biplane fighter of World War I.

buzz bomb A colloquial term for the German V-1 missile used during World War II. It was so called because of the buzzing sound of its pulse-jet engine. See **V-1.**

byrnie An early English term for mail body armor.

byssa An ancient cannon used for throwing stones.

BZ An incapacitating chemical agent designed to render men incapable of meeting military requirements. The general symptoms are interference with ordinary activity; dry, flushed skin; tachycardia; urinary retention; constipation; slowing of mental and physical activity; headache; giddiness; disorientation; hallucinations; drowsiness; sometimes maniacal behavior; and increase in body temperature. See **incapacitating chemical agents.**

C

C A U.S. Navy protected cruiser.

C1 See **Canadian 9mm submachine gun C1.**

C-1A See **Trader.**

C-2A See **Greyhound.**

C-5A See **Galaxy.**

C-7A See **Caribou.**

C-8A See **Buffalo.**

C-9A See **Nightingale.**

C-45 See **Expeditor.**

C-46 See **Commando.**

C-47 See **Skytrain.**

C-53 See **Skytrooper.**

C-54 See **Skymaster.**

C-56 See **Lodestar.**

C-69 See **Constellation.**

C-74 See **Globemaster I.**

C-82 See **Flying Boxcar.**

C-87 See **Liberator Express.**

C-97 See **Stratofreighter.**

C-118 See **Liftmaster.**

C-119 See **Flying Boxcar.**

C-121 See **Super Constellation.**

C-123 See **Provider.**

C-124 See **Globemaster II.**

C-130 See **Hercules,** sense 1.

C-131 See **Samaritan.**

C-133 See **Cargomaster.**

C-135 See **Stratoliner.**

C-140 See **JetStar.**

C-141 See **StarLifter.**

C-160 A twin-engine (turboprop) medium-range transport developed by the French-German team of Transall and first flown in

cabasset. (*The Smithsonian Institution, R. C. Abels Collection.*)

1963. It has a crew of four and carries 93 troops at a top speed of 333 mph.

CA A U.S. Navy heavy cruiser.

Cab The NATO code name for the Soviet Li-2 of World War II, a redesign of the C-47 Skytrain. A great many C-47's were supplied to the Soviet Union under lend-lease.

CAB Captured air bubble. The term refers to a boat which rides on an air bubble. Because hull drag is reduced, the speed is increased.

cabas A large buckler or shield once used by attacking archers.

cabasset A small type of open helmet with a brim and a keeled bowl worn by foot soldiers in the second half of the sixteenth century and throughout the seventeenth century. The name for this helmet derives from the Spanish *capacete*, a headpiece of the fifteenth century from which it developed. In early documents and in England today it is often called a "Spanish morion."

cable's length A unit of measure in the U.S. Navy that is equal to 120 fathoms, or 720 ft. In the British Navy it is equal to 608 ft.

cab rank An air-alert formation of patrolling fighters and fighter-bombers, usually in line astern, employed by the RAF on immediate call for close ground support. The cab rank was originated by the RAF Desert Air Force during the Italian campaign of World War II.

cabule A twelfth-century weapon used to throw stones.

Ca, Ch, Co, and Cr Classes of British destroyers (later modernized as antisubmarine destroyers) of 1,710 tons standard displacement built in 1944–1946. They had a speed of 33 knots, a complement of 186 men, and armament consisting of three or four 4.5-in. guns, two to seven 40mm and two to six 20mm antiaircraft guns, four 21-in. torpedo tubes, and two Squid depth-charge systems. There were 26 in the various classes.

CAD A cartridge-activated device.

cadence A standard time and pace set in marching.

California. (*U.S. Navy.*)

cadet A young man in training for the military or the naval service.

cadet ship A training ship for midshipmen.

cadre A group of officers and enlisted men which forms a core around which a new unit is developed.

Caesar The code name for an undersea surveillance system for detecting submarines off the U.S. coasts. Other systems include Artemis, Colossus, and Trident.

CAG U.S. Navy guided-missile heavy cruiser. Also stands for carrier air group.

cage An openwork steel framework used to support a gun.

Caisseur The French Army SE-4200 air-breathing surface-to-surface missile. It has a range of 60 nautical miles and a speed of about Mach 3. The prime contractor is Sud-Aviation.

caisson **1.** A two-wheeled vehicle used for carrying ammunition. It is designed to be joined with a limber. **2.** Originally, a chest filled with explosives and placed in the path of an enemy. It was exploded when he approached.

cal. The abbreviation for "caliber."

caliber A term that derives from the Latin *qua libra*, "what pound," first applied to the weight of a bullet and then to the diameter. (Cannons are still sometimes designated by the weight of the projectile they throw, such as a twenty-five-pounder.) The term now refers to the diameter of a projectile or the diameter of the bore of a gun or launching tube. Caliber is usually expressed in millimeters or inches. For example, a 105mm howitzer and a 6-in. gun have calibers of 105 millimeters and 6 inches respectively. The term "caliber" is also used to indicate the *length* of a gun's bore (or the length of the tube) measured from the breech face of the tube to the muzzle. For example, a 6-in. 50 cal. gun is 25 ft in length (fifty 6-in. calibers equal 300 in., or 25 ft).

calibration fire Preparatory fire to determine the separate corrections needed for the individual guns or launchers of a battery to cause all the weapons to hit the same point or burst to assume a desired pattern.

California **1.** A U.S. battleship of the **Tennessee** class, which see. It was commissioned in 1921 and was hit and sunk at Pearl Harbor on December 7, 1941. Subsequently refloated and repaired, it served in various operations in the Pacific (Marianas, Leyte, Luzon, Okinawa, etc.). In one operation (January 16, 1945, at Lingayen Gulf) the ship was hit by a Kamikaze plane and suffered a loss of 44 killed and 155 wounded. It was then repaired and re-entered service. **2.** The name of a class of 13,680-ton armored cruisers completed in 1905–1907. The class included *California, Colorado, Pittsburgh, Maryland, West Virginia,* and *South Dakota.* They had a length of 504 ft, a speed of 22 knots, a complement of 878 men, and main armament consisting of four 8-in. and fourteen 6-in. guns.

caliga The heavy-soled military footware worn by Roman soldiers.

caliver A sixteenth- or seventeenth-century light matchlock shoulder arm, a variation of the harquebus. It did not require the use of a forked rest.

call, call up To call reserves to active service with the armed forces.

call-fire Fire delivered on a specific target in response to a request from the supported unit.

calliope A U.S. Army 60-rocket launcher which fired a 4.5-in. rocket. It was mounted on a jeep or an M4 tank and had a range of 550 yd.

call mission A type of air support mission which is not requested sufficiently in advance of the desired time of execution to permit detailed planning and briefing of pilots prior to takeoff. Aircraft scheduled for this type of mission are on air, ground, or carrier alert and are armed with a prescribed load.

call to quarters A U.S. Army bugle call sounded 15 minutes before taps. It signals soldiers to repair to quarters.

calotte The backplate of a sword handle. Also, a type of iron or leather skullcap once worn by French cavalry.

caltrop A device with four sharpened iron points radiating from a common center. Caltrops are constructed so that when strewn on the ground, one point is always straight up (supported on three "feet"). They were used to prevent the advance of cavalry, to protect a defense perimeter, and to make a ford impassable and were hurled onto the decks of enemy ships. They have been used since at least 300 B.C. to the present with only minor changes in design. Modern army terminology refers to them as "tetrahedrons."

caltrop. (*The Smithsonian Institution, M. D. Day Collection.*)

camail. (*The Metropolitan Museum of Art, Bashford Dean Memorial Collection, purchase, 1929.*)

camail   Fourteenth-century mail for the protection of the neck and shoulders. It was often fastened to the basinet.

Camel   1. The NATO code name for a passenger-carrying version of the Tupolev Tu-16 bomber (Badger). **2.** A fighter aircraft of World War I. See **Sopwith Camel.**

camel load   In desert warfare, the load carried by a camel. It varies from 600 to 900 lb for short distances to 200 to 450 lb for long distances.

cam follower   See **contour follower.**

camisado   A night attack. Originally, one in which the soldiers wore shirts in order to recognize one another.

Camite   The French designation for **bromobenzylcyanide (BBC),** which see, the most powerful form of tear gas used in World War I.

cam lock   A U.S. Army single-shot breech-loading rifle and carbine used during a period dating from after the Civil War to as late as the Spanish American War. The breechblock was hinged at the top and locked by a cam piece at the right rear. Such an action extracts the fired case and leaves the chamber open for reloading.

camouflage   The disguise or concealment of persons, areas, equipment, or installations to deceive or divert the enemy.

camouflage-detection photography   Pho-

tography utilizing a special type of film (usually infrared) designed for the detection of camouflage.

camouflet   A small explosive mine designed to detonate underground and destroy an enemy's mining galleries without disturbing the surface of the ground.

Camp   The NATO code name for the Antonov An-3 twin-engine transport. It has accommodation for about 30 fully equipped troops.

camp   A group of tents, huts, or other shelter set up temporarily for troops; it is more permanent than a bivouac. A military post, temporary or permanent, may be called a "camp."

campaign   A military operation or connected series of operations undertaken as a distinct stage in a war or as an overall strategic operation. The term also refers to a military expedition conducted for a special purpose.

campaign plan   A plan for a series of related military operations aimed at accomplishing a common objective, normally within a given time and space.

campaign ribbon   A ribbon worn to indicate service in a particular campaign.

Campania   A British Fairey-built two-place single-engine floatplane (biplane) first flown in February 1917. It was armed with one Lewis gun and carried two 100-lb bombs. It flew at a top speed of about 80 mph.

camp follower   Originally, a male or female civilian who accompanied an army as a butler, servant, etc.

campilan   A straight-edged sword used by the Moros and Dyaks.

campmaster   A military officer's rank in the sixteenth and seventeenth centuries. It corresponded to the rank of colonel.

Campo Giro 9mm (Largo) automatic pistol Model 1913–16   This was the first automatic pistol used by Spain. The model 1913 is basically the Asta pistol and chambered for the 9mm Bergmann Bayard cartridge (in Spain called the "9mm Largo"). Modified slightly in 1916, the pistol was then referred to as the "Model 1913–16." This pistol has an overall length of 9.7 in., a barrel length of 6.7 in., and a weight of 2.1 lb. It features an eight-round detachable box magazine.

C.A.M.S. 37   A three-seat biplane observation flying boat developed by the French

Campo Giro 9mm (Largo) automatic pistol Model 1913-16. (*Spanish Ministry of Defense.*)

and first flown in 1926.

C.A.M.S. 55   French twin-engine biplane medium-range maritime reconnaissance flying boat first flown in 1928. It had a crew of five.

can   A slang term for a destroyer.

Canadian 9mm submachine gun C1   A weapon using the 9mm Parabellum cartridge and equipped with selective full automatic or semiautomatic fire. It is blowback-operated and has a cyclic rate of fire of 550 rounds per minute. It has an overall length (with stock extended) of 27 in. and a barrel length of 7.8 in. With a fully loaded 30-round magazine the weapon weighs 7.66 lb. A 10-round magazine is also available. It has a muzzle velocity of about 1,200 fps and a rear sight adjustable to 100 and 200 yd. The C1 is a slightly modified copy of the British Sterling submachine gun and has been manufactured in Canada, at Canadian Arsenals Limited, since the late 1950s. In most instances the components of the C1 and the Sterling are interchangeable.

Canadian armored carrier No. 2 Mark II*   A light full-tracked personnel carrier that served during World War II as a tracked jeep. It had a crew of two, carried two to four passengers, and was usually armed with a Bren light machine gun or a Boys antitank rifle. A version of the British Bren gun carrier, this vehicle remained in service with the Canadian Army until after the Korean conflict.

Canarias   A Spanish cruiser of 10,670 tons standard displacement completed in 1936 and refitted in 1954. It has a length of 636.5 ft, a beam of 64 ft, a speed of 31 knots, and a complement of 1,022 men. It is armed with eight 8-in. and eight 4.7-in. guns, plus

cam lock. (*The Smithsonian Institution, Military Service Institute Collection.*)

Canberra. (*U.S. Air Force.*)

four 1.5-in. (38mm) and four 37mm antiaircraft guns. A sister ship, the *Baleares*, was torpedoed and sunk during the Spanish Civil War.

Canberra **1.** A two-seat twin-engine turbojet all-weather tactical bomber, night intruder, and high-altitude weather reconnaissance aircraft originally produced in the United Kingdom by English Electric and first flown in 1949. It was built in the United States by Martin and designated the B-57. It has a speed of about 600 mph and carries a variety of armament, including bombs (nuclear and nonnuclear), cannons, and rockets. **2.** An Australian heavy cruiser. See **Australia** for details.

cancer Another name for a **penthouse,** which see. It was so called because the rounded upper portion resembled a crab.

candlebomb A pasteboard shell once used for signaling purposes. It is fired from a light paper or wooden mortar and makes a brilliant display when it explodes.

Canguru (Italian for "kangaroo") The Italian Savoia-Marchetti SM.82. Developed in 1938, this aircraft was used as a three-engine troop and cargo transport. It carried 40 troops and flew at a top speed of about 230 mph.

canister **1.** A special short-range antipersonnel projectile designed to be fired from guns, both artillery and small arms. It consists of a casing of light sheet metal, which is loaded with preformed submissiles such as small steel balls. The basing is designed so that it opens at, or just beyond, the muzzle of the gun. The submissiles are then dispersed in a cone, giving effective coverage of the area immediately in front of the gun. Another term for canister is "case shot." **2.** In certain special types of projectiles, the subassembly or inner container in which the payload is contained, such as canister or smoke. **3.** That part of a gas mask containing a filter for the removal of poisonous gases from the air being inhaled.

canister cartridge A cartridge assembled with a projectile consisting of a light metal case filled with steel balls, steel fragments, or steel slugs. When fired, the projectile breaks upon leaving the muzzle of the weapon, and the contents scatter in the manner of a shotgun cartridge.

canister shot See **canister,** sense 1. (Canister shot was first used in about 1400.)

canjar A Turkish saber with a crooked blade.

cannelure **1.** A groove in a bullet that contains a lubricant or into which the cartridge case is crimped; a groove in a cartridge case providing a purchase for the extractor; extractor groove. **2.** A ringlike groove for locking the jacket of an armor-piercing bullet to the core. **3.** A ringlike groove in the rotating band of a gun projectile to lessen the resistance offered to the

Canguru. (*Siai Marchetti.*)

gun rifling and to prevent fringing. **4.** A ringlike groove cut into the outside surface of a water-cooled machine-gun barrel into which packing is placed to prevent the escape of water from the breech end of the water jacket. **5.** The grooving of a blade to lighten it without impairing its stiffness.

cannibalize To remove serviceable parts from one item of equipment in order to install them on another item of equipment.

cannon In the sixteenth and seventeenth centuries a cannon was a specific type of artillery—a gun of large caliber and short barrel. Now "cannon" is a generic term for a complete assembly, consisting of a tube and a breech mechanism, firing mechanism, or base cap, which is a component of a gun, howitzer, or mortar. It may include muzzle appendages. The term is generally limited to calibers greater than 1 in.

cannonade An artillery barrage.

cannonball Originally, a round solid missile, usually made of cast iron, that was fired from a cannon. Later, the term was popularly extended to include missiles of any shape, solid and hollow, made for a cannon.

cannon baskets Another term for gabions.

cannon bullet A cannonball.

cannon cradle An item designed to support a cannon and allow it to recoil and counterrecoil. It also provides a means of securing the recuperator and recoil cylinders or the recoil piston rods. It has facilities for attaching to the mount or carriage of a gun or howitzer.

cannoneer An artilleryman.

cannon igniter A cannon lock or other device for firing a cannon.

cannon lock A device like the flint or percussion lock on a gun. It is placed over the vent of a cannon and is used to ignite the charge.

cannon of battery A medieval cannon that was somewhat shorter than a culverin.

cannon of eight A cannon having an 8-in. bore and firing a 65-lb ball; **cannon-royal,** which see

cannon-perrier An early type of cannon that fired stone shot.

cannon-petronel A piece of ordnance having a 6-in. bore and carrying a 24-lb shot.

cannon powder Materials used in separate-loading artillery ammunition. It now consists of large-sized grains of smokeless powder. In the nineteenth century, it consisted of large grains of black powder which were given subcategories according to size and shape.

cannon-royal A sixteenth- and seventeenth-century cannon having a bore of about 8 in. and a length of 8 to 12 ft. An 8-ft tube weighed 8,000 lb. It shot a 65-lb iron ball and is said to have had a range of about 2,000 paces.

cannon-serpentine An old name for a gun of 7-in. bore.

cannon shot A cannonball.

can opener A World War II slang term for the British Hawker Hurricane fighter equipped with 40mm guns.

Canopus. (*The Imperial War Museum.*)

Canuck. (*Canadian Armed Forces photograph.*)

capacete. (*The Metropolitan Museum of Art, gift of William H. Riggs, 1913.*)

Canopus A class of British 13,000-ton battleships completed in 1900–1902. There were six ships in the class: *Canopus, Goliath, Albion, Ocean, Glory,* and *Vengeance.* Each had a length of 418 ft, a complement of 750 men, and main armament consisting of four 12-in. and twelve 6-in. guns and four 18-in. torpedo tubes. They had a speed of 17 knots.

canopy A bubble canopy; the transparent enclosure over an airplane cockpit. The term also refers to the supporting fabric surface of a parachute.

Canso The Royal Canadian Air Force name for the **Catalina,** which see.

Cant Z.1007 See **Alcione.**

canteen **1.** A vessel for holding water. It is carried by soldiers on the march. **2.** A location on a military installation where food, drink and commodities are sold.

cantle The hind part of a saddle.

cantonment Temporary structures for the housing of troops. In British India the term referred to permanent military towns or stations.

Canuck The popular RCAF name for the Avro (Canada) CF-100 two-seat long-range all-weather twin-jet fighter first flown in 1950.

cap **1.** A percussion cap. **2.** The blunt nose on an armor-piercing projectile. **3.** A plug to protect a cannon bore.

capacete A fifteenth-century Spanish open helmet, often worn with a deep bevor (armor to protect the lower part of the face and neck).

cap and ball (percussion cap and lead ball) The percussion cap was a device for igniting the propelling charge of a weapon with a separate cap that detonated when struck by the hammer. Weapons of this sort usually fired a lead ball.

cap-a-pie armor Armor from head to toe; complete armor.

cap dispenser A container, often brass, for holding percussion caps. A capper.

capeline A thirteenth- and fourteenth-century visorless helmet made of iron or steel and worn by light troops.

capital In fortifications, the imaginary line bisecting the salient angle of a work.

capital ship A warship of the largest size and heaviest armament. The naval disarmament treaties held in 1921–1922 defined a capital ship as a warship (other than an aircraft carrier) with a standard displacement of over 10,000 tons and carrying a gun with a caliber larger than 8 in.

cap lock A percussion system for muzzle-loaders. It uses a cap containing a detonating powder.

caponier A covered passage across the ditch of a fortification.

capote A long, full overcoat once worn by soldiers.

capped bullet A bullet having a protective cap of harder metal on its nose.

capper A cap dispenser.

capping the T A naval tactic in which a commander succeeds in maneuvering his force at right angles across the enemy's intended track. The tactic allows the capping force to bring all its guns to bear on the enemy, while those of the capped force are masked by their own ships ahead in column. It may also be called "crossing the T."

Caproni bomber Ca 1-5 Italian four- or five-place three-engine biplane bombers developed during World War I. The Ca 4, for example, was introduced in late 1917, had a speed of 87 mph, and was armed with three Revelli machine guns. It carried a maximum bombload of 3,197 lb.

captain **1.** A naval officer ranking below a commodore or rear admiral and above a commander. His rank is equivalent with that of a colonel in the Army, Air Force, or Marine Corps, and his insignia consists of a silver spread eagle or four $\frac{1}{2}$-in. gold stripes on shoulder boards or uniform sleeeves. **2.** An Army, Air Force, or Marine Corps officer ranking below a major and above a first lieutenant. His insignia consists of two silver bars.

captain general Formerly, a rank conferred on the commander in chief of an army or armies. In Spanish historical usage, the term referred to the commander of a military division or the military governor of a Spanish colony.

captain lieutenant A rank that once existed in the British Army. This officer received the pay of a lieutenant but had the duties of a captain.

captain of the fleet In the British Navy, an officer of the rank of captain or commodore serving on the staff of a flag officer.

captain of the yard In the U.S. Navy, an assistant to the commandant of a navy yard.

captain's mast The process by which a commanding officer awards punishment, listens to requests (requests mast), or commends men for special services (meritorious

or commendatory mast). The term in the USMC is "office hours."

captive balloon A balloon restrained from free flight by a cable and winch assembly on the ground. At first they were used for observation purposes, then later as barrage balloons.

capture intelligence Military intelligence arising out of information gleaned from the examination of captured enemy documents and materiel, and from the interrogation of enemy prisoners of war, deserters, and civilians.

capucine A band holding the barrel of a gun or pistol to the stock.

carabineer, carabiniere A term derived from the French *carabinier*, or cavalry soldier armed with a carbine. In modern Italy a *carabiniere* is a policeman.

caravel A Turkish warship.

carbine A rifle of short length and light weight. It was formerly used chiefly by cavalry and mounted infantry, but in recent years has been used extensively by service troops and others. In the seventeenth century, carbines were sometimes smoothbores of a type later called "musketoons."

carbine butt A detachable buttstock that can be attached to a pistol so that the weapon can be used as a carbine.

carboazotine An explosive containing ferrous sulfate. It resembles gunpowder in composition.

Carcano See **Mannlicher Carcano 6.5mm carbine model 1891, 1891 TS; Mannlicher Carcano 6.5mm carbine Model 1938, 1938 TS; Mannlicher Carcano 6.5mm rifle Model 1891; Mannlicher Carcano 6.5mm rifle Model 1938; Mannlicher Carcano 7.35mm carbine Model 1938, 1938 TS;** and **Mannlicher Carcano 7.35mm rifle Model 1938.**

carcass Formerly, a shell used for incendiary purposes and filled with a very fiercely flaming composition of saltpeter, sulfur, resin, turpentine, antimony, and tallow. Some versions were equipped with three vents for the flame, and sometimes they had pistol barrels, so fitted in the interior as to discharge bullets at various times. These projectiles were fired from howitzers or

mortars to set fire to buildings and ships.

careen To turn a ship on its side in order to clean or repair a part of the hull normally below the water line.

cargo carrier An unarmored carrier, usually having a watertight hull, designed primarily to transport a small number of personnel or cargo.

cargo classification The division of military cargo for combat loading. It includes such classes as the following: *Chemical ammunition:* white phosphorous smoke, for example. *General:* cargo can be loaded in any place—boxes, bales, barrels, crates, etc. *Heavy lift:* single cargo units in excess of 5 long tons or, in Marine Corps usage, cargo exceeding 800 lb in weight or 100 cu ft in volume. *High explosive:* artillery ammunition, bombs, depth charges, demolition materials, rockets, and missiles. *Inflammable:* drummed gasoline, oils, etc. *Perishable:* materials requiring refrigeration such as meat, fruit, fresh vegetables, etc. *Special:* cargo which requires special handling or protection—detonators, precision instruments, etc. *Troop space:* cargo such as barracks bags, bedding, rolls or hammocks, locker trunks, etc. *Vehicle:* wheeled or tracked equipment, including weapons.

Cargomaster The Douglas C-133 Cargomaster is a four-engine (turboprop) long-range strategic transport developed for the USAF and first flown in 1956. It can carry cargoes equivalent to twice the payload of the Globemaster II. It has a speed of about 310 mph and a range of 4,030 mi. It can carry 200 troops or a maximum payload of about 90,000 lb. It can airlift an ICBM.

Caribou The de Havilland (Canada) DHC-4 Caribou is a twin-engine (piston) light tactical transport in service with Canadian forces, the U.S. Air Force, and the forces of about 10 other countries. It has a crew of 2 and can carry 32 troops at a top speed of 182 mph. It first flew in 1958. The USAF version is designated the C-7A. (Picture, next page.)

Carl Gustaf 9mm Parabellum submachine gun See **Swedish 9mm Parabellum submachine gun Model 45.**

Cargomaster. (*U.S. Air Force.*)

Caribou. (*U.S. Air Force.*)

carrier, the U.S. Army M-113 armored personnel carrier. (*U.S. Army.*)

carous A sort of gallery in ancient ships which turned on a pivot. It was hoisted to a given height by tackles and was thus brought to project over, or into, an enemy ship, furnishing a bridge for boarding.

carp A bombsight attachment for controlling weapons such as the razon bomb.

Carpenter A class of U.S. destroyers (DD) similar in many respects to the modernized **Gearing** class, which see.

carronade. (*The Smithsonian Institution, National Museum Collection.*)

carpet bombing The progressive distribution of a mass bombload upon an area defined by designated boundaries in such a manner as to inflict damage to all portions of it.

carquois A quiver for arrows.

carrack Formerly, a large cargo ship or galleon fitted for fighting.

carrago A kind of fortification built by surrounding an army with wagons.

carreau A bolt or arrow for a crossbow. It is also called a "quarrel."

carriage The mobile or fixed support for a cannon. It sometimes includes the elevating and traversing mechanisms. It may be called a "gun carriage," "howitzer carriage," or "mortar carriage." The term may also pertain to a support such as an armored vehicle, a gun motor carriage, a howitzer motor carriage, etc.

carrier **1.** A self-propelled tracked or half-tracked vehicle designed to transport personnel, cargo, weapons, and the like over difficult terrain and water, snow, sand, and swamp. **2.** A harness bag or device for carrying small loads, such as ammunition or gas masks. **3.** A part of the mechanism

of some automatic guns that helps to set the projectile in its proper firing position. **4.** An aircraft carrier.

carrier air group (CAG) Two or more aircraft squadrons formed under one command for administrative and tactical control of operations from a carrier.

carrier plane An airplane with wheeled takeoff and landing gear designed for use on an aircraft carrier.

carrier ring A ring that carries the breech-lock of a gun when it is withdrawn from the breech and swung out of the way during loading.

carrier striking force A naval task force composed of aircraft carriers and supporting combatant ships capable of conducting strike operations.

Carro Armato Tipo M 13-40 See **Italian tank, medium, Carro Armato Tipo M 13-40.**

carronade An iron cannon that was shorter and lighter than regular guns of the same caliber. It was used mostly for broadside guns on small ships where great range was not needed. So called because it was first made in Carron, Scotland, it fired projectiles ranging in weight from 6 to 68 lb. It is said to have been invented in 1759 by Col. Robert Melville, of the British Army, and was one of the first slide-mounted naval connons. In the early nineteenth century carronades were sometimes used as flank-defense guns in American forts.

carry To hold a weapon or standard in such a way that it is practically vertical at the right side. The term was once used in commands such as "carry arms" or "carry sabers."

carrying strap A strap on a rifle or lance for carrying purposes. A sling.

Cart The NATO code name for the Tupolev Tu-70, which is the transport version of the Tu-4 (Bull), itself a redesign of the World War II B-29 Superfortress.

cartel ship A ship that could sail under safe conduct between two belligerents during time of war. It was used for the exchange of prisoners and to convey proposals.

carthoun A variant of "cannon."

cartouche, cartouch **1.** An early variant of "cartridge." **2.** A cartridge made of a roll or case of paper. It might hold either the powder charge or the charge and bullet for a firearm. **3.** A special projectile fired from a howitzer. It consisted of a wooden case loaded with 400 musket balls and eight or ten 1-lb iron balls. It was used to defend a position.

cartridge The ammunition for a gun. In its modern form it contains in one unit assembly all the components required to function a gun once and is loaded into the gun in one operation. At one time the term was used to describe paper, cloth, or metal cases that held powder or powder and shot, but lacked a primer. It now applies to artillery-weapon assemblages that were formerly referred to only as "complete rounds" or "fixed shells."

cartridge bag A bag containing a propelling charge. It is used with large weapons which utilize separate-loading ammunition.

cartridge belt A belt having loops or pockets for cartridges or clips of cartridges.

cartridge box A leather box used to carry cartridges. It is suspended by a strap or worn on the belt. Cartridge boxes were displaced by the cartridge belt.

cartridge case A container used to hold the propelling charge. In fixed ammunition it also holds the projectile and a primer.

cartridge clip A metallic device used to contain rifle or pistol cartridges for ease of loading into a rifle or an automatic pistol.

cartridge cloth A special fabric used to hold the propelling charge for large guns. It is made so as not to leave burning residue when the gun is fired. Formerly silk was used exclusively for this purpose, but other satisfactory fabrics have been developed.

cartridge link A unit part of a link belt by means of which ammunition is fed into automatic weapons.

Casablanca directive A directive, issued as a result of the Casablanca conference (January 14 to 24, 1943), having as its object the destruction of the German military, economic, and industrial system by the RAF and the USAAF and, concomitantly, the undermining of German morale.

cascabel The projection behind the breech of certain muzzle-loading cannon. It consists of the knob (or breeching loop), the neck, and the fillet and was used to facilitate the handling of the piece in mounting and dismounting.

cascans A fortifications term for the holes which were used as entrances to galleries or which provided vents for enemy mines.

case The part of a cartridge that holds a charge, primer, and projectile. It may also be called a "shell case." The term is also short for "case shot."

case ejection chute A chute or passage through which empty shells are ejected after being fired in a machine gun.

case gun A U.S. Navy term referring to a gun with a caliber greater than 1 in. that used ammunition in which the powder charge was contained in a metallic case.

case head The base of a cartridge case where the primer is fitted.

casemate A bombproof structure used as a powder magazine, gun emplacement, or the like.

casernes Buildings or barracks for the soldiers of a garrison.

case shot The British term for canister. The term was once used in the United States to describe a hollow cast-iron projectile filled with musket balls. The projec-

tile was equipped with a bursting charge and a fuze and, when fired, was timed to burst a short distance in front of troops fired upon (thus differing from canister, where the bullet-filled case is disrupted in the gun). The European equivalent of U.S. case shot was shrapnel, named for Capt. Henry Shrapnel, who invented the projectile in the late 1700s.

Casey Cookie Early in World War II a number of civilian engineers in the Philippines were given military status and, under the direction of Maj. Gen. Hugh J. Casey, performed demolition work to block the Japanese advance. They were called "Casey's Dynamiters," and the Casey

cartridge. .30 cal. cartridges for a U.S. Springfield rifle Model 1903. (*U.S. Army.*)

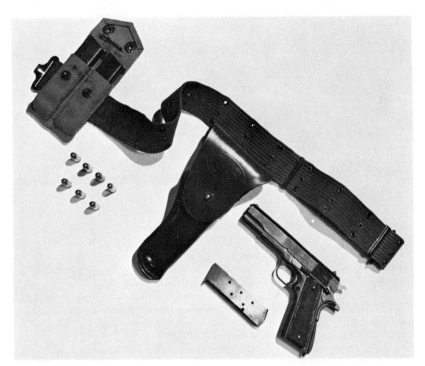

cartridge clip. (*U.S. Army.*)

Cookie was one of their innovations. It consisted of a grenade built from a joint of bamboo stuffed with nails, barbed wire, pieces of glass, and dynamite.

casque An open helmet such as a burgonet.

CASS An airborne antisubmarine-warfare detection and classification device.

casse-tête A wooden mace or war club.

castle A large fortified building or set of buildings.

Castle A class of British antisubmarine frigates (ex-corvettes) of 1,060 tons standard displacement built in 1943–1945. They had a speed of 16.5 knots and were armed with one 4-in. gun, two 40mm and two 20mm antiaircraft guns, and depth-charge throwers.

cascabel. (*The Smithsonian Institution, Department of Defense Collection.*)

Catalina. (*U.S. Navy.*)

Catamount. (*U.S. Army.*)

CASU Carrier Aircraft Service Unit.

casualty Any person who is lost to his organization by reason of having been declared dead, wounded, injured, diseased, interned, captured, or missing; also, a person whose whereabouts or status has not been determined.

casualty criteria Standards by means of which the ability of ammunition items or fragments therefrom to inflict disabling wounds on personnel may be classified. Three degrees of incapacitating wounds are recognized: *Type A:* wounds which will result in incapacitation within 5 minutes. *Type B:* wounds which will result in eventual incapacitation, without the limit of time. *Type K:* wounds which will result in incapacitation within 5 seconds.

casus belli An event or events which represent a cause of war or are alleged as a justification of war.

cat In medieval warfare, a movable building with a steep roof strapped with iron. After a ditch was filled up, the cat could be moved forward to the wall of the fortification under attack, and miners could then work without being fired upon. Crenelated cats were those with crenelles and openings from which arrows could be shot. A ram was also sometimes operated under the protection of a cat.

Cat The NATO code name for the Antonov An-10 four-engine (turboprop) airliner in service with Aeroflot in the Soviet Union. It can carry up to 130 passengers and flies at a speed of 444 mph.

Catalina The Consolidated PBY-1/6A twin-engine long-range maritime reconnaissance amphibian flying boat developed for the U.S. Navy and first flown in 1935. It was in continuous production for 10 years and was one of the most successful flying boats ever developed. During World War II, 3,290 aircraft were built and were in service with several countries, including the Soviet Union. It had a crew of seven to nine, was armed with three .30 cal. machine guns and two .50 cal. machine guns, and carried four 1,000-lb or twelve 100-lb bombs, or four 650-lb depth bombs, or two torpedoes. A version of the aircraft was called the "Nomad," and the Canadian nickname was "Canso."

catalytic attack An attack designed to bring about a war between major powers through the disguised machinations of a third power.

Catamount A U.S. Army lightweight air-droppable tracked cargo carrier. It has a payload of 6 tons and was designed for field-artillery support and other carrier duties.

cataphracta Armor made of leather or cloth and reinforced with iron links or scales. It was used for horses as well as people.

catapult **1.** A device for launching aircraft from a ship's deck. **2.** An ancient weapon used to throw heavy stones and burning objects against fortified positions. It consisted of a long upright arm terminating in a spoon-shaped end to hold the missile, the opposite end of which was affixed in heavy cords fastened to posts. The cords were twisted by winches until the arm was parallel to the ground. When released, the arm would fly upward by the torsion-generated force. Projectiles weighing several hundred pounds could be hurled to ranges up to 500 yd. Sometimes putrified bodies were hurled into besieged towns to cause sickness.

Caudron C.714 A lightweight single-engine single-place low-wing fighter aircraft produced by France in the late 1930s. It flew at speeds of 302 mph and was armed with four 7.5mm machine guns.

Caudron G.III A two-place single-engine biplane of nacelle-and-tailboom construction developed from the G.II and first flown in 1915. It was used for reconnaissance and artillery observation purposes during the first half of World War I. Some were armed with a machine gun in the front cockpit and a number of small bombs. They were later used by the Allied air forces as trainers.

Caudron G.IV A scaled-up version of the G.III, powered by two engines. It carried a 220-lb bombload and was armed with a free-firing Vickers or Lewis machine gun in the front cockpit and a machine gun mounted on the top wing to fire to the rear. It flew at speeds of 82 mph. It was used from November 1915 until 1917.

Caudron R.4 A three-place twin-engine biplane bomber that appeared in June 1915. It was designed to carry up to 220 lb of bombs and was armed with one or two Lewis machine guns on ring mountings in each of two cockpits. The pilot occupied the middle one of three cockpits, with gunners in front of him and behind him. It was not successful as a bomber, but the R.4A.3 was used as a three-seat photoreconnaissance aircraft with great success.

Caudron R.11 A replacement for the R.4 bomber, this aircraft was a smaller and lighter machine equipped with more powerful engines. It entered service in 1918, but had too light a bombload (265 lb) to be very effective. The R.11A.3, however, was a great success as an escort to Breguet 14 bomber squadrons. As a "flying gunboat" it was armed with twin Lewis machine guns in the front and rear cockpits and also with a downward-firing machine gun operated from the front gunner's position. In the last four months of the war it

CBC, the U.S.S. *Alaska*. (*U.S. Navy.*)

accompanied all French bombing squadrons.

cavalier In fortifications, a defensive work that rose above the main walls, often from the middle of a bastion. Cavaliers were also constructed by the besiegers of a fortress so that they could have a commanding position.

cavalier battery A battery in which the gun platforms are raised above the ground.

cavalry A military force that once utilized horses. The speed and mobility of mounted troops were often an asset against foot soldiers.

cavalryman A soldier belonging to the cavalry.

CAVU Ceiling and visibility unlimited.

Cayuse The Hughes OH-6A single-engine lightweight observation helicopter developed for the U.S. Army and first flown in 1963. It has a speed of 150 mph and a crew of two.

CB A U.S. Navy large cruiser.

CBC A U.S. Navy large tactical command ship.

CBR Chemical-bacteriological-radiological. A generic term applied to the use of these sciences to military operations.

CBU In U.S. Air Force usage, an end item consisting of a cluster bomb or dispenser.

CC A U.S. Navy battle cruiser or tactical command ship.

CCB A U.S. Navy command and control boat. It provides a floating command post for an assault force engaged in riverine warfare.

C Class A former class of U.S. submarines commissioned in 1934. They were armed with six 21-in. torpedo tubes and one 3-in. deck gun. Their speed, submerged, was 8 knots.

CCM Counter-countermeasures. A term applied to electronic devices and techniques designed to improve the extraction of radar target signals from a jamming environment.

ceiling **1.** In describing weather conditions, this term refers to the minimum height above the ground at which all clouds, at and below that height, cover more than one half the sky. **2.** The ceiling (or absolute ceiling) of an aircraft is the maximum altitude at which it can fly.

celestial guidance The guidance of a missile or other vehicle by reference to celestial bodies.

celestial navigation The determination of position by observation of celestial bodies.

cellulose nitrate Any of several esters of nitric acid used as explosives or propellants and produced by treating cotton or some other form of cellulose with a mixture of nitric and sulfuric acids. It is also called "nitrocellulose."

Centaur A British aircraft carrier of 23,670 tons standard displacement completed in 1953 and extensively refitted in the early 1960s. It was originally of the *Hermes* class, but the *Hermes* was completed to a modified design, and two sister ships, *Albion* and *Bulwark,* were converted to commando carriers; see **Modified Centaur.** *Centaur* has a length of 685 ft, a width of 123 ft, a speed

of 28 knots, and a complement of 1,390 men. It carries eighteen aircraft and eight helicopters and is armed with ten 40mm antiaircraft guns.

Centaur I A British cruiser tank of World War II. It had a loaded weight of up to 28 tons, a crew of five, and main armament consisting of one six-pounder gun.

Centauro **1.** A class of Italian frigates of 1,807 tons standard displacement completed in 1957–1958. They have a speed of 26 knots, a complement of 255 men, and armament consisting of three 3-in. guns, one three-barreled depth-charge mortar, and two triple torpedo tubes. **2.** The Fiat G.55 Centauro (Centaur) was an Italian Air Force single-seat single-engine interceptor fighter and fighter-bomber first flown in April 1942. It was considered the best single-seat fighter produced by Italy during World War II. Powered by a 1,475-hp engine, it reached speeds of 385 mph. Armament consisted of one 20mm Mauser cannon and two 12.7mm Breda-SAFAT machine guns.

center The portion of an army between its two wings.

center-fire When said of a cartridge, one having the primer in the center of the base of the case. When said of a firearm, one using center-fire cartridges. Center-fire is contrasted to rimfire, in which the primer

C Class, the U.S.S. *Cachalot* (C-1). (*U.S. Navy.*)

Centurion main battle tank. (*Vickers Ltd.*)

is in the rim of the base of the case.

center of burst A point about which the bursts of projectiles fired under like conditions are evenly distributed.

center of the bastion A fortifications term referring to the intersection made by the two demigorges.

Central Powers A World War I designation for Germany and Austria-Hungary, derived from their geographic position in Europe. The designation also included their allies, Bulgaria and Turkey.

Centre (Farman) F 222 A French five-seat four-engine heavy night bomber developed in 1935. It had a speed of 199 mph and carried a bombload of about 9,200 lb.

Centre NC 223 A French five-seat four-engine (two tractor and two pusher) heavy bomber and patrol bomber. It was developed in 1937, flew at a maximum speed of 248 mph, and carried a bombload of 9,240 lb. A conversion of this airplane, the Centre NC 223.4, was the first Allied aircraft to bomb Berlin in World War II. A single aircraft, the *Jules Verne*, made the flight on the night of June 7, 1940, dropped a 4,409-lb bombload, and successfully returned to France.

centurion A captain of a century (100 men) in the Roman Army.

Centurion main battle tank A British tank first placed in service in 1945 and the standard British Army tank for 20 years, having been replaced by Chieftain. In service with a number of countries, this tank has gone through 13 marks. The Mark 13 has a crew of four, a weight of 52 tons, a road speed of about 23 mph, and main armament consisting of one 105mm gun with a maximum antitank range of 2,000 (APDS) to 8,000 meters (HESH). It also carries a .50 cal. ranging machine gun.

CEP Circular error probability. The accuracy factor for a bomb or missile; the radius from the target in which it falls.

cervelière A thirteenth-century skullcap made of steel and worn under the coif of mail.

cessation of arms An armistice or truce.

CETME 7.62mm NATO assault rifle Model 58 This weapon is produced by the Centro de Estudios Tecnicos de Materials Especiales (CETME), a Spanish government research establishment. It operates on the delayed blowback system and is capable of selective fire. It has a cyclic rate of fire of 600 rounds per minute, a muzzle velocity of 2,493 fps, an overall length of 39.37 in., a barrel length of about 17 in., and a weight of 11.32 lb. It is fed from a 20-round detachable box magazine. It is presently the standard rifle in the Spanish service and was adopted in 1957.

cetra A Roman shield, 3 ft in diameter, carried by light infantry.

CEV Combat engineer vehicle. A special-purpose vehicle using the M60A1 tank chassis and turret and employed by combat engineers in forward battle areas.

Ceylon A class of British cruisers com-

pleted in 1942–1943. They had a standard displacement of 8,000 tons, a speed of 31.5 knots, a wartime complement of 950 men, and armament consisting of nine 6-in. and eight 4-in. guns, twelve 40mm and twelve 20mm antiaircraft guns, and six 21-in. torpedo tubes.

CF A U.S. Navy flying-deck cruiser.

CG **1.** A U.S. Navy guided-missile cruiser. **2.** The U.S. military designation for the war gas **phosgene**, which see.

CGM-13B See **Mace**.

CGM-16, CGM-16D, and CGM-16E See **Atlas ICBM**.

CGN A U.S. Navy nuclear-powered guided-missile cruiser.

Ch (Chequers) A class of British destroyers. See **CA**.

CH 17 and 18 Soviet missiles. See **Komet I** and **Komet II**.

chaff Radar-confusion reflectors made of strips of aluminum foil. Chaff was first used by the RAF during night raids against Hamburg in July 1943 and successfully jammed the German Wurzburg radar (see **Wurzburg**). The foil strips were ⅛-in. wide, with a length equal to half the wavelength of the radar. During World War II, about three-fourths of U.S. aluminum-foil production (5,000 tons) was devoted to this purpose. Some 20 billion strips were dropped over Germany (the Germans later collecting them for Christmas tree decorations).

Chaffee **1.** The U.S. tank, light, M24, developed in 1943 and used in both World War II and Korea. It had a weight of about 20 tons and was armed with one 75mm gun. **2.** A term sometimes applied to the Chaffee-Reese rifle used in small quantities by U.S. forces in the late nineteenth century.

Chaffroc A U.S. Navy program using modified Zuni rockets to disperse payloads of metal-foil chaff over ships as a protective cover from enemy radar.

chain armor Chain mail.

Chain Home During World War II, the early-warning and aircraft height-finding radar system used in the British Isles. "Chain Home Beamed" referred to inland aircraft reporting; "Chain Home Extra Low" referred to low-flying aircraft; and "Chain Home Low" referred to coastal locations for reporting low-flying aircraft.

chain mail Armor made of interlacing metal rings. It was first introduced in the period 1100 to 1300 and continued in use until the late 1600s. The term is now little used. Most students prefer to call this type of armor simply "mail."

chain of command The succession of commanding officers from a superior to a subordinate through which command is exercised.

chain shot A kind of shot that consisted

CETME 7.62mm NATO assault rifle Model 58. (*Spanish Ministry of Defense.*)

of two projectiles, round or half round, connected by a short chain. They were once used in naval warfare to tear a ship's sails and rigging.

chakra A thin, sharp circular weapon designed to be thrown. It was once a weapon of the Sikhs.

challenge Any process carried out by one unit or person with the object of ascertaining the friendly or hostile character or identity of another.

chaloupe A small French river and coast gunboat.

chamade A French military term for the drumbeat that signaled the moment of surrender.

chamber **1.** Any of the compartments in the cartridge cylinder of a revolver. **2.** To insert a round of ammunition in the chamber of a firearm or gun. **3.** The enlarged or diminished rear part of a cannon which holds the powder. **4.** In certain types of old ordnance, a detachable device which contained the charge. It was inserted at the breech of the weapon. **5.** In military mining, a cavity for a powder charge. It is located in a mine shaft or gallery.

chamber piece A small cannon loaded by the insertion of a separate chamber.

chamber pressure Pressure created in a gun's chamber by the expanding gases of the propellant charge.

chanfron A piece of armor to protect a horse's head. It was first made of leather and then later of iron or steel.

Chapaev A class of Soviet cruisers of 11,500 tons standard displacement completed in 1948–1950. They have a length of 656 ft, a beam of 64 ft, a speed of 34 knots, and a complement of 834 men. They are armed with twelve 5.9-in. guns, eight 3.9-in. guns, twenty-eight 37mm antiaircraft guns, and 100 to 200 mines.

Chaparral A battlefield surface-to-air missile adapted from the Sidewinder infrared homing air-to-air missile. It is produced by Philco-Ford. In operation, four missiles are mounted on a modified standard Army M730 self-propelled tracked cargo vehicle. In addition to the four in launching position, another four are stowed. The missile has a length of 9 ft 6½ in., a launching weight of about 185 lb, and a range in excess of two mi. See **Sidewinder.**

chape A metal mounting or trimming put on a scabbard or sheath. It is a confusing term since it means the tip of the scabbard in British usage and often means the mouth in American usage. It never applies to the middle band.

chapel-de-fer An open iron helmet first developed in the twelfth century.

chappe A gunpowder barrel. It consists of a barrel within a barrel.

Char B1 bis See **French tank, medium, Char B1 bis.**

Chaffee. (*U.S. Army.*)

chain mail. (*The Metropolitan Museum of Art.*)

chanfron. (*The Metropolitan Museum of Art, Bashford Dean Memorial Collection.*)

Chaparral. (*U.S. Army.*)

chapel-de-fer. (*The Metropolitan Museum of Art, Rogers Fund, 1904.*)

Charles F. Adams. (*U.S. Navy.*)

Chassepot rifle. (*The Smithsonian Institution, War Department Collection.*)

Chauchat 8mm machine gun Model 1915. (*The Smithsonian Institution, National Museum Collection.*)

charge   1. A given quantity of explosive, either by itself or contained in a bomb, projectile, mine, or the like or used as the propellant for a bullet or projectile. **2.** That with which a bomb, projectile, mine, or the like is filled, as a charge of explosive, thermite, etc. Also called the "fill," "filler," or "filling." **3.** In small arms, a cartridge or round of ammunition. **4.** To fill with a charge. **5.** To place a charge in a gun chamber. **6.** The act of rushing toward an enemy; an attack.

charger   The British term for a cartridge clip. Also, a term to describe a horse that has been trained to charge.

charger clip   A device for holding several cartridges while they are stripped from it into the magazine space of a gun.

charging cable   A cable attached to the bolt of an aircraft machine gun or cannon for drawing back the bolt manually in order to charge the piece.

Charles F. Adams   A class of U.S. guided-missile destroyers (DDG) of 3,370 tons standard displacement produced between 1960 and 1964. There are 23 ships in the class. They have a length of 437 ft, a beam of 47 ft, a speed of 35 knots, and a complement of 354 men. They are armed with two 5-in. guns, one ASROC eight-tube launcher, and two triple torpedo launchers.

charnel   The hinged staple or bolt fastening the helm or great basinet to the breastplate and backplate.

chase   The exposed part of a gun (artillery) between the trunnion band or cradle and the muzzle. The term is also used to describe the furrow on a crossbow in which the quarrel lies.

chase gun   The armament of a vessel used for pursuit. It may consist of a cannon in the bow or stern.

Chase-me-Charlie   A British slang term for a World War II German weapon which consisted of a remote-controlled glider with an explosive load and a rocket booster.

chase piece   A chase gun.

chase port   A porthole from which a chase gun is fired.

chase ring   In gunnery, the band at the front end of the chase.

Chassepot rifle   A rifle named for its French designer, Antoine A. Chassepot. It was a breechloading bolt-action rifle that fired a cartridge having a combustible envelope in the base of which was a percussion cap that was exploded by a firing pin. This 11mm rifle was adopted by the French in 1866.

chasseur   Originally, a body of light cavalry or infantry troops of the French Army.

chassis   In coast-artillery gun mounts, it is now the movable railway along which the carriage moves back and forth from firing position. It formerly referred to the lower traversing carriage.

CHAT   Crisis home alert technique. A concept for using commercial television and radio for nighttime warning of the public in times of international crisis.

chat échine   A French term meaning "prickly cat." The *chat échine* was a heavy beam bristling with sharp hardwood teeth. It was dropped from the wall of a defended place on the attackers.

Chatellerault 7.5mm machine gun Model 1929   A French gas-operated air-cooled machine gun with a rate of fire of 450 to 500 rounds per minute. It had a weight of 22 lb and was fed from a 30-round drum magazine.

Chauchat 8mm machine gun Model 1915   A French recoil-operated air-cooled machine gun with a rate of fire of 240 rounds per minute. It weighed 18 lb and was fed from a 20-round magazine. When the United States entered World War I, a contract was made to provide this weapon to American forces. A model revised to fire a .30 cal. service cartridge was designated U.S. .30 cal. machine gun Model 1918.

chausses   Linked mail armor of the Middle Ages. It protected the legs, the feet, and the body below the waist.

chauve-souris   A polearm with a long triangular blade and two shorter blades projecting from the base. *Chauve-souris* is a comparatively modern term. The older designation is "corsesque."

checkout A sequence of functional, operational, and calibrational tests to determine the condition and status of a weapon system or element thereof.

checkpoint 1. A predetermined point on the earth's surface used as a means of controlling movement, as a registration target for fire adjustment, or as a reference for location. **2.** The center of impact; a burst center. **3.** The geographic location on land or water above which the position of an aircraft in flight may be determined by observation or by electronic means. **4.** A place where military police check vehicular or pedestrian traffic in order to enforce circulation control measures and other laws, orders, and regulations.

Cheeseburger Another name for the U.S. daisy-cutter jungle-clearing bomb. See **Daisy-Cutter.**

chelone See **tortoise.**

chemical agent A solid, liquid, or gas which through its chemical properties produces lethal or damaging effects on man, animals, plants, or materiel or produces a screening or signaling smoke.

chemical ammunition Any ammunition, such as bombs, projectiles, bullets, flares, and the like, containing a chemical agent or agents. Such agents include war gases, smokes, and incendiaries.

chemical bomb An aerial bomb having a chemical agent for its main charge. Most bombs of this sort have bursters to break the case and spread the charge.

chemical-energy ammunition Ammunition intended to defeat armor and other resistant targets by chemical energy rather than kinetic energy, as in conventional armor-piercing ammunition. Examples are **HEAT** and **HEP** ammunition, which see.

chemical grenade The general term for any hand grenade or rifle grenade charged with a chemical agent.

chemical mortar A mortar that was designed to fire projectiles containing chemical agents. The term is now obsolete since all mortars may fire chemical types of projectiles as well as explosive types.

chemical operations The employment of chemical agents (excluding riot-control agents) (1) to kill, or incapacitate for a significant period of time, man or animals and (2) to deny or hinder the use of areas, facilities, or materials.

chemical spray Aerial release, or a device for aerial release, of liquid war gas for casualty effect or of liquid smokes for aerial smoke screens.

chemical warfare Warfare in which chemicals other than explosives are used.

chemical warhead A warhead designed to produce casualties by inhalation or contact with poisonous materials or to destroy targets by the use of incendiary materials.

chemise In medieval fortifications, an additional counterguard wall surrounding the donjon at a distance of a few yards.

Chesapeake The World War II British designation of the **Vindicator,** which see.

chauve-souris. (*The Metropolitan Museum of Art, gift of William H. Riggs, 1913.*)

Chester A class of U.S. heavy cruisers (CA) of about 9,050 tons standard displacement completed in 1930–1931. The class consisted of *Chester, Augusta,* and *Louisville.* They had a length of 569 ft, a beam of 66 ft, a speed of 32.7 knots, and a wartime complement of 1,200 men. They were armed with nine 8-in. and eight 5-in. guns, plus thirty-two 40mm and twenty-seven 20mm antiaircraft guns.

Chetverikov ARK-3 A Soviet twin-engine (tractor and pusher) five-seat reconnaissance-bomber and transport flying boat first flown in 1935 and used to some extent in convoy-protection duty during World War II.

cheval-de-frise A piece of timber traversed with iron-pointed spikes or spears 5 or 6 ft long. It was used to impede cavalry or troops and was sometimes strung with barbed wire to further increase its effectiveness.

chevet A small wedge once used in raising a mortar.

chevrette The apparatus once used for raising guns or mortars into their carriages.

chevron A type of insignia, often in the shape of a V, that indicates rank, class, length of service, etc.

Cheyenne A U.S. Lockheed-built combat helicopter developed for the U.S. Army and first flown in 1967. It is a two-seat com-

Chester. (*U.S. Navy.*)

Cheyenne. (*Lockheed Aircraft Corporation.*)

Chickasaw. (*U.S. Navy.*)

Chieftain main battle tank. (*Vickers Ltd.*)

pound helicopter with small, low-set, fixed wings; retractable landing gear; and armament consisting of a 40mm grenade launcher or 7.62mm Minigun in the nose, a 30mm cannon in a belly turret, and attachments under each wing for antitank missiles or 2.75-in. rocket pods. It has a range of 875 mi. and a speed of 253 mph.

Chiang Kai Shek rifle See **Chinese (Nationalist) 7.92mm "Chiang Kai Shek" rifle.**

Chicago piano A type of pom-pom, or antiaircraft weapon, that consists of four automatic cannons mounted and operating together.

Chickasaw The Sikorsky H-19 is a twelve-seat single-engine utility helicopter first flown in 1949 and once in use by all U.S. services. It has a speed of 101 mph.

chief of the boat The senior chief petty officer aboard a submarine. He is the executive officer's right-hand man in the ad-

ministration of the crew.

chief petty officer A petty officer of the highest rating.

Chieftain main battle tank A British tank developed in the late 1960s and currently in service in the British Army. It has a crew of four, a weight of 52 tons, a road speed of about 28 mph, and one 120mm high-velocity gun with a maximum antitank range of 3,000 (APDS) to 8,000 meters (HESH). It has secondary armament consisting of two .30 cal. machine guns.

Chilean 7mm Mauser carbine Model 1895 This weapon has an overall length of 37 in., a barrel length of 18.25 in., a weight of approximately 7.5 lb, and a muzzle velocity of about 2,600 fps. It has a nondetachable box magazine with a capacity of five cartridges. There is also a Chilean M95 short rifle that falls between the rifle and carbine in length and weight.

Chilean 7mm Mauser rifle Model 1895 This weapon is similar to the Spanish Mauser M1893. It is a bolt-action rifle with an overall length of 48.5 in., a barrel length of 29.06 in., a weight of 8.9 lb, and a muzzle velocity of about 2,700 fps. It has a five-round nondetachable box magazine.

Chimney A code name for a series of German early-warning radar stations used during World War II. They were also called "Wasserman." The stations could measure range, bearing, and height, and their radar towers consisted of very tall single masts.

Chinese landing A landing in which a boat or ship is brought alongside another, bow to stern. Also, a landing in which a ship is brought alongside down-current or in which an aircraft is landed down-wind.

Chinese (Nationalist) .45 ACP-M-36 submachine gun A submachine gun identical to the U.S. M3A1.

Chinese (Nationalist) 7.92mm "Chiang Kai Shek" rifle A weapon introduced in 1935 and a Chinese copy of the Mauser 7.92 "Standard Model."

Chinese (Nationalist) 7.92mm heavy machine gun Type 24 A 7.92mm modification of the German Maxim Model 08 (MG 08).

Chinese (Nationalist) 7.92mm Type 88 (Hanyang) rifle A weapon made by the Republic of China prior to World War II. It is a copy of the German 7.92mm M1888 rifle.

Chinese (Nationalist) 9mm Parabellum submachine gun M-37 A modified copy of the U.S. M3A1 submachine gun manufactured on Formosa since 1950.

Chinese (Nationalist) 9mm Parabellum submachine gun M-38 A close copy of the British Mk II Sten.

Chinese (People's Republic) 7.62mm assault rifle Type 56 A Chinese copy of the standard Soviet 7.62mm AK assault rifle.

Chinese (People's Republic) 7.62mm light machine gun Type 56 A Chinese copy of the Soviet R.P.D. light machine gun.

Chinese (People's Republic) 7.62mm pistol Type 51 A Chinese copy of the Soviet TT M1933 Tokarev pistol.

Chinese (People's Republic) 7.62mm rifle Type 53 A Chinese copy of the Soviet 7.62mm M1944 Mosin Nagant carbine.

Chinese (People's Republic) 7.62mm submachine gun Type 50 A Chinese copy of the Soviet PPSh M1941.

Chinese (People's Republic) 7.62mm submachine gun Type 54 A Chinese copy of the Soviet PPS-43 submachine gun.

Chinese (People's Republic) 7.92mm light machine gun Type 26 and Type 30 Czechoslovak- and Chinese-made 7.92mm ZB 26 and ZB 30 light machine guns.

Chinook The Boeing Vertol CH-47 medium transport helicopter developed for the U.S.

Army and first flown in 1961. It has a speed of 172 mph and a range of about 1,200 mi, and carries up to 44 troops.

Chiyoda A class of Japanese aircraft carriers that were converted in 1943 and 1944 from seaplane tenders that had been launched in 1936 and 1937. There were two ships in this class, *Chiyoda* and *Chitose*, both of which were sunk by U.S. carrier aircraft during the Battle of Leyte Gulf in October 1944. They had a displacement of 11,190 tons, flight-deck dimensions of 590 × 75 ft, a speed of 29 knots, and a force of 30 aircraft.

chlorine A pungent, suffocating greenish-yellow toxic chemical, gaseous at normal temperatures and pressures. It is irritating and harmful to the eyes, nose, throat, and lungs and may cause death. It was the first toxic gas used in World War I, having been introduced by the Germans at Ypres, France, on April 2, 1915.

chloroacetophenone (CN) A tear agent that has powerful lacrimatory effects and is also an irritant to the upper respiratory passages. In higher concentrations, it is irritating to the skin and causes a burning and itching sensation. High concentrations can cause blisters. Certain individuals experience nausea following exposure to CN. See **tear agents.**

chloroacetophenone, chloropicrin, and chloroform (CNS) A tear agent with an instantaneous irritating effect. In addition to having the same effects as chloroacetophenone (CN), it also has the effects of chloropicrin (PS), which acts as a vomiting agent, a choking agent, and a tear agent. This gas may cause lung effects similar to those produced by phosgene (CG) and also may cause nausea, vomiting, colic, and diarrhea which may persist for weeks. See **tear agents.**

chloroacetophenone in benzene and carbon tetrachloride (CNB) A tear agent with an instantaneous irritating effect. It is a powerful lacrimatory. See **tear agents.**

chloroacetophenone in chloroform (CNC) A tear agent with an instantaneous irritating effect. It causes a flow of tears, irritates the respiratory system, and causes a stinging of the skin. See **tear agents.**

chloropicrin A colorless liquid whose vapor is very irritating to the lungs and causes vomiting, coughing, and crying. It was first used by the Russians in 1916, during World War I. It was called "vomiting gas" by the British, *klop* by the Germans, and *aquinite* by the French.

Choctaw The Sikorsky S-58 transport and general-purpose helicopter developed for the U.S. Army and first flown in 1954. It carries up to 18 passengers, flies at a top speed of 123 mph, and has a range of 280 mi. The U.S. Navy version is called "Seabat" and is used as an antisubmarine-war-

Chinese (People's Republic) 7.62mm assault rifle Type 56. (*U.S. Army*)

Chinook. (*U.S. Army.*)

Choctaw. (*Sikorsky Aircraft.*)

fare helicopter (equipped with active-passive sonar and acoustic homing torpedoes). The U.S. Navy and Coast Guard version is called "Seahorse" and is a utility transport.

choke The narrowing of the bore of a gun toward the muzzle. In shotguns this tends to prevent the rapid spread of the shot.

choking agents War gases such as phosgene (CG) and diphosgene (DP) which injure the unprotected individual chiefly in the respiratory tract, that is, in the nose, throat, and particularly the lungs. In extreme cases membranes swell, lungs become filled with liquid, and death results

cinqueda. (*The Metropolitan Museum of Art, gift of William H. Riggs, 1913.*)

from lack of oxygen. Fatalities of this type are referred to as "dry-land drownings."

chopper A slang term for a helicopter.

chuffing The tendency of some rockets to burn intermittently and with an irregular noise.

chu-ko-nu A Chinese repeating crossbow which has bolts (quarrels) in a box on the top of the stock. Operating a lever on this weapon draws the bow, places a bolt in position, and discharges it.

Churchill Crocodile A Churchill tank equipped with flamethrowing equipment. It pulled its fuel supply in a 400-gal armored trailer.

Churchill tank Also known as the British tank, heavy, Mk IV (or infantry, MkIV), this tank was built in Marks I through VIII and was developed to replace the Matilda. It was built by Vauxhall Motors Ltd. and was

introduced in 1941 for use as an infantry support weapon. It had a crew of five and was armed with one six-pounder gun and two 7.92mm Besa machine guns. It had a weight of 43.1 tons and a maximum speed of 17 mph. 5,640 were produced.

Churruca A class of Spanish destroyers of 1,536 tons standard displacement completed in 1934–1936. They had a speed of 36 knots, a complement of 175 men, and armament consisting of four 4.7-in. guns, three 37mm and two 20mm antiaircraft guns, six 21-in. torpedo tubes, and depth-charge throwers.

Chu Sensha, Shiki 94 tank See **Japanese tank, medium, Model 94.**

chute A parachute.

CIC 1. Counterintelligence corps. **2.** Combat information center.

Cicogna The Fiat B.R.20 Cigogna (Stork) was a twin-engine bomber used by the Italians during World War II. It had a speed of 268 mph, a range of 1,150 mi with a 2,600-lb bombload, and armament con-

sisting of one 12.7mm and two 7.7mm machine guns.

Cigar The code name for an electronic communications-jamming device, both airborne and ground-based, that was used against German communications during World War II.

Cigarette The code name for an electronic communications-jamming device that was used against German bombers during World War II.

CIM-10 See **Bomarc.**

CINCEASTLANT The NATO abbreviation for Commander in Chief, Eastern Atlantic Area.

CINCENT The NATO abbreviation for Commander in Chief, Allied Forces, Central Europe.

CINCHAN The NATO abbreviation for the Commander in Chief, Channel and Southern North Sea.

CINCIBERLANT The NATO abbreviation for Commander in Chief, Iberian Atlantic Area.

CINCNORTH The NATO abbreviation for Commander in Chief, Allied Forces, Northern Europe.

CincPac Commander in Chief, Pacific Fleet Area.

CincPoa Commander in Chief, Pacific Ocean Area.

CINCSOUTH The NATO abbreviation for Commander in Chief, Allied Forces, Southern Europe.

CINCWESTLANT The NATO abbreviation for Commander in Chief, Western Atlantic Area.

cinqueda, cinquedea An Italian dagger or short sword of the fifteenth and sixteenth centuries. It was so-called because the blade, which was double-edged and tapered to a point, was five fingers wide at the hilt.

cipher Any cryptographic system in which arbitrary symbols represent units of plain text of regular length, usually single letters, or in which units of plain text are rear-

clamshell door. A Belfast aircraft is shown unloading three Saladin armored cars. (*Short Brothers and Harland Ltd.*)

Class of 1917–1918, the U.S.S. *Edsall.* (*U.S. Navy.*)

ranged, or both, in accordance with certain predetermined rules.

circular error probable (CEP) An estimate of the accuracy of a weapon used to determine the probable damage to a target.

circus An air armada made up primarily of a powerful fighter force sent out to bring enemy fighters into action.

citadel **1.** A fortress commanding a city. It served both to control the city and its inhabitants and to provide a defensive position during a siege. **2.** A term once used in reference to the protected central structure of an armored warship.

CIWS Close-in Weapon System. Also called **Phalanx,** which see, this U.S. Navy system is designed to provide nuclear-powered guided-missile frigates with a rapid-reaction lightweight 20mm to 25mm Gatling gun capable of providing last-ditch self-defense against enemy antiship missiles.

CK The U.S. military designation for the war gas **cyanogen chloride,** which see.

CL A U.S. Navy light cruiser.

CLAA A U.S. Navy antiaircraft light cruiser.

claim An assertion made by a pilot or crew member that claims credit for having destroyed or damaged an enemy target, such as an airplane or a locomotive.

clamshell door A cargo-loading door on the underside of the front of an airplane consisting of two panels that swing apart like a clamshell.

clandestine operation An operation, the purpose of which is to carry out intelligence, counterintelligence, and other, similar activities sponsored or conducted by governmental departments or agencies. A clandestine operation is carried out in such a way as to assure secrecy or concealment. (It differs from a covert operation in that emphasis is placed on concealment of the operation rather than on concealment of the identity of the sponsor.)

Clarion The code name for a World War II operation in which widespread air attacks were launched against communications all over Germany by fighters and light, medium, and heavy bombers. The attacks took place at the end of February 1945.

clasp A small metal device worn on the suspension ribbon of a service medal or on the ribbon bar. It denotes an additional award of the medal or identifies the nature of the service for which the medal was awarded.

Classic The NATO code name for the Ilyushin IL-62 four-engine (turbofan) long-range transport aircraft first flown in 1963. It can carry up to 186 passengers.

classified information Official information which has been determined to require, in the interests of national defense, protection against unauthorized disclosure and which

Claude. (*The Smithsonian Institution, National Air Museum.*)

CLC, showing the U.S.S. *Northampton* (CLC-1) at the right being replenished at sea by the U.S.S. *Alstede* (AF-48).

has been so designated. See **Defense classification.**

Class of 1917–1918 A class of U.S. four-stack destroyers of 1,190 tons standard displacement completed around 1920. They have a speed of 35 knots, a complement of 122 men, and main armament consisting of four 4-in. and one 3-in. gun and six 21-in. torpedo tubes. There were 58 ships in the class.

Claude A World War II code name used by the Allies to describe the Mitsubishi A5M4 single-seat shipboard fighter. It was the first fighter monoplane to be used by the Japanese Naval Air Force. It was first flown in February 1935, saw considerable service in China in the late 1930s, and was still standard carrier equipment when Japan attacked Pearl Harbor in 1941. It had a speed of 273 mph and was powered by

a 710-hp engine. It was armed with two 7.7mm machine guns.

Claymore **1.** A type of antipersonnel mine designed to produce a directionalized, fan-shaped pattern of fragments. **2.** A Scottish two-handed sword introduced in the fifteenth century. It has a long, heavy blade with a straight grip and straight *quillons* slanting toward the blade. By the eighteenth century this term had come to be applied to the Scottish basket-hilted broadsword, and it is still used in that way in the British Army.

CLC A U.S. Navy tactical command ship.

cleaning malkin A sponge with a jointed staff used for cleaning the bore of a cannon.

claymore. (*The Metropolitan Museum of Art, gift of Mrs. Alexander McMillan Welch, 1945.*)

Cleveland. (*U.S. Navy.*)

close air support, showing an F-4B Phantom II aircraft dropping its ordnance. (*U.S. Navy.*)

clean weapon One in which measures have been taken to reduce the amount of residual radioactivity relative to a "normal" weapon of the same energy yield.

clear 1. To approve or authorize or to obtain approval or authorization for: **a.** A person or persons with regard to their actions, movements, duties, etc. **b.** An object or group of objects, as equipment or supplies, with regard to quality, quantity, purpose, movement, disposition, etc. **c.** A request, with regard to correctness of form, validity, etc. **2.** Specifically, to give one or more aircraft a clearance. **3.** To give a person a security clearance. **4.** To fly over an obstacle without touching it. **5.** To pass a designated point, line, or object. The end of a column must pass the designated feature before the latter is cleared. **6. a.** To operate a gun so as to unload it or make certain that no ammunition remains. **b.** To free a gun of stoppages. **7.** To clear an engine; to open the throttle of an idling engine to free it from carbon. **8.** To clear the air to gain either temporary

or permanent air superiority or control in a given sector.

clearance An ordnance term referring to windage.

clearance minesweeping A procedure to make an area as safe as possible for all classes of shipping.

clearing block A wooden block placed in the action of an automatic weapon to prevent its closing and to show that the gun is unloaded.

Cleat The NATO code name for the Tupolev Tu-114 four-engine (turboprop) transport version of the Tu-20 "Bear" bomber. First flown in 1957, it was the largest and heaviest commercial airliner built up to that time. It utilized a crew of 10 to 15 and carried 220 passengers.

Clemenceau A class of French aircraft carriers of 22,000 tons standard displacement completed in 1961–1965. They have a length of 780 ft, a flight-deck width of 168 ft, a speed of 31 knots, and a complement of 2,150 men. They carry 30 aircraft and are armed with eight 3.9-in. guns. The

class includes *Clemenceau* and *Foch*.

Cleveland 1. A class of U.S. light cruisers (CL) of about 10,000 tons standard displacement completed between 1942 and 1946. This is the largest group of cruisers of a single design ever built, a total of 27 having been completed. They had a length of 610 ft, a beam of 66 ft, a speed of 33 knots, and a wartime complement of 1,200 men. They were armed with twelve 6-in. and twelve 5-in. guns, plus twenty-four to twenty-eight 40mm antiaircraft guns. They carried three aircraft. In 1959–1960, six ships of this class were converted to guided-missile light cruisers (CLG). The number of guns was reduced and twin Talos and Terrier launchers were added. **2.** The Curtiss SBC-4 single-engine two-seat dive bomber used by the U.S. Navy in World War II. It had a speed of 240 mph, armament consisting of two machine guns, and a bombload of about 1,300 lb.

CLG A U.S. Navy guided-missile light cruiser.

CLGN A U.S. Navy guided-missile light cruiser (nuclear-powered).

clice See **kilij.**

clide A machine of war developed in the Middle Ages. It was used to throw rocks at attackers.

CLINKER An antisubmarine-warfare system for sensing heat from the water trails of submarines.

clip A device to hold cartridges for insertion into some rifles and automatic pistols. See also **charger clip.** The term is popularly used to describe a box magazine.

clipeus A large, round shield used by the ancient Greeks and Romans. It had a convex outer face and a concave inner one.

CLK A U.S. Navy hunter-killer ship.

clobber A slang term coined by the RAF. It means to pound heavily; to cause great damage.

Clod The NATO code name for the Antonov An-14 twin-engine six-passenger light general-purpose aircraft in service with the Soviet Air Force and first flown in 1958.

close air support Air attacks against hostile targets which are in close proximity to friendly forces and which require detailed integration of each air mission with the fire and movement of those forces. The air attacks may utilize guns, bombs, guided airborne missiles, or rockets against enemy surface forces, installations, and vehicles.

close column A column of motor vehicles following one another as closely as is safely possible. A close column is usually formed when it is necessary to move a large volume of traffic a short distance in a minimum amount of time.

closed-breech action A system in a firearm in which the bolt or breechblock is closed, with a cartridge seated in the chamber immediately in front of it.

close-fights Barriers built aboard ships to protect men who were trying to repel boarders. They were equipped with loopholes and were also called "close quarters."

close formation A formation in which airplanes fly at minimum distances from one another. Bombers often fly in close formation for mutual protection against fighter attacks.

close helmet In armor, a type of helmet fitted with visor and bevor completely enclosing the head and face.

close order An arrangement of troops according to an exact system. Close-order drill may be performed in parades, in reviews, or in the performance of the manual of arms.

close stick A stick of bombs released in close train or salvo.

close support The action of the supporting force against targets or objectives which are sufficiently near the supported force to require detailed integration or coordination of the supporting action with the fire, movement, or other actions of the supported force.

close supporting fire Fire placed on enemy troops, weapons, or positions which,

close formation, showing three Cutlass aircraft. (*Vought Aeronautics Company.*)

because of their proximity, present the most immediate and serious threat to the supported unit.

closing plug A plug used to close the hole in the casing of certain kinds of ammunition after it has been filled with an explosive.

cloth-yard arrow An old English arrow 3 ft in length.

Cloud A class of Japanese destroyers of 2,050 tons standard displacement completed in the late 1960s, with others to be produced. They have a speed of 27 knots and a complement of 210 men and are armed with four 3-in. guns, an octuple ASROC launcher, and two triple torpedo launchers for antisubmarine homing torpedoes.

club A weapon used for dealing blows. Also called a "war club," typical examples have been made of wood and combinations of wood and stone or metal.

clubman A man armed with a club.

clunaculum An ancient Roman poniard.

cluster **1.** A fireworks signal in which a group of stars burn at the same time. **2.** Groups of bombs released together. A cluster usually consists of fragmentation or incendiary bombs. **3.** Two or more engines coupled together so as to function as one power unit. **4.** In land-mine warfare, the unit of minelaying. It may be antitank, antipersonnel, or mixed. It normally consists of several mines, but may contain only one mine.

cluster bomb A cluster bomb is an assembly of small bombs which may be suspended as a unit in a bomb station designed for a single large bomb. The small bombs are assembled into a single unit by means of a cluster adapter. The cluster is released as a unit for area bombing. After release from the aircraft, the individual bombs are separated from the cluster to arm and fall individually.

clutter Interference on a radarscope consisting of unwanted signals, echoes, or images other than the target return. It may be caused by buildings, trees, mountains, and other bodies that can reflect the signal.

Cloud. (*Japan Defense Agency.*)

CMC, the U.S.S. *Shawmut.* (*U.S. Navy.*)

CM A U.S. Navy minelayer. The term may also stand for **countermeasures,** which see.

CMC A U.S. Navy coastal minelayer.

CN A U.S. military designation for the war gas **chloroacetophenone,** which see.

CNB The U.S. military designation for the war gas **chloroacetophenone in benzene and carbon tetrachloride,** which see.

CNC The U.S. military designation for the war gas **chloroacetophenone in chloroform,** which see.

CNO Chief of Naval Operations.

CNS The U.S. military designation for the war gas **chloroacetophenone and chloropicrin in chloroform,** which see.

CO Commanding officer.

Co (Cossack) A class of British destroyers. See **Ca, Ch, Co,** and **Cr.**

Coach The NATO code name for the Ilyushin IL-12 twin-engine medium-range transport first flown in 1946. It carries up to 32 passengers and flies at a speed of 365 mph.

coal box See **Black Maria.**

Coastal Command A British air-sea organization providing reconnaissance, air-sea rescue, shipping and fleet protection, etc. During World War II its activities extended from the British Isles to Spitzbergen, Iceland, and West Africa.

coast artillery Artillery designed to defend a coastline.

Coast Guard In the United States, an organization charged with the responsibility for operating lifesaving stations along the coast and for operating ships to enforce U.S. customs, immigration, and other laws. It was organized in the 1890s to combine the Revenue Marine Service and the U.S. Life Saving Service.

coast watcher A person inside enemy-held territory who looks out for, and reports by radio, any coastwise movement, particularly shipping.

coat of fence A covering of leather or quilted fabric sufficiently strong to resist a sword cut.

coat of mail A piece of armor made of metal scales or chain mail.

coaxial machine gun A machine gun mounted integrally with the primary gun of a tank. The machine gun can be sepa-

Cobra. (*Ministry of Defense, Federal Republic of Germany.*)

rately bore-sighted so that its line of fire may cross that of the primary gun at any desired range.

cobalt bomb A theoretical atomic or hydrogen bomb encased in cobalt, the cobalt of which would be transformed into deadly radioactive dust upon detonation. This bomb is theoretical only in the sense that it is considered too dangerous to use since the dust would attack friend, foe, and neutrals. In the process of detonation, cobalt 59 would be converted into cobalt 60.

Cobra The Bölkow Bö 810 Cobra is a small wire-guided antitank missile which can be carried, launched, and controlled by one man. A standard weapon of the West German Army, it is also in use with the forces of numerous other countries. It has an overall length of 3 ft 1½ in., a launching weight of 22.5 lb (with a 5.5-lb warhead that can penetrate 18.7 in. of armor plate), and a range of up to 5,250 ft.

cock **1.** To draw back the hammer, bolt, or plunger of a firearm to make ready for firing. **2.** To set a bomb-release mechanism so as to make ready to drop the bomb or bombs. **3.** The striking arm holding the flint in a flintlock, snaphance, or miquelet lock.

Cock The NATO code name for the Antonov An-22 Antheus four-engine (turboprop) long-range heavy strategic transport used by the Soviet Air Force and seen for the first time in 1965. It carries 28 passengers plus freight and has a range of 6,800 mi at speeds up to 460 mph.

cockade A knot or loop of ribbon once worn on the hats of military and naval officers.

cocking indicator A pin that projects from certain rifles and automatic pistols to indicate that the hammer is cocked.

cocking lever A lever for drawing back (sometimes also for lowering) the striker or hammer of an automatic firearm or the mechanism of a bomb-release gear.

cocking piece The rearward extension of a striker or firing pin on some guns. It is pulled back to cock the gun.

cockpit **1.** The compartment in an aircraft from which it is controlled. **2.** A small well where the steering wheel is located in the after part of the upper deck of some sailing vessels. **3.** Formerly, the quarters of junior officers on the lower gundeck of a man-of-war. Also, the place where the wounded were treated, below the water line.

cockswain A term applied to one who steers a boat, usually a sailor in charge of a ship's boat and its crew.

cocooning The process of spraying a piece of equipment with a plastic protective material. It is also called "mothballing" and is used to protect against the effects of the atmosphere.

code Any system of communication in which arbitrary groups of symbols represent units of plain text of varying length. Codes may be used for brevity or for security.

code word A word which has been assigned a classification and a classified meaning to safeguard intentions and information regarding a classified plan or operation.

Codog Combined diesel or gas. A ship power plant having two diesels and one gas turbine. Used on U.S. Navy patrol boats, it provides the best features of both the diesel engine and the gas turbine.

codpiece A groin defense developed in the sixteenth century and repeating the padded civilian style of the period. See **breech of mail.**

coffee-mill carbine During the American Civil War a number of Sharp's carbines were altered to provide coffee mills, with detachable handles in their butts. It was the intent to issue one such carbine to each company of soldiers, but few were actually produced.

coffee-mill gun A repeating weapon invented by the American Wilson Ager and used in limited numbers by Union forces during the Civil War. It was crank-operated, and the hopper feed mechanism for the ammunition resembled a kitchen coffee grinder. It fired a .58 cal. round and had a rate of fire of about 120 shots per minute. It had a range of 1,000 yd.

coffer A trench made in the bottom of a dry ditch. It is used for defensive purposes.

cohort One of the 10 divisions of a Roman legion. A cohort contained from 500 to 600 soldiers.

coif de fer A thirteenth-century cap of mail.

coiffette A skullcap of iron worn in the eleventh and twelfth centuries.

coin In gunnery, a wedge placed under the breech of a gun to raise or depress it.

COIN An acronym for *counterinsurgency* aircraft. See **Bronco.**

Coke The NATO code name for the Antonov An-24 twin-turboprop transport used by Aeroflot in the Soviet Union and first flown in 1960. It can carry up to 50 passengers and has a speed of 310 mph.

Colbert A French antiaircraft cruiser of 9,080 tons standard displacement commissioned in 1959. It has a complement of 777 men, a speed of 32.4 knots, a length of 593 ft, and armament consisting of sixteen 5-in. guns and twenty 57mm antiaircraft guns.

cold steel A weapon or weapons made of steel and used for thrusting or cutting.

Coldstream Guards A regiment of foot guards first assembled in 1659 at Coldstream, Scotland.

cold war A state of international tension wherein political, economic, technological,

colletin. (*The Metropolitan Museum of Art, Bashford Dean Memorial Collection.*)

sociological, psychological, paramilitary, and military measures short of overt armed conflict involving regular military forces are employed to achieve national objectives.

coleopter A jet aircraft having an annular wing and the ability to take off and land vertically.

colichemarde A small sword with a blade that is wide near the hilt but narrows suddenly to a long, slender foible. Supposedly its name is derived from the eighteenth-century Swedish Count Königsmark.

collar See **gorget.**

collection station A medical station in the forward combat zone where battle casualties are prepared to be sent to a clearing station in the rear. Also, any place in a forward area for collecting and sorting salvaged materials.

colletin Plate armor for the protection of the neck and shoulders. It was introduced in the fourteenth century.

collingite The French term for **phosgene,** which see.

collision mat A mat constructed of canvas and fiber that is placed over the hole in a ship's hull after a collision or grounding.

Collossus See **Trident.**

colonel An officer ranking above a lieutenant colonel and below a brigadier general in the United States Army, Marine Corps, and Air Force. The insignia of a colonel is a silver eagle. The rank of captain in the Navy corresponds to that of colonel.

colonel commandant In the British Army, the commander of a brigade of artillery, engineers, or marines.

colonel general Formerly, an officer who had supreme command of an army.

Colorado A class of U.S. battleships of about 32,000 tons standard displacement completed between 1921 and 1923. The class included *Colorado, Maryland,* and

Colorado. (*U.S. Navy.*)

Colossus. (*The Imperial War Museum.*)

West Virginia. They had a length of 624 ft, a beam of 108 ft, a speed of about 21 knots, and a complement of 2,100 men. They were armed with eight 16-in. and sixteen 5-in. guns, plus thirty-two 40mm and fifty 20mm antiaircraft guns and three aircraft. They saw considerable action in the Pacific theater during World War II, including Kwajalein, Saipan, Marcus, Leyte, Okinawa, and Tinian.

color-bearer A person who bears the colors.

colored-marker projectile A projectile loaded with a charge consisting primarily of organic dye and provided with a burster charge. Upon impact the projectile is ruptured, and the dye is dispersed and vaporized by the heat of explosion. The dye then resolidifies in the air, forming a colored smoke cloud which serves as a marker and/or target indicator to supporting ground and air forces.

colored smoke Colored-smoke munitions are made in several forms, including projectiles, bombs, grenades, and candles. They may be employed as signals, target markers, zone-identification markers, and so forth. Distinctive smoke colors are red, green, yellow, and violet.

color guard A guard of honor which carries the colors of an organization.

colors The flag or ensign flown by a ship or by military organizations such as infantry regiments. Cavalry banners are called "standards."

colossus A passive ocean-bottom submarine-detection system using sonar to provide long-range directional information. It was developed as part of the Trident program.

Colossus **1.** A class of British aircraft carriers of 14,000 tons standard displacement commissioned in 1944–1945. The class included *Colossus, Vengeance, Venerable, Glory,* and *Ocean.* They had an overall length of 695 ft, an extreme flight-deck width of 80 ft, a top speed of 23 knots, and a complement of 950 men. They carried 33 aircraft and were armed with 88 antiaircraft guns (total barrels). **2.** A class of British 20,000-ton battleships completed in 1911. There were two ships in the class, *Colossus* and *Hercules.* They had a length of 546 ft, a complement of 900 men, and armament consisting of ten 12-in., sixteen 4-in., and four three-pounder guns, plus three 21-in. torpedo tubes. They had a speed of 20 knots. **3.** A part of the U.S. Navy's sound surveillance systems (SOSUS) for submarine detection, consisting of 5 to 15 sonar heads per mile connected to submerged cables. The sonars act as a direction-finding network, using the same cables on a time-share basis with land-based centers analyzing the signals and classifying submarine sound signatures. It is an additional refinement to the Caesar underwater detection system.

Colt 1. The NATO code name for the Soviet Antonov An-2 general-purpose transport aircraft first flown in 1947. It has a single engine and can carry 14 troops at a speed of 157 mph. **2.** A revolver manufactured by the Colt's Patent Firearms Company. In imprecise use, almost any revolver, especially with reference to the middle and late nineteenth century.

Colt 6mm machine gun Model 1895 A U.S. gas-operated air-cooled machine gun with a rate of fire of 500 rounds per minute. It had a weight of 40 lb and was fed from a fabric belt.

Colt .30 cal. machine gun M1917 This is a gas-operated machine gun with an overall length of 40.8 in., a barrel length of 28 in., and a weight of 35 lb. The mount for the gun weighs 61.25 lb. The weapon has a cyclic rate of fire of 480 rounds per minute, a muzzle velocity of 2,800 fps, and a feed device consisting of a 250-round fabric belt. This weapon has a jointed gas lever which swings down from the gun. For this reason it gained the nickname of the Colt "Potato Digger."

Colt .38 cal. Army, Navy, Marine revolver The predecessor of this model, in .41 cal., introduced the swing-out cylinder with simultaneous ejection and was the model from which the modern Colt design stemmed. This arm was produced from 1889 through 1908. In 1889 it became the standard side arm of the U.S. Navy, and in 1892 it was adopted as standard for the U.S. Army. The New Army and New Navy Models differed only in markings and stocks. The New Marine Corps Model was introduced in 1905 and differed only in having a rounded butt. With 6-in. barrels the overall length of these weapons was about 11 in. The cylinder capacity was six cartridges, and the weight was about 34 oz. This revolver fired the .38 Long and Short Colt, a cartridge that came into considerable disrepute during the war in the Philippines (1898–1900) because of its inability to stop savage Moros.

Colt .38 cal. automatic pistol Type 1899 A U.S. service pistol weighing 2 lb 6 oz and having a length of $9\frac{1}{4}$ in. and a barrel length of 6 in. The magazine held seven rounds of .38 cal. rimless ammunition. This weapon should not be confused with the .380 cal. pistol by Colt.

Colt .380 cal. automatic pistol A U.S. service pistol weighing 1 lb $7\frac{1}{2}$ oz. The overall length is $6\frac{3}{4}$ in., and the barrel length is $3\frac{3}{4}$ in. The magazine holds seven rounds of .380 rimless ammunition.

Colt .45 cal. Double Action Army revolver This was Colt's first heavy-frame double-action revolver. It was manufactured from 1877 to 1909 and had an overall

length (with a $7\frac{1}{2}$-in. barrel) of about $12\frac{1}{4}$ in. A $4\frac{3}{4}$-in. and a $5\frac{1}{2}$-in. barrel were also standard. The cylinder capacity was six cartridges, and the approximate weight was 39 oz. With the trigger guard made larger and with a longer trigger (to permit use with a gloved hand), this weapon was also known as the "Alaskan Model" and the "Philippine Model."

Colt .45 cal. Government Model 1911, 1911A1 This weapon evolved from an older .45 automatic called the "Old Model" or "Military Model." The M1911, as it was called, met the requirements of the U.S. government competition of 1911, which called for a weapon that was simple, could be completely disassembled without tools, used a heavy bullet, and had good reliability under unfavorable service conditions. The M1911 weighs 39 oz and has an overall length of 8.62 in. and a barrel length of 5 in. The magazine has a capacity of seven cartridges. A few minor changes were made in 1921, and the weapon became the M1911A1. It is also a standard arm of the Mexican Army.

Colt .45 cal. New Service revolver This weapon was introduced in 1897 and not discontinued until 1943. With a $4\frac{1}{2}$-in. barrel, it had an overall length of $9\frac{3}{4}$ in. and weighed 39 oz. In 1917–1918 some 150,000 of this model were produced to fire the .45 ACP cartridge. Three-shot half-moon clips were used.

Colt .45 cal. revolver Model 1917 A double-action revolver with an overall length of 10.8 in. and a barrel length of 5.5 in. The weight of the weapon is 2.5 lb, and the cylinder has a capacity of six cartridges. This weapon is the New Service Model adapted in 1917 to take .45 ACP rimless cartridges. It has a muzzle velocity of 830 fps. Colt manufactured 151,700 of these revolvers.

Colt .45 cal. Single Action Army revolver Introduced in 1873, this model, with slight modifications in caliber, is also referred to as the "Frontier" or the "Peacemaker." It has an overall length of 13 in., a $7\frac{1}{2}$-in. barrel (other barrel lengths are $4\frac{3}{4}$ and $5\frac{1}{2}$ in.), and a weight of about 40 oz. The cylinder capacity is six cartridges. This same model was also manufactured to shoot a large number of cartridges, including .32/20, .38 Special, .357 Magnum, .38/40, .44 Special, and, at one time, .45 ACP.

columbiads Tradition has long held that this large cast-iron smoothbore cannon was developed by Col. George Bomford and was used in the War of 1812. The term goes back at least to 1807, however, and was applied to relatively small iron guns as well as large ones. Probably the name derives from the Columbia Foundry, which made most U.S. iron cannons of this time, and Bomford probably had little to do with

Colt .45 cal. Government Model 1911, 1911A1. (*U.S. Army.*)

them. In 1860, General T. J. Rodman, of the U.S. Ordnance Department, developed a means of casting hollow tubes that were cooled from the bore outward, thereby securing a greater hardness and uniformity of grain inside the barrel. He also redesigned the exterior of the tube. These new cannons, though officially still called "columbiads," were produced for the Civil War in 8-, 10-, 15-, and 20-in. calibers.

column A formation of ships or aircraft in a single file, one astern of the other.

column cover The cover of a column by aircraft in contact therewith, providing for its protection by reconnaissance and/or attack of air or ground targets which threaten the column.

column formation A formation in which elements are placed one behind the other.

column, open-order A line of ships in column in which alternate ships are staggered to the right and to the left.

ComAirPac Commander Air Force, Pacific Fleet.

comb In armor, the keel-shaped ridge that passes from the front to the back of the top of a helmet. It adds strength and provides a better glancing surface.

combat Active fighting between armed forces.

combat aircrewmen Enlisted aviation crewmen aboard combat aircraft.

combat air patrol An aircraft patrol provided over an objective area, over the force protected, over the critical area of a combat zone, or over an air-defense area for the purpose of intercepting and destroying hostile aircraft before they reach their target.

combatant 1. Under international law, an individual member of a belligerent force subject to the laws, rights, and duties of war. **2.** A soldier or unit assigned to duty as an active fighter or fighting unit, as distinguished from duty in any of the services, such as administrative, supply, or medical.

combatant ship A ship such as a destroyer, attack transport, or submarine whose primary mission is combat with the enemy.

combat area A restricted area (air, land,

Combat Infantryman's Badge. (U.S. Army.)

or sea) which is established to prevent or minimize mutual interference between friendly forces engaged in combat operations.

Combat Arena The code name for a chronological and historical data base concerned with U.S. air operations over North Vietnam and Laos.

combat box A box formation of aircraft. During World War II this term applied to B-17 formations of three flights of six airplanes each.

combat branch A military organization specially organized, equipped, and trained for combat.

combat car An armed vehicle, tracked or wheeled, designed for combat.

combat control team During World War II, a team dropped into enemy territory to give navigational aid to airborne assault elements.

Combat Dawn A USAF drone aircraft developed by Teledyne Ryan and used to detect and position hostile radar emitters.

combat fatigue A nervous disorder caused by the demands of combat. A neurosis characterized by anxiety, tremor, nightmares, etc.

combat/fighting patrol A tactical unit sent out from the main body to engage in independent fighting; A detachment assigned to protect the front, flank, or rear of the main body, by fighting if necessary.

Combat Hornet A U.S. Air Force AC-119G and AC-119K gunship aircraft used in Vietnam. See **Flying Boxcar.**

Combat Infantryman's Badge A U.S. badge, showing a silver rifle on a blue field, signifying that the recipient has served in combat with ground forces.

combat information ship A designated ship charged with the coordination of the intership combat information center functions of the various ships in a task force so that the overall combat information available to commands will be increased. This ship normally is the flagship of the task-force commander.

combat intelligence That knowledge of the enemy, weather, and geographic features required by a commander in the planning and conduct of combat operations.

combat load Supplies and equipment prescribed to be taken into combat for a specific operation for a period of time during which resupply will not be available. The term may apply to a weapon, a vehicle, an individual, or an organization.

combat loading Loading assault troops and equipment for rapid debarkation in predetermined priority.

ComBatPac Commander Battleships, Pacific Fleet.

combat post A term that once described the smallest military tactical locality. The garrison of a combat post varied from a few men to a platoon.

combat range The range or distance from a base which a given airplane can fly on a combat mission.

combat ready Synonymous with "operationally ready" with respect to missions or functions performed in combat.

combat reserve A combat force held in reserve for immediate use if needed.

combat service Service in a combatant branch of the military.

combat support troops Those units or organizations whose primary mission is to furnish operational assistance for the combat elements.

combat surveillance A continuous, all-weather, day-and-night systematic watch over the battle area to provide timely information for tactical ground combat operations.

combat-surveillance radar Radar with the normal function of maintaining continuous watch over a combat area.

combat survival Those measures to be taken by service personnel when involuntarily separated from friendly forces in combat, including procedures relating to individual survival, evasion, escape, and conduct after capture.

combat team Pilots of a division of aircraft who train and fight together.

combat trail Interceptors in trail formation. Each interceptor behind the leader maintains position visually or with airborne radar.

combat train The transportation systems needed to carry material that is of immediate use during combat.

combat troops Those units or organizations whose primary mission is destruction of enemy forces and/or installations.

combat unit A unit organized, equipped, and trained for combat operations.

combat vehicle A land or amphibious vehicle, with or without armor or armament, designed for specific functions in combat or battle. The installation of armor or armament on vehicles other than combat vehicles does not change their original classification.

combat zone **1.** A region in a theater of operations where fighting takes place or where space is designated for the operations of friendly combat forces, extending from the front line to a line or boundary designated by the theater commander. **2.** In popular usage, a combat area. In sense 1, the size of a combat zone depends upon the size of the forces assigned, the nature of the operations contemplated, the character of the lines of communication, terrain features, and enemy capabilities.

combination fuze A fuze combining two different types of fuze mechanisms, especially one combining impact and time mechanisms.

combination weapons From the fifteenth through the nineteenth centuries a number of hybrid weapons were created by combining firearms with other weapons such as knives, axes, swords, maces, and polearms.

combined force A military force composed of elements of two or more allied nations.

combined operation An operation conducted by forces of two or more allied

Commando. (U.S. Army.)

nations acting together for the accomplishment of a single mission.

ComCarDiv Commander Carrier Division.

COMCN See **communication countermeasures.**

Comet 1 A British cruiser tank of World War II. Produced from late 1944, this vehicle had a crew of five, a speed of 29 mph, and armament consisting of one 77mm gun and two machine guns. It had a loaded weight of about 33 tons.

Comet 2 and 3 Comet 2 was a Soviet inertially guided surface-to-surface missile that drew heavily on German V-2 guidance technology. It was a solid-propellant missile with a range of about 600 mi. It was operational with the Army and was adapted for firing from surface ships and submarines. Comet 3 is a Soviet air-to-surface standoff missile, roughly equivalent to the British Blue Steel, with a range of about 100 mi.

Comfy Bee A U.S. Air Force high-altitude drone for electronic surveillance and photoreconnaissance missions.

Comfy Bridle A U.S. Air Force secure communications network in Southeast Asia.

Comfy Card U.S. air-transportable mobile huts with HF, VHF, and UHF radio equipment.

command **1.** The authority which a commander in the military service lawfully exercises over his subordinates by virtue of rank or assignment. Command includes the authority and responsibility for effectively using available resources and for planning the employment of, organizing, directing, coordinating, and controlling military forces for the accomplishment of assigned missions. It also includes responsibility for the health, welfare, morale, and discipline of assigned personnel. **2.** An order given by a commander, that is, the will of the commander expressed for the purpose of bringing about a particular action. **3.** A unit, organization, or area under the command of one individual. **4.** To dominate by a field of weapon fire or by observation from a superior position.

command active sonobuoy system (CASS) An airborne antisubmarine-warfare detection and classification device.

commandant The commanding officer of a place or of a body of men.

Commandant A class of French frigates of 1,750 tons standard displacement completed in 1962–1969. They have a length of 338 ft, a beam of 37.8 ft, a speed of 24.5 knots, and a complement of 214 men. They are armed with three 3.9-in. guns, two 30mm guns, one 12-in. quadruple A/S mortar, and six 21-in. torpedo tubes.

command car A military staff and reconnaissance vehicle.

command destruct signal A signal used to operate intentionally the destruction system in a missile.

Commando. (*U.S. Air Force.*)

commander The chief officer of an army or a subdivision of it. In the United States Navy, an officer whose rank is next below a captain and next above a lieutenant commander and equal to a lieutenant colonel in the Army. The insignia is a silver oak leaf or three ½-in. gold stripes.

commandeer To seize a thing for military purposes.

commander in chief An officer in supreme command of a nation's military or naval forces. The President of the United States is the commander in chief of all services, but the title is often applied to the general officer of highest rank in the Army. In the U.S. and British Navies the title is also applied to the senior flag officer in command of a fleet.

command guidance A guidance system wherein intelligence transmitted to the missile from an outside source causes the missile to traverse a directed flight path.

command net A communications network which connects an echelon of command with some or all of its subordinate echelons for the purpose of command control.

commando A soldier belonging to a specially trained amphibious organization of the British Army. The group engaged in hit-and-run raids into enemy territory for purposes of sabotage, destruction of stores and communications, and other shock tactics.

Commando **1.** The only wheeled armored fighting vehicle presently in service with the U.S. Army, this Cadillac Gage Company-produced armored personnel carrier was developed between 1960 and 1965. When equipped with a turret, it has a crew of nine (without a turret, it has a crew of twelve). Turret options include twin .30 cal. Brownings, twin 7.62mm machine guns, or a twin system consisting of one .50 cal. and one .30 cal. machine gun. Commando has a weight of 7.25 tons and a road speed of 62 mph. **2.** The Curtiss-Wright C-46 Commando is a twin-engine troop or cargo transport developed for the USAAF and used extensively in World War II; it is best known for "flying the hump" with the Air Transport Command. It is still in service with the U.S. Air Force and Navy and with

the air forces of numerous other countries. It has a speed of 227 mph and can carry 40 fully armed troops.

command post A unit's or subunit's headquarters where the commander and the staff perform their activities. In combat, a unit's or subunit's headquarters is often divided into echelons; the echelon in which the unit or subunit commander is located or from which he operates is called a "command post."

command-reconnaissance truck A truck equipped with an open body, fabric top, and automobile-type seats designed specifically to transport command and reconnaissance personnel in the field.

Commencement Bay A class of U.S. escort aircraft carriers (CVE) of about 11,000 tons standard displacement commissioned in 1944–1946. They had a speed of 19 knots and a wartime complement of over 1,000 men, and they carried 34 aircraft. They had a length of 557 ft and an extreme width of 105 ft. (Picture, next page.)

Commendation Ribbon A decoration consisting of a ribbon and a medallion. It is awarded to military persons who distinguish themselves by meritorious achievements or service.

commerce destroyer A fast, lightly armed vessel designed to capture or destroy merchant vessels.

commission **1.** To put in, or make ready for service or use, as to commission an aircraft or a ship. **2.** A written order giving a person rank and authority as an officer in the armed forces. **3.** The rank and authority given by such an order.

commissioned officer An officer who holds rank by virtue of a commission.

commitment position The point in a depth-charge attack at which the antisubmarine-warfare ship must be committed to the attack course and speed in order to reach the correct firing point.

commodore A U.S. Navy commissioned rank used in wartime. It is the rank immediately above a captain and below a rear admiral. It corresponds to the rank of brigadier general in the Army.

common projectile A penetrating projectile containing a bursting charge of high

Commencement Bay. (*U.S. Navy.*)

composite aircraft. (*U.S. Air Force.*)

explosive intended to explode after passing through the lighter protective armor of a vessel.

communications A method or means of conveying information of any kind from one person or place to another, except by direct, unassisted conversation or correspondence through nonmilitary postal agencies.

communications countermeasures (CONCM) The detection and location of enemy communications equipment by intercept search and the jamming of enemy communications.

communications intelligence Technical and intelligence information derived from foreign communications by other than the intended recipients.

communications zone The rear part of the theater of operations not included in the combat zone. It contains the lines of communications, establishments for supply and evacuation, and other agencies required for the immediate support and maintenance of the field forces.

communication trench A trench connect-

compensator. (*U.S. Army.*)

ing two other trenches and used for moving between them.

company The basic administrative and tactical unit in most arms and services of the Army. A company is on a command level below a battalion and above a platoon and is equivalent to a battery of artillery, etc.

company-grade officer A commissioned officer below the rank of major.

compass rose A graduated circle, usually marked in degrees, indicating directions and printed or inscribed in an appropriate medium.

compensating sight A gunsight incorporating a means of making corrections for wind, gravitation, target velocity, or other variables.

compensator On some small arms, a device used to hold down muzzle rise and reduce recoil.

complement The officers and men assigned to a ship; also, the crew of an aircraft.

complete round A term applied to an assemblage of explosive and nonexplosive components designed to perform a specific function at the time and under the conditions desired. Examples of complete rounds of ammunition are: (1) *Separate loading:* consisting of a primer, propelling charge,

and, except for blank ammunition, a projectile and a fuze. (2) *Fixed or semifixed:* consisting of a primer, propelling charge, cartridge case, and a projectile and a fuze, except when solid projectiles are used. (3) *Bomb:* consisting of all component parts required to drop and function the bomb once. (4) *Missile:* consisting of a complete warhead section and missile body with its associated components and propellants. (5) *Rocket:* consisting of all components necessary for it to function.

composite aircraft One airplane carrying another, or linked to another, with the two considered a single unit. The example shown was designated *Mistel* (Mistletoe) by the Germans in World War II. It consisted of a Focke Wulf FW 109 fighter (on top) and a Junkers JU 88 bomber (below). The JU 88 was employed as a pilotless missile carrying a large high-explosive warhead and guided to the target by the fighter.

Composite Air Strike Force A group of selected U.S. Air Force units composed of appropriate elements of tactical air power (tactical fighters, tactical reconnaissance, tankers, airlift, and command and control elements) and capable of employing a spectrum of nuclear and nonnuclear weapons.

composite defense In aitiaircraft artillery, a defense that employs two or more types of fire units which are integrated into a single defense.

compromise The known or suspected exposure of clandestine personnel, installations, or other assets, or of classified information or material, to an unauthorized person.

computed air release point A computed air position where the first paratroop or cargo item is released to land on a specified impact point.

computing gunsight A gunsight, especially one for aircraft machine guns, that automatically calculates for wind, range, and other variables and enables a gunner to hit his target. Some types of computing gunsights may be used also for rocket firing and bombing.

concealment The protection from observation only. See also **cover.**

concentrate To come together or join up, as ships or aircraft prior to making an attack.

concentrated fire **1.** The fire of the batteries of two or more ships directed against a single target. **2.** The fire from a number of weapons directed at a single point or small area.

concentration The assembling of troops within a given area. The simultaneous firing by a number of weapons on a common target.

concentration area **1.** An area, usually in the area of operations, where troops are assembled before beginning active operations. **2.** A limited area at which a volume of gunfire is placed within a limited time.

concentration camp A camp in which military and political prisoners are confined.

concertina A coil of barbed wire. It is compressed for carrying but is extended for use as an entanglement.

concrete dibber bomb A rocket-boosted bomb reportedly in use with the Israeli Air Force. In a French design study, the weight of the total system was 1,210 lb, of which 365 lb was the explosive warhead.

concrete-piercing projectile A projectile especially designed or adapted for penetrating concrete and other similarly resistant targets.

concussion fuze A bomb fuze designed to function in the air in response to the concussion produced by the explosion of a preceding bomb. It is also called an "airburst fuze" or an "air-pressure fuze."

condensation trail A visible cloud streak, usually brilliantly white in color, which trails behind a missile or other vehicle in flight under certain conditions. It is also called a "vapor trail" or a "contrail."

Condor **1.** The German Focke-Wulf Fw 200 Condor was originally designed as a commercial transport and first flown in 1937. During World War II it was used as a seven-seat four-engine long-range maritime reconnaissance bomber. It flew at speeds of 224 mph and was armed with one 20mm cannon, three 13mm machine guns, two 7.9mm machine guns, and a maximum bombload of 4,626 lb. This aircraft took a heavy toll of Allied shipping during the early part of the war, operating both by themselves and in cooperation with U-boat packs. **2.** The Curtiss B-2, a U.S. twin-engine biplane bomber developed in 1927. **3.** A television-guided air-to-surface missile developed as a follow-on to Bullpup.

condottiere The leader of a band of European mercenary soldiers of the fourteenth to the sixteenth centuries.

cone of burst See **cone of dispersion.**

cone of dispersion **1.** A term which can

concertina. (*U.S. Army.*)

Condor. (*Vereinigte Flugtechnishe Werke—Fokker.*)

Congreve rocket. (*The Smithsonian Institution, National Air Museum.*)

conning tower, of the U.S.S. *Permit.* (*U.S. Navy.*)

be applied to the pattern in space formed by any one of numerous phenomena which originate in a point source and spread out in conical form from the source. **2.** A cone-shaped pattern formed by the paths of a group of shots fired from a weapon with the same sight setting; synonymous in this sense with "cone of fire" and "sheaf of fire." **3.** The pattern in space from the opening of canister (or shrapnel, now obsolete) in which the preformed pellets, under the influence of forward velocity, spread out to form a cone in space.

cone of fire   See **cone of dispersion.**

confidential   See **defense classification.**

confirmed victory   In aerial combat, a victory that has been corroborated.

confusion reflector   In electronic countermeasures, any of several kinds of electromagnetic-wave reflectors dropped from aircraft to create false signals on radarscopes and confuse the enemy about the location of the aircraft. It may consist of lengths of wire, sheets of metal, or other metallic objects, but normally strips of metallic foil or paper are used. See also **chaff, rope,** and **window.**

Congreve rocket   A type of artillery rocket invented by Sir William Congreve (1772–1828) and used by the British and Ameri-

cans in the first half of the nineteenth century.

conn   To control the steering of a vessel. The officer in control is said to "have the conn." To guide or pilot a ship is spoken of as "conning."

Connecticut   A U.S. battleship of the **Louisiana** class, which see. It was commissioned in 1906.

conning tower   The control station in a submarine below the open bridge. Also, the armored control station on a cruiser. The conning tower contains means of communication with all parts of the ship.

conscript   One who has been drafted for military service.

conscription   A draft. The compulsory enrollment of men for military duty.

consolidate   To organize and strengthen a newly captured position so that it can be used against the enemy.

Conspicuous Gallantry Medal   A silver medal awarded to petty officers and seamen in the British Navy.

constant-helm plan   An evasive maneuver used by a ship which suspects the presence of an enemy submarine. Although the ship appears to be changing course constantly, it never varies much from its base track.

Constellation   The Lockheed C-69 Constellation was the Model 49 commercial airliner converted to a military role and first flown in 1943. It carried about 60 passengers and flew at a top speed of around 350 mph. A later version was the C-121 **Super Constellation,** which see.

Constitution   **1.** The oldest ship on the U.S. Navy list, it is now on view as a relic in Boston. It has a displacement of 2,200 tons, a length of 175 ft, a beam of 43.5 ft, and a speed (under sail) of about 13 knots. It is armed with twenty-eight 24-pounders and ten 12-pounders. It was completed in 1798 and saw action in the quasi-war with France, against Barbary pirates, and in the War of 1812 with Britain. After her 1812 defeat of H.M.S. *Java,* the ship was referred to as "Old Ironsides." **2.** The U.S. Lockheed-built R6V Constitution was a four-engine naval transport developed in the late 1940s and delivered to the U.S. Navy in January 1949. It had a designed cruising speed of 237 mph and a range of 2,300 mi.

contact   Indications of the presence of a target made by sight, sound, or electronic means.

contact fire   A method of firing a mine by which the mine is exploded immediately when touched by a vessel, vehicle, or person.

contact fuze   A device which initiates warhead detonation after a bomb or projectile impacts with a target surface. Initiation results from actual contact with the target to include such phenomena as impact,

Constellation. (*Lockheed Aircraft Corporation.*)

crush, tilt, or electrical contact.

contact lost The term used to signify that a target believed to be still within the area of visual, sonar, or radar coverage is temporarily lost but that the termination of track plotting is not warranted.

contact mine A mine fitted with a firing device which explodes the mine when it is touched by a vessel, person, or vehicle.

contact point **1.** In land warfare, a point on the terrain, easily identifiable, where two or more units are required to make contact. **2.** In air operations, the position at which a flight leader makes radio contact with an air-control agency.

contact report A report of visual, sonar, or radar contact with the enemy. The first report, giving the information immediately available when the contact is first made, is known as an "initial contact report." Subsequent reports containing additional information are referred to as "amplifying reports."

contain To stop, hold, or surround the forces of the enemy or to cause the enemy to center his activity on a given front and to prevent his withdrawing any part of his forces for use elsewhere.

containment A process whereby a hostile power is prevented from expanding beyond certain limits by the pressures of economics, politics, and propaganda or by the strengthening of adjacent friendly powers.

contamination The deposit and/or absorption of radioactive material or biological or chemical agents on and by structures, areas, personnel, or objects.

continuous cover The escort or cover provided by relays of fighters to protect bombers during a combat mission.

continuous fire **1.** Fire conducted at a normal rate without interruption for application of adjustment corrections or for other reasons. **2.** In field artillery, a succession of salvos, the pieces being fired consecutively at the interval designated in the command.

continuously pointed fire Antiaircraft fire directed at and following the target aircraft.

contour follower A cam-riding part designed to raise or lower a gun in an aircraft or to actuate a fire-interrupting device to avoid hitting any part of the aircraft. It is also called a "cam follower."

contraband of war According to international law, materials that cannot be supplied to one belligerent power without risk of seizure by the other.

contrail See **condensation trail.**

control **1.** Authority which may be less than full command exercised by a commander over part of the activities of subordinate or other organizations. **2.** The physical or psychological pressures exerted with the intent to assure that an agent or

Constitution. (*U.S. Navy.*)

group will respond as directed. **3.** An indicator governing the distribution and use of documents, information, or material. Such indicators are the subject of intelligence community agreement and are specifically defined in appropriate regulations.

control group An organization for the direction, supervision, and control of amphibious vehicles, landing craft, and landing ships during amphibious operations.

controlled-devices countermeasures
Electronic countermeasures against guided missiles, pilotless aircraft, proximity fuzes, or similar devices. The term also applies to the detection of these weapons and the use of jamming and deception to interfere with their operation.

controlled-effects nuclear weapons Nuclear weapons designed to achieve variation in the intensity of specific effects other than normal blast effect.

controlled forces Military or paramilitary forces under effective and sustained political and military direction.

controlled mine A mine fitted with firing devices capable of being activated by an electrical system leading to a central control station. It may be an underwater mine or a land mine.

controlled port A harbor or anchorage at which entry and departure, assignment of berths, and traffic within the harbor or anchorage are controlled by military authorities.

Constitution. (*Lockheed Aircraft Corporation.*)

Coontz. (*U.S. Navy.*)

controlled response The selection from a wide variety of feasible options of the one which will provide the specific military response most advantageous in the circumstances.

control point **1.** A position along a route of march at which men are stationed to give information and instructions for the regulation of supply or traffic. **2.** A position marked by a buoy, boat, aircraft, electronic device, conspicuous terrain feature, or other identifiable object which is given a name or number and used as an aid to navigation or control of ships, boats, or aircraft. **3.** A point located by ground survey with which a corresponding point on a photograph is matched, as a check, in making mosaics.

control vessel In an amphibious operation, the vessel that guides and directs the boats in the ship-to-shore movement.

conventional bomb Any nonatomic bomb designed primarily for explosive effect, as distinguished from a chemical bomb, leaflet bomb, incendiary bomb, or other special-purpose bomb.

conventional forces Those forces capable of conducting operations using nonnuclear weapons.

conventional warfare Warfare conducted without the use of bacteriological, chemical, or nuclear weapons.

conventional weapons Nonnuclear weapons. The term excludes all biological weapons and generally excludes chemical weapons except for existing smoke and incendiary agents and agents of the riot-control type.

converging fire Fire from a number of guns directed at the same spot.

conversion A change in the design or characteristics of a ship significant enough to necessitate altering its mission or assign-

Cooper bomb (far right), shown with a 112-lb and a 230-lb bomb at an airfield in France, 1918. (*The Imperial War Museum.*)

ing it to a different class.

convoy 1. A number of merchant ships, naval auxiliaries, or both, usually escorted by warships and/or aircraft, or a single merchant ship or naval auxiliary under surface escort, assembled and organized for the purpose of passage together. **2.** A group of vehicles organized for the purpose of control and orderly movement with or without escort protection.

convoy commodore A naval officer, or master of one of the ships in a convoy designated to command the convoy, subject to the orders of the escort-force commander. If no surface escort is present, he takes entire command.

convoy escort 1. Naval ships or aircraft in company with a convoy and responsible for its protection. **2.** An escort to protect a convoy of vehicles from being scattered, destroyed, or captured.

cookies The name for British 4,000-lb high-explosive bombs first used on Naples, Italy, in mid-October 1941.

cook-off The deflagration or detonation of ammunition caused by the absorption of heat from its environment. Usually it consists of the accidental and spontaneous discharge of, or explosion in, a gun or firearm caused by the igniting of a fuze, propellant charge, or bursting charge by an overheated chamber or barrel.

Cookpot The NATO code name for the Soviet Tupolev Tu-124 twin-engine (turbofan) transport first flown in 1960. It has a top speed of 603 mph and accommodations for 56 passengers.

Coontz A class of U.S. guided-missile frigates (DLG) of 4,700 tons standard displacement produced between 1959 and 1966. They have a length of 512.5 ft, a beam of 52.5 ft, a speed of 34 knots, and a complement of 375 men. They are armed with one 5-in. and four 3-in. guns, one twin Terrier launcher, one Asroc eight-tube launcher, and two triple torpedo launchers. There are 10 ships in this class.

Cooper bomb A small, streamlined bomb used in World War I. It was developed by the British and used by the Allies.

Coot The NATO code name for the Ilyushin IL-18 four-engine turboprop transport used in the Soviet Union by Aeroflot. It carries up to 110 passengers.

corbeau A weapon used in conjunction with a battering ram. After the ram had broken through the wall, the defenders would try to seize it. The *corbeau* was a long pole with an iron cutting edge at the end of it. It was suspended on a frame in a cart and was used to hack at the defenders while they tried to immobilize the ram.

corbeau à griffe A pole with strong nippers or pincers used for seizing and breaking objects.

corbel A projection, usually made of stone

Coronado. (*U.S. Navy.*)

or timber, from the face of a wall.

cordite A traditional British propellant. It is a double-base propellant in the form of cords and is composed of 65 percent guncotton, 30 percent nitroglycerin, and 5 percent mineral jelly. Cordite is used by some foreign nations, and to some extent in the United States, as a propellant.

cordon 1. A line of men placed at intervals to prevent others from passing. **2.** In fortifications, the ornamental projecting stonework at the junction of a parapet with rampart or with a sloping wall.

cored shot Formerly, a hollow cast projectile having a smaller cavity than a regular shell.

corium Leather body armor, consisting of overlapping scales or flaps, first used by the Romans.

corned powder When gunpowder is ground, moistened, and formed into grains, it is called "corned powder." If it is left dry, the resultant dustlike material is called "serpentine powder."

corner A World War II radar reflector consisting of four sheets of aluminum foil bent at right angles to one another to form a cross. When trailed from a small ship by a low-flying balloon, it gave the impression (to coastal and shipboard radar operators) of a large warship.

cornet 1. A sixteenth-century subdivision of cavalry. It consisted of from 100 to 300 men. **2.** Formerly, the fifth grade of commissioned officer in a British cavalry troop. He carried the standard. **3.** A nautical signaling flag or pennant. Formerly, a signal for all hands to report aboard a naval vessel at once; a general message from a flagship to a squadron; a signal for every ship to prepare to receive a message.

cornice An **astragal,** which see.

cornice ring Formerly, a ring next behind the muzzle ring on a cannon.

cornus A type of Roman battering ram with a hook.

Coronado The Consolidated PB2Y-2/5 four-engine long-range maritime reconnaissance-bomber flying boat developed for the U.S. Navy and first flown in 1937. It had a crew of 10, and armament consisting of eight .50 cal. machine guns, and it carried eight 1,000-lb bombs internally and four 1,000-lb bombs, four 650-lb depth charges, or two torpedoes externally. It flew at speeds of 223 mph and had a range of 1,370 mi.

corporal The lowest noncommissioned officer; the rank next below sergeant.

Corporal A mobile surface-to-surface liquid-propellant guided missile with nuclear-warhead capability. It is designed to attack targets up to a range of 75 nautical miles and is designated as MGM-5.

corps de garde Formerly, a body of guards. Later, the place where they stayed, such as the guardroom or guardhouse.

corps d'élite A corps or body of specially picked men.

corpsman An enlisted man in the U.S. Navy trained to give first aid and apprentice medical treatment.

corps of cadets The body of cadets under instruction at West Point (the United States Military Academy).

Corps of Engineers An arm of the U.S. Army. Its peacetime duties include the construction of lighthouses and the improvement of rivers, harbors, and waterways.

corps troops Troops assigned or attached to a corps, but not a part of one of the

Corsair. (*Vought Aeronautics Company.*)

divisions that make up the corps.

corrected azimuth The azimuth of the axis of the bore of a gun firing on a moving target after allowances have been made for atmospheric, materiel, and other variable conditions.

corrected deflection The horizontal angle between the line of sight and the axis of the bore of the gun after allowances have been made for atmospheric, materiel, and other variable conditions.

corrected range Actual range with allowances made for weather conditions, variation in ammunition, wear in the gun, or any other variations from standard conditions so that the projectile will carry to the target.

correction **1.** Any change in firing data to bring the mean point of impact or burst closer to the target. **2.** A communication proword to indicate that an error in data has been announced and that corrected data will follow.

corresponding range **1.** The range corresponding to a given angle of elevation of

a weapon. **2.** Specifically, the range corresponding to the lowest trajectory which passes safely over the heads of friendly troops.

corridor In fortifications, the covered way.

Corsair The Vought F4U Corsair was a single-seat single-engine shipboard interceptor and fighter-bomber developed for the U.S. Navy and first flown in May 1940. It was the first U.S. fighter to exceed 400 mph in level flight. In the Pacific, Corsairs destroyed 2,140 Japanese aircraft at a loss of only 189. The F4U-4 was powered by a 2,450-hp engine and flew at speeds of 446 mph. It was armed with six .50 cal. machine guns and two 1,000-lb bombs or eight 5-in. rockets. It had a span of about 41 ft, a length of 33 ft, and a height of 15 ft.

Corsair II The U.S. Ling-Temco-Vought A-7 Corsair II is a single-seat carrier-based light attack fighter developed for the U.S. Navy and first flown in 1965. Powered by a single jet engine, it has a speed of 607 knots and a normal radius of action of 620

mi. It is armed with two 20mm cannons and provisions for various combinations of rockets, missiles, and bombs (up to 15,000 lb of ordnance).

corselet Armor for the body, usually consisting of breastplate, backpiece, and often a gorget.

corsesque See **chauve-souris.**

cortellaggio A falchion, or large single-edged sword that often widens toward the point.

corvette **1.** Originally, a small warship with sails and having a row of guns along one deck only. It ranked next below a frigate and was called a "sloop of war" in the United States. **2.** An escort vessel, originally British or Canadian, smaller than a destroyer and armed with antisubmarine and antiaircraft weapons. About 150 ft long, they carried about one-half the crew of a destroyer.

corvus A huge hook mounted on the prow of a Roman warship. It was used to grapple on an enemy vessel so that a bridge could be dropped for boarding.

Corvus A U.S. Navy air-to-surface missile with a range of about 100 mi. It is powered with a prepackaged liquid propellant and is designed for use by carrier aircraft as a standoff weapon against heavily defended strongpoints.

Cossack post A four-man outguard which posted a single sentinel.

Cossacks Russian people of the steppes; cavalry troops first organized in the armies of the Czars.

Coston's lights Pyrotechnics in various colors used for night signaling. They were invented by B. Franklin Coston and patented by his widow in 1859. They were superseded largely by the Very lights, which can be projected into the air.

Cougar The Grumman F9F Cougar was a single-seat single-engine naval carrier-fighter that was a sweptwing modification of the straight-wing Grumman Panther. The aircraft had a speed of 712 mph and was armed with four 20mm cannon and under-wing racks for four 1,000-lb bombs.

couillard A machine used for throwing stones. See **clide.**

council of war An assembly of officers gathered to advise the commanding officer in matters of importance.

countdown The period of time during which final preparation and checking are done before the firing of a missile. The term is also applied to the process of "counting down," or indicating periodically the time remaining before "zero," which is the firing time.

counterapproach A trench made by the defenders of a fortified place to meet the approaches of the attackers.

counterarch A vertical arch connecting the tops of the counterforts.

Corsair II. (*Vought Aeronautics Company.*)

counterattack An attack by a part or all of a defending force against an enemy attacking force for such specific purposes as regaining ground lost or cutting off or destroying enemy advance units and with the general objective of denying to the enemy the attainment of his purpose in attacking. In sustained defensive operations, it is undertaken to restore the battle position and is directed at limited objectives.

counterbalance A spring-loaded device which aids in opening and closing a breechblock while at its loading angle.

counterbattery fire Fire delivered against active enemy weapons or fire-control stations.

counter-countermeasures (CCM) Warfare or equipment designed to impair or reduce the effectiveness of enemy countermeasures.

countered minefield A minefield expected to be swept or hunted by the enemy.

counterespionage A category of counterintelligence, the objective of which is the detection and neutralization of foreign espionage.

counterfire **1.** Fire delivered in answer to the fire of an attacker. **2.** Fire intended to destroy or neutralize enemy weapons.

counterforce The employment of strategic air and missile forces in an effort to destroy, or render impotent, selected military capabilities of an enemy force under any of the circumstances by which hostilities may be initiated.

counterforts Interior buttresses made to strengthen masonry revetments.

counterguard An outwork, not necessarily permanent, that protected the faces of a bastion or ravelin from breaching fire. The term may also refer to a part of a sword guard between the hand and the blade.

counterguerrilla warfare Operations and activities conducted by armed forces, paramilitary forces, or nonmilitary agencies of a government against guerrillas.

counterinsurgency Those military, paramilitary, political, economic, psychological, and civic actions taken by a government to defeat subversive insurgency.

counterinsurgency aircraft A light armed airplane with good maneuverability and low-altitude flying characteristics. Aircraft of this type are also used for reconnaissance and forward air-control duties.

counterintelligence That aspect of intelligence activity which is devoted to destroying the effectiveness of inimical foreign intelligence activities and to protecting information against espionage, individuals against subversion, and installations or materiel against sabotage.

countermarch The movement of troops back over the ground which they previously occupied or passed over. The maneuver whereby a marching body changes direc-

Cougar. (*Grumman Aerospace Corporation.*)

tion so as to reverse the direction of march.

countermeasures That form of military science which by the employment of devices and/or techniques has as its objective the impairment of the operational effectiveness of enemy activity.

countermeasures set A complete electronic set specifically designed to provide facilities for intercepting and analyzing electromagnetic energy propagated by a transmitter (or transmitters) and to provide a source of radio-frequency signals which prevent the enemy from using his electronic equipment effectively.

countermining **1.** The detonation of mines by nearby explosions, either accidentally or deliberately. **2.** The digging of mine tunnels by defending forces to destroy the mines of the besieging forces.

countermining distance The limiting distance between mines which will prevent chain countermining.

countermune In fortifications, a wall built in front of another wall to strengthen it.

counteroffensive A large-scale offensive undertaken by a defending force to seize the initiative from the attacking force.

counterparole A word sometimes used in addition to the password.

counterpoise A mechanism that counterbalances the weight of the breechblock of a large gun, making it easier to open and close.

counterpoise gun carriage A system in which a gun is moved into battery by the action of a counterpoise that is raised by the recoil of the gun.

counterpreparation fire Intensive prearranged fire delivered when the imminence of the enemy attack is discovered. It is designed to break up enemy formations; disorganize the enemy's systems of commands, communications, and observation; decrease the effectiveness of his artillery preparation; and impair his offensive spirit.

counterreconnaissance All measures taken to prevent hostile observation of a force, area, or place.

counterround An unexpected extra round made to assure that sentinels are vigilant.

countersabotage Action designed to destroy the effectiveness of foreign sabotage activities through the process of identifying, penetrating, manipulating, neutralizing, or repressing individuals, groups, or organizations conducting or capable of conducting such activities.

counterscarp In fortifications, the vertical

counterinsurgency aircraft, the Cessna A-37. (*Cessna Aircraft Company.*)

Courageous. (*The Imperial War Museum.*)

side of the ditch nearest the besiegers. In permanent works it was faced to make the descent into the ditch more difficult.

counterscarp galleries Galleries in the counterscarp at the salients. They were built to flank the ditch.

countersign A secret challenge and its reply.

countersubversion That part of counter-intelligence which is devoted to destroying the effectiveness of inimical subversive activities through the detection, identification, exploitation, penetration, manipulation, deception, and repression of individuals, groups, or organizations conducting or capable of conducting such activities.

countertrenches Trenches made against besiegers and having their parapets turned against the enemy's approaches. They are enfiladed from several places so that they can be rendered useless if occupied by the enemy.

counterwork In siege operations, fortifications constructed to oppose those of an enemy.

County A class of British guided-missile armed destroyers of 5,440 tons standard displacement completed in 1962–1966. They have a length of 520 ft, a beam of 54 ft, a speed of 32.5 knots, and a complement of 471 men. They are armed with four 4.5-in. and two 20mm guns, one Seaslug twin launcher, and two Seacat quadruple launchers. One helicopter is also carried.

coup de grâce A merciful blow. The death-blow dealt by an executioner or by a knight to dispatch a mortally wounded adversary.

coup de main A sudden or unexpected movement or attack.

coupures In fortifications, passages cut through the glacis to facilitate sallies on the part of the besieged.

Courageous A class of British 22,500-ton aircraft carriers completed in 1916. There were two ships in the class, and they had a length of 786 ft, a flight-deck width of 100 ft, a speed of 31 knots, and a comple-

ment of 1,216 men. They carried 48 aircraft. The class included *Courageous* (sunk by a German submarine in September 1939) and *Glorious* (sunk by the German battleships *Scharnhorst* and *Gneisenau* in June 1940).

courier A messenger (usually a commissioned or warrant officer) responsible for the secure physical transmission and delivery of documents and material; generally called a "command courier" or "local courier." At one time this term referred to a light-armed horseman or cavalryman.

course The direction or path of travel of an aircraft or ship; the compasss heading being steered.

courtel A weapon that served as both a knife and a dagger.

Courtney A class of U.S. escort ships (DE) identical with the **Dealey** class, which see.

courts-martial Military courts of law convened to try military personnel.

coustil a croc A fifteenth-century short sword with a straight, double-edged blade.

coustilliers Fifteenth-century light infantry.

couteau A large knife. Also, a two-edged dagger.

couteau-de-brèche See **glaive**.

coutel An obsolete term for a knife that served as both an eating utensil and a weapon.

coutere, couter A piece of armor to protect the elbow.

cover **1.** The action by land, air, or sea forces to protect by offense, defense, or threat of either. **2.** Shelter or protection, either natural or artificial. **3.** To maintain a continuous receiver watch with transmitter calibrated and available, but not necessarily available for immediate use. **4.** Photographs or other recorded images which show a particular area of ground. **5.** To keep fighters between force-base and contact designated at distance stated from force-base (e.g., "cover bogey" 27 to 30 mi). **6.** The protective guise used by a person, organization, or

installation to prevent identification with clandestine activities.

covered bridge gun See **Requa battery.**

covered way In fortifications, a road or broad path running along the top of the counterscarp. It is protected by an embankment whose outer slope forms the glacis. It is so named because soldiers standing in it cannot be seen by the besiegers. It was formerly called "covert way." Enlarged places, called "places of arms," are made in the covered way at certain spots to facilitate defensive activities or sorties.

covering fire **1.** Fire used to protect troops when they are within range of enemy small arms. **2.** In amphibious operations, fire delivered prior to the landing to cover preparatory operations such as underwater demolitions or minesweeping.

covering force **1.** A force operating apart from the main force for the purpose of intercepting, engaging, delaying, disorganizing, and deceiving the enemy before he can attack the force covered. **2.** Any body or detachment of troops which provides security for a larger force by observation, reconnaissance, attack, defense, or any combination of these methods.

covert operations Operations which are so planned and executed as to conceal the identity of, or permit plausible denial by, the sponsor. They differ from clandestine operations in that emphasis is placed on concealment of the identity of the sponsor rather than on concealment of the operation.

covert way See **covered way.**

C.O.W. 37mm aircraft cannon A World War I development by the British Coventry Ordnance Works. It was used to a limited extent in the war, but was unpopular because of the recoil of the weapon. (In one case, involving a Voisin aircraft, four shots were fired, and the wings came off the airplane. It crashed, killing all the occupants.) It was a recoil-operated air-cooled weapon with a rate of fire of 60 rounds per minute. It weighed 140 lb and was fed from a five-round magazine.

CP Command post.

Cr (Crescent) A class of British destroyers. See **CA**.

crabs A German innovation of World War II that consisted of armored steel pillboxes housing two men and a machine gun. They were towed on removable wheels to their places of installation.

crab tanks A type of World War II tank used for exploding mines. In practice, short lengths of chain were attached to a revolving drum on the front of the vehicle. As the chains beat the ground, the shock caused the mines to explode.

cradle The nonrecoiling structure of a weapon that houses the recoiling parts and rotates about the trunnions to elevate the gun.

crakys An ancient term for very large guns.

crampet The tip of a sword scabbard.

cranequin A crank-operated rack-and-pinion device used to draw back the cord of a crossbow.

craquemarte A seventeenth century heavy cutlass used at sea.

crash dolly A wheeled device for moving crashed aircraft on the flight deck of an aircraft carrier.

crash helmet A heavy padded helmet worn as protection against head injuries in a tank or an aircraft.

crash-land To land an airplane in such a way that the plane is damaged. The need for a crash landing may arise because of some difficulty with the landing gear.

Crate The NATO code name for the Ilyushin IL-14 twin-engine (piston) medium-range transport in service with the Soviet Air Force and the forces of more than 20 other countries. It carries up to 32 passengers and has a range of 937 mi and a speed of 258 mph.

cratering charge A demolition charge for use in blasting craters in roads and for similar demolition.

C rations U.S. military field rations consisting of a carton containing various types of canned goods, chocolate, toilet paper, cigarettes, etc.

Craven A class of U.S. destroyer. See **McCall and Craven**.

Crawfish (code) A code name for a type of electronic bomb release by which the leader of a formation may simultaneously release all the bombs carried by the aircraft in the formation.

C.R.D.A. Cant Z.501 Gabbiano An Italian single-engine four- or five-seat light reconnaissance-bomber flying boat. It entered service in 1936.

C.R.D.A. Cant Z.506B See **Airone**.

creeping attack A technique in ASW operations in which two ships are used. One makes a noiseless approach toward the target, using target information furnished by the other. The attacking ship does not echo-range.

creeping barrage A barrage in which the fire of all units participating remains in the same relative position throughout and which advances in steps of one line at a time. It is also called a "rolling barrage."

creeping method of adjustment A method of getting the range of an enemy position close to friendly troops by firing the first set of shots too far and then gradually and carefully shortening the range.

cremaille A parapet with a sawtooth pattern on the inside line.

crémaillère An indented or zigzagged trench line.

crénaux Small loopholes made through the walls of fortified places. They are narrow toward the enemy but broad within.

crenel 1. One of the embrasures alternating with merlons in a battlement; an indentation. 2. The peak of a helmet.

crenelated Furnished with battlements.

Créole A class of French submarines of 910 tons standard surface displacement completed in 1949–1952. They had a speed of 10 knots submerged and were armed with ten 21.7-in. torpedo tubes and one 3.5-in. deck gun.

cressit A small dagger.

Cressy A class of 12,000-ton British cruisers completed in 1901–1903. There were six ships in the class: *Cressy, Sutlej, Bacchante, Euryalus, Aboukir,* and *Hogue.* They had a length of 454 ft, a complement of 700 men, a speed of about 18 knots, and main armament consisting of two 9.2-in. and twelve 6-in. guns. On September 17, 1914, *Cressy, Aboukir,* and *Hogue* were sunk in the space of 1 hour by torpedoes from a single German submarine, the *U-9.* Fourteen hundred lives were lost.

Crested Dragon A code name for U.S. Air Force chemical and biological munitions capability and equipment.

Creusot gun Any cannon made at Le Creusot, in France, the location of the Schneider ordnance works.

crew The men who operate a ship, boat, aircraft, turret, or gun.

crew-served Of or pertaining to anything served or operated by a crew rather than an individual, e.g., a weapon operated by a crew of two or more persons.

cric A **cranequin,** which see.

crinet Armor for a horse's neck.

Cristobal .30 cal. automatic carbine M1962 A weapon developed in the Dominican Republic and similar in design to Beretta weapons. It utilizes the .30 cal. (U.S. M1 carbine) cartridge and operates on the delayed blowback principle. It has selective fire, a muzzle velocity of 1,870 fps, and a cyclic rate of fire of around 600 rounds per minute. The folding stock model weighs 8.2 lb and is 25.5 in. long when folded. The length of the barrel is 12.2 in.

critical altitude The altitude beyond which an aircraft or air-breathing guided missile ceases to perform satisfactorily.

critical intelligence Intelligence which is crucial and requires the immediate attention of the commander. It is required to enable the commander to make decisions

cranequin. (*The Smithsonian Institution, R. G. Packard Collection.*)

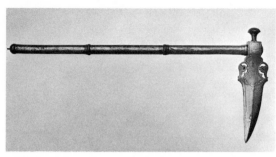

crowbill. (*The Metropolitan Museum of Art, bequest of George C. Stone, 1936.*)

which will provide a timely and appropriate response to actions by the potential or actual enemy. It includes but is not limited to the following: (1) Strong indications of the imminent outbreak of hostilities of any type (warning or attack). (2) Aggression of any nature against a friendly country. (3) Indications or use of nuclear-biological-chemical weapons. (4) Significant events within potential enemy countries that may lead to modification of nuclear strike plans.

critically wounded A nonevacuable patient.

critical mass The minimum mass, when related to a specific shape and environment, of a fissionable material necessary to sustain a nuclear chain reaction.

critical point 1. A key geographic point or position important to the success of an operation. 2. A crisis or turning point in an operation. 3. A selected point along a line of march used for reference in giving instructions. 4. A point at which there is a change of direction or change in slope in a ridge or stream. 5. Any point along a route of march where interference with a troop movement may occur.

critical zone The area over which a bombing plane engaged in horizontal or glide bombing must maintain straight flight so that the bombsight can be operated properly and the bombs dropped accurately.

crochert An ancient hackbut or hand cannon.

Croix de Guerre A French bronze cross awarded to officers and men for gallant action in war. It was instituted on April 9, 1915. The term also refers to a Belgian cross, similar to the Military Cross, instituted on October 25, 1905.

Cromwell IV A British cruiser tank of World War II. It was one of the fastest tanks of the war (up to 40 mph) because it was powered by a modified Merlin aircraft engine. It had a weight of about 27.5

cruciform hilt. (*The Smithsonian Institution, R. G. Packard Collection.*)

tons, a crew of five, and main armament consisting of one 75mm gun.

crossbar shot Two spheres, hemispheres, or cylinders connected by an iron rod.

crossbow A weapon used at least as early as the eleventh century for discharging quarrels, stones, etc. It is formed of a bow set crosswise on a stock. See also **arbalest.**

Crossbow The World War II Allied code word covering German preparations for, and Allied measures against, attacks by rockets and pilotless aircraft. See **V-1** and **V-2.**

crossbowman A soldier armed with a crossbow.

cross fire Two or more intersecting lines of gunfire.

cross hair An inscribed line or a strand of hair, wire, silk, or the like used in an optical sight for accurate sighting.

crossing target A moving target that crosses the line of sight at any angle. In firing at a crossing target, the firer must aim ahead of, or lead, the target so that the paths of the target and bullet will meet.

crossing the T See **capping the T.**

Crosslegs The NATO code name for a type of Chinese D-band early-warning and surveillance radar.

cross-level To level a weapon such as a mortar at right angles to the line of sight.

Cross of Merit An Italian award for gallantry in action, instituted January 19, 1922.

Crotale A French surface-to-air missile designed to attack low-flying aircraft. It has a launch weight of about 165 lb, a warhead weight of 33 lb, and a range of over 5 mi.

crotchet In fortifications, a passage around a traverse in the covered way.

crowbill A kind of ax with a blade usually at right angles to a long handle. It has a short, pointed blade.

crown In fortifications, the process of establishing works on the crest of the glacis or the summit of the breach.

crow's foot See **caltrop.**

crow's nest A lookout station aloft. In naval practice it is generally on the foremast of a ship.

Crozier wire-wound gun A gun consisting of a steel tube wrapped with steel wire under tension and finished by shrinking on a jacket and hoops.

cruciform hilt A sword or dagger with a plain crosspiece set at right angles to the hilt.

cruise missile A guided missile, the major portion of whose flight path to its target is conducted at approximately constant velocity; it depends on the dynamic reaction of air for lift and upon propulsion forces to balance drag.

cruiser An eighteenth-century privateer. In modern naval usage, a large armored warship having a minimum of protection

and capable of high speed.

cruising range The endurance of a ship in nautical miles at moderate or cruising speed.

crupper The steel plates or leather armor protecting a horse's hindquarters.

Crusader 1. The Ling-Temco-Vought F-8 Crusader is a single-seat carrier-based jet fighter developed for the U.S. Navy and first flown in 1955. It has a two-position variable-incidence wing and achieves speeds of about Mach 2. It is armed with four 20mm Colt cannons in the fuselage and up to four Sidewinder missiles mounted externally. 2. Another name for the British tank, medium, Mk III, which was introduced in 1938–1940 for use in armored divisions. It carried a crew of three and was armed with a six-pounder gun and a 7.93mm Besa tank machine gun. It had a maximum speed of about 27 mph and was first committed in the Western Desert of Africa in June 1941.

Crusader I A British cruiser tank of World War II. It had a crew of five, a weight of about 18 tons, and main armament consisting of one two-pounder gun. (This tank was powered by a modernized U.S. Liberty aircraft engine of World War I.)

Crusades Military expeditions by the Christian powers to recover the Holy Land from the Moslems. These expeditions took place in the eleventh, twelfth, and thirteenth centuries.

Crusty The NATO code name for the Soviet Tupolev Tu-134 rear-engine twin-jet transport first seen in 1964. It has a speed of 559 mph and accommodations for 64 passengers.

cryptanalysis The study of encrypted or coded texts; the steps or processes involved in converting encrypted text into plain text without initial knowledge of the key employed in the encryption.

cryptographer One who solves or deciphers cryptograms or decodes any secret communications.

Crystal Night The designation of the evening of raids in November 1938 that launched Hitler's campaign to eliminate German Jews. It was so named because the windows in thousands of Jewish shops and homes were broken by the Nazis.

CS 1. The U.S. military designation for the war gas **O-chlorobenzylmalononitrile,** which see. 2. A U.S. Navy scout cruiser.

CS-1 and CS-2 U.S. riot-control agents.

CSAWS Close Support Artillery Weapon System. A U.S. system that uses the M109 self-propelled 155mm howitzer to provide field-artillery direct fire support to infantry, mechanized, and armored units with mobility similar to that of supported weapons.

CSS A U.S. Navy Confederate States ship.

C stoff The German term for **methylchlorsulfonate,** which see, a tear gas used in

World War I.

CTB U.S. Navy coast torpedo boat.

Cub The NATO code name for the Antonov An-12, which is a cargo-carrying version of the An-10 (Cat) first flown in 1957. The military version is used by the Soviet Air Force as a paratroop and freight transport and is equipped with a tail gunner's position.

cuirass A piece of armor. Originally, it was a thick leather garment that covered the body from neck to waist. Later it was made of bronze and finally of steel. It usually consisted of a gorget and a breastplate and backpiece, fastened together with straps and buckles.

cuirassier A mounted soldier wearing a cuirass; specifically, a soldier of a certain type of heavy cavalry in the French and other modern European armies.

cuir-bouilli Leather that has been hardened by boiling in oil. Because of its lightness, it was often used as a substitute for iron or steel armor, particularly in the sixteenth century.

cuisse A type of plate armor for the protection of the thighs. It was first introduced in the fourteenth century.

cul-de-sac A French term meaning "bottom of the bag" and referring to a passageway or a place having only one outlet. An army may find itself in such a position, with no way out but to the front.

culverin Originally, a rude sort of hand cannon. Later, in the sixteenth and seventeenth centuries, a long cannon firing a shot weighing 18 lb.

culverineer A soldier armed with, or in charge of, a culverin.

cunette A trench in a ditch or moat for drainage. It could also be used for defense.

Crusader. (*U.S. Navy.*)

culverin. (*The Metropolitan Museum of Art, gift of William H. Riggs, 1913.*)

cup-hilt A form of hilt found on rapiers of the first half of the seventeenth century and sometimes later.

cup primer An early primer in which the rim of the cartridge was crushed when fired.

curly torpedo A torpedo which steers a sinuous course among the ships of a convoy to increase the chance of a random hit.

currier A seventeenth-century gun having the same bore as a **caliver,** which see, but with a longer barrel. It was often swivel-mounted.

currus falcatus A scythed war chariot.

curtain **1.** In fortifications, a bastioned front connecting two neighboring bastions. **2.** A smoke concentration laid down between friendly and enemy lines.

curtain angle The angle formed by a flank with a curtain.

curtal An obsolete short-barreled cannon.

Curtiss H.12 A U.S. four-place twin-engine biplane flying boat in production in 1916. It was armed with three machine guns and carried a bombload consisting of two 230-lb bombs or four 100-lb bombs. Some 50 of this type were supplied to the Royal Navy Air Service.

Curtiss JN Series A U.S. two-place single-engine biplane trainer first flown in 1915. Nicknamed "Jenny," the most widely produced version was the JN-4 type, of which more than 5,500 were produced. Some 1,035 JN-6H types were built, many of which remained in service with the U.S. Army until 1927. The JN-4 had a speed of 75 mph, a wingspan of 43 ft 7 in., a length of 27 ft 4 in., and a height of 10 ft 6 in. (Picture, next page.)

Curtiss N-9 A U.S. two-place single-engine

biplane seaplane version of the Curtiss Jenny. See **Curtiss JN Series.** It had a speed of about 70 mph.

curved fire Fire with low velocity and relatively large curvature of the trajectory at normal ranges.

cutlass A type of backsword; a short, curved cutting sword. In the eighteenth and nineteenth centuries the term referred specifically to such a sword as used by sailors. As late as 1969 the U.S. Navy ordered cutlasses for drill and ceremonies. (Picture, next page.)

Cutlass The Chance Vought F7U Cutlass is a single-seat jet fighter developed for the

cuirass. (*The Metropolitan Museum of Art, gift of George D. Pratt, 1926.*)

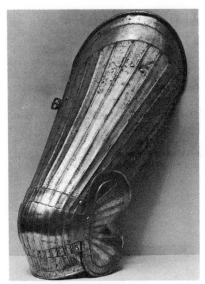

cuisse. (*The Metropolitan Museum of Art, gift of Prince Albrecht Radziwill, 1927.*)

Curtiss JN Series. (*U.S. Air Force.*)

Cutlass. (*Vought Aeronautics Company.*)

cutlass. (*The Smithsonian Institution, G. Heilborn Collection.*)

U.S. Navy and first flown in 1948. It was the first production naval aircraft to achieve supersonic flight. It was armed with four 20mm cannons, plus other armament of rockets and bombs.

cutoff 1. The deliberate shutting off of a reaction engine. **2.** In certain automatic weapons, a mechanical device to convert from automatic to semiautomatic operation.

cutter A small armed vessel in the United States Coast Guard.

cuvette In fortifications, a **cunette,** which see.

CV A U.S. Navy aircraft carrier.

CVA An attack aircraft carrier.

CVAN A U.S. Navy attack aircraft carrier, nuclear-powered.

CVB A U.S. Navy large aircraft carrier.

CVE A U.S. Navy escort aircraft carrier.

CVHA A U.S. Navy assault helicopter aircraft carrier.

CVHE A U.S. Navy escort helicopter aircraft carrier.

CVL A U.S. Navy small aircraft carrier.

CVS A U.S. Navy antisubmarine support aircraft carrier.

CVT A U.S. Navy training aircraft carrier.

CVU A U.S. Navy utility aircraft carrier.

CX The U.S. military designation for the war gas **phosgene oxime,** which see.

cyanogen chloride (CK) This war gas is a blood agent and has a quick-acting casualty effect. It is converted into hydrogen cyanide in the body. See **blood agents** and **hydrogen cyanide (AC).**

cyclic rate The rate at which a succession of movements repeats itself, applied especially to the rate of fire of an automatic weapon; the maximum rate of fire for a given automatic weapon.

cyclonite (RDX) A white crystalline explosive having high sensitivity and brisance. Cyclonite is used with other explosives or substances to form explosive mixtures and compositions. It is commonly used in bombs and shells.

cyclotol A high explosive composed of RDX (cyclonite) and TNT. Mixtures up to 75 percent RDX can be loaded by casting.

cylinder The rotating chambered breech of a revolver. A swing-out cylinder is one that swings out for easier loading.

cylinder stop The recesses in a revolver cylinder that are engaged by a lever to stop rotation and properly align the cylinder with the barrel.

CZ Combat zone.

czakany A type of war hammer used in Hungary and Poland. It was equipped with a sharp, beaklike fluke.

Czech 7.62mm assault rifle Model 58 This weapon is somewhat similar to the Soviet AK47 in appearance, but is different internally. It has selective semiautomatic and full automatic fire, with a cyclic rate of fire of 700 to 800 rounds per minute. The muzzle velocity is 2,300 fps, the overall length of the wooden-stock version is 33 in. (with folding stock in retracted position, the length is 25 in.), the barrel is 15.8 in., and the weight is 8.75 lb. Sights are adjustable from 100 to 800 meters. It is the standard shoulder weapon of the Czech Army.

Czech 7.62mm light machine gun Model 52 This weapon became standard for Czech forces in 1952. A slight modification in 1957 resulted in the Model 52/57, which is chambered for the Soviet-designed 7.62mm M43 cartridge. The weapon is gas-operated and can operate with either a 25-round box magazine or a 100-round belt. It weighs 17.6 lb unloaded and has an overall length of 41 in., a barrel length of 21.3 in., and a muzzle velocity of 2,450 fps. The cyclic rate of fire is 1,140 rounds per minute with belt and 900 rounds per minute with magazine.

Czech 7.62mm machine gun Model 59 This weapon is regarded as a general-purpose machine gun insofar as it can be used on a bipod as a light machine gun and on a tripod as a heavy machine gun. In these applications, light and heavy barrels are employed. With the heavy barrel (which is 27.3 in. long) and a tripod mount, the weight is 42.4 lb. With the light barrel (which is 23.3 in. long) and a bipod mount, the weight is 19.1 lb. It is gas-operated, has a cyclic rate of fire of 700 to 800 rounds per minute, and is fed by a 50-round link belt.

Czech 7.62mm pistol Model 52 The current service pistol of Czechoslovakia, this weapon was designed to fire the Czech-

CVA, the U.S.S. *Corregidor.* (*U.S. Navy.*)

made version of the Soviet 7.62mm Type P pistol cartridge. Loaded, the weapon weighs 2.31 lb; it has an overall length of 8.25 in., a barrel length of 4.71 in., and a muzzle velocity of about 1,600 fps. The magazine has a capacity of eight cartridges.

Czech 7.62mm rifle Model 52 This weapon was introduced in 1952 and utilizes a gas system similar to that of the German Mkb 42W. It has an overall length of 39.37 in. and a barrel length of 20.66 in. Its loaded weight is 9.8 lb. It uses a 10-round box magazine and has a muzzle velocity of 2,440 fps. A variation of this weapon was the 52/57, which was chambered for the Soviet-designed 7.62mm M43 cartridge.

Czech 7.62mm submachine gun Model 24 and Model 26 The Model 24 and Model 26 submachine guns superseded the Model 23 and Model 25 (9 mm) as the standard submachine guns used by the Czech Army. The 24 and 26 were adopted in 1952. The 7.62mm cartridge used by these weapons is loaded to achieve velocities about 20 percent higher than the standard Soviet 7.62mm round, although the latter can be fired without problem. The Model 24 corresponds with the earlier Model 23, since both have wooden stocks. The Model 26 corresponds with the Model 25, as both have the same folding stocks. The cyclic rate of fire is 600 rounds per minute. The length with the wooden stock is 26.60 in.; with the metal stock retracted, the length is 17.50 in. Muzzle velocity is 1,800 fps, and the weight, with a 32-round clip, is 8.55 lb.

Czech 7.65mm pistol Model 27 The CZ (Ceskoslovenska Zbrojovka) pistol incorporates a modified Colt barrel-mounting system and lockwork based on a Mauser Model 1910 design. It has a magazine capacity of eight cartridges, is 6.3 in. in length, has a barrel length of 3.9 in., and weighs approximately 25 oz. Certain World War II versions may have the German markings of Bohmische Waffenfabrik A.G. Prague. The Germans called it "Pistol

27(t)" and used it extensively during the war. This was made in the largest quantity of all pre-World War II Czech pistols.

Czech 7.65mm pistol M1950 This pistol is similar in functioning to the Walther PP and PPK. It was used as the service pistol in Czechoslovakia after World War II. It has a weight of about 1.5 lb, an overall length of 6.8 in., a barrel length of 3.8 in., and a muzzle velocity of 919 fps. The magazine holds eight rounds.

Czech 7.65mm submachine gun Model 61 Also called the "Skorpion," this weapon might be described as a machine pistol since it can be fired from one hand as well as from the shoulder. It is made for a 7.65mm (.32 ACP) cartridge, which is relatively low-powered, and it is therefore more easily controlled in automatic fire. The weapon has an overall length with stock folded of 10.62 in. and a barrel length of 4.5 in. The weight of the weapon is 2.87 lb, the muzzle velocity is 1,040 fps, and the cyclic rate of fire is 750 rounds per minute. It can be fired selectively in full or semi-automatic operation. Ten- and twenty-round magazines are used with this weapon.

Czech 7.92mm heavy machine gun Model 37 (ZB53) This weapon is the forerunner of the British-made Besa tank machine gun. It is air-cooled and gas-operated and has two cyclic rates of fire—450 to 550 rpm and

cylinder. (*The Smithsonian Institution, National Museum Collection.*)

700 rpm. It has a weight of 41.8 lb, an overall length of 43.5 in., and a barrel length of 26.7 in. It is fed by a metallic link belt with 100- and 200-round capacity and has a muzzle velocity of about 2,600 fps.

Czech 7.92mm light machine gun ZB26 and ZB30 Weapons developed by Vaclav Holek in 1924 and modified to become the Praga Model 24 and then ZB26. The ZB26 and ZB30 were used in 24 countries throughout the world and represent the ancestors of the Bren gun. The ZB26 was

Czech 7.62mm submachine gun Model 24. (*Military Historical Institute, Prague.*)

Czech 9mm Parabellum submachine gun Model 25. (*Military Historical Institute, Prague.*)

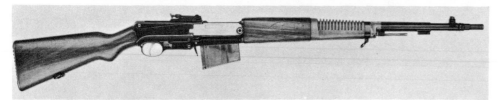

Czech 7.92mm rifle ZH29. (*Military Historical Institute, Prague.*)

the standard light machine gun of the Czech Army. Many ZB26 and ZB30 guns were used during World War II by the Germans. The ZB26 is a gas-operated weapon with an overall length of 45.8 in. and a barrel length of 23.7 in. It has a muzzle velocity of 2,500 fps and a cyclic rate of fire of 550 rounds per minute. The loaded weight is 21.28 lb, and the magazine has a capacity of 20 cartridges.

Czech 7.92mm rifle Model 24 This Mauser rifle was standard in Czechoslovakia prior to World War II. It uses the basic Mauser 98 action and differs from the German Kar 98K mainly in fittings. It

weighs 8.98 lb and has an overall length of 43.3 in. and a barrel length of 23.2 in. The magazine is nondetachable and has a capacity of five rounds. This rifle has a muzzle velocity of 2,700 fps and sights graduated from 300 to 2,000 meters. This Czech Mauser was designated as the Model 24(t) by the German Army, and at the beginning of World War II, 11 divisions were equipped with it and other Czech weapons.

Czech 7.92mm rifle Model 98/29 This was a Czech-made Mauser sold in large numbers to Iran. See **Iranian 7.92mm rifle Model 1938.**

Czech 7.92mm rifle ZH29 The first Czech

semiautomatic rifle to be exported in any quantity, this weapon was introduced in 1929 and was used to some extent by Ethiopia and Thailand. It is gas-operated and has a muzzle velocity of 2,650 fps. It weighs about 10 lb and has an overall length of 45.5 in. and a barrel length of 21.5 in. It uses 10- and 25-round box magazines and has sights adjustable from 100 to 1,400 meters.

Czech 7.92mm rifle ZK420 This weapon was first developed in 1942, with subsequent modifications made until the late 1940s. It has an overall length of 41.73 in. and a barrel length of 21.65 in. It weighs 10.58 lb and has a muzzle velocity of about 2,700 fps and a 10-round detachable box magazine.

Czech 9mm Parabellum submachine gun Model 23 and Model 25 These models went into production in 1949 and were produced until 1952, by which time over 100,000 had been made. Originally issued to Czech troops, they were also sold in large numbers to Syria in the 1950s and to Cuba in the 1960s. The Model 23 was made with a wooden stock, and the Model 25 has a folding metal stock. Both fire the 9mm Parabellum cartridge and have selective full automatic and semiautomatic fire. The overall length with the wooden stock is 27 in.; with the folding stock retracted, the length is 17.50 in. Barrel length is 11.20 in. The loaded weight of the weapon is about 8.50 lb, and the muzzle velocity is approximately 1,470 fps. Magazines are available in capacities of 24 or 40 rounds, and the open V rear sight is adjustable to 100, 200, 300, and 400 meters.

Czech 9mm Parabellum submachine gun

Czech 47mm antitank gun Model 38. (*Military Historical Institute, Prague.*)

Model ZK 383 The standard submachine gun of the Bulgarian Army during World War II, this weapon was first patented in 1933 and remained in production until about 1948. It has selective full automatic and semiautomatic fire, is blowback-operated, and has a cyclic rate of fire of 500 and 700 rounds per minute. With a 30-round magazine, the weight of the weapon is 10.65 lb. The overall length is 34.40 in., and the barrel length is 12.80 in. The muzzle velocity is 1,250 fps, and an open V rear sight is adjustable from 100 to 800 meters in 100-meter increments.

Czech 9mm pistol Model 38 This pistol was adopted by the Czech Army in 1938 and, when used by the Germans in World War II, was called the "Pistole Modell 39(t)." It has a weight of 2 lb, a length of 7.8 in., and a barrel length of 4.7 in. The muzzle velocity is 1,000 fps, and the magazine has a capacity of eight rounds.

Czech 9mm Short pistol Model 22 This was the first service automatic designed and manufactured in Czechoslovakia. It was based on the German Nickl design and was also produced by Mauser. It fires the 9mm Short cartridge (same as .380 ACP), is recoil-operated, and has a weight of 1.37 lb. The overall length is 6 in., and the barrel length is 3.44 in. It has a muzzle velocity of 984 fps and a magazine with a capacity of eight rounds.

Czech 9mm Short pistol Model 24 This pistol was a follow-on to the Model 22 and was made in considerable quantities until about 1937.

Czech 12.7mm quad DShK M1938/46 heavy machine gun This system consists of four Czech-made DShK M1938/46 12.7mm machine guns mounted on a Czech-designed two-wheeled antiaircraft mount. The weight of the unit is 1,411 lb, and it is capable of 360° traverse and 90° elevation. Its operation is hampered by the fact that the guns have magazines that hold only 50 rounds.

Czech 47mm antitank gun Model 38 A weapon used in World War II by the Germans. The projectile weight is 3.7 lb, and

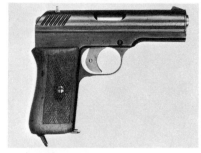

Czech 9mm Short automatic pistol Model 22. (*Military Historical Institute, Prague.*)

the range is about 5,500 yd.

Czech Mauser rifles In 1924, Ceskaslovenske Zobrojovka Brno (ZB) began the production of Mauser rifles for the Czech Army and for export. All the weapons produced by ZB were based on the M98 action. Among the models produced were the rifle 98/22, the rifle 98/29, and the rifle Model 24.

D

DA The U.S. military designation for the war gas **diphenylchloroarsine,** which see. Also used as an abbreviation for "double action."

Dackel (German for "dachshund") A German World War II long-range pattern-running torpedo. It had a length of 33 ft and was first used in June 1944.

dag In the sixteenth and seventeenth centuries, a pistol of any sort. As now used,

dag. (*The Smithsonian Institution, R. G. Packard Collection.*)

Dahlgren gun. (*The Smithsonian Institution, Department of Defense Collection.*)

the term means a short, heavy wheel-lock pistol introduced in the latter part of the sixteenth century.

dagger A short double-edged sharp-pointed weapon used for stabbing.

Dahlgren gun A type of cannon employed during the American Civil War and named after its inventor, Rear Adm. John A. Dahlgren of the U.S. Navy. It was a smooth-bore cannon made of cast iron, and the thickness of the tube varied proportionately with the pressure of the exploding gases. It was introduced in 1856.

daikyu A large Japanese military bow.

daisho A term that refers to the two swords once carried by Japanese of the military class. The *dai* was the long fighting sword (the *katana*), and the *sho* was the shorter supplementary weapon (the *wakizashi*). The latter was also used for com-

mitting ceremonial suicide.

Daisy-Cutter 1. A slang term for the U.S. BLU-82/B 15,000-lb bomb. It has a diameter of 4.5 ft, a length of more than 11 ft, and an explosive weight of 12,600 lb of DBA-22M (an aqueous gel of ammonium nitrate, aluminum powder, and an intermediary agent). The bomb is set to explode before touching the ground, and the explosion does not produce a crater. It is used to produce landing spaces for helicopters. Also called "Cheeseburger." **2.** A slang term for an antipersonnel fragmentation bomb fuzed to burst on impact.

Dakota The World War II British name for the C-47 Skytrain.

daiwei See **DHA.**

damage assessment 1. The determination of the effect of attacks on targets. **2.** The determination of the effect of a compromise of classified information on the national security.

damage categories Two damage-category classifications applying to combat materiel subject to attack have been accepted. The first classification, used in evaluating damage to *aircraft* and the damage potential of ammunition, employs the following damage-evaluation terms: *K damage:* damage such that the aircraft will fall out of control immediately after the damage occurs. *KK damage:* damage such that the aircraft will disintegrate immediately after the damage occurs. *A damage:* damage such that the

128

aircraft will fall out of control within 5 minutes after damage occurs. *B damage:* damage such that the aircraft will be unable to return to its base. *C damage:* damage that will prevent the aircraft from completing its mission. The second classification, used in evaluating damage to *armored vehicles,* employs the following damage-evaluation terms: *K damage:* damage that will cause the vehicle to be destroyed. *F damage:* damage that will cause complete or partial loss of the vehicle's ability to fire its main armament and machine guns. *M damage:* damage that will cause immobilization of the vehicle.

damage cone A wooden cone formerly used to plug holes in the sides of vessels struck by enemy cannons.

damage control In naval usage, measures necessary aboard ship to preserve and reestablish watertight integrity, stability, maneuverability, and offensive power; to control list and trim; to effect rapid repairs of materiel; to limit the spread of, and provide adequate protection from, fire; to limit the spread of, remove the contamination caused by, and provide adequate protection from, toxic agents; and to provide for the care of wounded personnel.

Damascus barrel A barrel that is produced by welding two or more rods or wires of iron or steel together, rolling them into a ribbon shape, and then wrapping the ribbon around a mandrel. The ribbon is then welded, and the tube is finished inside and out.

Damascus steel A hard, elastic steel once highly regarded for the production of sword blades. Like the steel in Damascus barrels, it is made by welding various strips of iron and steel together and then folding and refolding them. The material is characterized by wavy surface patterns.

dan To mark a position or sea area with dan buoys.

dan buoy A temporary marker buoy used during minesweeping operations. It indicates the boundaries of the swept path, swept areas, and known hazards.

danger area A specified area on land or sea within, below, or over which activities may be taking place that constitute a potential danger to aircraft, persons, property, or traffic.

danger signal In naval usage, five or more rapid, short blasts of a whistle to indicate the possibility of a collision or other emergency.

danger space **1.** That portion of the range within which a target of given dimensions could be hit by a projectile with a given angle of fall. Specifically, the danger space is the space in which the trajectory of rifle or machine-gun bullets does not rise above the average height of a man. **2.** The space around the bursting point of an antiaircraft projectile.

Danish 8mm Krag–Jorgensen rifle Model 1889. (*The Smithsonian Institution, Department of Defense Collection.*)

Danish 8mm Krag-Jorgensen rifle Model 1889 Denmark was the first country to adopt the Krag rifle, which, with slight alterations, was the weapon adopted a few years later by Norway and the United States. It is bolt-operated and has a five-round in-line magazine that is loaded singly through a side gate. The overall length is 52.28 in., and the barrel length is 32.78 in. It weighs 9.5 lb. This rifle and several varieties of Model 1889 carbines were used by Danish forces until the end of World War II.

Danish 9mm Parabellum (Madsen) Suomi submachine gun In 1940 the Danish firm of Madsen acquired the manufacturing rights to the **Suomi 9mm Parabellum submachine gun M/1931,** which see, from Finland. From 1940 until the end of World War II this weapon (the Suomi model M/1931) was produced for the Danish, German, and Finnish forces.

Danish 9mm pistol M1910 and M1910/21 The Model 1910 pistol is the **Bergmann Bayard automatic pistol Model 1910,** which see. In 1922 the pistol was altered slightly, and the designation was changed to M1910/21.

Daphne A class of French submarines of 850 tons standard surface displacement completed in 1964–1970. They have a speed (surface and submerged) of 16 knots, a complement of 45 men, and armament consisting of twelve 21.7-in. torpedo tubes.

D.A.R.10F A single-engine two-seat light reconnaissance bomber and dive bomber first flown in 1941. It represented the only indigenous Bulgarian combat aircraft to attain production.

Daring A class of British destroyers of 2,800 tons standard displacement completed in 1952–1954. They have a length of 390 ft, a beam of 43 ft, a speed of 34 knots, and a complement of 297 men. They are armed with six 4.5-in. and six 40mm guns, one Squid 3-barreled depth-charge mortar, and five 21-in. torpedo tubes.

darken ship To black out all lights visible from outside a ship.

Darky System A network of low-power radio stations used in England during World War II to advise pilots of their approximate location.

Darne 7.5mm aircraft machine gun Type 33 Model 29 A French gas-operated air-cooled machine gun with a rate of fire of 900 to 1,200 rounds per minute. It had a weight of 18.5 lb and was fed from a 250-round link belt.

dart A hand-thrown pointed missile weapon such as a short lance or javelin.

Dart A U.S. Army solid-propellant short-range rocket developed in 1953. It has a winged configuration.

DART Deployable Automatic Relay Terminal. A U.S. transportable ground station that receives, processes, and displays data relayed from QU-22 Pave Eagle and P-2 aircraft. The reconnaissance planes obtain intelligence from drones and ground sensors placed along infiltration routes.

DASH See **drone antisubmarine helicopter.**

DATB Deamino-trinitro-benzine. A pressed explosive used in missile warheads.

Dauntless The Douglas SBD-3 Dauntless was a U.S. Navy carrier-based dive bomber used during World War II. Also designated the A-24, this aircraft had a maximum speed of 250 mph and armament consisting of two .50 cal. and two .30 cal. machine guns. It carried a bombload of 1,000 lb and had a range of 1,580 mi. (Picture, next page.)

David A small boat that carried a torpedo (naval mine) and was submerged until almost awash. Boats of this type were constructed by the Confederates in the Civil War. See **torpedo,** sense 2.

davits Steel arms or cranes that project from the sides of ships and are used for lowering and lifting aboard boats, torpedoes, accommodation ladders, and so forth.

Davy Crockett A mobile launcher designed to provide firepower with a nuclear warhead. It is essentially a recoilless rifle and can be airlifted or mounted on a jeep, mechanical mule, or armored personnel carrier. The M-28 version is a 120mm system with a weight of 116 lb and a range of 1½ mi. It is served by a three-man crew. The M-29 has a weight of 379 lb, a range of 3 mi, and a warhead with an equivalent of 40 tons of TNT. (Picture, next page.)

day bomber A World War II heavily armed and armored bomber developed for use during the day.

day of fire See **day of supply.**

day of supply The ammunition day of supply is the estimated quantity of conventional ammunition required per day to sustain operations in an active theater.

dayroom A room in a barracks set aside for reading, writing, and recreation.

Davy Crockett. (*U.S. Army.*)

dazzle   A temporary loss of vision or a temporary reduction in visual acuity. It is caused by an intense flash of light.

dazzle system   A World War I system of antisubmarine camouflage by means of which a ship's lines were distorted to give an erroneous impression of its course.

DB   **1.** The letters used in designations of U.S. Army aircraft around 1920. They referred to "day bombardment."   **2.** The letters used in the names of Russian aircraft from 1925 to 1945. They referred to *Dal'nii bombovos*, or long-range bomber.

DB-7   An early version of the A-20 Havoc as used by England and France in the early part of World War II.

DC   The U.S. military designation for the war gas **diphenylcyanoarsine,** which see.

D Class   A class of British 4,850-ton light cruisers completed between 1918 and 1922. It included *Danae, Dauntless, Delhi, Despatch, Diomede, Dragon, Dunedin,* and *Durban.* They had a length of 472 ft, a speed of 29 knots, a complement of 460 men, and main armament consisting of six 6-in. guns, three 4-in. guns, and twelve

21-in. torpedo tubes.

DCM   Distinguished Conduct Medal.

DD   A U.S. Navy destroyer.

D-day   The unnamed day on which a particular operation begins or is to begin. A D-day may mark the commencement of hostilities, the date of a major military effort, the execution date of an operation, or the date the operations phase is implemented, by land assault, air strike, naval bombardment, parachute assault, or amphibious assault. The most famous D-day was June 6, 1944, when the Allies landed in Normandy in Operation Overlord.

DDC   A U.S. Navy corvette.

DDE   A U.S. Navy antisubmarine destroyer.

DDG   A U.S. Navy guided-missile destroyer.

DDK   A U.S. Navy hunter-killer destroyer.

DDR   A U.S. Navy radar picket destroyer.

DE   A U.S. Navy escort vessel, formerly called a "destroyer escort," with a displacement of 1,500 tons, armament consisting of 5-in. guns, and a speed of about 20 knots.

Deacon   A British four-wheeled self-propelled six-pounder carrier developed during World War II. Employed in North Africa as antitank batteries, Deacons were sometimes called "Yellow Devils."

deactivate   **1.** To break up or abolish a unit or an organization.   **2.** To render a bomb, a shell, or other explosive charge inert.   **3.** To render a weapon, such as a machine gun, inoperable.

dead angle   In fortifications, the space outside a work that cannot be seen by the defenders or reached by their fire.

dead in the water   The condition of a vessel that has stopped and has no way on.

dead space   **1.** An area within the maximum range of a weapon, radar transmitter, or observer which cannot be covered by fire or observation from a particular position because of intervening obstacles, the nature of the ground, the characteristics of the trajectory, or the limitations of the pointing capabilities of the weapon.   **2.** An area or zone which is within range of a radio transmitter but in which a signal is not received.   **3.** The volume of space about and around a gun or guided-missile system into which it cannot fire because of mechanical or electronic limitations.

dead zone   See **dead space.**

Dealey   A class of U.S. escort ships (DE) of 1,450 tons standard displacement produced in 1954–1955. They have a length of 314.5 ft, a beam of 36.8 ft, a speed of 25 knots, and a complement of 149 to 170 men. Armament consists of two or four 3-in. guns, one Weapon Alpha rocket launcher, two triple torpedo launchers, and two drone antisubmarine helicopters (DASH). The first three ships of this class are designated as *Dealey* class. The following ten, of the same design, are designated as *Courtney* class.

Dauntless. (*McDonnell Douglas Corporation.*)

Dealey. (*U.S. Navy.*)

death organs Multibarreled muzzle-loading guns that date back to the fourteenth century, some of which are said to have had as many as 33 barrels. They were fired in volley.

death's-head burgonet A heavy seventeenth-century burgonet. It had round openings for the eyes, with hoods that projected over them, causing it to resemble a skull.

debarkation The unloading of troops, equipment, or supplies from a ship or aircraft.

debarkation net A specially prepared type of cargo net employed for the debarkation of troops over the side of a ship.

deblai The excavation formed when earth is removed for the construction of parapets in fortifications. The earth removed was called the "remblai."

debouch To march out of a combined or sheltered spot into open ground.

debrief To interrogate someone, such as a combat pilot, upon his return from a mission.

DEC A U.S. Navy control escort ship.

decagon A 10-sided fortification.

decay (radioactive) The decrease in the radiation intensity of any radioactive material with respect to time.

decay rate (radioactive) The time rate of the disintegration of radioactive material generally accompanied by the emission of particles or gamma radiation.

deck-piercing shell A shell once used with large coastal mortars. It was delivered by high-angle fire with the object of penetrating the decks of ships and bursting within.

declaration of war An announcement made either before or after an act of hostility stating that a condition of war exists between two countries.

decontamination The process of making any person, object, or area safe by absorbing, destroying, neutralizing, making harmless, or removing chemical or biological agents or by removing radioactive material clinging to or around it.

decoration A medal or ribbon awarded an individual for exceptional courage, skill, or meritorious achievement.

decoy guided missile A guided missile specifically designed to lead another missile from the intended target.

decoy ships (Q ships) Warships or other ships camouflaged as merchantmen or converted commerce raiders. Their armament and other fighting equipment is hidden, and they have special provisions for unmasking their weapons quickly.

decumana One of the two main gates of a Roman camp. Also called "abesia."

decury The squad of Roman cavalrymen commanded by a decurion.

deep air support Air action against enemy forces at such a distance from friendly forces that detailed integration of each air mission with the fire and movement of friendly forces is not required.

deep creep attack A surprise depth-charge attack used against submarines that are deeply submerged and traveling at slow speeds. It is effective only when it is possible to surprise the submarine under attack.

deep-fording ability The ability of a gun or vehicle that is equipped with built-in waterproofing and whose suspension is in contact with the ground to negotiate a water obstacle after application of a special waterproofing kit.

deep-penetration bomb A bomb designed to penetrate the target before exploding. Bombs of this sort designed in World War II had a bursting charge amounting to about 43 percent of their total weight.

deep supporting fire Fire directed on objectives not in the immediate vicinity of friendly forces. Its purpose is to neutralize and destroy enemy reserves and weapons and to interfere with enemy command, supply, communications, and observations.

defector A person who for political or other reasons has repudiated his country and may be in possession of information of sufficient interest to justify special treatment.

Defender The code name for a project which is an omnibus effort first under the direction of the Advanced Research Projects Agency, and then of the Advanced Ballistic Missile Defense Agency, to provide the missile and reentry technology associated with strategic offensive and defensive weapons systems. The project is also assigned the responsibility of developing concepts for advanced defensive systems against satellite and ballistic-missile attacks.

defense In fortifications, the works that cover and defend the opposite posts, such as flanks, parapets, casements, and so forth.

defense classification A category or grade assigned to defense information or material which denotes the degree of danger to national security that would result from its unauthorized disclosure and for which standards in handling, storage, and dissemination have been established. These categories are defined as follows: (1) *Confidential:* defense information or material whose unauthorized disclosure could be prejudicial to the defense interests of the United States. (2) *Secret:* defense information or material whose unauthorized disclosure could result in serious damage to the nation, such as jeopardizing the international relations of the United States, endangering the effectiveness of a program or policy of vital importance to the national defense, or compromising important military or defense plans, scientific or technological developments important to national defense, or information revealing important intelligence operations. (3) *Top secret:* defense information or material which requires the highest degree of protection. This classification is applied only to that information or material the defense aspect of which is paramount and the unauthorized disclosure of which could result in exceptionally grave damage to the nation, such as leading to a definite break in diplomatic relations affecting the defense of the United States, an armed attack against the United States or its allies, a war, or the compromise of military or defense plans, intelligence operations, or scientific or technological developments vital to the national defense.

defense emergency An emergency condition which exists when (1) a major attack is made upon United States forces overseas or on allied forces in any theater and is

Defiant. (*The Smithsonian Institution, National Air Museum.*)

confirmed by either the commander of a command established by the Secretary of Defense or higher authority or (2) an overt attack of any type is made upon the United States and is confirmed by either the commander of a command established by the Secretary of Defense or higher authority.

defense in depth The siting of mutually supporting defense positions designed to absorb and progressively weaken attack, to prevent initial observations of the whole position by the enemy, and to allow the commander to maneuver his reserve.

defensive minefield A minefield which is laid in accordance with the divisional plan and whose purpose is to defeat penetration between positions and also to strengthen the defense of the positions themselves.

defensive position Ground that is occupied or organized for defense.

defensive zone An outpost area and battle position developed as a defensive system.

Defiant The Boulton Paul Defiant was a single-engine two-seat night fighter first flown by the British in 1939. It was powered by a 1,030-hp engine and flew at speeds up to 304 mph. Armament consisted of a power-operated turret with four .303 cal. machine guns. This turret was located just aft of the pilot's position.

defilade **1.** Protection from hostile observation and fire provided by an obstacle such as a hill, ridge, or bank. **2.** A vertical distance by which a position is concealed from enemy observation. **3.** To shield from enemy fire or observation by using natural or artificial obstacles.

deflection The horizontal angle between the line of sight and the axis of the bore. In naval gunnery, the lateral angular correction applied to the target bearing to obtain hits.

deflection error **1.** In artillery, the distance to the right or left of the target between the point aimed at and the burst of the projectile, or the mean point of a salvo burst. **2.** In bombing, the distance between the point of impact or the mean point of impact and the center of the target measured at right angles from the line of

the aircraft's approach.

defoliant A biological agent that destroys leaves or green plants or a chemical agent that causes trees, shrubs, and other plants to shed their leaves prematurely.

DEG A U.S. Navy guided-missile escort ship.

de Gaullist A follower of General Charles de Gaulle, particularly during World War II. General de Gaulle repudiated the Vichy government's armistice with Germany in 1940. He went to England, where he organized the Fighting French.

degauss To reduce the magnetic field of a ship to protect it against magnetic mines and torpedoes.

De Grasse A French antiaircraft cruiser of 10,238 tons standard displacement commissioned in 1956. It has a complement of 651 men, a speed of 33 knots, a length of 617.8 ft, and armament consisting of twelve 5-in. guns.

Degtyarev machine guns See **Soviet 7.62mm heavy machine gun Model 1939 DS (Degtyarev), Soviet 7.62mm light machine gun DP (Degtyarev), Soviet 7.62mm light machine gun DPM (Degtyarev), Soviet 7.62mm light machine gun RPD (Degtyarev), Soviet 7.62mm machine gun DP (Degtyarev),** and **Soviet 7.62mm machine gun DS (Degtyarev Medium).**

dehors An old fortifications term for any sort of outwork placed at some distance from the walls of a fortified place.

Delaware A class of U.S. battleships of 20,000 tons normal displacement commissioned in 1910. The class included *Delaware* and *North Dakota*. They had a length of 518 ft, a beam of 85 ft, a speed of 21 knots, and a complement of 937 men. Main armament consisted of ten 12-in. guns, fourteen 5-in. guns, and two 21-in. torpedo tubes.

delayed-action bomb A bomb having a delay fuze. The delay action may vary from a fraction of a second to several days after impact, depending on the type of fuzing. Bombs or other projectiles having short-delay fuzes are used to penetrate targets before exploding. Bombs having medium-delay fuzes are used for the safety of the plane in low-altitude bombing; the plane may move away from the point of impact before detonation. Bombs having long-delay fuzes are normally used to deny territory to the enemy for a period of time or to allow successive waves of planes to drop their bombs before any of them detonate.

delayed-action mine An explosive charge designed to go off some time after planting. Delayed-action mines are often left behind by a retreating enemy to harass or destroy pursuing forces.

delayed-contact fire A firing system arranged to explode a mine at a set time after it has been touched or disturbed.

Delfinen A class of Danish submarines of 595 tons standard surface displacement

DEG, the U.S.S. *Brooke* (Deg-1). (*U.S. Navy.*)

Delaware. (*U.S. Navy.*)

built in 1958–1960. They have a submerged speed of 17 knots, a complement of 21 men, and armament consisting of eight 21-in. torpedo tubes.

deliberate defense A defense normally organized when out of contact with the enemy or when contact with the enemy is not imminent and time for organization is available. It normally includes an extensive fortified zone incorporating pillboxes, forts, and communications systems.

deliberate fire Fire which is conducted at a rate intentionally less than the normal rate for the purpose of applying adjustment corrections between each round or salvo, for tactical reasons, or in order to conserve ammunition. Also called "slow fire."

deliberate trenches In the days of trench warfare, a system of carefully designed trenches that were very strong and capable of resisting assault.

delivery error The inaccuracy associated with a given weapon system resulting in a dispersion of shots about the aiming point.

delivery system The means of delivering atomic weapons to the target.

delousing In World War II naval usage in the Pacific, the process of weeding out Japanese Kamikaze aircraft that would attempt to join American aircraft formations returning from missions in order to attack their carriers.

Delta Dagger The Convair F-102 Delta Dagger is a supersonic single-seat all-weather delta-wing jet fighter developed for the U.S. Air Force and first flown in 1953. It has a speed of Mach 1.25 and a range of about 1,100 mi and is armed with six Falcon air-to-air missiles.

Delta Dart The Convair F-106 Delta Dart is a single-seat all-weather interceptor and

Delta Dagger. (*General Dynamics.*)

Delta Dart. (*General Dynamics.*)

demipauldron. (*The Metropolitan Museum of Art, Bashford Dean Memorial Collection.*)

a developed version of the F-102 Delta Dagger. It was produced for the U.S. Air Force and was first flown in 1956. It has a speed of Mach 2.3 and a range of 1,150 mi. It is armed with one Genie rocket (with a nuclear warhead) and four Super Falcon air-to-air missiles.

Delta Platform A 22-ft platform used for off-loading troops in swampy areas. This U.S. development is also used as a weapons platform, command post, shelter, and helicopter landing pad.

delta wing An airplane or wing design in which the swept-back wings, looked at from below or above, give the appearance of an isosceles triangle, the trailing edges of the wings forming one straight line to become the base of the triangle. Such a wing is a feature of certain transonic airplanes.

demibastion A half bastion. It consists of one face and one flank.

demibrigade A half brigade. Specifically,

a special organization in the French Army from 1793 to 1803. It consisted of a regiment of three battalions.

demicannon An ancient type of ordnance that had a bore of about 6½ in. and fired a ball weighing from 30 to 36 lb.

demicaponier In fortifications, a caponier that is protected on only one side.

demicuirass In armor, a partial cuirass. The term refers particularly to a covering, or reinforcing, piece on the breastplate.

demiculverin A type of culverin having a bore of about 4½ in. It fired a ball weighing about 10 lb.

demigardebras A *gardebras* for the upper arm.

demigorge In fortifications, half the gorge or entrance into the bastion, taken from the curtain angle to the center of the bastion.

demihag A variety of hackbut, a sixteenth-century pistol.

demijambe A piece of armor covering only the front of the leg.

demilance **1.** A light lance or half-pike used in the fifteenth and sixteenth centuries. **2.** A demilancer.

demilancer A light cavalryman armed with a demilance.

demilitarization **1.** The taking away of all military organization and installations. **2.** Disassembly, destruction, or any other action which renders munitions, weapons, and other materiel which is lethal, hazardous, classified, or of a specialized nature harmless and ineffectual for military purposes.

demilitarized zone A defined area in which the stationing or concentrating of military forces, or the retention or establishment of military installations of any description, is prohibited.

demilune A crescent-shaped work designed to defend the entrance to a fort. At first it was inside the line of the main ditch, but later developed into the ravelin.

demiparallel In siege works, a place of arms formed between the two parallels nearest to the enemy.

demipauldron A small, light fifteenth-cen-

tury pauldron, or armor for the shoulder.

demipike A half-pike.

demirevetment The revetment of a rampart when it is carried only as high as the cover in front.

demisuit A suit of armor covering only a part of the body, such as one which protects the body as far down as the thighs.

demobilization A process of dismantling or demobilizing a military organization at the end of a war.

demobilize To dismiss from active military service.

demolition The destruction of structures, facilities, or materiel by use of fire, water, explosives, mechanical, or other means.

demolition belt A selected land area sown with explosive charges, mines, and other available obstacles, the purpose of which is to deny use of the land to enemy operations and to protect friendly troops.

demolition bomb Formerly, a bomb that explodes after a short penetration, accomplishing damage and destruction by both blast and underground explosion. During World War II a demolition bomb had a charge approximately equal to 50 percent of its total weight. Now called a "general-purpose bomb."

demolition duty A hazardous military duty involving the demolition or disarming of explosives or the destruction of objects or obstacles by detonating planted or fixed explosives.

demolition guard A local force positioned to ensure that a target is not captured by an enemy before orders are given for its demolition and before the demolition has been successfully fired. The commander of the demolition guard is responsible for the operational command of all troops at the demolition site, including the demolition firing party. He is responsible for transmitting the order to fire to the demolition firing party.

Demon The McDonnell F-3 Demon is a single-seat single-jet sweptwing carrier-based fighter developed for the U.S. Navy and first flown in 1951. It flies at supersonic speeds and is armed with four 20mm cannons, Sparrow missiles, and other armament, including nuclear weapons.

demonstration An attack or a show of force on a front where a decision is not sought, made with the aim of deceiving the enemy.

denial measures Action to hinder or deny the enemy the use of space, personnel, or facilities. It may include destruction, removal, contamination, or erection of obstructions.

density In land-mine warfare, the average number of mines per a specified unit of measure of front of the minefield.

density bombing Bombing in which a given tonnage of bombs is dropped onto an

Demon, armed with Sparrow missiles. (*U.S. Navy.*)

area in order to make certain of striking particular targets within the area.

Department of the Air Force (U.S.) The executive part of the Department of the Air Force at the seat of government and all field headquarters, forces, reserve components, installations, activities, and functions under the control or supervision of the Secretary of the Air Force.

Department of the Army (U.S.) The executive part of the Department of the Army at the seat of government and all field headquarters, forces, reserve components, installations, activities, and functions under the control or supervision of the Secretary of the Army.

Department of the Navy (U.S.) The executive part of the Department of the Navy at the seat of government; the headquarters, U.S. Marine Corps; the entire operating forces of the U.S. Navy, including naval aviation, and of the U.S. Marine Corps, including the reserve components of such forces; all field activities, headquarters, forces, bases, installations, activities, and functions under the control and supervision of the Secretary of the Navy; and the U.S. Coast Guard when operating as a part of the Navy pursuant to law.

deploy 1. To send personnel or units to combat positions, or simulated combat positions, so as to cover an extended front or area. **2.** To spread out personnel, forces, or equipment, according to a plan, so as to meet a military situation. **3.** To release or open a parachute.

deployment 1. The act of extending battalions and smaller units in width, in depth, or in both width and depth to increase their readiness for contemplated action. **2.** In naval usage, the change from a cruising approach or contact disposition to a disposition for battle. **3.** In a strategic sense, the relocation of forces to desired areas of operation. **4.** The designated location of troops and troop units as indicated in a troop schedule.

depot A facility for the receipt, classification, storage, accounting, issue, maintenance, procurement, manufacture, assembly, research, or salvage of supplies or for the reception, processing, training, assignment, and forwarding of personnel replacements. It may be an installation or activity of the zone of the interior or area of operations. At one time this term was used in the British Army to identify that portion of a regiment that remained at home while the rest was on foreign service.

depot ship A tender; a vessel equipped to provide stores or make repairs to other ships.

depress To decrease or lower the angle of elevation of a gun or launcher.

depth The space occupied by a formation from front to back.

depth charge. (*U.S.Navy.*)

depth bomb A light-case aerial bomb designed to explode underwater and used against ships or submarines. Water pressure created by the explosion of a depth bomb produces the damage done to the target.

depth charge An explosive item designed to be dropped or catapulted from a watercraft and used against underwater targets. The slang term for this weapon is "ashcan."

depth-charge arbor A device designed to provide a means of launching and supporting a depth charge in a depth-charge gun.

DER A U.S. Navy radar picket escort ship.

derringer, deringer A small pocket pistol originally made by Henry Deringer, of Philadelphia, but copied by many others.

De Ruyter A Dutch cruiser of 9,529 tons standard displacement completed in 1953. It has a length of 614 ft, a beam of 56.7 ft, a speed of 32 knots, and a complement of 926 men. It is armed with eight 6-in. guns, plus eight 57mm and eight 40mm antiaircraft guns.

descending branch That portion of a trajectory between the summit and a point beyond the summit where the trajectory terminates, as a result of either impact or airburst. On this branch the projectile falls and its altitude constantly decreases.

descents In fortifications, the holes and vaults made by undermining the ground.

deserter A person found legally guilty by court-martial of the act of desertion.

Desert Fox The nickname for German Field Marshal Erwin Rommel, who led the Afrika Korps in World War II.

desertion The act of being absent without leave with the intent of never returning, done to avoid hazardous duty or to shirk military service of any kind. In the U.S. services, desertion during wartime is punishable by death.

Desert Rats The popular name for veterans of the British Eighth Army, commanded by Field Marshal Bernard L. Montgomery in North Africa in World War II. The name was taken from a genuine desert rat that had been picked up as a mascot as the army moved between Alexandria and Tripoli.

design class Ships of a type which, at the time of issue of specifications, are intended to be identical. Change orders issued may eventually make them dissimilar in some respects.

desired ground zero (DGZ) The point on the surface of land or water at, vertically below, or vertically above, the center of a planned nuclear detonation.

Des Moines A class of U.S. heavy cruisers (CA) of 17,000 tons standard displacement completed in 1948–1949. The class consisted of *Des Moines*, *Newport News*, and *Salem*. They had a length of 716 ft, a beam of 75 ft, a speed of 33 knots, and a complement of 1,860 men. They were armed with

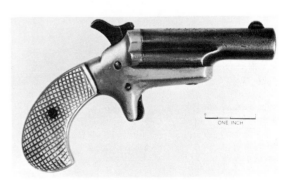

derringer. (*The Smithsonian Institution, Remington Collection.*)

Destroyer. (*U.S. Air Force.*)

nine 8-in. and twelve 5-in. guns, plus twenty-four 3-in. and twenty 20mm antiaircraft guns. One helicopter was carried.

destrier A war-horse of the Middle Ages.

destroyed Said of aircraft, materiel, installations, or the like that have been ruined beyond repair and are unfit for further military use. In air combat, an enemy aircraft is officially considered destroyed (1) when it is seen to hit the ground or sea, (2) when it is seen to break up in the air or descend in flames, (3) when it is forced to descend and is captured, or (4) when it is a single-seat plane and is abandoned by bailout.

destroyer A high-speed warship designed to operate offensively with strike forces, with hunter-killer groups, and in support of amphibious assault operations. Destroyers also operate defensively to screen support forces and convoys against submarine, air, and surface threats. The normal arma-

ment consists of 3-in. and 5-in. dual-purpose guns and various antisubmarine-warfare weapons. Designated as DD, the slang term for this warship is "can" or "tin can."

Destroyer The Douglas B-66 Destroyer is a land-based version of the A-3 **Skywarrior**, which see. It is used by the USAF as a tactical all-weather light bomber. It has a speed in the 600-mph class and internal storage for 15,000 lb of bombs.

destroyer escort A lightly armored ship smaller than a destroyer. It is used for antisubmarine operations, and its principal offensive weapons are depth charges.

destroyer leader A warship like a destroyer that has facilities for accommodating the squadron commander and his staff.

destroyer minelayer A converted destroyer designed to conduct high-speed minelaying operations. The average load is 80 mines laid from two stern racks. Desig-

nated as DM.

destruct To destroy a missile or similar vehicle intentionally for safety or other reasons.

destruction fire Fire delivered for the sole purpose of destroying material objects.

Destructor The code name for a U.S. combination bomb-mine which does not detonate until an object of a specified weight passes over it or until it is jarred into action by vibrations from nearby vehicles.

destruct system A system which, when operated by external command or preset internal means, destroys a missile or similar vehicle.

detached bastion In fortifications, the basis separated from the *enceinte* by a ditch.

detached scarp A wall in the ditch of a fortified place, separated from the embankment of the parapet by a path.

detached works In fortifications, outworks that are detached or located some distance from the main works.

detachment 1. A part of a unit separated from its main organization for duty elsewhere. **2.** A temporary military or naval unit formed from other units or parts of units.

detail To assign men to a particular duty. Also, the men assigned to the duty. The term once referred to the written list of orders or exercises for the day, either for the entire command or for a part of it.

detection In arms control, the first step in the process of ascertaining the occurrence

Deutschland class, showing the battleship *Schleswig Holstein.* (*The Imperial War Museum.*)

of a violation of an arms-control agreement.

detent The mine-release gear on a mine-layer.

deterrence The restraint from action by fear of the consequences. Deterrence is brought about by the existence of a credible threat of unacceptable counteraction.

detonate To explode suddenly and violently.

detonating agent An explosive which is extremely sensitive to heat and shock and which is normally used to initiate a secondary high explosive. It is capable of building up from a deflagration to detonation at an extremely short distance and in a very short period of time.

detonating fuze A fuze designed to initiate its main munition by a detonating action, as compared with the igniting action of an **igniting fuze,** which see. This type of fuze is required for adequate initiation of a high-explosive main charge.

detonating powder A material such as mercury fulminate which, when heated or struck, explodes violently.

detonator An explosive train component which can be activated by either a nonexplosive impulse or the action of a primer and which is capable of reliably initiating high-order detonation in a subsequent high-explosive component or train. When activated by a nonexplosive impulse, a detonator includes the function of a primer. In general, detonators are classified in accordance with the method of initiation, such as percussion, stab, electric, flash, etc.

Deutschland A class of German 13,200-ton battleships completed in 1906–1908. They included the *Deutschland, Hannover, Pommern, Schleswig-Holstein,* and *Schlesien.* These ships had a length of 430 ft, a speed of 19 knots, a complement of 729 men, and main armament consisting of four 11-in. guns, fourteen 6.7-in. guns, and six 17.7-in. torpedo tubes.

Devastator The Douglas TBD-1 Devastator was developed in the late 1930s and was used during World War II. It was a single-engine three-place torpedo bomber and flew at speeds up to 225 mph.

deviation **1.** The distance by which a point of impact or burst misses the target. **2.** The angular difference between magnetic and compass headings.

Devonshire A class of British 10,850-ton cruisers completed in 1904–1905. There were six ships in the class, and they had a length of 450 ft, a complement of 655 men, and main armament consisting of four 7.5-in. and six 6-in. guns. They had a speed of 22 knots. Lord Kitchener was among those lost when *Hampshire,* a ship of this class, struck a mine on June 5, 1916.

Dew Line (from Distant Early Warning) A line of radar stations at about the 70th parallel on the North American continent,

Devastator. (*U.S. Air Force.*)

financed by the American government but undertaken in cooperation with the Canadian government.

Dewoitine D.520 A French single-engine single-seat low-wing fighter-interceptor that went into large-scale production in 1940. It was powered by a 910-hp engine, flew at speeds of 329 mph, and was armed with one 20mm Hispano-Suiza cannon and four 7.5mm machine guns. After the German occupation of France, a number of these airplanes were sent to the Bulgarian and Rumanian Air Forces, where they were used operationally.

De Zeven Provincien A Dutch cruiser of 9,850 tons standard displacement completed in 1953. It has a length of 609 ft, a beam of 56.7 ft, a speed of 32 knots, and a complement of 940 men. It is armed with four 6-in. guns, six 57mm and four 40mm antiaircraft guns, and one twin Terrier launcher.

DFC Distinguished Flying Cross.

DFM Distinguished Flying Medal.

D.F.W. B.I and C.I German (Deutsche Flugzeug-Werke) two-place single-engine observation biplanes that first appeared in mid-1914. They had a speed of about 75 mph. The B.I was unarmed; the C.I was equipped with a free-firing Parabellum mounted over the top wing. They were used on both the Eastern and Western fronts.

D.F.W. C.V A German two-place single-engine observation and reconnaissance biplane that went into service in midsum-

mer 1916. It was soon seen in France, Italy, Macedonia, and Palestine. About 600 C.V's were in service on all fronts when World War I ended. It had a speed of 96.3 mph.

DGZ **Desired ground zero,** which see.

D.H.I and D.H.IA British two-place single-engine pusher biplanes designed by Geoffrey de Havilland and first flown early in 1915. An observer in the front cockpit was armed with a machine gun. The D.H.IA had a slightly more powerful engine and flew at a speed of 88 mph. It was used as an escort airplane early in World War I.

D.H.2 A single-seat scaled-down version of the D.H.I, this airplane appeared in the spring of 1915 and was in quantity production by the beginning of 1916. A Lewis machine gun was mounted in the nose. It had a speed of 93 mph and remained in service until early 1917.

D.H.4 A British two-place single-engine biplane bomber first flown in August 1916. It was armed with a forward-firing synchronized Vickers gun and a Lewis gun in the observer's cockpit. It had a maximum bombload of two 230-lb bombs or four 112-lb bombs. It was also used for artillery spotting, reconnaissance, and antisubmarine patrol and had a maximum speed of 143 mph. Britain produced 1,449 aircraft of this type, and the United States produced 4,800. (D.H.4 variants were in U.S. service until 1932.) (Picture, next page.)

D.H.5 A British single-seat single-engine biplane fighter first flown in December 1916. It had a speed of 102 mph and was

D.H.4. (*The Smithsonian Institution, National Air Museum.*)

armed with a forward-firing Vickers machine gun. It was the least successful de Havilland design of World War I and was operational for only 8 months.

D.H.6 A British two-place single-engine biplane trainer that entered production in January 1917. A total of 2,950 were ordered. It had a maximum speed of 66 mph.

D.H.9 and D.H.9a British two-place single-engine bombers developed in 1917–1918. The D.H.9 had a speed of 123 mph, was armed with one forward-firing synchronized Vickers machine gun and one Scarff-mounted Lewis gun in the rear cockpit, and could carry an internal bombload of two 230-lb bombs or four 112-lb bombs. Production of this type of aircraft totaled 3,204. The D.H.9A was a refined version with a more powerful engine. It appeared in 1918. About 2,500 of this type were produced, some staying in service until 1931.

dha The Burmese national sword. It has a single-edged blade with a slight curve and a hilt without a guard.

Dhool-Dhanee A huge bronze cannon of Agra, India, having a bore of 23.2 in. and said to be capable of firing stone balls weighing 520 lb.

DI A slang term for a drill instructor.

Diadem A class of British 11,000-ton cruisers completed in 1899–1902. There were six in the class, and they had a length of 462 ft, a complement of 677 men, and main armament consisting of sixteen 6-in. and twelve 12-pounder guns. They had a speed of about 18 knots.

Diana The World War II code name for a German navigational system for day bombing.

DICASS Directional Command Activated Sonobuoy System. A technique using sonobuoys dropped by U.S. Navy antisubmarine-warfare aircraft to detect and track submerged submarines.

DICE Digital Interface Countermeasures Equipment. The code name for a U.S. Air Force program involving jamming and electronic countermeasures for strategic aircraft such as the B-52.

Dick A German war gas of World War I. See **ethyldichloroarsine.**

Dido A class of British cruisers of 5,770 tons standard displacement completed in 1940–1942. Four ships in this class of ten were lost during World War II. They had a length of 512 ft, a beam of 50.5 ft, a speed of 32 knots, and a complement of 550 to 620 men. They were armed with eight 5.25-in. guns, two to twelve 40mm and four to thirteen 20mm guns, and eight to twelve 2-pounder antiaircraft guns. They also carried six 21-in. torpedo tubes. Five modified Dido class vessels were completed in 1943–1944, and one was lost in action. They were similarly armed.

died of wounds received in action Used to describe all battle casualties who die of wounds or other injuries received in action, after having reached a medical treatment facility. It is essential to differentiate these cases from battle casualties who are found dead or who die before reaching a medical treatment facility (the "killed in action" group). It should be noted that reaching a medical treatment facility while still alive is the criterion.

diminished angle The angle formed by the exterior side and the face of a bastion.

Ding-Dong A U.S. Air Force air-to-air rocket later named "Genie." It was developed by the Douglas Aircraft Co. and carries an atomic warhead.

dinghy A small (less than 20 ft) boat with a transom stern. It may be rigged for oars or sail.

Dingo A British Daimler-built four-wheeled armored scout car of World War II. It had a weight of about 3 tons and carried a crew of two.

diphenylaminechloroarsine A solid material that is dispersed by heat to produce an aerosol causing skin and eye irritation, chest distress, and nausea. In popular usage, "adamsite." One of the "vomiting gases," it is relatively nontoxic.

diphenylchloroarsine (DA) This war gas (also a mob- and riot-control gas) has a very rapid rate of action. Effects are felt within 2 or 3 minutes after 1 minute of exposure. It causes irritation of the eyes and mucous membranes, viscous discharge from the nose similar to that caused by a cold, sneezing and coughing, severe headache, acute pain and tightness in the chest, and nausea and vomiting. In moderate concentrations the effects last about 30 minutes after an individual leaves the contaminated atmosphere. At higher concentrations the effects may last up to several hours.

diphenylcyanoarsine (DC) This war gas (also a mob- and riot-control gas) has a very rapid rate of action. It causes the same symptoms as DA, but is more toxic.

diphosgene (DP) This war gas is a choking agent and has a delayed-action casualty

D.H.9a. (*The Smithsonian Institution, National Air Museum.*)

effect. Because DP is converted to CG (phosgene) in the body, the effects of the two gases are the same. This gas was first used by Germany in May 1916 and was fired in shells at Verdun. During World War I, the U.S. designation was "Superlite." It was called *Surpalite* by the French and *Perstoff* by the Germans. See **phosgene.**

direct-action fuze   See **impact-action fuze.**

direct bombing   Bombing by aiming at the target, as distinguished from offset bombing.

direct damage assessment   A direct examination of an actual strike area by air observation, air photography, or direct observation.

direct fire   Gunfire delivered on a target, using the target itself as a point of aim for either the gun or the director.

direct hit   A hit directly on the target.

directing piece   That piece of a battery for which the initial firing data are computed.

direction of attack   A specific direction or route which the main attack or center of mass of the unit will follow. The unit is restricted and required to attack as indicated and is not normally allowed to bypass the enemy. The direction of attack is used primarily in counterattacks or to ensure that supporting attacks make the maximum contribution to the main attack.

directive   **1.** A military communication in which policy is established or a specific action is ordered.   **2.** A plan issued with a view to placing it in effect when so directed or in the event that a stated contingency arises.   **3.** Broadly speaking, any communication which initiates or governs action, conduct, or procedure.

direct laying   Laying in which the sights of the weapons are aligned directly on the target.

director   **1.** A mechanical and electronic device for the control of gunfire.   **2.** The name given to a 13-in. seacoast mortar mounted on a railway car and used in the siege of Petersburg, Va., in 1864.

direct support   A mission requiring a force to support another specific force and

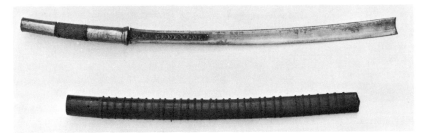

dha. *(The Metropolitan Museum of Art, gift of George Cameron Stone, 1936.)*

dirigible, the *Akron*. *(Goodyear Aerospace.)*

authorizing it to answer directly the supported force's request for assistance.

direct-support artillery   Artillery whose primary task is to provide fire requested by the supported unit.

dirigible   A lighter-than-air aircraft which has its own motive power and which may be steered in any desired direction by its crew.

dirigible torpedo   A torpedo steered electrically by the operating station.

dirk   A kind of short dagger worn by the Scottish Highlanders. It normally has a heavy single-edged blade that tapers uniformly from hilt to point. Also, a dagger once worn by naval officers in undress uniform and on shore in the eighteenth and nineteenth centuries. There was also a Mediterranean dirk popular in Spain and Italy. (Picture, next page.)

disappearing carriage   A type of fixed mount in which a balancing mechanism

Dido. *(Vickers Ltd.)*

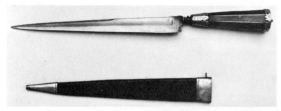

dirk. (*The Metropolitan Museum of Art, gift of Jean Jacques Reubell, 1926.*)

lifts the major-caliber cannon to a position above its protective parapet for the act of firing, after which the cannon again "disappears" behind the parapet. It was formerly used in seacoast defense, but is now considered obsolete because of its inability to fire at high angles and the lack of advantage of the "disappearing" feature against bombs and other missiles with high angles of fall.

disarm To remove the detonating device or fuze of a bomb, mine, or other piece of explosive ordnance or otherwise render it incapable of exploding in its usual manner.

disarmament The reduction of a military establishment to some level set by international agreement.

disarmed mine A mine which has been rendered inoperative by breaking a link in the firing sequence.

disassemble To take apart a firearm in order to clean or repair it.

disaster control Measures taken before, during, or after the occurrence of a hostile action or a natural or man-made disaster to reduce the probability of damage, min-

imize its effects, and initiate recovery.

discharge **1.** The process of separating enlisted men from the service. The discharge may be labeled "honorable," "general," "undesirable," "bad conduct," or "dishonorable." **2.** To cause a weapon to fire.

disconnector The device in an automatic pistol that ensures that firing will not take place until the action is completely closed. It also prevents the firing of more than one shot for each pull of the trigger.

disk primer A small fulminate-loaded copper disk that is exploded by the fall of a hammer to ignite a propellant charge.

dismount To remove a weapon or piece of equipment from its setting, mount, or carriage.

dispart A type of seventeenth-century wire foresight on a cannon.

dispensary A medical treatment facility intended primarily and appropriately staffed and equipped to provide outpatient medical service for nonhospital-type patients. Examination and treatment of emergency cases are types of services rendered. A dispensary is also intended to perform certain nontherapeutic activities related to the health of the personnel served, such as physical examinations, immunizations, medical administration, and other preventive medical and sanitary measures necessary to support a primary military mission. A dispensary is equipped with the supporting services necessary to perform the assigned mission. It may be equipped with beds (normally fewer than 25) for observation of patients awaiting transfer to

a hospital and for care of those who cannot be treated on an outpatient basis but who do not require hospitalization. Patients whose expected duration of illness exceeds 72 hours do not occupy dispensary beds for periods longer than are necessary to arrange transfer to a hospital.

dispersal The spreading out of equipment, supplies, or personnel, especially for protection against enemy action; the practice of building or establishing industrial plants, government offices, or the like in separated areas to reduce vulnerability to enemy attack.

dispersal airfield An airfield, military or civil, to which aircraft can move before H hour on either a temporary-duty or permanent-change-of-station basis and from which they can conduct operations.

dispersed-movement pattern A pattern for ship-to-shore movement which provides additional separation of landing craft both laterally and in depth. This pattern is used when nuclear-weapon threat is a factor.

dispersion **1.** A scattered pattern of hits, by bombs dropped under identical conditions or by projectiles fired from the same gun or group of guns with the same firing data. **2.** In antiaircraft gunnery, the scattering of shots in range and deflection about the mean point of impact. As used in flak analysis, the term includes scattering due to all causes, and the mean point of impact is assumed to be the target. **3.** The spreading or separating of troops, materiel, establishments, or activities which are usually concentrated in limited areas for the purpose of reducing vulnerability to enemy action. **4.** In chemical warfare, the dissemination of agents in liquid or aerosol form from bombs and spray tanks.

dispersion error The distance from the point of impact or burst of a round to the mean point of impact or burst.

dispersion pattern The distribution of a series of rounds fired from one weapon or group of weapons under conditions as nearly identical as possible, the points of bursts or impacts being dispersed about a point called the "mean point of impact."

displaced person A person who is involuntarily outside the national boundaries of his country.

disposition **1.** The distribution of the elements of a command within an area, usually the exact location of each unit headquarters, and the deployment of the forces subordinate to it. **2.** A prescribed arrangement of the stations to be occupied by the several formations and single ships of a fleet, or major subdivisions of a fleet, for any purpose, such as cruising, approach, maintaining contact, or battle. **3.** A prescribed arrangement of all the tactical units composing a flight or group of aircraft. **4.** The removal of a patient from a medical

disappearing carriage. A U.S. 10-in. seacoast gun. (*U.S. Army.*)

treatment facility by reason of return to duty, transfer to another treatment facility, death, or other termination of medical care.

dissemination In intelligence operations, the timely distribution of information and/or intelligence in the most suitable form to those who need it.

distance **1.** The space between adjacent individual ships or boats measured in any direction between foremasts. **2.** The space between adjacent men, animals, vehicles, or units in a formation measured from front to rear.

distilled mustard (HD) This war gas is a blistering agent and has a delayed-action casualty effect. The symptoms usually appear 4 to 6 hours after exposure. Local action results in conjunctivitis, or inflammation of the eyes; erythema (redness of the skin), which may be followed by blistering or ulceration; and inflammation of the nose, throat, trachea, bronchi, and lung tissue. Injuries produced by HD heal much more slowly and are more liable to infection than burns of similar intensity produced by physical means or by other chemicals. This is due to the fact that HD makes the blood vessels incapable of carrying out their functions of repair and to the fact that necrotic (dead or dying) tissue acts as a good medium for bacterial growth. This gas has a garlic-like odor. See **blistering agents.**

Distinguished Conduct Medal (DCM) A British silver medal instituted in 1854 and awarded to enlisted men for distinguished conduct in the field.

Distinguished Flying Cross (DFC) A military decoration awarded in the United States for heroic or extraordinary achievement while participating in aerial flight. It was established in 1917. Also, a similar British decoration.

Distinguished Flying Medal (DFM) A British military decoration awarded noncommissioned officers and men for valor or devotion to duty while flying in active operations against the enemy.

distinguished marksman A soldier who has won three badges or medals for rifle fire in competitions designated by the Department of the Army.

distinguished pistol shot A soldier who has won three badges or medals for pistol fire in competitions designated by the Department of the Army.

Distinguished Service Cross (DSC) **1.** A U.S. cross of bronze awarded persons for extraordinary heroism in operations against the enemy. It was established in 1919. **2.** A British cross of silver awarded to officers in the Royal Navy below the rank of lieutenant commander for distinguished service before the enemy.

Distinguished Service Medal (DSM) **1.** A bronze medal awarded persons for exceptionally meritorious service in a duty

dive bomber. A Douglas Dauntless dive bomber over Wake Island, December 1943. (*U.S. Navy.*)

of great responsibility. This U.S. military decoration was established in 1917. **2.** A British medal of bronze awarded to enlisted men in the Royal Navy and Marines for distinguished conduct in war.

Distinguished Service Order (DSO) A British decoration established in 1866 and awarded for distinguished service in war.

Distinguished Unit Citation The highest award given by the United States to any military unit in the United States or allied armed forces. The Distinguished Unit Citation, first established by executive order in 1942, is given "for extraordinary heroism in action against an armed enemy of the U.S." It takes precedence over all other U.S. unit citations.

distributed fire Fire so dispersed as to engage an area target most effectively.

distribution **1.** The arrangement of troops for any purpose, such as a battle, march, or maneuver. **2.** A planned pattern of projectiles about a point. **3.** A planned spread of fire to cover a desired frontage or depth. **4.** An official delivery of anything, such as orders or supplies. **5.** That functional phase of military logistics which embraces the act of dispensing materiel, facilities, and services.

distribution point A point at which supplies and/or ammunition, obtained from supporting supply points by a division or other unit, are broken down for distribution to subordinate units. Distribution points usually carry no stocks; items drawn are issued completely as soon as possible.

ditch **1.** A trench dug in the earth and used by soldiers for protection from enemy fire; a trench along the outside of a fort wall. **2.** To crash-land a landplane on water.

ditching The controlled landing of a distressed aircraft on water.

dive A rapid descent by an aircraft or missile, nose downward, with or without power or thrust. The airspeed is greater than the maximum speed in horizontal flight.

dive-bomb To release one or more aerial bombs at a target when the bombing plane is in a dive, especially a steep dive.

dive bomber An airplane especially designed and equipped to carry out dive-bombing attacks. The dive bomber must be built so that it can pull out of a steep dive, if necessary, with its bomb or bombs still attached and without breaking apart.

dive bombing The action of bombing a target from a diving airplane.

Diver A U.S. Navy radar-guided air-to-surface torpedo based on a 1,000-lb bomb. It was developed by the National Bureau of Standards after World War II and was part of a family of winged torpedos that led to the development of **Petrel,** which see.

diversion **1.** The act of drawing the attention and forces of an enemy from the point of the principal operation; an attack, alarm, or feint which diverts attention. **2.** A change made in a prescribed route for operational or tactical reasons. A diversion order will not constitute a change of destination. **3.** The rerouting of cargo or passengers to a new transshipment point of destination or on a different mode of transportation prior to arrival at the ultimate destination.

diversionary attack An attack wherein a force attacks, or threatens to attack, a target other than the main target for the purpose of drawing enemy defenses away from the main effort.

diversionary landing An operation in which troops are actually landed for the purpose of diverting enemy reaction away from the main landing.

divert **1.** A command meaning "proceed to divert field or carrier as specified." **2.** To change the target, mission, or destination of an airborne flight.

Dodge weapons carrier. (*U.S. Army.*)

divided fire Fire of a ship's batteries that is directed against two targets.

diving planes (bow and stern) Control surfaces on the bow and stern of a submarine used to control motion underwater in a vertical plane.

division **1.** A tactical unit or formation as follows: **a.** A major administrative and tactical unit or formation which combines in itself the necessary arms and services required for sustained combat, larger than a regiment or brigade and smaller than a corps. **b.** A number of naval ships of similar type grouped together for operational and administrative command, or a tactical unit of a naval aircraft squadron, consisting of two or more sections. **c.** An air division is an air combat organization normally consisting of two or more wings with appropriate service units. The combat wings of an air division will normally contain similar units. **2.** An organizational part of a headquarters that handles military matters of a particular nature, such as personnel, intelligence, plans and training, or supply and evacuation. **3.** A number of personnel of a ship's complement grouped together for operational and administrative command.

division artillery Artillery that is perma-

nently an integral part of a division. For tactical purposes, all artillery placed under the command of a division commander is considered division artillery.

division direct-support missile See **Missile A.**

division support missile See **Missile B.**

Dixie Cup A U.S. ballistic-missile penetration aid in the form of a metallic reentry vehicle-shaped decoy that radiates electronic jamming signals before the ICBM enters the earth's atmosphere.

DL A U.S. Navy frigate; a large destroyer-type vessel of about 3,700 tons displacement.

DLG A U.S. Navy guided-missile frigate.

DLGN A U.S. Navy guided-missile frigate, nuclear-powered.

DM **1.** A U.S. Navy destroyer minelayer. **2.** The U.S. military designation for the war gas **adamsite,** which see.

DMS A U.S. Navy high-speed minesweeper.

DMZ A demilitarized zone, such as the zone separating North and South Vietnam.

DNSS Defense Navigation Satellite System. A U.S. Air Force system using a radio-ranging concept to provide data for latitude, longitude, and altitude calculation by aircraft, ships, or land-based vehicles.

dock A large basin either permanently filled with water (wet dock) or capable of being filled and drained (dry dock or graving dock). It is an inaccurate term for "pier" or "wharf."

Dodge weapons carrier A ¾-ton 4 × 4 (four-wheeled, four-wheel drive) weapons carrier developed by Dodge in 1942 and produced in large numbers during World War II. Also called "Beep," possibly from "beefed-up Jeep," this vehicle had a weight of 5,650 lb and was powered by a six-cylinder engine of 92 bhp (brake horsepower).

dogface A slang expression (particularly in World War II) for an infantryman or ordinary soldier in the U.S. Army.

dogfight Aerial combat between fighter-type aircraft. It usually involves considerable maneuvering and violent aerobatics by both sides.

doghead The viselike device which holds the pyrite on a wheel lock.

dog lock An English lock having a horizontal sear and a dog catch or safety which enables the shooter to place the weapon at half cock.

dog tag A slang term for an identification disk.

dolabra An ancient hatchet. The earliest forms were made of flint.

Dolphin The name of a Douglas twin-engine amphibian built for the U.S. Army and Navy in 1931–1932.

dolphins The handles cast on cannon, the early ones being in the form of dolphins. The two handles were placed over the center of gravity.

Dominator. (*U.S. Air Force.*)

Dornier Do 18. (*The Smithsonian Institution, National Air Museum.*)

dome The mound of water spray thrown up into the air when the shock wave from an underwater detonation of a nuclear (or atomic) weapon reaches the surface.

Dominator A large U.S. four-engine bomber first flown in 1942. Built by Convair and sometimes referred to as the "Super B-24," this airplane had a crew of 10 and could carry 8,000 lb of bombs. Only 115 were made.

Dominie A de Havilland twin-engine biplane first used by the British RAF in the mid-1930s. See **Dragon Rapide.**

doodlebug A slang term for the V-1, or German flying bomb.

Doolittle raid An air raid carried out by B-25's against Tokyo on April 18, 1942. It represented the first strike against the home islands of Japan during World War II. The bombers, flown from an aircraft carrier, were led by Lt. Col. (later Lt. Gen.) James H. Doolittle.

door bundle A bundle for manual ejection in flight, normally followed by parachutists.

dope A cellulose-nitrate liquid, normally colorless, applied to the fabric surfaces of aircraft to render the fabric taut, waterproof, airtight, or gastight.

Doppler radar A radar system which differentiates between fixed and moving targets by detecting the apparent change in frequency of the reflected wave due to motion of the target or the observer.

Doria A class of Italian battleships of 23,622 tons standard displacement completed in 1915–1916 and rebuilt in 1937–1940. *Andrea Doria* and *Caio Duilio* were in the class. They had a length of 611 ft, a beam of 92 ft, a speed of 27 knots, and a complement of 1,198 men. They were armed with ten 12.6-in., twelve 5.3-in., and ten 3.5-in. guns, plus nineteen 37mm and twelve 20mm antiaircraft guns.

Dornier Do 17 A four-seat twin-engine medium bomber developed by Germany in 1935. The Do 17Z was introduced in 1938 and flew at a top speed of 224 mph. It was armed with six 7.9mm machine guns and carried an internal bombload of about 2,200 lb.

Dornier Do 18 A German twin-engine (tractor and pusher) maritime reconnaissance flying boat first flown in 1935.

Dornier Do 24 A German three-engine maritime reconnaissance and transport flying boat first flown in 1937.

Dornier Do 217 A German four-seat twin-engine aircraft that was originally developed as a heavy bomber and first flown in 1938. Later versions of the aircraft were used as night bombers and high-altitude reconnaissance bombers. The Do 217M was introduced in 1942 and was equipped with two 1,750-hp engines. It had a maximum speed of 348 mph and was armed with two 13mm machine guns and four 7.9mm ma-

Dornier Do 217. (*The Smithsonian Institution, National Air Museum.*)

chine guns. It carried a bombload of about 8,800 lb.

Dornier Do 217J and 217N German twin-engine three-seat night fighters developed in 1942 by converting Do 217E-2 bombers. The conversion consisted mostly of redesigning the nose to carry four 20mm cannons and four 7.9mm machine guns. Radar was also installed on later models.

Dornier Do 335 Pfeil The Pfeil (Arrow) was a German single-seat fighter-bomber of unconventional design that was first flown in 1943. It had an engine in the nose and a second engine amidships in the fuselage that drove a pusher propeller behind the tail. It reached speeds of 413 mph and was armed with one cannon and two machine guns.

Dorsetshire A class of British 9,950-ton cruisers completed in 1930. They included *Dorsetshire* and *Norfolk*, and each had a length of 630 ft, a speed of 32 knots, a complement of 650 men, and main armament consisting of eight 8-in. and eight 4-in. guns, plus eight 21-in. torpedo tubes and one aircraft.

double action A method of fire in a revolver and in old-style rifles and shotguns in which a single pull of the trigger both cocks and fires the weapon.

double balteus A belt used by the Romans to carry the sword and dagger.

double-banked frigate See **frigate,** sense 3.

double banker See **frigate,** sense 3.

double-base powder A propellant containing nitrocellulose and nitroglycerin. A single-base powder has only nitrocellulose as its base.

double-decker An old nautical term for a man-of-war with two gun decks.

double-headed shot A bar shot.

double pieces Supplementary pieces of a suit of armor to adapt the basic unit for use in the field or in a tournament.

double time A rate of marching at 180 steps per minute, each step being 3 ft in length; also, the command to march at this rate. It was formerly called "double-quick."

doublet of defense An obsolete term for a brigandine.

doughboy A World War I slang term for a U.S. Army infantryman.

Dove 1. A U.S. Navy air-to-surface solid-propellant infrared homing rocket of World War II. It was developed by Eastman Kodak Company and was identified as XASM-N-4 and XASM-N-5. **2.** Operation Dove was the code name for the main Allied glider operation during the invasion of Southern France on August 15, 1944. It involved the landing of 332 towed gliders and 2,762 paratroopers.

down 1. A term used by an observer or spotter to indicate that he is unable to determine the difference in range between the target and a round or rounds. **2.** To

Dornier Do 335 Pfeil. (*The Smithsonian Institution, National Air Museum.*)

Dragon. (*McDonnell Douglas Corporation.*)

shoot down an aircraft or other object.

downgrade To lower a security classification previously assigned.

DP **1.** The U.S. military designation for the war gas **diphosgene,** which see. **2.** The abbreviation for "displaced person."

draft The induction of persons into military service, especially under the U.S. Selective Training and Service Act of 1940 and the Selective Service Act of 1948. See **selective service.**

dragon **1.** An old name for a musketoon or short musket carried hooked on a soldier's shoulder belt. **2.** An armored tractor once used for towing artillery. **3.** An old type of artillery that fired a 40-lb ball.

Dragon The XFGM-77A medium antitank assault weapon (MAW), the name formerly applied, is a one-man-operated weapon designed to defeat tanks and other tactical targets and fills the medium role in the U.S. Army's family of such weapons—the M72 (light) and TOW (heavy). Either shoulder-fired or bipod-launched, Dragon is guided by electronic pulses sent through wires which accompany the missile in flight. Lateral and vertical direction are accomplished through the triggering of short jetlike bursts vented through nozzles completely encircling the missile. It has a weight of 27 lb and a range of 3,280 ft. It was developed by McDonnell Douglas and first fired in 1968.

Dragonfly A U.S. Cessna-built two-place twin-turbojet light close-support and counterinsurgency aircraft. It is used by the forces of the United States and South Vietnam, has a speed of 476 mph, and carries a 7.62mm Minigun and other weapons. The A-37A was developed from the T-37 trainer in 1963. The A-37B (twice as heavy as the T-37) was first flown in 1967.

Dragon Rapide The de Havilland DH.89 was a twin-engine biplane first flown in 1934. Called the **Dominie** (which see) by the British RAF, this aircraft remained in con-tinuous production until 1946.

Dragonship The U.S. Air Force AC-47 gunship aircraft.

Dragon's Teeth A World War II term for concrete pillars or iron posts erected as tank barriers.

dragon volant An old type of artillery piece that fired a 32-lb ball.

dragoon A mounted infantryman armed with a short musket called a "dragon" or "dragoon." The term later referred to heavily equipped cavalry soldiers. Dragoons were first employed in Europe in the sixteenth century.

Dragoon The World War II code name for the Allied invasion of the southeastern Mediterranean coast of France. It began on August 15, 1944.

drake **1.** A small artillery piece used in the seventeenth and eighteenth centuries. **2.** A Viking ship or galley.

Drake **1.** The popular name for a U.S. Army 8-ton amphibious truck. **2.** A class of 14,000-ton British cruisers completed in 1902–1903. There were four ships in the class, and they had a length of 529 ft, a complement of 900 men, and main armament consisting of two 9.2-in. and sixteen 6-in. guns. They had a speed of about 25 knots.

Draken **1.** A class of Swedish submarines of 835 tons standard surface displacement completed in 1961–1962. They have a length of 229.7 ft, a submerged speed of 25 knots, and armament consisting of four 21-in. torpedo tubes. **2.** The Saab-35 Draken (Dragon) is a jet interceptor and ground-attack aircraft first flown in 1955 and currently in service with the Swedish Air Force. It has a top speed of Mach 2, is armed with two 30mm Aden guns, and has nine attachments for weapons such as bombs, rocket packs, and missiles.

drakkar A Norse sailing craft capable of carrying men and horses. The vessel had a high prow shaped like a dragon.

Dreadnought **1.** The first British nuclear-powered submarine, commissioned in 1963 and having a standard surface displacement of 3,000 tons. It has a length of 265.8 ft, a beam of 32.2 ft, a speed of about 30 knots, and a complement of 88 men. It is armed with six 21-in. torpedo tubes. **2.** A British 17,900-ton battleship completed in 1906. It was 526 ft in length and had a crew of 800, a speed of 22 knots, and main armament consisting of ten 12-in. guns and twenty-four 12-pounders, plus five 18-in. torpedo tubes.

Dresden A class of German small cruisers of 3,600 tons completed in 1908–1909. They had a speed of 24.5 knots, a complement of 321 men, and main armament consisting of ten 4.1-in. guns, eight 5-pounder guns, and two 17.7-in. torpedo tubes. A sister ship, the *Emden,* operated in the Indian

Draken. (*U.S. Navy.*)

Ocean as a raider in the early part of World War I. She sank 15 ships before she was finally sunk by H.M.A.S. *Sydney* in November 1914.

dress To arrange soldiers in exact lines at proper distances.

dress cap A cap worn with dress uniforms.

dress coat The coat worn as part of a dress uniform.

dressing station A place for the early treatment of the wounded in battle. Sometimes called an "aid station."

dress uniform A uniform for formal wear.

Dreyse 7.92mm machine gun Model 1912 A German recoil-operated water-cooled machine gun with a rate of fire of 550 to 600 rounds per minute. It had a weight of 37.5 lb and was fed from a 200-round link belt.

Dreyse machine gun M1918 See **German 7.92mm machine gun MG 13.**

Dreyse rifle The Dreyse rifle, or "needle gun," was developed by J. N. von Dreyse, a German inventor, in 1836. It was a single-shot breechloading rifle with a bolt-breech action. It fired a conical bullet encased in a paper cartridge with a powder charge. The bolt of the rifle contained a long needle that penetrated the paper cartridge, passed through the propellant, and detonated a primer attached to the base of the bullet. This weapon, in .607 cal., was adopted by the Prussian Army in 1840 and remained in service through the war with Austria (1866) and the war with France (1870).

drift 1. The lateral deviation of the trajectory from the plane of departure, caused by rotation of the projectile. As a result of drift, the horizontal trace of the trajectory is a curved, rather than a straight, line. 2. The amount of sidewise movement or displacement caused by a side wind acting on an aircraft, ship, or barrage balloon. 3. The slow spreading of a chemical cloud by gravity and wind.

drifting mine A mine which is designed with no provision for maintaining a fixed position after planting. It is free to move with the waves, current, and wind. Drifting mines may watch at the surface or may be kept at a set depth by depth-control devices. A special type of drifting mine is the oscillating mine, which rises and falls gently as it continuously seeks its point of balance.

drill Exercises for instructing troops consisting of the manual of arms, marching, and other repetitive exercises for discipline or training.

drill ammunition Inert ammunition used for training.

drill book A manual of instructions in military drill.

drill sergeant A noncommissioned officer responsible for training recruits. Later

Dreyse rifle. (*The Smithsonian Institution, R. G. Packard Collection.*)

called a "drill instructor."

drogue 1. A fabric-covered piece of equipment shaped like the frustum of a cone and normally used as a towed target, a wind sock, a sea anchor, or a kind of parachute to stabilize or slow down an aircraft in flight. 2. A funnel-shaped piece of equipment at the end of a hose. It is trailed behind a tanker aircraft and is used in a certain method of air refueling.

droman A Byzantine warship, usually a two-banked galley with two lateen-rigged masts, 30 to 40 oars to a side, and a complement of about 300 men.

drone antisubmarine helicopter (DASH) A small, lightweight, remotely controlled helicopter capable of operating from a destroyer and delivering an antisubmarine-warfare weapon to an enemy submarine. It provides destroyers with a standoff weapon. The popular name is DASH. Designated as QH-50, the QH-50A can carry a 265-lb weapon within a combat radius of 29 mi; the QH-50B, a 500-lb weapon within a combat radius of 30 mi; and the QH-50C, a 750-lb weapon within a combat radius of 30 mi.

drones 1. Basically, unmanned vehicles that take the place of manned aircraft. They include modified aircraft that have been removed from service as well as craft designed specifically for target or reconnaissance missions. 2. Landing craft loaded with explosives and used in landing operations during World War II. See **apex boats** for details.

droop 1. The bending of a structure due to its own weight, such as the curvature of a very long tube in a heavy-artillery piece. 2. Formerly, the wearing away of the muzzle of a smoothbore gun after much firing.

drop 1. The action of dropping a bomb. 2. The vertical drop of a projectile. 3. A

drone antisubmarine helicopter (DASH), carrying a Mark 46-0 torpedo. (*U.S. Navy.*)

drone. (*U.S. Army.*)

drop tank.   Two 100-gal fuel drop tanks are on each wing of this U.S. Air Force A-37B aircraft. (*U.S. Air Force.*)

parachute jump, individual or en masse; supply delivery by parachute; or the act of making such a jump or delivery.

drop angle   See **range angle.**

dropmaster   1. An individual qualified to prepare, perform acceptance inspection, load, lash, and eject material for airdrop. **2.** An aircrewman who, during parachute operations, relays any required information between pilot and jumpmaster.

drop panel   A strip of cloth, usually in combination with other panels, used to mark on the ground the area in which

personnel or equipment is to be dropped from aircraft.

dropping angle   In bombing, the angle formed by the line of sight to the aiming point and a vertical line at the bomb-release point.

drop point   The point in the air at which personnel or supplies are dropped into a drop zone or area.

drop tank   A tank, generally used to carry additional fuel, which can be detached while in flight and dropped. Drop tanks are sometimes used in napalm bombing.

drop zone   A specified area upon which airborne troops, equipment, or supplies are dropped.

Drottning Victoria   The sister ship of the Swedish armored ship **Gustaf V,** which see.

drum   1. A cylindrical magazine for feeding ammunition to certain types of automatic weapons.   **2.** A musical percussion instrument long used for military signals and for marching cadences.

drumfire   The continuous firing of weapons along a front. The sound is similar to that of a drum.

drumhead court-martial   A court-martial convened on the battlefield or on the line of march; so called because it was sometimes held around a drumhead used as a table.

dry dock   See **dock.**

dry firing   Aiming, cocking, and squeezing the trigger of an unloaded firearm.

dry run   A rehearsal of any kind, as in torpedo firing, when all motions are gone through except the release of the torpedo.

DSC   Distinguished Service Cross, which see.

DSM   Distinguished Service Medal, which see.

DSO   Distinguished Service Order, which see.

D-Stoff   See **phosgene.**

DSU   Distinguished Unit Citation, which see.

dual (multicapable) weapons   1. Weapons, weapon systems, or vehicles capable of selective equipage with different types or mixes of armament or firepower. **2.** Sometimes restricted to weapons capable of handling either nuclear or nonnuclear munitions.

dual-purpose weapon   A weapon designed for delivering effective fire against air or surface targets.

duck   See **DUKW.**

Duck   The Grumman J2F-1/6 was a general-utility amphibian float seaplane first flown in 1933 and used by the U.S. Navy and Coast Guard. In production until 1945, this aircraft flew at speeds of 176 mph and was armed with two 100-lb bombs or two 325-lb bombs and sometimes a flexible .30 cal. machine gun.

Duckbill   A 12-gauge shotgun tested for possible use in Vietnam and so named because of its flat muzzle, which spreads buckshot in a fan-shaped pattern. It was developed by the U.S. Army's Frankford Arsenal.

dud   Explosive munition such as a bomb or shell which has not been armed as intended or which has failed to explode after being armed.

dudgeon   A kind of wood used for the handles of daggers.

duffel bag   A water-repellent canvas bag for holding clothing and other personal belongings.

dugout   An underground shelter built to protect troops, ammunition, and materiel from gunfire.

Duke of Edinburgh   A class of British 13,550-ton cruisers completed in 1905–

drum, of a Soviet 7.62mm light machine gun DPM. (*U.S. Army.*)

Duck. (*Grumman Aerospace Corporation.*)

1906. There were two ships in the class, the name ship and *Black Prince*. They had a length of 480 ft, a complement of 704 men, and main armament consisting of six 9.2-in. and ten 6-in. guns. They had a speed of about 22 knots.

DUKW A U.S. Army 2½-ton amphibious truck. It has a speed of 50 mph and a range of 400 mi and is used for ferrying, lighter service, or the landing of troops. It is also called "duck."

Dulle-Griete A 13-ton wrought-iron bombard in Ghent that was made in 1430. It had a bore of 25 in. and fired a 700-lb stone.

Dumbo Originally, a World War II code word for the Cataline flying boat; it was named after the flying elephant in the Walt Disney animated cartoon. The term was later used to describe any seaplane used for search and rescue operations.

dumdum, dumdum bullet A bullet that flattens excessively on contact; a kind of expanding manstopping bullet. The name derives from Dumdum, India, where such bullets were first manufactured. The use of this type of bullet is forbidden under international law.

dummy 1. A nonexplosive bomb, projectile, or the like, or an object made to appear as one of these. 2. An object made to appear as an airplane, gun emplacement, tank, or the like from the air.

dummy ammunition Inert ammunition designed or adapted for use in training of the weapon's crew.

dummy cartridge A cartridge, used for drill purposes, that has no primer charge or powder charge.

dummy-head torpedo A torpedo that has no bursting charge in the warhead.

dummy message A message sent for some purpose other than its content; it may consist of dummy groups or have a meaningless text.

dummy mine A false or imitation land mine used to deceive the enemy or for training purposes.

dummy torpedo An item designed to be substituted for a torpedo when proof-checking the fitment requirements of the various launching devices. It is similar to its legitimate counterpart in outside configuration.

dump A temporary storage area, usually in the open, for bombs, ammunition, equipment, or supplies.

Duncan A class of British 14,000-ton battleships completed in 1903–1904. The class included *Duncan, Russell, Albemarle, Cornwallis,* and *Exmouth,* all of which had a length of 429 ft, a complement of 750 men, and main armament consisting of four 12-in. guns, twelve 6-in. guns, and four 18-in. torpedo tubes. They had a speed of 20 knots.

dunking (dunked) sonar Sonar gear towed submerged by an airship or helicopter. Also

DUKW. (*U.S. Army.*)

called "dipping sonar."

Dunkirk See **Dynamo.**

dunnite A high explosive developed in the United States by Lt. Col. B. W. Dunn; explosive D.

dusack A roughly made sixteenth-century German cutting sword made without a separate hilt.

Duster A self-propelled twin 40mm antiaircraft weapon developed for use against low-flying aircraft. Designated as M-42.

Dustoff Medical evacuation missions by helicopters in Vietnam.

Dutch 6.5mm machine gun Model 1920 A version of the **Lewis machine gun,** which see.

Dutch 6.5mm Madsen machine guns Dutch forces used seven models of the Madsen machine gun, from Model 1919 to Model 1939. See **Madsen machine guns.**

Dutch armored personnel carrier DAF YP 408 This system, developed between 1956 and 1958, has a crew of two (plus ten infantrymen), a weight of 12 tons, and a road speed of 50 mph; it is armed with one .50 cal. machine gun.

Dutch Mannlicher 6.5mm rifle Model 95 This weapon, adopted by the Netherlands in 1895, is basically the same as the Rumanian Model 1893 Mannlicher. Several carbine versions were made, including one with a folding bayonet for gendarmery use.

dynamite A high explosive consisting of nitroglycerin and/or nitroglycol and/or ammonium nitrate and other materials

with or without an inert base, packed in cylindrical paper cartridges or in bags. It is set off by a detonator and is used for general blasting purposes.

dynamite bomb A bundle of dynamite sticks used as a bomb.

dynamite gun A type of pneumatic cannon developed in the 1880s that fired a projectile filled with dynamite. The largest cannons of this type were 15-in. guns, a few of which were adopted by the U.S. Army for coast artillery purposes. Part of the system included a 10-ton air reservoir that held 680 cu ft of air at 1,000 psig. The 15-in. version placed 1,000-lb projectiles to a range of 2,100 yd (about 1.2 mi).

dynamite, military A blasting explosive in cartridges especially suitable for use in military construction, quarrying, and service demolition work. It has good storage stability, is rifle-bullet-insensitive, and can be detonated when wet.

Dynamo An Allied operation in which 338,226 men were evacuated from Dunkirk, France, to Dover, England, between May 26 and June 4, 1940.

Dynatrac A U.S. Army utility carrier (XM571) that is a fully tracked tactical and support vehicle consisting of two units with all tracks driven by a single air-cooled engine in the forward unit. Lightly armored and highly mobile, it can bridge a 4-ft trench and negotiate an 18-in. vertical wall; it has a speed of 32 mph on land (2 mph on water).

Duster. (*U.S. Army.*)

E

E I A class of Soviet nuclear-powered submarines armed with two 21-in. torpedo tubes and six launching tubes for Shaddock missiles. There are five submarines in the class. They have a standard surface displacement of 4,600 tons, a length of 385 ft, a beam of 33 ft, a speed of about 20 knots, and a complement of 92 men.

E-1 See **Tracer.**

E II A class of Soviet nuclear-powered submarines armed with six 21-in. torpedo tubes and eight launching tubes for Shaddock missiles. There are 25 submarines in the class. They have a standard surface displacement of 5,000 tons, a length of 393 ft, a beam of 33 ft, a speed of 22 knots, and a complement of 100 men.

E-2 See **Hawkeye.**

Eagle A British aircraft carrier (ex-*Audacious*) of 43,000 tons standard displacement completed in 1951 and reconstructed in 1959–1964. It has a length of 811 ft, a maximum flight-deck width of 171 ft, a speed of 31.5 knots, and a complement of 2,750 men with air squadrons. It carries 34 aircraft and 10 helicopters and is armed with eight 4.5-in. guns and six quadruple launchers for Seacat missiles. (An earlier aircraft carrier also bore the same name. The first *Eagle* had a displacement of 22,600 tons and was completed in 1918. It had a length of 667 ft, a speed of 32 knots, a complement of 748 men, and armament consisting of 35 antiaircraft guns. It carried 21 aircraft.)

Eagle Boats World War I U.S. Navy escort vessels.

Eagle Squadron Any of three RAF squadrons, composed of American volunteer pilots, that existed during the early days of World War II. The nucleus of the first Eagle Squadron consisted of former members of the French Squadron, modeled after the Lafayette Escadrille of World War I. Pilots in the Eagle Squadrons were transferred to the AAF in September 1942 and organized into the Fourth Fighter Group of the VIII Fighter Command.

Early Spring An antireconnaissance satellite-weapon system.

early warning See **air-defense early warning.**

early-warning radar In aircraft control and warning, a radar set or system set up or used near the periphery of a defended area to warn of approaching aircraft. Early-warning radar is designed to detect aircraft

Eagle. (*The Imperial War Museum.*)

Edsall. (*U.S. Navy.*)

at as great a distance as possible.

earthwork A temporary or permanent fortification for attack or defense made chiefly of earth.

Eastern Air Command A combined air command in India during World War II with operational control over AAF and RAF units in India and on the Burma front. It was organized under Maj. Gen. George E. Stratemeyer in December 1943 and dissolved on June 1, 1945.

East Wind A German antiaircraft tank consisting of a PzKpfw. IV chassis on which was mounted a 37mm gun. This gun, designated Flak 43, fired at the rate of 250 rounds per minute. The projectile weight was 1.4 lb, and the effective vertical range was about 5,000 ft. These vehicles were introduced in March 1944 and were employed as AA platoons of tank battalions. They had a crew of seven.

EB Early burst, indicating premature explosion of a warhead.

EC-2 The U.S. Navy designation for a Liberty-ship cargo vessel. This 441-ft ship is designated GR when converted to a patrol or picket vessel. See **GR** for photograph.

échauguette A kind of bartizan or watchtower.

echelon **1.** A subdivision of a headquarters, e.g., forward echelon or rear echelon. **2.** A separate level of command. As compared with a regiment, a division is a higher echelon; a battalion is a lower echelon. **3.** A fraction of a command, in the direction of depth, to which a principal combat mission is assigned, e.g., attack echelon, support echelon, or reserve echelon. **4.** A formation in which the subdivisions are placed one behind another, extending beyond and unmasking one another wholly or in part.

echo A radar echo; The signal received by

a radar set as a result of the reflection of a transmitted pulse from objects in the field of scan.

ECM Electronic countermeasures.

economic warfare The defensive use in peacetime, as well as during a war, of any means by military and civilian agencies to maintain or expand the economic potential for war of a nation and its (probable) allies and, conversely, the offensive use of any measure in peacetime or wartime to diminish or neutralize the economic potential for war of the (likely) enemy and his accomplices.

ecoutes Small galleries made in front of the glacis of a fortification. They serve to interrupt enemy miners.

EC powder See **EC smokeless powder.**

ecrasite A high explosive, related to lyddite and melinite, formerly used in filling shells, especially in the Austrian service during World War II.

EC smokeless powder An explosive powder used chiefly in blank cartridges; also called "EC blank fire," "EC blank powder," and "EC powder." EC powder is used in some .22 cal. and shotgun ammunition and was formerly used in fragmentation grenades.

ecu A small shield of the fourteenth and fifteenth centuries. It was carried by mounted soldiers.

ED The U.S. military designation for the war gas **ethyldichloroarsine,** which see.

EDC The NATO abbreviation for European Defense Community.

edge The cutting part of a sword or similar weapon.

Edinburgh A class of British 10,000-ton cruisers that included *Edinburgh* and *Belfast*, completed in 1939. They had a length of 613 ft, a speed of 32.5 knots, and main armament consisting of twelve 6-in. guns,

twelve 4-in. guns, six 21-in. torpedo tubes, and four aircraft.

Edsall A class of U.S. escort ships (DE) of 1,200 tons standard displacement commissioned in 1943–1944. They had a length of 306 ft, a beam of 36.6 ft, a speed of 21 knots, and a complement of 149 men. They were armed with three 3-in. guns and up to eight 40mm antiaircraft guns, plus hedgehogs and depth charges. Thirty-six were converted to radar picket escort ships (DER), with two 3-in. guns, two triple torpedo launchers, and one trainable hedgehog.

effective ceiling AA The maximum vertical range within which an antiaircraft gun may engage for a period of 20 seconds an aircraft approaching directly at 300 mph, firing the last round at a quadrant elevation of 70°.

effective damage That damage necessary to render a target element inoperative, unserviceable, nonproductive, or uninhabitable.

effective firing time The period of time during which an aircraft can deliver effective fire at a moving or a stationary target.

effective range The maximum distance at which a weapon may be expected to fire accurately to inflict casualties or damage.

egg An escape capsule for multiplace high-speed aircraft.

eggs A World War II slang term, used by both the Allies and the Germans, for "bombs."

Eiche The code name for a German World War II operation which rescued Mussolini from a resort hotel on Gran Sasso Mountain in the Abruzzi, central Italy, after the Armistice with the Allies. It was led by S.S. Hauptsturmfuehrer Count Otto Skorzeny and took place on September 12, 1943.

ejection Escape from an aircraft by means

Emden. (*The Imperial War Museum.*)

of explosively propelled seats.

ejection seat A device which expels the pilot safely in an emergency from a high-speed airplane.

ejector A device in the breech mechanism of a gun, rifle, or the like which automatically throws out an empty cartridge case or unfired cartridge from the breech or receiver.

elbow cop A modern armor term, coined to correspond with the older "knee cop" and denoting the armor protecting the elbow.

elbow gauntlet In armor, a gauntlet made of plate that reached to the elbow. It was normally worn on the left arm only.

electron bomb A German World War II bomb having an incendiary charge and a combustible casing of magnesium. The name derives from the German trade name "Elektron."

electronic counter-countermeasures That major subdivision of electronic warfare involving actions taken to ensure effective use of electromagnetic radiations despite the enemy's use of countermeasures.

electronic countermeasures That major subdivision of electronic warfare involving actions taken to prevent or reduce the effectiveness of enemy equipment and tactics employing or affected by electromagnetic radiations and to exploit the enemy's use of such radiations.

electronic deception The deliberate radiation, reradiation, alteration, absorption, or reflection of electromagnetic radiations in a manner intended to mislead an enemy in the interpretation of data received by his electronic equipment or to present false indications to electronic systems. See also **electronic countermeasures** and **radio deception.**

Electronic Fence A U.S. program designed to create an electronic barrier across the demilitarized zone (DMZ) in Vietnam. It consisted of various anti-intrusion devices and detection and warning systems.

electronic fuze A fuze, such as a radio proximity fuze, set off by an electronic device incorporated in the fuze.

electronic intelligence Also called ELINT, the intelligence information product of activities involving the collection and processing, for subsequent intelligence purposes, of foreign noncommunications electromagnetic radiations emanating from other than nuclear detonations and radioactive sources.

electronic jamming The deliberate radiation, reradiation, or reflection of electromagnetic signals, including window jamming, with the object of impairing the use of electronic devices by the enemy.

Elephant 1. A German tank destroyer of World War II. It consisted of an 88mm antitank gun mounted on a Tiger chassis. Manufactured by Porsche KG/Alkett, this system was introduced in 1943 and carried a crew of six. It weighed 71.7 tons and had a road speed of 12 mph. In addition to the 88mm gun, it was armed with one 7.9mm MG-34. **2.** The World War I nickname for the Martinsyde G.100 and G.102 biplanes.

elevate To increase the angle of elevation of a gun or launcher.

elevating arc An upright, geared arc attached to a weapon or a carriage by means of which the weapon is elevated and depressed.

elevating screw A system employed on certain types of old ordnance in which a screw is used to raise the breech. This results in depression of the muzzle.

elevation 1. The angle of elevation. **2.** In antiaircraft artillery, the angular height is sometimes called "elevation," and dials on some equipment, which indicate angular height, are marked "elevation." **3.** The vertical distance, usually measured in feet or meters, above mean sea level (plus elevation) or below mean sea level (minus elevation).

elevation scale The scale on a gun carriage that shows the quadrant elevation of the gun.

elevation table A firing table giving a list of ranges, with the corresponding quadrant-elevation settings to be applied to a gun.

elevator A control surface, usually attached to the horizontal stabilizer, moved to make the tail of an aircraft go up or down.

ELF Electronic location finder. A U.S. electronic helicopter-to-ground locating system capable of finding and rescuing downed pilots under all weather and light conditions.

ELINT Electromagnetic intelligence. The U.S. Air Force 466L system which provides a worldwide network for the collection of intelligence by electromagnetic means and processing for transmission to users. Using fixed stations, specially equipped aircraft, and reconnaissance satellites, the system monitors, analyzes, and records electromagnetic emissions, thus identifying a foe's electronic order of battle, the nature and deployment of warning and missile-guidance radars, and fire-control and countermeasures systems.

El Kaher and El Zahir V-2-type ballistic missiles first fired by the United Arab Republic in July 1962. They use single-stage liquid-propellant engines and have a range of 220 to 300 mi.

embarkation The loading of troops with their supplies and equipment into ships and/or aircraft.

embattled parapet   A parapet having indentations alternating with solid parts, or "merlons."

emboîtment   A cuirass made from two or more plates, one overlapping the other.

embrasure   An opening in a wall or parapet, especially one through which a gun is fired. It is usually cut wider at the outside to permit the gun to swing through a greater arc.

emcon   *Em*ission *con*trol. A U.S. Navy term for electronic silence, a countermeasure against hostile ELINT (electronic intelligence) measures.

Emden   A German cruiser of 5,400 tons standard displacement built in 1925. It had a length of 508 ft, a beam of 47 ft, a speed of 29 knots, and a complement of 534 men. It had main armament consisting of eight 5.9-in. and three 3.5-in. guns, plus four torpedo tubes. It was scuttled at Kiel after a bombing attack in April 1945. (*Emden* was also the name of a German light cruiser completed in 1908. For details, see **Dresden.**)

emergency anchorage   An anchorage, which may have a limited defense organization, for naval vessels, mobile support units, auxiliaries, or merchant ships.

emergency barrage   An artillery barrage, essentially a standing (defensive) barrage for which the battery has target data and which is used to reinforce the normal barrage of some other battery.

emergency landing field   A place which is adapted, but not equipped, for the landing and taking off of aircraft.

Emily   The Allied code name for the Japanese Kawanishi H8K1/4 four-engine long-range maritime reconnaissance-bomber flying boat first flown in 1940. It had a crew of 10 and was armed with five 20mm cannons and four 7.7mm machine guns. It carried a 4,000-lb bombload and was the fastest (290 mph) flying boat used by any of the combatants in World War II. The first operational service of this aircraft took place when three Emily flying boats attempted a night attack on Oahu Island in March 1942. Based in the Marshall Islands, 2,000 mi distant, the aircraft refueled from a submarine en route. The attack had to be aborted because of a thick cloud cover over Oahu.

empennage   The assembly at the rear end of an aircraft comprised of the horizontal and vertical stabilizers and their associated control surfaces. Also called the "tail assembly."

emplace   To put in position; to fix a gun or launcher in a prepared position from which it may be fired.

emplacement   A prepared position for one or more weapons or pieces of equipment which provides protection against hostile fire or bombardment and from which they can execute their missions. (Picture,

Emily. (*U.S. Air Force.*)

next page.)

enarme, enarmes   The strap or straps that hold a shield on the arm.

encampment   The place where a body of troops encamps; a camp.

enceinte   The main wall or rampart constituting the enclosure of a fortress; also called the "body."

encipher   To convert a plain-text message into unintelligible language by means of a cipher system.

encounter   Formerly, combat or a battle.

encrypt   To convert a plain-text message into unintelligible form (cryptogram) by means of a cryptographic system.

endurance   The time an aircraft can continue flying or a vehicle or ship can continue operating under given conditions without refueling.

enemy capabilities   Those courses of action of which the enemy is physically capable and which, if adopted, will affect the accomplishment of a mission. The term "capabilities" includes not only the general courses of action open to the enemy, such as attack, defense, or withdrawal, but also all the particular courses of action possible under each general course of action. Enemy capabilities are considered in the light of all known factors affecting military opera-

empennage, of an OV-10A Bronco aircraft. (*U.S. Navy.*)

emplacement. (*U.S. Army.*)

Enfield rifle Pattern 1914 (P-14). (*The Smithsonian Institution, W. R. Arco Collection.*)

tions including time, space, weather, terrain, and the strength and disposition of enemy forces. In strategic thinking, the capabilities of a nation represent the courses of action within the power of the nation for accomplishing its national objectives in peacetime or wartime.

enfans perdus A term meaning "forlorn hope." Formerly, officers or men who were selected, usually from among volunteers, for dangerous service, such as leading an attack.

Enfield Pertaining to weapons (rifles, carbines, and pistols) made by the Royal En-

Entac. (*U.S. Army.*)

field Manufactury in Great Britain.

Enfield .380 cal. British Service Pistol (Revolver No. 2 Mk I) This revolver is based on the Webley pattern, and the only differences between it and the Revolver No. 1 Mark VI (Webley .455 cal.), besides caliber, are in the type of cylinder catch and the arrangement of the safety. The weapon has an overall length of $10\frac{1}{4}$ in., a barrel length of 5 in., a weight of about $27\frac{1}{2}$ oz., and a muzzle velocity of 600 fps. The cylinder capacity is six cartridges.

Enfield .577 cal. rifle-musket A single-shot muzzle-loading weapon used by the British Army from 1852 to 1866. It had a length of 54 in. and a weight of 8.9 lb. Many of these arms were used in the United States during the Civil War.

Enfield musket A muzzle-loading .577 cal. rifled musket generally used by the British Army from 1852 to 1866 and used in considerable numbers by U.S. troops in the Civil War.

Enfield rifle The popular name for the U.S. .30 cal. rifle Model 1917. It is a bolt-type breechloading magazine rifle and is the same as the Enfield rifle P-14.

Enfield rifle Pattern 1913 (P-13) A prototype rifle made with a modified Mauser-type action and an integral five-round magazine. It was designed for a high-velocity .276 cartridge. One thousand were made. This rifle was the forerunner of the P-14.

Enfield rifle Pattern 1914 (P-14) This rifle is basically the same weapon as the P-13 except that it is chambered for the .303 cartridge. It has a weight of about 9.5 lb, a barrel length of 26 in., and an overall length of approximately 46 in. In 1926 the British changed the nomenclature of this rifle from the P-14 to Rifle No. 3 Mark 1*. As produced in the United States in .30 cal., this weapon was called the "U.S. Rifle .30 cal. M1917."

enfilade To rake with gunfire; to fire down the length of a trench or line of troops.

engage To join battle or enter into conflict.

engagement An action or encounter with an enemy on land or sea.

engagement stars Small metal stars worn on campaign ribbons to denote the wearer's participation in specific battles or operations.

engineer The former title of an artillery-man or gunner. Now one of a corps or division of men who perform military engineering work.

engineering test An evaluation test of materiel under development conducted by, or under the supervision of, the technical service concerned, the purpose of which is to determine the inherent structural, electrical, or other physical and chemical qualities of the item or system tested, including those of an environmental nature. It is designed to provide a basis for decisions as to subsequent developmental action or the suitability of the item for **user test,** which see.

engine order telegraph A device on a ship's bridge by means of which orders are given to the engine room; also called an "annunciator."

engines, gyns Machines such as catapults, ballistas, and trebuchets used for throwing stones, arrows, and other missiles.

English lock A type of early seventeenth-century flintlock firing mechanism with a laterally acting sear and no half-cock position.

enlisted men Military personnel below the grade of warrant officer.

ensign 1. The most junior commissioned officer in the U.S. Navy. The insignia consists of a gold bar on the epaulets and $\frac{1}{2}$-in. gold strips on the shoulder marks and uniform sleeves. The grade is equivalent to that of a second lieutenant in the Army. 2. The national flag flown by a warship. 3. Formerly, a commissioned officer in the British Army who carried the ensign or flag of a company or regiment.

ensis The cavalry sword of the Romans.

Entac A roll-stabilized wire-guided anti-tank missile adopted by the French Army in 1957 and now standard equipment with a number of other countries, including the United States (where it is designated the MGM-32A). It has an overall length of 2 ft 8½ in., a launching weight of 26.9 lb, and a warhead weight of 9 lb. The shaped-charge warhead will penetrate more than 25 in. of steel armor. It has a range of 6,600 ft.

entanglement A system of defense consisting of concertina wire (coils of barbed wire) and supporting posts.

Enterprise **1.** A U.S. nuclear-powered attack aircraft carrier (CVAN) of 75,700 tons standard displacement commissioned in 1961 and, at that time, the largest warship ever built. It has a length of 1,123 ft, a flight-deck width of 257 ft (maximum), a speed of 35 knots, and a complement of over 5,000 men. It carries 70 to 100 aircraft, depending on type, and is armed with Sea Sparrow missiles. **2.** A U.S. aircraft carrier (CV) of 19,800 tons standard displacement commissioned in 1938. It had an overall length of 809.5 ft, an extreme flight-deck width of 109.5 ft, a top speed of 32.5 knots, and a complement of 2,919 men. It carried 85 aircraft and was armed with over 100 antiaircraft guns (total barrels). Other ships in this class were *Hornet* and *Yorktown*.

entrench To place in, or surround with, a trench.

entrenching tool Any tool, such as a folding shovel-pick combination, that can be used for making an entrenchment, a foxhole, etc.

entrenchment A defensive work consisting of a trench and a parapet.

envelope In fortifications, a small rampart raised in the ditch, or beyond it, to cover a weak part in the defensive works.

envelopment A two-part attack designed to envelop an enemy. It consists of a frontal, or *holding*, attack and a flanking or, *enveloping*, attack.

Enzian (German code word) A subsonic ground-to-air winged guided rocket directed by radio pulse signals. It was developed by the Germans during World War II.

EOD Explosive-ordnance disposal. A term applied to missions and units for deactivating and disposing of excess munitions.

epaule In fortifications, a work of earth forming a rough parapet. It is used chiefly as a cover from flanking fire.

epaulet, epaulette An ornament or badge worn on the shoulders of the uniforms of some military and naval officers. It usually consists of a strap ending in a fringed pad.

épaulière, espauliere A piece of armor that protected the shoulder and connected the breastplate and backpiece. It was made of flexible, overlapping plates.

épée A sharp-pointed sword without a cutting edge used in fencing and dueling. It has a bowl-shaped guard.

Epperson A class of U.S. destroyers (DD) similar in most respects to the modernized **Gearing** class, which see.

Enterprise. (*U.S. Navy.*)

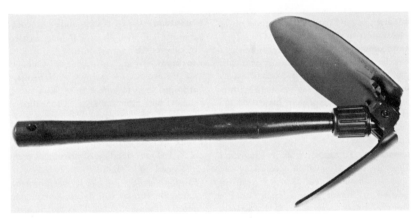

entrenching tool. (*U.S. Army.*)

eprouvette A device for testing gunpowder. In the days before strict quality control of powder, it was necessary to test each lot to determine its strength.

equipage The accouterments or necessary equipment of a soldier or a body of troops. Also, the furnishings and supplies of a vessel fitting her for service.

equipment All articles needed to outfit an individual or organization. The term refers to clothing, tools, utensils, vehicles, weapons, and other similar items. As to type of authorization, equipment may be divided into special (or project) equipment, equipment prescribed by tables of allowances, and equipment prescribed by tables of organization and equipment.

equivalent service rounds (ESR) A standard for indicating gun erosion. All rounds fired, including reduced charges, are recorded in terms of service rounds.

Erika A Swedish Navy ship-to-underwater

missile with a weight of 550 lb and a range of 2,000 meters. The prime contractor is A. B. Bofors.

erosion The enlargement or wearing away of the bore of a weapon as a result of the

epaulet. (*The Smithsonian Institution.*)

espontoon. *(The Smithsonian Institution.)*

movement of high-temperature gases and residues generated from the burning of the propellant, chemical action, and friction between the projectile and the bore.

escadrille A French air unit comprised of six airplanes. Also, a squadron of warships, usually eight in number.

escalade A military attack on a fortified place in which ladders are used to scale the ramparts.

escalation An increase in the scope or violence of a conflict, deliberate or unpremeditated.

escape and evasion intelligence Intelligence prepared for use by military personnel who may be captured by the enemy or at large in enemy territory.

escapee Any person who has been physically captured by the enemy and succeeds in freeing himself.

escape hatch A submarine compartment specially fitted to receive a rescue chamber or to charge submarine escape lungs.

escarp In fortifications, the surface of the ditch next to the rampart.

escarpment The ground surrounding a fortified place, cut away nearly vertically to prevent an enemy's approach.

escopette, escopet A seventeenth-century wheel-lock carbine or short firearm with a hinged stock. When folded back on itself, it could be carried in a holster like a long pistol.

escort 1. To convoy. 2. A combatant unit or units assigned to accompany and protect another force. 3. An aircraft assigned to protect other aircraft during a mission. 4. An armed guard that accompanies a convoy, a train, prisoners, etc. 5. An armed guard accompanying persons as a mark of honor. 6. A member of the armed forces assigned to accompany, assist, or guide an individual or group, e.g., an escort officer.

escort carrier In the U.S. Navy, a small auxiliary aircraft carrier or a converted tanker or cargo ship with flight deck and hangar decks added.

escort fighter A fighter designed or equipped for long-range missions, usually as

an escort for heavy bombers on raids.

escort forces Combat forces of various types provided to protect other forces against enemy attack.

escort ship A warship designed to screen support forces and convoys and to operate against submarines. The normal armament consists of 5-in. or 3-in. dual-purpose guns and various antisubmarine-warfare weapons. Designated as DE.

espadon A fifteenth-century double-edged two-handed sword.

espingole A type of muzzle-loading firearm which was loaded with several balls and charges separated from one another but connected by a powder train. After the first ball was fired, the others fired in succession.

espionage Actions directed toward the acquisition of information through clandestine operations.

esplanade In fortifications, the clear space between a citadel and the nearest houses of a city. Such a space made it impossible for an enemy to erect breaching batteries under cover of the houses.

espontoon A seventeenth- and eighteenth-century half-pike, about 7 ft long, carried by officers who served on foot.

espringal An ancient engine of war used for throwing vires (arrows with feathers arranged so as to impart spin), large darts, stones, and other missiles. Also called a "springal" or "springald."

ESR See **equivalent service rounds.**

Essex A class of U.S. aircraft carriers (CV) of 27,100 tons standard displacement commissioned in 1942–1946. Included were *Essex, Yorktown, Intrepid, Hornet, Franklin, Lexington, Bunker Hill, Wasp, Bennington,* and *Bonhomme Richard.* They had an overall length of 872 ft, an extreme flight-deck width of 147.5 ft, a top speed of 33 knots, and a complement of 3,488 men. They carried 100 aircraft and were armed with over 80 antiaircraft guns (total barrels). Twenty-three ships of this class were completed.

establishment 1. An installation, together with its personnel and equipment, organized as an operating entity. 2. The table setting out the authorized numbers of men and pieces of major equipment in a unit-

formation; sometimes called "table of organization" or "table of organization and equipment."

estacade A dike made of piles or stakes driven in the sea or a river to check an enemy's approach.

estimate of the situation A logical process of reasoning by which a commander considers all the circumstances affecting the military situation and arrives at a decision as to the course of action to be taken in order to accomplish his mission.

estoc A sixteenth-century thrust sword with a stiff blade of triangular or square section.

estramacon A type of double-edged sword.

ETA Estimated time of arrival.

ETD Estimated time of departure.

ETE Estimated time en route.

Etendard IV-M A French Dassault single-seat carrier-based jet fighter and fighter-bomber first flown in 1956. It has a speed of Mach 1.02 and is armed with one or two 30mm cannons and 3,000 lb of bombs, rockets, or air-to-surface missiles.

Ethan Allen A class of U.S. fleet ballistic-missile submarines (SSBN) of 6,900 tons standard surface displacement commissioned in 1960–1962. There are five of these nuclear-powered submarines in the class. They have a length of 410.5 ft, a beam of 33 ft, a speed of about 30 knots submerged, and a complement of 112 men. They are armed with four 21-in. torpedo tubes and carry 16 tubes for Polaris missiles.

ethyldichloroarsine (ED) This war gas is a blister agent and has a delayed-action casualty effect. As with other chemical agents containing arsenic, ED is irritating to the respiratory tract and produces lung injury upon sufficient exposure. The vapor is irritating to the eyes, and the liquid may produce severe eye injury. The absorption of either vapor or liquid through the skin in sufficient amounts may lead to systemic poisoning or death. Called "Green Cross 3" and *Dick* by the Germans during World War I, this gas also causes vomiting and paralysis of the hands. See **blistering agents.**

ETO In World War II, the European theater of operations.

etoiles Small redoubts in fortifications.

ETR Estimated time of return.

Essex. *(U.S. Navy.)*

European–African–Middle-Eastern Campaign Medal A U.S. military decoration awarded persons under certain specified conditions for service within the European–African–Middle-Eastern theater of war between December 7, 1941 and November 8, 1945.

European theater A World War II theater of operations covering Europe, exclusive of Italy, Greece, and the Balkans, and included in the European–African–Middle-Eastern theater of war.

evacuation **1.** The process of moving any person who is wounded, injured, or ill to or between medical treatment facilities. **2.** The clearance of personnel, animals, or materiel from a given locality. **3.** The controlled process of collecting, classifying, and shipping unserviceable or abandoned materiel, U.S. and foreign, to appropriate reclamation, maintenance, technical intelligence, or disposal facilities.

evacuation-control ship In an amphibious operation, a ship designated as a control point for landing craft, amphibious vehicles, and helicopters evacuating casualties from the beaches.

evacuation hospital A mobile hospital or hospital unit used near the front for providing major medical and surgical care and for preparing and sorting casualties for further evacuation.

evacuee A civilian removed from his place of residence by military direction for reasons of his own security or because of the requirements of the military situation.

evader Any person who has become isolated in hostile or unfriendly territory and who eludes capture.

evaluation (intelligence) The appraisal of an item of information in terms of credibility, reliability, pertinency, and accuracy. Appraisal or evaluation of items of information or intelligence is indicated by a standard letter-number system. The evaluation of the reliability of sources is designated by a letter from A through F, and the accuracy of the information is designated by a numeral from 1 through 6. These are two entirely independent, separate appraisals, and they are indicated in accordance with the system shown below. Thus, information adjudged to be "probably true" received from a "usually reliable" source is designated "B-2" or "B2," while information of which the "truth cannot be judged" received from a "usually reliable" source is designated "B-6" or "B6."

Reliability of source	Accuracy of information
A—Completely reliable	1—Confirmed by other sources
B—Usually reliable	2—Probably true
C—Fairly reliable	3—Possibly true
D—Not usually reliable	4—Doubtful
E—Unreliable	5—Improbable
F—Reliability cannot be judged	6—Truth cannot be judged

evasion and escape The procedures and operations whereby military personnel and other selected individuals are enabled to emerge from an enemy-held or hostile area to areas under friendly control.

evasive steering Ship tactics to confuse submarines, including zigzagging, sinuating, and weaving.

evening gun The firing of a gun as a signal for the lowering of a flag at retreat. The gun is fired after the sounding of the last note of the bugle call at retreat. Also called "retreat gun."

evolution A maneuver, either of a body of troops or of a ship or fleet of ships; the process of passing from one formation to another.

evzone At one time, a member of a select Greek infantry corps.

examining post A post set up in the field to examine all persons attempting to pass the lines.

executive officer The second in command of a ship, station, aircraft squadron, etc.

exercise A military maneuver or simulated wartime operation involving planning, preparation, and execution. It is carried out for the purpose of training and evaluation. It may be a combined, unified, joint, or single service exercise, depending on the participating organizations.

Exeter A British 8,390-ton cruiser completed in 1931. It had a length of 540 ft, a beam of 58 ft, a speed of 32 knots, and a complement of 600 men. It was armed with six 8-in., eight 4-in., and four 3-pounder guns, plus six 21-in. torpedo tubes and two aircraft.

Exocet A French solid-propellant two-stage surface-to-surface tactical missile developed to protect surface warships against other surface vessels. It entered service in 1971, and has a weight of about 1,540 lb (of which 330 to 440 lb is warhead) and a range of about 20 nautical miles.

expanding bullet A bullet with a soft nose, such as a **dumdum,** which see, designed to flatten out when it hits its target.

expeditionary force An armed force or-

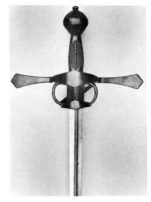

estoc. (*The Metropolitan Museum of Art, gift of William H. Riggs, 1913.*)

ganized to accomplish a specific objective in a foreign country.

Expeditor A U.S. Beech-built aircraft first flown in 1937 and used during World War II by the Allies as a light transport and trainer. When operational with the U.S. Air Force, it was designated C-45.

expendable supplies and material Supplies which are consumed in use, such as ammunition, paint, fuel, cleaning and preserving materials, surgical dressings, drugs, medicines, etc., or which lose their identity, such as spare parts, etc. Sometimes referred to as "consumable supplies and material."

expenditure The consumption of ammunition by an organization. For purposes of record, with certain exceptions (nuclear weapons and designated missile items), ammunition is considered expended when issued to the user. Special ammunition is considered expended when a delivery unit notifies a supporting-ordnance special-ammunition unit and the fire-direction center of this fact.

experimental aircraft An aircraft built to try out an idea or to try to develop certain capabilities or characteristics; an aircraft that embodies a new principle or a new application of an old principle. The purpose of the Chance Vought XF5U-1 experimental fighter was to develop an aircraft

Ethan Allen. (*U.S. Navy.*)

experimental aircraft, the XF5U-1, developed for the U.S. Navy at the end of World War II. (*Vought Aeronautics Company.*)

extraction parachute. (*U.S. Air Force.*)

with a wide speed range (a landing speed of 40 mph and a maximum speed of 425 mph), but testing was discontinued in 1947. This airplane was nicknamed the "Flying Pancake."

expert The highest classification given for skill in the use of small arms in the U.S. military. The next classifications, in order, are Sharpshooter and Marksman.

exploitation **1.** Taking full advantage of success in battle and following up initial gains. **2.** Taking full advantage of any information that has come to hand for tactical or strategic purposes. **3.** In intelligence usage, the process of getting information from any source.

exploratory minesweeping A minesweeping operation whose purpose is to determine the presence or absence of mines rather than to destroy them.

explosive A substance or mixture of substances which may be made to undergo a rapid chemical change, without an outside supply of oxygen, with the liberation of large quantities of energy generally accompanied by the evolution of hot gases. Explosives are divided into two classes—high explosives and low explosives—according to their rate of reaction in normal usage.

explosive bullet A bullet which contains an explosive and is detonated on contact with its target or via a time fuze. Such bullets were banned for small arms by international agreement in 1868.

explosive D So called from the initial of Col. B. W. Dunn, the inventor. Also called "dunnite." A high explosive consisting mainly of ammonium picrate. It is used in some armor-piercing projectiles because of its comparative insensitivity to shock and friction.

explosive ordnance Ordnance materiel which normally contains or consists of explosives, for example, bombs, mines, torpedoes, missiles, and projectiles.

explosive-ordnance-disposal unit Personnel with special training and equipment who render explosive ordnance safe (such as bombs, mines, projectiles, and booby traps), make intelligence reports on such ordnance, and supervise the safe removal thereof.

explosive paravane See **paravane.**

explosive-pellet warhead A warhead that consists of numerous separately fused explosive pellets that do not explode unless they contact or penetrate a target.

explosive train A train of combustible and explosive elements arranged in order of decreasing sensitivity inside a fuze, projectile, bomb, gun chamber, or the like. The function of the explosive train is to accomplish the controlled augmentation of a small impulse into one of suitable energy to cause the main charge of the munition to function.

extended order An arrangement of either troops or ships that places them at greater intervals than would be the case in a normal formation.

exterior ballistics The branch of ballistics which deals with the motion of the projectile while in flight.

exterior crest In fortifications, the line of intersection of the superior and the exterior slopes.

exterior side In fortifications, the side of the polygon upon which a front of a fortification is formed.

exterior slope In fortifications, the slope connecting the exterior crest with the berm.

extraction parachute An auxiliary parachute designed to release and extract cargo from aircraft in flight and to deploy cargo parachutes.

extractor A device in the breech mechanism of a gun, rifle, or the like for pulling an empty cartridge case or an unfired cartridge out of the chamber.

extreme range The greatest range of a weapon, e.g., the greatest distance a gun will shoot.

F2A See **Buffalo,** sense 2.

F2H See **Banshee.**

F-3 1. See **Demon,** a U.S. Navy jet fighter. **2.** A World War II reconnaissance version of the A-20 Havoc.

F-4 See **Phantom II.**

F4F See **Wildcat.**

F4U See **Corsair.**

F-5 The Northrop F-5 is a single-seat lightweight jet fighter first flown in 1963 and presently in service with the U.S. Air Force and the forces of at least 13 other countries. It has a range of 1,750 mi, a speed of Mach 1.4, and armament consisting of two 20mm guns in the nose, plus attachment points for missiles, bombs, gun packs, and rockets. It is also called the "Freedom Fighter."

F6F See **Hellcat,** sense 2.

F7F See **Tigercat,** sense 2.

F7U See **Cutlass.**

F-8 See **Crusader,** sense 1.

F8F See **Bearcat.**

F9F See **Cougar.**

F-11 See **Tiger,** sense 2.

F-14 See **Tomcat.**

F-51 See **Mustang.**

F-59 See **Airacomet.**

F-61 See **Black Widow.**

F-80 See **Shooting Star.**

F-82 See **Twin Mustang.**

F-84F See **Thunderstreak.**

F-84G See **Thunderjet.**

F-86 See **Sabre.**

F-5. (*U.S. Air Force.*)

F-89 See **Scorpion,** sense 1.

F-94 See **Starfire.**

F-100 See **Super Sabre.**

F-101 See **Voodoo.**

F-102 See **Delta Dagger.**

F-104 See **Starfighter.**

F-105 See **Thunderchief.**

F-106 See **Delta Dart.**

F-111 The General Dynamics F-111 (formerly the TFX) is a two-seat twin-jet all-weather multipurpose fighter and fighter-bomber using variable sweptwing configurations. It was developed for use by both the USAF and the U.S. Navy and Marine Corps and was first flown in 1964. It has a speed of Mach 2.5, a range of about 3,800 mi, and armament consisting of up to eight missiles or bombs under the wings. (Picture, next page.)

FAADS Forward Area Air Defense System.

The forerunner of the present Surface-to-Air Missile Development (SAM-D), which was originally conceived to fill the U.S. Army's requirement for the provision of an improved battlefield defense against aircraft over that provided by Hawk and Hercules surface-to-air missile batteries.

face 1. In fortifications, the portion formed by one side of a salient angle. Also, the front between two neighboring bastions or other salient works. **2.** One side of a formation (particularly a square) of men.

facings The trimmings, collar, and cuffs of a military coat, usually of a different color from that of the coat and indicating the arm of the service or, in former times, the regiment of the wearer.

factory buster The name for a World War II British 12,000-lb high-explosive bomb first used against Limoges, France, in Feb-

F-111. (*U.S. Navy.*)

ruary 1944.

Fagot The NATO code name for the Mikoyan-Gurevich MiG-15 single-seat jet fighter and two-seat trainer in service with the Soviet Air Force and used by several other countries. It first appeared in about 1949 and has a speed of about 668 mph. It is armed with one 37mm cannon and two 23mm cannons and is provided with attachments for two 1,000-lb bombs.

fail-safe device A device built into a potentially hazardous piece of equipment which provides that the equipment will remain safe to friendly users even though it fails in its intended purpose. This includes devices which destroy the item being operated. They may be self-destructive in the event of equipment failure or may be destroyed by command if operated by remote control.

Fakir (code) A World War II designation for a German antijamming radar system.

Falangist A member of a Spanish fascist organization called the "Falange."

falarica An engine of the Middle Ages developed to throw burning darts.

falchion A seventeenth-century short, single-edged, broad-bladed, slightly curved sword.

Falco The Fiat C.R. 42 Falco was an Italian single-seat fighter and the last biplane to be produced by any of the combatants in World War II. Produced until 1939, this airplane had a speed of 266 mph and was armed with two 12.7mm Breda-SAFAT machine guns. Aircraft of this type were also sold to Hungary, Belgium, and Sweden.

Falco I The Reggiane Re.2000 Falco I was a single-seat single-engine low-wing fighter-interceptor and fighter-bomber built in Italy and first flown in 1938. It was called "Falco" by it builders, although the name was adopted officially by the Regia Aeronautica for the Fiat C.R. 42. This airplane had a speed of 329 mph and was armed

falchion. (*The Metropolitan Museum of Art, gift of Mrs. D. H. Schmidt.*)

with two 12.7mm Breda-SAFAT machine guns. A small number were operational with the Italian Navy, and a few were exported to Sweden and Hungary.

Falco II The Reggiane Re.2001 Falco II was a follow-on to the Falco I and was accepted for use by the Italian Air Force. It had a maximum speed of 337 mph and was armed with two 12.7mm and two 7.7mm Breda-SAFAT machine guns.

falcon A light piece of ordnance of the fifteenth to the seventeenth centuries. It fired a ball weighing 2 lb.

Falcon 1. A series of air-to-air guided missiles developed by Hughes for the U.S. Air Force and first produced in 1950. USAF designations for earlier models were AIM-4A, C, and D, and these were produced until 1959. AIM-4D has a length of 6.5 ft, a weight of about 120 lb, and a range of about 5 mi. For AIM-4E and 4F, see **Super Falcon.** For AIM-26A, see **Nuclear Falcon.** AIM-47A is similar to Super Falcon but much larger, having a length of about 12 ft. The HM-55 and HM-58 Falcon are similar to AIM-26A, but have a high-explosive warhead, an overall length of 7 ft 1 in., a weight of 262 lb, and a range of 6.2 mi. **2.** In gunnery, a radar-ranging device developed by Bell Telephone Laboratories. **3.** A popular name for a single-engine observation biplane developed by Curtiss between World War I and World War II and used in a number of different series and designations. **4.** A former code name for the Russian MiG 15.

falconet A smaller falcon, firing a ball weighing 1.5 lb.

fall The capture or surrender of a place.

fallback That part of the material carried into the air by an atomic explosion that ultimately drops back to the earth or water at the site of the explosion.

fall back To retreat to a stronger or safer position.

fall in A command meaning "form in lines or ranks."

falling block An action for a single-shot rifle. It consists of a vertically moving

breechblock.

fallout The precipitation of radioactive particulate matter that falls to earth from a nuclear cloud; also, the particulate matter itself.

fall out To leave one's place in the ranks.

false fire Lights or fires used to deceive an enemy, to lead an enemy to make a false estimate of numbers of encamped troops, etc.

false muster An incorrect report of the number of available personnel.

false ogive A rounded or pointed hollow cup added to the nose of a shell to improve streamlining. Also called a "windshield."

Fanning A class of U.S. destroyers completed in the late 1930s. They had a standard displacement of 1,500 tons, a speed of 36.5 knots, and main armament consisting of five 5-in. guns and twelve 21-in. torpedo tubes.

Fan Song (A and B) The NATO code name for a type of Soviet E/F-band surface-to-air missile (SAM) and surface-to-surface missile (SSM) acquisition and fire-control radar.

Fan Song (D and E) The NATO code name for a type of Soviet G-band surface-to-air missile (SAM) and surface-to-surface missile (SSM) acquisition and fire-control radar.

fantail The aftermost deck area topside on a ship.

Fantail The NATO code name for a Lavochkin-designed single-jet fighter with swept-back wing and tail.

Fantasque A class of French escort vessels (former light cruisers) of 2,569 tons standard displacement built in 1935. They had a speed of 37 knots, a complement of 220 men, and armament consisting of five 5.5-in. guns, eight 40mm and eight 20mm antiaircraft guns, four depth-charge throwers, and six 21.7-in. torpedo tubes.

fantassin An infantry soldier.

FAO 7.62mm machine gun Model 59 This weapon, a copy of the Czech ZB26 machine gun, was first called the "FAO" and chambered for 7.92mm. It was made at the Fabrica de Armas de Oviedo (FAO) during the Spanish Civil War. Later this weapon was modified to belt feed and rebarreled for the 7.62mm NATO cartridge. In this modification the weapon is called the "FAO 59."

Fargo 1. A class of U.S. light cruisers (CL) of about 10,000 tons standard displacement completed in 1945–1946. The class consisted of *Fargo* and *Huntington*. They had a length of 600 ft, a beam of 66 ft, a speed of 32.5 knots, and a wartime complement of 1,200 men. They were armed with twelve 6-in. and twelve 5-in. guns, plus twenty-four 40mm and nineteen 20mm antiaircraft guns. Three seaplanes were carried. **2.** The NATO code name for the Mikoyan/Gurevich MiG-9 single-seat single-engine jet fighter that entered service with the Soviet Air Force in 1946.

Farman F.40 series French two-seat sin-

Falcon. (*U.S. Air Force.*)

falconet. (*The Metropolitan Museum of Art, Bashford Dean Memorial Collection.*)

Fanning. (*U.S. Navy.*)

Fargo. (*U.S. Navy.*)

fauchard. (*The Metropolitan Museum of Art, Rogers Fund, 1904.*)

gle-engine (pusher) biplanes used for reconnaissance and bombing, operational during 1916 and 1917. They had a speed of 84 mph and were armed with one Lewis gun in the front cockpit.

Farman HF.20 series French two-seat single-engine (pusher) biplanes introduced in 1913. They had a speed of about 62 mph. Later versions were used as bombers and carried about 550 lb of bombs.

Farman MF.7 A French two-place single-engine pusher biplane that first appeared in 1913 and was in service with British and French forces a year or so before World War I. Because of long, curved outriggers that held the forward elevator, the British nicknamed the aircraft "Longhorn." It was widely used for observation early in the war

and had a speed of about 59 mph.

Farman MF.11 A 1914 follow-on to the Farman MF.7, this pusher-type aircraft no longer carried a forward elevator, but had short skids in front of the wheels (and was therefore dubbed "Shorthorn"). It was armed with one forward-firing machine gun. An airplane of this type made the first night bombing raid of World War I when it dropped eighteen 16-lb bombs on German gun emplacements near Ostend.

Farmer The NATO code name for the Mikoyan-Gurevich MiG-19 single-seat supersonic jet fighter in service with the Soviet Air Force and the forces of Pakistan, China, and several east European countries. Aircraft of this type first appeared in 1955, have speeds up to 850 mph, and are armed with three 30mm cannons plus under-wing attachments for rockets, missiles, and bombs.

Farragut A class of U.S. destroyers (DD)

of about 1,375 tons standard displacement commissioned in 1934–1935. They had a length of 341 ft, a beam of 34 ft, a speed of 36.5 knots, and a complement of 162 men. They were armed with five 5-in. guns and eight 21-in. torpedo tubes.

farrier Formerly, a noncommissioned officer in a cavalry regiment. He was in charge of the horses or their shoeing.

fascines Tightly tied bundles of brushwood used for building temporary fortifications and to strengthen earthworks.

Fast Fix A development of the USAF Systems Command, this special cement hardens in 30 minutes and is used for repairing runways damaged by enemy rocket or mortar fire.

fastness A fortified place or stronghold; a fortress.

FAT Field-artillery tractor.

fathom A measure of length or depth equal to 6 ft.

fatigue dress A soldier's working attire.

fatigue duty Nonmilitary work done by soldiers, such as cleaning grounds, etc.

fauchard A word found in French and some English texts of the twelfth to the fourteenth centuries. It refers to a weapon with a scythelike blade having a point at the back.

faucre A type of lance rest that was secured to the breastplate.

fauld In armor, an extension of the breastplate to protect the lower part of the abdomen.

faulx A scythelike weapon once used in the defense of a place.

faussebraie In fortifications, a second, lower rampart constructed parallel to the main rampart.

F.B.A. A series of World War I Franco-British aviation two- and three-seat single-engine biplane flying boats. The F.B.A. Type S, for example, was armed with one machine gun, carried a bombload of about 220 lb, and flew at a speed of about 70 mph. It was in production during 1918. The photograph shows an F.B.A. built under license in Italy by the firm of Rinaldo Piaggio.

FBM See **fleet ballistic missile.**

F Class A class of Soviet attack submarines of 2,000 tons standard surface displacement. There are some 40 in the class. They have a length of 300 ft, a beam of 27 ft, a speed of 15 knots submerged, and a complement of 70 men. They are armed with eight 21-in. torpedo tubes.

FCS Fire-control system.

FDL A U.S. Navy fast-deployment logistics ship.

F.E.2b A British two-place single-engine pusher biplane fighter first flown in March 1915. It had a speed of about 80 mph and was armed with two Lewis machine guns. It could carry one 230-lb bomb or three

F.B.A. (*Rinaldo Piaggio Aircraft.*)

Farragut. (*U.S. Navy.*)

Felixstowe. (*The Smithsonian Institution, National Air Museum.*)

112-lb bombs.

F.E.2d An improved version of the F.E.2b, with increased wingspan and a more powerful engine. It flew at speeds up to 95 mph.

F.E.8 A single-seat single-engine biplane (pusher) fighter armed with one machine gun. Production began in 1916, and it flew at a top speed of 94 mph. By the time it entered service, it was no match for German twin-gunned single-seaters.

Feather The NATO code name for the Yakovlev Yak-17 single-seat jet fighter developed for the Soviet Air Force in the late 1940s. It is an improved version of the Yak-15.

Federov 6.5mm semiautomatic rifle "Automat" This Russian recoil-operated weapon was developed in 1916 to fire the 6.5mm Japanese cartridge. One of the first assault rifles, this was a selective-fire weapon with a length of about 39 in., a weight of 9.7 lb, and a magazine with a capacity of 25 rounds. It was produced in limited numbers during World War I.

feed chute A chute or passage through which ammunition is guided into the breech mechanism of a machine gun.

feeder A device that supplies ammunition to a weapon; it is usually actuated by an automatic or semiautomatic mechanism.

feet per second The unit of measurement used to indicate the velocity or speed of a projectile.

feint A mock attack or assault designed to throw an enemy off guard.

Feldgrau Field gray. The neutral gray color of German war uniforms.

Felix A U.S. Army Air Force air-to-ground radio-guided bomb with a heat-seeking

F.E.8. (*The Imperial War Museum.*)

Fiat C.R.32. (*The Smithsonian Institution, National Air Museum.*)

warhead. It had an octagonal tail configuration for control and a total weight of about 1,000 lb. It was developed during World War II.

Felixstowe A series of British twin-engine biplane flying boats developed from Curtiss designs and first delivered in November 1917. They were armed with four to seven machine guns and carried two 230-lb bombs. They had a speed of 95 mph.

fer à cheval A horseshoe-shaped fortification with a parapet.

Fiat (Revelli) 8mm machine gun Model 35. (*The Smithsonian Institution, Treasury Department Collection.*)

Ferdinand See **Elephant** (German tank destroyer), sense 1.

ferret **1.** An aircraft, ship, or vehicle especially equipped for the detection, location, recording, and analyzing of electromagnetic radiation. **2.** A person who poses as a prisoner in order to obtain information in a concentration camp.

Ferret The code name for satellites used by the U.S. Air Force 466L electromagnetic intelligence system (see **ELINT**) to monitor, analyze, and record electromagnetic emissions. The satellites are of the Samos type.

Ferret scout car A four-wheeled British vehicle developed between 1951 and 1953 from the Daimler scout car. It has been produced in large numbers for the British Army and for the forces of at least 24 other countries. It has a crew of two, a weight of about 9,460 lb, a road speed of 58 mph,

and armament consisting of one .30 cal. Browning machine gun. See also **Big-wheel Ferret.**

ferry **1.** To deliver aircraft or ships by operating them under their own power. **2.** To transport personnel and materiel by air.

FFAR A 2.75-in. folding-fin aircraft rocket used by the U.S. Army and Navy as helicopter armament.

FG42 See **German 7.92mm paratroop rifle Model 42.**

German 7.92mm aircraft machine gun FG-42 A German gas-operated air-cooled machine gun with a rate of fire of 400 to 450 rounds per minute. It weighed 14 lb and was fed from a 20-round magazine.

Fiat 6.5mm machine gun Model 1914 An Italian blowback-operated water-cooled machine gun with a rate of fire of 450 to 500 rounds per minute. It had a weight of 37.5 lb and was fed from 50-round magazine compartments.

Fiat 7.7mm aircraft machine gun Model 1928 An Italian recoil-operated air-cooled machine gun with a rate of fire of 700 to 800 rounds per minute. It had a weight of 28 lb and was fed from a 250-round link belt.

Fiat B.R.20 See **Cicogna.**

Fiat C.R.32 An Italian single-seat interceptor–close-support biplane fighter first flown in 1933. Approximately 400 were in service with the Italian Air Force (Regia Aeronautica) at the beginning of World War II. They had a top speed of 221 mph and were armed with two 12.7mm Bredo-SAFAT machine guns and twelve 4.4-lb antipersonnel bombs. (Picture, p. 161.)

Fiat C.R.42 Falco See **Falco.**

Fiat G.50 Freccia See **Freccia.**

Fiat G.55 Centauro See **CENTAURO,** sense 2.

Fiat G91R/3 An Italian-built single-seat light tactical strike-reconnaissance fighter in service with the German Air Force and first flown in 1956. It has a speed of 650 mph and is armed with two 30mm cannons, plus bombs, rockets, and missiles.

Fiat G91Y An Italian Air Force single-seat lightweight reconnaissance jet fighter-bomber first flown in 1966. It has a speed of Mach 0.93. It is armed with two 30mm cannons in the nose and is equipped with under-wing attachments for bombs, napalm tanks, or rocket packs.

Fiat (Revelli) 8mm machine gun Model 35 This weapon operates on a delayed-blowback principal and is capable of selective fire. The overall length is 49.75 in., and it has a barrel length of 25.75 in. and a weight of 39.75 lb. The tripod weighs 41.5 lb. The cyclic rate of fire is 500 rounds per minute, and the muzzle velocity is 2,600 fps. The weapon is fed from a 300-round nondisintegrating belt.

field artillery, the U.S. 105mm howitzer M102. (*U.S. Army.*)

field stripping. A disassembled Australian 9mm submachine gun Model F.1. (*Australian Department of Supply.*)

Fiat R.S.14 A four- or five-seat twin-engine reconnaissance-bomber twin-float seaplane first flown in 1938 and used by the Italian Air Force during World War II.

fid A block of wood used in mounting and dismounting heavy guns.

Fiddler The NATO code name for a Soviet Tupolev twin-jet all-weather fighter in service with the Soviet Air Force. It has a speed of Mach 1.75 and is armed with two Ash air-to-air missiles under each wing. It was first seen in 1961.

Fido A World War II homing torpedo developed by the U.S. Navy for use by airplanes against submarines.

field A space or plain on which a battle is fought.

field armor Armor for war, as opposed to tilt armor.

field army An administrative and tactical organization composed of a headquarters, certain organic army troops, service-support troops, a variable number of corps, and a variable number of divisions.

field artillery Artillery mounted on carriages and mobile enough to accompany infantry or armored units in the field.

Field Artillery A former branch of the U.S. Army.

field-artillery direct-support weapons Artillery assigned the task of executing the fire requested by the supported unit.

field-artillery general-support weapons Artillery which fires in support of the operation as a whole rather than a specific unit.

field-artillery observer A person who watches the effects of artillery fire, adjusts the center of impact of that fire onto a target, and reports the results to the firing agency.

field battery A battery of field artillery.

field colors Small flags to mark the boundaries of squadrons and battalions either in camp or on the battlefield. Also, the colors that are carried in the field or on parade.

field exercise An exercise conducted in the field under simulated war conditions in which troops and armament of one side are actually present, while those of the other side may be imaginary or in outline.

field fortification A fortification constructed in the field to strengthen the natural defenses of the ground features. Field fortifications include foxholes, obstacles, trenches, gun emplacements, etc.

field grade An officer's grade covering major, lieutenant colonel, and colonel; hence, field-grade officer.

field gun A field-artillery piece; a cannon mounted on a carriage for use in the field.

field hospital A temporary military hospital established in the field.

field marshal In some armies, an officer of the highest rank except that of commander in chief.

field officer A field-grade officer; a major,

fifty. (*The Smithsonian Institution.*)

lieutenant colonel, or colonel.

field of fire The area which a weapon or a group of weapons may cover effectively with fire from a given position.

field of search The space that a radar set or installation can cover effectively.

field order A combat order that communicates instructions for a specific operation.

fieldpiece A field-artillery gun or howitzer; a gun mounted on a carriage for use in the field.

field plotter A field plotting board.

field ration The ration provided troops in the field.

field staff A staff used by gunners to hold a lighted match for discharging a gun.

field-strip To disassemble the major components of a machine gun, cannon, or other firearm for cleaning, inspection, or the like.

field telegraph, telephone, radio Communications systems that can be used in the field of battle.

field train A transportation unit that carries reserve stocks of equipment not required during combat.

field training The training of troops for wartime service.

fieldwork Temporary fortifications constructed by an army in the field.

fifteen-pounder A gun whose solid projectile weighs 15 lb.

fifth column A translation of the Spanish *quinta columna*, used in a radio address

given during the Spanish Civil War in October 1936 by Nationalist General Emilio Mola. It referred to the four columns of troops advancing against Madrid, plus the Franco sympathizers within the city; hence, secret sympathizers and supporters of the enemy engaged in espionage, sabotage, and other subversive activity within defense lines.

fifty A popular term for a .50 cal. machine gun. Used in the plural, the term refers to guns mounted in multiple mounts, such as twin fifties, quad fifties, etc.

fighter A fighter airplane. Formerly, in the U.S. Air Corps the term was "pursuit."

fighter-bomber An airplane used both to fight and to drop bombs; a fighter equipped to carry and release bombs.

fighter cover The maintenance of a number of fighter aircraft over a specified area or force for the purpose of repelling hostile air activities.

fighter direction The control of fighter aircraft. A fighter-direction ship or aircraft is one especially equipped for that purpose. A fighter director is one who does the controlling.

fighter-direction ship or aircraft A ship or aircraft equipped and manned for directing fighter-aircraft operations.

fighter-interceptor A fighter aircraft designed to intercept its target. It may or may not carry devices to assist in interception

fighter-bomber, the Saab Viggen. (*Swedish Air Force.*)

fighter sweep, showing a flight of Spitfires. *(Vickers Ltd.)*

and in aiming its weapons.

fighter strip An airstrip used especially by fighter planes.

fighter sweep An offensive mission by fighter aircraft to seek out and destroy enemy aircraft or targets of opportunity in an allotted area of operations.

fighting compartment The portion of a fighting vehicle in which the occupants service and fire the principal armament. It takes up a portion of the hull and the whole turret, if any.

Fighting French See **de Gaullist.**

fighting load The items of individual clothing, equipment, weapons, and ammunition which are carried by the combat soldier and are essential to his effectiveness and the accomplishment of the immediate mission of his unit when he is on foot.

fighting patrol See **combat fighting patrol.**

figure The plan or interior polygon of a fortified place.

Fiji The first designation of a class of British cruisers later referred to as the **Mauritius** class, which see.

file Soldiers in a row one behind another. When soldiers are in a row standing abreast, they are arranged in "rank."

file firing The process of firing by file, in which each file of soldiers fires independently of the others.

file off To march in single file at right angles to the original direction.

filler 1. A substance carried in an ammunition container such as a projectile, mine, bomb, or grenade. A filler may be an explosive, chemical, or inert substance. **2.** One of a number of individuals, officer or enlisted, required initially to bring a unit, organization, or approved allotment to authorized strength.

filter center The location in an aircraft control and warning system at which information from observation posts is filtered for further dissemination to air-defense control centers and air-defense direction centers.

filtering The process of interpreting reported information on movements of aircraft, ships, and submarines in order to determine their probable true tracks and, where applicable, their heights or depths.

Fin The NATO code name for the **La-7,** which see.

fin assembly An assembly of a quantity of metal blades, usually mounted lengthwise on a sleeve and used on a missile, such as a bomb or rifle grenade, to give directional stability.

fine sight The adjustment of the sight of a gun so that only the tip of the front sight can be seen through the notch of the rear sight.

finger guard The portion of a sword guard which protects the fingers.

Finnish 7.62mm assault rifles M60 and M62 This weapon is a modified copy of the Soviet AK-47 assault rifle. It is capable of selective full automatic and semiautomatic fire and has a cyclic rate of fire of 650 rounds per minute and a muzzle velocity of 2,362 fps. It has an overall length of 36 in., a barrel length of 16.5 in., and a loaded weight of about 9 lb. It utilizes a staggered box magazine with a capacity of 30 cartridges. The Model 62 is a more recent version of the Model 60 and features a change in the trigger guard and improvements in the stock.

Finnish 7.62mm heavy machine guns MO9, M21, and M32 These weapons were basically adaptations of the Maxim heavy machine gun.

Finnish 7.62mm light machine gun M60 This is a gas-operated weapon used on a bipod or a lightweight tripod. It has a cyclic rate of fire of 1,050 rounds per minute, a weight of 16.8 lb, and a feed device consisting of a nondisintegrating metallic link belt with a capacity of 100 cartridges.

Finnish 7.62mm Mosin-Nagant rifles M91, M24, M27, M28, M28/30, and M39 When Finland became free of czarist rule in 1917, it solved its weapons problem by appropriating a large quantity of Russian-made Mosin-Nagant M91 rifles and M91 actions. The latter were used with Finnish-made parts. The Finnish M91 was a Russian M91 with a heavier barrel. The M27 was a Finnish M91 with the barrel shortened by 4½ in. and redesigned sights. Subsequent model changes included modifications in sights and stock fittings. The M39 is 46.73 in. long and has a barrel length of 26.97 in. It weighs 9.7 lb.

Finnish 9mm submachine gun Model M44 A weapon very similar in design to the Soviet PPS 43 submachine gun, except that it used the 9mm Parabellum cartridge and was fabricated to use existing Suomi box and drum magazines. Introduced in 1944, it is the standard submachine gun of the Finnish Army.

fin-stabilized Said of a missile or craft on which airfoils or fins are used for purposes of directional stability.

fire 1. The discharge of a gun, launching of a missile, or the like. **2.** The projectiles or missiles fired. **3.** To discharge a weapon.

fire adjustment The correction of the elevation and direction of a weapon or the regulation of the explosion time of its projectile that ensures that the projectile will strike or burst at the desired point. Fire adjustment for automatic weapons is an operation which is continuous from the instant the first rounds reach the vicinity of the target until the command "cease firing" is given.

fire area A portion of land or water effectively covered by gunfire.

firearm 1. In a general sense, a gun. **2.** Specifically, a small arm, such as a pistol or rifle, designed to be carried by an individual.

fire arrow An arrow that has a flaming substance attached to it and is used to set fire to the sails of ships and other flammable targets.

fireball The luminous sphere of hot gases which forms a few millionths of a second after detonation of a nuclear weapon and immediately starts expanding and cooling. The term once referred to a ball filled with powder and other flammable materials that was thrown among the enemy.

Fireball The Ryan FR-1 Fireball was a single-seat shipboard fighter-bomber developed for the U.S. Navy and first flown in June 1944. It was powered by both a radial engine and a turbojet and reached maximum speeds of 426 mph. It was armed with four .50 cal. machine guns, plus one 1,000-lb bomb or eight 5-in. rockets.

Firebar The NATO code name for the Yakovlev Yak-28 two-seat all-weather jet fighter in service with the Soviet Air Force and first seen in 1961. It flies at speeds of Mach 1.1 and is armed with Anab or Atoll missiles under each wing. The Firebar and two other versions (the Maestro trainer and the Brewer tactical bomber) stem from the Yak 25 Flashlight.

Firebird A large air-to-air missile produced by the Ryan Aeronautical Company and first fired in 1950.

fire block A roadblock achieved by concentrated gunfire to stop or hinder enemy movement.

fire bomb A device designed to be dropped from an aircraft to destroy or reduce the utility of a target by the effects of combustion. It contains an incendiary mixture which spreads on impact to burn or envelop in flames personnel and material targets, such as vehicles and tents. Such bombs often consist of thin-skinned containers of gasoline gel.

fire by direct laying See **direct fire.**

fire by indirect laying See **indirect laying.**

Fire Can The NATO code name for a type of Soviet E-band antiaircraft artillery-fire-control radar.

fire chart A map, photomap, or grid sheet showing the relative horizontal and vertical positions of batteries, base points, base-point lines, checkpoints, targets, and other details needed in preparing firing data.

fire command A term formerly used in the U.S. Coast Artillery to refer to a group of guns or batteries under the command of one officer.

fire commander The senior officer of a fire command.

fire control Control over the direction, volume, and time of fire of guns or launchers by the use of certain electrical, optical, or mechanical systems, devices, or aids; a fire-control system.

fire-control equipment The equipment required and used to direct air guns or controlled missiles at a particular target. Fire-control equipment includes all instruments used in calculating and adjusting the proper elevation and deflection of guns and missiles in flight. Included are such items as radars, telescopes, range finders, predictors, directors, other computers, power plants, and communication-control systems connecting these elements.

fire-control quadrant A mechanical device having scales graduated in mils and a fine micrometer adjustment and a leveling or a cross-leveling vial. It may be physically

attached to the gun, gun mount, or gun carriage and is used for setting and/or measuring the elevation angles of a weapon in order to obtain the horizontal range of a target.

fire-control radar Radar used to provide target-information inputs to a weapon fire-control system.

fire coordination The planning and executing of fire so that targets are adequately covered by a suitable weapon or group of weapons.

fire-direction center That element of a command post, consisting of gunnery and communication personnel and equipment, by means of which the commander exercises fire direction and/or fire control. The fire-direction center receives target intelligence and requests for fire and translates them into appropriate fire direction.

fire effect The effect of fire, as on enemy personnel.

fire fight The exchange of fire between opposing units, as distinguished from the fighting which occurs when the two forces close with each other, as during an assault.

Fireflash A British Royal Air Force air-to-air missile with a range of several miles and a speed of more than Mach 2.

Fire Fly See **Sherman V C (M4A4).**

Firefly 1. A Korean conflict designation for U.S. Air Force C-47 transport aircraft modified for flare-dropping missions. Also called "Lightning Bug" and "Old Lamplighter of the Korean Hills." **2.** A British single-engine two-seat low-wing shipboard reconnaissance fighter built by Fairey for the British Navy. Although it was not committed to action until mid-1944, it operated in practically every theater of war and became one of the most effective British carrier airplanes of World War II. It was powered by a 1,730-hp engine and flew at speeds of 386 mph. It was armed with four 20mm Hispano cannons plus eight 60-lb rockets or two 1,000-lb bombs.

fire for adjustment Fire delivered for the purpose of determining firing data that will place the center of impact or burst on the desired portion of the target.

fire for effect 1. Fire which is delivered after the mean point of impact or burst is within the desired distance from the target of the adjusting or ranging point. **2.** Used in a fire message to indicate that the adjustment or ranging is satisfactory and that fire for effect is desired.

firelock An old term usually indicating a wheel lock or flint arm which ignites the priming by a spark.

fire message See **call for fire.**

fire mission 1. A specific assignment given to a fire unit as part of a definite plan. **2.** The order used to alert the weapon-battery area and indicate that the message following is a call for fire.

fire plan A tactical plan for using the weapons of a unit or formation so that their fire will be coordinated.

firepot A small clay pot filled with burning substances that was thrown at an enemy.

firepower 1. The amount of fire which may be delivered by a position, unit, or weapon system. **2.** The ability to deliver fire.

fire raft A raft laden with burning material and used to set fire to enemy ships or a waterfront.

fire raid An air raid in which incendiary, or fire, bombs are used.

fire registration Fire delivered to obtain accurate data for subsequent effective engagement of targets.

fire rockets Rockets tipped with fire. See also **agny astra.**

fire ship A vessel loaded with burning materials or explosives that is sent among enemy ships to set them on fire.

fire stone A material once placed in hollow shells, with a bursting charge, to set fire to ships and buildings.

fire storm A stationary mass fire, generally in a built-up urban area that generates strong inrushing winds from all sides; the winds keep the fire from spreading, while

fin stabilization. A Martin Lacrosse missile. (*Martin Marietta Aerospace Group.*)

adding fresh oxygen to increase its intensity.

Firestreak An infrared homing air-to-air missile built by Hawker Siddeley Dynamics and presently in service with the RAF and the Royal Navy. It has an overall length of about 10.5 ft, a launching weight of 300 lb, a warhead weight of 50 lb, and a range of up to 5 mi.

fire superiority Fire with greater effect than that of the enemy because of its greater accuracy and volume. Fire superiority makes advances against the enemy possible without heavy losses.

fire support Gunfire to aid or assist a unit ashore. It may be close-support, deep-support, or direct-support fire.

fire trench A trench constructed for the delivery of small-arms fire.

Fire Wheel The NATO code name for a type of Soviet E-band antiaircraft artillery-fire-control radar.

fireworks Military fireworks include such things as signal lights, signal smokes, and flares.

Fireye An improved U.S. Navy fire bomb designed to deliver a new type of burning agent.

firing base The part of the mechanism in some cannons that supports the gun carriage when it is in position for firing.

firing line A line, usually the front line, from which fire is delivered against the enemy.

firing lock The mechanism in the breech of a gun which contains the firing pin.

firing party A military squad detailed to fire three volleys of blank cartridges over the grave of a person buried with military honors.

firing pin A device used in the firing mechanism of a gun, mine, bomb, fuze, projectile, or the like which strikes and detonates a sensitive explosive to initiate an explosive train or a propelling charge.

firing platform See **launching platform.**

firing range The distance from a gun to the target. Also the distance between a firing ship and the target at the instant a torpedo is fired.

firing squad A detachment of riflemen who carry out a sentence of death by shooting.

firing step A ledge or board about 1 ft from the bottom of a trench used to stand on when firing.

firing stop mechanism A device that prevents a gun from firing into its own ship's structure.

firing table A table or chart giving the data needed for firing a gun accurately on a target under standard conditions and also the corrections that must be made for special conditions, such as winds or variations of temperature.

first lieutenant In the U.S. Army, Air Force, and Marine Corps, an officer next in rank below a captain and above a second

lieutenant. His insignia of rank is a single silver bar. Also, a naval officer in charge of the construction and repair department of a warship and generally responsible for her cleanliness and upkeep.

first light The beginning of morning nautical twilight, which occurs when the center of the morning sun is 12° below the horizon.

first line The troops or ships in the line immediately confronting the enemy.

first sergeant The ranking noncommissioned officer in a company, etc.

first strike The first offensive move of a war. (Generally associated with nuclear operations.)

fish A slang term that is short for "tin fish," or torpedo.

Fishbed The NATO code name for one of several versions (A, B, C, and D) of the Mikoyan/Gurevich MiG-21 single-seat jet fighter developed for the Soviet Air Force and first seen in 1956. Fishbed C is in service with a number of countries and has a speed of Mach 2 and a combat radius of 375 mi. It is armed with one or two 30mm cannons, plus under-wing attachments for two Atoll air-to-air missiles.

Fishpot The NATO code name for the Sukhoi Su-9 single-seat all-weather jet fighter in service with the Soviet Air Force and first seen in 1956. It has a speed of Mach 2.5 and is armed with two Anab air-to-air missiles under the wings.

Fitter The NATO code name for the Sukhoi Su-7B single-seat ground-attack jet fighter first seen in 1956 and presently in service with the Soviet Air Force and the forces of several other countries. It has a speed of Mach 1.6 and is armed with two 30mm cannons and attachments for rocket packs and bombs.

fix bayonets A command indicating that the bayonets are to be attached to the rifles.

fixed ammunition Ammunition with primer and propellant contained in a cartridge case permanently crimped or attached to a projectile. It is loaded into the weapon as a unit and is usually termed a "cartridge."

fixed armament Guns or weapons that are permanently emplaced.

fixed artillery Artillery weapons permanently installed on land and sea frontiers for the protection of important areas; artillery of position.

fixed bayonet A bayonet that is fitted in its place on the end of a rifle.

fixed emplacement A fixed setting for a gun. A fixed emplacement is usually made of reinforced concrete, with the baseplate and base ring set in the concrete and bolted down.

fixed gun Specifically, an aircraft machine gun that is mounted rigidly to the aircraft and is aimed by moving the aircraft, as

fixed ammunition, being handled on a 3-in. mount aboard the U.S.S. *Canberra.* (*U.S. Navy.*)

distinguished from a flexible gun.

fixed-station patrol One in which each scout maintains a station relative to an assigned point on a barrier line while searching the surrounding area. Scouts are not stationary, but remain under way and patrol near the center of their assigned stations. A scout is a surface ship, submarine, or aircraft.

FJ See **Fury.**

F.K.3 and F.K.8 British two-place single-engine reconnaissance-bomber biplanes produced by Armstrong Whitworth and designed by Frederick Koolhoven. The F.K.3 was first flown in 1916 and was succeeded by the F.K.8, basically a scaled-up version. It had a speed of about 93 mph, carried a bombload of 160 lb, and was armed with a front-firing synchronized Vickers machine gun and a Scarff-mounted Lewis gun in the rear cockpit. It was used throughout 1917 and 1918 for day and night bombing, ground attack, and patrol and reconnaissance duties. The F.K.3 was nicknamed "Little Ack," and the F.K.8, "Big Ack."

flag The flag of a flag officer. It is hoisted aboard his vessel, which is called the "flagship." Also, a flag flown over a camp or permanent establishment on land.

flag bag A container on the bridge of a ship for holding the signal flags.

flaghoist A method of communicating between ships by using flags run up on signal halyards.

flag lieutenant An officer on the staff of a flag officer. He serves in the capacity of a personal aide.

flag officer An officer in the U.S. Navy with the rank of commodore or above. A commodore is entitled to fly a flag with one star.

flag of truce A white flag displayed to an enemy as an invitation to parley. It renders the bearer inviolate.

Flagon-A The NATO code name for the Soviet Sukhoi single-seat twin-jet delta-wing fighter first seen in 1967. Flagon-B appears to be a STOL version of the same aircraft.

flag rank A naval rank of commodore or higher. It is also called "star rank."

flagship The ship from which an admiral or other unit commander exercises command.

flail A weapon dating at least to the thirteenth century and probably earlier. It consists of a haft to which a ball or a shorter spiked haft is attached by a length of chain.

flail tank A specially constructed tank equipped with a flailing device consisting of chain flails attached to a roller powered by the tank engine. It is employed to detonate antitank mines. See also **crab tanks.**

Flak (The abbreviation for Fliegerabwehrkanone, or "antiaircraft gun")

1. Explosive or exploding missiles fired from antiaircraft cannons. **2.** An antiaircraft cannon, especially in some attributive uses, as in "flak battery" or "flak installation."

flak analysis The examination and study of flak intelligence to determine the nature, effectiveness, or probable effectiveness of enemy antiaircraft defenses.

flak battery A battery of flak guns.

flak jacket A jacket or vest made of heavy fabric containing metal, nylon, or ceramic plates and designed especially for protection against flak. The usual type of flak jacket covers the chest, abdomen, back, and genitals, leaving the arms and legs free. Also called "flak vest."

flak ship A ship or boat on which antiaircraft cannons are mounted and which is used especially for air defense.

flak suit A garment consisting of two or more pieces of armored clothing, such as a flak jacket with thigh protectors attached.

flak tower A towerlike structure in which one or more antiaircraft automatic weapons are mounted.

flak vest See **flak jacket.**

flamberge Almost any large sword of the early Middle Ages. From about 1600 onward, the term referred to a rapier with a long, slender blade.

flameout The extinguishment of the flame in a reaction engine, especially in a jet engine.

flamethrower An offensive weapon used to project ignited fuel and equally capable of causing casualties to personnel and destruction of materiel. It was invented by the Germans during World War I. (Picture, next page.)

flancard, flanchard A piece of armor for the thigh or flank.

flank The left or right side of a fleet or an army. Also, any part of a fortification that defends another part by fire along the outside of its parapet.

flanked angle The angle formed by the bastion flank and a curtain.

flanker Men who protect the flank of a column on the march.

flanking angle The angle formed by a flank with a curtain; a curtain angle.

flap A control surface on an airplane. Also, a slang term meaning "excitement" or "confusion."

Flap Track The NATO code name for a type of Soviet I-band antiaircraft artillery-fire-control radar.

Flap Wheel The NATO code name for a type of Soviet I-band antiaircraft artillery-fire-control radar.

flare A pyrotechnic item designed to produce a single source of intense light for purposes such as target or airfield illumination.

flare pistol A pistol for shooting flares; a

fixed bayonet. *(U.S. Army.)*

flaghoist. *(U.S. Navy.)*

flak jacket. *(U.S. Army.)*

flamethrower. (*The Smithsonian Institution.*)

flare pistol. (*The Smithsonian Institution.*)

flashpan. (*The Smithsonian Institution, L. Baird Collection.*)

flash hider. (*The Smithsonian Institution.*)

Very pistol or signal pistol. The earliest flare pistols served only to ignite and hold the flare, which burned in place.

Flash   This U.S. Army system is a four-barreled flame weapon that fires rocket-propelled 66mm incendiary shells instead of a fire stream. It has a weight of 26.6 lb and a maximum range of 700 meters. The flame agent of the shell ignites on exposure to air or after impact has exploded the shell.

flash blindness   Temporary or permanent impairment of vision resulting from an intense flash of light. It includes loss of night adaptation and dazzle and may be associated with retinal burns.

flash burn   The burn from the flash of a bomb or projectile.

flash hider   A metallic cone and/or flat disks which are attached to the muzzle of a gun to conceal the flash when it is fired and to prevent temporary blindness of the gun crew while firing.

flashing light   Communication using code transmitted by blinker or signal searchlight.

flash in the pan   The igniting (and flashing) of the priming in the pan of a flintlock musket without discharging the piece. The term thus applies to other sorts of unsuccessful efforts.

flashless charge   A charge containing powder that reduces the flash of detonation; used for concealment at night.

Flashlight   The NATO code name for the Yakovlev Yak-25 two-place twin-jet all-weather jet fighter in service with the Soviet Air Force and first seen in 1955. Flashlight-A has a radius of action of about 200 mi and a speed of Mach 0.9. It is armed with two 37mm cannons and has provision for a pack of unguided air-to-air rockets. Flashlight-B has a glazed nose to accommodate a navigator-bombardier. Flashlight-C is similar to Flashlight-D, a tactical reconnaissance version (also called "Mangrove").

flash message   A category of precedence reserved for initial enemy-contact messages or operational combat messages of extreme urgency.

flashpan   The pan beside the touchhole of a flintlock, wheel-lock, or matchlock firearm in which the flash powder is ignited to fire the charge.

flash ranging   Finding the position of the burst of a projectile or of an enemy gun by observing its flash.

flash reconnaissance   Observation from ground posts or from aircraft to locate enemy gun positions by the flashes of the enemy guns.

flash suppressor   A device attached to the muzzle of a weapon which reduces the amount of visible light or flash created by burning propellant gases.

flask   See **powder flask.**

Flat Face   The NATO code name for a type of Soviet C-band antiaircraft artillery-fire-control radar.

flat fire   Flat trajectory fire.

flattop   A slang term for an aircraft carrier.

Flattop   Also called "Floating Aircraft Maintenance Facility," this project was a U.S. Army effort to provide depot-level maintenance of its combat aircraft in Southeast Asia. The first Flattop (U.S.N.S. *Corpus Christi Bay*), a converted seaplane tender, was deployed in Vietnam waters.

flat trajectory   A trajectory which is relatively flat, that is, described by a projectile of relatively high velocity. Often used to describe the trajectory of a rifle or gun, as opposed to that of howitzers and mortars.

flèche   In fortifications, a salient outwork of two faces with an open gorge.

fléchette   (French for "small arrow")   **1.** A small steel dart dropped from an airplane.   **2.** A small fin-stabilized missile, a large number of which can be loaded in an artillery canister or in a warhead.

fleet   An organization of ships, aircraft, marine forces, and shore-based fleet activities, all under the command of a commander or commander in chief who may exercise operational as well as administrative control. Also, all Navy operating forces.

Fleet Air Arm   The British aviation service of the Royal Navy.

fleet admiral   The highest commissioned rank in the U.S. Navy, corresponding to general of the army; a person holding this rank. The insignia of this rank is five silver stars. It was established on December 14, 1944.

fleet ballistic missile   A shipborne ballistic missile, such as **Polaris** or **Poseidon,** which see.

fleet ballistic-missile submarine   A nuclear-powered submarine designed to deliver ballistic-missile attacks against targets from either a submerged or a surfaced condition. Designated as SSBN.

fleet engineer   The senior engineering officer of a fleet, usually aboard the flagship of the commander in chief and serving on his staff.

fleeting target   A moving target that remains within observing or firing distance for such a short period that it affords little time for deliberate adjustment and fire against it; a transient target. Fleeting targets may be aircraft, vehicles, marching troops, etc.

Flensburg   The code name for a kind of German airborne electronic equipment of World War II that was capable of homing on radar transmissions.

fletcher   An arrow maker.

Fletcher   A class of U.S. destroyers (DD) of about 2,100 tons standard displacement produced in 1942–1945. Some 119 ships were completed. Numerous original and modernized versions are currently in commission. They have a length of 376.5 ft, a beam of 39.5 ft, a speed of 35 knots, and a complement of about 250 men. Original armament included four or five 5-in. guns, plus either six 3-in. guns or ten 40mm guns, depth charges, hedgehogs, and torpedo launchers. Modernized versions carry 5-in. guns, Weapon Alpha, hedgehogs, and DASH.

fleuret A light foil or small sword.

Flexbee A U.S. Marine Corps lightweight flexible-wing reconnaissance drone.

flexible gun A machine gun mounted in an aircraft turret or on a post, tripod, or other mount in such a manner that the gun may be swung in both a vertical and a horizontal plane. It is distinguished from a *fixed* gun. The illustration shows an early example—twin Vickers-Berthier .303 aircraft machine guns mounted in the rear cockpit of a British biplane.

Flexitroper An individual flexible-wing drop glider for use by airborne troops.

flight **1.** In U.S. Navy and Marine Corps usage, a specified group of aircraft usually engaged in a common mission. **2.** The basic tactical unit in the Air Force, consisting of four or more aircraft in two or more elements. **3.** A single aircraft airborne on a nonoperational mission.

flight deck **1.** In certain airplanes, an elevated compartment occupied by the crew from which they operate the airplane in flight. **2.** The upper deck of an aircraft carrier that serves as a runway.

flight leader The pilot in tactical command of a mission, flight, sweep, or patrol station.

flight lieutenant A commissioned rank in the RAF and RCAF corresponding to that of captain in the USAF.

flight line **1.** On an airfield, a general area including the hangars and the ramps and other grounds between and surrounding the hangars where aircraft are parked, serviced, etc., but not including runways or taxiways. **2.** The line of flight of an aircraft. (Picture, next page.)

flight path The path of the center of gravity of a missile, usually with reference to the earth.

flight plan Specified information provided to air-traffic service units relative to the intended flight of an aircraft.

flight sergeant An enlisted rank or person in the RAF and RCAF corresponding to master sergeant in the USAF.

flight surgeon A physician specially trained in aviation medical practice. His primary duty is the medical examination and medical care of aircrew members.

flight test The test of an aircraft, rocket, missile, or other vehicle by actual flight or launching. Flight tests are planned to achieve specific test objectives and gain operational information.

flintlock A lock for a gun or pistol. Invented early in the seventeenth century, it consists of a cock that holds a piece of flint. When the flint in the cock strikes against a piece of steel (called the "frizzen"), it creates a shower of sparks that ignite the priming powder in the pan, which in turn fires the charge. This system was employed until superseded by the percussion lock early in the nineteenth century. Students differentiate between the French or "true" flintlock and a number of other mechanisms that employ the same general principle for

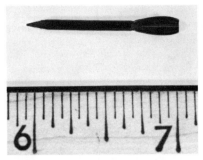

fléchette. (*U.S. Army.*)

flexible gun. Shown here are twin Vickers-Berthier machine guns. (*Vickers Ltd.*)

flight deck, showing a Corsair II attack bomber aboard the U.S.S. *Independence.* (*U.S. Navy.*)

flintlock. (*The Smithsonian Institution, H. Caldwell Collection.*)

flight line, showing Focke-Wulf Fw 190 fighters. (*Vereinigte Flugtechnische Werke—Fokker.*)

floatplane, an OS2U Kingfisher. (*Vought Aeronautics Company.*)

flying boat, a PBM Mariner. (*U.S. Navy.*)

producing a spark, e.g., the English lock, snaphaunce, miquelet lock, etc.

float   A watertight structure attached to an aircraft to give it buoyancy in the water.

float flare   A signal launched from an aircraft to mark a location at sea. It floats on the surface and emits smoke and flame for up to 1 hour.

floating battery   An artillery battery on rafts or the hulls of ships. They were used for coastal defense and to attack fortifications.

floating bridge   A double bridge, the top part of which projected beyond the lower part and could be moved forward by pulleys. It was used by troops for crossing narrow moats in the process of attacking a fortification.

floating dock   A dock which partly submerges to permit a ship to enter. It is then floated, and the ship is raised as in a dry dock.

floating smoke pot   A smoke pot which emits dense smoke when ignited and which floats on the surface of water to provide a temporary screen.

floatplane   A seaplane that is supported on water by one or more floats. A floatplane may use one float to support the fuselage and smaller floats, called "outriggers," on the wings.

Flogger   The NATO code name for the Soviet Mikoyan variable-geometry Mach 2 single-seat fighter first seen in 1967.

floodcock   A cock in a vessel which, when opened, can admit seawater to flood the powder magazines, etc.

floor plate   The bottom of a self-contained box magazine. The follower spring is attached to it.

Flora   The NATO code name for the Yakovlev Yak-23 single-seat jet fighter developed for the Soviet Air Force. It superficially resembles the Yak-17 (Feather) but is entirely different in construction, power plant, and performance.

Florida   **1.** The code name for a Hughes Aircraft-produced air-defense radar system provided the Swiss government. It consists of a network of air-defense centers interfaced with Switzerland's aircraft and surface-to-air missiles. **2.** A battleship of the **Utah** class, which see. It was commissioned in 1911.

flotation   **1.** The capacity of a vehicle, gun, or trailer to negotiate water obstacles without being in contact with the bottom. **2.** The capacity of a vehicle to negotiate soft, unfavorable terrain such as mud, sand, or snow.

flotilla   An administrative or tactical organization consisting of two or more squadrons of destroyers or smaller types, together with such additional ships as may be assigned, for example, flagships and tenders.

Flower   A class of British frigates (ex-corvettes) of 1,020 tons standard displacement completed in 1940–1942. They had a speed of 16 knots, a complement of 78 men, and armament consisting of one 4-in. gun, one 2-pounder, and two 20mm antiaircraft guns. They also carried two hedgehog A/S weapons.

Flume The code name for a German electronic device of World War II for locating radar transmitting sets.

Fly 1, 2, and 3 Subdivisions of a carrier flight deck. Fly 1 is under the direction of the flight-deck officer and catapult officer, Fly 2 is under the direction of the taxi-signal officer, and Fly 3 is under the direction of the landing-signal officer.

flying boat A kind of seaplane having a boatlike hull or fuselage, which allows the craft to float, take off, and land on water.

flying bomb Popularly, any explosive robot plane, guided missile, rocket bomb, or the like; specifically, the German V-1 explosive robot plane of World War II.

Flying Boxcar The Fairchild twin piston-engine tactical cargo and troop transport developed for the USAAF and first flown in 1944. The first version was called the "C-82" (Packet) and was replaced by an improved version in 1948. The latter, designated the C-119, carries 62 troops or 30,000 lb of cargo and has a range of 2,280 mi and a speed of about 200 mph.

flying camp Formerly, a company, squadron, or other body of troops that could move rapidly from one place to another.

flying circus A squadron or force of fighter planes, such as the Richthofen flying circus of World War I.

flying column A strong detachment which operated at a distance from the main force.

Flying Fortress The Boeing B-17 Flying Fortress was a four-engine heavy bomber first flown in 1935 and produced, in several versions, until the end of World War II. The size of the crew varied from 6 to 10, and the aircraft was armed with thirteen .50 cal. Browning machine guns. It had a maximum speed of 300 mph and a range of 1,100 mi with a 6,000-lb bombload. It was the mainstay of U.S. daylight raids against Germany, and it dropped approximately 640,000 tons of bombs on European targets during the war years.

Flying Pancake See **experimental aircraft.**

Flying Pencil A popular name for German Dornier Do 17 series bomber.

flying squadron A Naval squadron that can move rapidly from one place to another, but is detached from the main command.

flying the hump Flying cargo planes (and other aircraft) that flew over the Himalayas between India and China during World War II were said to be "flying the hump." Cargo duties were largely the responsibility of the U.S. Air Transport Command.

Flying Boxcar. (*U.S. Air Force.*)

Flying Fortress. (*U.S. Air Force.*)

FN 7.62mm light automatic rifle (FAL), as produced in Canada. (*Canadian Armed Forces Photograph.*)

Flying Tigers A popular name for the **American Volunteer Group (AVG),** which see, a volunteer air force serving in China in the early part of World War II.

FM A U.S. military field manual.

FM smoke See **titanium tetrachloride.**

FN The abbreviation for Fabrique Nationale d'Armes de Guerre, the Belgium firearms manufacturer.

FN 5.56mm CAL rifle This is a gas-operated weapon with selective-fire capability. It has an overall length of 38.6 in. and a barrel length of 18.4 in. It has a loaded weight of 7.3 lb, a cyclic rate of fire of about 850 rounds per minute, and a muzzle velocity of 3,182 fps. The initials CAL stand for *Carbine Automatique Légère,* or light automatic carbine. The magazine is of the staggered-row box type and has a capacity of 20 cartridges.

FN 7.62mm light automatic rifle (FAL) The FAL (*Fusil Automatique Légère*—light

automatic rifle) has the widest distribution of any postwar weapon in the non-Communist world. It is currently used in some 30 countries around the world and has been manufactured in 7 of them. This weapon is made in numerous variations, but all are chambered for the 7.62 NATO cartridge. The weapon has an overall length of 40 in. and a barrel length of 21 in. It weighs 9.06 lb unloaded and has a cyclic rate of fire of 650 to 700 rounds per minute and a magazine with a capacity of 20 cartridges.

FN Browning automatic rifle Model 30 Before World War II, FN produced this variation of the Browning automatic rifle for Chile, China, Belgium, and other countries. It is similar to the U.S. Model 1918A1 BAR. It was made in the following calibers: 7mm, 7.65mm, and 7.92mm.

FN Browning automatic rifle Type D This weapon was a postwar version of the BAR and included many refinements and major

FN Browning automatic rifle Type D. (*Belgian Ministry of Defense.*)

FN MAG machine gun. (*Belgian Ministry of Defense.*)

Focke-Wulf Fw 189. (*Vereinigte Flugtechnische Werke—Fokker.*)

improvements not found in other models. It was purchased by Belgium in .30/06 cal. and by Egypt in 7.92mm. This weapon has a barrel length of 19.7 in. and a total length of 45.1 in. With magazine, the weight of the Type D is 20.86 lb.

FN MAG machine gun This weapon has been developed to fire the 7.62mm NATO cartridge or the 6.5mm Swedish. It is designed for use as a light machine gun (on a bipod) or as a heavy machine gun (on a tripod). It has an adjustable rate of fire, with cyclic rates varying from 700 to 1,000 rounds per minute. The weight of the weapon with butt and bipod is 23.92 lb.

The weight of the FN tripod is 22 lb. The overall length of the weapon is 49.21 in., and the barrel length is 21.44 in. The muzzle velocity is about 2,800 fps with the 7.62 NATO ball cartridge, and the weapon has sights adjustable to 1,400 meters. Sweden was the only one of twenty-three countries that purchased this machine gun in a caliber other than 7.62mm.

FN self-loading rifle Model 1949 A weapon developed before World War II, but not produced until after the war. It was developed for use with the following cartridges: .30 cal., 7mm, 7.65mm, and 7.92mm. In .30 cal. it was adopted by Bel-

gium, Brazil, Luxembourg, Argentina, Colombia, and the former Belgian Congo. In 7mm it was bought by Venezuela, and in 7.92mm by Egypt. It is a gas-operated weapon with an overall length of 43.7 in. and a barrel length of 23.2 in. It weighs 9.48 lb and has a capacity of 10 cartridges.

Focke-Achgelis Fa 330 A German rotary-wing observation kite designed to be towed behind a U boat and provide an airborne observation platform.

Focke-Wulf Fw 189 A three-seat twin-engine twin-boom tactical-reconnaissance and Army cooperation aircraft first flown in Germany in 1938. Its top speed was 217 mph and it had armament consisting of six 7.9mm machine guns; it carried a bombload of about 440 lb.

Focke-Wulf Fw 190 This extremely successful German single-engine single-seat low-wing fighter was first flown on June 1, 1939. Manufactured throughout World War II, a total of 13,367 were produced as fighters, and 6,634 as fighter-bombers and close-support aircraft. The FW 190A-8 was introduced at the end of 1943 and had a maximum speed of 408 mph at 18,000 ft. Powered by a 1,700-hp engine, it had a range of 500 mi and a ceiling of 37,400 ft. The armament consisted of two 13mm machine guns MG 131 and four 20mm cannons. It had a span of 34.5 ft, a length of 29 ft, and a height of 13 ft. It was nicknamed *Wurger* (German for "Butcher Bird").

Focke-Wulf Fw 200 See **Condor**, sense 1.

foible The portion (about two-thirds) of a sword blade nearest the point.

Fokker D.I through D.V A series of German single-seat single-engine biplane fighters first flown in early 1916. They flew at a speed of about 95 mph and were armed with one forward-firing Spandau machine gun. They were no match against Allied Neuports and were soon withdrawn for use as trainers.

Fokker D.VI A biplane fighter with a speed of 121 mph and armament consisting of twin forward-firing Spandau machine guns. Limited numbers were produced.

Fokker D.VII A German single-seat single-engine biplane fighter that entered service in April 1918. It was regarded as the best German fighter of World War I. It flew at speeds of about 118 mph and was armed with twin 7.92mm Spandau machine guns mounted directly in front of the pilot. It had excellent flying characteristics and was able to maintain performance at high altitudes. It had a wingspan of about 29 ft, a length of 22.75 ft, and a height of about 9 ft. Its operational ceiling was 19,685 ft.

Fokker D.XXI A single-seat single-engine fighter-interceptor used by the Dutch Army Air Service and first flown in 1936. It had a speed of 286 mph and was armed with four 7.9mm Browning machine guns. Finland acquired a manufacturing license to build this aircraft.

Fokker Dr.I A German single-seat single-engine triplane fighter that began to be delivered in October 1917. It flew at speeds up to about 105 mph and was armed with two forward-firing Spandau machine guns. While flying an airplane of this type, Manfred von Richthofen was shot down and killed on April 21, 1918.

Fokker E types A series of German single-place single-engine midwing monoplanes first flown in 1913. They were armed with the first of the Fokker interrupter gears that made it possible to fire a machine gun through the spinning blades of a propeller. The E.III was the version produced in the greatest numbers; it had a speed of about 83 mph.

Fokker E.V/D.VIII A German single-seat single-engine high-wing monoplane that was produced in limited numbers at the end of World War I. It had a speed of 115 mph and was armed with forward-firing twin Spandau machine guns.

Fokker F.27M Troopship This short- to medium-range military transport aircraft was developed in the Netherlands and first flown in 1955. It has a speed of 295 mph and carries 45 fully equipped paratroops.

Fokker G.I A three-seat twin-engine twin-boom heavy fighter and close-support aircraft first flown in March 1937. The first sale of this aircraft was to Spain, but these were diverted to the Army Air Service. It had a maximum speed of 295 mph and was armed with eight forward-firing 7.9mm Browning machine guns and one rear-firing flexible Browning gun.

folding fin A fin on a rocket or missile that is hinged to permit outward extension when the missile is in flight.

Folgore The Macchi C.202 Folgore (Lightning) was an Italian single-seat single-engine fighter-interceptor and fighter-bomber and the first Italian fighter to compare favorably with the aircraft of other countries. The prototype first flew in August 1940, and by 1943 some 1,500 aircraft had been built. Used in the Mediterranean area and in Russia, this airplane had a 1,175-hp engine and flew at speeds of 364 mph. It was armed with two 12.7mm Breda-SAFAT machine guns and two 7.7mm Breda-SAFAT machine guns.

follower In a box magazine, the metallic plate between the magazine spring and the cartridges.

foot Infantrymen; soldiers who fight on foot.

forage To collect supplies and food for men and animals.

forage cap A small undress hat for an officer or enlisted man. In the U.S. service the term was superseded by "service cap."

Focke-Wulf Fw 190. (*Vereinigte Flugtechnische Werke—Fokker.*)

Fokker D.VII. (*The Smithsonian Institution, National Air Museum.*)

Fokker E.III. (*The Imperial War Museum.*)

foray A sudden raid.

force **1.** A body of troops, ships, or aircraft, or a combination thereof. **2.** A major subdivision of a fleet.

forced landing A landing, either on land or on water, made when it is impossible for the aircraft to remain airborne as a result of mechanical failure, combat damage, etc.

force rendezvous A navigational checkpoint at which formations of aircraft or ships join and become part of the main force.

forcing cone The tapered beginning of the lands at the origin of the rifling of a gun tube. The forcing cone allows the rotating band of the projectile to be gradually engaged by the rifling, thereby centering the projectile in the bore.

forecastle Formerly, warships were equipped with a short upper deck that was

formation, Swedish Saab 29F single-seat jet fighters. (*Swedish Air Force.*)

formation bombing, Martin B-26 Marauders. (*U.S. Air Force.*)

raised like a castle and located on the forward part of the ship. It was used to command an enemy's deck. The term now refers to the forward section of the weather deck.

fore-end The portion of the stock forward of the action and below the barrel.

foreland The ground between the wall of a fortification and the moat.

forelock A fastening, in medieval armor, for holding the helmet to the gorget or breastplate in front.

fork A musket rest. See also **fourquine**.

forlorn hope See **enfans perdus**.

formation **1.** An ordered arrangement of troops and/or vehicles for a specific purpose. **2.** An ordered arrangement of two or more ships, units, or aircraft proceeding together.

formation bombing Bombing by aircraft in formation; pattern bombing.

Formidable A class of British 15,000-ton battleships completed in 1901–1902. There were three ships in the class: *Formidable*, *Irresistible*, and *Implacable*. They had a length of 430 ft, a complement of 780 men, and main armament consisting of four 12-in. and twelve 6-in. guns, plus four 18-in. torpedo tubes. They had a speed of 18.5 knots. *Formidable* was sunk by a German U Boat on January 1, 1915.

forming-up place The last position occupied by the assault echelon before crossing the start line or line of departure.

Forrestal A class of U.S. attack aircraft carriers (CVA) of about 60,000 tons standard displacement commissioned in 1955–1959. They have a length of about 1,000 ft, a maximum flight-deck width of about 260 ft, a speed of 33 to 35 knots, and a complement of 4,700 men. They carry 70 to 90 aircraft, according to type, and are armed with 5-in. guns and Sea Sparrow missiles.

Forrest Sherman A class of U.S. destroyers (DD) and guided-missile destroyers (DDG) of about 2,800 tons standard displacement produced between 1955 and 1959. There

Forrest Sherman. (*U.S. Navy.*)

are 14 DD's and four DDG's in the class. They have a length of 418 ft, a beam of 45 ft, a speed of 33 knots, and a crew of about 300 men. The DD's are armed with two 5-in. and four 3-in. guns, plus hedgehogs and torpedo launchers. The DDG's carry one 5-in. gun, one Asroc eight-tube launcher, and two triple torpedo launchers.

fort **1.** A permanent post, as opposed to a camp, which is a temporary installation. **2.** A land area within which harbor defense units are located. **3.** A strong, fortified building or place that can be defended against an enemy.

fortification **1.** A structure or earthworks, usually heavily armed, constructed as a defense; a fortified place or position. **2.** The act or art of fortifying.

fortress A large, permanent fortification which sometimes includes a town.

Fortress The British World War II designation for the **Flying Fortress,** which see.

forward area An area in proximity to combat.

forward echelon The combat echelon of a command.

forward observer An observer operating with front-line troops and trained to adjust ground or naval gunfire and pass back battlefield information. In the absence of a forward air controller he may control close air-support strikes.

fosse, foss A ditch or moat.

fougasse A mine constructed so that upon explosion of the charge, pieces of metal, rock, gasoline, or other substances are blown in a predetermined direction.

fouling Deposit that remains in the bore of a gun after it is fired. It consists of burned powder residue, scrapings from projectiles, etc.

four-by-four In regard to motor vehicles, four wheels, all of which are driving wheels, dual wheels being considered one wheel. It is usually written "4 × 4."

four-by-two In regard to motor vehicles, four wheels, two of which are driving wheels, dual wheels being considered one wheel. It is usually written "4 × 2."

four-pounder A gun that fires a 4-lb projectile.

fourquine A stick with a fork on one end that is used to support a firearm.

fourragère A unit decoration given by France or Belgium. The emblem of the *fourragère* consists of braided cords worn on a service uniform around the right shoulder. It differs from an aiguillette in color, in the insignia it bears on its metal tips, and in the place worn. The aiguillette is worn around the left shoulder.

fourrier A quartermaster.

four-striper A U.S. Navy captain, so called because of the four gold stripes worn on the sleeves of his uniform.

Fox **1.** A British four-wheeled armored car developed by Daimler in the late 1960s. It has a crew of three and is armed with a

fourquine. (*Metropolitan Museum of Art, gift of Charles M. Schott, Jr., 1917.*)

Rarden 30mm cannon, which see, and one 7.62mm machine gun. The range of the Rarden cannon is over 1,000 meters. **2.** The Fairey Fox was a two-seat reconnaissance, observation, and light bombing aircraft first flown in 1925 and used by the RAF and the Belgian Aeronautique Militaire. It had a maximum speed of 224 mph and was armed with two or three 7.62mm machine guns.

Foxbat The NATO code name for the Mikoyan/Gurevich MiG-23 single-seat supersonic interceptor and strike reconnaissance aircraft in service with the Soviet Air Force and first seen in 1965. It has a speed of Mach 3.

Foxer A defensive device produced by the Allies during World War II and carried by transatlantic escort vessels. It consisted of parallel rods which clacked together when towed, making a noise that attracted and detonated German acoustic torpedoes.

foxhole A small pit used for cover, usually for one or two men, and so constructed that an occupant can fire effectively from it.

fps The abbreviation for "feet per second." It is the measurement for expressing the velocity of a projectile.

frag bomb Short for "fragmentation bomb."

Forrestal. (*U.S. Navy.*)

fragmentation grenade. (*U.S. Army.*)

frag cluster Short for "fragmentation cluster."

fragmentation A term describing ammunition that is intended primarily to produce a fragmentation effect.

fragmentation bomb Fragmentation bombs are used against personnel and materiel. The body of a fragmentation bomb usually consists of a thin steel tube with square wire spirally wound on the outside. The wire provides the principal source of fragments when the bomb is detonated. The explosive filler constitutes about 14 percent of the total bomb weight. Small fragmentation bombs (23 lb or less) are used against personnel and light materiel. Larger ones, however, are used against materiel such as vehicles, machinery, and other equipment. Some are equipped with parachute units for low-altitude bombing.

fragmentation-bomb cluster A cluster of fragmentation bombs, so arranged that more than one bomb can be suspended and dropped from a single station of a bomb rack on an airplane. Popularly called "frag cluster."

fragmentation grenade A hand grenade designed to give fragmentation which is effective against personnel. The thrower needs protective cover, and hence the grenade is used primarily for defensive operations and is often called a "defensive grenade."

fragmentation warhead A warhead which ejects metal fragments of the casing at high velocity to achieve damage to the target.

fraises Rows of palisades planted horizontally to protect a position. They were about 8 ft long and 5 in. thick. To fraise a battalion was to cover it in every direction with bayonets, thus enabling it to withstand a cavalry assault.

FRAM Fleet Rehabilitation and Modernization. A U.S. Navy program to upgrade World War II-era ships.

frame The basic structure of a firearm.

framea A kind of ancient Teutonic spear.

Frances 26 The World War II code name for the Kawanishi P1Y2-S Kyokko (Aurora), a three-seat twin-engine night fighter derived from a land-based bomber, the P1Y1 Ginga (Milky Way). Equipped with two 1,850-hp engines, this aircraft flew at speeds of 325 mph and was armed with three 20mm cannons. The prototype first flew in June 1944.

francisca A battle-ax so named because it was used by the sixth-century Franks. It dates, however, to Roman times. It has a single-bladed head with a long blade curved on the outer face. It was often used as a missile.

frangible bullet A brittle plastic or other nonmetallic bullet used for firing practice which, upon striking a target, breaks into powder or small fragments without penetrating. Frangible bullets are usually designed to leave a mark at the point of impact.

frangible grenade An improvised incendiary hand grenade consisting of a glass container filled with a flammable liquid, with an igniter attached. It breaks and ignites upon striking a resistant target, such as a tank. Sometimes called a "Molotov cocktail."

Frank **1.** The NATO code name for the **Yak-9,** which see. **2.** The World War II Allied code name for the Nakajima Ki.84 Hayate (Gale) single-seat single-engine general-purpose fighter-interceptor and fighter-bomber built for the Japanese Army Air Force and first flown in May 1943. It was one of Japan's best wartime fighters and could outclimb and outmaneuver both the Mustang and the Thunderbolt. It had a speed of 388 mph and armament consisting of two 20mm cannons and two 12.7mm machine guns. A total of 3,413 aircraft were produced.

Frankish sword The sword of the Franks from about 450 to 760. It was a short, straight, broad-bladed, double-edged, somewhat obtusely pointed weapon and usually had a length of about 30 to 32 in.

Freccia The Fiat G.50 Freccia (Arrow) was the first all-metal monoplane fighter designed and flown in Italy. A single-seat general-purpose fighter, it was flown for the first time in 1937, and several were tested operationally in Spain in 1938. It was armed with two 12.7mm Breda-SAFAT machine guns and had a speed of 293 mph.

Fred The NATO code name for the P-63 Kingcobra as supplied to the Soviet Union under lend-lease during World War II.

Freedom The World War II code name for the rescue, in the fall of 1944, of some 300 U.S. prisoners of war in Bulgaria and their transportation to Italy by way of Turkey and Egypt.

Freedom Fighter A designation of the **F-5,** which see.

free drop The dropping of equipment or supplies from an aircraft without the use of parachutes.

free fall A parachute maneuver in which the parachute is manually activated at the discretion of the jumper or automatically at a preset altitude.

free-falling antipersonnel missile A nonexplosive missile designed to be dropped from aircraft for effect against personnel.

free-falling tire-puncturing missile A nonexplosive missile designed to be dropped from aircraft on roads and airfield runways; it causes damage to tires of vehicles or aircraft by contact. See also **caltrop.**

free lance A mercenary knight or soldier of the Middle Ages. He would fight for any state or commander who paid him.

free rocket A rocket not subject to guidance or control in flight.

free run As applied to guns, the travel of a projectile from its original position in the gun chamber until it engages with the rifling in the gun bore.

French 7.5mm light machine gun Model 1924 M29 This weapon is similar to the U.S. Browning automatic rifle Model 1918. It has selective-fire capability, an overall length of 42.6 in., a barrel length of 19.7 in., a weight of 24.51 lb (with bipod), and a cyclic rate of fire of 550 rounds per min-

Frank. (*The Smithsonian Institution, National Air Museum.*)

ute. It has a muzzle velocity of 2,590 fps.

French 7.5mm machine gun Model 52 (AAT) This weapon is called the "AAT" (Arme Automatique Transformable) by the French because it can be used as either a light or a heavy machine gun. The length of this weapon with stock extended is 45.9 in. It has a cyclic rate of fire of 700 rounds per minute and a muzzle velocity of 2,690 fps. In the light-machine-gun role it is used with a light barrel (having a length of 19.3 in.), a bipod, and a butt support. As a heavy machine gun it uses a heavy barrel (with a length of 23.6 in.) and a U.S. M2 tripod with a French adapter. The weight of the weapon with the light barrel is 21.7 lb; with the heavy barrel, 23.29 lb.

French 7.5mm machine gun Model 1931A This is a tank and fortress version of the French 7.5mm M1924 M29 (Chatellerault) machine gun, and some are still in use on French-made armored vehicles. This is a gas-operated weapon that functions on automatic fire only. It has an overall length of 40.5 in. and a barrel length of 23.5 in. The empty weight is 27.48 lb. This weapon is fed from either 36-round box magazines or 150-round drum magazines and has a cyclic rate of fire of 750 rounds per minute and a muzzle velocity of 2,750 fps.

French 7.5mm rifle M1907/15 M34 This rifle has an integral five-round staggered-row box magazine, an overall length of 43.2 in., a barrel length of 22.8 in., a weight of 7.85 lb, and a muzzle velocity of 2,700 fps.

French 7.5mm rifle M1932 This rifle is the prototype of the M1936 and was manufactured in limited quantities.

French 7.5mm rifle M1936 This rifle utilizes an integral five-round staggered-row box magazine and has an overall length of 40.13 in., a barrel length of 22.6 in., a weight of 8.29 lb, and a muzzle velocity of 2,700 fps. It evolved from the M1932 rifle, which was the prototype weapon to use the standardized M1929 7.5mm cartridge.

French 7.5mm rifle M1936 CR39 This rifle utilizes an integral five-round staggered-row box magazine and has an overall length of 34.9 in. with stock extended, a barrel length of 17.7 in., a weight of about 8 lb, and a muzzle velocity of 2,700 fps.

French 7.5mm semiautomatic rifles M1949 and M1949/56 (MAS) These weapons evolved from the 7.5mm MAS Model 1944 and were designed at the French government arsenal Manufacture d'Armes de Saint-Étienne (MAS). They use the same gas system as the Swedish Ljungman AG42 semiautomatic rifle. The M1949 is capable of semiautomatic fire only. It weighs 10.4 lb and has an overall length of 43.3 in. and a barrel length of 22.8 in. It utilizes a 10-round detachable box magazine and has a muzzle velocity of 2,705 fps. The M1949/56 is identical to the M1949

except for a shorter forearm and handguard. Grenade-launching rings and sights have also been added, as have provisions for a bayonet.

French 7.65mm automatic pistols M1935A and M1935S These were the standard French service pistols during World War II and continued in service until the mid-fifties. The M1935A has an overall length of 7.6 in. and a barrel length of 4.3 in. The magazine has a capacity of eight cartridges, and the weight of the weapon is 1.62 lb. The M1935S differs only slightly.

French 7.65mm Long submachine gun MAS Model 1938 The MAS (Manufacture d'Armes de Saint-Étienne) Model 1938 was adopted as standard for the French Army in 1938 and remained in production until 1949. It uses the 7.65mm Long cartridge and is capable of only full automatic fire. It is blowback-operated and has a cyclic rate of fire of 600 rounds per minute. It has an overall length of 24.8 in. and a barrel length of 8.80 in. With a 32-round clip, the weapon weighs 7.48 lb. It has a muzzle velocity of about 1,150 fps and a rear sight adjustable to ranges of 100 and 200 meters. The weapon saw limited service in World War II, but was used to a large extent during the early parts of the Indochinese War.

French 8mm carbine M1890 (Mannlicher Berthier) This weapon utilizes an integral

French 7.65mm automatic pistol M1935A. (The Smithsonian Institution, Treasury Department Collection.)

three-round Mannlicher-type magazine and has an overall length of 37.2 in., a barrel length of 17.7 in., a weight of 6.83 lb, and a muzzle velocity of 2,080 fps.

French 8mm carbine M1892 (Mannlicher Berthier) A modified form of the M1890, this 8mm Mousquetoon (carbine) utilizes an integral three-round Mannlicher-type magazine and has an overall length of 37.2 in., a barrel length of 17.7 in., a weight of 6.8 lb, and a muzzle velocity of 2,080 fps.

French 8mm carbine M1916 This carbine utilizes an integral five-round Mannlicher-type magazine and has an overall length of 37.2 in., a barrel length of 17.7 in., a weight of 7.17 lb, and a muzzle velocity of 2,080 fps.

French 8mm light machine gun Model 1915 (Chauchat/C.S.R.G.) This is a long-recoil selective-fire weapon with an

French 7.5mm rifle M1936. (*The Smithsonian Institution, Department of Defense Collection.*)

French 7.65mm Long submachine gun MAS Model 1938. (*The Smithsonian Institution, G.S.A. Administration Collection.*)

French 8mm carbine M1892 (Mannlicher Berthier). (*The Smithsonian Institution, National Museum Collection.*)

French 8mm light machine gun Model 1915 (Chauchat/C.S.R.G.). *(The Smithsonian Institution, National Museum Collection.)*

French 8mm rifle M1907/15. *(The Smithsonian Institution, War Department Collection.)*

French 8mm semiautomatic rifle Model 1918. *(The Smithsonian Institution, War Department Collection.)*

French 9mm Parabellum submachine gun M.A.T. Model 1949. *(The Smithsonian Institution, Department of Defense Collection.)*

overall length of 45.2 in. and a barrel length of 18.5. With a bipod it weighs 20 lb. It has a cyclic rate of fire of 240 rounds per minute and a muzzle velocity of 2,300 fps. For more details see **French .30 cal. light machine gun M1918 C.S.R.G.**

French 8mm machine gun Model 1915 See **Chauchat 8mm machine gun Model 1915.**

French 8mm machine gun Model 1922 A version of the **Lewis machine gun,** which see. It was used as a ground weapon.

French 8mm Madsen machine gun France used four models of the Madsen machine gun, ranging from Model 1915 to Model 1924. See **Madsen machine guns.**

French 8mm rifle M1886 M93 This rifle, the Lebel, was introduced in 1886 and was the first weapon to use the new smokeless powder invented by Paul Vielle. This bolt-action rifle was designed with a tubular magazine holding eight cartridges. It has an overall length of 51.3 in., a barrel length of 31.4 in., a muzzle velocity of 2,380 fps, and a weight of 9.35 lb. This rifle continued in service with the French through both world wars. The M1886 M93 R35 is the above rifle altered to a carbine form in 1935. The tubular magazine is retained but holds only three rounds. The M1886 M27 is a carbine version of the M1886 M93 modified to use a 7.5mm cartridge and a five-round Mauser-type magazine.

French 8mm rifle M1902 (Indochina Model) This rifle utilizes an integral three-round Mannlicher-type magazine and has an overall length of 38.6 in., a barrel length of 24.8 in., a weight of 7.9 lb, and a muzzle velocity of 2,180 fps.

French 8mm rifle M1907 (Colonial Model) This rifle utilizes an integral three-round Mannlicher-type magazine and has an overall length of 52 in., a barrel length of 31.4 in., a weight of 8.6 lb, and a muzzle velocity of 2,380 fps.

French 8mm rifle M1907/15 This rifle utilizes an integral three-round Mannlicher-type magazine and has an overall length of 51.43 in., a barrel length of 31.4 in., a weight of 8.38 lb, and a muzzle velocity of 2,380 fps. The M1907/15 M34 is a variant cut down and rebarreled for the 7.5mm cartridge. It is fitted with a five-round Mauser-type magazine.

French 8mm rifle M1916 This rifle utilizes an integral five-round Mannlicher-type magazine and has an overall length of 51.42 in., a barrel length of 31.4 in., a weight of 9.25 lb, and a muzzle velocity of 2,380 fps.

French 8mm rifles M1917-35 and M1918-35 A conversion of the M1917 and M1918 semiautomatic rifles into manually operated magazine rifles.

French 8mm semiautomatic rifles Model 1917 and Model 1918 Popularly known as the "Saint-Étienne rifles" and the "R.S.C." (after Ribeyrolle, Sutter, and Chauchat, who worked on the design). The Model 1917 fired the 8mm Lebel cartridge and is a gas-operated semiautomatic rifle with an overall length of 52.4 in., a barrel length of 31.4 in., and a weight of 11.6 lb. It utilizes a five-round nondetachable box magazine and has a muzzle velocity of 2,180 fps. The Model 1918 was a modification that included a shorter barrel and had a lighter weight, but it was manufactured too late to see active service during World War I.

French 9mm Parabellum automatic pistol Model 1950 A pistol similar in some respects to the U.S. Colt .45 automatic. It has an overall length of 7.6 in. and a barrel length of 4.4 in. The weight of the weapon is 1.8 lb, and the magazine has a capacity of nine cartridges. It has a muzzle velocity of 1,156 fps. It is presently the official French service pistol.

French 9mm Parabellum submachine gun Hotchkiss "Type Universal" See **Hotchkiss 9mm Parabellum submachine gun "Type Universal."**

French 9mm Parabellum submachine gun M.A.T. Model 1949 The M.A.T. (Manufacture Nationale d'Armes de Tulle) Model 1949 was adopted by the French Army in 1949 and is still in use, having seen extensive service in Indochina and Algeria. It is of blowback operation and fires full automatic only. It has a cyclic rate of fire of 600 rounds per minute. The overall length with stock extended is 28 in., and it has a barrel length of 9.05 in. With a 32-round magazine the weight is 9.40 lb. The muzzle velocity is about 1,200 fps, and an aperture rear sight is adjustable to 100 and 200 meters.

French 11mm revolver M1873 A weapon similar in operation to the U.S. .45 cal. M1873 (the Colt Frontier or Peacemaker Model), except that the French revolver is double-action, while the other is single-action. It was designed for a low-pressure black-powder cartridge.

French 11mm rifle Model 1866 (Gras Chassepot conversion) This rifle has an overall length of 51 in., a barrel length of 32.3 in., and a weight of 9.3 lb. It was modified in 1874 and 1878. The 1874 modification is still often found in the Balkans.

French 11mm rifle Model 1874 (Gras) The first French service rifle to use a metallic cartridge. It evolved from the Chassepot Needle Fire and was also made in carbine form.

French 11mm rifle Model 1878 (Kropatcheck–Marine Infantry) This rifle has a tubular magazine with a capacity of seven rounds, an overall length without bayonet of 49 in., a barrel length of 29.5 in., and a weight of 10.3 lb. It was used by the French Navy.

French .30 cal. light machine gun M1918 C.S.R.G. This weapon was called the "Chauchat" and was used widely during World War I. The United States ordered considerable quantities of this weapon in 8mm and in .30/06 cal. It is the same as the French 8mm light machine gun Model 1915 except for having a straight 16-round magazine rather than the crescent-shaped magazine required by the French 8mm cartridge. C.S.R.G. refers to the three designers of the weapon. After World War I the weapon was adopted by Belgium in 7.65mm and by Greece in 8mm. It saw certain amounts of service during World War II. The English call this weapon the "Chauchard."

French 75mm gun, Model 1897 The famous "French 75" of World War I was the finest fieldpiece of its time and was widely used by Allied forces. It had a length of 34.5 calibers, a weight of 1,015 lb, and a range of 13,500 yd. It fired either a 16-lb shrapnel shell or a 12.3-lb high-explosive shell at the rate of 15 to 20 rounds per minute.

French 105mm self-propelled howitzer AMX 105A A fully tracked basic artillery weapon, this system has been in service with the French Army since 1952. It has a crew of five, a weight of 18.2 tons, and a road speed of 37 mph. The range of the 105mm howitzer is about 15,000 meters.

French 155mm gun, Models 1917 and 1918 Also designated the Saint-Chamond 155mm G. P. F. (by the Saint-Chamond Company; the G. P. F. meaning *Grande puissance Filloux*, or "great range Filloux," named after the designer). It was the best Allied medium gun of World War I. It had a

length of 232 in. and a weight (on a wheeled mount) of 20,100 lb. It fired a 95-lb projectile to a range of more than 21,000 yd. Mounted on a Sherman tank chassis, it became the U.S. 155mm Gun Motor Carriage M12 of World War II (also designated the **U.S. 155mm self-propelled gun M12,** which see).

French 155mm self-propelled howitzer Mk F3 A full-track system presently in service with French forces, it has a weight of 37,480 lb, a road speed of up to 37 mph, and a crew of eight. The 155mm howitzer has a maximum rate of fire of four rounds per minute and a range of 20,000 meters.

French .303 cal. machine gun Model 1916 The **Lewis machine gun,** which see, used for aircraft applications during World War I.

French 340mm railway gun A World War I weapon that fired a 940-lb projectile to a distance of 20.5 mi.

French armored car Panhard AMD 35 Introduced in 1935, this armored car was used by cavalry reconnaissance units. It had a crew of four, a weight of 8.3 tons, and a road speed of 50 mph. It was armed with one 25mm gun and one 7.5mm machine gun. Numbers of these vehicles were captured by the Germans during World War II and redesignated SdKfs 178(f).

French armored personnel carrier AMX-

French 11mm revolver M1873. (*The Smithsonian Institution, War Department Collection.*)

VTP M-56 See **AMX-VTP M-56.**

French light armored car AML 245 See **AML 245.**

French light tank AMX 13 See **AMX 13.**

French main battle tank AMX 30 See **AMX 30.**

French self-propelled twin 30mm AA guns AMX D.C.A. 30 First produced in 1964, this system is presently in service with the French Army. It has a crew of five, a weight of 30,860 lb, and a road speed of up to 37 mph. It carries two radar-controlled 30mm antiaircraft guns.

French Squadron A fighter squadron made up of American volunteers serving in

French 11mm rifle Model 1874 (Gras). (*The Smithsonian Institution, War Department Collection.*)

French 105mm self-propelled howitzer AMX 105A. (*French Ministry of Defense.*)

Friedrichshafen G.III. (*The Smithsonian Institution, National Air Museum.*)

the spring of 1940 in World War II under French command.

French tank, cavalry, Somua S35 This tank was introduced in 1936 and saw service in the early part of World War II. It had a crew of three, a weight of 20 tons, a length of about 17 ft, and a speed of 23 mph. It was armed with one 47mm gun and one 7.5mm machine gun.

French tank, heavy, Char de Manoeuvre B-1 A tank introduced in 1936 for use with armored divisions. It had a crew of four, a weight of 31 tons, and a road speed of 17 mph. It was armed with one 75mm howitzer, one 37mm gun, and two 7.5mm machine guns.

French tank, light, Renault FT This vehicle was designed in 1916 and entered service in May 1918. It was the most successful light tank in World War I. It had a crew of two, a speed of 6 mph, a weight of 7 tons, and armament consisting of one

37mm gun or one machine gun. More than 4,000 were produced.

French tank, light, Renault R35 Introduced in 1935, this tank was the standard infantry tank when France entered World War II. It had a weight of 10.8 tons, a length of about 13 ft, a crew of two, and a speed of 12 mph. It was armed with one 37mm cannon and one 7.5mm machine gun.

French tank, medium, Char B1 bis A tank introduced in 1936 and used as the main battle tank when France entered World War II. It had a crew of four, a weight of 32 tons, a length of about 21 ft, and a speed of 18 mph. It was armed with one 75mm gun (mounted in the front hull), a 47mm antitank gun, and a 7.5mm machine gun.

Fresco The NATO code name for one of several versions (A, B, C, or D) of the Mikoyan/Gurevich MiG-17 single-seat jet fighter in service with the Soviet Air Force

and first seen in 1953. It is used by at least 15 other countries. It has a speed of Mach 0.975 and a range of 750 mi and is armed with three 23mm cannons, plus four 8-rocket pods or two 550-lb bombs. It is an update of the MiG-15 (Fagot).

frette A wrought-iron or steel hoop that was shrunk on a cast-iron gun to make it stronger.

Freya A World War II German radar installation for the long-range early warning of the approach of Allied bombers.

friction primer A type of primer that is fired by pulling a toothed wire or plug through an explosive mixture.

Friedrichshafen floatplane series German two-place single-engine floatplanes (biplanes) first flown in the spring of 1915. Their major duties included coastal and ocean patrol, fleet observation and cooperation, and antisubmarine work. They had a speed of about 72 mph and were armed with one rear-mounted Parabellum machine gun.

Friedrichshafen G types A series of German three-place twin-engine (pushers) biplane bombers first tested in 1914. By 1916 the G.II had appeared, and this was followed in 1917 by the G.III. It was armed with single or double Parabellum guns in each of the front and rear cockpits, had a speed of 87.6 mph, and carried 1,102 lb of bombs. They were used chiefly as night bombers against targets in France and Belgium.

Friesland A class of Dutch antisubmarine destroyers of 2,497 tons standard displacement completed in 1956–1958. They have a speed of 36 knots, a complement of 284 men, and armament consisting of four

frigate, the U.S.S. *England* of the *Leahy* class. (*U.S. Navy.*)

4.7-in. guns, four 40mm antiaircraft guns, and two four-barreled depth-charge mortars.

frigate 1. A warship designed to operate independently or with strike, antisubmarine-warfare, or amphibious forces against submarine, air, and surface threats. (Normal armament consists of 3- and 5-in. dual-purpose guns and advanced antisubmarine-warfare weapons.) 2. During World War II, an escort vessel in the British and Canadian Navies. It was of a size between a corvette and a destroyer. 3. Originally, in the days of sail, a three-masted square-rigged sailing ship. A typical U.S. frigate carried 36 to 44 guns. A double-banked frigate carried guns on two decks.

fringing groove A groove cut into a rotating band on a projectile to collect metal from the band while it travels through the bore. Excess metal so collected is prevented from forming a fringe in back of the rotating band. Fringe formation has been a cause of excess dispersion and short range.

frisrutter A device for blocking a harbor or a river. It consists of iron beams holding projecting iron bars. The bars were about 12 ft long.

Fritz 1. The NATO code name for the Soviet **La-9** aircraft, which see. 2. A World War I slang expression for a German and also for a German weapon, such as an artillery shell, an airplane, etc.

Fritz-X The German code name for a World War II air-to-surface armor-piercing bomb, radio-guided to its target. It was unpowered and was designed principally for use against ships. When released from a 3-mi altitude, it had a range of 4.5 mi.

frizzen In a flintlock firing mechanism, the upright steel plate against which the flint strikes to produce sparks.

frizzen pick A metal pick used to clean out the clogged flash holes of flintlocks.

frog The metal hook on a rifle sling that permits adjustment for length.

Frog-1 The NATO code name for a Soviet missile that appears to be a counterpart of the U.S. Honest John. It has a length of 31 ft, an estimated firing weight of 6,000 lb, a range of 15 mi, and a thermonuclear warhead. It has been since 1960.

Frog-3 through 5 The NATO code designations for a series of Soviet unguided spin-stabilized missiles. The Frog-4 is a two-stage missile with a length of about 33 ft, an estimated weight of 4,400 lb, and a range of about 30 mi.

frogmen A slang term for underwater demolition personnel.

Frommer Stop pistol See **Hungarian 7.65mm Frommer Stop pistol model 19.**

fronde A large sling used for throwing stones.

front 1. The lateral space occupied by an element, measured from the extremity of

one flank to the extremity of the other flank. 2. The direction of the enemy. 3. The line of contact of two opposing forces. 4. When a combat situation does not exist or is not assumed, the direction toward which the command is faced.

front sight A metallic bead, blade, post, or the like, attached on the muzzle end of military carbines, pistols, revolvers, rifles, shotguns, and other similar items as a sighting device. It may be provided with a hood or protective wings.

FS A U.S. Navy freight supply ship.

FU-1 fighter The first biplane fighter built by Chance Vought for the U.S. Navy in 1924. It was powered by a 220-hp Wright J-3 engine and flew at a top speed of 153 mph.

fubar See **snafu.**

Fubuki A class of Japanese 2,000-ton destroyers produced in the late 1920s and early 1930s. They had a speed of 34 knots, a complement of 197 men, and armament consisting of six 5-in. guns, two 13mm guns, and nine 24-in. torpedo tubes. Only one ship of this class of twenty survived World War II.

full automatic A weapon that provides continuous fire as long as the trigger is depressed, as distinguished from semiautomatic.

full charge The largest of the two propelling charges available for naval guns.

full colonel A colonel. Sometimes used as a distinguishing term in contexts where the word "colonel" may be considered to refer to either a colonel or a lieutenant colonel.

full-dress uniform The uniform worn on ceremonial occasions.

Full House The code name of the World War II operation in which Allied fighter planes interfered with enemy air and land movement in France during the Normandy invasion (Operation Overlord), in June 1944.

full-track combat engineer vehicle A self-propelled armored vehicle, utilizing a combat tank chassis, designed to accomplish essential pioneer tasks within combat

frizzen. (*The Smithsonian Institution.*)

areas. It includes a demolition gun in a revolving turret and attachments, such as winches, booms, bulldozer, and A-frame. It may have provisions for special attachments, such as mine exploder, mine detector, or minelaying devices.

full-track vehicle A vehicle entirely supported, driven, and steered by an endless belt, or track, on each side. Tanks are full-track vehicles. (Picture, next page.)

Fulmar A British single-engine two-seat low-wing general-purpose shipboard fighter built by Fairey and first flown in 1940. This aircraft saw considerable service aboard Royal Navy carriers in the Mediterranean. They were powered by a 1,300-hp engine and flew at speeds of 272 mph. Armament consisted of eight forward-firing .303 cal. Browning machine guns, and some were also fitted with a single .303 cal. Vickers machine gun in the rear cockpit.

functional bombing The bombing of a specially selected class of key targets, such as dams or marshaling yards, that function within an industrial complex or transportation system, as opposed to the bombing of the entire system.

funda, funditor A seventh-century stone-ball throwing machine used by the Visigoths.

Furious A British 22,450-ton aircraft car-

FU-1 fighter. (*Vought Aeronautics Company.*)

full-track vehicle, the British Centurion medium tank. (*Vickers Ltd.*)

Fury. (*U.S. Marine Corps.*)

fusil. (*The Smithsonian Institution, L. H. White Collection.*)

rier completed in 1916. It had a length of 735 ft, a speed of 30 knots, a complement of 1,200 men, and a total of 42 antiaircraft guns. It carried 33 aircraft.

furlough An authorized leave of absence from military service.

furniture **1.** In naval usage, the masts, rigging, sails, and general stores of a ship. **2.** In military terminology, the metal mounts of a sword, dagger, or firearm.

Furrer 7.5mm machine gun Model 1925 This Swiss recoil-operated air-cooled machine gun had a rate of fire of 400 to 450 rounds per minute. It had a weight of 18 lb and was fed from a 30-round magazine.

Furrer 20mm aircraft cannon A weapon invented by Col. Adolf Furrer and introduced to the Swiss Air Force in 1933. It was a blowback-operated air-cooled cannon with a rate of 650 to 700 rounds per minute. It weighed 98 lb and was fed from a 200-round link belt.

Furrer 34mm aircraft cannon A Swiss weapon with the same action as the 20mm cannon, but with a cyclic rate of fire of 350 rounds per minute.

Furutaka A class of Japanese cruisers of 9,150 tons standard displacement built in the mid-1920s. They had a length of 602 ft, a beam of 55 ft, a speed of 33 knots, and a complement of 625 men. Main armament consisted of six 7.9-in. and four 4.7-in. guns, eight 24-in. torpedo tubes, and two aircraft. The two ships in the class, *Furutaka* and *Kako*, were lost during World War II, the former by gunfire from the U.S. cruiser *Boise* (of the **Brooklyn** class, which see), and the latter by a submarine.

Fury The North American FJ Fury is a single-seat sweptwing carrier fighter developed from the F-86 Sabre. It was first flown in 1952.

fuse (Not to be confused with "fuze.") An igniting or explosive device in the form of a cord, consisting of a flexible fabric tube and a core of low or high explosive. Used in blasting and demolition work and in certain munitions.

fusee A variation of **fusil,** which see.

fuselage A basic, load-carrying body of heavier-than-air aircraft of approximately streamlined form to which may be attached the wings and the empennage. The fuselage provides space for the crew, passengers, and cargo and in some cases contains the power plant.

fuseplug A plug fitted to the fuse hole of a shell to hold the fuse.

fusil A light flintlock musket.

fusilade The simultaneous or rapid firing of firearms.

fusileers Soldiers armed with fusils. The term dates from the seventeenth century.

Fuso A class of Japanese battleships of about 29,330 tons standard displacement built in 1914–1917, modernized in 1934, and used during World War II. They had a length of 673 ft, a beam of 94 ft, a speed of 22.5 knots, and a complement of 1,300 men. They were armed with twelve 14-in., sixteen 6-in., and eight 5-in. guns, plus three seaplanes. There were only two ships in the class, *Fuso* and *Yamashiro*, and both were lost in the Battle of Leyte Gulf in October 1944.

fuze **1.** A device with explosive components designed to initiate a train of fire or detonation in an item of ammunition by means of hydrostatic pressure, electrical energy, chemical action, impact, mechanical timing, or a combination of these. Excludes "fuse." **2.** A nonexplosive device designed to initiate an explosion in an item of ammunition by an action such as continuous or pulsating electromagnetic waves, acceleration or deceleration forces, or piezo-electric action.

fuze safety Two terms have been commonly used to describe the safety built into a fuze to prevent premature functions at the time of employment and to provide the required safety in transportation. One term, "bore safety," is strictly applicable only to fuzes used in artillery or mortar projectiles or rockets and refers to the provision of means to prevent functioning while in the bore of the gun or in the launching tube. Such fuzes are said to be "bore-safe." "Detonator safety" is the second term and may relate to fuzes for any application. It refers to the provision of means to prevent functioning of the succeeding element(s) of the explosive train if the detonator functions while the fuze parts are in the safe position. Such a fuze is said to be "detonator-safe." In general the terms are interchangeable with respect to artillery, mortar, and rocket fuzes, but "bore safety" applies only to those types of fuzes.

FX-1400 A German radio-controlled glide bomb first used against the Allies during the landings at Salerno, Italy, in September 1943. It used a four-tone radio control system, controlling the bomb by instructing it to fly up, down, left, and right.

FZG-76 The abbreviation for the German *Funkzielgerat* radio-aiming device. The official German name for the V-1 robot bomb used in World War II.

G

G-1 Formerly, the personnel division of the U.S. War Department General Staff.

G-2 Formerly, the intelligence division of the U.S. War Department General Staff.

G-3 Formerly, the operations and training division of the U.S. War Department General Staff.

G-4 Formerly, the supply division of the U.S. War Department General Staff.

GA The U.S. military designation for the war gas **tabun,** which see.

gabion A wickerwork (sometimes strapiron) cylinder shaped like a basket without a bottom. Gabions were filled with earth and were used to build fieldworks, revetments, etc. Most were about three ft high, and some were six ft in diameter.

gabionade A fieldwork made with gabions, particularly a protecting traverse between guns or on their flanks.

gabionage Gabions used in fieldworks or fortifications. Also, the sections built with gabions.

Gabriel An Israeli surface-to-surface missile with a length of 11 ft, a diameter of 1.7 ft, and a launch weight of 882 lb. It is a ship-launched missile, and the guidance is by automatic homing.

gad **1.** The point of a spear. **2.** A metal spike.

gadaru A Turkish saber with a broad blade.

gadling A small gad, or metal spike, located on the knuckle or back of a gauntlet.

gaffle **1.** A steel lever used to bend a crossbow. **2.** A musket rest, or fork.

G agent Any one of a group of war gases known as "nerve gases." The group is known as the "G series."

Gainful The NATO code name for a Soviet single-stage surface-to-air missile (SA-6) first seen in 1967. It has a length of about 19.5 ft (somewhat larger than the U.S. Hawk). In use, three are mounted on a tracked vehicle.

gainpain A kind of gauntlet.

gain twist A twist that is more rapid at the muzzle of a gun than at the breech; this gradually increases the rotation of the projectile.

gaintwist A firearm having a gain twist.

galapago A testudo-like defense of shields used in medieval times. Also, a mantelet.

Galaxy The Lockheed C-5A Galaxy is a heavy strategic transport powered by four turbofan engines. Developed for the U.S. Air Force and first flown in 1968, this airplane can carry 220,000 lb of cargo and fly at a maximum speed of 550 mph.

galea A light Roman helmet.

galeass A large galley of the sixteenth and seventeenth centuries. It mounted heavy guns and was propelled by both sails and oars.

Galeb See **Jastreb.**

galet A round stone thrown from a sling or a bow.

Galicia A class of Spanish cruisers of 7,457 tons standard displacement completed between 1925 and 1931. They had a speed of

Galaxy. (*Lockheed Aircraft Corporation.*)

33 knots, a complement of 564 men, and main armament consisting of eight 6-in. guns and eight 3.5-in. guns.

galiot, galliot A small, fast vessel used in the Mediterranean in the Middle Ages. It was propelled by both sails and oars.

galleon A sailing vessel of about the fifteenth and sixteenth centuries, although the term appeared in England during the reign of Elizabeth. They often had three or four decks and were used for vessels of war as well as commerce. The galleons were the first line of defense, supported by the lighter but faster galleasses.

gallery In fortifications, an underground passage that is either cut in the soil or built of masonry. It serves to connect the inner and exterior works of a fortified place. In military mining, a gallery is an under-

ground passage connecting the mine chambers.

gallery deck A partial deck below a flight deck on an aircraft carrier.

galley In the Middle Ages, a one-decked large vessel propelled by both oars and sails and used mostly in the Mediterranean. A war galley might have a complement of as many as 1,200 men and a length of 200 ft. In classical antiquity, the term referred to a vessel propelled chiefly by oars.

galloper A small, light piece of ordnance that could be pulled easily and quickly with horses. It was called also a "galloper gun." The term also once referred to an orderly or aide-de-camp.

Galosh The NATO code name for a Soviet surface-to-air (SA-7) antimissile missile first seen in 1964. It has a four-nozzle first stage

and a length of 67 ft.

GAM Guided aircraft missile.

Gama Goat A U.S. Army and Marine Corps 1¼-ton cargo carrier or ambulance. This six-wheel amphibious vehicle can travel at speeds of 55 mph on land and 2.5 mph on water.

gambeson A defensive medieval garment made of cloth or leather, often stuffed or quilted, and originally worn under the hauberk as a pad. It was the sole defense of foot soldiers.

Game Warden The code name for a U.S. Navy operation in which lightweight shallow-water boats (**PBR,** which see) were developed to intercept and search enemy riverboats in Vietnam.

Ganef The NATO code name for a Soviet surface-to-air missile (SA-4) first seen in

Galicia. (*Spanish Ministry of Defense.*)

Garcia. (*U.S. Navy.*)

1964. It is a mobile army air-defense weapon with a length of 26 ft and a diameter of 2.7 ft. It is air-transportable in the An-22 (Cock) transport.

gangplank A temporary bridge from the ship to the dock or to another ship alongside.

gangway 1. An opening in the rail or bulwarks giving access to a ship. **2.** An order to stand aside or to stand clear.

Gapa A ground-to-*air*-*p*ilotless *a*ircraft; a post-World War II Boeing missile project for the U.S. Air Force. The first firings were made in 1948, and the findings were later applied to the Bomarc program.

gap marker In land-mine warfare, markers used to identify a minefield gap. Gap markers at the entrance to, and exit from, the gap are referenced to a landmark or intermediate marker.

GAR Guided aircraft rocket.

Garand rifle The **U.S. .30 cal. rifle M1,** which see. It was invented by John C. Garand, a Canadian-born American citizen, and was adopted by the U.S. Army in 1936.

garble An error in transmission, reception, encryption, or decryption which renders a message incorrect or undecryptable.

Garcia A class of U.S. escort ships (DE) of 2,620 tons standard displacement built in 1964–1968. They have a length of 414.5 ft, a beam of 44.2 ft, a speed of 27 knots, and a complement of 241 men. They are armed with two 5-in. guns, one Asroc eight-tube launcher, two triple torpedo launchers, and two fixed torpedo tubes. There are 10 ships in the class.

gardebras A piece of armor to protect the arm.

garde-collet A raised plate on the pauldron to protect the neck.

Gargoyle An air-launched radio-controlled glide bomb equipped with a flare for visual tracking. It was developed by the U.S. Navy near the end of World War II.

Garibaldi A class of Italian cruisers of 9,802 tons standard displacement completed in 1937 and modernized in the early 1950s. They had a speed of 35 knots, a complement of 600 men, and main armament consisting of ten 6-in. and ten 3.9-in. guns.

garote Any method whereby a victim is seized around the throat and strangled.

garrison The troops stationed in a fort or the fortified place itself. Also, to place troops in a fortification to defend it.

garrison force All units assigned to a base or area for defense, development, operation, and maintenance of facilities.

garrot A lever used to wind a crossbow.

gas 1. Short for **war gas,** which see. **2.** Short for "gasoline." **3.** To expose to, or be affected by, a war gas. **4.** To fill tanks with gasoline.

gas alert A state of preparedness against a gas attack.

gas attack An attack by the use of poisonous or irritant gas.

gas-attack alarm A U-shaped tubular metal device equipped with a carrying strap and a hand-operated striker. When struck, it produces a ringing sound. It is usually carried and used by military personnel to sound an alarm when a gas attack is anticipated.

gas bombs Gas bombs are designed to produce casualties among personnel and for purposes of area contamination. These bombs contain a burster charge which splits the bomb case and disperses the filler over the area to be contaminated.

gascheck A device in a gun to prevent the escape of gas through the breech.

gas cloud A mixture of air and war-gas vapor.

gas cumulative action The building up within the human body of small, ineffective doses of certain war gases to a point where the eventual effect is similar to that of one large dose.

gas cylinder A tube fixed to the barrel of a gas-operated automatic weapon and containing a piston, the movement of which operates the extracting and reloading mechanisms.

gas grenade The popular name for a chemical grenade, designed to release a war gas. The types of gases released are usually limited to tear gas and other irritants.

gas mask A mask worn over the face to protect the eyes and to remove gases from the air as it is inhaled.

gas munition A munition such as a bomb, projectile, pot, candle, or spray tank containing a war gas and a means of release.

gas-operated Said of an automatic or semiautomatic weapon that utilizes part of the gas from the explosion in the barrel to unlock the bolt and actuate the loading mechanism.

gas-operated gun An automatic gun operated solely by gas, utilizing a portion of the gas pressure to act on some form of piston-and-cylinder arrangement. The relative movement, between the piston and the cylinder, drives the bolt to the rear with sufficient force to unlock and open the breech. The gas may be taken from the barrel through a hole drilled in the barrel at any point between the chamber and the muzzle. In some weapons, gas is taken at the muzzle itself.

gas port An opening for the passage of gas. The gas cylinder of a gas-operated automatic weapon has gas ports that admit some of the propellant gases from the barrel of the gun.

gas shell or bomb A projectile filled with gas, usually liquefied, that is released when the projectile explodes.

Gast 7.92mm aircraft machine gun (double-barreled) Model 1918 A German

gardebras. (*The Metropolitan Museum of Art, Bashford Dean Memorial Collection.*)

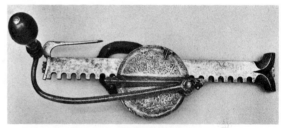

garrot. (*The Metropolitan Museum of Art, gift of William H. Riggs, 1913.*)

gas mask. (*U.S. Army.*)

gate. (*The Smithsonian Institution, National Museum Collection.*)

air-cooled machine gun that operated through a system in which energy from the fired bolt operated the other bolt. It had a rate of fire of 1,600 to 1,800 rounds per minute and a weight of 60 lb and was fed from 180-round flat drums, one for each gun.

gastrapheten A Roman weapon similar in operation to a crossbow.

Gatling gun. (*The Smithsonian Institution, A. Sherman Collection.*)

gas-turbine engine A continuous-combustion-type engine consisting primarily of a compression chamber, combustion chamber, and turbine. Air is compressed and heated by a combustible fuel and is expanded through the turbine. It is designed to furnish a source of rotary shaft and/or pneumatic power. The pneumatic power is obtained by a bleed-off of the engine compressor.

gas vent A venthole in a rifle receiver to release excess gas pressures should they develop. Also, the slotted vents in a muzzle brake.

gas warfare Warfare in which poisonous, asphyxiating, or corrosive gases may be used as weapons.

gate A metal part in the rear of the cylinder of old-pattern revolvers that was turned out to expose the cylinders for loading.

gate tower In medieval fortifications, to tower at a gate.

gate vessels Ships that are used to open and close the gates or openings in the antisubmarine nets used to protect a harbor or a narrow passage.

Gatling gun A type of machine gun using multibarrels which fire in rotation, an early principle which has come back into use in the Vulcan machine guns. It permits very rapid fire because it reduces the problem of overheating a single barrel. On a Gatling gun as each barrel comes opposite a hopper on the left side of the cylinder, a cartridge falls into a groove of the carrier, is pressed into the breech by a plunger, and is held there until struck by the firing pin. The standard rate of fire is about 600 rounds per minute. Named after the American inventor R. J. Gatling, the weapon was patented in 1862 and was for many years the standard machine gun of the U.S. Army.

Gato A class of U.S. submarines (SS) of 1,525 tons standard surface displacement commissioned during World War II. They had a length of 311 ft, a beam of 27 ft, a speed of 21 knots on the surface (10 knots submerged), and a complement of 85 men. They were armed with ten 21-in. torpedo tubes, one to three 5-in. guns, and two 20mm antiaircraft guns. Nineteen of this class were lost to enemy action during World War II.

GAU-2/A and GAU-2A/A Army versions of U.S. Air Force M-133 and M-134 Minigun systems. See **Minigun.**

gauge The unit of bore measurement for shotguns. Originally it referred to the number of solid lead balls of bore diameter that could be cast from 1 lb of lead; the larger the bore, the lower the number.

gauntlets In the Middle Ages, armor for protection of the hands. It was made of chain mail or of leather partly covered with metal plates or scales.

gazons In fortifications, pieces of earth, or sods, covered with grass. They were cut in wedges to line the outsides of earthworks.

GB **1.** The U.S. military designation for the war gas **sarin,** which see. **2.** An abbreviation for "glide bomb."

GB-4 A glide bomb with a mounted television camera and transmitter, controlled in azimuth and range by radio and guided from a mother aircraft by means of the television. Often called "GB-4 missile."

GCA See **ground-controlled approach.**

GCI See **ground-controlled interception.**

G Class **1.** A class of current Soviet submarines armed with three launching tubes for ballistic missiles. There are 25 submarines in the class. They have a standard surface displacement of 2,350 tons, a length of 320 ft, a beam of 28 ft, a speed of 17 knots submerged, and a complement of 86 men. They also carry six 21-in. torpedo tubes. Construction on this class began in 1958. **2.** A former class of U.S. submarines, later designated as *Gato,* which see.

GD The U.S. military designation for the war gas **soman,** which see.

Gearing A class of U.S. destroyers (DD) of about 2,425 tons standard displacement produced between 1944 and 1947 and modernized in FRAM (Fleet Rehabilitation and Modernization) programs in the late 1950s and early 1960s. They have a length of 390.5 ft, a beam of 40.9 ft, a speed of 34 knots, and a complement of 274 men. They were originally armed with six 5-in. guns plus 40mm and 20mm antiaircraft guns. They are presently equipped with four 5-in. guns plus various combinations of Asroc eight-tube launchers, triple torpedo launchers, and facilities for DASH. There are over 90 vessels in this class.

Geiger counter A counter used to detect and measure radiation.

gelb kreuz (German for "yellow cross") See **mustard gas.**

Gelb Operation (German for "Yellow Operation") The German plan for invasion of the Low Countries and France, which began on May 10, 1940. This plan originated in Hitler's "Directive No. 6 for the Conduct of the War," which was issued on October 9, 1939.

GEM **Ground-effect machine,** which see.

gendarme Formerly, a French horse soldier in full armor; later, a cavalryman.

general A general officer next above a lieutenant general and next below a general of the army. The insignia for this rank is four stars. The term is also used to refer to an officer of one of the six highest grades: general of the armies, general of the army, general, lieutenant general, major general, and brigadier general.

general alarm A sound signal used on board ship for calling all hands to general quarters.

general issue See **GI, G.I.**

General Lee The British name for the **U.S. tank, medium, M3A5,** which see.

general mobilization A mobilization of the entire military forces of a nation, either to engage in hostilities already begun or to prepare for an all-out war.

general officer Any officer of the U.S. Army, Air Force, or Marine Corps above the rank of colonel, i.e., a brigadier general, major general, lieutenant general, general, or general of the air force or army.

general of the armies The highest-ranking officer in the Army of the United States;

a special title created by Congress for General Pershing.

general of the army A general officer next above a general. The insignia is five stars.

general orders **1.** Permanent instructions, issued in order form, that apply to all members of a command, as compared with special orders, which affect only individuals or small groups. General orders are usually concerned with matters of policy or administration. **2.** A series of permanent guard orders that govern the duties of a sentry on post.

General Pershing Also called the U.S. tank, medium, M26 (T26E3), this tank was introduced in 1945 for use with armored divisions. It has a crew of five and is armed with one 90mm gun M3 (caliber length 53), one .50 cal. machine gun M2 (for antiaircraft use and mounted on the top of the turret), and two .30 cal. machine guns M1919A4. It weighs 46 tons and can travel 30 mph on roads. It was used during the last 6 weeks of World War II and was the first U.S. tank to mount the 90mm tank gun M3.

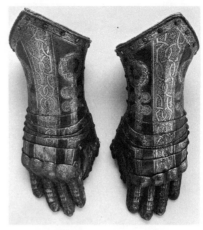

gauntlets. (*The Metropolitan Museum of Art, gift of William H. Riggs, 1913.*)

general-purpose bombs Bombs designed to be dropped from an aircraft to destroy or reduce the utility of a target by explosive effect. They may be used against both material targets and personnel. General-purpose bombs are used in the majority of

General Pershing. (*U.S. Army.*)

Gearing. (*U.S. Navy.*)

general-purpose machine gun, the FN MAG machine gun M3. *(Belgian Ministry of Defense.)*

General Sheridan. *(U.S. Army.)*

General Sherman. *(U.S. Army.)*

bombing operations against targets requiring some penetration. Their cases are relatively light, and approximately 50 percent of their complete weight is explosive material.

general-purpose machine gun A weapon that may be used as a light machine gun (usually bipod-mounted and fed from small ammunition boxes) or as a medium machine gun (usually tripod-mounted and belt-fed). Examples include the FN MAG, the French M52, and the U.S. M60.

general-purpose vehicle A motor vehicle designated to be used interchangeably for movement of personnel, supplies, ammunition, or equipment for towing artillery carriages, trailers, or semitrailers and used without modification to body or chassis to satisfy general automotive transport needs.

general quarters A condition of readiness when naval action is imminent. All battle stations are fully manned and alert, ammunition is ready for instant loading, and guns and guided-missile launchers may be loaded.

general reserve The reserve of troops retained under the control of the overall commander.

general-reserve artillery Consists of all artillery units not organic to divisions and corps. It is a pool of reserve artillery available to the field-forces commander for assignment or attachment to subordinate commands as required by combat conditions.

General Sheridan The U.S. Army ARAAV (armored reconnaissance airborne assault vehicle) is a lightweight full-track airdroppable assault vehicle utilizing a 152mm gun-launcher capable of firing either a conventional round or the Shillelagh surface-to-surface missile. It is built by General Motors Corp.

General Sheridan (M-551) A U.S. Army armored reconnaissance airborne assault full-track lightweight vehicle armed with Shillelagh surface-to-surface guided missiles and conventional 152mm shells. It is built by GMC.

General Sherman Also called the "U.S. tank, medium, M4A4," this tank was introduced in 1943 for use with armored divisions. It has a crew of five and is armed with one 75mm gun M3 (caliber length 40) and two .30 cal. machine guns M1919A4. It has a weight of about 36 tons and a speed of 25 mph on roads. British versions of this tank included the Sherman II (M4A1), the Sherman III (M4A2), and the Sherman V (M4A4). The M4A2 in Russia was the M4C.

general staff A group of officers in the headquarters of Army or Marine divisions, Marine brigades and aircraft wings, or similar or larger units which assist their commanders in planning, coordinating, and supervising operations.

General Stuart Also called the "U.S. tank, light, M3A1," this tank was manufactured by American Car and Foundry and was introduced in 1941 for use in armored divisions. It has a crew of four and is armed with one 37mm gun M6 (caliber length 53), two .30 cal. machine guns M1919A4, and one .45 cal. submachine gun 1928A1. It has a weight of 14.3 tons and a top speed of 37 mph on roads. This tank was introduced by the British in World War II, having been provided via lend-lease.

general-support artillery Artillery which executes the fire directed by the commander of the unit to which it organically belongs or is attached. It fires in support of the operation as a whole rather than in support of a specific subordinate unit.

general war Armed conflict between major powers in which the total resources of the belligerents are employed and the national survival of a major belligerent is in jeopardy.

Geneva Convention An international agreement dealing with the humane treatment of combatants and noncombatants in time of war. The original convention, signed at Geneva in 1864, concerned wounded soldiers and prisoners of war. Later amendments and revisions extended the provisions to victims of maritime actions and to civilian populations. In 1949 existing provisions were reformulated into four conventions for the protection of war victims. The United States has been a signatory of the successive conventions, and since 1964 the Convention has been the charter of the International Red Cross.

Genie An unguided air-to-air rocket missile with a nuclear warhead, developed for the U.S. Air Force by McDonnell Douglas and first flown in 1957. It has an overall length of 9 ft 7 in., a launching weight of about 820 lb, and a range of 6 mi. While in development, this system was referred to as "Ding-Dong" and "High Card."

genouillère Armor to protect the knee.

George 11 The code name for the Japanese Kawanishi N1K1-J Shiden (Violet Lightning) single-seat single engine fighter-interceptor and fighter-bomber. First flown in 1943, it was equipped with a 1,990-hp engine and flew at speeds of 362 mph. It was armed with four 20mm cannons and two 7.7mm Type 97 machine guns.

George 21 The code name for the Japanese Kawanishi N1K2-J Shiden-Kai single-seat fighter-interceptor and fighter-bomber. It represented a complete redesign of the Shiden fighter, and the result was the finest fighter used by the Japanese Naval Air Force in World War II. This aircraft utilized a 1,990-hp engine and flew at speeds of 369 mph. It was armed with four 20mm cannons and carried two 550-lb bombs. (Picture, next page.)

General Stuart. (*U.S. Army.*)

George Washington A class of U.S. fleet ballistic-missile submarines (SSBN) of 5,900 tons standard surface displacement commissioned in 1959–1961. They have a length of 381.7 ft, a beam of 33 ft, a speed of about 30 knots submerged, and a complement of 112 men. They are armed with six 21-in. torpedo tubes and carry 16 tubes for Polaris missiles. This was the first class of submarines (of the Western powers) to be armed with ballistic missiles. (Picture, next page.)

Georgia A U.S. battleship of the old **New Jersey** class, which see. It was commissioned in 1906.

Gerät Potsdam submachine gun This German 9mm Parabellum submachine gun was an identical copy of the British Mk II Sten submachine gun and was duplicated to the smallest detail, including the markings. The purpose in copying the Sten was

Genie. (*U.S. Air Force.*)

George 11. (*The Smithsonian Institution, National Air Museum.*)

George 21. (*Shin Meiwa.*)

George Washington. (*U.S. Navy.*)

to cover the origin of the weapons. They were intended to be dropped behind the lines to arm German guerrilla units fighting the Allies. Production of these weapons totaled 25,000 to 28,000 early in 1945, and the majority were used in France in the closing stages of the war.

German 7.62mm machine gun MG 42/59 This weapon is made by the German firm of Rheinmettal and is almost identical to the World War II MG42. It is made to fire the 7.62mm NATO cartridge and is a standard machine gun in West Germany, Austria, Italy, Denmark, Yugoslavia (in 7.92mm), and other countries.

German 7.62mm rifle G3 A West German weapon based on the Spanish CETME assault rifle. It is manufactured by Heckler and Koch and is a delayed-blowback selective-fire weapon with a cyclic rate of fire of 500 to 600 rounds per minute and a muzzle velocity of 2,624 fps. It has an overall length of 40.2 in., a barrel length of 17.7 in., and a weight of 9.9 lb. It has been adopted by Portugal, Pakistan, the Dominican Republic, Sweden, Norway, and Denmark. See also **Heckler and Koch assault rifles.**

German 7.65mm automatic pistols PP and PPK See **Walther 7.65mm automatic pistols PP and PPK.**

German 7.92mm aircraft machine gun FG42 A German gas-operated air-cooled machine gun with a rate of fire of 400 to 450 rounds per minute. It weighed 14 lb and was fed from a 20-round magazine.

German 7.92mm automatic rifle FG42 The German 7.92mm paratroop rifle Model 42 (FG42).

German 7.92mm L.M.G. 34 A German light machine gun weighing about 26 lb and capable of both automatic and semiautomatic fire. It is belt-fed and has a cyclic rate of fire of 800 to 900 rounds per minute and a range of about 3,800 yd. The M.G. 34/41 is shorter than the 34 and has a heavier barrel and a higher rate of fire (about 1,000 rounds per minute).

German 7.92mm machine gun MG08 (Maxim) The standard German heavy machine gun of World War I was the 7.92mm Maxim machine gun Model 1908. It was made in extremely large quantities. It is recoil-operated, has a cyclic rate of fire of 400 to 500 rounds per minute, and a muzzle velocity of 2,750 fps. The overall length of the weapon is 46.25 in., the barrel length is 28.25 in., and the weight of the gun is 40.5 lb. The sled mount for this machine gun weighs 83 lb, while the tripod mount weighs 65.5 lb. The weapon is water-cooled and is fed by 100- and 250-round fabric belts.

German 7.92mm machine gun MG 08/15 This is a lightened version of the MG08 and is fitted with a shoulder stock, bipod, modified barrel jacket, and receiver; the ammunition belt is carried in a reel-type drum magazine. It was adapted for aircraft use by replacing the water jacket with a ventilated barrel jacket. It and the Parabellum, a modified Maxim, were the principal German aircraft guns of World War I. Later the MG 08/18 became the ground version of the 08/15.

German 7.92mm machine gun MG

08/18 See **German 7.92mm machine gun MG 08/15.**

German 7.92mm machine gun MG 13 This 7.92mm machine gun was adopted as standard by the German Army in 1932. It was fabricated from Dreyse M1918 water-cooled light machine guns manufactured at the end of World War I. These existed in limited numbers. They are recoil-operated and air-cooled and have an overall length of 57 in., a barrel length of 28.25 in., and a weight (with bipod) of 26.4 lb. The cyclic rate of fire is 750 rounds per minute, and the muzzle velocity is about 2,750 fps. It is fed from a 25-round box magazine or a 75-round saddle magazine.

German 7.92mm machine gun MG 15 and 17 See **Solothurn 8mm machine gun Model 30S.**

German 7.92mm machine gun MG 34 This is the first modern general-purpose machine gun ever produced in large quantities. Developed by Mauser, this weapon was the standard 7.92mm ground machine gun used by the Germans in World War II. It was used on a bipod as a light machine gun and on a tripod as a heavy machine gun. An aircraft version, the MG 81, was also used. The MG 34 is a recoil-operated selective-fire weapon with an overall length of 48 in., a barrel length of 24.6 in., and a weight of 26.5 lb with bipod. The weight of the mount is 42.3 lb. It is air-cooled and has a cyclic rate of fire of 800 to 900 rounds per minute and a muzzle velocity of 2,750 fps. It is fed from 50-round nondisintegrating belts (which can be put together to form a 250-round belt), a 50-round belt drum, and a 75-round saddle drum. It has a range of about 3,800 yd. The MG 34.S was very similar but was simplified for mass production. The MG 34/41 was shorter than the 34 with a heavier barrel and a higher rate of fire (about 1,000 rounds per minute). Since World War II this weapon has been used by the Czechs, the Israelis, the French, and the Viet Cong.

German 7.92mm machine gun MG 42 This machine gun made great use of stamping and fabrications and cut down on machine-tool usage in Germany during World War II. It introduced a recoil-operated roller locking system and an extremely rapid barrel-change system (needed because of the high cyclic rate of fire of this weapon). It has an overall length of 48 in., a barrel length of 21 in., and a weight (with bipod) of 25.5 lb. The tripod mount weighs 42.3 lb. The cyclic rate of fire is 1,100 to 1,200 rounds per minute, and the muzzle velocity is 2,480 fps. The gun is fed by 50-round nondisintegrating belts (often joined into 250-round belts) or a 50-round drum. It is used in West Germany in 7.62mm NATO as the MG 1 (MG 42/59). It has also been adopted by Italy and Yugoslavia, where it is known as the "Model 53" or "SARAC."

German 7.92mm machine gun MG 81 See German 7.92mm machine gun MG 34.

German 7.92mm machine guns, Maxim types Numerous Maxim guns were employed by German forces, both ground and air. The model numbers included 1899, 1901, 1908, '08/15, '08/18, 1914, and '14/17. The latter two were referred to as "Parabellum" machine guns.

German 7.92mm Mauser rifles and carbines See Mauser 7.92mm carbine Models 98a and 98b, Mauser 7.92mm rifle Model 98k (Kar 98k), Mauser 7.92mm rifle Model 33/40, and Mauser 7.92mm rifle Model 98 (Gew 98).

German 7.92mm paratroop rifle Model 42 (FG42) The *Fallschirmjager Gewehr* 42 (FG42) was developed at the request of the Luftwaffe, since German paratroops during World War II were under the Air Force. A limited number of these weapons were produced. It has an overall length of 37 in., a barrel length of 19.75 in., and a weight of 9.93 lb. It is capable of semiautomatic and full automatic fire and has a cyclic rate of fire of 750 to 800 rounds per minute and a muzzle velocity of about 2,500 fps. It utilizes a detachable 20-round magazine.

German 7.92mm rifle Model 1888 This weapon was developed by a German Army commission and combines the magazine of the Mannlicher with bolt features of the Mauser Model 1871/84. It was used by Austria during World War I. The Chinese bought many of these rifles and made a modified copy called the "Type 88" or "Hanyang." It has an overall length of 37.4 in., a barrel length of 17.6 in., a weight of 6.88 lb, and a muzzle velocity of 1,935 fps. It makes use of a five-round fixed box magazine.

German 7.92mm rifle Model 98/40 This weapon is not a Mauser, but is based on the design of the Hungarian 8mm rifle Model 1935. It was made in Hungary by the Danuvia Arms Works. It has an overall length of 43.6 in., a barrel length of 23.6 in., a weight of 8.9 lb, and a muzzle velocity of 2,476 fps. It has a staggered-row fixed box magazine with a capacity of 10 cartridges.

German 7.92mm rifle Volkssturm Gewehr 1 (VG1) See Volkssturm Gewehr (VG1) 7.92mm rifle.

German 7.92mm rifle Volkssturm Karabiner 98 (VK98) See Volkssturm Karabiner 98 (VK98) 7.92mm rifle.

German 7.92mm self-loading rifle G.41 W. A gas-operated rifle capable of semiautomatic fire only. It has a length of 45 in. and a weight of about 11 lb. The magazine has a capacity of 10 rounds.

German 7.92mm semiautomatic rifle Model 43 (Gewehr 43) This weapon was produced in great quantities during World

German 7.92mm machine gun, Maxim type. (*The Smithsonian Institution, War Department Collection.*)

German 7.92mm machine gun MG08 (Maxim). (*The Smithsonian Institution, War Department Collection.*)

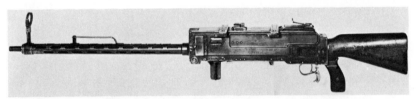

German 7.92mm machine gun MG 13. (*The Smithsonian Institution, War Department Collection.*)

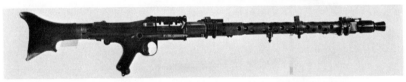

German 7.92mm machine gun Mg 34. (*The Smithsonian Institution, Treasury Department Collection.*)

German 7.92mm machine gun MG 42. (*The Smithsonian Institution, National Museum Collection.*)

German 7.92mm rifle Model 1888. (*The Smithsonian Institution, War Department Collection.*)

War II and is very roughly made with many stampings, castings, and forgings. It is gas-operated and capable of semiautomatic fire only. It has an overall length of 44 in., a barrel length of 21.62 in., and a weight of approximately 9.5 lb. It has a detachable box magazine holding 10 rounds and a muzzle velocity of about 2,550 fps. (Picture, next page.)

German 9mm (Luger) automatic pistol P-38 See Walther 9mm (Luger) automatic pistol P-38.

German 7.92mm semiautomatic rifle Model 43 (Gewehr 43). *(The Smithsonian Institution, William B. Culver Collection.)*

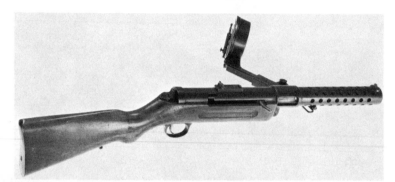

German 9mm Parabellum submachine gun MP 18, I. *(Swiss Military Department.)*

German 9mm Parabellum submachine gun MP 38. *(The Smithsonian Institution, Department of Defense Collection.)*

German 9mm Parabellum submachine gun MP 18, I This weapon was designed by Hugo Schmeisser, the noted German small-arms designer, and was introduced in 1918. It was produced by the Theodor Bergmann Factories, and by the middle of 1918 it had been issued to German troops on all fronts. Slightly over 35,000 were produced by the armistice of November 11, 1918. It was the first true straight blowback submachine gun. It operated with full automatic fire with a cyclic rate of fire of 350 to 450 rounds per minute. The overall length was 32.10 in., and the barrel length was 7.88 in. The loaded weight of the weapon was 11.55 lb, including the special 32-round Parabellum drum magazine. It fired the 9mm Parabellum cartridge and had a muzzle velocity of approximately 1,250 fps. The Allies valued this weapon highly and prohibited its use by the 100,000-man German Army authorized by the Treaty of Versailles.

German 9mm Parabellum submachine gun MP 18, II This weapon was substantially modified over the earlier MP 18, I. It included a selective-fire mechanism and

a number of other changes. It was produced under Schmeisser license in Belgium and saw its greatest use during the Spanish Civil War between 1936 and 1939. It was produced for use with the following cartridges: 9mm Parabellum, 9mm Bergmann Bayard, 7.65mm Parabellum, 7.63mm, and .45 cal. ACP. It uses 20-, 25-, 32-, and 50-round magazines. Its cyclic rate of fire is 500 rounds per minute, and it has a muzzle velocity of 1,250 fps. This weapon went out of production in the late 1930s.

German 9mm Parabellum submachine gun MP 28, II A further modification of the MP 18, II, this weapon weighed about 9.4 lb and had a length of 33.25 in. and a magazine capacity of 32 rounds. It is equipped with selective fire and has a cyclic rate of fire of 500 to 600 rounds per minute. It was never a standard weapon of the German Army, but was used by police units during World War II.

German 9mm Parabellum submachine gun MP 34 (Ö) The **Steyr-Solothurn 9mm Mauser submachine gun MP 34,** which see, was manufactured in Austria. When the Germans took over Austria in 1938, they

called this weapon the "Maschinene Pistole 34 Österreich" (Österreich meaning "Austrian"). The weapon is of German design but is manufactured outside Germany because of restrictions in the Versaille Treaty against arms development in that country. This weapon was used during World War II by German police and rear-area military units.

German 9mm Parabellum submachine gun MP 38 This weapon was developed in the mid-1930s by the Erma factory in Germany and, contrary to popular belief, was *not* designed by Hugo Schmeisser. It was adopted by the German army in mid-1938 and continued to be produced until early 1940. It was the first weapon to be made entirely of steel and plastics, with no wood used. It fires the 9mm Parabellum cartridge and has a muzzle velocity of approximately 1,250 fps. Using a blowback type of operation, it operates only on full automatic. It has a cyclic rate of fire of 500 rounds per minute. The length with stock retracted is 24.80 in., and it has a barrel length of 9.90 in. Loaded with a 32-round magazine, the weight is 9.5 lb. The MP 38 was the second submachine gun officially adopted by the German Army, the first having been the MP 18,I, adopted in 1918.

German 9mm Parabellum submachine gun MP 38/40 The MP 38/40 was a conversion of the German MP 38. To avoid accidental discharges caused by the fact that the safety locks the bolt only in the open position on the MP 38, these weapons were modified by adding a two-piece retracting handle of the new model MP40/I.

German 9mm Parabellum submachine gun MP 40 The general characteristics of the MP 40 are the same as those of the MP 38, the difference being a few new design features and a manufacturing process that facilitated mass production. The MP 40 was the first submachine gun to be produced quickly and economically. It made use of stamped sheet steel and plain carbon steel in the metal parts. Fabrication was by spot welding, fusion welding, brazing, soldering, riveting, and crimping. Mass-production methods resulted in the fabrication of well over a million of these weapons from 1940 to 1944.

German 9mm Parabellum submachine gun MP 3008 The German MP 3008 is a modified copy of the British Sten Mk II submachine gun. It fires the 9mm Parabellum cartridge in a standard Schmeisser-designed MP 38 magazine. Some 10,000 of these weapons were produced during the last months of World War II for issue to Volkssturm units. The common designation was the "Volks MP." Although the German copy follows the Sten system very closely, there is a major difference in that the magazine feeds from below the weapon instead of from the side. It weighed 8 lb loaded and had a muzzle velocity of 1,250 fps and a cyclic rate of fire of 500 rounds per minute.

German 13mm machine gun MG 131 See **Solothurn 8mm machine gun Model 30S.**

German 13mm machine gun Model 1918
A scaled-up weapon of Maxim design.

German 20mm antiaircraft cannon Flak 30 The Rheinmetall 20mm antiaircraft gun MK-ST-5 used by German forces early in World War II, both for antiaircraft applications and as a tank gun. It was a recoil-operated air-cooled cannon with a rate of fire of 200 to 280 rounds per minute. It weighed 141 lb and was fed from 20-, 40-, or 50-round magazines.

German 20mm antiaircraft cannon Flak 38 A Mauser-produced cannon that was similar in appearance and identical in principle to the MG-151 20mm aircraft cannon. It was a recoil-operated air-cooled cannon with a rate of fire of 420 to 480 rounds per minute. It weighed 123 lb and was fed from a 20-round magazine. The projectile weighed 0.3 lb.

German 37mm antiaircraft cannon Flak 18 A recoil-operated air-cooled cannon with a rate of fire of 160 to 180 rounds per minute. It weighed 595 lb and was fed from an eight-round magazine. Thousands of Flak 18's were installed before World War II by all German services. It was the first-line automatic weapon for AA defense by the German Navy and was employed as a dual-purpose gun by the Army, which used it mainly for AA applications but could also use it for antitank work.

German 37mm antiaircraft gun Flak 43
A German weapon firing a projectile weighing 1.4 lb and having a vertical range of about 5,000 ft. It fired at the rate of 250 rounds per minute.

German 37mm antitank gun PAK 36 A World War II weapon with a weight of 952 lb and a projectile weight of 1.5 lb. It fired fixed ammunition and had a range of 6,000 yd.

German 50mm antiaircraft gun Flak 41
A World War II weapon with a weight of 3.3 tons and a projectile weight of 5 lb. It fired fixed ammunition and had an effective ceiling of 18,400 ft.

German 50mm antitank gun PAK 38 A World War II weapon with a weight of 1 ton and a projectile weight of 4.5 lb. It fired fixed ammunition and had a range of 3,000 yd.

German 50mm gun KwK 39 This gun fired a projectile weighing 4.54 lb.

German 75mm antitank gun 40 on Czech 38 chassis See **Marten.**

German 75mm antitank gun 40 on Panzer II chassis See **Marten.**

German 75mm antitank gun PAK 40 A World War II weapon with a weight of 1.6 tons and a projectile weight of 12.6 lb. It

German 9mm Parabellum submachine gun MP 40. (*The Smithsonian Institution, Department of Defense Collection.*)

German 20mm antiaircraft cannon Flak 30. (*U.S. Army.*)

German 37mm antiaircraft cannon Flak 18. (*U.S. Army.*)

German 88mm antiaircraft gun, being fired by an American artillery crew. (*U.S. Army.*)

fired fixed ammunition and had a range of 8,400 yd.

German 75mm assault gun on PzKpfw III chassis   This self-propelled gun was manufactured by Krupp and was introduced in 1941 for assault and infantry-support purposes. It had a crew of four, and later models were armed with a 75mm Stu. K 40 gun, caliber length 48. It weighed 24.3 tons and traveled at a speed of 25 mph on roads.

German 75mm gun KwK 42   This gun fired an armor-piercing projectile weighing 15 lb.

German 75mm gun 1eFK 18   A World War II weapon with a weight of 1.2 tons and a projectile weight of 13 lb. It fired fixed ammunition and had a range of 10,300 yd.

German 75mm gun 1eIG 18   A World War II weapon with a weight of 880 lb and a projectile weight of 12 lb. It fired fixed ammunition and had a range of 4,150 yd.

German 75mm gun Pak 40   The gun fired an armor-piercing projectile weighing 15 lb to a range of about 8,500 yd.

German 75mm gun Stu. K 40   This gun fired a projectile weighing 15 lb to a range of about 7,700 yd.

German 75mm recoilless rifle LG 40   A World War II weapon with a weight of 321 lb and a projectile weight of 13 lb. It fired fixed ammunition and had a range of 7,435 yd.

German 76.2mm gun Pak 36 (r)   This gun was the Soviet 76.2mm gun Model 36, rechambered to take the German Pak 40 cartridge case. An armor-piercing projectile for this weapon weighed 16.8 lb and had a maximum range of about 8,300 yd.

German 77mm gun, Model 1896   A weapon with a range of 9,260 yd with a 15-lb shell. Germany had more than 5,000 of these guns at the outbreak of World War I.

German 77mm gun, Model 1916   A World War I weapon that fired a 13.4-lb shell to a range of 11,264 yd.

German 88mm antiaircraft gun Flak 18, 36, and 37   A series of World War II weapons with a weight of 5.6 tons and a projectile weight of 20 lb. They employed fixed ammunition and had an effective ceiling of 26,250 ft and a range of about 11,550 yd. They could be fired at the rate of 15 to 20 rounds per minute.

German 88mm antiaircraft gun Flak 41   A World War II weapon with a weight of 8.4 tons and a projectile weight of 21 lb. It fired fixed ammunition and had an effective ceiling of 38,000 ft.

German 88mm antitank gun PAK 43   A World War II weapon with a weight of 5.5 tons and a projectile weight of 20.3 lb. It fired fixed ammunition and had a range of 14,100 yd.

German 88mm gun KwK 43   This weapon fired an armor-piercing projectile weighing 22.4 lb. It could penetrate 9.4 in. of armor at 100 yd at O° and had a range of about 12,000 yd. The KwK 43/2 had a range of about 14,000 yd.

German 105mm antiaircraft gun Flak 38   A World War II weapon with a weight of 11.2 tons and a projectile weight of 33 lb. It fired fixed ammunition and had an effective ceiling of 35,000 ft.

German 105mm assault howitzer on PzKpfw III chassis   This system was introduced in 1942 and was employed with artillery-assault gun brigades. It had a crew of four and was armed with one 105mm Stu. H. 42 howitzer, caliber length 28. Some models also carried a 7.9mm MG 34.

German 105mm gun 1eFH 18   A World War II weapon with a weight of 2.1 tons and a projectile weight of 33 lb. It fired fixed ammunition and had a range of 11,675 yd.

German 105mm gun 1eFH 44   A World War II weapon with a weight of 2.5 tons and a projectile weight of 33 lb. It fired fixed ammunition and had a range of 16,400 yd.

German 105mm gun sK 18   A World War II weapon with a weight of 1.2 tons and a projectile weight of 33 lb. It fired fixed ammunition and had a range of 20,860 yd.

German 105mm howitzer L.F.H. 18   This weapon fired a high-explosive projectile weighing 32.7 lb to a range of about 11,500 yd. Equipped with a muzzle brake and extra charge (*Fernladung*), the range was increased to about 13,500 yd.

German 105mm howitzer Stu. H. 42   This weapon fired a high-explosive projectile weighing 32.7 lb to a range of about 9,000 yd.

German 105mm recoilless rifle LG 42   A World War II weapon with a weight of 1,217 lb and a projectile weight of 33 lb. It fired fixed ammunition and had a range of 8,700 yd.

German 105mm self-propelled howitzer on Panzer II chassis   See **Wasp**, sense 3.

German 128mm antiaircraft gun Flak 40   A World War II weapon with a weight of 19 tons and a projectile weight of 57 lb. It fired fixed ammunition and had an effective ceiling of 35,000 ft.

German 128mm antitank gun PAK 44   A World War II weapon with a weight of 11 tons and a projectile weight of 57 lb. It fired fixed ammunition and had a range of 26,700 yd.

German 128mm gun PJK 80   This weapon fired an armor-piercing projectile weighing 62.4 lb to a range of about 17,250 yd.

German 150mm assault howitzer Sturmpanzer 43   See **Grizzly Bear**.

German 150mm (15cm) coast gun SK C/28   A World War II weapon with a weight of 21.6 tons and a projectile weight of 100 lb. It fired separate-loading ammunition and had a range of 25,700 yd.

German 150mm gun, Model 1916   A Krupp-built weapon developed during World War I. It had a weight of more than 11 tons and fired a 115.8-lb projectile about 25,000 yd.

German 150mm (15cm) gun sFH 36   A World War II weapon with a weight of 6.3 tons and a projectile weight of 96 lb. It fired fixed ammunition and had a range of 16,500 yd.

German 150mm (15cm) gun sIG 33 A World War II weapon with a weight of 1.7 tons and a projectile weight of 83 lb. It fired fixed ammunition and had a range of 5,140 yd.

German 150mm heavy howitzer sFH 13 This weapon fired a projectile weighing 90 lb and had a muzzle velocity of 1,250 fps. The maximum range was about 9,500 yd. This model was developed prior to World War I.

German 150mm howitzer, Model 1917 A World War I weapon that could fire a 93-lb projectile about 10,000 yd.

German 150mm howitzer sFH 18/1 This weapon fired a high-explosive projectile weighing 96 lb to a range of about 15,000 yd. The muzzle velocity was 1,706 fps.

German 150mm howitzer sIG 33 This weapon had a high-explosive projectile weight of 83.3 lb and a range of about 5,000 yd. The muzzle velocity was 787 fps.

German 150mm howitzer Stu. H. 43 This weapon fired a high-explosive projectile weighing 83.8 lb to a range of about 4,500 yd. The muzzle velocity was 787 fps.

German 150mm (15cm) railroad gun K A World War II weapon with a weight of 81.7 tons and a projectile weight of 95 lb. It fired separate-loading ammunition and had a range of 24,600 yd.

German 150mm recoilless rifle LG 240 A World War II weapon with a weight of 1,875 lb and a projectile weight of 83 lb. It fired fixed ammunition and had a range of 5,570 yd.

German 150mm rocket launcher Nebelwerfer 41 See **Nebelwerfer.**

German 150mm self-propelled gun This weapon was produced with the chassis of a PzKpfw II tank and a 150mm gun. It was introduced in 1942 and had a crew of five, a combat weight of 12 tons, and a road speed of 30 mph.

German 150mm self-propelled howitzer on Czech 38 chassis A system that consisted of a 150mm infantry howitzer (sIG 33) mounted on a Czech 38 tank chassis. It was introduced in 1942 and had a crew of four.

German 150mm self-propelled howitzer on French Lorraine chassis A system that was introduced in 1942 and consisted of a 150mm howitzer (sFH 13, of World War I manufacture) mounted on the chassis of a French Lorraine tank chassis. It weighed 9.4 tons and had a crew of four.

German 150mm self-propelled howitzer on Panzer IV chassis See **Bumble Bee.**

German 170mm (17cm) coast gun SK L/40 A World War II weapon with a weight of 112 tons and a projectile weight of 138 lb. It fired separate-loading ammunition and had a range of 30,000 yd.

German 170mm (17cm) gun K 18 A World War II weapon with a weight of 19.2 tons and a projectile weight of 138 lb. It fired fixed ammunition and had a range of 32,375 yd.

German 170mm (17cm) railroad gun K A World War II weapon with a weight of 87.8 tons and a projectile weight of 138 lb. It fired separate-loading ammunition and had a range of 29,300 yd.

German 210mm (21cm) gun K 39 A World War II weapon with a weight of 37 tons and a projectile weight of 298 lb. It fired separate-loading ammunition and had a range of 32,800 yd.

German 210mm howitzer This howitzer fired a 249-lb projectile a distance of about 18,000 yd (slightly over 10 mi).

German 232mm "Paris" guns Special weapons developed by Germany in World War I to fire on Paris from ranges of up to 75 mi. See **Paris guns.**

German 240mm (24cm) gun K4 A World War II weapon with a weight of 60.4 tons and a projectile weight of 352 lb. It fired separate-loading ammunition and had a range of 53,600 yd.

German 240mm (24cm) railroad gun Bruno A World War II weapon that consisted of a naval gun mounted on a railroad mounting. It had a weight of 103.6 tons and a projectile weight of 327 lb. It fired separate-loading ammunition and had a range of 22,100 yd.

German 280mm (28cm) railroad gun K5 A World War II weapon with a weight of 240.8 tons. It fired a conventional projectile

German 128mm antiaircraft gun Flak 40. (*U.S. Army.*)

German 170mm (17cm) gun K 18. (*U.S. Army.*)

German tank, medium, PzKpfw III. (*U.S. Army.*)

that weighed 561 lb to a range of 68,000 yd and a rocket-assisted projectile that weighed 547 lb to a range of 94,600 yd. A third projectile type was shaped like an enormous dart, having a diameter of 12 cm, a length of 180 cm, a weight of 300 lb, and four stabilizing fins. It utilized a discarding sabot and had a muzzle velocity of 5,000 fps and a range of 160,000 yd (almost 80 mi). See also **Anzio Annie (Annies).**

German 300mm (30cm) coast gun SK L/50 A World War II weapon with a weight of 194.8 tons and a projectile weight of 551 lb. It fired separate-loading ammunition and had a range of 46,800 yd.

German 340mm (34cm) howitzer M1 A World War II weapon with a weight of 82.3 tons and a projectile weight of 1,267 lb. It fired separate-loading ammunition and had a range of 21,900 yd.

German 380mm (38cm) railroad gun Siegfried A World War II weapon with a weight of 323.6 tons and a projectile weight of 1,091 lb. It fired separate-loading ammunition and had a range of 61,000 yd.

German 600mm (60cm) self-propelled howitzer A World War II weapon with a weight of 136.7 tons. It fired a 3,746-lb projectile (with a range of 7,300 yd) or a 4,840-lb projectile (with a range of 4,900 yd).

German 800mm (80cm) railroad gun Gustav The largest railroad gun ever used operationally, this World War II weapon had a weight of 1,350 tons. It was operated, maintained, and protected by a force of 1,420 men under the command of a major general. Actual firing was conducted by 500 men under the command of a colonel. This gun fired a high-explosive projectile weighing 5 tons to a range of about 29 mi. It fired a 7.5-ton concrete-piercing projectile (re-puted to penetrate 80 meters of concrete) to a range of 23 mi.

German aircraft self-loading carbine Model 15 This weapon was the 7mm Mondragon, a semiautomatic rifle of Mexican design and Swiss manufacture. It was gas-operated and was used by Germans in aircraft.

German antiaircraft tank, 20mm guns See **Whirlwind.**

German antiaircraft tank, 37mm guns See **East Wind.**

German armored car Kfz-13 and Kfz-14 A four-wheeled vehicle introduced in 1933. The Kfz-13 had a crew of two, a weight of 4,850 lb, and a road speed of 35 mph. It was employed with cavalry regimental machine-gun units, and later with reconnaissance platoons, and was armed with one 7.9mm machine gun. The Kfz-14 was a three-man unarmed radio-command car built on the same chassis.

German armored car SdKfz 222 A four-wheeled vehicle introduced in 1938 and used with reconnaissance companies of tank battalions. It had a crew of three, a combat weight of 10,582 lb, a road speed of 30 mph, and armament consisting of one 20mm automatic gun, one 7.9mm MG 34 machine gun, and one 9mm MP 38 or MP 40 submachine gun.

German armored car SdKfz 223 A four-wheeled vehicle introduced in 1937 and employed with reconnaissance companies. It had a crew of three, a weight of 9,700 lb, a road speed of 30 mph, and armament consisting of one 7.9mm MG 34 machine gun and one 9mm MP 38 or MP 40 submachine gun. This vehicle resembled the SdKfz 222, but differed in that it contained radio equipment and could be used for command functions.

German armored car SdKfz 232 A six-wheeled armored car introduced in 1933 and used as a radio-command vehicle in armored reconnaissance companies. It had a crew of four, a combat weight of 13,778 lb, a road speed of 45 mph, and armament consisting of one 20mm automatic gun and one 7.9mm machine gun.

German armored personnel carrier M-1966 See **Marder-Schutzenpanzer Neu M-1966.**

German armored personnel carrier SPZ 12-3 (HS-30) See **SPZ 12-3 (HS-30).**

German DFS-230A glider The Germans used gliders of this type during their invasion of Crete in April 1941. Made of wood covered with fabric, each glider carried a pilot and 10 troops and was towed (often in strings of as many as 10) by Junkers Ju 52's and Ju 86's.

German light amphibious car Kfz-1/20 See **Schwimmwagen.**

German light armored car SdKfz 221 A four-wheeled vehicle introduced in 1937 and used with reconnaissance companies and armored reconnaissance battalions. It had a crew of three, a road speed of 30 mph, and a combat weight of 8,818 lb. It was armed with one 7.9mm MG 34 machine gun and one 9mm MP 38 or MP 40 submachine gun.

German light car Kfz-1 Type 82 (Volkswagen) See **Kübelwagen.**

German manned torpedo See **Negro.**

German S mine Set off by trip wires, this mine would pop into the air before exploding. It would detonate at 3 to 6 ft above the ground and project fragments as far as 100 yd. The explosive charge weighed $1\frac{1}{4}$ lb. It was also called **Bouncing Betty,** which see.

German tank destroyer, 47mm gun on PzKpfw I chassis This system was introduced in late 1939 for use in tank-destroyer battalions. It was operated by a crew of three and was armed with one Czech 47mm antitank gun. It weighed 8.4 tons.

German tank destroyer, 75mm gun on Caterpillar Tractor East This system was introduced in 1944 and carried one 75mm Pak 40 gun. It weighed 4.5 tons and had a speed of about 11 mph.

German tank destroyer, 75mm gun on Czech 38 chassis See **Baiter.**

German tank destroyer, 75mm gun on PzKpfw IV chassis This system was introduced in 1944 and was employed in tank-destroyer units of infantry and armored divisions. Built by Krupp, it had a crew of four and was armed with a 75mm gun and one 7.9mm machine gun. It weighed 26.9 tons and could travel at speeds of 25 mph on roads.

German tank destroyer, 76.2mm gun on Czech 38 chassis This system was introduced in 1941 and was used in motorized units. It was operated by a crew of four and was armed with one 76.2mm Pak 36 gun (actually a Soviet 76.2mm gun Model 36 rechambered to take the German Pak 40 cartridge case) and one 7.9mm MG 37 machine gun. The weight was 11.6 tons. It saw considerable action in North Africa, where it could outgun a Sherman tank.

German tank destroyer, 88mm gun on PzKpfw IV chassis See **Rhinoceros.**

German tank destroyer, 88mm gun on Tiger chassis See **Elephant,** sense 1.

German tank destroyer, 88mm gun Pak 43 on Panther chassis This system was introduced in 1944 and carried a crew of five. Armament consisted of one 88mm Pak 43/3 gun, caliber length 71, and one 7.9mm MG 34 machine gun. By mounting this gun on the Panther chassis, the Germans achieved a low-silhouette tank destroyer of great mobility. It could destroy any Allied tank in the field. The gun could penetrate 9.4 in. or armor at 100 yd at 0°. The entire system weighed 51.3 tons.

German tank destroyer, 128mm gun on Tiger B chassis This system was introduced in 1944 and was used in heavy tank-destroyer battalions. It had a crew of six and was armed with a 128mm antitank gun PJK 80 and one 7.9mm MG 34 machine gun. It weighed 79 tons and could travel at speeds up to 26 mph on roads.

German tank, heavy, King Tiger See **King Tiger tank.**

German tank, heavy, PzKpfw V See **Panther tank.**

German tank, heavy, PzKpfw VI See **Tiger tank.**

German tank, light, PzKpfw I ("PzKpfw" is a German abbreviation for *Panzerkampfwagen,* which means "tank") This was a light German tank introduced in 1934 and used in armored divisions in Poland, France, Africa, and Russia. When obsolete it was used to mount self-propelled guns. These tanks had a crew of two and were armed with two 7.9mm MG 13 machine guns. They weighed 6.4 tons and could travel at speeds of 25 mph on roads.

German tank, light, PzKpfw II A light tank of World War II. It was introduced in 1938 for use with armored divisions. It had a crew of three, a weight of 9.8 tons, a length of about 15 ft, and a speed of about 25 mph on roads. It was armed with one 20mm KwK or KwK 38 gun and one coaxially mounted 7.9mm machine gun. It saw considerable service with Rommel's Afrika Korps in the Western Desert.

German tank, light, SPZ 11-2 See **SPZ 11-2 (Hotchkiss SPIA).**

German tank, main battle, Leopard See **Leopard,** sense 1.

German tank, medium, PzKpfw III A tank which first appeared in 1939 but which was not introduced until 1942. It was used with armored divisions, had a crew of five, weighed 25.4 tons, and had a road speed of about 28 mph. It was originally armed with a 37mm gun, but this was replaced with a 50mm KwK 39 (caliber length 60), which could easily destroy a Sherman. A version armed with a 75mm low-velocity gun was designated a "Sturmpanzer III." Other armament on this tank included two 7.9mm MG-34 machine guns.

German tank, medium, PzKpfw IV This tank appeared in about 1937 but was not introduced to armored divisions until later. It had a crew of five, a weight of 23 tons, a length of about 19 ft, and a road speed of 25 mph. It was armed with one 75mm KwK gun, plus two 7.9mm MG-34 machine guns. Other models were armed with the 75mm KwK 40. It was used in Poland and France in 1940 and could destroy any French tank with the low-velocity gun. With the more powerful gun it could destroy a Sherman tank.

German tank, TNHP, PzKpfw 38 (t) Actually a Czech tank with a German 37mm gun. It had a crew of four, a weight of 9.7 tons, a length of about 16.5 ft, and a road speed of 30 mph. Some 1,200 tanks of this type were produced, some of them seeing action in France and Poland and in the early attacks on the Soviet Union.

German U Boats, World War II See **Type IIA (B, C, and D), Type VIIC and VIIC41/42, Type IXC and IXC40, Type IXD2, Type XXI, Type XXIII, Type XXVIIA,** and **Type XXVIIB.**

Gew(ehr) 33/40 See **Mauser 7.92mm rifle Model 33/40.**

Gew(ehr) 43 semiautomatic rifle See **German 7.92mm semiautomatic rifle Model 43 (Gewehr 43).**

Gew(ehr) 98 rifle See **Mauser 7.92mm rifle Model 98 (Gew 98).**

Gew(ehr) 98/40 rifle See **German 7.92mm rifle Model 98/40.**

ghost signal An unwanted echo on the screen of a radar indicator.

GI, G.I. Originally this was an unofficial U.S. quartermaster term for "galvanized iron," but later came to be understood as "government issue." In popular or slang usage it came to designate an American soldier, particularly an enlisted man. It was also used as an adjective to describe clothing, haircuts, housing, etc. To have the GI's was to have diarrhea.

giberne At one time, a bag used by grenadiers to hold their hand grenades. Also, a cartridge box.

Gibson Girl A portable watertight radio transmitter used by men adrift at sea. Distress signals were automatically sent by the turn of a crank. The name derives from the hourglass contour of the transmitter.

gig A ship's boat for the use of the commanding officer.

Gigant See **Messerschmitt Me 321 glider and Messerschmitt Me 323 transport.**

Gimlet A 2-in. folding-fin unguided, air-to-surface rocket.

gisarme A weapon carried by foot soldiers in medieval times. It was a scythe-shaped weapon mounted on a long staff.

glacis The slope of earth that rises from open country to the top of the covered way or the counterscarp. It serves to bring an attacker into clear view from the parapet of the fortification.

glacis plate In naval terminology, the sloping armor plate on a deck that is set around a hatch or at the base of a turret.

Gladiator A British single-seat fighter and one of the last biplanes to see active service. Built by Gloster and first flown in 1934, this airplane was used at the beginning of World War II by the British and several European countries to which it had been exported. Powered by an 840-hp engine, it flew at speeds of 253 mph and was armed with four .303 cal. Browning machine guns. A carrier version was called the "Sea Gladiator," and in April 1940, four aircraft of this type were sent to Malta for fighter defense of the island. One was held in reserve, and the other three (called *Faith, Hope,* and *Charity*) stood alone against the Italian Air Force for 18 days until the arrival of RAF Hurricane fighters.

German tank, medium, PzKpfw IV. (*U.S. Army.*)

Gleaves. (*U.S. Navy.*)

gladius   The short thrusting sword of the Roman legionnaire. See **Roman sword.**

glaive   A weapon dating from medieval times and consisting of a large curved blade fixed on the end of a pole.

Gleaves   A class of U.S. destroyers (DD) of 1,630 tons standard displacement commissioned between 1940 and 1943. They had a length of 348 ft, a beam of 36 ft, a speed of 37 knots, and a wartime complement of 250 men. They were armed with four 5-in. guns, four 40mm and seven 20mm antiaircraft guns, and five 21-in. torpedo tubes. Twelve of the class were lost to action during World War II.

Gleaves-Livermore   A class of U.S. destroyers (DD) of 1,700 tons standard displacement produced in the period 1940–1943. In 1944-1945, twenty-four (of sixty-six) ships in the class were converted to high-speed minesweepers (DMS). Thirteen ships were lost to enemy action during World War II. They have a length of 348.2 ft, a beam of 36 ft, a speed of 37.6 knots, and a complement of 240 men. Armament consists of three or four 5-in. guns, plus four 40mm and four to seven 20mm antiaircraft guns, depth charges, and torpedo tubes.

Glen   The Allied code name for the Yokosuka E14Y1 two-seat single-engine submarine-borne twin-float reconnaissance seaplane. First flown in 1939, this Japanese airplane was designed to be transported in a waterproof cylindrical hangar on the deck of a submarine. It would be assembled for use and then catapulted from the deck. It was built in larger numbers than any other submarine-borne aircraft, had a speed of 153 mph, and was armed with one 7.7mm machine gun and two 110-lb bombs. This was the only Axis aircraft to drop bombs on the North American continent. This event took place in September 1942 on the southern coast of Oregon. Two bombs were dropped in a forested area where they caused no damage.

glide bomb   A bomb, fitted with airfoils to provide lift, carried and released in the direction of a target by an airplane. A glide bomb may be remotely controlled. Certain glide bombs, such as the Henschel 293, are initially propelled by a rocket engine; others depend upon the force of gravity for thrust.

glide bombing   1. The action of bombing a target from a gliding airplane.   **2.** The action of using glide bombs for bombing a target.   **3.** Bombing of a target by releasing one or more bombs at it when the bombing plane is gliding.

glide paths   1. The flight path of an aircraft or winged missile as it glides downward, the line of which forms an angle with the longitudinal axis of the aircraft or missile.   **2.** The line to be followed by an aircraft as it descends from horizontal flight to land upon the surface. Also called "glide slope."

glider   A fixed-wing airplane having no power plant and constructed so as to glide and soar. Military gliders, used to carry troops, supplies, etc., are normally carried aloft by being towed by a powered airplane. Released from the tow, they have limited range, but are given lift by their airfoils and thrust by the force of gravity combined with momentum and the reaction of aerodynamic forces upon the lifting surfaces. See also **military glider.**

Glisenti 9mm automatic pistol Model 1910   The official Italian service pistol in World War I and World War II, this weapon fires the special 9mm Glisenti cartridge. The cartridge is very similar to the

9mm Luger, but American and German ammunition should not be used for pistols designed for this cartridge. The model 1910 pistol is 8½ in. long, with a barrel length of 4 in. and a weight of about 32 oz. The magazine has a capacity of seven cartridges. The Glisenti pistol was developed from the 1906 Brixia and is quite similar to it.

Glisenti 10.35mm revolver Model 1889
This double-action revolver was adopted in 1889, with production continuing well into the 1920s. It has an overall length of 10.25 in., a barrel length of 5.25 in., and a weight of 2.2 lb. The cylinder has a capacity of six cartridges, and the muzzle velocity is about 840 fps.

Globemaster I The Douglas C-74 Globemaster I was a four-engine transport aircraft first flown in 1945. It had a crew of 13, a speed of 300 mph, and a range of 7,800 mi.

Globemaster II The Douglas C-124 Globemaster II is a four-engine (piston) long-range strategic transport developed for the USAF and first flown in 1949. It has a range of 4,030 mi and a speed of 272 mph and can carry 200 troops or 68,500 lb of cargo.

Gloire A class of French cruisers of 7,600 tons standard displacement completed in 1937. Of six ships in the class, three were scuttled at Toulon in November 1942. They had a length of 580 ft, a beam of 57.5 ft, a speed of 31 knots, and a complement of 764 men (wartime). They were armed with nine 6-in. and eight 3.5-in. guns, twenty-four 40mm and sixteen 20mm antiaircraft guns, and four 21.7-in. torpedo tubes.

Glomb (glide bomb) A glider adapted by the U.S. Navy for use as a glide bomb. This World War II development was towed to the target area and then released. It was guided to the target by radio control and monitored by television. It was designed to carry either 3,000 gal of gasoline or 18,000 lb of high explosive.

Glory A class of British light aircraft carriers of 13,190 tons standard displacement completed in 1945–1946. They had a length of 695 ft, a flight-deck width of 80 ft, a speed of 25 knots, and a complement of 1,300 men. They carried 35 aircraft and were armed with two-pounder pompoms and 40mm antiaircraft guns.

GM Guided missile. Also, gunner's mate.

Gnat The British Hawker Siddeley Gnat is a single-seat lightweight fighter or fighter-bomber presently in service with the Indian Air Force and the Finnish Air Force; it was first flown in 1955. It has a speed of Mach 0.98, is armed with two 30mm Aden cannons, and has provisions for the under-wing mounting of two 500-lb bombs or twelve 3-in. rockets.

Gneisenau 1. A German battle cruiser of 32,000 tons displacement produced in 1936. It had a length of 741.5 ft, a beam of 98.5 ft, a speed of 31.5 knots, and a complement of 1,800 men. It was armed with nine 11-in., twelve 5.9-in., fourteen 4.1-in., sixteen 37mm, and thirty-eight 20mm guns, plus six 21-in. torpedo tubes and four air-

glider, a Waco CG-4. (*U.S. Army.*)

Globemaster II. (*U.S. Air Force.*)

Glory. (*The Imperial War Museum.*)

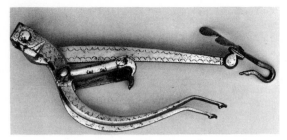

goats foot lever. (*The Metropolitan Museum of Art, gift of William H. Riggs, 1913.*)

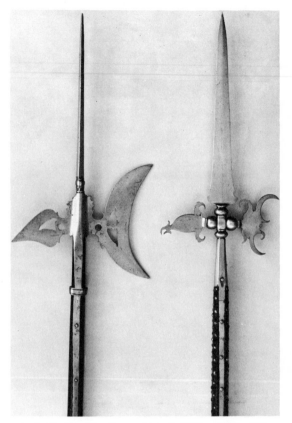

godenda. (*The Metropolitan Museum of Art, gift of William H. Riggs, 1913.*)

craft. It had one sister ship, *Scharnhorst.* *Gneisenau* was decommissioned after it was damaged by an RAF raid on Kiel in February 1942. **2.** An armored cruiser completed in 1907. For details see **Scharnhorst,** sense 1.

Goa The NATO code name for a Soviet two-stage surface-to-air missile (SA-3) first shown in 1964. In appearance it is the Soviet counterpart of the U.S. Hawk missile. Both a field and a shipboard missile, it has an overall length of 22 ft.

goats foot lever The system whereby smaller crossbows were drawn. It consisted of a set of articulated levers.

gob A slang term for a U.S. Navy sailor.

godbertum A thirteenth-century hauberk.

godenda A twelfth-century Flemish halberd.

goedendag A weapon consisting of a long, heavy clublike shaft with a spike at its upper end. It could be used as a club or thrust like a spear.

Goer The name given to a highly mobile cross-country amphibious transport vehicle having low-pressure tires and exoskeletal construction.

golandause An Anglo-Indian expression meaning "artilleryman."

Golden Rain The code name for a World War II German pyrotechnic device fired from antiaircraft guns as a navigational aid to aircraft.

Golem I A Soviet Navy underwater-to-surface missile with a range of about 400 mi. Based on German V-2 technology, this liquid-fueled missile has a radio-inertial guidance system and a nuclear warhead. Two or three of these missiles can be towed behind a submarine and, by flooding the base of the missile container, raised to the vertical and fired.

Golem II A Soviet Navy underwater-to-surface missile with radio-inertial guidance, a nuclear warhead, and a range of 1,200 to 1,300 mi. An advanced version of Golem I, the missile is towed behind a submarine in a sealed firing tube. When ready to fire, the base of the tube is flooded, raising the missile to a vertical position.

Golem III A Soviet underwater-to-air or surface-to-air infrared guided missile which can be launched from submarines, surface ships, or land-based mobile carriers. It can reach an altitude of about 10 mi at ranges out to 30 mi.

Golem IV A Soviet surface-to-air missile with a range of 45 mi. Used aboard surface ships, it uses a radar guidance system and solid-fuel engines.

goli A musket ball.

Goliath The code name for a high-powered very-low-frequency radio station operated by the Germans during World War II. It made possible radio communications to German U Boats that were 5 to 15 ft below the surface. Prior to this, submarines surfaced to receive instructions and were vulnerable to air attack.

gollette The shirt of mail once worn by foot soldiers.

gondola 1. A car or cabin suspended from an airship. **2.** Loosely applied to a bulging part on the underside of certain airplanes, such as the gunner's compartment on a Heinkel 111.

gonne, gunne The twelfth- and thirteenth-century spellings of "gun."

Good Conduct Medal A service award granted to enlisted men in recognition of exemplary behavior.

Gooney Bird A popular name for the C-47.

goop A compound in paste form containing finely divided magnesium used as a constituent of certain incendiary-bomb fillings.

Goose 1. A former U.S. Air Force turbo-

jet-powered missile. **2.** See **Grumman G-21A Goose.**

goose step The English and American name for the stiff-kneed, straight-legged parade step once used by the German infantry.

Gordi A class of Soviet destroyers of 1,657 tons standard displacement completed in 1936–1941. They had a speed of 36 knots, a complement of 240 men, and main armament consisting of four 5.1-in. guns, two 3-in. guns, and six 21-in. torpedo tubes.

gorge In fortifications, the rear entrance into a bastion or other outwork. Also, the rear part of a fortification.

gorget A piece of armor protecting the throat. It is usually formed of several lames. In the eighteenth and nineteenth centuries it became a crescent-shaped insignia worn by officers.

Goryunov machine guns See **Soviet 7.92mm heavy machine gun SG43 (Goryunov)** and **Soviet 7.62mm heavy machine gun SGM (Goryunov).**

Gosling The British name for the **Grumman G-44 Widgeon,** which see.

Gotha G.I to G.V A series of German three-place twin-engine biplane bombers first flown in 1915–1916. G.IV's and G.V's were widely used in carrying out raids on the United Kingdom. G.V's had a speed of 87 mph, a range of 522 mi, and defensive armament consisting of two machine guns; they carried six 110-lb bombs.

Gotha Go 242 glider A German glider of World War II. It had a wingspan of about 79 ft and a length of 52½ ft and could carry 5,300 lb of cargo or 25 fully equipped men. Gliders of this type were towed by Junkers Ju 52's and were used to ferry men and supplies to Rommel's Afrika Korps.

Gothic Line (Gotenstellung) The German defense line across Italy during World War II (1944). It ran from the coastal plain south of Spezia to the Foglia River and Pesaro on the Adriatic. Also called "Green Line" by the Germans.

Gourdou-Leseurre GL-810/812 A single-engine three-seat observation and scout twin-float seaplane that operated from French warships and coastal bases. It went into service in 1931 and was armed with two 7.7mm machine guns.

GR A U.S. Navy picket or patrol vessel converted from an EC-2 cargo ship (Liberty ship). It has a length of 441 ft and a beam of 56 ft. (Picture, p. 202.)

graffle A hook that was fastened to the belt and used to bend early crossbows.

grain 1. The unit of measurement used to express the weight of a powder charge or a bullet; 437.5 grains equal 1 oz avoirdupois, and 7,000 grains equal 1 lb. **2.** A single piece of solid propellant regardless of size or shape used in a gun or rocket. For the latter, a grain is often very large and shaped to fit the requirements of the rocket. It is termed "propellant grain."

Grand Army The army organized and commanded by Napoleon between 1804 and 1814. The term refers particularly to the army (consisting of 300,000 to 400,000 men) with which he invaded Russia in 1812.

Grand Army of the Republic Another name for the Union forces of the American Civil War.

Grand Slam **1.** A British 22,000-lb aircraft bomb developed during World War II. It was a relatively heavy-walled bomb with approximately 45 percent explosive. It was designed for use against heavily fortified targets such as U boat pens and underground factories. It was the largest bomb employed in the war and was first used against Bielefeld, Germany, on March 14, 1944. **2.** A U.S. Army 24-tube rocket launcher developed during World War II for use with either chemical or high-explosive rockets.

Grant MK I Another designation for British tank, medium, M3. It was introduced in 1941 and used in armored divisions. With a crew of six, it was armed with a 75mm gun, a 37mm gun, and two .30 cal. machine guns. It weighed 31.1 tons and traveled (on roads) at a speed of 22 mph. It was the first U.S. medium tank to see action and was used against the Germans in Libya in June 1942. (Picture, next page.)

granulation The size and shape of propellant powder granules.

grapeshot A type of charge used in a cannon. It consisted of a cluster of small cast-iron balls, usually nine, held together by plates, rings, and a connecting rod. In flight the balls would spread. (Picture, next page.)

grapnel A small four-pronged anchor formerly used to hold an enemy ship alongside for hand-to-hand combat.

Gras rifle See **French 11mm rifle Model 1874 (Gras).**

grasshopper **1.** A light scouting airplane used to direct artillery fire. **2.** An eighteenth-century colloquial term for a galloper gun.

Gravel A U.S. antipersonnel mine, designated the XM27. It is a small canvas-covered charge of lead azide that can be seeded by hand or by helicopters, aircraft, or trucks.

graves registration The supervision and execution of matters pertaining to the identification, removal, and burial of the dead and to the collection and processing of their effects.

Grayback A term used (by Union soldiers) to describe a Confederate soldier during the American Civil War. Graybacks were so called because of the color of their uniforms.

graze **1.** To pass close to the surface, as a shot that follows a path nearly parallel to the ground and low enough to strike a standing man. **2.** The burst of a projectile

gondola, of the *Akron*. (*U.S. Navy.*)

at the instant of impact with the ground. In this meaning, also called "graze burst."
3. The sensing, in time fire, for a burst on impact with the ground or other material object on a level with or below the target.

grazing fire Fire which is approximately parallel to the ground and does not rise above the height of a man.

Grease Gun The nickname given to the U.S. .45 cal. submachine gun M3 and M3A1 used in World War II and the Korean conflict. (Picture, p. 203.)

Great Mortar of Moscow A giant mortar built slightly after 1500. It had a 36-in. bore and fired a 1-ton stone projectile.

gorget. (*The Metropolitan Museum of Art, Rogers Fund, 1917.*)

Gotha G. III. (*The Smithsonian Institution, National Air Museum.*)

GR. (*U.S. Navy.*)

Grant MK I. (*The Imperial War Museum.*)

grapeshot. (*The Smithsonian Institution, Department of Defense Collection.*)

greaves Defensive armor for the legs below the knees.

Greek fire A material that was known to the Byzantine Greeks and said to have taken fire on wetting. The term also refers to any of several flammable mixtures. It may also be called "wildfire."

Greek Mannlicher 7.92mm rifle Model 95/24 This weapon uses a standard Austrian Model 95 receiver (for 8mm) with the necessary magazine and barrel alterations needed to fire the German 7.92mm cartridge. This weapon saw service during World War II.

Greek Mannlicher Schoenauer 6.5mm rifle Model 1903 This rifle was adopted in 1903 and was modified slightly in the Model 1903.14. It has an overall length of 48.3 in., a barrel length of 28.5 in., and a weight of 8.31 lb. The carbine versions of this weapon had a barrel length of 20.5 in.

and a weight of about 8 lb. Most of these weapons were lost during World War I.

Greek Mauser 7.92mm rifle Model 1930 This weapon saw service during World War II and was essentially a 7.92mm Mauser on the German Kar 98k system. It was made in Belgium by F-N. It has an overall length of 43.3 in. and a barrel length of 23.2 in. and utilizes a five-round nondetachable box magazine. It weighs 8.5 lb.

Green Cross 3 See **ethyldichloroarsine**.

Green Dragons A World War II nickname given by U.S. Marines in the Pacific to jungle-camouflaged LST's (landing ship, tank).

greenhouse The canopy of an aircraft cockpit, cabin, turret, or nose.

Green Quail The popular name for an Air Force air-to-surface missile designed to confuse enemy radar.

Greif 1. The Heinkel He 177 Greif was a

German six-seat twin-engine heavy bomber, reconnaissance, and antishipping aircraft of World War II. It was equipped with two 2,950-hp engines and flew at a top speed of 303 mph. It was armed with two 20mm cannons, three 13mm machine guns, and three 7.9mm machine guns, plus a bombload of about 2,200 lb carried internally and two sea mines, torpedoes, or missiles carried externally. **2.** Operation Greif was a World War II German plan to spread confusion at the beginning of their Ardennes offensive in December 1944. It involved the use of German officers and men dressed in U.S. uniforms and driving U.S. vehicles. They issued false orders and seized key positions. This operation also included the airdrop of 800 parachutists into the Malmedy, Belgium, area. It was directed by S.S. Col. Count Otto Skorzeny (who also led Operation **Eiche,** which see).

grenade A small explosive or chemical missile, originally designed to be thrown by hand, but now also designed to be projected from special grenade launchers, usually fitted to rifles or carbines. Grenades may be classified in a broad sense as hand grenades or rifle grenades. Many varieties and variations of these have been used, including a number of improvised ones.

grenade carrier A container of flexible material specifically designed to carry hand grenades. It is designed to be attached to a belt.

grenade net A net of chicken wire or similar material placed over a trench, etc., as a protection against grenades.

grenade pit A pit, usually at the bottom of an incline, to catch hand grenades and limit the effects of their explosion.

grenadier Formerly, a soldier who carried and threw grenades. Later the term was attached to picked troops composed of large men who served in a special company attached to each regiment or battalion. In the eighteenth century the men of these companies were armed with grenades and hatchets. In modern times, the term refers to a member of a special regiment or corps.

Greyhound 1. The Grumman C-2A Greyhound is a cargo and combat-support transport used by the U.S. Navy and Marine Corps and first flown in 1964. It is powered by two turboprops and has a speed of 425 mph. **2.** The World War II British designation for the **U.S. armored car, light, M8 (T22E2),** which see. (Picture, next page.)

grid Two sets of parallel lines intersecting at right angles and forming squares. The grid is superimposed on maps, charts, and other similar representations of the earth's surface in an accurate and consistent manner to permit identification of ground locations with respect to other locations and the computation of direction and distance to other points. The term is also used in

Grease Gun. (*U.S. Army.*)

greenhouse of the Heinkel He 111. (*Vereinigte Flugtechnische Werke—Fokker.*)

Greif. (*Vereinigte Flugtechnische Werke—Fokker.*)

giving the location of a geographic point by grid coordinates.

Gridley A class of U.S. 1,500-ton destroyers later referred to as **McCall and Craven** classes, which see.

Griffon The NATO code name for a Soviet surface-to-air missile (SA-5) first seen in 1963. It is a two-stage missile with a length of 49 ft and a diameter of 2.9 ft. It can reach altitudes of 95,000 ft and is claimed to have antimissile capability.

grip One of a pair of wooden or plastic

grenade. (*U.S. Army.*)

Greyhound. (*U.S. Navy.*)

grip. (*The Smithsonian Institution.*)

pieces designed to be attached by threaded fasteners to the two sides of the frame of a weapon, such as a revolver or bayonet. It is shaped to fit the hand and to provide a formed gripping surface to hold the weapon. Also, the part of a sword or dagger grasped by the hand.

Grizzly Bear The German 150mm assault howitzer (Sturmpanzer 43) on a PzKpfw IV chassis. It was armed with one 150mm Stu. H. 43 howitzer, caliber length 12. It was employed by cannon companies of armored infantry regiments, armored artillery battalions, and army armored battalions. It was introduced in 1943.

groove diameter The diameter of a bore of a gun as measured from the bottom of one groove to the bottom of the opposite groove.

grooves The spiral depressions in the rifling of a gun. They impart a spinning motion to a projectile which stabilizes it in flight.

gross weight The weight of a vehicle including fuel, lubricants, coolant, on-vehicle materiel, cargo, and operating personnel.

ground alert That status in which aircraft on the ground or deck are fully serviced and armed, with combat crews in readiness to take off within a specified short period of time (usually 15 minutes) after receipt of a mission order.

ground attack **1.** An attack by ground forces upon a ground target. **2.** An air attack upon a ground target.

ground-controlled approach (GCA) The technique or procedures for talking down, through the use of both surveillance and precision-approach radar, an aircraft during its approach so as to place it in a position for landing.

ground-controlled interception (GCI) The technique by which a pilot is guided to intercept his target by provision of speeds, headings, and altitudes from a controller ashore.

ground crew **1.** A detail or team of engine mechanics and other technicians who maintain, service, or handle aircraft on the ground. **2.** A landing crew.

ground-effect machine A machine which

normally flies within the zone of the ground effect or ground cushion. It is also known as an "air-cushion vehicle."

ground fire Small-arms ground-to-air fire directed against aircraft.

ground handling The handling of an airplane, atomic bomb, or any other object, while moving it on the ground. Specifically, the action of moving an aircraft around on the ground, either by taxiing or by use of manual labor, tugs, or tractors.

ground-influence mine A **ground mine,** which see, designed to be dropped from aircraft and to rest on the bottom. It is detonated by magnetic or other influence.

ground mine An underwater mine possessing considerable negative buoyancy and intended to rest on the bottom. For this reason it is suitable for use in relatively shallow water only.

ground readiness That status wherein aircraft can be armed and serviced and personnel alerted to take off within a specified length of time after receiving orders.

ground return The indication on a radar indicator screen caused by radio waves, being reflected back by the surface of the ground.

ground strafing An attack upon ground troops by low-flying aircraft using bombs, machine guns, and cannons.

ground-support equipment (GSE) That part of a military weapon system which includes all the ground equipment required for test, operation, storage, and maintenance.

ground troops Troops employed in ground warfare, such as infantry, artillery, etc., as distinguished from personnel of the air or naval forces.

ground zero The point on the surface of land or water at, or vertically below or above, the center of a planned or actual nuclear detonation.

group **1.** A flexible administrative and tactical unit composed of either two or more battalions or two or more squadrons. The term also applies to combat-support and combat-service units. **2.** A number of ships and/or aircraft, normally a subdivision of a force, assigned for a specific purpose.

group captain An RAF rank equivalent to that of colonel in the U.S. Air Force.

group rendezvous A checkpoint at which formations of the same type will join before proceeding.

grouser One of a number of projections on a tractor or tank track or automobile wheel to increase traction.

Grumman G-21A Goose A small twin-engine utility navigational training and coastal-patrol amphibian flying boat first developed for the U.S. Army Air Corps and flown in 1937. Later used by the U.S. Navy and Coast Guard, it carried antisubmarine

Grumman G-44 Widgeon. (*Grumman Aerospace Corporation.*)

armament consisting of two 250-lb bombs.

Grumman G-44 Widgeon   A small twin-engine two-seat coastal-patrol flying boat developed for the U.S. Coast Guard and first flown in 1940. Its only armament consisted of one 200-lb depth bomb carried under the starboard wing root. It had a maximum speed of 153 mph. This unlikely aircraft sank the German submarine U-166 in the Gulf of Mexico in 1942.

Gruppe   In the German Luftwaffe of World War II, an operational unit consisting of four *Staffeln*. A *Staffel* was made up of three *Schwarm*, and a *Schwarm* consisted of two *Rotten*. A *Rotte* was a two-aircraft formation.

GSE   See **ground-support equipment.**

guard   1. Soldiers detailed to protect a person or a position.   **2.** A curved metal piece, called a "trigger guard," that is set below the trigger to prevent accidental firing. A handguard protects the hand from the heat of a gun barrel.   **3.** In the British Army, guards are certain troops attached to the person of the sovereign, e.g., foot guards and royal horse guards.

guardapolvo   A circular plate, usually pierced with ornament, fixed inside the cup of a cup-hilt rapier.

guard chamber   A guardroom.

guardhouse   A building that accommodates the members of a military guard and provides space for the detention or confinement of military prisoners.

guard report   The report of the commander of a guard unit at the end of each guard-duty period.

guardroom   The room occupied by a guard during guard duty. It may also be a room where prisoners are confined.

guardship   A ship ordered to maintain a readiness to get under way immediately. Also, a ship maintaining a prescribed communication guard or watch on certain radio frequencies.

guardsman   A member of any military organization called "guards."

Guedes 8mm rifle Model 1885   This weapon was a single-shot rifle with falling block action. It was used by Portugal, but manufactured by Steyr in Austria. It is 48 in. long, with a barrel length of 38.3 in. and a weight of 9 lb.

Guerlich 20mm antitank gun   This German antitank gun had a bore that tapered from 28mm at the breech to 20mm at the muzzle. Its shells were ringed with soft iron bands which compressed 8mm as the shell traveled down the barrel. The muzzle velocity of this weapon was 4,400 fps.

guerrilla   A combat participant in guerrilla warfare.

guerrilla warfare   Operations carried on by independent or semi-independent forces in the rear of the enemy. These operations usually are conducted by irregular forces acting either separately from or in conjunction with regular forces, but may at times be conducted entirely with regular troops. The objective of these operations is to harass, delay, and disrupt the military operations of the enemy, possibly leading to civil war, and they normally are characterized by the extensive use of unorthodox tactics, passive resistance, espionage, sabotage, diversion, assassination, and propaganda.

guichet   A small door made in the gates of fortified towns.

guidance   1. Policy, direction, decision, or instruction having the effect of an order when promulgated by a higher echelon.   **2.** The entire process by which target intelligence information received by the guided missile is used to effect proper flight control to cause timely direction changes for effective target interception.

guidance system   Concerning missiles, that system which performs data analysis, processes intelligence, and issues the necessary commands enabling a guided missile to reach a specified destination, with special emphasis on the flight path or orbit and on the information for determining the proper course whether computed externally or within the missile itself.

guide   A person or vessel against which others in a formation regulate their positions.

guided bomb   An aerial bomb guided dur-

guard. (*The Smithsonian Institution.*)

ing its drop in range, in azimuth, or in both.

guided missile   An unmanned self-propelled vehicle, with or without a warhead, which is designed to move in a trajectory or flight path all or partially above the earth's surface and whose trajectory or course, while in flight, is capable of being controlled remotely, by homing systems, or by inertial and/or programmed guidance from within. Excludes drones, torpedoes, rockets, and other vehicles whose trajectory or course cannot be controlled while in flight. Guided missiles may be air-to-air (AAM), surface-to-surface (SSM), surface-to-air (SAM), air-to-surface (ASM), air-to-underwater (AUM), surface-to-underwater (SUM), underwater-to-air (UAM), underwater-to-surface (USM), and underwater-to-underwater (UUM).

guided-missile cruiser   With the exception of CGN's, these ships are a full conversion of heavy cruisers. All guns are removed and replaced with Talos or Tartar missile launchers. The CGN is a nuclear-

guided missile. Pershing. (*Martin Marietta Aerospace Group.*)

powered long-range ship equipped with Talos or Terrier missile and Asroc launchers. Designated as CG and CGN.

guided-missile destroyer This destroyer type is equipped with Terrier or Tartar guided-missile launchers, improved naval gun battery, long-range sonar, and antisubmarine-warfare weapons, including Asroc. It is designated as DDG.

guided-missile frigate A frigate equipped with Terrier or Tartar missile launchers and 5-in./54 gun battery; also Asroc. Designated as DLG and DLGN. The DLGN is nuclear-powered.

guided-missile heavy cruisers These ships are converted heavy cruisers, with one triple 8-in./55 turret removed and replaced with a twin Terrier missile launcher. It is designated as CAG.

guided-missile light cruisers Converted light cruisers. In addition to 6-in./47 guns, either Terrier or Talos missile launchers have been added to the main armament. It is designated as CLG.

guided-missile submarine A submarine designed to have an additional capability to launch guided-missile attacks from surface condition. Designated as SSG and SSGN. The SSGN is nuclear-powered.

Guideline The NATO code name for a Soviet two-stage surface-to-air (SA-2) guided missile first seen in 1957. It is in service with Soviet forces and the forces of several other countries. It has a length of

35 ft, a launching weight (with booster) of about 5,000 lb, a slant range of 25 mi, and an effective ceiling of 60,000 ft. The weight of the high-explosive warhead is 288 lb.

guidon A company identification pennant for naval units ashore. Formerly, a small flag or streamer carried by mounted troops; also, a similar flag carried by almost all units of the U.S. Army.

guige A strap supporting a shield. It passed across the body and over the right shoulder.

Guild The NATO code name for a Soviet surface-to-air (SA-1) missile first seen in 1960. It has a length of about 40 ft and a maximum diameter of 2.3 ft.

guisarme A weapon in wide use from the eleventh to the fifteenth centuries. It is an obsolete term for a polearm, and students disagree on its exact meaning. Most believe it was a kind of bill or glaive.

gulaigorod A combination camp-fortification used in fifteenth-century Russia. The term means "moving town," and a gulaigorod consisted of numerous wagons which conveyed large numbers of shields set up as protection. The shields were equipped with loopholes.

gun 1. In general, a piece of ordnance consisting essentially of a tube or barrel and used for throwing projectiles by force, usually the force of an explosive, but sometimes that of compressed gas, a spring, etc. The general term embraces such weapons as are sometimes specifically designated as guns—howitzers, mortars, cannons, firearms, rifles, shotguns, carbines, pistols, and revolvers. **2.** Specifically, a gun (sense 1) with a relatively long barrel (usually over 30 cal.) and a relatively high initial velocity,

capable of being fired at low angles of elevation. **3.** A discharge of a cannon in a salute, such as a signal or the like—for example, a salute of 17 guns; the evening gun. **4.** To fire upon with guns. **5.** To advance the throttle or apply full power to an engine or motor.

gun blister A blister protuberance on an airplane from which a gunner fires his guns.

gunboat A small, moderate-speed, heavily armed vessel for general patrol and escort duty. Gunboats are usually unarmored and weigh less than 2,000 tons.

gun-bomb-rocket sight A computing sight used in a fighter aircraft in which different data may be set for use in aiming gunfire, bombs, or rockets.

gun book A log that records the history of the operations and inspections of a particular gun.

gun breech The rear end of a cannon from the front slope back to the rear face, exclusive of the breech mechanism. In this metal are formed the seat for the breech mechanism, the powder chamber, and the slopes connecting the latter with the rifled portion of the bore.

gun brig An armed square-rigged sailing vessel with two masts.

Gunbus See **Vickers F.B.5.**

gun camera A camera synchronized to operate when an aircraft's guns fire. It provides a photographic record of hits, both in target practice and in combat.

gun captain In the U.S. Navy, a petty officer in command of a gun crew.

gun carriage The mobile or fixed support for a gun. It sometimes includes the elevating and traversing mechanism. Some-

guided-missile heavy cruiser, the U.S.S. *Chicago* of the Albany class. (*U.S. Navy.*)

times called "carriage."

gun chamber The part of a gun that receives the charge.

gun charger A mechanism on a gun that operates to retract the breech mechanism or bolt to the rear and to insert a charge into the chamber. Often shortened to "charger." On a machine gun, the charger retracts the breech mechanism to the rear of the receiver, lining up a round with the barrel and allowing the breech mechanism to move forward to chamber the round. A gun charger may be operated manually or by other means.

guncotton Nitrocellulose of high nitration (13.35 to 13.4 percent nitrogen); nitrocotton. An explosive made by treating cotton with nitric and sulfuric acids. Guncotton is used principally in the manufacture of single-base and double-base propellants.

gun cover A fabric cover, usually of canvas, to protect a gun and sometimes its carriage from rain, dust, and the like.

gun crew The personnel assigned to the service of a gun.

gun deck At one time, a deck below the spar deck, on which guns were carried. In modern warships, the deck carrying guns next below the main deck.

gun direction The distribution and direction of the gunfire of a ship.

Gun Dish The NATO code name for a type of Soviet I/J-band 23mm antiaircraft-artillery-gun director radar.

gun emplacement The firing location of a gun together with necessary installations, such as camouflage, ammunition supply, etc.

gunfire The use of such things as artillery, rifles, and small arms, as distinguished from the use of bayonets, swords, torpedoes, and bombs.

gun flash Muzzle flash.

gunflint The flint used in a flintlock firearm to produce a spark which ignites the priming.

gun fore-end A wood or plastic piece that is usually designed with a semicircular groove to fit under the barrel of a gun and attached by metal fastening devices. It is shaped to fit the hand and is used to steady the weapon during firing.

gun handguard A wood or plastic piece that is usually designed with a semicircular groove to fit over the top of the barrel of a carbine or rifle and attached by metal fastening devices. It is shaped to fit the hand and to protect it during firing. It excludes the gun fore-end.

gun hoist A device placed near the breech of a gun for lifting propellant and projectiles.

gunhouse The visible part of a turret extending above the barbette.

gun-laying radar Any radar equipment specifically designed for determining the

gun carriage, a special sled mount for a U.S. 75mm pack howitzer. (*U.S. Army.*)

range, azimuth, and elevation of a target for purposes of fire direction.

gunlock A term originally used to refer to the types of ignition systems required to produce spark or flame. Types of locks include the flintlock, matchlock, percussion lock, and wheel lock.

gunmetal The material from which guns are made. Specifically, a type of bronze (9 parts copper and 1 part tin) once much used for the manufacture of cannons.

gun mount A system designed to support a gun; it includes machine-gun mounts. In vehicles, the assembly which consists of the cradle, recoil cylinders, rotor, elevating mechanism, and fire solenoids that hold the gun; in armored vehicles, the supporting and protective device for the armament which connects the armament to the hull and turret. Tank and armored-car guns are in practically all cases based on, and carried by, some portion of the hull walls. These

gun mount, the turret mount of a Saladin armored car. (*The Rover Co. Ltd.*)

gunner's quadrant. (*The Smithsonian Institution.*)

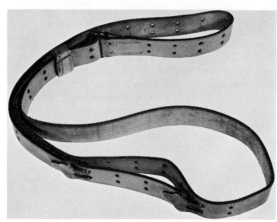

gunsling. (*The Smithsonian Institution.*)

gun tub, showing a 40mm antiaircraft gun. (*U.S. Navy.*)

mounts may be divided into three classes: (1) turret mounts, (2) sponson mounts, and (3) ball mounts. (1) *Turret mount:* A gun mount positioned in the turret of a tank or combat vehicle. Multiple gun turret mounts, for more than one gun, give improved control in tracking aerial targets and increased firepower and are power-driven. (2) *Sponson mount:* A gun mount positioned on the sponson of a tank or combat vehicle. Practically abandoned on account of vulnerability and limited field of fire, although widely used in earlier tanks. (3) *Ball mount:* A gun mount used for mounting automatic small arms for use against personnel targets.

gunnage   The number of guns carried by a warship. At one time, prize money was given to crew members according to the number of guns on the prize vessel.

gunner   A U.S. Navy warrant officer in charge of a vessel's ordnance. Also, a soldier whose duty is to adjust and aim a gun.

gunner's calipers   Calipers (inside or outside) that measure the bore of a cannon or the diameter of a spherical projectile and indicate the weight of the solid shot. They were in use from the 1600s to the late 1800s.

gunner's mate   A petty officer who is responsible for the upkeep and repair of ordnance.

gunner's quadrant   The modern gunner's quadrant is a mechanical device having scales graduated in mils, with fine micrometer adjustments and leveling or cross-leveling vials. It consists of a separate, unattached instrument for hand placement on a reference surface. Early specimens consisted of an L-shaped piece of wood with an arc at the joint marked in degrees. A plumb line indicated the angle of elevation. The data are used with cannons or mortars in adjusting the piece to the correct elevation to achieve a desired range.

gunner's rule   An early form of tangent sight.

gunnery   The art or practice of using machine guns or cannons either on the ground or in the air.

gunnery officer   The officer in charge of the gunnery department aboard a warship. He is responsible for the ship's or the squadron's armament, superintends gun drills, and directs the training of gun crews.

gun pit   An excavation, with or without a parapet dug to protect a fieldpiece and its men from direct fire.

gunport   An aperture in the front armor plate of a turret through which a gun projects.

gunpowder   A term usually applied to black powder, which is composed of potassium nitrate (saltpeter), charcoal, and sulfur. It consists of 70 to 80 percent saltpeter and 10 to 15 percent of each of the other ingredients. The mixture contains the necessary amount of oxygen for combustion and, when ignited, produces gases that occupy 1,000 to 1,500 times more space than the powder itself.

gunpower   A measure of the total weight of the projectiles thrown by the major battery of a battleship in one broadside.

gun rail   The track for machine-gun-carriage mounts that extends around the body of a scout car or a similar open, armored vehicle.

gun rest   See **fourquine.**

gun room   In the British Navy, the space located aft on the berth deck that was once used by the gunner and his mates, but is now used by midshipmen and junior officers. In the U.S. Navy this location is called the "steerage" or "junior officers' quarters."

gunrunning   Contraband traffic in arms and ammunition.

Gunship   A U.S. Air Force program to convert transport aircraft into day or night reconnaissance and interdiction aircraft equipped with multiple guns, searchlights, and sensors. The series includes Gunship 1 (Douglas AC-47's) and Gunship 2 (Lockheed AC-130's), both of which were deployed in Southeast Asia.

gunshot   Formerly, the reach or range of a gun.

gunsling   The adjustable strap on a musket, rifle, or carbine used to facilitate carrying and to steady the weapon when firing.

gunsmith   A person who makes or repairs small firearms; an armorer.

gunstick   A ramrod.

gunstock   The wooden stock in which the barrel and mechanism of a gun are fixed.

gunstone   An obsolete word for a cannon ball.

Gustaf V. (*Swedish Defense Staff.*)

gun tackles The tackles used to move a cannon on board ship and to return a gun to its original position after firing.

gun tub The cylindrical splinter protection around a deck gun aboard ship.

gun turret A turret built into the surface structure of an airplane, especially a bomber, in which one or more guns are mounted.

gun-type weapon A device in which two or more pieces of fissionable material, each less than a critical mass, are brought together very rapidly so as to form a supercritical mass which can explode as the result of a rapidly expanding fission chain.

GUPPY Greater Underwater Propulsion Program. A U.S. Navy modernization program evolved after World War II to improve the underwater performance of existing submarines. The concept borrowed from the design features of German Type XXI submarines (streamlined hull and superstructure, snorkel, and increased battery power), which were mass-produced in 1944–1945. A large number of *Balao* and *Tench* class submarines were thus converted.

Gurkha knife A **kukri**, which see.

gurries Mud forts, sometimes surrounded by ditches, once made in India.

gusset In armor, a piece of mail or plate armor to protect the point between the breast and the arm.

Gustaf V A Swedish armored ship of about 7,200 tons standard displacement completed in 1922 and the sister ship of *Drottning Victoria*. Both ships had a length of 397 ft, a beam of 61 ft, a speed of 22.5 knots, and a complement of 600 men. Main armament consisted of four 11-in., six 6-in., and four 3-in. guns.

Gustav See **German 800mm (80cm) railroad gun Gustav.**

Gustav Line A strongly fortified southern portion of the German **Winter Line,** which see, of World War II (1943–1944). It extended across Italy from Monte Cassino

gun turret. Quadruple mountings for battleships of the King George V class. (*Vickers Ltd.*)

gusset. (*The Metropolitan Museum of Art, gift of Prince Albrecht Radziwill, 1927.*)

along the west bank of the Rapido-Gari-Garigliano River to the Gulf of Gaeta.

GVAI A Soviet army barrage rocket fired in salvos.

Gypsy Moth A de Havilland biplane trainer of the 1920s used by the British RAF. It was the forerunner of the widely used Tiger Moth.

gyrene A slang term for a U.S. Marine.

gyrostabilization A mechanism which stabilizes the vertical motion of a tank gun, regardless of the pitching motion of the tank while moving.

GZ **Ground zero,** which see.

H

H I A class of Soviet nuclear-powered submarines armed with three launching tubes for ballistic missiles. There are 10 submarines in the class. They have a standard surface displacement of 3,500 tons, a length of 344 ft, a beam of 32.9 ft, a speed of 25 knots, and a complement of 90 men.

H II A class of Soviet nuclear-powered submarines armed with five launching tubes for ballistic missiles. There are five submarines in the class. They have a standard surface displacement of 3,700 tons, a length of 344 ft, a beam of 33 ft, a speed of 25 knots, and a complement of about 100 men.

habergeon A short coat of mail. Often, loosely, a hauberk.

haches d'armes Poleaxes or battle-axes.

hackbut It was formerly thought that "hackbut" was a variant of "arquebus" or "harquebus." Modern students point out that the two terms sometimes appear in the same ancient document as different arms. They contend, with good evidence, that the word "hackbut" derives from the German *Hakbuchse*, a gun with a hook, and that it means those heavier firearms provided with a hook on the underside of the barrel—the hook being placed over a wall or some

similar support to help absorb some of the recoil.

hackbuteer, hackbutter A soldier armed with a hackbut.

Hadrian The nickname of the **Waco CG-4** combat glider, which see. Nearly 14,000 were built during World War II.

haft The hilt of a sword, dagger, knife, or polearm.

Haganah A body of Zionist militia formed in Palestine during Turkish rule and used to protect settlers from Arab attack. Later formed as an army, it took a leading part in the formation of the state of Israel in 1947–1948.

hagbut See **hackbut.**

hagg See **hackbut.**

hailshot Buckshot.

hair trigger A delicately adjusted trigger that requires only a light touch to fire the gun.

Hajen A class of Swedish submarines of 785 tons standard surface displacement completed in 1956–1960. They have a length of 216.5 ft, a submerged speed of 20 knots, a complement of 44 men, and armament consisting of one 20mm antiaircraft gun and four 21-in. torpedo tubes.

hake An old term for a handgun.

Hakim 7.92mm rifle A rifle of Egyptian manufacture, this is a modification of the 6.5mm Ljungman Model 42.

halberd A weapon on a long shaft that was

Hajen. (*Swedish Defense Staff.*)

210

widely used in the fifteenth and sixteenth centuries. The head consists of an ax head with a peak or pointed fluke opposite it and a long spike or blade on the end. In the seventeenth and eighteenth centuries it became the distinctive weapon of a sergeant, honor guard, or court official.

halberdier A soldier or guard who is armed with a halberd.

halberdman, halberdsman A halberdier.

Halberstadt C.V A German two-place single-engine photoreconnaissance biplane used during the closing months of World War I. It had a speed of 105 mph and was armed with a Parabellum machine gun in the rear cockpit and a synchronized Spandau machine gun in the front. C.V's also carried wireless equipment.

Halberstadt CL.II A German two-place single-engine escort fighter that entered service in mid-1917. It had a speed of 102.5 mph and was armed with one or two 7.92mm Spandau machine guns synchronized to fire through the propeller and a Parabellum machine gun on a ring in the rear. When it entered service, it was pressed into the role of close-support operations and was very successful. A variant, the CL.IV, appeared early in 1918 and had somewhat greater maneuverability.

Halberstadt D Series A series of German single-place single-engine biplane fighters first flown in early 1916. They employed a single forward-firing Spandau gun and had a speed of about 90 mph. They began leaving operational service in the spring of 1917, being replaced by later Albatros variants.

Halcón 9mm submachine gun M.L. 57 An Argentine-produced weapon firing a 9mm Parabellum cartridge and capable of selective full automatic and semiautomatic fire. It has a cyclic rate of fire of 520 rounds per minute. With its folding stock extended, it is 30.7 in. long. The barrel length is 8.86 in. The weapon weighs 8.65 lb with a loaded 40-round magazine. A later version of the M.L. 57 is the M.L. 60 (Model Light 1960). Instead of a selector lever, this version employs a dual trigger system, similar to those used on various Beretta submachine guns. The forward trigger produces semiautomatic fire, and the rear trigger provides full automatic fire. The two models are otherwise the same.

Halcón .45 cal. submachine guns Models 1943 and 1946 Weapons produced in Argentina and designed to fire the .45 cal. ACP cartridge. They are capable of selective full automatic and semiautomatic fire. The Model 1943 has a wooden stock. It is blowback-operated and has a cyclic rate of fire of 700 rounds per minute. The overall length is 33.40 in., and the weight, with a 30-round clip, is 12.52 lb. The model 1946 has a retractable stock and weighs 10 lb

fully loaded. It has most of the general design features of the Model 1943. The weapons utilize mostly machine-turned components and are therefore unnecessarily heavy and expensive to produce.

half-armor Armor protecting only a part of the body, usually the head, arms, and trunk.

half bastion A demibastion. The half of a bastion cut off by the capital; it consists of one base and one front.

half block See **block.**

half cock The position of the hammer of a small-arms weapon when it is held by the first cocking notch, with the trigger locked and the weapon relatively safe. It was possible to carry certain types of loaded flintlock weapons in the half-cocked position, fully cocking them before pulling the trigger. When the secondary sear notch became worn, however, the gun was capable of discharging accidentally, giving rise to the expression "going off half-cocked," or doing something before being fully prepared to do it.

half deck **1.** The after part of the gun deck of a naval vessel. **2.** In the high-pooped ancient vessels, the deck which ran aft from about the center of the vessel.

half-life The time required for the activity of a given radioactive species to decrease to half of its initial value as a result of radioactive decay. The half-life is a characteristic property of each radioactive species and is independent of its amount or condition. The effective half-life of a given isotope is the time in which the quantity in the body will decrease to half as a result of both radioactive decay and biological elimination.

half-loaded In automatic arms, a half-loaded weapon is one in which the belt or magazine has been inserted and the receiver charged, but in which the first cartridge is not actually in the chamber.

halberd. (*The Smithsonian Institution, National Air Museum.*)

half-merlons The merlons at the ends of a parapet.

half-moon A polearm of the sixteenth and seventeenth centuries. It consisted of a crescent-shaped blade at right angles to the shaft. This is also a fortifications term. See **demilune.**

half-moon clips A revolver clip for holding the cartridges for one-half of the cylinder. In some cases it adapts rimless ammunition for revolver use.

half-pike A short pike, at one time carried by officers; a spontoon.

half-track personnel carrier An armored combination wheeled and tracklaying carrier which may or may not have armament. Excludes all half-track vehicles mounting major guns, howitzers, mortars, multiple guns, and combination guns.

half-track vehicle A combination wheeled and tracklaying vehicle in which the rear end is supported by a complete band track and the front end is supported on wheels; half-track. (Picture, next page.)

HAL HF-24 The HAL (Hindustan Aeronau-

half-moon clips. (*The Smithsonian Institution.*)

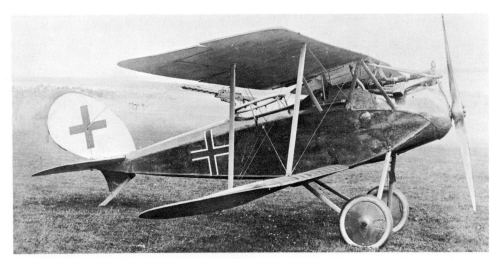

Halberstadt C.V. (*The Smithsonian Institution, National Air Museum.*)

half-track vehicle, the U.S. M-2 of World War II. (*U.S. Army.*)

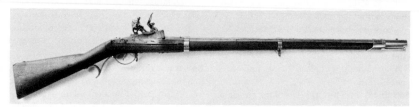

Hall rifle. (*The Smithsonian Institution, Military Service Institute Collection.*)

tics Ltd.) HF-24 Marut (Wind Spirit) is a single-seat fighter powered by two turbojet engines. It is armed with four 30mm Aden cannons and a retractable pack of 48 air-to-air rockets. First flown in 1961, the aircraft has a speed of Mach 1.02.

Halifax The British Handley Page Halifax was a heavy four-engine bomber first flown in 1939 and produced, in various versions, until 1945. In all, 6,176 aircraft were manufactured. The Halifax had a maximum speed of 278 mph, a range of 1,030 mi with maximum bombload, and armament consisting of nine .303 cal. Browning machine guns. It carried a bombload of 13,000 lb.

Halland A class of Swedish destroyers of

2,650 tons standard displacement completed in 1955–1956. They have a speed of 35 knots, a complement of 290 men, and armament consisting of one rocket launcher, four 4.7-in. guns, two 57mm and six 40mm antiaircraft guns, and eight 21-in. torpedo tubes.

hallebardier An archaic variant of "halberdier."

Hall rifle One of the first reasonably successful breechloading rifles, invented by the Americans Col. John H. Hall and William Thornton in 1811. It was first a flintlock, but was later adapted to the percussion system. It was developed as a .54 cal. weapon. Hall also designed the machines,

jigs, and gauges for manufacturing the rifle at the U.S. Harpers Ferry Armory and made it the first American firearm with completely interchangeable parts.

halt A stop in marching or walking or in any action.

Hamburg A class of German destroyers of 3,340 tons standard displacement completed in 1964–1968. They have a length of 439 ft, a beam of 44 ft, a speed of 35.8 knots, and a complement of 282 men. They are armed with four 3.9-in. guns, eight 40mm antiaircraft guns, two Bofors four-barrel depth-charge mortars, and five 21-in. torpedo tubes.

Hamilcar A British military tank or vehicle-carrying glider first flown in March 1942. It had a length of 68 ft, a wingspan of 110 ft, and a maximum towing speed of 150 mph. Towed by British bombers such as the Halifax, Lancaster, or Stirling, this glider could carry up to 17,500 lb of military cargo. It was built by the firm of General Aircraft Ltd. (G.A.L.).

Hamilcar X A powered version of the G.A.L. Hamilcar glider. It was first flown in February 1945.

hammer A metallic pivoted item, part of the firing mechanism of a firearm, designed to strike a firing pin or percussion cap and fire a gun.

hammerbox A noisemaking device for sweeping acoustic mines.

hammer cap A cap over the hammer of a gun.

hammerless A type of gun with the striking mechanism enclosed within the frame.

Hamp The Allied code name for a variation of the Japanese "Zero" fighter. See **Zeke.**

Hampden The British Handley Page Hampden was a four-seat twin-engine bomber first flown in 1936. It remained in service until 1943, by which time some 1,580 had been produced. It had a speed of 265 mph and a range of 870 mi with its

Hamburg. (*Ministry of Defense, Federal Republic of Germany.*)

maximum bombload of 4,000 lb. It was armed with four .303 cal. machine guns.

hanapier The front part of a cuirass or breastplate.

hand A member of a ship's crew. "All hands" means "every person on board."

hand-and-a-half sword A fifteenth- and sixteenth-century long sword with a straight blade and a long grip. It was ordinarily used with one hand, but two or three fingers of the left hand could be used for added weight to the blow.

hand cannon The earliest shoulder arm, developed about 1350. It consisted of a simple barrel tube with a touchhole and a straight handle. It was ignited with a burning match.

hand-fired parachute flare A complete, self-contained device which is fired from the hand and provides a rocket-projected parachute-borne pyrotechnic light.

hand grenade A grenade designed to be thrown by hand. Certain kinds may be projected by a rifle or carbine when the grenade is fitted with an adapter. In the seventeenth and eighteenth centuries, grenade launchers were developed as mortars or cup attachments for muskets to hurl hand grenades.

handgrip The handle or hilt of a sword or other edged weapon.

handguard A wooden part on a rifle to protect the shooter's hands from the hot barrel. Also, the part of a sword or dagger designed to protect the hand.

handgun A firearm carried in the hand. A pistol or a revolver.

handles Handles placed over the center of gravity on bronze cannons. Because of the sculptured shape of many early pieces, they were also called **dolphins,** which see.

Handley Page 0/100 A British four-place twin-engine bomber with a wingspan of 100 ft, a speed of about 95 mph, a bombload of eight 250-lb bombs or sixteen 112-lb bombs, and armament consisting of twin Lewis machine guns in the nose and dorsal locations and a fifth Lewis gun firing downward and to the rear through a trap in the bottom of the fuselage. It entered service in November 1916 and was subsequently used on several fronts.

Handley Page 0/400 A British bomber similar to the Handley Page 0/100, but with shorter engine nacelles. They were produced in greater numbers than the 0/100, some 800 having been ordered during the war period. The 0/400 carried a 1,650-lb bombload and flew at a speed of about 97 mph. It entered service in April 1917.

Handley Page V/1500 A British four-engine biplane bomber with a wingspan of 126 ft, a length of 64 ft, and a height of 23 ft. It was the first British four-engine bomber to go into production and was the

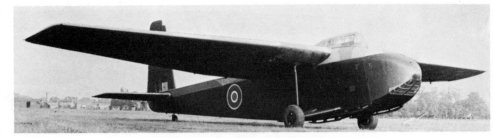

Hamilcar. (*The Smithsonian Institution, National Air Museum.*)

largest British aircraft produced between 1914 and 1919. Delivered too late in 1918 to see service in World War I, this aircraft was armed with six machine guns and could carry a 3-ton bombload. (Picture, next page.)

handstaff An obsolete term for a javelin.

hand-to-hand combat Combat between two persons in a close fight.

hand weapon A weapon, such as a pistol, knife, or sword, used with one hand. Distinguished especially from a shoulder weapon, in regard to firearms.

Handy Talky A U.S. two-way voice radio set of World War II. It was battery-powered, weighed 6 lb, and had a range of 1½ mi.

hangar A building in which aircraft and airships are stored and serviced.

hangar deck A deck, below the flight deck of a carrier, where aircraft are parked and serviced.

hanger A term for a short cutting sword of the seventeenth and eighteenth centuries, often applied to the side arm of infantry privates in the eighteenth century.

hangfire A brief, undesired delay in the functioning of an ammunition item after initiating action is taken. The term usually refers to a delay in the ignition of a propelling charge.

hangier A poniard once used by the Turks.

hangwire A length of wire connecting the fuze assembly of an aerial flare or bomb to

the structure of an aircraft. The wire removes the safety and arms the fuze after the flare or bomb has fallen the wire's length from the aircraft; in some flares it opens a parachute or stabilizing sleeve.

Hanover CL series German two-place single-engine biplane fighters developed in 1917. Used as escort fighters, they had a speed of about 102 mph and were armed with a forward-firing Spandau machine gun and a Parabellum gun for the observer. Various types were used through the end of World War I.

handgrip. (*The Smithsonian Institution, A. Lansing Collection.*)

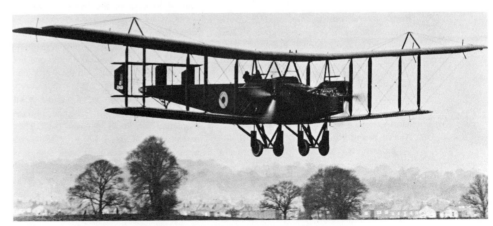

Handley Page 0/400. (*The Smithsonian Institution, National Air Museum.*)

Handley Page V/1500. (*The Smithsonian Institution, National Air Museum.*)

Hansa-Brandenburg W. 12. (*The Imperial War Museum.*)

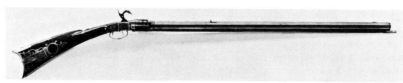

harmonica rifle. (*The Smithsonian Institution, Patent Office Collection.*)

Hanriot HD-1   A French single-seat single-engine biplane fighter that first appeared in mid-1916 and was later used by the Belgian and Italian Air Forces. It had a speed of 114 mph and was armed with one Vickers machine gun.

Hansa-Brandenburg C.I   An Austro-Hungarian two-place single-engine biplane designed by Ernst Heinkel. From the spring of 1916 until the end of World War I, this airplane was employed as a reconnaissance, artillery observation, and light bombing aircraft. It was armed with a Schwarzlose machine gun, flew at speeds up to 87 mph, and carried a bombload of 220 lb.

Hansa-Brandenburg CC   A German single-place single-engine (pusher) biplane flying boat introduced in 1917. It had a speed of about 108 mph and was armed with one forward-firing machine gun.

Hansa-Brandenburg D.I   A German single-seat single-engine biplane fighter that began production in mid-1916. Nicknamed *Spinne* (Spider), it had a speed of 116 mph and was armed with one 8mm machine gun mounted above the top wing to fire over the propeller. (The gun was inaccessible to the pilot during flight.) The design was carried forward in the **Phönix D.I to D.III** series, which see.

Hansa-Brandenburg KDW   A German single-place single-engine biplane seaplane adapted from the Hansa-Brandenburg D.I landplane. First flown in mid-1916, it had a speed of about 106 mph.

Hansa-Brandenburg W.12 and W.19   German two-place single-engine biplane seaplanes first flown in early 1917. They had a speed of about 100 mph and were armed with twin forward-firing Spandaus and one Parabellum machine gun in the rear cockpit. The W.19 was a somewhat larger version with a more powerful engine.

Hansa-Brandenburg W.29 and W.33   Two-place monoplane seaplane versions of the W.12 biplane seaplane. They had a

speed of about 110 mph.

hante   An ornamental pike with a banner attached.

Hanyang rifle   See **Chinese (Nationalist) 7.92mm Type 88 (Hanyang) rifle.**

haqueton   See **acton.**

harass   To worry or impede by repeated attacks.

harassing agent   A chemical agent, such as irritating gas or smoke, that forces troops to wear masks and so cuts down their efficiency. It produces irritating effects only.

harassing fire   Fire of less intensity than neutralization fire and designed to inflict losses or, by the threat of losses, to disturb the rest of the enemy troops, to curtail movement, and in general to lower morale. In naval terminology, sporadic shore bombardment to prevent enemy rest, regrouping, or movement.

harassment   An incident in which the primary objective is to disrupt the activities of a unit, installation, or ship, rather than to inflict serious casualties or damage.

harbor defense   The defense of a harbor or anchorage and its water approaches against (1) submarine, submarine-borne, or small surface-craft attack; (2) enemy mine-laying operations; and (3) sabotage. The defense of a harbor from guided or dropped missiles while such missiles are airborne is considered to be a part of air defense.

hard   A section of a beach especially prepared with a hard surface for amphibious operations. Also, an adjective meaning "full" or "extreme," as in the command "hard right rudder."

hard base   A launching base that is protected against a nuclear explosion.

hard beach   A portion of a beach especially prepared with a hard surface extending into the water and employed for the purpose of loading or unloading directly into or from landing ships or landing craft.

hardened site   A site constructed to withstand the blast and associated effects of a nuclear attack and likely to withstand a chemical, biological, or radiological attack.

hardstand   **1.** A paved or stabilized area where vehicles or aircraft are parked. **2.** An open ground area having a prepared surface and used for storage of materiel.

Hare The NATO code name for the Mil Mi-1 four-place helicopter developed for the Soviet Air Force and first flown in 1950.

Harke The NATO code name for the Mil Mi-10 heavy flying-crane helicopter derived from the Mi-6 (Hook). It can carry a payload of about 33,000 lb.

harmonica pistol or rifle A weapon having a number of barrels, in line, with a moving block. Also, a single-barreled weapon with a rectangular feed block holding several rounds. The barrels or the block makes the weapon resemble a harmonica.

harness Originally, an English word meaning "a suit of armor." It was from this sense of the word that the expression "to die in harness" evolved.

Harp The NATO code name for the Soviet Kamov Ka-20 antisubmarine helicopter first shown in 1961 and armed with a pair of air-to-surface missiles.

Harpon A French surface-to-surface missile with the same characteristics as the Nord 5210 (SS.11) but with an improved guidance system.

Harpoon A U.S. twin-engine light bomber developed by Lockheed during World War II and otherwise designated PV-2. Delivered to the U.S. Navy in March 1944, it was a variation of the **Ventura** (PV-1), which see.

Harpune The code name for the Germans' cover operations during World War II (May to August 1941) to divert attention from their attack on the Soviet Union. It was directed at leading the Allies to believe that an attack on England was imminent.

harquebus A fifteenth-century portable firearm with a matchlock operated by a trigger or, later, by a wheel lock or perhaps a flint.

harquebusade A volley from harquebuses.

harquebusier A soldier armed with a harquebus.

Harrier A British Hawker Siddeley single-seat V/STOL strike and reconnaissance jet fighter in service with the Royal Air Force and first flown in 1966. It has a speed of Mach 0.95 and can carry up to 5,000 lb of external weapons. A number of these aircraft have been purchased by the United States and are now in use by the Marine Corps.

Harry Hopkins Tank The popular name for the **British tank, light, MK VIII,** which see. This Vickers-built tank weighed 8½ tons and was armed with one 2-pounder gun and one Besa 7.92mm machine gun. It was introduced in 1942.

HAS An acronym for Helicopter Armament Subsystem.

hash mark Military slang for a service stripe.

hastati Spearmen who often formed the first line in the Roman order of battle.

hasty defense A defense normally organized while in contact with the enemy or when contact is imminent and time available for the organization is limited. It is characterized by improvement of the natural defense strength of the terrain by utilization of foxholes, emplacements, and obstacles.

hasty minefield A field of mines quickly laid as a protection against an enemy attack. When practicable it is laid in a definite pattern, as is a deliberate field, but measurements are approximate rather than exact.

hatch An access opening in the deck of a ship.

hatchway Steps leading from one deck to another aboard ship.

Harpoon. (*Lockheed Aircraft Corporation.*)

harquebus. (*The Metropolitan Museum of Art, gift of William H. Riggs, 1913.*)

Harrier. (*Hawker Siddeley Aviation Ltd.*)

Havoc. (*U.S. Air Force.*)

Hawk. (*U.S. Army.*)

Hatsuharu A class of Japanese 1,700-ton destroyers produced in the mid-1930s. They had a speed of 33 knots and a complement of 228 men and were armed with five 5-in. guns, two 13mm guns, and six 24-in. torpedo tubes. There were six ships in this class, all of which were lost in action during World War II.

hauberk In the eleventh, twelfth, and thirteenth centuries, a long tunic or coat of mail. It extended from the neck to the knees and was worn over a quilted gambeson which prevented bruises when the mail was struck. The sleeves at first reached only to the elbows, but later came down to the wrist and sometimes descended over the hand to form a glove.

hausse A type of graduated breech sight once used on ordnance.

hausse-col A piece of armor that protected the lower neck and chest. Later, a crescent-shaped piece of steel, like a gorget, worn over the uniform in front of the throat as a badge of rank.

haustement A body garment worn just under the armor.

havelock A light cloth covering for the cap. It hangs over the neck and is worn as protection from the sun. It is named after Sir Henry Havelock, the English general in the Sepoy Mutiny in 1857.

haversack **1.** A bag for carrying a soldier's rations on a march. It was worn on the side and suspended by a strap from the right shoulder. **2.** A leather bag used to carry cartridges to an artillery piece from an ammunition chest.

havildar In the British Indian armies, a native noncommissioned officer.

havildar major In the British Indian armies, a native sergeant major.

Havoc As first produced, this twin-engine attack bomber was designated the Douglas DB-7. First flown in late 1938, it was produced for the air forces of Britain and France. It was known to the RAF as the "Boston." This designation was changed to "Havoc" when the aircraft was modified for the use as a night fighter. When accepted for use by the USAAF, the designation "A-20 Havoc" was created. As an RAF two-seat night fighter, the airplane was equipped with as many as twelve .303 cal. machine guns. As a bomber, it was armed with nine .50 cal. machine guns and a 2,000-lb bombload.

Hawk **1.** (Homing All-the-Way Killer.) A small surface-to-air missile developed by Raytheon and first operational with U.S. Army and Marine Corps forces in July 1959. It is designed to destroy enemy aircraft flying anywhere between treetop height and operational altitude (its homing system is able to distinguish a moving target from the signals reflected by hills, buildings, trees, etc.). It has a length of 16.5

ft, a firing weight of 1,295 lb, a speed of Mach 2.5, and a range of 22 mi. **2.** The Curtiss P-36 Hawk was a single-seat single-engine fighter-interceptor developed for the U.S. Army Air Corps and first flown in April 1936. An export version, the Hawk 75A, was sold to France, the Netherlands, the United Kingdom, China, Thailand, and Argentina. The P-36 was equipped with a 1,200-hp engine and flew at speeds of 323 mph. It was armed with one .50 cal. machine gun and three .30 cal. machine guns. The British called this aircraft the "Mohawk."

Hawkeye The Grumman E-2 Hawkeye is a carrier-borne early-warning aircraft developed for the U.S. Navy and first flown in 1960. It has a crew of five and is powered by two piston engines. It has a maximum speed of about 400 mph.

Hawkins A class of British heavy cruisers of 9,800 tons standard displacement completed in 1919. They had a top speed of 29.5 knots, a complement of 800 men, and main armament consisting of seven 7.5-in. guns, four 4-in. guns, and four 21-in. torpedo tubes.

Hawkins Grenade An Allied grenade of World War II. It weighed 2¼ lb and could be buried like an antitank mine, thrown at moving vehicles, or used as a portable demolition charge.

Hawk Screech The NATO code name for a type of Soviet I-band antiaircraft artillery-fire-control radar.

Hayashio A class of Japanese submarines of 750 tons standard surface displacement completed in 1962–1963. They have a length of about 200 ft, a beam of 21.3 ft, a speed of 14 knots submerged, and a complement of 40 men. They are armed with three 21-in. torpedo tubes.

HBAR A U.S. Army 5.56mm heavy-barreled automatic rifle. It is built by Colt.

H-bomb See **hydrogen bomb.**

HBX Several explosive compositions used primarily for blast effect and carrying distinguishing nomenclature, such as HBX-1, etc. They differ in proportions and constituents, being essentially mixtures of TNT, RDX, and aluminum.

HD The U.S. military designation for the war gas **distilled mustard,** which see.

HE High explosive.

head **1.** The angle measured clockwise from an aircraft, ship, or ground vehicle between a reference datum point such as true or magnetic north and the longitudinal axis of the aircraft, ship, or ground vehicle. The respective angles are true heading and magnetic heading. **2.** The leading element of a column. **3.** The forward explosive-carrying section of a rocket or torpedo.

heading The direction in which a ship or aircraft is pointed.

Headlight The NATO code name for a type

Hawk. (*U.S. Air Force.*)

Hawkeye. (*Grumman Aerospace Corporation.*)

of Soviet G/H-band surface-to-air missile (SAM) and surface-to-surface missile (SSM) acquisition and fire-control radar.

headquarters The quarters of a commanding officer; the place from which orders issue.

headspace The distance between the face of the locked bolt or breechblock of a gun and some specified point in the chamber.

With guns designed for rimless bottle-necked cartridges, headspace is the space between the bolt face and a specified point on the shoulder of the chamber. With guns using rimmed cartridges, it is the space between the bolt face and the ridge or abutment in the chamber against which the rim rests. With guns using rimless straight-case cartridges, it is the space be-

Hayashio. (*Japan Defense Agency.*)

heavy bomber, a U.S. B-52 Stratofortress. *(U.S. Air Force.)*

heavy field artillery, U.S. 8-in. howitzers. *(U.S. Army.)*

tween the bolt face and ridge or point in the chamber where the mouth of the cartridge case rests.

Heartbreak Ridge The UN name for a topographic feature in the **Punchbowl** area, which see, of eastern Korea. It was the scene of heavy fighting in September and October 1951.

HEAT High-explosive antitank (cartridge).

heat seeker A guided missile or the like incorporating a heat-sensitive device for homing on heat-radiating machines or installations, such as an aircraft engine, blast furnace, etc.

HEAT-T High-explosive antitank (cartridge) with tracer.

heaume A large helmet, particularly in the thirteenth century, that was worn over a hood of mail or a steel cap. It covered the whole of the face, except the eyes, which were protected by small iron bars laid crosswise.

heavy antiaircraft artillery Conventional antiaircraft artillery pieces larger than 90mm, the weight of which in a trailed mount is greater than 40,000 lb.

heavy artillery Specifically, artillery, other than antiaircraft artillery, consisting entirely of howitzers and longer-barreled cannons of a caliber larger than the caliber of those included in the classification of medium artillery, i.e., 155mm.

heavy assault weapon A weapon capable of operating from ground or vehicle and used to defeat armor and other material targets.

heavy bombardment **1.** A bombardment of great intensity, especially one with large aerial bombs or other missiles. **2.** Formerly, short for "heavy bombardment aviation."

heavy bomber Any large bomber considered to be relatively heavy, such as, in 1955, a bomber having a gross weight, including bombload, of 250,000 lb or more, as in the case of the B-36 and the B-52. During World War II, bombers such as the B-17 and B-24 were considered heavy bombers. The B-29 was also classed as a heavy bomber, although at first it was considered a very heavy bomber.

heavy-case bomb Any high-explosive bomb in which the weight of the container is relatively large in proportion to the weight of the bursting charge.

heavy cavalry Cavalry was once divided into light and heavy cavalry, according to the size of the men and horses and the type and weight of the equipment and the armor used.

heavy cruiser A warship designed to operate with strike, antisubmarine-warfare, or amphibious forces against air and surface threats. The main battery consists of 8-in. guns; some CA's have Regulus capability. The full load displacement is approximately 21,000 tons. Designated as CA.

heavy drop An airdrop in which heavy articles, such as trucks or artillery pieces, are dropped by parachute.

heavy field artillery Field artillery of the largest calibers, such as the 155mm gun, the 6-in. gun, the 8-in. howitzer, and the 240mm howitzer.

heavy machine gun **1.** In army usage, any machine gun of relatively heavy weight, including .30 cal. water-cooled machine guns and .50 cal. machine guns. **2.** Any aircraft machine gun above .30 cal.

heavy rocket Any rocket-type weapon, without guidance equipment, which is 318mm in diameter or over.

heavy tank A full-track combat tank with a weight of from 56 to 85 tons.

heavy weapon Any antiaircraft weapon having a caliber of 120mm or greater. In the Army, "heavy weapons" is an infantry term applied to mortars, howitzers, long-barreled cannons, heavy machine guns, recoilless rifles, and other crew-served ordnance.

Hecht 1. The code name for a German air-to-surface guided missile of World War II. It weighed 308 lb, was 6.5 ft in length, and had a winged configuration. **2.** A class of World War II German midget submarines (Type XXVIIA) of about 11.75 tons displacement. They had a length of 34 ft, a beam of 5.5 ft, a surface speed of 5.75 knots (6 knots submerged), and a crew of two. They carried one mine or one 21-in. torpedo.

Heckler and Koch assault rifles West German assault rifles based upon the G3 rifle design. They consist of the HK32 and 32K (for the 7.62 × 39 Soviet M1943 cartridge) and the HK33 and 33K (in .223 cal.). The HK13 is a belt-fed light machine gun designed to fire the .223 cal. cartridge, and the HK21 is similar in 7.62mm NATO. The Model HK25 is a .50 cal. machine gun, and the Model HK54 is a 9mm Parabellum submachine gun.

hecklers Night-bombing aircraft which harass the enemy during darkness.

hedgehog 1. a. A portable obstacle, made of crossed poles laced with barbed wire, in the general shape of an hourglass. **b.** A beach obstacle, usually made of steel bars, channel iron, or the like, embedded in concrete and used to interfere with beach landings. **2.** A concentration of troops securely entrenched or fortified, with arms and defenses facing all directions. **3.** Hedgehog round, which see.

hedgehog round A small, mortarlike antisubmarine projectile. Called "7.2-in. high-explosive projector charge."

hedgehop 1. A slang term meaning to fly close to the ground, rising up over hedges, trees, houses, or other obstacles as they present themselves. **2.** In a less exact sense, to fly at a very low level; hence, hedgehopping.

hedgehopper A small, light airplane, especially one of the cub type.

hedgehopping bombing Bombing from a very low altitude.

heel 1. In small arms, the upward corner of the butt when the weapon is in firing position. **2.** The part of a sword blade next to the hilt; also, the handle end of a pike.

heelpiece Armor to protect the heel.

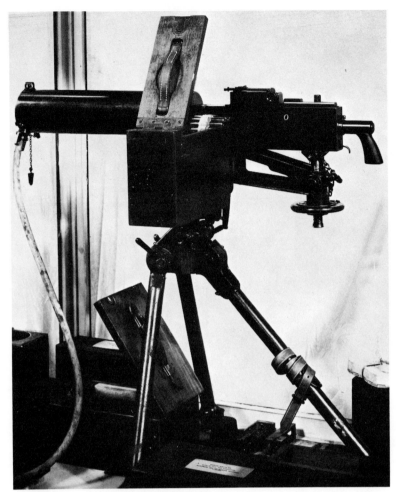

heavy machine gun. (*The Smithsonian Institution.*)

Hecht. (*Ministry of Defense, Federal Republic of Germany.*)

Heinkel He 59. (*Vereinigte Flugtechnische Werke—Fokker.*)

Heinkel He 111. (*Vereinigte Flugtechnische Werke—Fokker.*)

Heinkel He 114. (*Vereinigte Flugtechnische Werke—Fokker.*)

heelplate A metal plate on the butt end of a gunstock; a butt plate.

height finder A piece of radar equipment used to determine the height of aerial targets.

height of burst 1. The vertical distance from the earth's surface or target to the point of burst. **2.** For nuclear weapons, the optimum height of burst for a particular target (or area) is that at which it is estimated a weapon of a specified energy yield will produce a certain desired effect over the maximum possible area.

Heinie The nickname for "Heinrich" and the World War I Canadian and American slang term for a German soldier, airplane, or the like.

Heinkel He 59 A German four-seat twin-engine torpedo-bomber and reconnaissance, navigational training, and air-sea rescue twin-float seaplane. It was first flown in 1932, saw action as a night bomber in the Spanish Civil War, and was used in a variety of missions during World War II. It was armed with three 7.9mm machine guns and could carry one torpedo or a 2,200-lb bombload. It had a top speed of about 137 mph.

Heinkel He 60 A German two-seat single-engine shipboard reconnaissance twin-float seaplane first flown in 1933. It was used as a catapult plane on German cruisers until replaced by the Arado Ar 196. It was armed with one 7.9mm machine gun and flew at a speed of 149 mph.

Heinkel He 111 A German five-seat twin-engine medium bomber first flown in 1935 and produced in several versions. The Heinkel He 111H, in production at the beginning of World War II, was equipped with two 1,350-hp engines and flew at a top speed of 270 mph. It was armed with one 20mm cannon, one 13mm machine gun, and two or three 7.9mm machine guns, plus a bombload of about 6,000 lb. (The photograph also shows a Heinkel He 100, a single-seat fighter first flown in 1938. Only 12 production He 100's were made, but these were repainted with different insignia several times, and photographs were widely distributed. Allied Intelligence was led to believe, therefore, that this aircraft was in widespread use.)

Heinkel He 114 A German two-seat single-engine reconnaissance twin-float seaplane first flown in 1936 and operated from coastal seaplane stations during World War II. It was armed with two 7.9mm machine guns, carried two 110-lb bombs, and flew at speeds of 208 mph.

Heinkel He 115 A German three-seat twin-engine torpedo-bomber, minelaying, and reconnaissance twin-float seaplane first flown in 1936. It was the Luftwaffe's most important torpedo-bomber and reconnaissance seaplane during World War II. It was armed with two 7.9mm machine guns and could carry one 1,760-lb torpedo and two 550-lb bombs, or one 2,028-lb mine and two 550-lb bombs, or five 550-lb bombs. It flew at a top speed of 203 mph.

Heinkel He 162A Salamander Popularly known as the "Volksjäger" or "People's fighter," this German airplane flew for the first time in 1944, having progressed from the drawing board to flight tests in the unusually short time of 69 days. Powered by a turbojet engine with a 1,760-lb thrust, this airplane could reach speeds of 522 mph. It was armed with two 30mm cannons.

Heinkel He 177 See **Greif,** sense 1.

Heinkel He 219 Uhu This German airplane, called the "Uhu" (Owl), was first flown on November 15, 1942. It was produced in various versions throughout the war years, but it was basically a two-seat twin-engine, high-altitude night fighter. It was powered by two 1,900-hp engines, reached speeds of 416 mph, and was armed with two 30mm cannons in the wing roots, two 30mm cannons and two 20mm cannons in a ventral tray, and two 30mm cannons firing obliquely upward.

Helen The Allied code name for the Nakajima K1.49 heavy bomber used by the Japanese during World War II. It had a speed of 304 mph, a range of 1,000 mi with a 1,654-lb bombload, and armament consisting of one 20mm cannon and five 7.7mm machine guns. (Picture, next page.)

Helgoland A class of German battleships of 21,000 tons normal displacement completed in 1911–1912. They had a length of 546 ft, a beam of 93.5 ft, a speed of about 20 knots, and a complement of 1,106 men. The class included *Helgoland, Thüringen, Ostfriesland,* and *Oldenburg.* Main armament consisted of twelve 12-in. guns, fourteen 6-in. guns, and six 20-in. torpedo tubes.

helicopter An aircraft supported in flight by rotating airfoils instead of fixed wings and used for spotting, rescue, evacuation, transport, and general utility. Also called "pinwheel," "eggbeater," "whirlybird," "windmill," "copter," and "chopper."

helicopter assault force A task organization combining helicopters, supporting units, and helicopter-borne troop units for use in helicopter-borne assault operations.

helicopter drop point A designated point within a landing zone where helicopters are unable to land because of the terrain, but in which they can discharge cargo or troops while hovering.

helicopter landing site A designated subdivision of a helicopter landing zone in which a single flight or wave of assault helicopters lands to embark or disembark troops or cargo.

helicopter landing zone A specified

Heinkel He 115. (*Vereinigte Flugtechnische Werke—Fokker.*)

Heinkel He 162A Salamander. (*Vereinigte Flugtechnische Werke—Fokker.*)

Heinkel He 219 Uhu. (*Vereinigte Flugtechnische Werke—Fokker.*)

helicopter, the amphibious Sea King. (*U.S. Navy.*)

Helen. (*U.S. Air Force.*)

Hellcat. (*Grumman Aerospace Corporation.*)

helmet. (*The Smithsonian Institution.*)

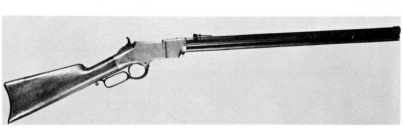

Henry .44 cal. rifle. (*The Smithsonian Institution, War Department Collection.*)

machine guns, plus two 1,000-lb bombs or six 5-in. rockets. **3.** A U.S. 76mm gun motor carriage M18, built by Buick and introduced in 1943 for use in tank-destroyer battalions. It had a crew of five and was armed with one 76mm gun and one .50 cal. antiaircraft machine gun. It weighed 19.5 tons and had a road speed of about 45 mph.

Helldiver   The Curtiss SB2C-1 Helldiver was a single-engine carrier-based dive bomber developed for the U.S. Navy and used during World War II. A USAAF version of the same airplane was designated the A-25. It had a speed of 281 mph and armament consisting of four .50 cal. and two .30 cal. machine guns. It carried a bombload of 1,000 lb and had a range of 1,750 mi. (An earlier Curtiss Helldiver was the F8C, a shipboard biplane fighter of 1932–1933.)

helm   The tiller of a ship. In giving orders to the quartermaster, the helm is referred to in the merchant service, but the rudder in the naval service.

helmet   Any special piece of headgear designed to protect the wearer from blows, shell fragments, crash injury, cold, etc. It is usually made of steel or leather and is lined or padded.

helmet liner   A detachable plastic or fiber inner layer of a metal helmet.

Henry .44 cal. rifle   A 15-shot lever-operated repeating rifle developed by the American Benjamin Tyler Henry from the Volcanic rifle and used during the American Civil War. It utilized a tubular magazine and served as the pattern for the Winchester rifles Models 1866 and 1873.

Henschel Hs 123   A German single-seat single-engine dive bomber and close-support aircraft first flown in 1935 and remaining in first-line service until 1944. It flew at a top speed of 212 mph and was armed with two 7.9mm machine guns and four 110-lb bombs.

Henschel Hs 129   A German single-seat twin-engine close-support and antitank aircraft first flown in 1939 and used during World War II. It flew at a maximum speed of about 253 mph and was armed with one 30mm cannon, two 20mm cannons, and six 7.9mm machine guns. It carried a bombload of about 550 lb.

HEP   High-explosive plastic projectiles.

HEPAT   High-explosive plastic antitank.

HEP-T   High-explosive plastic with tracer.

herbicide   A chemical compound which will kill or damage plants.

Herbstreise (German for "Autumn Journey")   A deception measure planned by the Germans early in World War II (fall 1940) to feign a landing on the northeast coast of Great Britain between Aberdeen and Newcastle before the **Seeloewe,** which see, landings in the south.

Hercules   **1.** The Lockheed C-130 Hercules

ground area for landing assault helicopters to embark or disembark troops or cargo. A landing zone may contain one or more landing sites.

helicopter team   The combat-equipped troops lifted in one helicopter at one time.

Hellcat   **1.** The air-launched version of the **Seacat,** which see.   **2.** The Grumman F6F Hellcat single-seat single-engine shipboard fighter and fighter-bomber was developed for the U.S. Navy and first flown in June 1942. It became operational in mid-1943 and replaced the **Wildcat,** which see. A total of 12,272 Hellcats were produced and were credited with the destruction of 5,156 enemy aircraft. The F6F-5 was equipped with a 2,000-hp engine and flew at speeds of 386 mph. It was armed with six .50 cal.

is a four-engine (turboprop) medium assault transport developed for the USAF and first flown in 1954. It flies at a speed of 368 mph and can carry 92 fully equipped troops. It has a range of 4,700 mi. **2.** A class of British light aircraft carriers of 14,000 tons standard displacement completed in the 1950s. They had a length of 695 ft, a flight-deck width of 80 ft, a speed of 24.5 knots, and a complement of 1,343 men. They carried 35 aircraft and were armed with twenty-eight 40mm antiaircraft guns.

herisson A long beam or bar set with a number of iron spikes and mounted on a pivot. It revolves when touched, always presenting a front of spikes. It was used to block up passages and approaches.

Hermes A British aircraft carrier (ex-*Elephant*) and originally the name ship of a class that included *Albion, Bulwark,* and *Centaur.* It has since been modified to a different type, now having a length of 744 ft, a width of 160 ft, a speed of 28 knots, and a complement of 2,100 men. It carries twenty aircraft and eight helicopters and is armed with two quadruple Seacat surface-to-air systems. It has a standard displacement of 23,900 tons. (An earlier British aircraft carrier also had the name *Hermes.* It had a normal displacement of 10,850 tons and was completed in 1924. It had flight-deck dimensions of 598 × 90 ft, a speed of 25 knots, and a complement of 664 men; it carried 15 aircraft.)

herse In fortifications, a door made of strong pieces of wood and stuck full of iron spikes. It was suspended on a rope, which was cut in order to effect a surprise blockage of passageways or gates.

hersillon A strong beam, stuck full of spikes, that is thrown into a breach made by an enemy to render it impassable.

HE-S High explosive with spotting charge.

HESD High explosive, self-destroying.

HESH High explosive, squash head. A type of antitank projectile.

HE-T High explosive with tracer.

HETSD High explosive with tracer, self-

Hercules. (*Lockheed Aircraft Corporation.*)

destroying.

Hetzer See **Baiter.**

hexanite A mixture of 60 percent TNT and 40 percent hexanitrodiphenylamine (hexite). It is slightly superior to TNT in brisance and power and is called *novit* by the Germans.

HGM-16 See **Atlas ICBM.**

HGM-25 See **Titan.**

H-hour **1.** The specific hour on D-day at which hostilities commence. **2.** When used in connection with planned operations, the specific hour at which an operation commences.

Higgins boats The World War II Allied nickname for LCVP's (landing craft, vehicle and personnel).

high-angle fire Fire delivered at elevations greater than the elevation of maximum range; fire the range of which decreases as the angle of elevation is increased. Typical of mortar and howitzer fire.

high-angle gun A cannon, such as an antiaircraft cannon, capable of firing at a high angle of elevation. (Picture, next page.)

High Card A former name of **Genie,** which see.

high command The supreme headquarters

or highest command echelon of a military or naval establishment, service, or field force.

high explosive Any powerful nonatomic explosive characterized by extremely rapid detonation and having a powerful disruptive or shattering effect. Typical examples are trinitrotoluene (TNT), amatol, tetryl, and picric acid.

high-explosive bomb Any aerial bomb charged with a high explosive; specifically, any such bomb that is dependent chiefly upon only its explosion, or blast effect, to create damage. In a broader sense, "high-explosive bomb" is a generic term encompassing armor-piercing bombs, general-purpose bombs, light-case bombs, and semi-armor-piercing bombs. A high-explosive bomb is distinguished from a chemical bomb or an atomic bomb and, in its specific sense, from a fragmentation bomb.

high-explosive plastic A high-explosive substance or mixture which, within normal ranges of atmospheric temperature, is capable of being molded into desired shapes; also called "plastic explosive" or "PE."

high-explosive-plastic antitank (HEPAT) A shaped charge and a high-explosive-

Hermes. (*Vickers Ltd.*)

high-angle gun, a U.S. 120mm antiaircraft gun. (*U.S. Army.*)

plastic charge, intended to produce jet penetration followed by a detonated plastic charge.

high-explosive-plastic projectile (HEP projectile) A thin-walled projectile filled with plastic explosive. The projectile is designed to "squash" against an armored target before detonation and to defeat the armor by producing spalls which are detached with considerable velocity from the back of the target plate. Also called "squash head," especially by the British.

high-explosive projectile A projectile with a bursting charge of high explosive.

High Fix The NATO code name for a type of Soviet airborne I-band radar.

high-order detonation An explosion that is complete and instantaneous.

high-speed submarine A submarine capable of submerged speeds of 20 knots or more.

high velocity As used in connection with artillery, small arms, and tank cannons, generally accepted to have the following meanings: **1.** The muzzle velocity of an artillery projectile of from 3,000 fps to, but not including, 3,500 fps. **2.** The velocity of small-arms ammunition between 3,500 and 5,000 fps. **3.** The velocity of tank-cannon projectiles between 1,550 and 3,350 fps.

high-velocity aircraft rocket (HVAR) Any large air-to-ground aircraft rocket specially designed for high velocities, especially such a rocket (6 ft in length) developed by the

United States during World War II. Nicknamed "Holy Moses," the HVAR was first used operationally in July 1944.

hilt The handle of a sword, dagger, or knife.

Hindenburg line The strong line of defense established by the Germans during World War I. Named after the German general Paul von Hindenburg, it was established in 1916 across the northeast portion of France.

Hip The NATO code name for the Mil Mi-8 transport helicopter in service with the Soviet Air Force and first seen in 1961. It has a range of 223 mi and a speed of 124 mph and can carry 24 persons.

HIPEG High-performance external gun. A 20mm gun pod for aircraft. It has a very high firing rate.

Hiroshima bomb The atomic-fission bomb dropped at Hiroshima, Japan, on August 6, 1945. It was the first atomic bomb to be used against an enemy.

Hispano-Suiza 20mm aircraft cannon Type 404 The designation of the British-made Type 404 cannon. It was equipped with an improved, disintegrating-link feed system and was produced by the firm of British Manufacture & Research Co. The latter initials gave rise to the nickname "Mark."

Hispano-Suiza 20mm gun An automatic weapon with a cyclic rate of fire of 800 to 1,000 rounds per minute and a range of 7,200 meters. This weapon is interchangeable with the M-2 .50 cal. machine gun on the M-114 command and reconnais-

sance carrier.

Hispano-Suiza Birkigt 20mm aircraft cannon Type 404 A French gas-operated air-cooled cannon with a rate of fire of 450 to 500 rounds per minute. It weighed 110 lb and was fed from a 60-round drum magazine. This weapon was designed by Marc Birkigt, of Hispano-Suiza, in the early 1930s. The British bought manufacturing rights and began production in late 1938.

Hispano-Suiza twin 30mm naval mounting A.32 A weapon that is presently in production in the United Kingdom. The weight of each gun is 343 lb, and the mount weighs 2,744 lb. The mounting provides a rate of fire of 1,300 rounds per minute.

hit **1.** Specifically, a blow or impact on a target by a bullet, bomb, or other projectile. **2.** An instance of striking something with a bomb, or the like, as in "he had two hits and one miss."

hitch A slang term for a period of enlistment.

Hiyo A Japanese aircraft carrier of 27,500 tons standard displacement commissioned in July 1942. It had a top speed of 25.5 knots and carried 54 planes. It was sunk by U.S. carrier planes during the Battle of the Philippine Sea in June 1944. It was the name ship of a class that also included the *Junyo,* which survived the war and was scrapped in 1947.

HL The U.S. military designation for the war gas **mustard-lewisite,** which see.

HN-1, HN-2, and HN-3 The U.S. military designations for the war gas **nitrogen mustard,** which see.

hobbies In the fourteenth century, small horses used by light cavalry.

hobilers Fourteenth-century light cavalrymen. They were later called "demilances."

hobits Small mortars mounted on gun carriages and having a bore of 6 to 8 in. They were in use before howitzers. The word derives from the German *Haubitz,* which became the standard term for "howitzer."

HOBO *H*oming *o*ptical *b*omb. A U.S. Air Force development consisting of an electrooptic guidance kit which is strapped onto a conventional 2,000-lb demolition bomb.

Hohentwiel The code name for a German airborne radar system of World War II used for locating ships and submarines. Also designated as Fug 200.

Holbein dagger A sixteenth-century dagger that stemmed from the baselard. It had a double-edged blade and an I-shaped hilt. In Nazi Germany this design was reintroduced in the regulation SS and SA daggers.

hold **1.** A cargo stowage compartment aboard ship **2.** To maintain or retain possession of by force, as a position of an area. **3.** In an attack, to exert sufficient pressure to prevent movement or redistribution of enemy forces. **4.** As applied to air traffic, to keep an aircraft within a specified space or location which is identified by visual or other means in accordance with air-traffic-control instructions.

holding attack An attack designed to hold the enemy in position, to deceive him as to where the main attack is being made, to prevent him from reinforcing the elements opposing the main attack, or to cause him to commit his reserves prematurely at an indecisive location.

holding pattern A pattern flown by an aircraft while awaiting landing instructions.

holding war A war in which both sides make little or no progress.

Holland A class of Dutch antisubmarine destroyers of 2,215 tons standard displacement completed in 1954–1955. They have a speed of 32 knots, a complement of 247 men, and armament consisting of four 4.7-in. guns, one 40mm antiaircraft gun, and two four-barreled depth-charge mortars.

hollow bastion A bastion in which the rampart extends only along the faces and the flanks.

hollow square A formation in which soldiers form a square to resist a charge.

holster A pocket-type device with a single compartment designed to be worn on a belt or shoulder harness, which may be furnished with it. It is used to carry a pistol, revolver, or the like. Other types of holsters are carried on horseback, usually in front of the saddle.

Holy Moses The U.S. 5-in. HVAR aircraft rocket of World War II. It weighed 140 lb and had a velocity of 1,300 fps. It had an accurate range of 1,000 yd, and the weight of its high explosive was 7.8 lb.

holy-water sprinkler Also called a "morning star," this was a shafted weapon with a head studded with spikes.

home The ability of a rocket or torpedo to direct itself to its target by guiding on heat radiations, radar echoes, radio waves, sounds, or other energy coming from the target.

home guards A military body for local or home defense.

homing **1.** Of a missile, one that homes. **2.** The action implied by the verb "to home." The homing of a missile may be active, semiactive, or passive. If active, the missile is both the originator and the receiver of radar signals, and as such it is subject both to detection and to jamming by window or tinsel. If semiactive, the missile uses a radar receiver to pick up the target from echoes of pulses sent out by a cooperating ground facility, in which case the missile's guidance system is subject to jamming but not readily to detection. If passive, the missile depends only on radiation from the target, such as noise, infrared rays, or electrostatic discharge, in which

Hispano-Suiza 20mm gun, mounted on a U.S. M-114 armored personnel carrier. (*U.S. Army.*)

case the missile's guiding system is more or less resistant to detection.

homing guidance A system by which a missile steers itself toward a target by means of a self-contained mechanism which is activated by some distinguishing characteristics of the target.

Honest John A U.S. large-caliber fin-stabilized field-artillery rocket, the development of which was started in 1950 by Douglas. The first type, produced in large numbers, was designated the MGR-1A. An improved version, the MGR-1B, has a smaller airframe, reduced weight, and in-

Honest John. (*U.S. Army.*)

Horsa glider. (*The Smithsonian Institution, National Air Museum.*)

creased performance. It has a length of 26 ft, a launching weight of 4,719 lb, and a range of 20 mi (at a speed of Mach 1.5). A conventional or nuclear (100 to 150 kilotons) warhead can be used.

Honey The British tank, light, M3A1. It was also called the "Stuart MK IV" and was the first U.S.-made tank to see action, having been used by the British against German forces in Libya in 1941. It had a crew of four and was armed with one 37mm gun and two .30 cal. machine guns. The weight was 14.3 tons, and the speed on roads was 34 mph. It was called "Honey" because British tank crews were so impressed with it.

honorable discharge A formal release of a soldier indicating honest and faithful service.

honors of war Certain privileges shown a defeated enemy, such as allowing him to march out of a town or camp armed and with colors flying.

hood 1. A covering for a mortar. **2.** The protective cover over a fuze of a projectile. **3.** The metal covering for a motor-vehicle engine.

Hood A British battle cruiser of 42,100 tons displacement completed in 1920. It had a length of 860 ft, a beam of 105 ft, a speed of 31 knots, and a complement of 1,241 men. It was armed with eight 15-in., twelve 5.5-in., and eight 4-in. guns, plus four 3-pounders and four 21-in. torpedo tubes.

Hoodlum The NATO code name for the Soviet Kamov Ka-26 twin-engine light helicopter first flown in 1965.

Hook The NATO code name for the Mil Mi-6 heavy transport helicopter in service with the Soviet Air Force and first seen in 1957. It carries up to 65 passengers or a maximum internal payload of 26,450 lb. It has a range of 620 mi and a speed of 155 mph.

hoop A cylindrical metal forging that is shrunk in rows on the tube of a built-up gun.

hoplite The infantry soldier of ancient Greece, typically armed with a 10-ft spear, a short cut-and-thrust sword, and a round shield worn on his left arm. He wore greaves and a bronze helmet and cuirass. The total weight of his armor and arms was about 70 lb and was carried by a slave when on the march.

horizontal bombing Bombing from an airplane in horizontal flight, as distinguished from dive bombing, glide bombing, toss bombing, etc. Also called "level bombing."

horizontal error The error in range, deflection, or radius which a weapon may be expected to exceed as often as not. The horizontal error of weapons making a nearly vertical approach to the target is described in terms of circular error probable. The horizontal error of weapons producing an elliptical dispersion pattern is expressed in terms of probable error.

horizontal range The distance measured horizontally between a gun and its target; specifically, in antiaircraft gunnery, the distance between the gun and a spot on the ground directly beneath the target.

Hormone The NATO code name for the Kamov Ka-25 twin-turbine flying crane helicopter in service with the Soviet Naval Air Force and first seen in 1967. It has a range of 250 mi and a speed of 136 mph.

It can carry a 4,400-lb payload.

horned scully An underwater beach obstacle designed to tear holes in the bottoms of boats.

Hornet 1. A U.S. aircraft carrier completed in the early part of World War II. It was a sister ship of the old **Enterprise,** sense 2, for details which see. It was sunk by the Japanese at the Battle of Vera Cruz in October 1942. **2.** A German tank destroyer of World War II. See **Rhinoceros.**

horn work In fortifications, two bastions connected by a curtain and located in front of a fortified place. It is connected to the main works by wings.

Horsa glider A British glider developed by the firm of Airspeed and used with success in the World War II airborne invasions of Sicily, Italy, Normandy, and Germany. It had a length of 67 ft, a wingspan of 88 ft, and a speed of 150 mph. It had a capacity of 30 troops. It was used, with U.S. Waco CG-4's, in the largest glider operation of World War II, an unsuccessful attempt to seize the Rhine crossing at Arnheim in September 1944.

horse Mounted soldiers; cavalry.

Horse The NATO code name for the Yakovlev Yak-24 tandem-rotor transport helicopter developed for the Soviet Air Force and first seen in 1955. It can carry a load of about 8,800 lb and flies at a speed of about 110 mph.

horse armor Also called "bard," complete horse armor would consist of chanfron (head), crinet (neck), peytral (breast), saddle, crupper (hindquarters), and flanchards (flanks). Such armor was made of either steel or leather.

horse artillery Light artillery that usually served with cavalry, with cannoneers mounted on horseback or riding the limber.

horse bow A short bow used by horsemen.

horseman's hammer A short-handled war hammer much used in the fifteenth and early sixteenth centuries.

horse pistol Any large pistol formerly carried by a horseman.

horseshoe A small round or oval fortification with a parapet.

Hosho Japan's first aircraft carrier, the

Hornet. (*U.S. Navy.*)

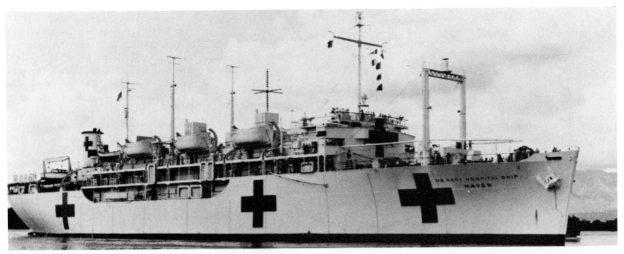

hospital transport, the U.S. Navy hospital ship *Haven*. (*U.S. Navy*.)

Hosho was completed in 1922. It had a displacement of 7,470 tons, a length of 551.5 ft, a flight-deck width of 74.5 ft, a speed of 25 knots, and a complement of 550 men. It carried 21 aircraft.

hospital ship An unarmed ship, marked in accordance with the Geneva convention and staffed and equipped to provide hospitalization for armed forces and also to evacuate casualties. Designated as AH.

hospital transport A transport provided with additional medical personnel and increased facilities for the evacuation of casualties.

hostage A person held as a pledge that certain terms or agreements will be kept. (The taking of hostages is forbidden under the Geneva convention of 1949.)

hostile track The classification assigned to a track which, on the basis of established criteria, is determined to be an enemy airborne, ballistic, and/or orbiting threat.

hostilities The state or situation under which armed conflict takes place or can be expected to take place.

hot Radioactive, as "hot" material.

Hot A tube-launched wire-guided antitank missile of a larger size and higher performance than the Milan missile. Built by Nord/Bölkow, it has an overall length of 4 ft 3 in, a weight of 55 lb, and a range of 13,100 ft.

hot caseman A man who disposes of the ejected cases from a gun using case ammunition. Also called "hot shellman."

Hotchkiss The name of several guns invented by the American inventer Benjamin B. Hotchkiss (1826–1885). He lived in France and invented numerous small arms, a small semiautomatic cannon, and an air-cooled gas-operated machine gun.

Hotchkiss 8mm machine gun Model 1914 A mass-produced Hotchkiss gun that was used in great numbers by France during World War I. U.S. troops were armed chiefly with this weapon when America entered the war. They later switched to a .30/06 cartridge, however. See **Hotchkiss machine gun Model 1914.**

Hotchkiss 8mm machine gun "Portative" A French gas-operated air-cooled machine gun with a rate of fire of 650 to 700 rounds per minute. It had a weight of 27 lb and was fed from 24- or 30-round strips.

Hotchkiss 9mm Parabellum submachine gun "Type Universal" This French-manufactured weapon is blowback-operated and has selective full automatic and semiautomatic fire. It has a cyclic rate of fire of 650 rounds per minute, an overall length of 30.6 in., and a barrel length of 10.8 in. It weighs 8.9 lb with a loaded 32-round magazine. This weapon was introduced in 1949 and was used to a limited extent in the Indochinese War.

Hotchkiss 11mm antiballoon gun A French gas-operated air-cooled machine gun with a rate of fire of 400 rounds per minute. It had a weight of 66 lb and was fed from a 24-round strip.

Hotchkiss 13.2mm machine gun M1932 This is a gas-operated weapon capable of automatic fire only. It has a cyclic rate of fire of 450 rounds per minute, an overall length of about 95 in., a barrel length of 65 in., and a weight, with tripod, of about 215 lb.

Hotchkiss 25mm cannon A weapon developed in the late 1930s and used for both aircraft and antiaircraft applications. This French-produced cannon was gas-operated and air-cooled and had a rate of fire of 150 to 180 rounds per minute (0.7-lb projectiles). It weighed 164 lb and was fed from a 10-round magazine.

Hotchkiss .303-in. light machine gun This weapon was widely used by the British during World War I. The basic version had a cyclic rate of fire of about 550 rounds per minute, an overall length of 46.75 in., a barrel length of 35.5 in., and a weight of about 27 lb. It had selective semiautomatic and automatic fire and was fed by metal strips holding 9, 14, or 30 rounds or by a belt holding 50 rounds.

Hotchkiss machine gun Model 1914 This was the principal machine gun used by the French during World War I and was still in service when France fell in 1940. It was used by the French in Indochina. Twelve U.S. divisions were equipped with this weapon in 1918, mostly in conversions to .30/06 cal. It was later used by Spain in 7mm and by China in 7.92mm. The weapon is gas-operated and capable of automatic fire only. It has a cyclic rate of fire of 450 to 500 rounds per minute, a muzzle velocity of 2,325 fps, and a feed device consisting of 24- or 30-round strips or a 250-round belt consisting of articulated strips.

Hotchkiss machine guns French gas-operated air-cooled weapons with a rate of fire of 600 rounds per minute. First fired in 1896, they had a weight (depending on mount) of between 20 and 55 lb and were fed from 24- or 30-round strips. First used by the French (Model 1897), they were also in service with various other countries, including Mexico, Spain, Norway, Belgium, and Japan.

Hotchkiss revolving cannon A cannon invented in 1875 that consisted of five barrels grouped around a common axis in its interior workings. The 37mm version of this weapon fired a round that weighed (complete) 2.42 lb and had a rate of fire of about 80 rounds per minute. Other versions of this crank-operated weapon were produced in 40mm, 47mm, and 57mm.

hot line A communication channel providing instantaneous communication without switching.

Hotpoint A U.S. Navy weapon with a nuclear warhead for use against planes on the ground.

hot shot Also called "heated shot." It was

Hound Dog. (*U.S. Air Force.*)

an old ordnance practice to heat shot until red-hot and then fire it at buildings and ships in order to set them on fire. There are records of hot shot being used in Cherbourg in 1418, and it continued in use until the mid-nineteenth century.

Hound The NATO code name for the Soviet Mil Mi-4 transport and general-purpose helicopter. It carries 14 troops and has a range of 250 mi at speeds up to 130 mph. It is used by the Soviet Air Force and by the air forces of about 12 other countries.

Hound Dog A turbojet-propelled air-to-surface missile designed to be carried externally on the B-52. It is equipped with a nuclear warhead and can be launched for either high- or low-altitude attacks against enemy targets, supplementing the inter-

nally carried firepower of the B-52. Designated as AGM-28. It weighs 9,600 lb and has a range of 500+ mi and a speed of 1,200+ mph. It is built by McDonnell-Douglas.

Hounskull (from the German *Hundsgugel*, or "dog's hood") A bascinet with a pointed visor bearing a resemblance to a dog's snout.

hourd A wooden gallery built outside the battlements of a fortification. It enabled the defenders to see the base of the walls and towers and to drop stones and other missiles on the approaching enemy.

Hovea 9mm submachine gun M.49 The standard submachine gun used by the Danish Armed Forces. It was developed in 1944 by the Swedish firm of Husqvarna, and is very similar to the Swedish M/45. It is blowback-operated and fires at full auto-

matic only. The cyclic rate of fire is 600 rounds per minute, and the muzzle velocity is approximately 1,250 fps. The weapon is 21.60 in. long with stock retracted, and the barrel is 8.50 in. long. With a 36-round magazine it weighs 8.85 lb. In the late 1940s the weapon went into production in Denmark.

hovering ceiling The highest altitude at which a helicopter is capable of hovering in standard atmosphere. It is usually stated in two figures: hovering in ground effect and hovering out of ground effect.

Høver M.F.11 A Norwegian single-engine three-seat reconnaissance twin-float seaplane first flown in 1931. It was armed with three .30 cal. machine guns and flew at speeds of 146 mph.

howitz An early name for a howitzer.

howitzer A complete projectile-firing weapon with bore diameter greater than 30 mm. The howitzer is used to deliver curved fire, with projectiles of lower muzzle velocities than those from the gun. The length of bore of a modern howitzer usually lies between 20 and 35 cal., and the maximum angle of elevation is about 65°. The muzzle velocity, and hence the range and curvature of the trajectory, can be altered by the use of any of several propelling charges or zones, thus permitting a howitzer to reach targets hidden from gunfire. In length, weight, and muzzle velocity the howitzer lies generally between the gun and the mortar. The first howitzers were invented at about the end of the sixteenth century, but were not widely used until the eighteenth century. Muzzle-loading models normally had a chamber of smaller diameter than the bore and were much shorter than guns.

H sight A rear gunsight consisting of two small uprights with a wire between them.

HT The U.S. military designation for the war gas **mustard-T,** which see.

hub cannon A cannon mounted through a propeller hub of an aircraft.

Hubuki A class of Japanese destroyers of about 1,700 tons standard displacement built in the late 1920s and early 1930s and used during World War II. They had a length of 371 ft, a beam of 34 ft, a speed of 34 knots, and a complement of about 240 men. They were armed with six 5-in. guns, four 47mm antiaircraft guns, and nine 21-in. torpedo tubes.

Hudson The Lockheed A-29 Hudson was developed in the late 1930s and first produced for the RAF (later for the USAAF). It is a twin-engine bomber with a speed of 250 mph, a range of 700 mi with a bomb-load of 1,400 lb, and armament consisting of six .50 cal. machine guns.

HueyCobra A high-speed close-support helicopter developed by Bell for the U.S. Army and Marine Corps and first flown in

howitzer, a U.S. 240mm howitzer as used during World War II. (*U.S. Army.*)

1965. It has a top speed of 219 mph and a range of 425 mi and is armed with a 7.62mm Minigun machine gun and other armament such as rockets, missiles, and 40mm grenade launchers.

HUK See **hunter-killer force.**

hulk An old ship with little but the hull remaining.

hull The body or shell of a ship or seaplane.

hull down Said of a ship that is just visible over the horizon.

Hun A derogatory word for a German, used in both World War I and World War II.

Hungarian 7.62mm rifle Model 48 A Hungarian copy of the Soviet 7.62mm Mosin Nagant rifles.

Hungarian 7.62mm submachine gun Model 48 A post-World War II copy of the Soviet 7.62mm submachine gun PPSh M1941.

Hungarian 7.65mm Frommer Stop pistol Model 19 This pistol was used by the Hungarians during World War I. Despite the model designation, the pistol appeared in 1912 and was adopted by the Hungarian Army prior to the war. It has an overall length of 6.5 in., a barrel length of 3.8 in., and a weight of 1.31 lb. It has a detachable box magazine with a capacity of seven rounds and a muzzle velocity of 920 fps.

Hungarian 7.65mm (and 9mm) pistol Model 37 This weapon appeared in 1937 and was made in large quantities for the Hungarian Army. It has an overall length of 6.8 in., a barrel length of 3.9 in., and a weight of 1.62 lb. It utilizes a seven-round detachable box magazine and has a muzzle velocity of 984 fps.

Hungarian 7.92mm Mannlicher rifle Model 43 This weapon was the Model 35 redesigned for German use. The caliber was changed from 8mm to 7.92mm, and provisions were made for a staggered-row Mauser-type box magazine and German-type bands and bayonet lugs. The Germans called it the **German 7.92mm rifle Model 98/40,** which see.

Hungarian 8mm machine gun Model 31 The **Solothurn 8mm machine gun Model 30S,** which see.

Hungarian 8mm Mannlicher Model 35 This weapon was adopted in 1935 and is a composite of several Mannlicher designs. It has an overall length of 43.7 in., a barrel length of 23.6 in., and a weight of 8.9 lb. It uses a fixed box magazine with a capacity of five cartridges and has a muzzle velocity of 2,395 fps. It fires the 8 × 56mm rimmed Model 31 cartridge.

Hungarian 9mm (Mauser) submachine gun Model 39 A submachine gun introduced in Hungary in 1934 and firing the 9mm Mauser cartridge. It employs a modified blowback system and has selective full automatic and semiautomatic fire. The cyclic rate of fire is 750 rounds per minute.

hub cannon, shown on a Messerschmitt Bf 110. (*U.S. Air Force.*)

Hudson. (*Lockheed Aircraft Corporation.*)

HueyCobra. (*Bell Helicopter Company.*)

It has an overall length of 41.25 in. and a barrel length of 19.65 in. The weight of the weapon, with a standard 40-round magazine, is 10 lb. It has a muzzle velocity of 1,475 fps.

Hungarian 9mm (Mauser) submachine gun Model 43 This weapon was a further development of the original Model 39 submachine gun and was manufactured in much larger numbers. It was produced from mid-1943 until the close of World War II. It utilizes the 9mm Mauser cartridge and has a muzzle velocity of about 1,450 fps. It operates on a retarded-blowback

system and has selective full automatic and semiautomatic fire. It has a cyclic rate of fire of 750 rounds per minute. The length with stock retracted is 29.50 in., and the barrel length is 16.70 in. Loaded with a 40-round magazine, the weapon weighs 9.8 lb.

Hungarian pistols Model 48 There are two Hungarian pistols with the designation "Model 48." One was developed after World War II and is a modified copy of the German 7.65mm Walther PP. The other weapon, in 7.62mm, is a copy of the Soviet Tokarev TT33 pistol. The latter is the

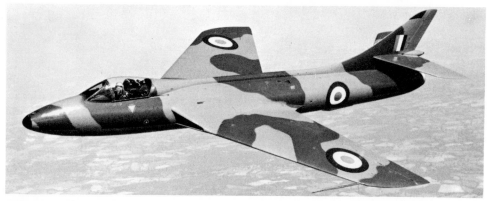

Hunter. (*Hawker Siddeley Aviation Ltd.*)

HUP Retriever. (*U.S. Navy.*)

Hurricane. (*The Smithsonian Institution, National Air Museum.*)

standard handgun of the Hungarian forces.

hung bomb A bomb which accidentally remains hanging to the bomb rack after the releasing action has been taken.

Hunter A British single-seat jet fighter and two-seat trainer built by Hawker and used, in a number of versions, by the forces of several countries. Later versions have a speed of Mach 0.92 and are armed with four 30mm Aden guns, with provisions for the external mounting of bombs, napalm, and rockets. The first aircraft in the series was flown in 1952.

Hunter 2 A U.S. Air Force program to equip AC-130 (Hercules) aircraft with battlefield illuminating devices, sensors, and 20mm Vulcan cannons.

hunter-killer force A naval force consisting of an antisubmarine-warfare carrier and associated aircraft and escorts combining specialized searching, tracking, and attacking capabilities of air and surface antisubmarine-warfare units operated as a coordinated group for the conduct of offensive antisubmarine operations in an area of submarine probability.

hunter-killer operation 1. A coordinated air and sea operation for seeking out and destroying an enemy submarine or submarines. **2.** A procedure developed by the U.S. Air Force in Korea in September 1952. In practice, a "Hunter" B-26 medium bomber would create a roadblock by dropping general-purpose, fire, and butterfly bombs, after which a "Killer" B-26 would be called in to attack the enemy vehicles backed up behind the roadblock.

HUP Retriever A single-engine tandem-rotored helicopter developed by Vertol Aircraft for the U.S. Navy and delivered until July 1954. It was used in shipboard operations such as rescue, observation, and transport. It accommodated a crew of two (plus up to four passengers) and had a speed of 105 mph.

hurdles In fortifications, a framework woven of willow or some other wood used to hold earth in defensive works. They are similar to gabions except that the pickets are in a straight line instead of a circle.

Hurricane The Hawker Hurricane was a single-seat fighter-interceptor and one of the mainstays of the Royal Air Force in the Battle of Britain. Design of this airplane was commenced in 1934, and the first production aircraft was delivered in October 1937. It was the first combat airplane to exceed a speed of 300 mph in level flight. During the Battle of Britain the Hurricane was used against German bombers, while Spitfires handled the escorting fighters. Earlier versions were powered with 1,030-hp engines and flew at speeds of 324 mph. Armament consisted of eight .303 cal. Browning machine guns. The aircraft had a wingspan of 40 ft, a length of about 32 ft, and a height of 8.75 ft.

Husky The World War II code name for the invasion of southeastern Sicily by the British Eighth and the U.S. Seventh Armies. It began on July 10, 1943.

hussar Originally, one of the bodies of light cavalry of Hungary or Croatia, and later a class of European light cavalry.

Hustler The General Dynamics B-58 Hustler is a three-seat four-jet supersonic strategic bomber developed for the USAF and first flown in November 1956. It has a speed of over Mach 2.0+ and a range of about 2,000 mi and is armed with one Vulcan 20mm cannon in a radar-operated tail mounting, plus nuclear or conventional weapons in a missile pod under the fuselage.

HVAP Hypervelocity armor-piercing, which see.

HVAPDS Hypervelocity armor-piercing discarding sabot, which see.

HVAPDSFS Hypervelocity armor-piercing discarding sabot fin-stabilized, which see.

HVAP-T Hypervelocity armor-piercing with tracer.

HVAR High-velocity aircraft rocket.

HVAT Hypervelocity antitank.

HWLS Hostile Weapons Locating System. The abbreviation for the U.S. AN/TPQ-28 mortar-locating radar. The term is also used generically to mean any system locating hostile weapons.

Hydra The U.S. Navy code name for all its studies and tests of sea-launched missile concepts and systems.

hydrofoil A surface vessel that utilizes submerged foils to lift the hull from the water, thus reducing drag and permitting greater speed.

hydrogen bomb A fusion bomb in which an isotope of hydrogen is made to fuse under intense heat, with a resultant loss of weight and release of energy. Also called "H-bomb."

hydrogen cyanide (AC) This war gas is a blood agent and has a very quick-acting casualty effect. AC interferes with the utilization of oxygen by the body tissues, and death occurs within 15 minutes after a

Hustler. (*General Dynamics.*)

lethal dosage has been received. This gas has an odor similar to that of peach kernels. Popularly called "prussic acid." See **blood agents.**

hydrostatic fuze A fuze employed with depth bombs or charges to cause underwater detonation at a predetermined depth. Initiation is caused by the ambient fluid pressure.

hypergolic fuel Fuel which will spontaneously ignite with an oxidizer, such as aniline with fuming nitric acid. It is used as the propulsion agent in certain missile systems.

hypersonic Of or pertaining to speeds equal to, or in excess of, five times the speed of sound.

hypervelocity As used in connection with artillery, small arms, and tank cannons, generally accepted to have the following meanings: **1.** The muzzle velocity of an artillery projectile of 3,500 fps or more. **2.** The muzzle velocity of a small-arms projectile of 5,000 fps or more. **3.** The muzzle velocity of a tank-cannon projectile in excess of 3,350 fps.

hypervelocity armor-piercing (HVAP) A term used to designate a type of artillery projectile consisting of a core of extremely hard, high-density material, such as tungsten carbide, contained within a light-weight carrier called a "sabot." Because of the low total weight, hypervelocity is obtainable within the allowable pressure of the gun tube. The velocity is rapidly lost, but at short ranges the projectile is effective against armor.

hypervelocity armor-piercing discarding sabot (HVAPDS) A term used to designate a type of HVAP projectile in which the sabot is designed so that it will become separated from the core a short distance from the muzzle of the gun. Separation of the sabot from the core results in the core's becoming the free-flight projectile with lowered air resistance.

hypervelocity armor-piercing discarding sabot fin-stabilized (HVAPDSFS) A term used to designate a type of HVAPDS projectile in which the free-flight projectile (core) is stabilized in flight by fins rather than by spin.

I

I The abbreviation for "fighter" (*Istrebital*), used in the designations of Russian aircraft from 1925 to 1945, as in I-15, I-17, I-26, etc.

I 1 Class (Type J1) A class of Japanese 1,970-ton submarines produced in the mid-1920s. They made 8 knots submerged, had a complement of 80 men, and were armed with six 21-in. torpedo tubes and two 5.5-in. deck guns.

I 9 Class A class of 2,434-ton Japanese submarines produced in 1939–1940. They were equipped with a seaplane hangar and catapult fitted to the hull casing in front of the conning tower. They carried one aircraft (see **Glen**). The submarines had a complement of 100 men and were armed with six 21-in. torpedo tubes and one 5.5-in. deck gun.

I 15 Class A class of Japanese 2,198-ton submarines produced between 1939 and 1942. They were originally designed to carry a seaplane in a hangar in front of the conning tower, but many of these were later removed. This class had a length of 356 ft, a submerged speed of 8 knots, a complement of 100 men, and armament consisting of six 21-in. torpedo tubes and one 5.5-in. deck gun. Of 20 produced, 19 were lost in action during World War II.

I 16 Class A class of 2,184-ton Japanese submarines produced in the late 1930s. They had a length of 358 ft, a submerged speed of 8 knots, and a complement of 100 men; they were armed with eight 21-in. torpedo tubes, one 5.5-in. deck gun, and one midget Type A submarine. All five ships of this class were lost during World War II.

I 40 Class A class of Japanese submarines produced in 1942–1943; they were somewhat improved versions of the I 15 Class submarines. Specifications are the same. All six ships of this class were lost in action during World War II.

I 46 Class A class of Japanese submarines that were similar to the I 16 Class submarines but did not carry midget submarines.

I 52 Class The last major submarine type produced by Japan toward the end of World War II. They had a displacement of 320 tons, a length of 174 ft, a submerged speed of 13 knots, a complement of 22 men, and armament consisting of two 21-in. torpedo tubes. Most of this class of 38 were scuttled or scrapped after the war.

I 121 Class A class of Japanese 1,142-ton submarines that were practically identical to the ex-German U 125, from which they were developed. They had four torpedo tubes and a complement of 75 men.

I 153 and I 156 Classes Classes of Japanese submarines of 1,635 tons displacement produced in the middle to late 1920s. They were armed with eight 21-in. torpedo tubes and had a complement of 60 men.

I 164 and I 165 Classes Classes of Japanese submarines produced in the late 1920s and early 1930s. They were armed with six 21-in. torpedo tubes and had a complement of 60 to 75 men.

I 168 Class A class of Japanese 1,400-ton submarines produced in the mid-1930s. They had a submerged speed of 8 knots, a length of 384 ft, a complement of 70 men, and armament consisting of six 21-in. torpedo tubes. All six ships of the class were lost to action during World War II. The name ship of the class (*I 168*) sank the U.S. carrier *Yorktown* at the Battle of Midway in June 1942.

I 176 Class A class of Japanese 1,630-ton submarines produced between 1941 and 1943. They were armed with six 21-in. torpedo tubes and one 4.7-in. deck gun, made a speed of 8 knots submerged, and had a complement of 80 men. None of the 10 submarines in the class survived World War II.

IAGS Improved Aircraft Gun System.

I.A.R.80 A single-seat single-engine fighter-interceptor and fighter-bomber and the only fighter designed and manufactured by Rumania during World War II. First flown in 1938, it had a speed of 317 mph and was armed with two 20mm cannons, four 7.7mm machine guns, and two 220-lb bombs.

ICBM *Intercontinental ballistic missile.* A missile able to travel over 5,000 mi.

Idaho. (*U.S. Navy.*)

ice mine A waterproof mine placed in or under river or lake ice and detonated by a pressure device on the surface or exploded deliberately to break the ice.

ICS Integrated Communications System. A system that consisted of 53 sites in Vietnam and provided the U.S. Army with strategic and tactical communications. It was linked to worldwide communications systems.

Idaho Two battleships were named for the state of Idaho. The first *Idaho* was commissioned in 1908 and was the sister ship of the old *Mississippi*. Both had a normal displacement of 13,000 tons, a length of 382 ft, a beam of 77 ft, a speed of 17 knots, and a complement of 834 men. Main armament consisted of four 12-in. guns, eight 8-in. guns, and two 21-in. torpedo tubes. (In 1914, *Idaho* was turned over to the Greek government, where it became the coastal defense ship *Lemnos*. It was sunk by the German Luftwaffe in April 1941.) The second *Idaho* was a ship of the *New Mexico* class and was commissioned in 1919. It saw considerable service in the Pacific theater during World War II.

identification **1.** In air defense and antisubmarine warfare, the process of determining the friendly or hostile character of a detected contact. **2.** In arms control, the process of determining which nation is responsible for the detected violations of an arms-control measure.

Identification Friend or Foe (IFF) A system using electronic transmissions to which equipment carried by friendly forces automatically responds, for example, by emitting pulses, thereby distinguishing itself from equipment of enemy forces. It is a method of determining the friendly or unfriendly character of aircraft or ships by other aircraft or ships and by ground forces using electronic detection equipment and associated Identification Friend or Foe units.

identification panel A strip of cloth or other material employed by ground troops in using the identification-panel code.

identification-panel code A code that is displayed with identification panels by ground troops to identify themselves to friendly aircraft.

identification tag Either of two metal tags usually worn about the neck by a person in the military service. Often called "dog tags," they are used in identifying wounded or killed personnel. Each tag has the name, service number, blood type, religious preference, and tetanus record of the wearer stamped upon it.

IFF **Identification Friend or Foe,** which see.

IFS The U.S. Naval designation for an inshore fire-support ship.

igloo space The area in an earth-covered structure of concrete or steel designed for the storage of ammunition and explosives.

Igloo White The U.S. code name for the use of airdropped sonobuoys over Southeast Asian land infiltration routes to detect enemy troop movements, with signals processed by U.S. Air Force EC-121 aircraft.

igniter **1.** Any device—chemical, electrical, or mechanical—used to ignite. **2.** A specially arranged charge of a ready-burning composition, usually black powder, used to assist in the initiation of a propelling charge. **3.** A device containing such a composition and used to amplify the initiation of a primer in the functioning of a fuze.

igniting fuze A fuze designed to initiate its main munition by an igniting action, as compared with the detonating action of a detonating fuze. This type of fuze is suitable only for munitions using a main charge of low explosive or other readily ignitable material.

IJN Imperial Japanese Navy.

Ikara An Australian rocket-propelled missile launched from a ship and directed at submarine targets. When near its target, it releases an American Type 44 lightweight torpedo, which has an acoustic detection and homing system. The missile has an overall length of 11 ft and a wingspan of 5 ft. (Picture, next page.)

Ikarus IK-2 A single-seat single-engine high-wing fighter designed and built in Yugoslavia in the late 1930s. It was armed with one 20mm cannon and two 7.92mm machine guns and flew at a maximum speed of 266 mph.

IL A designation for Soviet aircraft designed by Sergei Vladimirovich Ilyushin.

IL-2 The two-seat assault bomber developed for the Soviet Air Force during World War II and called by them the "Stormo-

Ikara. (*Royal Australian Navy.*)

vik." This aircraft had a speed of about 280 mph and was armed with two 23mm cannons, two 7.6mm machine guns, and eight 56-lb rockets. Later it carried the NATO code name "Bark."

IL-3 A Soviet twin-engine bomber and torpedo carrier used during World War II and developed from a transport aircraft produced in the late 1930s. It had a speed of 265 mph and carried a 4,400-lb bombload.

IL-4 An improved version of the IL-3, this aircraft carried a bombload of 5,950 lb and was armed with two machine guns. It was later given the NATO code name "Bob."

IL-10 See **Beast.**

IL-12 See **Coach.**

IL-14 See **Crate.**

IL-18 See **Coot.**

IL-28 See **Beagle** (ex-Butcher).

IL-62 See **Classic.**

Illinois A U.S. battleship commissioned in 1901. It had the same specifications as the first battleship **Alabama,** which see.

illuminating fire Gunfire employing illuminating projectiles delivered to silhouette the enemy, aid observation, and facilitate movements of friendly troops.

illuminating grenade A hand grenade or rifle grenade designed to be placed or projected and to provide illumination by a burning action. It may be used also as a trip flare or as an incendiary device.

illuminating mortar A lightweight system for projecting a parachute-borne illuminating flare. A typical system is the Bofors-built **Lyran,** which see.

illuminating projectile A projectile, with a time fuze, that releases a parachute flare at any desired height. It is used for lighting

up an area and is popularly called "star shell."

Illustrious A class of British aircraft carriers of 23,000 tons standard displacement commissioned in 1940–1941. Included were *Illustrious, Formidable, Victorious,* and *Indomitable.* They had an overall length of 753 ft, an extreme flight-deck width of 96 ft, a top speed of 30.5 knots, and a complement of 1,600 men. They carried 55 aircraft and were armed with 120 antiaircraft guns (total barrels).

Ilya Mourometz V A Russian five-place four-engine biplane bomber designed by Igor Sikorsky and first flown early in 1914. A follow-on of the **Sikorsky Grand** (which see), this airplane had a wingspan of 102 ft, a speed of about 85 mph, armament consisting of three or four machine guns (although up to seven could be carried, including a turret in the tail), and a typical bombload of 992 to 1,543 lb. They were used in bombing raids over Germany and Lithuania between 1915 and 1917.

IM Gasoline thickened with isobutyl methacrylate and used in incendiary, or fire, bombs.

I.M.A.M. Ro.43/44 An Italian single-float seaplane used either as a single-seat fighter or as a two-seat reconnaissance aircraft and first flown in 1935. It was the standard catapult aircraft aboard Italian warships. Armament consisted of two 2.7mm machine guns. The aircraft had a top speed of 193 mph.

immediate air support Air support to meet specific requests which arise during the course of a battle and which, by their nature, cannot be planned in advance.

immediate message A category of precedence reserved for messages relating to situations which gravely affect the security of national or allied forces or populace and which require immediate delivery to the addressee.

Immelmann turn An aircraft maneuver in which an airplane completes half a loop and then rolls half a complete turn. It amounts to a reverse turn. It was named after Max Immelmann, a German aviator (1890–1916).

impact-action fuze A fuze that is set in action by the striking of a projectile or bomb against an object.

impact area An area in which projectiles or bombs strike or are expected to strike.

impact fuze A fuze, as for a bomb, in which the action is initiated by the force of impact; sometimes called a "contact fuze."

impact point The point on the drop zone where the first parachutist or airdropped cargo item should land.

Impavido A class of Italian guided-missile armed destroyers of 3,201 tons standard displacement completed in 1963–1964. They have a speed of 34 knots, a complement of 344 men, and armament consisting of one Tartar launcher, two 5-in. guns, four 3-in. guns, and two triple torpedo tubes.

Impetuoso A class of Italian destroyers of 2,755 tons standard displacement completed in 1958. They have a speed of 34 knots, a complement of 393 men, and armament consisting of four 5-in. guns, sixteen 40mm guns, one three-barreled depth-charge mortar, and two triple torpedo tubes. This was the first class of Italian destroyers constructed since World War II.

Implacable A class of British aircraft carriers of 23,000 tons standard displacement commissioned in 1944. The class (modified *Illustrious* class) consisted of *Implacable* and *Indefatigable.* They had an overall length of 766 ft, an extreme flight-deck width of 96 ft, a top speed of 32.5 knots, and a complement of 1,650 men. They carried 70 aircraft and were armed with 125 antiaircraft guns (total barrels).

implosion weapon A device in which a quantity of fissionable material, less than a critical mass, has its volume suddenly decreased by compression so that it becomes supercritical and an explosion can take place. The compression is achieved by means of a spherical arrangement of specially fabricated shapes of ordinary high explosive which produce an inwardly directed implosion wave, the fissionable material being at the center of the sphere.

INA .45 cal. submachine gun Model 953 A Brazilian submachine gun made under Madsen license by the Industria National de Armas S.A. This weapon is a slightly modified version of the Danish submachine gun Model 1946. The Brazilian variation fires the .45 cal. ACP cartridge, while all Madsen weapons fire the 9mm Parabellum cartridge.

inactivate To place a ship in the reserve fleet.

in battery A tube or barrel is *in battery* when it has fully returned from recoil upon its cradle. A tube *out of battery* is one which has not fully returned from recoil.

incapacitating agent BZ See **BZ**.

incapacitating chemical agents Incapacitating chemical agents are capable of producing physiological or mental effects that prevent exposed personnel from performing their primary military duties for a significant period of time. There is, however, complete recovery from these effects. The incapacitating agents fall into two general groups: those which produce temporary physical disability, such as paralysis, blindness, or deafness, and those which produce temporary mental aberrations. The incapacitating agents suggest employment where military necessity requires control of a situation but where there is good reason for not harming the surrounding population or even the troops. They also suggest covert uses either to confuse defense or retaliatory forces or to affect the rationality of an important leadership group at some particularly crucial point. See **BZ**.

incapacitating gas See **incapacitating chemical agents**.

incendiary **1.** Any chemical agent designed to cause combustion, used especially as a filling for certain bombs, shells, bullets, or the like. **2. Short for "incendiary bomb," "incendiary bullet," etc.**

incendiary bomb A bomb designed to be dropped from an aircraft to destroy or reduce the utility of a target by the effects of combustion. It contains an incendiary mixture and is designed to penetrate and destroy relatively noncombustible targets such as buildings and fortifications. There are two basic types: scatter and intensive. The scatter bomb contains a thickened fuel mix which is projected from the bomb case upon impact and adheres to the target while it burns. The intensive bomb is composed of metallic fuels which burn at very high temperatures at the point of contact.

incendiary-bomb cluster A cluster of incendiary bombs, so arranged that more than one bomb can be suspended and dropped from a single station of a bomb rack of an airplane.

incendiary bullet A bullet having an incendiary charge, used especially against flammable targets.

incendiary grenade A hand grenade designed to be filled with incendiary materials or used primarily for incendiary purposes.

incidents Brief clashes or other military disturbances generally of a transitory nature and not involving protracted hostilities.

increase twist A gain twist in a gun barrel.

increment An amount of propellant added to, or taken away from, a propelling charge of semifixed or separate-loading ammunition to allow for differences in range. Increments are commonly packed in propellant bags made of cartridge cloth, as for the main propelling charge.

indefatigable A British 18,750-ton battle cruiser completed in 1911. It and its sister ship, *New Zealand*, had a length of 580 ft, a complement of 800 men, and armament consisting of eight 12-in. and sixteen 4-in. guns, plus three 21-in. torpedo tubes. They had a speed of 29 knots. *Indefatigable* was sunk by German gunfire at the Battle of Jutland on May 31, 1916. Also, the name of a British aircraft carrier. See **Implacable**.

indented line A serrated fortification line with alternate salient and receding angles; each face flanks the front of the next, thus defending it.

Independence A class of U.S. light aircraft carriers (CVL) of 11,000 tons standard displacement commissioned in 1943. Included were *Independence, Princeton, Belleau Wood, Cowpens, Monterey, Langley, Cabot, Bataan,* and *San Jacinto*. They had an overall length of 622 ft, an extreme flight-deck width of 109 ft, a top speed of 33 knots, and a complement of 1,569 men. They carried 45 aircraft and were armed with 24 antiaircraft guns (total barrels). These ships were laid down as light cruisers of the *Cleveland* class but were completed as carriers.

Independent Air Force In World War I, a British strategic air force set up in June 1918, composed of bomber units of the RAF, but never a part of the RAF. It was under the command of Maj. Gen. Sir Hugh M. Trenchard, and its targets were enemy airdromes, munition plants, and other war-making installations.

independent company A company not incorporated in any regiment.

Indian .303 cal. Vickers-Berthier machine gun This weapon is similar in appearance and construction to the Bren, the main differences being in the breechblock, the gas cylinder arrangement, the sight, the feed, and the hold-open device. The weapon has an overall length of 45.5 in., a barrel length of 23.9 in., and a loaded weight of 24.4 lb. It is fed by a 30-round box magazine and has a muzzle velocity of 2,400 fps.

Indiana Two battleship classes have been named for the state of Indiana. The first *Indiana* was the name ship of a class of ships that also included *Massachusetts* and *Oregon*. Commissioned in 1895–1896, they had a normal displacement of 10,288 tons, a length of 350 ft, a beam of 69 ft, a speed of 15 knots, and a complement of 473 men. Main armament consisted of four 13-in., eight 8-in., and twelve 3-in. guns. The second *Indiana* was the name ship of a class of battleships of about 35,000 tons standard displacement completed in 1942. The class also included *Alabama, Massachusetts,* and *South Dakota*. They had a length of 680 ft, a beam of 108 ft, a speed of 28 knots, and a wartime complement of 2,500 men. They were armed with nine 16-in. and twenty 5-in. guns, plus fifty-six 40mm and forty 20mm antiaircraft guns. *Indiana* saw considerable service in the Pacific theater during World War II.

Indianapolis A class of U.S. heavy cruisers (CA) of about 9,800 tons standard displacement completed in 1932–1933. The class consisted of *Indianapolis* and *Portland*. They had a length of 584 ft, a beam of 66 ft, a speed of 33 knots, and a complement of about 1,000 men. Main armament consisted of nine 8-in. and eight 5-in. guns. Four aircraft were carried. (Picture, next page.)

indications (intelligence) Information in various degrees of evaluation, all of which bears on the intention of a potential enemy to adopt or reject a course of action.

Illustrious. (*The Imperial War Museum.*)

Indianapolis. (*U.S. Navy.*)

Inflexible. (*The Imperial War Museum.*)

indirect fire Gunfire delivered at a target that cannot be seen from the gun position or firing ship.

indirect laying Aiming a gun either by sighting at a fixed object, called the "aiming point," instead of at the target or by using a means of pointing other than a sight, such as a gun director, when the target cannot be seen from the gun position.

individual equipment Equipment, such as arms, packs, kits, and the like (exclusive of clothing), issued to an organization for distribution to its individual members for use in carrying out the mission of the organization.

Indomitable A British aircraft carrier of 23,500 tons standard displacement completed in 1941 and extensively refitted and modernized in 1948–1950. It had a length of 754 ft, a beam of 97.75 ft, a speed of 30.5 knots, and a complement of 1,600 men. It carried 65 aircraft.

inert Descriptive of the condition of a munition, or component thereof, which contains no explosive, pyrotechnic, or military chemical agent.

inert ammunition Any shell, bomb, grenade, cartridge, rocket, or the like with its explosive charge, fuze, or other component essential to its normal functioning removed. Usually collective. Ammunition with all explosives removed is usually described as completely inert or totally inert.

inertia fuze A kind of impact fuze that functions by inertial force. Upon impact of the projectile to which an inertia fuze is attached, either a striker will fly forward against a primer or detonator, or the primer or detonator will move forward against a fixed firing pin.

inertial guidance A guidance system designed to project a missile over a predetermined path, wherein the path of the missile is adjusted after launching by devices wholly within the missile and independent of outside information. The system measures and converts accelerations experienced to distance traveled in a certain direction.

infantry A branch of an army in which soldiers are organized, trained, and equipped to fight on foot.

infantryman An infantry soldier.

infernal machine A disguised or cleverly concealed explosive device, usually intended for sabotage.

infiltration 1. The movement through or into an area or territory occupied by either friendly or enemy troops or organizations. The movement is made, whether by small groups or by individuals, at extended or irregular intervals. When used in connection with the enemy, the term implies that contact is avoided. 2. In intelligence usage, placing an agent or other person in a target area in hostile territory. This usually involves crossing a frontier or other guarded line. Methods of infiltration are black (clandestine), gray (through a legal crossing point but under false documentation), and white (legal).

Inflexible A British warship of about 11,880 tons displacement that was launched in 1876. One of the first iron, steam-propelled warships, it had a length of 320 ft, a beam of 75 ft, and a speed of about 14 knots. It was armed with four 80-ton guns. *Inflexible* and two other British battleships, *Ocean* and *Irresistible*, were lost within 1 hour and 15 minutes when they struck mines in the Dardanelles on

March 18, 1915.

in-flight refueling Air refueling, from one aircraft to another, during the course of a flight.

in-flight report A standard form of message whereby aircrews report mission results while in flight. Also used for reporting any other tactical information sighted of such importance and urgency that the delay, if reported by normal debriefing, would negate the usefulness of the information.

informant **1.** A person who, wittingly or unwittingly, provides information to an agent, a clandestine service, or the police. **2.** In reporting, a person who has provided specific information and is cited as a source.

information (intelligence) Unevaluated material of every description, including that derived from observations, reports, rumors, imagery, and other sources which, when processed, may produce intelligence.

informer A person who intentionally discloses to police or to a security service information about persons or activities he considers suspect, usually for a financial reward.

infrared imagery Imagery produced as a result of sensing electromagnetic radiations emitted or reflected from a given target surface in the infrared portion of the electromagnetic spectrum (approximately 0.72 to 1,000 microns).

initial aiming point The point on which a gun is sighted to establish a reference line from which direction angles for targets are measured. From this reference line, other aiming points that give the direction of the targets are measured off. This method of aiming is used in indirect laying.

initial lead The amount a gun is pointed in front of, above, or below a moving target when opening fire. This amount allows for the distance the target will travel while the projectile is in flight.

initial mass The mass of a rocket missile at the beginning of its flight.

in-flight refueling of a Cessna A-37B. (*Cessna Aircraft Company.*)

initial point **1.** A point on the ground, identified visually or by electronic means, over which an aircraft begins a bomb run, a run over a drop zone, or the like. **2.** An assembly point at which a march or movement begins.

initial radiation The radiation, essentially neutrons and gamma rays, accompanying a nuclear explosion and emitted from the resultant fireball; immediate radiation.

initial velocity The velocity of a projectile at the moment it ceases to be acted upon by propelling forces. For a gun-fired projectile the initial velocity, expressed in feet or meters per second, is also called "muzzle velocity." It is obtained by measuring the velocity over a distance forward of the gun and correcting back to the muzzle for the retardation in flight. For a rocket a slightly fictitious value is used. The fictitious initial velocity is the velocity at the launcher which would produce the actual velocity at the point of burnout if there were no thrust. The initial velocity of a bomb dropped from an airplane is the speed of the airplane.

inshore fire-support ship (IFS) An amphibious warfare vessel of shallow draft capable of providing heavy fire cover for military landings.

insignia Any distinctive device that identifies a person or object as to nationality, organization, office, rank, or branch of service, such as a shoulder patch, aircraft markings, or the like.

Insomnia The code name of U.S. Navy night operations by carrier-based planes against rail communications and truck movements in North Korea during the Korean conflict. They started in the spring

insignia. Three U.S. Navy Skyhawk aircraft. (*U.S. Navy.*)

intercontinental ballistic missile, the U.S. Titan. (U.S. Air Force.)

of 1952 and used irregular launching schedules to catch the enemy by surprise.

inspection The examination of personnel, organizations, activities, or installations to determine their effectiveness and economy of operation, adequacy of facilities, readiness to perform assigned missions, or compliance with directives; the examination of materiel to determine quality, quantity, or compliance with standards.

inspector general An officer at the head of a department or system of inspection. He reports on the state of readiness, effectiveness, and efficiency, and he is accountable for the activities of inspection, security, and investigation.

installation A military facility in a fixed or relatively fixed location, together with its buildings, building equipment, and subsidiary facilities such as piers, spurs, access roads, and beacons.

instrument bombing Bombing by the use of radar or other instruments without visual reference to the ground.

insurgency A condition resulting from a revolt or insurrection against a constituted government which falls short of civil war.

Integrated Satellite This U.S. Air Force 1,800-lb, 23-ft-tall satellite was developed to be positioned south of the Soviet–Red China ICBM test-launch corridors, where it would track fired ICBM's and provide trajectory and probably target information. It would provide the United States with a 30-minute warning of long-range ballistic-missile attack. It uses a variety of sensors, including infrared, visual, electrooptic, laser, ultraviolet, and radiation detection devices, and possibly electromagnetic sensors, depending upon the type of mission flown. In addition to the detection of missile launches, it can also detect nuclear explosions and meteorological phenomena and provide reconnaissance. It incorporates under one program the technologies of several Air Force reconnaissance-detection-warning satellite programs.

intelligence The product resulting from the collection, evaluation, analysis, integration, and interpretation of all information which concerns one or more aspects of foreign countries or areas and which is immediately or potentially significant to the development and execution of plans, policies, and operations.

intelligence estimate An appraisal of the elements of intelligence relating to a specific situation or condition with a view to

intermediate-range ballistic missile, the U.S. Pershing missile. (U.S. Army.)

determining the courses of action open to the enemy or potential enemy and the probable order of their adoption.

interceptor A manned aircraft utilized for the identification or engagement of airborne objects. An interceptor may or may not be equipped with radar to assist in the interception.

intercept point A computed point in space toward which an interceptor is vectored to complete an interception.

intercontinental ballistic missile (ICBM) A ballistic missile with a range capability of from about 3,000 to 8,000 nautical miles.

intercontinental bomber A bomber capable of flying from one continent to targets on another without landing either in going out or return. It may be refueled while in the air.

interdiction The prevention or destruction of, or interference with, enemy movements, communications, and lines of communication, as by gunfire, shelling, or bombing; the action of making it very difficult for the enemy to move from one place to another.

interdiction bombing Bombing done for purposes of interdiction.

interdiction fire Gunfire delivered in the process of interdiction; specifically, the fire placed on a specified place, as a railyard, assembly area, crossroad, or the like, and intended to prevent its effective use.

interior ballistics The science of the movement of projectiles within the bore of a gun, with the combustion of powder, development of pressure, etc., to determine the effect of such factors as weight, size, shape, rifling, and so forth. Also called "internal ballistics."

interior crest In fortifications, the line of the junction of the interior and superior slopes.

interior flanking angle In fortifications, that angle which is formed by the meeting of the line of defense and the curtain.

interior side In fortifications, the line drawn from the center of one bastion to that of the next.

interior slope The slope toward the inner part of the fortification work; the earth forming the rampart or parapet.

intermediate-range ballistic missile (IRBM) A ballistic missile with a range capability of from about 1,500 to 3,000 mi.

internal ballistics See **interior ballistics**.

International Code A code adopted by many countries to facilitate sight communication between persons of different nations. The code uses some 26 flags, each standing for a letter of the Latin alphabet. They may be used in different combinations, each signifying a certain message, or used as letters to spell out a word or sentence. If flags are not used, the international Morse code is employed.

interphone, intercom A telephone apparatus by means of which personnel can talk to one another within an aircraft, tank, or ship or during an activity.

interrupted fire Automatic fire delivered in short series of bursts.

interrupter gear A synchronizing gear for machine guns, so called because it interrupts the firing mechanism of the gun or guns to allow a propeller blade to pass the muzzle.

interval **1.** The space between adjacent groups of ships or boats measured in any direction between the corresponding ships or boats in each group. **2.** The space between adjacent individuals, ground vehicles, or units in a formation that are placed side by side, measured abreast. **3.** The space between adjacent aircraft measured from front to rear in units of time or distance.

intervalometer **1.** An electrical device used in bombing, by means of which data are preset in order to drop a desired number of bombs at a constant predetermined interval. **2.** In aerial photography, a device connected to an automatic camera; it can be preset to make exposures at desired constant intervals of time.

Intrepid **1.** The name of a captive balloon used by the Union Balloon Corps during the Civil War. **2.** A U.S. aircraft carrier of the **Essex** class, which see.

Intruder The Grumman A-6A Intruder is a two-seat twin-engine carrier-based low-level attack bomber developed for the U.S. Navy and first flown in 1960. It is powered by two 9,300-lb thrust engines and flies at a top speed of over 620 mph. A typical weapon load is thirty 500-lb bombs, in clusters of three, or two Bullpup missiles and three 2,000-lb general-purpose bombs.

intruder mission A mission, especially a night mission of fighters or attack bombers, sent into enemy territory to destroy hostile aircraft, to attack airdromes, or otherwise to dislocate the enemy air forces.

intruder operations Offensive operations by day or night over enemy territory with the primary objective of destroying enemy aircraft in the vicinity of their bases.

Invader The Douglas A-26 Invader was a twin-engine three-place attack bomber developed for the USAAF and first flown in 1942. It had a speed of 359 mph, a range of 700 mi with 5,000 lb of bombs, and armament consisting of eighteen .50 cal. machine guns. A version of this aircraft, the YB-26K, is still in service with the USAF as a counterinsurgency bomber. It carries a weapon load of 8,000 lb and has a speed of 375 knots.

invasion The act of invading a place or a country with the use of warlike or hostile force.

invasion currency Currency of a distinctive design prepared by an invading power and declared legal tender in the invaded territory.

Invincible A class of British 17,250-ton battle cruisers completed in 1908. The class included *Invincible, Inflexible,* and *Indomitable,* all of which had a length of 562 ft, a complement of 750 men, and armament consisting of eight 12-in. guns, sixteen 4-in. guns, and three 18-in. torpedo tubes. They had a speed of 28 knots. In the Battle of Jutland in May 1916, *Invincible* was hit by German gunfire and was blown in half in the ensuing explosion. There were only five survivors.

inworks The inner defenses of a fortification.

Iowa Two battleships were named for the State of Iowa. The first *Iowa* was commissioned in 1897 and was the only ship of its type. It had a displacement of 11,346 tons, a length of 360 ft, a beam of 72 ft, a speed of 17 knots, and a complement of 683 men. Main armament consisted of four 13-in., eight 8-in., and four 4-in. guns. *Iowa* fired the first shot in the Battle of Santiago de Cuba during the Spanish-American War and accounted for the destruction of several Spanish ships. The second *Iowa* was the name ship of a class of battleships that also included *Missouri, New Jersey,* and *Wisconsin.* They had a length of 888 ft, a beam of 108 ft, a speed of 35 knots, and a wartime complement of 2,700 men. They were armed with nine 16-in. guns, twenty 5-in. guns, and eighty 40mm antiaircraft guns. They were originally equipped with catapults for two aircraft, which were later

Intruder. (*U.S. Navy.*)

Invader. (*U.S. Air Force.*)

replaced with observation helicopters. *Iowa* saw considerable service in combat, both in the Pacific theater during World War II and in Korea.

IPDSMS Improved Point Defense Surface Missile System. Also known as "NATO Sea Sparrow," this system uses modified AIM-7E Sparrow 3 missiles and an integrated fire-control–launch system. It provides surface-to-air point defense for sur-

Iowa. (*U.S. Navy.*)

Iroquois. (*Bell Helicopter Company.*)

face ships.

IRA   Irish Republican Army.

IRAN   Inspect, Repair as Necessary. A U.S. Air Force system of periodic maintenance and modification.

Iranian 7.92mm rifle Model 1938   This weapon is the Czech (Mauser) model 98/29. It is made in both a rifle and a carbine version. The rifle has an overall length of 49.2 in., a barrel length of 29.13 in., and a weight of 9.1 lb. It has a muzzle velocity of about 2,800 fps and features a staggered-row nondetachable magazine with a capacity of five rounds.

IRBM   Intermediate-range ballistic missile,

which see.

IRDU   Infrared detection unit. See **infrared imagery.**

Irgun (Irgun Zvai Leumi)   The Irgun Zvai Leumi, or National Military Organization, consisted of militant, rightist Jewish Zionists in Palestine. They organized to fight for a free Israel.

IRIS   Infrared intruder system. A small, self-contained and compact intruder detector.

ironclad   A wooden ship clad with iron plates, especially during the American Civil War.

Iron Duke   A class of British battleships of

25,000 tons standard displacement completed in 1914. There were four ships in the class: *Iron Duke, Emperor of India, Benbow,* and *Marlborough.* They had a length of 620 ft and main armament consisting of ten 13.5-in., twelve 6-in., and four 3-pounder guns, plus four 21-in. torpedo tubes. They had a speed of 22 knots.

Iron Hand   A U.S. Air Force code name applied to all electronic-countermeasure equipment introduced aboard U.S. aircraft during the Southeast Asia conflict to meet the threat posed by Soviet-built surface-to-air missiles (SAM) used in North Vietnam. It also involved firing Shrike antiradiation missiles at launching complexes.

iron hat   A headpiece of iron or steel. Originally, it was a general term, but by the seventeenth century it had come to refer to a steel variant that was a copy of the contemporary civilian hat.

Iron Hump   A World War II nickname for the French coast, as given by Allied pilots. So called because of the intensity of radar-controlled flak. See **Wurzburg.**

iron sight   Any metallic gunsight, such as a blade sight, as distinguished from an optical or computing sight.

Iron Triangle   A term used in the Korean conflict to describe an area bounded by Chormon, Kumhwa, and Pyongyang, Korea; the central anchor of North Korea's defense line north of the 38th parallel. It was the hub of a communication and supply network.

Iroquois   A utility helicopter developed by Bell for the U.S. Army and first flown in 1956. It has a range of 327 mi and a speed of 148 mph and carries a pilot and 12 troops.

irregular forces   Armed individuals or groups who are not members of the regular armed forces, police, or other internal security forces.

irritant gas   A nonlethal gas that causes irritation of the skin and a flow of tears. Any one of the family of tear gases used for training and riot control. See **tear gas.**

Irving   The code name for the Nakajima J1N1-S Gekko (Moonlight) twin-engine two-seat night fighter developed for the Japanese Naval Air Force and first flown in May 1941. It was on an aircraft of this type that Commander Yasuna Kozono of the 251st JNAF Air Corps devised a system of obliquely mounted 20mm cannons that fired forward and upward (or downward) at an angle of 30°. This system was adopted by the German Luftwaffe and called by them *Schräge Musik* (Jazz Music). The J1N1-S had a speed of 315 mph and was armed with four 20mm cannons.

Ise   A class of Japanese battleships of about 29,990 tons standard displacement built in 1916–1918 and reconstructed in 1936. Used during World War II, they had a length of

Irving. (*U.S. Air Force.*)

683 ft, a beam of 94 ft, a speed of 23 knots, and a complement of 1,360 men. They carried twelve 14-in., eighteen 5.5-in., and eight 5-in. guns, plus three seaplanes. There were two ships in the class, *Ise* and *Hyuga*, and both were sunk during World War II.

island The structure above the flight deck of a carrier.

isopropyl   methylphosphonofluoridate See **sarin.**

Israeli 9mm Parabellum revolver A modified copy of the Smith & Wesson Military and Police pistol. Because it is chambered for the 9mm Parabellum cartridge, it is necessary to use two 3-shot clips (moon clips).

Israeli 9mm Parabellum UZI submachine gun See **UZI 9mm submachine gun.**

Italian 6.5mm machine gun Model 1914 (Revelli) See **Revelli 6.5mm machine gun Model 1914.**

Italian 6.5mm Madsen machine gun Italy has used five models of the Madsen machine gun, ranging from the Model 1908 to the Model 1931. See **Madsen machine guns.**

Italian 6.5mm and 7.35mm rifles and carbines See **Mannlicher Carcano 6.5mm carbine Model 1891, 1891 TS; Mannlicher Carcano 6.5mm carbine Model 1938, 1938 TS; Mannlicher Carcano 6.5mm rifle Model 1891; Urannlicher Carcano 6.5mm rifle Model 1938; Mannlicher Carcano 7.35mm carbine Model 1938, 1938 TS;** and **Mannlicher Carcano 7.35mm rifle Model 1938.**

Italian 9mm Parabellum submachine gun Model TZ-45 A blowback-operated weapon utilizing the 9mm Parabellum cartridge and having selective full automatic and semiautomatic fire. The cyclic rate of fire is 550 rounds per minute. The weight of the weapon is 8.90 lb with a 40-round magazine. The length of the weapon, with stock retracted, is 21.50 in., and the barrel length is 9 in. It was introduced in 1944 and produced for a limited time in 1945. It was adopted in a modified form by Burma after World War II. As manufactured there, it is called the "BA52."

Italian 9mm Parabellum Villar Perosa (Revelli) submachine gun See **Villar Perosa 9mm (Glisenti) submachine gun Model 1915** and **Villar Perosa 9mm (Glisenti) submachine gun O.V.P.**

Italian 47mm antitank gun 47/27 A World War II weapon with a weight of 582 lb and a projectile weight of 5.3 lb. It fired fixed ammunition and had a range of 3,800 yd.

Italian 47mm self-propelled gun Semovente 47/32 This system was introduced in 1941 for use with tank-destroyer units of armored divisions. It was equipped with one 47mm gun, had a weight of 7.5 tons, and could travel at a speed of about 25 mph on roads.

Italian 75mm gun 75/27 A World War

Italian 90mm antiaircraft gun 90/53. (*U.S. Army.*)

II weapon with a weight of 1.1 tons and a projectile weight of 14 lb. It fired fixed ammunition and had a range of 11,200 yd.

Italian 75mm howitzer A World War II weapon with a projectile weight of about 14 lb and a range of 8,200 yd.

Italian 75mm self-propelled howitzer Obice DA 75/18 Semovente A howitzer mounted on an M13/40 tank chassis. Introduced in 1940, this system was employed with armored divisions. It had a crew of four and was armed with one 75mm howitzer, caliber length 18. It weighed 14.4 tons and traveled at a speed of about 20 mph on roads.

Italian 90mm antiaircraft gun 90/53 A World War II weapon with a weight of 5.7 tons and a projectile weight of 22 lb. It fired fixed ammunition and had an effective ceiling of 32,000 ft.

Italian 90mm gun model 41 A World War II weapon with a projectile weight of about 22 lb and an estimated range of 15,000 yd.

Italian 90mm self-propelled gun 90/55 Semovente This system, introduced in

1942, consisted of a 90mm AA gun on an M14/41 tank chassis. It was armed with a 90mm gun Model 41 and was used for ground targets only. It weighed 17 tons and traveled at speeds of about 20 mph on roads. This gun was almost the equal of the German 88mm gun and could destroy any Allied tank of its time.

Italian 100mm howitzer 100/17 A World War II weapon with a weight of 1.5 tons and a projectile weight of 30 lb. It fired fixed ammunition and had a range of 10,125 yd.

Italian 102mm antiaircraft gun A World War II weapon that fired a 29-lb projectile to an effective ceiling of 26,000 ft.

Italian 104mm gun 104/40 A World War II weapon with a weight of 4.4 tons and a projectile weight of 38 lb. It fired fixed ammunition and had a range of 19,250 yd.

Italian 105mm pack howitzer Model 56 This weapon entered service with the Italian Army in 1957. It has a weight of 2,843 lb, a barrel length of 7 ft 2 in., and a range of 10,575 meters (with a projectile weight

Italian 90mm self-propelled gun 90/55 Semovente. (*U.S. Army.*)

Iwo Jima. (*U.S. Navy.*)

Italian tank, medium, Carro Armato Tipo M13-40. (*U.S. Army.*)

of 33 lb). The howitzer is serviced by a crew of six. This weapon is used by the forces of at least 17 countries.

Italian 127mm/54 antiaircraft gun COMPACT An Italian shipboard gun with a weight of 32 tons, a maximum rate of fire of 45 rounds per minute, and a projectile weight of 70 lb.

Italian 149mm gun 149/35 A World War II weapon with a weight of 7.84 tons and a projectile weight of 101 lb. It fired fixed ammunition and had a range of 19,100 yd.

Italian 149mm howitzer 149/20 A World War II weapon with a weight of 6.2 tons and a projectile weight of 90 lb. It fired fixed ammunition and had a range of 16,000 yd.

Italian 149mm self-propelled gun Model 35 Semovente 149 A system that was introduced in 1942 and employed by artillery divisions. It was armed with one 149mm gun Model 35, caliber length 40.

Italian 152mm gun 152/47 A World War II weapon with a weight of 18.3 tons and a projectile weight of 103 lb. It fired separate-loading ammunition and had a range of 21,200 yd.

Italian 210mm howitzer 210/28 A World War II weapon with a weight of 17.4 tons and a projectile weight of 225 lb. It fired separate-loading ammunition and had a range of 17,500 yd.

Italian Beretta weapons See **Beretta 7.62mm Nato rifle BM59 series, Beretta**

7.65mm automatic pistol Model 1915, Beretta 7.65mm automatic pistol model 1915–1919, Beretta 7.65mm automatic pistol Model 1931, Beretta 9mm automatic pistol Model 1934, Beretta 9mm (Glisenti) automatic pistol Model 1923, Beretta 9mm (Glisenti) submachine gun Model 1918, Beretta 9mm Parabellum automatic pistol Model 1951, Beretta 9mm Parabellum submachine gun Model 12, Beretta 9mm Parabellum submachine gun Model 1938A, Beretta 9mm submachine gun Model 38/42, Beretta 9mm Parabellum submachine gun Model 38/44, and **Beretta 9mm submachine gun Model 38/49.**

Italian main battle tank M60 A1 These are tanks of the U.S. M60 A1 design that have been manufactured under license in Italy. Several hundred are now in service with the Italian Army.

Italian tank, medium, Carro Armato Tipo M13-40 This tank was introduced in 1940 for employment by armored divisions. It had a crew of four and was armed with one 47mm gun and four 8mm Breda machine guns. It weighed 15.4 tons and traveled at a speed of about 20 mph on roads.

Iwo Jima A class of U.S. amphibious assault ships of about 17,000 tons standard displacement commissioned between 1961 and 1969. They have a length of 592 ft, a beam of 84 ft, a flight-deck width of 105 ft, a speed of 20 knots, and a complement of 528 men. In addition to the ship's complement, 2,090 troops are carried. They are deployed in the ship's 20 to 24 helicopters.

IX U.S. Navy unclassified miscellaneous ships.

J

J-3 A Soviet Navy and Army supersonic-speed surface-to-surface missile with a range of 450 to 600 mi.

J-12 A U.S. Army and Marine Corps bayonet knife.

JAAF Japanese Army Air Force.

jack Soft body armor of the fifteenth to the seventeenth centuries. It often consisted of a coat that was quilted and covered with leather and was worn particularly by horsemen. Sometimes metal rings or plates were sewn in for added protection. The sixteenth-century example shown is made of plates of iron laced between two folds of canvas.

Jack The code name for the Mitsubishi J2M2-7 Raiden (Thunderbolt), a single-seat single-engine fighter-interceptor developed for the Japanese Naval Air Force and first flown in March 1942. It was equipped with a 1,820-hp radial engine and flew at speeds up to 371 mph. It was armed with four 20mm cannons. (Picture, next page.)

jackboot A boot worn in the seventeenth and eighteenth centuries by cavalry soldiers. They were made of thick leather and were sometimes lined with plates of iron.

jacket **1.** A cylinder of steel covering and strengthening the breech end of a gun or howitzer tube. **2.** The water jacket on some machine guns. **3.** See also **bullet jacket.**

Jack Johnson See **Black Maria.**

Jackpot Joint Airborne Communications Center–Command Post. A U.S. Air Force system to provide a joint-task-force commander with the control of forces during limited warfare. Once in the contingency area, the four shelters of Jackpot can be off-loaded from C-130 aircraft and operated on the ground. One shelter houses a command post; another, a communications center; and the remaining two, power generators, air conditioners, antennas, and collapsible fuel tanks. The units may be used aboard aircraft through utilization of a special antenna system for voice air-to-ground communications.

jaculum A light Roman javelin.

Jagdstaffel A German term for a fighter squadron.

jager One of a body of light infantry armed with rifles.

Jaguar A single-seat light tactical-support jet aircraft developed by BAC (UK) and Breguet (France) and first flown in 1968. It is in service with the British and the French Air Forces, flies at a speed of Mach 1.7, and is armed with two 30mm Aden cannons and under-wing armament such as missiles and bombs.

Jake The Allied code name for the Japanese Aichi E13A1 three-seat single-engine long-range reconnaissance twin-float seaplane first flown in 1938 and produced in larger numbers than any other Japanese

jack. (*The Metropolitan Museum of Art, Bashford Dean Collection, 1929.*)

floatplane. In service throughout World War II, this aircraft had a speed of 234 mph and was armed with one 7.7mm machine gun and one 550-lb bomb or four 132-lb bombs. (Picture, next page.)

Jaktrobot The Swedish B04.

jam **1.** Of a machine gun or full automatic, semiautomatic, or other firearm, to stick or become inoperative because of improper loading, ejection, or the like. **2.** To make the transmissions of a radio unintelligible;

243

Jack, shown with U.S. markings. (*The Smithsonian Institution, National Air Museum.*)

to make a radio or radar set ineffective, either by the use of countertransmissions or by the use of a confusion reflector.

jamb   A piece of armor to protect the leg.

jambeaux   A pair of jambs.

jambiya   A curved, double-edged Arab knife with a rib down the middle.

jamming   Deliberate radio or radar interference.

Janes and Joes   Allied female and male secret agents dropped by plane behind enemy lines in Europe during World War II.

Janizary   From the fourteenth to the nineteenth centuries, a Turkish infantry soldier.

Japanese 6.5mm aircraft machine gun Type 3   A machine gun of Hotchkiss design that was introduced in 1943.

Japanese 6.5mm light machine gun Types 11 and 96   Machine guns of Hotchkiss design. Type 11 was introduced in 1922, and Type 96 in 1936.

Japanese 6.5mm machine gun Type 3   The Japanese adopted the Hotchkiss machine gun during the Russo-Japanese War in 1904–1905. The Type 3 is a modification of the 1914 Hotchkiss in 6.5mm. It has an overall length of about 47 in., a barrel length of about 29 in., and a weight of 122 lb with tripod. This is a gas-operated weapon capable of full automatic fire only. The cyclic rate of fire is 450 to 500 rounds per minute, and the muzzle velocity is 2,434 fps. It is fed from a 30-round strip.

This weapon was modified by General Nambu and uses the ejection system of the Lewis gun.

Japanese 6.5mm machine gun Type 11   This weapon was introduced in 1922 and is a modification of the Type 3 machine gun. It is lighter, and the barrel can be removed more rapidly. Although designed for use as a light machine gun (it weighs 22 lb), it was also used on a tripod.

Japanese 6.5mm machine gun Type 91   This weapon, introduced in 1931, is the tank version of the Type 11 machine gun. It has a larger feed hopper than the Type 11 and is equipped with a telescopic sight. This version is 33 in. long, with a barrel length of 19.2 in. The weight is 22.4 lb, and the muzzle velocity is 2,300 fps.

Japanese 6.5mm machine gun Type 96   This light machine gun was introduced in 1936. It has an overall length of 41.5 in. and a barrel length of 21.7 in. It weighs 20 lb and has a cyclic rate of fire of 550 rounds per minute and a muzzle velocity of 2,400 fps. It is fed by a 30-round box magazine. This weapon represented an improvement over the Type 11, which in turn was a modification of the Type 3. All three of these machine guns lack the feature of slow initial extraction, which means that the cartridges have to be oiled. In the Types 3 and 11 this is accomplished by a gravity-fed oil reservoir. On the Type 96 there is an oiler built into the magazine loader. The Type 99 machine gun was designed to overcome the need for lubricated cartridges.

Japanese 6.5mm rifle Type 30   This was the first Ariska rifle and was introduced in 1897. It represented the first Japanese use of the modified Mauser action, and also of the 6.5mm semirimmed cartridge. This weapon was the standard Japanese rifle in the Russo-Japanese War of 1904–1905. It was a bolt-action weapon with a detachable magazine holding five cartridges. It weighed 8 lb 4 oz and had an overall length of 49 in. and a barrel length of about 30 in. It was also called the "Meiji rifle."

Japanese 6.5mm rifle Type 38   This Ariska rifle was introduced in 1905 and was one of two principal rifles used during World War II. The action of the Type 38 is very similar to that of the 98 Mauser. The overall length of this weapon is 50.2 in., the barrel length is 31.4 in., and the weight is 9.25 lb. It has a five-round nondetachable box magazine and a muzzle velocity of 2,400 fps. It has an accurate range of about 500 yd.

Japanese 6.5mm rifle Type 97   This weapon, adopted in 1937, is a sniping version of the 6.5mm rifle Type 38. It is equipped with a 2.5-power telescopic sight, which brings the total weight of the weapon to 11.2 lb.

Jake. (*The Smithsonian Institution, National Air Museum.*)

Japanese 6.5mm tank machine gun Type 91 A machine gun of Hotchkiss design, this weapon was introduced in 1931.

Japanese 7.62mm NATO machine gun Type 62 This weapon is a general-purpose machine gun developed in Japan by the Nittoku Metal Industry Company according to requirements laid down by the JGSDF (Japanese Ground Self-Defense Forces) in 1956. It has an overall length of 47.3 in., a barrel length of 23.6 in., and a weight of 23.6 lb. The muzzle velocity is 2,800 fps, and the cyclic rate of fire, with full-charge cartridges, is 650 rounds per minute. It utilizes a disintegrating metallic link belt.

Japanese 7.62mm NATO rifle Type 64 This weapon was developed by Howa Machinery Ltd. in Japan over a period of time beginning in 1957. In 1962 the Japanese Ground Self-Defense Forces adopted the Type R6E (modified) and called it the "Type 64." This weapon is gas-operated and has selective-fire capabilities. The cyclic rate of fire is 450 to 500 rounds per minute, the muzzle velocity is 2,650 fps, and the weapon is fed from detachable 20-round box magazines. The overall length is 38.97 in., the barrel length is 17.71 in., and the weight is 9.5 lb without a magazine.

Japanese 7.7mm aircraft machine gun Models 89 and 97 Machine guns of Hotchkiss design introduced in 1929 and 1937, respectively.

Japanese 7.7mm machine gun Model 1932 A version of the Lewis machine gun, which see. It was used both on the ground and in aircraft.

Japanese 7.7mm machine gun Type 1 This weapon was adopted by the Japanese late in 1942. It evolved from a need, first stated in 1937, for a lightened modification of the Type 92—a weapon that, with mount, would weigh less than 88 lb and could be easily carried by two men. This weapon weighs 70 lb and has a cyclic rate of fire of 550 rounds per minute and a muzzle velocity of about 2,400 fps. The length is 42.4 in., and the barrel has a length of 23.2 in.

Japanese 7.7mm machine gun Type 89 An aircraft machine gun copied from the British .303 cal. Vickers aircraft machine gun.

Japanese 7.7mm machine gun Type 92 This weapon is essentially an improved Type 3 (6.5mm) in a larger caliber. It was the heavy machine gun most widely used by the Japanese during World War II. It was developed in 1932. With tripod, this machine gun weighs 122 lb. It is 45.5 in. long and has a barrel length of about 29 in. The cyclic rate of fire is 450 to 500 rounds per minute, and the muzzle velocity is about 2,400 fps. It utilizes a 7.7mm semi-

Japanese 6.5mm machine gun Type 3. (*The Smithsonian Institution, Department of Defense Collection.*)

Japanese 6.5mm machine gun Type 96. (*The Smithsonian Institution, Treasury Department Collection.*)

Japanese 6.5mm rifle Type 30. (*The Smithsonian Institution, Department of Defense Collection.*)

Japanese 7.62mm NATO machine gun Type 62. (*Japan Defense Agency.*)

Japanese 7.7mm machine gun Type 92. (*The Smithsonian Institution, Department of Defense Collection.*)

Japanese 7.7mm machine gun Type 99. (*The Smithsonian Institution, National Museum Collection.*)

Japanese 7.7mm rifle Type 99. (*The Smithsonian Institution, National Museum Collection.*)

rimmed cartridge. Because of lack of coordination between the Japanese Army and Japanese Navy ordnance authorities, the Navy and Navy Air Corps adopted the Lewis gun for certain ground and air requirements. They also called *this* weapon the "Type 92 machine gun." It fires the 7.7mm rimmed cartridge, which is the same as the .303 cal. British cartridge.

Japanese 7.7mm machine gun Type 97 This machine gun is a copy of the Czech BZ26 and was introduced in 1937. It and the Type 11 were the standard tank machine guns used by the Japanese in World War II. With stock, this weapon has an overall length of 46.5 in., a barrel length of 28 in., and a weight of 24.5 lb. One of the shortcomings of this weapon is that it is magazine-loaded, the magazine holding only 30 rounds. The cyclic rate of fire of this machine gun is 500 rounds per minute. The muzzle velocity is 2,400 fps.

Japanese 7.7mm machine gun Type 99

Japanese 8mm automatic pistol Pattern 14 (1925). (*The Smithsonian Institution, Department of Defense Collection.*)

This light machine gun was introduced in 1939 and is based upon the design of the Type 96; however, it has features which eliminate the need for a lubricated cartridge. This weapon has an overall length of 46.75 in., a barrel length of about 21.5 in., and a weight of 23 lb. It has a cyclic rate of fire of 850 rounds per minute and a muzzle velocity of about 2,350 fps. It is fed from a 30-round box magazine.

Japanese 7.7mm machine guns (Vickers) Weapons of the Maxim machine-gun type, they included Types 89, 97, and 98.

Japanese 7.7mm rifle Type 99 Two versions of this rifle were developed in Japan in the late 1930s and adopted in 1939. They arose from a need for a more powerful cartridge than the 6.5mm, which was standard at the time. The long version of the Type 99 was used by infantry and has an overall length of 50 in. with a barrel length of 31.4 in. and a weight of 9.1 lb. It has a muzzle velocity of 2,390 fps. The short version was designed for use by cavalry and special troops and has an overall length of 43.9 in., a barrel length of 25.8 in., and a weight of 8.6 lb. In 1942, a Type 99 rifle with a four-power telescopic sight was adopted for sniper use.

Japanese 7.7mm tank machine gun Type 4 and Type 97 Browning machine guns.

Japanese 7.92mm machine gun Type 98 An aircraft machine gun copied from the German MG15.

Japanese 8mm automatic pistol Pattern 14 (1925) An automatic pistol that replaced the **Nambu 8mm automatic pistol Model 1904,** which see, in Japanese service during World War II. It fires the 8mm Nambu cartridge and has the same general specifications as the Model 1904, with a few

differences imposed by the needs of mass production.

Japanese 8mm automatic pistol Pattern 94 A weapon firing the 8mm Nambu Japanese service cartridge. It has a magazine capacity of six cartridges, an overall length of 7.2 in., a barrel length of 3.8 in., and a weight of 1 lb 11 oz. This weapon is of poor construction, and because of disconnector malfunction it may fire before the slide is fully closed and locked. It is also dangerous because the sear is exposed on the outside of the pistol and, if accidentally pressed, will cause the weapon to fire.

Japanese 8mm rifle Type 20 (1887) This rifle was adopted in 1887 to use a new 8mm rimmed cartridge. The weapon has an overall length of 47.5 in., a barrel length of 29.5 in., and a weight of 8.68 lb. The capacity of the tubular magazine is eight rounds. This was the major infantry rifle used by the Japanese in their war with China in 1894.

Japanese 8mm submachine gun Type 100 (1940) A weapon adopted in 1940 but not produced in quantity until 1942. Blowback-operated, this submachine gun utilizes the 8mm Nambu cartridge and fires on full automatic only. The cyclic rate of fire is 450 rounds per minute, and the muzzle velocity is 1,100 fps. With a standard 30-round magazine the weight of the weapon is 8.70 lb. It is 22.25 in. long with stock retracted (the wooden stock is hinged), and the barrel length is 9 in.

Japanese 8mm submachine gun Type 100 (1944) A modification of the earlier Type 100 (1940) model. Fewer than 8,000 of this model were produced between 1944 and 1945.

Japanese 9mm revolver Model 26 A hinge-frame revolver made to fire the special Japanese 9mm cartridge. It has a cylinder with six cartridge chambers, an overall length of 9.4 in., a barrel length of 4.7 in., and a weight of 2 lb. It was primarily a Japanese cavalry weapon.

Japanese 11mm rifle Type 13 (Model 1887) This weapon, the Murata, was the first Japanese service rifle. It was modified in 1887 to a tube repeater. This rifle has an overall length of 50.25 in., a barrel length of about 32 in., and a weight of 9 lb. It was replaced by the Type 20.

Japanese 12.7mm aircraft machine gun Type 1 A Japanese copy of the Browning .50 cal. machine gun, developed to use a 12.7mm cartridge.

Japanese 13.2mm antiaircraft machine gun Type 93 A machine gun of Hotchkiss design that was introduced in 1933.

Japanese 13.2mm machine gun Type 93 This weapon was the standard heavy-caliber ground and naval machine gun. It was introduced in 1933 and was basically a copy of the French 13.2mm M1932 Hotchkiss machine gun.

Japanese 20mm cannon H05 A World War II weapon with a weight of 84 lb and a rate of fire of 960 rounds per minute. It was designed by scaling up a captured Browning .50 cal. machine gun.

Japanese 20mm cannon Model 98 A weapon that was constructed so that it could be used for both aircraft and antitank mountings. First tested in 1939, it had a rate of fire of 450 rounds per minute and a weight of 152 lb.

Japanese 25mm antiaircraft gun Type 96 A permanently emplaced dual antiaircraft cannon used by the Japanese throughout World War II.

Japanese 47mm antitank gun Model 01 A World War II weapon with a weight of 1,660 lb and a projectile weight of 3.4 lb. It fired fixed ammunition and had a range of 8,400 yd.

Japanese .50 cal. machine gun Model 1 A Browning machine gun.

Japanese 50mm grenade launcher This weapon was sometimes mistakenly referred to as a "knee mortar" because its round-ended concave baseplate looked as if it could be placed on the operator's thigh. (If the weapon was fired in this position, however, the recoil would break a man's leg.) It fired a fused projectile weighing about 2 lb to ranges up to 700 yd.

Japanese 70mm howitzer M92 A World War II weapon with a weight of 468 lb and a projectile weight of 8.3 lb. It fired fixed ammunition and had a range of 3,050 yd.

Japanese 70mm howitzer Type 32 A World War II weapon that is still in service with Chinese (People's Republic) infantry divisions. It has an overall weight of 468 lb and a range of about 3,050 yd. The weight of the projectile is 8.3 lb (HE).

Japanese 75mm antiaircraft gun Model 88 A World War II weapon with a weight of 2.6 tons and a projectile weight of 14.4 lb. It fired fixed ammunition and had an effective ceiling of 20,000 ft. (Picture, next page.)

Japanese 75mm gun Meiji 41 A World War II weapon with a weight of 1 ton and a projectile weight of 12.5 lb. It fired fixed ammunition and had a range of 12,000 yd.

Japanese 75mm gun type 90 This weapon fired a projectile weighing 14 lb and had a range of about 13,000 yd.

Japanese 75mm mountain gun Type 94 A World War II weapon that continues in service with Chinese (People's Republic) forces. It breaks into eight pack loads for transport and was designed to be carried by mules. It has an overall weight of 1,200 lb and a maximum range of 9,000 yd. The weight of the projectile is 14 lb (HE).

Japanese 75mm self-propelled gun This weapon consisted of a 75mm gun Type 90 on a Type 97 (1937) tank chassis. It was

Japanese 8mm submachine gun Type 100 (1940). (*The Smithsonian Institution, Department of Defense Collection.*)

Japanese 13.2mm machine gun Type 93. (*The Smithsonian Institution, National Museum Collection.*)

Japanese 50mm grenade launcher. (*The Smithsonian Institution, C. L. Smives Collection.*)

Japanese 9mm revolver Model 26. (*The Smithsonian Institution, Department of Defense Collection.*)

introduced in 1942 and was served by a crew of three. It weighed about 15 tons, traveled at speeds of about 25 mph, and represented the only Japanese armored vehicle capable of destroying any U.S. tank committed against it. (Picture, next page.)

Japanese 80mm antiaircraft gun Model 10 A World War II weapon that fired a 13.5-lb projectile to a height of 15,000 ft.

Japanese 105mm antiaircraft gun Model 14 A World War II weapon with a weight of 5.4 tons and a projectile weight of 35 lb. It fired fixed ammunition and had an effective ceiling of 31,000 ft.

Japanese 105mm gun M92 A World War II weapon with a weight of 4 tons and a projectile weight of 34.6 lb. It fired fixed ammunition and had a range of 20,000 yd.

Japanese 25mm antiaircraft gun Type 96. (*U.S. Army.*)

Japanese 75mm antiaircraft gun Model 88. (*U.S. Army.*)

Japanese 75mm self-propelled gun. (*U.S. Army.*)

Japanese 150mm howitzer Type 38. (*U.S. Army.*)

Japanese 105mm howitzer M91 A World War II weapon with a weight of 1.6 tons and a projectile weight of 31.5 lb. It fired fixed ammunition and had a range of 11,500 yd.

Japanese 150mm gun M89 A World War II weapon with a weight of 11.4 tons and a projectile weight of 90 lb. It fired fixed ammunition and had a range of 21,000 yd.

Japanese 150mm howitzer M4 A World War II weapon with a weight of 3 tons and a projectile weight of 68 lb. It fired fixed ammunition and had a range of 10,800 yd.

Japanese 150mm howitzer Type 38 A weapon used by the Japanese in World War II. It had a range of 6,500 yd and fired a projectile weighing about 79 lb.

Japanese 150mm self-propelled howitzer This weapon was introduced in 1942 for use with armored-division artillery. It had a crew of five and was armed with one 150mm howitzer Type 38. It weighed 15 tons and could travel at speeds of about 25 mph.

Japanese amphibious tank Type 2 This vehicle was introduced in 1942 and was used with special landing forces. It had a crew of five, a combat weight of 24,915 lb (with pontoons), and a speed of 23 mph on roads or 6 mph on water. It was armed with one 37mm gun and two 7.7mm tank machine guns.

Japanese armored personnel carrier Type 60 First tested in 1958, this system has a crew of two (plus eight infantrymen), a weight of 12 tons, a road speed of 28 mph, and armament consisting of one .50 cal. and one .30 cal. machine gun.

Japanese blades Japanese sword and knife blades are made in the same way and have the same shape and section. The differences lie solely in the lengths. The following are characteristic lengths: Jin Tachi, 33 in. and over; Katana and Tachi, 24 to 30 in.; Chisa Katana, 18 to 24 in.; Wakizashi, 16 to 20 in.; Tanto and Aikuchi, 11 to 16 in.; Yoroi Toshi, 9 to 12 in.; and Kwaiken, 3 to 6 in.

Japanese "Knee Mortar" See **Japanese 50mm grenade launcher.**

Japanese main battle tank Type 61 A tank that is based somewhat on the design of the U.S. M48 tank and was first produced in 1962. It has a crew of four, a weight of 35 tons, a road speed of 28 mph, and main armament consisting of one 90mm gun. Secondary armament consists of one .50 cal. and one .30 cal. machine gun.

Japanese midget submarine Type A A class of Japanese 46-ton submarines built between 1938 and 1942. They had a length of 78.5 ft, a top speed of 19 knots submerged, a crew of two, and armament consisting of two 18-in. torpedoes. (Picture, p. 250.)

Japanese midget submarine Type D A class of midget submarines built near the end of World War II. They had a displacement of 59 tons, an overall length of 86 ft, a complement of five men, and armament consisting of two 18-in. torpedoes. When no torpedoes were available, some of these vessels were fitted with an explosive warhead and used as suicide craft.

Japanese paper balloons A weapon system developed by the Japanese during World War II. These balloons were released from the Japanese home islands and allowed to drift across the Pacific to the U.S. mainland, carried there by prevailing winds. It was hoped that the balloons would start forest fires, but such was not the case. The balloons were 33½ ft in diameter and held 19,000 cu ft of hydrogen gas. A barometric system released ballast to maintain altitude, and the gondola portion carried two incendiary bombs and one 15-kilogram antipersonnel bomb.

Japanese suicide aircraft See **Kamikaze.**

Japanese suicide bomb See **Baka bomb.**

Japanese suicide motorboat See **SHINYO,** sense 2.

Japanese suicide submarine See **Kaiten 1** and **Japanese midget submarine Type D.**

Japanese tank, light, Model 95 (Kei Sensha, Shiki 95) A tank introduced in 1935 for use with armored divisions and independent tank regiments. It had a crew of three and was armed with one 37mm tank gun and two 7.7mm Type 97 machine guns. It had a weight of 8.5 tons and could travel at a speed of 30 mph on roads.

Japanese tank, medium, Model 94 (Chu Sensha, Shiki 94) A tank introduced in 1934 for use with armored divisions. It had a crew of four and was armed with one 57mm gun and two 6.5mm tank machine guns Type 91. It weighed 15.4 tons and could travel at 28 mph on roads.

Japanese tank, medium, Type 97 A tank that was introduced in 1937, but improved in 1942. It was designed for use with armored divisions and had a crew of five. The 1937 models were armed with 57mm guns; 1942 versions had a 47mm gun. Both were armed with two 7.7mm machine guns Type 97, weighed 15 tons, and could travel at speeds of about 25 mph. The improved version was the best of the Japanese World War II tanks.

Japanese torpedo Type 93 This oxygen-driven torpedo was introduced in 1933 and, at the time, was the best in the world. It had a range of 43,500 yd, a speed of 36 knots, and a warhead weight of 1,100 lb. Nicknamed "Long Lance," this torpedo had a diameter of 24 in.

Jarman 10.15mm rifle Model 1887 This rifle is a modification of the Jarman 1881, the first bolt-action rifle ever adopted by Norway. It utilizes a tubular magazine and has an overall length of 53 in., a barrel length of 32.3 in., and a weight of 9.8 lb. (Picture, next page.)

Japanese amphibious tank Type 2. (*U.S. Army.*)

Japanese armored personnel carrier Type 60. (*Japan Defense Agency.*)

Japanese main battle tank Type 61. (*Japan Defense Agency.*)

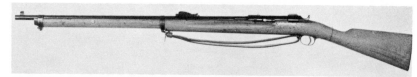

Jarman 10.15mm rifle Model 1887. (*Norwegian Defense Department.*)

JASDF Japanese Air Self-Defense Force.

Jastreb The Yugoslavian Soko-built Jastreb (Hawk) is a single-seat light attack jet-aircraft version of the Galeb (Seagull) jet trainer first flown in 1961. The attack version has a range of 945 mi, a speed of 510 mph, and armament consisting of three .50 cal. machine guns plus provisions for bombs, flares, and rockets.

JATO Jet-assisted takeoff; an auxiliary rocket device providing short, intense thrust during takeoff of an aircraft.

javelin The short, light spear used by the Romans.

Javelin 1. This British aircraft was the first twin-jet delta-wing all-weather fighter. Built by Gloster, it flew at speeds of Mach 0.94 and was armed with four 30mm Aden guns and had provision for rockets on under-wing pylons. It first flew in 1951. **2.** A class of British 1,690-ton destroyers produced in 1938–1939. They had a length of 348 ft, a speed of 36 knots, a complement of 183 men, and armament consisting of six

4.7-in. guns and ten 21-in. torpedo tubes. There were 24 ships in this class.

Jay Bird The NATO code name for the Soviet J-band airborne radar carried aboard the MiG-23 interceptor.

Jazerant A type of mail reinforced by small plates and once popular in India, Turkey, and Persia.

JB-2 An American version of the German V-1 flying bomb. It is also called the "Loon." The Navy adapted the system for submarine launch.

JB10 A U.S. Army Air Corps missile copied from the V-1. It could carry 2 tons of explosive.

J Class A class of Soviet submarines of 1,800 tons standard surface displacement first launched in 1962. They have a length of 328 ft, a beam of 27 ft, a speed of 15 knots submerged, and a complement of 90 men. They are armed with four Shaddock launching tubes and six 21-in. torpedo tubes.

JCS Joint Chiefs of Staff (the Air Force and

Army Chiefs of Staff, the Chief of Naval Operations, and the Chairman of the Joint Chiefs). The highest U.S. military unit.

Jean Bart A French battleship of 35,000 tons standard displacement completed in 1949. It had a length of 813 ft, a beam of 116 ft, a speed of 30 knots, and a complement of about 2,300 men. It was armed with eight 15-in., nine 6-in., and twenty-four 3.9-in. guns, plus twenty-eight 57mm and eight 20mm antiaircraft guns.

Jedburgh ax A kind of poleaxe with a steel head. Some had hooks shaped like a gaff. So named from Jedburgh, Scotland.

jeep 1. A small multipurpose cross-country vehicle (four-wheeled, four-wheel drive) of ¼-ton capacity. It has a 71-hp engine, a speed of 65 mph, and a range of 300 mi. The U.S. Marine Corps designation is M-38A1, and the Army designation is M-151. The name was derived from "GP" (general purpose) through association with the sound "jeep" made by a rodentlike character (Eugene) in the comic strip "Popeye," by E. C. Segar. The jeep was introduced in 1941, and between that time and the end of World War II, over 639,000 were produced. **2.** A small aircraft carrier.

jejeemy A salvage rig to rescue swamped or stranded boats during an amphibious landing.

Jenny See **Curtiss JN Series.**

jerrican A 5-gal flat-sided narrow can,

Japanese midget submarine Type A. (*U.S. Navy.*)

J Class. (*U.S. Navy.*)

adapted from a German-made can. It is easily stacked and transportable and can be adapted by special openings for discharging fuel. Also called "blitz can" (slang).

Jerry A slang expression for a German, especially one of the military forces.

jerry can See **jerrican**.

jet engine A species of reaction engine, namely, an engine that takes in air from outside for use as a fuel oxidizer and projects a jet of hot gases backward to create thrust, the gases being derived from combustion within the engine.

jet propulsion Reaction propulsion in which the propulsion unit obtains oxygen from the air, as distinguished from rocket propulsion, in which the unit carries its own oxygen-producing material. In connection with aircraft propulsion, the term refers to a gasoline or other fuel turbine jet unit which discharges hot gas through a tail pipe and a nozzle, affording a thrust which propels the aircraft.

Jet Provost A series of two-seat jet basic trainer and light attack aircraft built by British Aircraft Corporation (originally by Hunting Percival) and first flown in 1950. They have a speed of 410 mph and are armed with two .303 cal. machine guns, plus under-fuselage packs of .50 cal. guns and under-wing rockets.

JetStar The Lockheed C-140 JetStar is a USAF four-engine light jet transport with a crew of two and accommodation for eight or ten passengers. It was first flown in 1957 and has a speed of 566 mph and a range of about 2,250 mi.

jezail An Afghan gun with a long barrel and a crooked stock. Originally matchlocks, many were later converted to flintlocks.

Jezebel A sonobuoy system employed by the U.S. Navy in antisubmarine-warfare operations. In operation, a Jezebel-type sonobuoy is dropped from antisubmarine-warfare aircraft (such as the P-3 Orion and the S-2 Tracker) and, upon entering the water, deploys a hydrophone which transmits target sounds to the aircraft, where the signals are recorded on paper and displayed visually. The passive Jezebel system works in conjunction with the active **Julie** sonobuoy system, which see.

Jill The Allied code name for the Nakajima B6N1 single-engine carrier attack and torpedo bomber used by the JNAF during World War II. It had a speed of 300 mph, a range of about 700 mi. with a 1,764-lb bombload or one torpedo, and armament consisting of three 7.7mm machine guns.

jingal A long, heavy musket or other small, portable piece of ordnance designed to be fired from a rest or mounted on a swivel.

JMSDF Japanese Maritime Self-Defense Force.

JNAF Japanese Naval Air Force.

John C. Butler A class of U.S. escort ships

jeep. (*U.S. Army.*)

JetStar. (*Lockheed Aircraft Corporation.*)

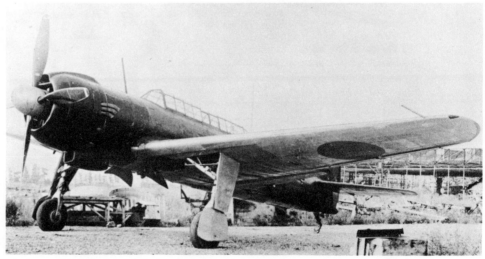

Jill. (*The Smithsonian Institution, National Air Museum.*)

Jolly Green Giant. (*Sikorsky Aircraft.*)

Junkers D.I. (*The Smithsonian Institution, National Air Museum.*)

(DE) of 1,350 tons standard displacement commissioned in 1943–1945. They had a length of 306 ft, a beam of 36.6 ft, a speed of 24 knots, and a wartime complement of 222 men. Original armament consisted of two 5-in. guns, ten 40mm and six 20mm antiaircraft guns, and one bank of three 21-in. torpedo tubes. Four ships of this class were lost in World War II.

Johnson .30 cal. machine gun Model 1941 A light machine gun developed by the American Melvin Johnson and used to a limited extent by the Marine Corps and the Army First Special Service Force during World War II. It is recoil-operated and has a cyclic rate of fire of 400 to 450 rounds per minute and a muzzle velocity of 2,800 fps. It is fed from a 20-round detachable box magazine. It has selective-fire capability, an overall length of 42 in., a barrel length of 22 in., and a weight of about 13 lb.

Johnson semiautomatic rifle See **U.S. .30 cal. rifle (Johnson M1941).**

joint Connotes the activities, operations, organizations, etc., in which elements of more than one service of the same nation participate.

joint staff A staff formed of two or more of the services of the same country.

joint zone (air, land, or sea) An area established for the purpose of permitting

Junkers Ju 52. (*The Smithsonian Institution, National Air Museum.*)

Juneau. (*U.S. Navy.*)

friendly surface, air, and subsurface forces to operate simultaneously.

Jolly Green Giant See **Sea King.**

Judy The Allied code name for the Aichi D4Y3 Suisei single-engine carrier dive bomber used by the JNAF during World War II. It had a speed of 261 mph, a range of 940 mi with a 1,103-lb bombload, and armament consisting of three 7.7mm machine guns.

Jug A World War II slang term for the **Thunderbolt,** which see.

Julie A sonobuoy system employed by the U.S. Navy in antisubmarine-warfare operations. In operation, the system uses TNT dropped as a sound source—picking up direct detonation sound and echo from the target. It then relays data (range, bearing, etc.) via UHF to the antisubmarine-warfare aircraft. The active Julie system works in conjunction with the passive Jezebel sonobuoy by pinpointing the target after Jezebel has localized it.

jumpmaster The assigned airborne qualified individual who controls parachutists from the time they enter the aircraft until they exit.

Juneau A class of U.S. antiaircraft cruisers (CLAA) developed from the *Atlanta* class of light cruisers. They had a standard displacement of 6,000 tons and were completed between 1942 and 1946. They had a length of 541 ft, a beam of 52 ft, a speed of 35 knots, and a wartime complement of 700 men. They were armed with twelve 5-in. guns, twenty-four to thirty-two 40mm guns, and twelve to sixteen 20mm antiaircraft guns.

Junkers CL.I A German two-seat ground-attack version of the **Junkers D. I,** which see. It had the additional armament of a ring-mounted Parabellum gun for the observer.

Junkers D. I A German single-place single-engine low-wing monoplane first flown in December 1915. It had a speed of about 115 mph and was armed with twin forward-firing Spandau machine guns.

Junkers J.I A German two-place single-engine infantry patrol and support biplane that went into service at the beginning of 1918. Because of its size and weight it was nicknamed *Möbelwagen* ("Furniture Wagon"). It featured all-metal construction, armor protection for the engine and crew positions, and armament consisting of two forward-firing Spandau guns and one Parabellum gun in the rear cockpit. It

Junkers Ju 88. (*The Smithsonian Institution, National Air Museum.*)

had a speed of about 96 mph.

Junkers Ju 52/3mW A German twin-float transport-seaplane version of the Junkers Ju 52. It was used extensively in the German invasion of Norway. It was armed with one 13mm machine gun and two 7.9mm machine guns and flew at a maximum speed of 163 mph.

Junkers Ju 86 A German four-seat twin-engine bomber first built in 1934 and used, in a variety of versions, during World War II. The Ju 86D was armed with three 7.9mm machine guns and carried eight 220-lb bombs. It had a service ceiling of about 25,000 ft. The Ju 86R was a two-seat high-altitude photo reconnaissance version with a ceiling of 47,250 ft.

Junkers Ju 87 See **Stuka.**

Junkers Ju 88 A German three-seat twin-engine bomber first flown in 1936 and used, in various modifications, until the end of World War II. It flew at speeds up to 279 mph, was armed with one 20mm cannon and four machine guns, and had a range of 1,553 mi. Maximum bomb capacity was about 5,000 lb. One version of this aircraft was called the *Mistel* (Mistletoe) and consisted of a Ju 88 employed as a pilotless missile, carrying a large high-explosive warhead and guided to the target by a single-engine fighter (usually a Focke Wulf FW 190) temporarily attached to it. For a picture of Mistel, see **composite aircraft.**

Junkers Ju 88C A three-seat night-fighter version of the German Ju 88 bomber, this airplane flew at speeds of 311 mph and was armed with three 20mm cannons and three 7.9mm machine guns firing forward, one 13mm machine gun firing rearward, and optional armament of two 20mm cannons firing obliquely upward.

Junkers Ju 188 A German follow-on design of the Ju 88, this four-seat medium bomber was first flown in 1943. It flew at a top speed of 310 mph and was armed with one 20mm cannon, two 13mm machine guns, and two 7.9mm machine guns, plus a bombload of about 6,600 lb.

Junkers Ju 390 A German six-engine bomber developed in 1943 as an ultra-long-range aircraft capable of attacking New York from European bases. Only two prototypes were built, one of which was tested in a long-range mission in January 1944. Carrying fuel for an endurance of 32 hours, this aircraft took off from a field south of Bordeaux, France; flew to a point about 12 mi off the U.S. coast north of New York; and then returned to its base.

Junyo A Japanese aircraft carrier of 27,500 tons standard displacement commissioned in May 1942. It had a top speed of 25.5 knots and carried 54 planes.

Jupiter A liquid-propellant one-stage rocket-powered intermediate-range ballistic missile equipped with a nuclear warhead and an all-inertial guidance system. Designated as PGM-19, it has a range of about 1,500 mi and a speed of 10,000 mph.

jus angaria A belligerent's use of a neutral's ships, etc., by consent or force, through the necessity of war. The ship must be taken in the belligerent's harbors, not on high seas.

K

K-14 sight A U.S. gyroscopic computing gunsight employing a mechanical range-control system.

K-18 sight A U.S. gyroscopic computing gunsight employing an electrical range-control system.

K-38 A Smith and Wesson .38 cal. revolver used by all U.S. services. It weighs 14.5 oz.

Ka A designation for Soviet helicopters designed by Nikolai I. Kamov.

Ka-20 See **Harp.**

Ka-25 See **Hormone.**

Ka-26 See **Hoodlum.**

KA-band radar See **radar frequencies.**

Kaga A Japanese aircraft carrier that was originally laid down as a battleship. Entering service in 1930, this ship had a displacement of 38,200 tons, a flight-deck length of 816.5 ft (and width of 100 ft), a speed of about 28 knots, and a complement of 2,019 men. It carried 90 aircraft. *Kaga* was sunk by U.S. carrier aircraft during the Battle of Midway in 1942.

Kagero A class of Japanese destroyers of about 2,000 tons standard displacement built in 1939 and the early 1940s and used during World War II. They had a length of 364 ft, a beam of 35 ft, a speed of 36 knots, and a complement of 250 men. They were armed with six 5-in. guns, four 47mm antiaircraft guns, and eight 24-in. torpedo tubes. Of the eighteen ships in this class, only one survived the war.

Kaiser A class of German battleships of 24,700 tons displacement completed in 1912–1913. They had a length of 564 ft, a beam of 95 ft, a speed of about 20 knots, and a complement of 1,088 men. Ships of this class included *Kaiser, Friedrich der Grosse, Kaiserin, Prinz Regent Luitpold,* and *König Albert.* The main armament consisted of ten 12-in. guns, fourteen 6-in.

Kaiser. (*The Imperial War Museum.*)

254

guns, and five 20-in. torpedo tubes.

Kaiten 1 A one-man suicide submarine developed by the Japanese near the end of World War II. They had a weight of about 8 tons (of which 1.7 tons was the TNT warhead), a length of about 48 ft, and a radius of action ranging from 25,000 to 85,000 yd (at speeds ranging from 12 to 30 knots).

Kaiyo A Japanese aircraft carrier with a displacement of 13,600 tons produced by converting a luxury liner (*Argentina Maru*). It carried 24 aircraft and a crew of 829 and was sunk by U.S. aircraft in August 1945.

KAM-3D See **KAWASAKI KAM-3D (Type 64 ATM-1).**

kamikaze (Japanese for *"divine wind."*) An action taken by certain Japanese pilots during World War II, in which they flew their airplanes as missiles against Allied targets, involving self-destruction on the part of the pilots. The airplanes were often laden with explosives.

Kamikaze A class of Japanese destroyers of about 1,270 tons displacement built in the early to the mid-1920s. They had a speed of about 37 knots, a complement of 148 men, and main armament consisting of four 4.7-in. guns and six 21-in. torpedo tubes. Seven of the nine ships in this class were lost during World War II (the *Hayate* being the first ship to be lost in the war when it was sunk by U.S. Marine shore batteries during the attack on Wake Island on December 11, 1941).

KAN-2 A radio-controlled rocket-propelled ship-to-air missile. Popularly called "Little Joe," it was developed during World War II as a defense against Japanese Kamikaze air attacks, but was introduced too late for active service.

Kangaroo 1. A U.S. Navy antisubmarine-warfare technique using a sonar probe attached to 2,200 ft of nylon rope that is reeled out of the tail of an aircraft flying about 500 ft above the ocean. The probe is plunged below the surface, where it transmits sonar signals and listens for any target return. **2.** The NATO code name for a large Soviet air-to-surface missile first seen in 1961. It is a winged missile similar in shape and size to a sweptwing jet fighter. **3.** The British Blackburn Kangaroo was a four-place twin-engine bomber delivered to operational squadrons in April 1918. It was armed with Lewis guns in front and rear Scarff rings, and it carried four 230-lb bombs. It had a speed of 100 mph and could remain aloft for 8 hours.

Kanin A class of Soviet guided-missile armed destroyers similar in design and construction to those in the **Krupny** class, which see.

Kanone JPZ 4-5 A German (Federal Republic) self-propelled antitank gun developed in the early 1960s and currently in use with German forces. It has a crew of four,

Kanone JPZ 4-5. (*Ministry of Defense, Federal Republic of Germany.*)

Kate, shown in U.S. markings. (*U.S. Air Force.*)

a weight of 26 tons, a road speed of 43 mph, and main armament consisting of one 90mm high-velocity gun (with a maximum antitank range of 2,000 meters). Secondary armament consists of two 7.62mm machine guns.

Kansas A class of U.S. battleships of about 16,000 tons normal displacement commissioned in 1907–1908. The class included *Kansas, Vermont, Minnesota,* and *New Hampshire.* They had an overall length of 456 ft, a beam of about 77 ft, a speed of 18 knots, and a complement of 850 men. Main armament consisted of four 12-in., eight 8-in., and twelve 7-in. guns, plus four 21-in. submerged torpedo tubes.

Kar 98a, 98b, and 98k See **Mauser 7.92mm carbine Models 98a and 98b** and **Mauser 7.92mm rifle Model 98k (Kar 98k).**

Karlsruhe A German 5,600-ton light cruiser produced in 1927. It had two sister ships, *Köln* and *Königsberg.* These ships had a length of 508 ft, a beam of 47 ft, a speed of 29 knots, and a complement of 630 men. Their main armament consisted of eight 5.9-in. and three 3.5-in. guns, plus four 21-in. torpedo tubes. All three ships were lost during World War II.

Kashin A class of Soviet guided-missile armed destroyers of 4,300 tons standard displacement produced in the early 1960s. They have a length of 475 ft, a beam of 53 ft, a speed of 35 knots, and armament consisting of twin Goa launchers, four 3-in. guns, and five 21-in. torpedo tubes.

katar A Hindu weapon with a flat triangular blade and a crossbar grip. Made in

lengths varying from a few inches to 3 ft, it is the oldest of the Indian knives.

Kate The World War II Allied code name for the Japanese Nakajima B5N2 single-engine low-wing torpedo bomber. It had a crew of two or three and a speed of 225 mph and was armed with two 7.7mm machine guns, one of which was mounted in the rear cockpit.

Katsuragi A Japanese aircraft carrier of 20,200 tons standard displacement commissioned in October 1944. It had a top speed of 32 knots and carried 63 planes.

Katy mine A World War II German anti-shipping mine, usually planted in growth

katar. (*The Metropolitan Museum of Art, gift of George Cameron Stone, 1936.*)

Kawasaki KAM-3D (Type 64 ATM-1.) *(Japan Defense Agency.)*

Kawasaki P-2J. *(Lockheed Aircraft Corporation.)*

K class. *(Goodyear Aerospace Corporation.)*

kepi. *(The Smithsonian Institution, War Department Collection.)*

on the floor of harbors.

Katyusha rocket launcher The Soviet 132mm rocket launcher M-13. It consisted of a truck-mounted system for firing 16 rockets from eight rails. Actually "Katyusha" could be used to designate a series of launchers consisting of simple metal racks in which were placed as many as 36 rockets of varying size. The M-13 weighed 7.1 tons and fired 94-lb rockets a maximum range of 9,846 yd.

Kawanishi E7K1/2 See **Alf.**

Kawanishi H6K1/5 See **Mavis.**

Kawanishi H8K1/4 See **Emily.**

Kawanishi N1K1 Kyofu See **Rex.**

Kawanishi N1K1-J Shiden See **George 11.**

Kawanishi N1K2-J Shiden-Kai See **George 21.**

Kawanishi P1Y2-S Kyokko See **Frances 26.**

Kawasaki KAM-3D (Type 64 ATM-1) A wire-guided antitank missile presently in service with the JGSDF (Japanese Ground Self-Defense Force). It has a length of 3 ft 1.4 in., a launching weight of 34.6 lb, and a range of 5,900 ft.

Kawasaki Ki.45 Toryu See **Nick.**

Kawasaki Ki.48 Type 99 See **Lily.**

Kawasaki Ki.61 Hien See **Tony.**

Kawasaki Ki.100 An extremely successful single-seat single-engine fighter-interceptor and fighter-bomber developed toward the end of World War II and used by the Japanese Army Air Force for defense of the home islands. It was largely an improvization, utilizing the airframe of the Ki.61 and a large 1,500-hp Mitsubishi radial engine. It had a maximum speed of 367 mph and was armed with two 20mm cannons and two 12.7mm machine guns.

Kawasaki Ki.102 See **Randy.**

Kawasaki P-2J A Japanese eight-seat maritime patrol bomber powered by two turboprops and two auxiliary turbojets and first flown in 1966. It is basically a modification of the P2V-7 Neptune. It has a speed of 230 mph; an internal capacity for 8,000 lb of bombs, depth charges, or torpedoes; and attachments on the wings for sixteen 5-in. rockets.

KC-97 See **Stratofreighter.**

KC-130 The aerial-tanker version of the C-130 Hercules.

KC-135 See **Stratoliner.**

K class A class of Goodyear dirigibles having a helium capacity of 456,000 cu ft.

K Class A class of Soviet submarines of 1,457 tons standard surface displacement completed between 1939 and 1943. They had a speed of 10 knots submerged, a complement of 62 men, and armament consisting of ten 21-in. torpedo tubes and two 4-in. deck guns.

Kearsarge A U.S. battleship commissioned in 1900 and a sister ship of the **Kentucky,** which see. (It is also the name of an *Essex* class aircraft carrier.)

keep In the Middle Ages, an inner tower and citadel of a castle. It was used by the besieged in their last efforts at defense.

Kei Sensha, Shiki 95 tank See **Japanese tank, light, Model 95.**

Kelt The NATO code name for a Soviet air-to-surface missile (AS-5) carried by the Navy version of the Tupolev TU-16 (Badger) bomber. It has a length of 31 ft, a wingspan of 15 ft, and a range of 100+ mi.

Kennel The NATO code name for a Soviet

air-to-surface (AS-1) antishipping missile. It is a turbojet-powered weapon and resembles a scaled-down unpiloted MiG 15 fighter aircraft. It has a length of 26 ft, a wingspan of 14 ft, and a range of 50 mi. It is carried by the Tupolev Tu-16 (Badger) bomber.

Kent A class of British 10,000-ton cruisers completed in 1928. They had a length of 630 ft, a speed of 31.5 knots, a complement of 679 men, and main armament consisting of eight 8-in. guns and eight 4-in. antiaircraft guns. Three aircraft were carried. This class included *Kent, Berwick, Cornwall, Cumberland,* and *Suffolk.*

Kentucky A U.S. battleship of 11,540 tons standard displacement. It and a sister ship, *Kearsarge,* were commissioned in 1900. They had a length of 375 ft, a beam of 72 ft, a speed of 16 knots, and a complement of about 555 men. Main armament consisted of four 13-in., four 8-in., and eighteen 5-in. guns.

Kentucky rifle A long-barreled muzzle-loading rifle of .32 to .60 cal. developed in the eighteenth century by Pennsylvanians of German descent. It was first a flintlock rifle, but it evolved into a percussion rifle. It is also called the "Pennsylvania rifle" or the "American long rifle."

kepi A military cap with a close-fitting band; a flat, round top slanting to the front; and a visor.

Kettering aerial torpedo A small pilotless and expendable bombing airplane designed during World War I by the American inventor Charles Franklin Kettering. Original U.S. Army Signal Corps plans called for a plane that could carry 300 lb of explosive, fly 50 mi or more under its own controls, and bomb a given spot with reasonable accuracy. Direction was controlled by means of a gyroscope, altitude was regulated by an aneroid barometer, and distance by means of an air log. This weapon was perfected too late to see service in World War I.

kettle-hat From the Middle Ages to about 1500, an open iron helmet worn by knights. It is the equivalent English term for the French **chapel-de-fer,** which see.

key area An area which is of paramount importance.

key point A concentrated site or installation, the destruction or capture of which would seriously affect the war effort or the success of operations.

keyserlick During the days of the Holy Roman Empire, a soldier in the Imperial Army.

Keystone bomber A U.S. biplane bomber of the early 1930s. The B-3A, B-4A, B-5A, and B-6A versions of this aircraft were all known as "Panthers," and all had a wingspan of about 75 ft, a crew of five, and armament consisting of three .30 cal.

Kentucky rifle. (*The Smithsonian Institution.*)

Kettering aerial torpedo. (*The Smithsonian Institution, National Air Museum.*)

Keystone bomber. (*The Smithsonian Institution, National Air Museum.*)

Browning machine guns. The B-3A shown had a top speed of 114 mph, a service ceiling of 12,700 ft, and a range of 860 mi.

key terrain Any locality or area, the seizure or retention of which affords a marked advantage to either combatant.

Kfz. The abbreviation for *Kraftfahrzeug,* German for "motor vehicle."

K-gun The common name for the **U.S. depth-charge projector Mark 6 Model 1,** which see.

khaki 1. A stout, tan-colored cotton cloth; the color of this cloth. **2.** *pl.* A uniform or uniforms made of this cloth and used as summer wear by U.S. Air Force, Army, and Navy personnel.

KIA Killed in action, which see.

Kiangnan A class of Chinese (People's Republic) frigates of 1,200 tons standard displacement built in the mid- to the late 1950s. They have a speed of 28 knots, a complement of 150 men, and armament consisting of three 3.9-in. guns, four 37mm antiaircraft guns, four depth-charge projectors, and three 21-in. torpedoes. Fifty mines may also be carried.

kick 1. The violent backward movement of a gun after it is fired, caused by the rearward force of the propellant gases acting on the gun. **2.** To move backward under the force of a propelling explosion. In both meanings, also called "recoil."

kidney dagger A dagger used from the fourteenth to the seventeenth centuries. It had a pair of rounded lobes instead of quillons. The term originated in the Victorian era to replace the original name "ballock dagger."

kidney dagger. (*The Metropolitan Museum of Art, Rogers Fund, 1904.*)

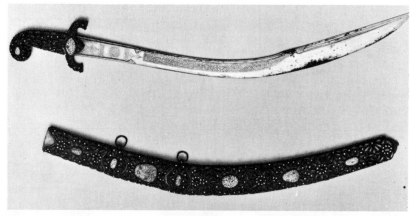

kilij. (*The Metropolitan Museum of Art, gift of J. Pierpont Morgan.*)

Kingcobra. (*Bell Aerospace Company.*)

Kingfisher. (*Vought Aeronautics Company.*)

kilij A long, curved Turkish saber, sometimes also called a "clice."

kill 1. An act or instance of destroying an enemy aircraft or submarine, especially as vouched for by supporting evidence or testimony. **2.** An aircraft or submarine that is destroyed.

killed in action A battle casualty who is killed outright or who dies as a result of wounds or other injuries before reaching any medical treatment facility.

killer submarine (SSK) One designed to detect and destroy other submarines.

killese The groove in a crossbow.

kill probability The probability that, given a hit, a single projectile or missile will kill the target against which it is fired.

kiloton energy The energy of a nuclear explosion which is equivalent to that produced by the explosion of 1 kiloton (i.e., 1,000 tons) of trinitrotoluene (TNT).

kiloton weapon A nuclear weapon, the yield of which is measured in terms of thousands of tons of trinitrotoluene (TNT) explosive equivalents, producing yields from 1 to 999 kilotons.

kinetic-energy ammunition Ammunition designed to inflict damage to fortifications, armored vehicles, or ships by reason of the kinetic energy of the missile upon impact. The damage may consist of shattering, spalling, or piercing. The missile may be solid or may contain an explosive charge, intended to function after penetration. See also **chemical-energy ammunition**.

King Air The Beechcraft C-6A King Air is a 10-place twin-turboprop transport used by the U.S. Air Force and first delivered in 1964. It has a speed of 270 mph.

Kingcobra The Bell P-63 Kingcobra was a U.S. single-seat single-engine interceptor and fighter-bomber that was first flown in December 1942. Although it closely resembled the Airacobra, it was actually of an entirely different design. Of the 3,303 built, 2,500 were supplied to the Soviet Union under lend-lease. Russian pilots used the airplane primarily for close-support and ground strafing. It was equipped with a 1,325-hp engine and had a maximum speed of 410 mph. It was armed with one 37mm cannon, four .50 cal. machine guns, and three 500-lb bombs.

King Edward A class of British 16,350-ton battleships completed in 1905–1906. The class included *King Edward, Commonwealth, Dominion, Hindustan, Zealandia, Hibernia, Africa,* and *Britannia*. These ships had a length of 453 ft, a complement of 777 men, and main armament consisting of four 12-in. guns, four 9.2-in. guns, and five 18-in. torpedo tubes. They had a speed of 18 knots.

Kingfisher The Vought OS2U-1/3 single-engine two-seat observation and scout float seaplane was developed for the U.S. Navy and first flown in 1938. It was used for naval gunfire spotting, reconnaissance, and anti-submarine patrol and as a catapult aircraft from battleships and cruisers. It was armed with two .30 cal. machine guns, carried two 100-lb or 325-lb bombs, and flew at speeds up to 172 mph. (An airplane of this type rescued Capt. Eddie Rickenbacker and his crew in the South Pacific by taxiing through 40 mi of rough sea.)

King George A class of 23,000-ton British battleships completed in 1913. There were four ships in the class: *King George, Centurion, Ajax,* and *Audacious.* They had an overall length of 596 ft, a complement of 900 men, and main armament consisting of ten 13.5-in., sixteen 4-in., and four 3-pounder guns, plus three 21-in. torpedo tubes. They had a speed of 22 knots.

King George V A class of British battleships of 35,000 tons standard displacement completed in 1940–1942. Included were *King George V, Howe, Duke of York, Anson,* and *Prince of Wales* (the latter lost in December 1941). They had a length of 745 ft, a beam of 103 ft, a speed of 28 knots, and a complement of 2,000 men (wartime). Armament consisted of ten 14-in. and sixteen 5.25-in. guns, plus antiaircraft protection from sixty to sixty-four 2-pounders, two to fourteen 40mm guns, and eight to fourteen 20mm guns. *Prince of Wales* was sunk by Japanese land-based aircraft near Singapore on December 10, 1941.

King Tiger tank A German heavy tank built by Henschel and introduced in 1944 for use with army armored battalions. With a crew of five, it was armed with one 88mm gun KwK 43 and two 7.9mm MG 34's. This tank weighed 75 tons and had a length of 23.8 ft, a height of 10.2 ft, and a width of 12.2 ft. It could make a speed of 26 mph on roads. The tank was heavy and under-powered, but the gun could penetrate 9.4 in. of armor at 100 yd at 0° elevation.

Kiowa. (*Bell Helicopter Company.*)

Kiowa The OH-58A Kiowa is a five-place observation helicopter built by the Bell Helicopter Company for the U.S. Army. It has a weight of 3,000 lb, a maximum airspeed of 138 mph, and a range of about 300 mi.

Kipper The NATO code name for a Soviet air-to-surface (AS-2) antishipping missile. It has a sweptwing aircraft design with an underslung turbojet power plant. It has a length of 31 ft, a wingspan of 16 ft, and a range of 120 mi. It is belly-mounted on the Tupolev TU-16 (Badger) bomber.

Kirov A class of Soviet cruisers of 8,800 tons standard displacement completed between 1938 and 1950. They have a length of 613.5 ft, a beam of 59 ft, a speed of 34 knots, and a complement of 734 men. They are armed with nine 7.1-in. and eight 3.9-in. guns, sixteen 37mm and six 13mm antiaircraft guns, six 21-in. torpedo tubes, and 60 to 80 mines. (Picture, next page.)

kit bag A closed baglike container that is carried as a piece of luggage and designed to hold a group of related special-purpose items.

Kitchen The NATO code name for a Soviet air-to-surface missile (AS-4) belly-mounted on the Tupolev Tu-22 (Blinder-B) bomber.

It has a length of 36 ft, a wingspan of 8 ft, and a range of 200+ mi.

Kitty Hawk A class of U.S. attack aircraft carriers (CVA) of about 60,000 tons standard displacement commissioned between 1961 and 1968. Included are *Kitty Hawk, Constellation, America,* and *John F. Kennedy.* They have an overall length of about 1,050 ft, a flight-deck width of about 255 ft, a speed of 35 knots, and a complement of 2,700 men. They carry 70 to 90 aircraft and are armed with Terrier and Sea Sparrow missiles. (Picture, next page.)

Kittyhawk The British World War II designation for later models of the P-40, specifically the Warhawk.

klinkets Small gates in the palisades of a fortification.

klop The German designation for **chloropicrin,** which see, a gas used in World War I.

knee-cop In armor, a small domed plate for the protection of the knee. (Picture, next page.)

knee mortar See **Japanese 50mm grenade launcher.**

knife bayonet A bayonet with a handle and sufficient breadth of blade to be used as a knife or a dagger. (Picture, next page.)

knight A mounted man-at-arms who served

King George. (*Vickers Ltd.*)

Kirov. (*U.S. Navy.*)

Kitty Hawk. (*U.S. Navy.*)

knee-cop. (*The Metropolitan Museum of Art, Bashford Dean Memorial Collection.*)

knobkerrie. (*The Smithsonian Institution, Ethnology Collection.*)

knife bayonet. (*The Smithsonian Institution.*)

a sovereign or feudal superior in time of war. A gentleman-soldier elevated to special status by the sovereign after training and service.

knob The rounded rear portion of a cascabel on old cannons.

knobkerrie A short club with a knobbed end. It was often thrown.

knot A velocity of 1 nautical mile per hour, i.e., 1.1508 statute miles per hour.

Knox A class of U.S. escort ships (DE) of 3,011 tons standard displacement built from 1969 to the present. Forty-six ships of this type are planned, the largest destroyer-

Köln class, the *Augsburg.* (*Ministry of Defense, Federal Republic of Germany.*)

type warship class to be produced since World War II. They have a length of 438 ft, a beam of 46.75 ft, a speed of 27+ knots, and a complement of 220 men. Armament consists of one 5-in. gun, one Asroc eight-tube launcher, four fixed torpedo launchers, and facilities for a small antisubmarine-warfare helicopter.

knuckle bow   The part of the sword guard which protects the knuckles. It curves from the base of the grip to the pommel.

Kobben   A class of Norwegian submarines of 350 tons standard surface displacement completed in 1964–1967. They have a length of 149 ft, a beam of 15 ft, a speed of 17 knots, and a complement of 18 men. They are armed with eight 21-in. torpedo tubes.

Kola   A class of Soviet destroyer escorts of 1,200 tons standard displacement produced in the early 1950s. They have a length of 305 ft, a beam of 32.8 ft, a speed of 31 knots, and a complement of 190 men. They are armed with four 3.9-in. guns, three 21-in. torpedo tubes, and depth-charge throwers and racks.

Köln   A class of German frigates of 2,100 tons standard displacement completed in 1961–1963. They have a length of 360 ft, a beam of 36 ft, a speed of 30 knots, and a complement of 210 men. They are armed with two 3.9-in. guns, six 40mm antiaircraft guns, two Bofors four-barreled depth-charge mortars, and two torpedo tubes.

Komet   The Messerschmitt Me 163 Komet was the only rocket-powered fighter-interceptor to see operational service during World War II. Designed by Germany in 1939, it made its first powered flights in October 1941, attaining speeds of 623 mph. It was introduced operationally in mid-1944 and enjoyed considerable success against Allied bombers. Powered by a bipropellant liquid rocket motor with a 3,750-lb thrust, the aircraft was armed with two 30mm cannons and twenty-four unguided rockets. It was an extremely dangerous airplane to fly.

Komet. (*The Smithsonian Institution, National Air Museum.*)

Kobben. (*Norwegian Defense Department.*)

Komet I   A Soviet Army and Navy solid-propellant surface-to-surface missile having a range of 100 mi and a speed of 3,000 mph.

Komet II   A Soviet Army and Navy solid-propellant surface-to-surface missile having a range of 600 mi.

Komet D   A Soviet Air Force air-to-surface standoff missile having a range of 55 mi.

Kondor Legion   An air force made up of elements of the German Air Force used by the Luftwaffe to gain experience while supporting General Francisco Franco in the nationalist rebellion against the Spanish republic (1936–1939).

kukri. (*The Metropolitan Museum of Art, gift of George Cameron Stone, 1936.*)

Krag-Jörgensen 6.5 × 55mm rifle Model 1894. (*Norwegian Defense Department.*)

Kongo A class of Japanese battleships of about 31,720 tons displacement launched in 1912–1913, modernized or reconstructed during the 1920s and 1930s, and used during World War II. The class included *Kongo, Haruna, Hiei,* and *Kirishima.* They had an overall length of 728.5 ft, a beam of 95 ft, a speed of about 30 knots, and a complement of 1,437 men. Their main armament consisted of eight 14-in., sixteen 6-in., and eight 5-in. guns, plus three seaplanes. All four were sunk during World War II.

König A class of German battleships of 25,575 tons displacement completed in 1914–1915. The class included *König, Grosser Kurfurst, Kronprinz,* and *Markgraf.* These ships had a length of 580 ft, a beam of 96 ft, a speed of 21.5 knots, and a complement of 1,100 men. Main armament consisted of ten 12-in. guns, fourteen 6-in. guns, and five 20-in. torpedo tubes.

Koolhoven F.K.58 A single-seat single-engine fighter-interceptor developed by the Netherlands and first flown in 1938. It had a speed of 300 mph and was armed with four 7.5mm Browning machine guns.

kopfring A metal ring which is attached to the nose of a bomb to reduce its penetration in earth or water.

kora A heavy sword with a curved single-edged blade with a pronounced widening at the end. It is the national sword of Nepal.

Korean Service Medal (KSM) A U.S. military decoration awarded persons for service within the Korean theater or adjacent areas during a given period and under certain specified conditions.

Koryu See **Japanese midget submarine Type D.**

Kotlin A class of Soviet destroyers of 2,850 tons standard displacement built in 1954–1957. They have a length of 425 ft, a beam of 41.5 ft, a speed of 36 knots, and a complement of 285 men. They are armed with four 5.1-in. guns, sixteen 45mm antiaircraft guns, six side-thrown depth-charge projectors, ten 21-in. torpedo tubes, and eighty mines. Some ships of the class have been converted to guided-missile armed destroyers with the addition of Goa and Strela

Kotlin. (*U.S. Navy.*)

Kronor. (*Swedish Defense Staff.*)

Krupny. (*U.S. Navy.*)

rocket launchers.

kozuka, kodzuka A small knife that is carried in a pocket of a Japanese sword scabbard.

Krag-Jörgensen A five-shot military rifle developed in 1889 and adopted by Denmark and Norway. A modified version was adopted by the United States in .30 cal. and was the standard arm from 1892 to 1903. The rifle is named after the inventors, Capt. O. Krag and E. Jörgensen, of Norway.

Krag-Jörgensen 6.5 × 55mm carbine Model 1895 The carbine version of the Krag-Jörgensen Model 1894. It is a bolt-operated weapon with an overall length of 40 in., a barrel length of 20.5 in., and a weight of 7.5 lb. It is fed with a five-round horizontal box magazine and has a muzzle velocity of 2,575 fps. Variations of this carbine appeared as the Model 1904, Model 1907, and Model 1912.

Krag-Jörgensen 6.5 × 55mm rifle Model 1894 This rifle, which fires the 6.5 × 55mm rimless Mauser cartridge, was adopted by Norway in 1894. It, and various carbine versions, constituted the mainstay of the Norwegian Army until Norway was occupied by the Germans in World War II. The M1895 is a bolt-operated rifle with an overall length of 49.9 in., a barrel length of 29.9 in., and a weight of 9.38 lb. It is fed from a five-round horizontal box magazine and has a muzzle velocity of about 2,625 fps. Sniper versions of this rifle appeared as the Model 1923, Model 1925, and Model 1930.

Krag-Jörgensen 8mm rifle Model 1889 This bolt-operated rifle was the Danish service rifle from its adoption in 1889 until World War II. It has an overall length of 52.28 in., a barrel length of 32.78 in., and a five-round horizontal hinged box magazine.

Kraguj A Yugoslavian Soko-built single-seat close-support aircraft with a speed of about 183 mph and armament consisting of two 7.7mm machine guns plus attachments for napalm tanks, bombs, and rockets.

K ration A lightweight, packaged, emer-

Kübelwagen. (*The Imperial War Museum.*)

gency ration issued during World War II especially for use in the field.

kraut A derisive term for a German in World War I and World War II.

Kresta The NATO designation for a class of Soviet armed destroyer leaders (light cruisers) of about 6,000 tons standard displacement, the prototype of which carried out sea trials in 1967. They have a length of 508 ft, a beam of 55 ft, a speed of 34 knots, and a complement of 400 men. Armament consists of two twin Shaddock launchers, two twin Goa launchers, two 12-barreled and two 6-barreled depth-charge launchers, four torpedo tubes, four 57mm guns, and one helicopter.

kris A Malay sword or dagger with a straight or waved blade, made in various lengths.

Kronor A class of Swedish cruisers of 8,200 tons standard displacement completed in the mid-1940s. One ship, *Göta Lejon*, is still in commission. It has a length of 590.5 ft, a beam of 54 ft, a speed of 33 knots, and a complement of 610 men. It is armed with seven 6-in. guns, plus four 57mm and eleven 40mm antiaircraft guns.

Kropatchek rifle See **French 11mm rifle Model 1878.**

Krupny A class of Soviet guided-missile armed destroyers of 3,650 tons standard displacment that began construction in 1958. They have a length of 453 ft, a beam of 44 ft, a speed of 34 knots, and a complement of 360 men. They are armed with two Strela missiles, sixteen 57mm antiaircraft guns, and six launchers for homing torpedoes.

Krupp gun A breechloading steel cannon made by Krupp in Essen.

KU-band radar See **radar frequencies.**

Kübelwagen A popular name for the German light car Kfz.1 Type 82 produced by Volkswagen and used by German forces during World War II. It had a weight of about 1,500 lb and was powered by a four-cylinder engine of about 25 bhp (brake horsepower).

KUD-1 A kind of remote-controlled glide bomb, popularly called the "Gargoyle."

kukri A curved knife with a heavy single-edged blade. It is used by the Gurkhas of Nepal.

Kuma A class of Japanese cruisers of about

kytoon. (*U.S. Army.*)

5,100 tons standard displacement that were built in the early 1920s and used during World War II. They had a length of 535 ft, a beam of 47 ft, a speed of 33 knots, and a complement of 450 men. They were armed with seven 5.5 in. and two 3-in. guns, plus four torpedo tubes and one seaplane. (*Kuma, Kiso, Oi,* and *Tama* were lost in 1944. A fifth ship, *Kitakami,* was scrapped after World War II.)

Kw.K. The abbreviation for *Kampwagen-Kanone,* German for "battlewagon cannon."

Kynda A class of Soviet guided-missile armed destroyer leaders (light cruisers) of 4,800 tons standard displacement, the first example of which was completed in 1962. They have a length of 492 ft, a beam of 51 ft, a speed of 35 knots, and a complement of 390 men. They are armed with two Shaddock quadruple mounts, one twin Goa launcher, two 12-barreled antisubmarine rocket launchers, four 3-in. antiaircraft guns, six 21-in. torpedo tubes, and one helicopter.

kytoon A helium-filled balloon supporting a temporary radio antenna.

L

L **1.** The abbreviation for "light" in unit designations. **2.** The abbreviation for "liaison" in designations of USAF aircraft, as in L-3, L-5, etc. **3.** The U.S. military designation for the war gas **lewisite,** which see.

L2A2 and L2A3 9mm Parabellum submachine guns See **Sterling 9mm Parabellum submachine gun L2A3.**

L4A2 machine gun See **Bren .303 light machine gun.**

L7A1 machine gun This is the British version of the **FN MAG machine gun,** which see. Enfield has made some modifications, particularly in the barrel. When used as a heavy machine gun, on a tripod, a heavier barrel is used. It has an overall length of 49.7 in. and a barrel length of 24.75 in. It weighs 24 lb (light-barrel version), and the tripod weighs 29 lb. The muzzle velocity is about 2,800 fps, and the cyclic rate of fire is 700 to 900 rounds per minute. The weapon has also been used as a tank machine gun. Other versions include the L7A2 (with 50-round belt box), the L8A1 (a tank version), the L20 (an experimental gun-pod version for aircraft), and the L37A1 (for both armored vehicles and ground use).

La A designation for Soviet aircraft designed by Semyon A. Lavochkin.

La-5 A single-seat single-engine interceptor and fighter-bomber produced for the Soviet Air Force. It was first used operationally in the Stalingrad area in 1942 and was later flown by many of the leading Russian aces. It was equipped with a 1,540-hp engine and flew at speeds of about 400 mph. It was armed with two 20mm cannons and carried a 440-lb bombload.

La-7 Basically an improved version of the La-5, this aircraft was powered by a 1,775-hp engine and flew at speeds up to 413 mph. It was armed with three 20mm cannons, six rockets, and two 110-lb bombs or one 220-lb bomb. It was later given the NATO code name "Fin."

La-9 A Soviet single-seat single-engine interceptor and escort fighter that first appeared in 1945. It has a speed of 428 mph and armament consisting of four 20mm cannons. It later received the NATO code name "Fritz."

labeled cargo Cargo of a dangerous nature, such as explosives, flammable or corrosive liquids, and the like, which is designated by different colored labels to indicate the requirements of special handling and storage. Examples of such colored labels are as follows: *Green labels:* Required on shipments of nonflammable gases. *Red labels:* Required on shipments of articles of a flammable nature. *White labels:* Required on shipments of acids or corrosive liquids. *Yellow labels:* Required on shipments of flammable solids and oxidizing materials.

La Coruña submachine gun See **Rexim F. V. Mk 4 submachine gun.**

lacrimators **Tear agents,** which see.

Lacrosse A mobile, accurate surface-to-surface guided missile, with a nuclear and nonnuclear warhead capability, designed to engage hardened-point targets or area targets up to a range of 30,000 meters. Designated as MGM-18. The prime contractor is Martin Marietta. (Picture, next page.)

ladder **1.** Stairs aboard a ship. **2.** A method of hitting gun range by firing a succession of salvos with established differences in elevation.

Lafayette A class of U.S. fleet ballistic-missile submarines (SSBN) of 7,320 tons standard surface displacement commissioned between 1963 and 1967. These nuclear-powered submarines are the largest undersea craft ever built. There are 31 in the class. They have a length of 425 ft, a beam of 33 ft, a speed of about 30 knots submerged, and a complement of 140 men. They are armed with four 21-in. torpedo tubes and carry 16 tubes for Polaris missiles. (Picture, next page.)

Lafayette Escadrille **1.** A volunteer squadron made up principally of American fliers who fought for the French in World War I. **2.** In World War II, a fighter squadron of French pilots under American command and equipped with American aircraft which fought in North Africa. In sense 1, the Lafayette Escadrille, first named the "Escadrille Américaine," was

Lacrosse. (*U.S. Army.*)

lames. (*The Metropolitan Museum of Art, Bashford Dean Memorial Collection.*)

formed in 1916 within the French service. A few of its pilots were French. In 1918, it was transferred to the American service and became the 103d Pursuit Squadron.

LaGG-3 A single-seat single-engine interceptor and fighter-bomber designed by the team of Lavochkin, Gorbunov, and Gudkov that went into production for the Soviet Air Force in 1940. It had a maximum speed of 348 mph and was armed with one 20mm cannon and two 12.7mm machine guns, plus six 56-lb rockets or two 220-lb bombs.

Lafayette class, the U.S.S. *Alexander Hamilton* (SSBN 617). (*General Dynamics.*)

Lahti 7.92mm machine gun Model 26/32 A Finnish recoil-operated air-cooled machine gun with a rate of fire of 450 to 550 rounds per minute. It weighed 19.5 lb and was fed from a 25- or 75-round magazine.

Lahti 9mm Parabellum automatic pistol This weapon has been used by the armed forces of both Finland and Sweden. The Model 40, as used in the Swedish forces, is recoil-operated and has an overall length of 10.7 in., a barrel length of 5.5 in., and a weight of 2.4 lb. It utilizes a nine-round detachable box magazine.

Lahti 20mm aircraft cannon A Finnish gas-operated air-cooled cannon with a rate of fire of 450 to 500 rounds per minute. It weighed 84 lb and was fed from a 60-round drum magazine. It was adopted in the 1930s by the Finnish Air Force and saw much action in the Russo-Finnish War.

Lahti Saloranta 7.62mm light machine gun Model 26 The recoil-operated selective-fire weapon made before World War II in 7.62mm for Finnish forces and in 7.92mm for Chinese forces. It has a cyclic rate of fire of 500 rounds per minute and a muzzle velocity of 2,625 fps. It is fed from either a 20-round box magazine or a 75-round drum magazine. The weight of the weapon with a 20-round magazine is 23 lb, and the length is 46.5 in.

lamboys Fifteenth- and sixteenth-century armor consisting of a steel skirt that protected the area from the waist to the knees.

lames Overlapping metal plates mounted with rivets on leather straps or with the rivets of one lame sliding in slots on the next, thus making the whole system flexible.

Lancaster The British Avro Lancaster was a four-engine heavy bomber first flown in 1941 and manufactured throughout World

War II. It had a speed of 270 mph and a range of 1,160 mi with a normal 14,000-lb bombload. It was armed with eight .303 cal. Browning machine guns. Special modifications of the Lancaster could carry the Grand Slam 22,000-lb deep-penetration bomb or the famous "spinning bombs" used against German dams. The design of this aircraft led to a scaled-up version called the **Lincoln,** which see.

lance A long shaft with a sharp steel head once carried by horsemen. The medieval lance was very long and heavy and was often supported on a rest attached to the breastplate. More modern lances were 9 or 10 ft long and were supported by a sling over the arm.

Lance A combat ballistic missile developed for the U.S. Army by LTV (Ling-Temco-Vought) and first tested in 1965. It has a length of 20 ft, a launching weight of 3,200 lb, and a range of up to 30 mi. Either nuclear or nonnuclear warheads can be used.

lance corporal A private with the duties of a corporal but the pay of a private; an acting corporal.

lance head The head of a lance.

lance-knight A foot soldier, or **lansquenet,** which see.

lanceman A soldier armed with a lance or pike.

lancer A soldier who carries a lance, particularly a light cavalry soldier in a regiment called "lancers."

Lancer The Republic P-43 Lancer was a progressive development of the Republic (Seversky) **P-35A,** which see. First delivered in 1940, this aircraft had a speed of 356 mph and was armed with four .50 cal. machine guns and one 200-lb bomb. China was provided with 108 Lancers under lend-lease.

lance rest A bracket on the breastplate in armor to aid in supporting the lance.

lance sergeant A corporal with the duties of a sergeant but the pay of a corporal; an acting sergeant.

lance socket A leather socket used to support the butt of the lance when on horseback. It was sometimes called a "lance bucket."

Lanchester 9mm submachine gun Mark I A blowback-operated weapon with selective full automatic or semiautomatic fire and a cyclic rate of fire of 575 to 600 rounds per minute. It has an overall length of 33.5 in. and a barrel length of 7.9 in. It carries a 50-round box magazine and has a muzzle velocity of 1,280 fps and a weight of 9.62 lb. It was designed by G. H. Lanchester and was manufactured by the Sterling Engineering Company. The overall design is based on the German MP 28 11. The Lanchester was introduced in 1941 and saw service with the British Navy. The Mark I* was introduced later and was capable of full automatic fire only.

land diameter The diameter of a bore as measured from the top of one land to the top of the land opposite.

land dreadnought A tank.

land force A military force serving on land.

landing area 1. That part of the objective area within which are conducted the landing operations of an amphibious force. It includes the beach, the approaches to the beach, the transport areas, the fire-support areas, the air occupied by close-supporting aircraft, and the land included in the advance inland to the initial objective. **2.** (Airborne.) The general area used for landing troops and materiel by either airdrop or air landing. This area includes one or more drop zones or landing strips. **3.** Any specially prepared or selected surface of land, water, or deck designated or used for takeoff and landing of aircraft. ·

landing attack Any attack against enemy defenses by troops landed from ships, aircraft, boats, or amphibious vehicles.

landing beach That portion of a shoreline usually required for the landing of a battalion landing team. However, it may also be that portion of a shoreline constituting a tactical locality (such as the shore of a bay) over which a force larger or smaller than a battalion landing team may be landed.

landing craft A craft employed in amphibious operations and specifically designed for carrying troops and equipment and for beaching, unloading, and retracting. Also used for logistic cargo resupply operations.

landing craft, mechanized A twin-propeller steel landing craft, with a ramp bow, designed to land military equipment, such as trucks, trailers, and tanks, directly on the beach and to retract under its own power. (Picture, next page.)

Lancaster. (*The Smithsonian Institution, National Air Museum.*)

Lancer. (*U.S. Air Force.*)

landing flare A flare dropped by an aircraft or positioned on the ground to provide illumination for landing.

landing force The troops organized for an amphibious assault.

landing gear The complete apparatus on an aircraft for supporting it during landing or while resting or moving about on the surface. Landing gear consists of wheels, skids, endless tracks, floats, or skis, together with the necessary axles, struts, wires, shock absorbers, and other assemblies or parts.

landing mat A prefabricated portable mat so designed that any number of planks (sections) may be rapidly fastened together to form surfacing for emergency runways, landing beaches, etc.

landing party An organized force of infan-

Lance. (*Vought Missiles and Space Company.*)

landing craft. (*U.S. Navy.*)

land mine. (*The Smithsonian Institution.*)

Langenhan (F. L. Selbstader) .32 cal. ACP automatic pistol. (*The Smithsonian Institution, Treasury Department Collection.*)

Lansen. (*The Swedish Air Force.*)

try from a ship's company detailed for emergency or parade duty ashore.

landing ship An assault ship which is designed for long sea voyages and for rapid unloading over and onto a beach.

landing ship dock A ship designed to transport and launch loaded amphibious craft or amphibious vehicles with their crews and embarked personnel and equipment and to render limited docking and repair services to small ships and craft.

landing strip An airstrip or that part of an airstrip where the airplanes actually touch the surface in landings or takeoffs. Also a part of, or an area adjoining, an airfield, especially an unimproved area, as distinguished from improved runways, suitable for landing and takeoff.

landing vehicle, tracked A track-propelled vehicle, with or without armor protection or fixed armament, for use in amphibious landing operations to carry personnel or cargo on rough waters or over coral reefs and other obstacles.

landing vehicle, tracked, engineer, Model 1 A lightly armored amphibious vehicle designed for minefield and obstacle clearance in amphibious assaults and operations inland. It is equipped with line charges for projection in advance of the vehicle and with bulldozer-type blades with scarifier teeth. It is designated LVTE-1.

landing vehicle, tracked, howitzer, Model 6 A lightly armored self-propelled amphibious 105mm howitzer. It is designed to provide close fire support during a landing operation by initially delivering direct fire on the landing beaches and, after landing,

by providing field-artillery fire in support of operations ashore. It is designated LVTH-6

landing vehicle, wheeled A self-propelled wheeled vehicle designed to transport cargo and/or personnel on land or water. Popularly called "DUKW," pronounced "duck."

landmark In land-mine warfare, a feature, either natural or artificial, that can be accurately determined on the ground from a grid reference.

land mines Land mines are explosive items which may be planted in the path of the enemy to hinder his movement or to deny him access to certain territory. The mines are generally concealed and so rigged that they will be initiated by the enemy's presence or contact, except in instances where they may be initiated by remote control. Land mines may produce casualties by direct explosive force, fragmentation, shaped-charge effect, or the release of harassing agents or lethal gas.

lands The raised part of the rifling of a gun between the grooves.

Landsturm A term used in Germany to describe the last line of defense; a force consisting of all men liable to service but not already in the armed forces or the reserves.

Landwehr The organized reserves of Germany, Austria, etc.

lane marker In land-mine warfare, a device used to mark a minefield lane. Lane markers at the entrance to, and exit from, the lane are referenced to a landmark or intermediate marker.

Langenhan (F. L. Selbstader) .32 cal. ACP automatic pistol This weapon was a substitute standard pistol for German forces during World War I. It has a magazine capacity of eight cartridges, an overall length of 6.75 in., a barrel length of 4.2 in., and a weight of about 20 oz. This weapon is commonly known by the initials "FL" (standing for the inventor, Fritz Langenhan). With these initials, and the exterior similarity to the Model 1900 Browning (marked "FN" for "Fabrique Nationale"), there can be confusion. The Browning is a safe and reliable weapon, while the Langenhan is dangerous because of its breech-lock design.

langrage In former ordnance usage, a type of shot that consisted of bolts, nails, and other pieces of metal fastened together or enclosed in a canister. It was used for destroying an enemy ship's sails and rigging and for antipersonnel work.

langue de boeuf **1.** A fifteenth-century pike having a blade that was wide at the head and tapered rapidly to a point. **2.** An Italian dagger or short sword.

languet, languette **1.** A strip of metal to protect and strengthen the haft of a staff weapon. **2.** The part of a sword hilt that overhangs the scabbard.

Lansen The Saab-32 Lansen is a two-seat all-weather jet fighter, attack fighter, and photo reconnaissance aircraft in service with the Swedish Air Force and first flown in 1952. It has a speed of 700 mph and is armed with four 20mm cannons and underwing attachments for two air-to-surface rockets, 2,200 lb of bombs, or twenty-four rockets.

lansquenet In the fifteenth and sixteenth centuries, a mercenary foot soldier (usually German or Swiss) in foreign service.

lantaca, lantaka A piece of native brass ordnance similar to a swivel gun and once used in the Philippines, Malaya, etc. Lantacas are of varying sizes, but most have bores less than 2½ in. Normally there is a socket at the breech for the insertion of an aiming tiller.

lanterne A ladle for putting gunpowder in a cannon. It resembles a long scoop or ladle and is fixed to a long pole.

lanyard **1.** A cord or thong attached to a pistol butt; it is looped around the neck to prevent loss of the pistol. **2.** A cord or cable of specific length, usually with a hook on one end and a handle on the opposite end. It is designed to be attached to a component of the firing mechanism of a gun, rocket launcher, smoke-puff discharger, or the like and is used to fire the weapon by remote control.

lanyard ring A ring located on the butt of certain revolvers, or the side of certain saddle carbines, to which a lanyard can be attached.

LARA Light armed reconnaissance aircraft. A U.S. aircraft requirement that eventually evolved into the North American OV-10 **Bronco,** which see.

LARC *L*ighter, *a*mphibious, *r*esupply *c*argo. Usually pronounced "lark." A U.S. over-the-beach amphibious wheeled vehicle designed to deliver general cargo from ship to inland storage or distribution areas. The LARC-5 weighs 5 tons, has a 270-hp engine, and travels 35 mph on land and 10 mph on water. The LARC-15 is a 15-ton resupply cargo lighter. The LARC LX is a 60-ton-capacity barge.

large spread A report by an observer or a spotter to a ship to indicate that the distance between the bursts of a salvo is excessive.

Largo See **Astra 9mm (Largo) automatic pistol model 1921.**

Lark A U.S. Navy rocket-powered guided missile, designed as a short-range antiaircraft weapon.

Larynx The earliest British guided weapon, the development of which began in 1927. It consisted basically of a flying bomb that was radio-controlled, traveled at speeds up to 200 mph, and flew a distance of 100 mi.

LARC. (*U.S. Army.*)

launcher, for the Lance missile. (*U.S. Army.*)

This remote-controlled aircraft carried 250 lb of high explosives.

lascar **1.** In British India, a low-ranking native artilleryman. **2.** A native army servant.

LAT Light-artillery tractor.

latch **1.** A device designed to fasten a rocket in or on a launcher prior to firing. **2.** The part on a revolver that withdraws the locking bolt which holds the cylinder in place and enables it to be swung out.

Latécoère 298 A single-engine two- or three-seat torpedo-bomber and reconnaissance twin-float seaplane developed for the French Navy and first flown in 1936. It saw considerable service during World War II. It was armed with three 7.5mm machine guns and carried one 1,477-lb torpedo, three depth charges, or two 330-lb bombs.

lateral spread A technique used to place the mean point of impact of two or more units 100 meters apart on a line perpendicular to the gun-target line.

launch **1.** To release or send forth, under its own power only, a rocket missile, robot bomb, or the like from a special launcher, rack, ramp, or other device or installation. **2.** To drop or release an aerial torpedo from an aircraft. **3.** To catapult, especially to catapult or discharge a torpedo from a torpedo tube or to catapult an airplane, as from a ship's deck. **4.** The largest boat belonging to a warship. It is used for carrying materiel and personnel and is often fitted with a light gun in the bow.

launcher A structural device—airborne, fixed, mobile, portable, seaborne, or transportable—designed to support and hold in position for firing a rocket or guided missile. It may have limited means for directing the flight. It is not equipped with any form of powered device for catapulting the rocket or guided missile into the air.

launching platform A platform from which a guided missile or the like is launched or fired. Also called a "firing platform."

launching rack A structure, as on an airplane, used to hold missiles for launching.

launching tube, for the Bofors antisubmarine rocket. (A. B. Bofors.)

LAW. (U.S. Army.)

LCC, the amphibious command ship U.S.S. *Mount McKinley* (LCC-7). (U.S. Navy.)

launching rail A rail that guides, or aids in guiding, a rocket missile or other projectile in launching.

launching site Any site or installation with the capability of launching missiles from surface to air or surface to surface.

launching tube A tube used to guide a rocket, missile, or other projectile during launching. See **rocket launcher.**

launch pad A concrete or other hard-surface area on which a missile launcher is positioned.

Laura The code name for the Aichi E11A1 single-engine biplane three-seat night-reconnaissance flying boat first flown in 1934.

LAW Light assault weapon. The U.S. Army M-72 66mm antitank missile that fires an unguided antitank rocket. It has a range of about 500 to 600 yd.

lay **1.** To direct or adjust the aim of a weapon. **2.** The setting of a weapon for a given range, a given direction, or both. **3.** To drop one or more aerial bombs or aerial mines onto the surface from an aircraft. **4.** To spread a smoke screen on the ground from an aircraft. **5.** To calculate or project a course. **6.** To lay on. **a.** To execute a bomber strike. **b.** To set up a mission.

laydown bombing A very low-level bombing technique wherein delay fuzes or devices are used to allow the attacker to escape the effects of his bomb.

lazarette A storage compartment in the stern of a ship or boat.

Lazy Dog An air-to-ground antipersonnel rocket used by the U.S. Air Force in the early stages of the war in Vietnam.

LB-30 A B-24 Liberator bomber built to British specifications during World War II. The plane had no American counterpart.

L-band radar See **radar frequencies.**

LBP A U.S. Navy personnel landing boat.

LBV A U.S. Navy vehicle landing boat.

LCA A U.S. Navy landing craft, assault, personnel and cargo carrier, 30 tons.

LCC(1) A U.S. Navy landing craft, control Mk I.

LCC(2) A U.S. Navy landing craft, control Mk II.

LCFF A U.S. Navy landing craft, infantry (flotilla flagship).

LCI A U.S. Navy landing craft, infantry.

LCI(FF) A U.S. Navy landing craft, infantry (flotilla flagship).

LCIG A U.S. Navy landing craft, infantry (gunboat).

LCI(L) A U.S. Navy landing craft, infantry (large).

LCIM A U.S. Navy landing craft, infantry (mortar).

LCIR A U.S. Navy landing craft, infantry (rocket).

L class A class of Goodyear dirigibles having a helium capacity of 123,000 cu ft.

L Class A class of Soviet submarines of

LCI. (*U.S. Navy.*)

1,100 tons standard surface displacement launched between 1929 and 1935. They had a speed of 9 knots submerged and a complement of 50 men and were armed with eight 21-in. torpedo tubes and one 4-in. deck gun.

LCM A U.S. Navy landing craft, medium; an amphibious assault boat capable of beaching and discharging personnel and tanks.

LCM(2) A U.S. Navy landing craft, mechanized, Mk II.

LCM(3) A U.S. Navy landing craft, mechanized, Mk III.

LCM(6) A U.S. Navy landing craft, mechanized, Mk VI. (Picture, next page.)

LCM(8) A U.S. Navy landing craft, mechanized, Mk VIII.

LCP(L) A U.S. Navy landing craft, personnel (large).

LCP(N) A U.S. Navy landing craft, personnel (nested).

LCP(R) A U.S. Navy landing craft, personnel (with ramp).

LCR(L) A U.S. Navy landing craft, inflatable boat (large).

LCR(L) or (S) A U.S. Navy landing craft, rubber, for ten people (L) or seven people (S).

LCR(S) A U.S. Navy landing craft, inflatable boat (small).

LCSL A U.S. Navy landing craft, infantry (support).

LCSR A U.S. Navy landing craft, swimmer reconnaissance.

LCSS(1) A U.S. Navy landing craft, support (small), Mk I.

LCSS(2) A U.S. Navy landing craft, support (small), Mk II.

LCT A U.S. Navy landing ship, utility or landing craft, tank.

LCU A U.S. Navy landing craft, utility. (Picture, next page.)

LCV A U.S. Navy landing craft, vehicle.

LCVP A U.S. Navy landing craft, vehicle and personnel; a small amphibious assault boat capable of beaching.

LE, L.E. The abbreviation for "low explosive."

lead **1.** Bullets or projectiles in general. **2.** The action of aiming ahead of a moving target with a gun, bomb, rocket, or torpedo so as to hit the target, including whatever action is necessary to correct for deflection. **3.** The lead angle. **4.** The distance between the moving target and the point at which the gun or missile is aimed.

lead aircraft **1.** The airborne aircraft designated to exercise command of other aircraft within the flight. **2.** An aircraft in the van of two or more aircraft.

lead crew An aircrew specially trained to fly the lead bomber in certain bomber formations, navigating for the entire formation and signaling or indicating, by one means or another, the proper time for the dropping of bombs by all the other aircraft in the formation.

leade The bore of a gun barrel just ahead of the chamber. It is slightly enlarged over the rest of the bore so as to accommodate the bullet.

leaflet bomb A light-case bomb (made of

LCIR. (*U.S. Navy.*)

L class. (*Goodyear Aerospace Corporation.*)

LCM(6). (*U.S. Navy.*)

LCU. (*U.S. Navy.*)

leaf sight. (*The Smithsonian Institution.*)

sheet metal or laminated plastic) designed to be filled with leaflets. It is provided with a fuze to cause opening before impact and is released from an aircraft for the purpose of distributing the leaflets.

leaflet raid A raid in which leaflets are dropped, especially in leaflet bombs.

leaf sight A rear sight for small arms, hinged so that it can be raised for aiming or lowered to keep it from being broken when not in use. A leaf sight often contains a peep sight that can be moved up and down to make adjustments for range. Sometimes two or three leaves of different sizes are hinged on the same pivot to adjust for range.

Leahy A class of U.S. guided-missile frigates (DLG) of 5,670 tons standard displacement produced in 1962–1964. There are nine ships in the class. They have a length of 533 ft, a beam of 54.9 ft, a speed of 34 knots, and a complement of 396 men. They are armed with four 3-in. guns, two twin Terrier launchers, one Asroc eight-tube launcher, and two triple torpedo launchers.

Leander 1. A class of British general-purpose frigates of 2,450 tons standard displacement completed between 1963 and 1970. They have a length of 372 ft, a beam

of 41 ft, a speed of 30 knots, and a complement of 263 men. They are armed with two 4.5-in. guns, two 40mm and two 20mm antiaircraft guns, one Seacat launcher, and one Limbo three-barreled depth-charge mortar. They also carry one helicopter armed with homing torpedoes. **2.** A class of British 7,270-ton light cruisers completed in 1933–1935. It included *Leander, Orion, Neptune, Achilles,* and *Ajax.* They had a length of 554 ft, a speed of 32 knots, a complement of 550 men, and armament consisting of eight 6-in. and eight 4-in. guns, eight 21-in. torpedo tubes, and one (or two) aircraft.

leapfrog A form of movement in which like supporting elements are moved successively through or by one another along the axis of movement of supported forces.

leatherneck A slang term for a U.S. Marine. It derives from the leather stock worn around the neck by early Marines.

Lebel 8mm revolver Model 1892 This was the official French Army double-action revolver for many years and was technically referred to as the "French Modèle D'Ordonnance 1892 (Lebel)." It has a cylinder containing six cartridge chambers, an overall length of about 9¼ in., a barrel length

Leahy. (*U.S. Navy.*)

of 4.5-in., and a total weight of 1.8 lb. It was the first swing-out cylinder revolver adopted in Europe.

Lebel rifle See **French 8mm rifle M1886, M93.**

Leberecht Maass A class of 16 German 2,200-ton destroyers built in 1937–1938. They had a speed of 30 knots, a complement of 315 men, and armament consisting of five 5-in. guns, four 37mm and eight 20mm antiaircraft guns, and eight 21-in. torpedo tubes. Ten were lost to action during World War II.

Le Corse A class of French frigates of 1,290 tons standard displacement completed in 1955–1956. They have a speed of 28.5 knots, a complement of 174 men, and armament consisting of six 2.25-in. and two 20mm antiaircraft guns, depth-charge mortars, and 12 tubes for homing torpedoes.

Ledo Road A military road constructed by the Allies during World War II. It began at Ledo in Assam, intersected the Burma Road, and ended in Kunming, China. It was also called the "Stilwell Road."

Lee-Enfield .303 rifles Bolt-action repeating rifles of .303 cal. The name derives from that of the inventor, James P. Lee, a Scottish-born U.S. citizen, and Enfield, a town near London, England. They were first adopted by Great Britain in 1895. The rifle has a detachable magazine holding 10 cartridges. See also **British .303 Lee-Enfield rifle Mark I, British .303 Lee-Enfield rifle Mark I*, British .303 S.M.L.E. rifle No. 1 Mark I, British .303 S.M.L.E. rifle No. 1 Mark I*, British .303 S.M.L.E. rifle No. 1 Mark I**, British .303 S.M.L.E. (converted) rifle No. 1 Mark II*, British .303 S.M.L.E. rifle No. 1 Mark III and Mark III*, British .303 S.M.L.E. (converted) rifle No. 1 Mark IV, British .303 S.M.L.E. rifle No. 1 Mark V,** and **British .303 S.M.L.E. rifle No. 1 Mark VI.**

Lee-Metford rifles A bolt-action .303 cal. military rifle adopted by the British in 1888. It was succeeded by the Lee-Enfield in 1895. See also **British .303 Lee-Metford rifle Mark I, British .303 Lee-Metford rifle Mark I*,** **British .303 Lee-Metford rifle Mark II,** and **British .303 Lee-Metford rifle Mark II*.**

left (right) **1.** A term used to establish the relative position of a body of troops. The person using the term "left" or "right" is assumed to be facing in the direction of the enemy regardless of whether the troops are advancing toward, or withdrawing from, the enemy. **2.** A directional deviation used by an observer or a spotter in adjusting ground or naval gunfire. **3.** A fire correction used by an observer to indicate that a lateral shift perpendicular to the spotting line is desired.

left-hand dagger A sixteenth- and seventeenth-century dagger designed to be held in the left hand in fencing with sword or rapier. The rapier was held in the right hand. A special form of this dagger, used in Italy and Spain, was called a *main-gauche.*

legion A body of Roman soldiers numbering anywhere from about 3,500 in earlier times to 5,000 to 6,000 under the empire.

Legion of Merit (LM) A decoration established in 1942 and awarded to military personnel for distinguished service to the United States in time of war or peace. Awards of this decoration to members of foreign armed forces are made in the degrees of Chief Commander, Commander, Officer, and Legionnaire.

Leigh light A particular make of searchlight that was used on airplanes in World War II for antisubmarine operations.

Leipzig A German light cruiser of World War II. It had a displacement of 6,650 tons, a speed of 32 knots, and a complement of 820 men. Main armament consisted of nine 5.9-in. and six 3.5-in. guns, twelve 21-in. torpedo tubes, and two aircraft. In July 1946 it was sunk in the North Sea with a cargo of poison gas.

lend-lease A system developed by the lend-Lease Act of March 11, 1941, by which the Allies during World War II could lend and lease war materials to one an-

Lebel 8mm revolver Model 1892. (*The Smithsonian Institution, Department of Defense Collection.*)

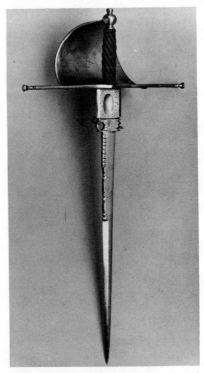

left-hand dagger. (*The Metropolitan Museum of Art, gift of William H. Riggs, 1913.*)

Leopard. (*Ministry of Defense, Federal Republic of Germany.*)

Letov Š-328. (*Military Historical Institute, Prague.*)

Lewis machine gun. (*Vickers Ltd.*)

other. Between March 1941 and July 1946, the United States shipped goods valued at some 50 billion dollars, the British Empire, the U.S.S.R., France, and China being the principal recipients. Some 7 billion dollars' worth of goods were returned on reverse lend-lease.

Leningrad A class of Soviet destroyers of 2,225 tons standard displacement completed in 1933–1941. They had a speed of 38 knots, a complement of about 250 men, and main armament consisting of four 5.1-in. guns, two 3-in. guns, and eight 21-in. torpedo tubes.

Le Normand A class of French frigates of 1,295 tons standard displacement completed in 1956–1960. They have a length of 325 ft, a beam of 33.8 ft, a speed of 28 knots, and a wartime complement of 200 men. Armament includes six 2.25-in. and two 20mm antiaircraft guns, homing torpedoes, and hedgehog-type depth-charge mortars.

Leon mine Named for Captain Karl Iskar Leon, its Swedish inventor, this is a floating naval mine that can be set to remain submerged within certain limits by an arrangement of hydrostatic valves.

Leopard 1. A German (Federal Republic) main battle tank in service since 1965 and presently used by Germany, the Netherlands, Belgium, and Norway. This tank has a crew of four, a weight of 40 tons, a road speed of 40 mph, main armament consisting of one **British 105mm QF gun (L7AI)** (which see), and secondary armament consisting of two 7.62mm machine guns. 2. A class of British antiaircraft frigates of 2,300 tons standard displacement completed in 1957–1959. They have a length of 339 ft, a beam of 40 ft, a speed of 25 knots, and a complement of 205 men. They are armed with four 4.5-in. guns, one 40mm antiaircraft gun, and one Squid three-barreled depth-charge mortar.

LES A U.S. Navy support landing boat.

lesse A Greek mantelet covered with hides.

lethal radius The distance from point of burst or ground zero at which a projectile, missile, or the like will probably destroy a target or kill persons.

Letov Š-328 A single-engine two-seat light tactical biplane reconnaissance bomber developed in Czechoslovakia in 1935 and used by Czech, German, and Bulgarian forces during World War II.

level To aim a gun or other weapon in direct line with the intended target.

level bombing Bombing in which bombs are released in level flight.

lewisite (L) This war gas is one of the **blistering agents,** which see, and has a rapid rate of action. It produces effects similar to those produced by HD (distilled mustard) but, in addition, acts as a systemic poison,

Lexington. (*U.S. Navy.*)

causing pulmonary edema, diarrhea, restlessness, weakness, subnormal temperature, and low blood pressure. Liquid L causes an immediate searing sensation in the eye and permanent loss of sight if not decontaminated within 1 minute. When inhaled in high concentrations, it may be fatal in as short a time as 10 minutes. It has a geranium-like smell.

Lewis machine gun A weapon developed in 1911 by Isaac N. Lewis, a U.S. Army lieutenant colonel. Based on a system invented by Samuel McClean, it was a gas-operated air-cooled light machine gun with a cyclic rate of fire of 500 to 600 rounds per minute. It had an overall length of 50.5 in., a barrel length of 26.04 in., and a weight of 25 lb. It was fed from 47- or 96-round flat drum magazines. It was an effective weapon and was used for both ground and aircraft applications. It saw service in the forces of numerous countries (including the United States, Great Britain, France, Italy, Belgium, Japan, and Holland) and was the light machine gun most used by the British Army during World War I. It was still in service as an antiaircraft weapon in World War II. The Lewis was the first machine gun ever fired from an aircraft (June 7, 1912).

Lexington A U.S. aircraft carrier completed in 1927 and a sister ship of the **Saratoga**, for details which see. *Lexington* was sunk by Japanese carrier aircraft in the Battle of the Coral Sea on May 5 and 6, 1942.

LFR A U.S. Navy inshore fire-support ship.

LFS A U.S. Navy amphibious fire-support ship.

LGM-25C See **Titan**.

LGM-30B(WS-133A) See **Minuteman**.

LGM-30 F/G (WS-133B) See **Minuteman**.

LHA A U.S. Navy amphibious assault ship, general purpose.

LHT A U.S. Navy lighthouse tender.

Liberator. (*U.S. Air Force.*)

liaison A contact or intercommunication maintained between elements of military forces to ensure mutual understanding and unity of purpose and action. It is often aided by exchange of personnel.

liberated territory Any area—domestic, neutral, or friendly—which, having been occupied by an enemy, is retaken by friendly forces.

Liberator The Consolidated B-24 Liberator was a U.S. four-engine bomber first flown in 1939 and produced, in various models, until 1945, by which time 18,188 aircraft had been manufactured. It had a maximum speed of 300 mph and a range (with a 5,000-lb bombload) of 1,700 mi. It was armed with ten .50 cal. machine guns and carried a maximum short-range bombload of 12,800 lb. It was used for a variety of duties, including strategic bombing, reconnaissance, antisubmarine operations, and passenger and freight transportation, and was used successfully in every theater of war. The PB4Y-1 and the PB4Y-2 (Privateer) were U.S. Navy versions and were equipped with single vertical stabilizers.

Liberator Express A popular name for the

C-87, a B-24 Liberator bomber converted to a cargo carrier.

liberator pistol See **U.S. .45 cal. Flare Projector**.

Liberty Eagle Also called the "Bug" or the "Kettering aerial torpedo," this was the first U.S. flying bomb. In production at the end of World War I, it consisted of a pilotless biplane powered by a 40-hp engine and guided by a gyro and a sensitive aneroid barometer. It carried 300 lb of TNT.

Lichtenstein A type of radar developed for use with German night-fighter aircraft during World War II. It was very successful, partly because of the failure of Allied airborne jammers to counter it. This led to the development of **Tuba**, which see.

lide A machine for throwing large stones against a fortified place.

lieutenant In the U.S. Army, Air Force, and Marine Corps there are two grades of this rank: second lieutenant and first lieutenant. The former, lower in rank, has a gold bar as insignia. A first lieutenant has a silver bar. In the U.S. Navy, there are two grades of this rank: lieutenant junior grade and lieutenant. The former, lower in rank,

Liftmaster. (*U.S. Air Force.*)

light artillery, a U.S. 105mm howitzer. (*U.S. Army.*)

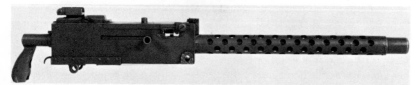

light machine gun, (U.S. .30 cal. T-66). (*The Smithsonian Institution.*)

has a silver bar (or two stripes of gold lace, one ½ in. wide and the other a ¼-in. stripe). A lieutenant has two silver bars (or two ½-in. stripes of gold lace).

lieutenant colonel In the U.S. Air Force, Army, and Marine Corps, the rank next below that of colonel and next above that of major. The insignia of this rank is a silver oak leaf. The rank corresponds with that of a commander in the Navy.

lieutenant commander In the U.S. Navy, an officer who ranks just below a commander and just above a lieutenant. The insignia of rank is a gold oak leaf or two

½-in. gold stripes with a ¼-in. stripe between them. The stripes appear on shoulder boards or the sleeves of uniforms.

lieutenant general A commissioned rank in the U.S. Air Force, Army, or Marine Corps ranking next below general and next above major general. The insignia is three silver stars.

lieutenant junior grade (JG) A U.S. Navy officer who ranks just above an ensign and just below a full lieutenant. The insignia of rank is one silver bar or two stripes on the uniform sleeve, one stripe being ½ in. wide and the other being ¼ in. wide.

lifeguard Aircraft and ships detailed to recover aircraft personnel at sea.

lifeguard submarine A submarine employed for rescue in an area which cannot be adequately covered by air or surface rescue facilities because of enemy opposition, distance from friendly bases, or other reasons. It is stationed near the object and sometimes along the route to be flown by the strike aircraft.

lift fire **1.** To advance the range of fire by elevating the muzzle of a weapon. **2.** To cease or suspend fire.

Liftmaster The Douglas C-118 Liftmaster is a four-engine (piston) long-range transport developed in the late 1940s and basically a modification of the C-54 Skymaster. It carries 74 troops or 27,000 lb of cargo and has a cruising speed of about 300 mph. The range is about 3,860 mi.

liftoff The initial motion of a space vehicle or missile as it rises from the launcher.

light antiaircraft artillery Conventional antiaircraft-artillery pieces, usually under 90mm, the weight of which in a trailed mount, including on-carriage fire control, does not exceed 20,000 lb. Self-propelled versions are rated in the same category as the trailed version.

light-armed Armed with light weapons and equipment, such as light troops.

light artillery All guns and howitzers of 105mm caliber (4.13 in.) or smaller.

light battery A battery of light artillery.

light bomber Any bomber considered to be relatively light in weight such as a bomber having a gross weight, including bombload, of less than 100,000 lb. In World War II, the A-20 and the A-26 were considered light bombers.

light-case bomb A type of general-purpose bomb having a thin, light metal casing; giving a high charge-weight ratio; and designed to accomplish damage primarily by blast. Also called a "blast bomb." A light-case bomb usually contains a charge of from 70 to 80 percent of the total weight.

light cavalry See **heavy cavalry.**

light cruiser A warship with 6-in. naval guns as main battery. It is designed to operate with strike, antisubmarine, or amphibious forces against air and surface threats. Full load displacement is approximately 18,000 tons. In the U.S. Navy the designation is CL.

lighter-than-air aircraft An aircraft that rises and is supported in air by virtue of a contained gas weighing less than the air displaced by the gas. Examples are blimps and dirigibles.

light field artillery Artillery used in field operations, such as the 75mm gun, 105mm howitzer, 3-in. gun, etc.

light horse Light cavalry.

light machine gun **1.** Any aircraft machine gun of .30 cal. or smaller. **2.** In

U.S. Army usage, any lightweight machine gun, including the .30 cal. air-cooled machine gun and excluding full automatic rifles, submachine guns, and machine pistols. **3.** In specific nonofficial context, any full automatic rifle or any machine gun having a total weight with mount, if any, of between 20 and 30 lb, approximately. The Browning automatic rifle and the Lewis machine gun typify this type.

Lightning **1.** A single-seat supersonic all-weather interceptor, strike, and reconnaissance jet fighter first flown in 1959 and manufactured by the British Aircraft Corporation. It has a speed above Mach 2, and later versions are armed with two 30mm Aden guns and two Hawker Siddeley Firestreak air-to-air missiles. **2.** The Lockheed P-38 Lightning was a twin-engine single-seat long-range fighter and fighter-bomber and the first USAAF fighter with a twin-boom configuration. It was first flown in January 1939, and successive models were developed throughout World War II. Later versions were equipped with two 1,425-hp engines and flew at speeds of 414 mph. They were armed with one 20mm Hispano cannon and four .50 cal. machine guns, plus two 1,000-lb bombs or ten 5-in. rockets. Lightnings claimed more Japanese aircraft destroyed than any other fighter. The leading U.S. fighter ace, Maj. Richard Bong, scored all 40 of his victories with this aircraft. **3.** See also **Folgore,** an Italian fighter of World War II.

light tank A full-track combat tank designed for missions requiring speed and mobility, such as those for security and reconnaissance. It may weigh up to 25 tons.

light weapon Any antiaircraft weapon having a caliber of 75mm or smaller. The term "automatic weapon" is sometimes used to refer to a light weapon, since antiaircraft light weapons are all automatic.

Lily The Allied code name for the Kawasaki Ki.48 Type 99 twin-engine light bomber used by the Japanese during World War II. It had a speed of 313 mph, a range of 1,491 mi with a 1,100-lb bombload, and armament consisting of four 7.7mm machine guns.

limber A detachable front part of a gun carriage or caisson consisting of two wheels, an axle, and the pole to which horses are attached. This frame is also used to support ammunition chests.

limber chest The ammunition chest or box carried on the limber.

Limbo A British shipborne surface-to-surface medium-range antisubmarine mortar system. In operation, the ship's sonar provides submarine position data to a predictor which computes mortar elevation and lateral tilt. The triple-barreled mortar fires a pattern of three mortar bombs programmed to give a three-dimensional pat-

Lightning. (*Lockheed Aircraft Corporation.*)

Lightning, shown armed with a Red Top missile. (*Hawker Siddeley Aviation Ltd.*)

tern ahead of the firing ship. The system has a range of about 2,000 meters, a missile length of about 5.75 ft, and a missile weight of about 440 lb. They became operational in the early 1960s.

lime pots Earthenware pots filled with quicklime. They were thrown in the faces of the attacking enemy.

limited war Armed conflict short of general war, exclusive of incidents, involving the overt engagement of the military forces of two or more nations.

limit of fire **1.** The boundary marking off the area on which gunfire can be delivered. **2.** Safe angular limits for firing at aerial targets.

limit stop An arm or part used to limit angular motion, as of a gun turret.

limpet mines Small explosives attached to the hull of a ship by swimmers.

Lince The Breda 88 Lince (Lynx) was a twin-engine bomber and fighter-bomber used by the Italians during World War II. It had a speed of 310 mph, a range of 900 mi with a 2,200-lb bombload, and armament consisting of three 12.7mm and three

linked ammunition. (*The Smithsonian Institution.*)

7.7mm machine guns.

Lincoln This British Avro-built four-engine bomber was a scaled-up version of the Lancaster bomber. It was intended for use in the Pacific theater during World War II, but appeared too late to see service. It had a speed of 310 mph, a range of 1,150 mi with a bombload of 22,000 lb, and armament consisting of two 20mm cannons and four .50 cal. machine guns.

line **1.** The front line; the line of defense presented to the enemy. **2.** The regular troops of an army. **3.** A formation of men or ships formed in any direction from a guide. **4.** In naval usage, a general term for "rope." **5.** In aviation usage, a general term for "shroud line" or "flight line."

line ahead A British naval term for "column"; a formation in which ships are placed one behind another.

line astern A line of aircraft, one after another.

line crew A ground crew that works on a flight line.

line defense The defense of a line, or a defense established along a line, as distinguished from area defense or point defense in air-defense operations.

line forces Soldiers on the line; combatant forces, as distinguished from noncombatant forces.

line of aim The line from a person's eye, such as that of a gunner or bombardier, through a sight, along which aim is taken.

line of battle The position of troops or ships drawn up to deliver an attack or receive a charge.

line-of-battle ship See **ship of the line.**

line of columns Parallel columns with their heads in a straight line.

line of communications See **lines of communication.**

line of counterapproach A trench made by the besieged in a fortification to move forward from the glacis and counteract the enemy's works.

line of defense **1.** An artificial or natural barrier which can be used against attack; a body of water, a fortification, etc. **2.** A nation's military forces, modified by the terms "first," "second," "third," etc. The first line of defense would be the standing army. The others would represent various reserve categories. **3.** In fortifications, the distance between the salient angle of the bastion and the opposite flank; the bastioned front.

line of departure **1.** The direction of a projectile at the instant it clears the muzzle of the gun. **2.** The direction of a bomb or rocket at the instant of launching. **3.** A line designated to coordinate the departure of attack or scouting elements; a jump-off line. **4.** A suitably marked offshore coordinating line to assist assault craft in landing on designated beaches at scheduled times.

line of elevation The prolongation of the bore when the piece is set to fire.

line of fall The line tangent to the trajectory at the level point, i.e., the point of the trajectory when the projectile is at the same height as the muzzle of the gun.

line officer In the U.S. Navy, an officer concerned with the operation of the forces afloat, in contrast to a staff officer.

line of fire The flight path or paths followed by projectiles fired from a weapon or group of weapons.

line of flight The line of movement, or the intended line of movement, of an aircraft, guided missile, projectile, or the like in the air. The line of flight may or may not be coincident with, or parallel to, the longitudinal axis of the aircraft, projectile, etc.

line of impact or arrival A line tangent to the trajectory at the point of impact or burst.

line of march A line along which troops advance or march.

line of position The straight line connecting the point of origin with the point of position. The point of origin is usually the gun or a position-finding instrument. Thus, corresponding to the three positions of the target, there are the line of position at observation, the line of present position, and the line of future position.

line of sight The line of vision; the optical axis of an observation instrument; the straight line between an observer's eye and a target or other observed object or spot, along which sight is taken.

line of site The straight line between the origin of the trajectory and the target. It is sometimes called "line of position."

line of supply The systems to the rear of an army by which it is supplied. Such a line may consist of a waterway, a road, a railway, etc.

liner **1.** The inner tube, in a cannon, which bears the rifling and which may be replaced when worn out. **2.** The detachable plastic or fiber inner layer of a metal helmet; a helmet liner. **3.** A metal inner box, usually with soldered or welded seams, designed to be placed within a sturdily constructed exterior container for the protection of ammunition or explosives against deterioration. **4.** The cone of material used as an integral part of shaped charges; a shaped-charge liner.

lines crémaillère Lines composed of alternate short and long faces at right angles to one another.

lines of bastion A succession of bastion-shaped parapets consisting of two faces and two flanks and connected by a curtain.

lines of circumvallation The defensive works by which a besieging army covers its rear and flanks.

lines of communication **1.** All the routes—land, water, and air—which connect an operating military force with a base of operations and along which supplies and reinforcements move. **2.** In fortifications, the trenches that unite one work with another so that men may pass from one place to another without being exposed to fire.

lines of retreat Generally, when a force retreats, it takes the same routes that it took to advance.

lines of tenailles Parapets which form a series of salient and reentering angles.

link In communications, a general term used to indicate the existence of communications facilities between two points.

link belt An ammunition feed belt for an automatic weapon in which metal links connect the cartridges and with them form the belt.

linked ammunition Cartridges fastened to one another side by side with metal links, forming a belt for ready feed to a machine gun. As the linked ammunition runs through the breech mechanism, the links and cartridge cases separate.

Linse (German for "lentil.") A German radio-controlled motorboat of World War II. It operated in units of three boats, one of which was the control boat and the other two of which carried explosives. The latter were controlled by human pilots until they neared the target, at which time the pilots jumped overboard and were picked up by the control boat, which also directed the explosive boats into their targets by radio.

linstock A long-handled device which held the burning quick match sometimes used to ignite muzzle-loading cannons. Early versions sometimes had a spear point and metal clamps. Late ones had only a slot or hole in the wood.

Lion A class of British 26,350-ton battle cruisers completed in 1912. There were two ships in the class, *Lion* and *Princess Royal,* and they had a length of 680 ft, a complement of 1,000 men, and armament consisting of eight 13.5-in. guns, sixteen 4-in. guns, and three 21-in. torpedo tubes. They had a speed of 31 knots.

Lioré-et-Olivier H-257bis, H-258 A six-seat twin-engine torpedo-bomber twin-float seaplane developed for the French Navy and first flown in 1932.

liquid-cooled Cooled by a liquid, such as

water or glycol, and said especially of engines or machine guns.

liquid propellant Any liquid combustible fed to the combustion chamber of a rocket engine.

lis 1. A French term for a system of defense similar to palisades. It consists of upright stakes tied together with vines or twigs. **2.** In ancient times, an Irish fortification consisting of a circular mound or trench, often surrounding dwellings.

listen To maintain a continuous radio-receiver watch.

litter A basket or frame utilized for the transport of injured persons.

Little David (914mm mortar T1) An experimental rifled mortar of 36-in. diameter developed during World War II. This mortar and its special ammunition were secretly developed in case they should be required in reducing German fortifications; however, this proved to be unnecessary. The mortar weighed 172,900 lb, and the projectile weighed 3,650 lb, of which 1,589 lb was high explosives. It was fired by a maximum propelling charge of 218 lb of powder and had a range of about 9,000 yd.

Little Joe A popular name for the KAN-2 missile. It derived from an earlier Little Joe (KAN-1) designed during World War II for use against Japanese kamikaze aircraft. KAN-1 was a radio-controlled winged missile with a 100-lb high-explosive warhead.

Littlejohn 1. A U.S. surface-to-surface artillery rocket developed by the U.S. Army Missile Command. It is composed of a 318mm MGR-3A (formerly M-15) rocket and the M-34 launcher. The system can be towed by a jeep or a 3/4-ton truck. It has an overall length of 14 ft 5 in., a firing weight of 780 lb, and a range of over 10 mi. Development of the system began in 1957. **2.** A highly mobile Allied two-pounder antitank gun of World War II.

Little Willie The nickname of the first tank to be produced. Designed by Sir William Tritton and demonstrated before King George V in 1915, this vehicle had a weight of 28 tons, a speed of 3.5 mph, and armament consisting of one 2-pounder gun and two machine guns. An improved model was called "Mother" or "Big Willie."

live ammunition Ammunition containing explosives or active chemicals, as distinguished from inert or drill ammunition.

Liverpool A British cruiser of 9,400 tons standard displacement completed in 1938. (Two sister ships, *Gloucester* and *Manchester*, were lost during World War II.) It had a length of 592 ft, a beam of 62 ft, a speed of 32.3 knots, and a complement of 850 men. It was armed with nine 6-in. and eight 4-in. guns, twenty-six 2-pounder pompoms, eight 40mm Bofors antiaircraft guns, and six 21-in. torpedo tubes.

liziere The berme of a parapet.

Ljungman semiautomatic rifle This weapon was adopted by Sweden in 1942 and is referred to as the "AG 42B." It has been manufactured in Egypt in both 7.92 mm and 7.62mm. The Swedish version fires the 6.5 × 55mm cartridge. It is a gas-operated semiautomatic weapon with an overall length of 47.6 in., a barrel length of 24.5 in., and a weight of 10.4 lb. It uses a 10-round nondetachable box magazine and has a muzzle velocity of 2,460 fps. (Picture, next page.)

LKA A U.S. Navy amphibious cargo ship.

Lloyd C types Austro-Hungarian two-place single-engine reconnaissance aircraft first flown in mid-1914. The C.II appeared in 1915. It had a speed of about 79 mph and was later armed with a Schwarzlose machine gun for the observer.

load 1. A single round of ammunition. **2.** A command to put ammunition into a gun. **3.** To stow supplies into a boat, vehicle, ship, or aircraft.

loader A mechanical device which loads guns with cartridges.

loading The process of putting troops, equipment, and supplies into ships, aircraft, trains, or road transport or other conveyances.

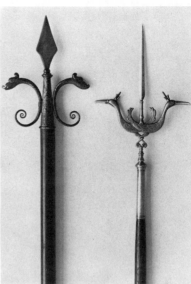
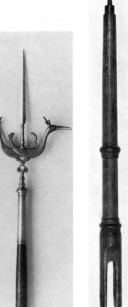

linstock. (*The Metropolitan Museum of Art, gift of William H. Riggs. The Smithsonian Institution, H. Williams Collection.*)

Littlejohn. (*U.S. Army.*)

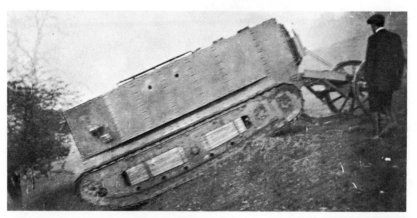

Little Willie. (*The Imperial War Museum.*)

Lochaber ax. *(The Metropolitan Museum of Art, Bashford Dean Memorial Collection.)*

loading angle The angle of elevation specified for loading a particular weapon with its ammunition.

loading gate A magazine or breech cover that is hinged and closed except during loading and unloading operations.

loading tray A trough-shaped carrier on which heavy projectiles are placed so that they can be more easily and safely slipped into the breech of a gun.

loafer's loops A slang term for "aiguillettes."

Lobber The name given to an Army solid-propellant cargo-carrying rocket with a range of 10 to 15 mi.

Loch A class of British antisubmarine frigates of 1,435 tons standard displacement completed in 1944–1946. They had a speed of 19.5 knots, a complement of 103 men, and armament consisting of one 4-in. gun, four 2-pounder pompoms, four 40mm antiaircraft guns, two depth-charge throwers, and two Squid depth-charge mortars.

Lochaber ax A polearm with a long single-edged ax head, often with a hook at the top. The name derives from Lochaber, Scotland.

lochage In ancient Greece, the commander of a lochus.

lochus A small Greek army division or company containing from 100 to 200 men.

lock **1.** The position of a safety mechanism which prevents a weapon from being fired.

2. The fastening device used to secure against accidental movement, as on a control surface. **3.** To secure or make safe, as to set the safety on a weapon. **4.** To lock on; to fasten onto and automatically follow by means of a radar beam. Said of a radar set or antenna. **5.** The part or apparatus of a firearm by means of which the charge is exploded, such as a matchlock, miquelet, percussion lock, wheellock, or flintlock.

locket The metal reinforcement at the mouth of a scabbard.

lockhole The open recess in a gunstock to accommodate the lock; the lock mortise.

locking lugs Metal projections on the bolt of a small-arms weapon which cam into recesses cut in the side of the receiver to lock the weapon prior to firing.

lock on A term signifying that a tracking or target-seeking system is continuously and automatically tracking a target in one or more coordinates (e.g., range, bearing, and elevation).

Lodestar The Lockheed C-56 Lodestar was a twin-engine transport developed in the late 1930s and used in military service during World War II.

lodgment **1.** In general terms, the occupation or holding of enemy territory; specifically, a footing obtained inside an enemy's fortification. **2.** Quarters for soldiers.

LOF Line of fire, a straight line joining the gun and the point of impact (or burst) of the projectile.

loft bombing A method of aerial bombing in which the delivery plane approaches the target at a very low altitude, makes a definite pull-up at a given point, releases a bomb at a predetermined point during the pull-up, and tosses the missile onto the target.

logistics The science of planning and carrying out the movement and maintenance of forces.

Lohner B and C types Austro-Hungarian two-place single-engine reconnaissance biplanes first flown in 1914. They were used through 1916, had a speed of about 85 mph, and were armed with one Schwarzlose machine gun in the rear (for use by the observer).

Lohner L An Austro-Hungarian two-place single-engine biplane reconnaissance flying boat that entered service in the second half of 1915. They had a speed of 65 mph and armament consisting of one Schwarzlose machine gun, and they carried up to 441 lb of bombs or depth charges. They operated in the Adriatic area against Allied shipping and targets on the Italian mainland.

Loire 130 A French single-engine three-seat shipboard or shore-based observation flying boat first flown in 1934.

Loki A fin-stabilized unguided solid-propellant rocket developed during World War II

Ljungman semiautomatic rifle. *(Swedish Defense Staff.)*

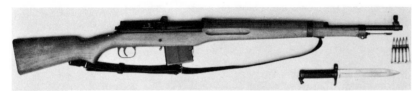

longbow. *(The Metropolitan Museum of Art, gift of William H. Riggs, 1913.)*

Long Tom, M53. *(U.S. Army.)*

for antiaircraft use, but never used in combat.

lombard An ancient form or size of cannon.

London **1.** The name of a biplane flying boat of the 1930s. See **Saro London.** **2.** A class of British heavy cruisers of 9,830 tons standard displacement completed in 1929. There were four ships in the class: *London, Devonshire, Sussex,* and *Shropshire.* They had a speed of 32 knots, a complement of 800 men, and main armament consisting of eight 8-in. and eight 4-in. guns, eight 21-in. torpedo tubes, and one aircraft. **3.** A class of British 15,000-ton battleships completed in 1902. It included *London, Bulwark,* and *Venerable,* each of which had a length of 430 ft, a complement of 750 men, and main armament consisting of four 12-in. and twelve 6-in. guns, plus four 18-in. torpedo tubes. They had a speed of 18 knots.

Long Beach A U.S. nuclear-powered guided-missile cruiser (CGN) completed in 1961. It has a standard displacement of 14,200 tons, a length of 721 ft, a beam of 73 ft, a speed of 35 knots, and a complement of 1,000 men. It is armed with two 5-in. guns, one twin Talos surface-to-air launcher, two twin Terrier surface-to-air launchers, one Asroc eight-tube launcher, and two triple torpedo launchers.

longbow An important English and Welsh weapon of the thirteenth to the fifteenth centuries. They were usually made of yew, were about 5 ft long, and used arrows 1 yd in length. An experienced archer was accurate at ranges up to 240 yd.

long-delay fuze A type of delay fuze, especially for bombs, in which the fuze action is delayed for a relatively long period of time, usually anywhere from 2 minutes to 5 days.

longeron A principal longitudinal member of the structural framework of a fuselage, nacelle, or empennage boom.

Long Eye The NATO code name for a type of Soviet I-band antiaircraft artillery-fire-control radar.

Longhorn See **Farman MF.7.**

Long Lance A nickname for the **Japanese torpedo Type 93,** which see.

Long Talk The NATO code name for a type of Soviet C-band early-warning and surveillance radar.

Long Tom **1.** The 155mm self-propelled gun M-53 used by the U.S. Army and Marine Corps. It is full-tracked to provide mobility for the gun and protection for the crew in offensive combat. It has a crew of six. **2.** In World War II, the 155mm self-propelled gun M2. Extremely accurate, it fired a 95-lb projectile a distance of 25,700 yd. It weighed 15 tons and had a barrel length of about 23 ft. During the assault on the Siegfried Line these tanks assisted in the destruction of 120 pillboxes, obliterating one with each round fired from a range

of 300 yd. **3.** Any long pivot gun once carried on the deck of a ship. Also, sometimes, any large gun of long range, especially when used ashore.

Long Track The NATO code name for a type of Soviet I-band early-warning and surveillance radar.

Looking Glass The code name for the U.S. Air Force EC-135C airborne command post under the 465L Strategic Air Command Control System for the transmission, collection, processing, and displaying of data to assist the SAC in command and control of forces. See also **SACCS.**

lookout **1.** A man stationed to keep a visual watch over air, horizon, surface, fog, etc. **2.** A crow's nest.

Look Two The NATO code name for a type of Soviet airborne I-band radar.

Loon **1.** The U.S. Navy designation for the JB-2, an American version of the German V-1 flying bomb. **2.** A long-range navigational aid used by ships and airplanes.

loopholes Small openings in walls, stockades, and parapets through which small arms could be fired.

loose ammunition Firearm ammunition in which two or more components of each round, usually the projectile and the pro-

pelling charge, are separate from one another and are handled separately in loading, as distinguished from fixed ammunition. Loose ammunition is used in certain large cannons and is the usual form of ammunition for old-fashioned muzzle-loading arms.

loose round A defective cartridge in which the bullet is loose in the cartridge case.

loran A long-range-radio navigation position-fixing system using the time difference of reception of pulse-type transmissions from two or more fixed stations. (This term is derived from the words "*long-range* electronic *navigation.*")

Lord Nelson A class of British battleships of 16,500 tons displacement completed in 1907–1908. It included *Lord Nelson* and *Agamemnon,* both of which had a length of 445 ft, a complement of 865 men, and armament consisting of four 12-in. guns, ten 9.2-in. guns (plus smaller weapons), and five 18-in. torpedo tubes. They had a speed of 19 knots.

lorica The Roman cuirass or coat of mail made variously of overlapping plates of iron, linked iron rings, or hard leather or metal.

Los Angeles A rigid airship built by the

Los Angeles, landing aboard the U.S.S. *Saratoga,* January 1929. (*U.S. Navy.*)

Louisiana. (*U.S. Navy.*)

LPH, The U.S.S. *New Orleans* (LPH-11). (*U.S. Navy.*)

LSD, the U.S.S. *Monticello* (LSD-35). (*U.S. Navy.*)

German Zeppelin Works. It was commissioned into the U.S. Navy in 1924, but was withdrawn from service in June 1932. It was also known as the "Z.R.III." The *Los Angeles* was used as a training ship in 1933 and was later used in mooring-mast experiments.

Louisiana A class of U.S. battleships of 16,000 tons standard displacement. It included *Louisiana* and *Connecticut*. *Louisiana* was commissioned in 1906 and had a length of 456 ft, a beam of about 77 ft, a complement of 827 men, and main armament consisting of four 12-in., eight 8-in., and twelve 7-in. guns, plus four 21-in. torpedo tubes.

low-altitude bombing Horizontal bombing with the height of release at an altitude between 900 and 8,000 ft.

low-angle fire Gunfire delivered at angles of elevation below the elevation that corresponds to the maximum range of the piece; the ranges thus increase with increases in angles of elevation.

low-angle loft bombing A type of loft bombing of free-fall bombs wherein weapon release occurs at an angle less than 35° above the horizontal.

Low Blow The NATO code name for a type of Soviet I-band surface-to-air missile (SAM) and surface-to-surface missile (SSM) acquisition and fire-control radar. It is used with the **GOA** missile, which see.

low explosive Any nonatomic explosive, such as smokeless gunpowder, characterized usually by deflagration rather than detonation and used especially as a propellant in guns or rockets.

low-order burst (detonation) The incomplete, less destructive detonation of an explosive.

low velocity Specifically, a muzzle velocity of an artillery projectile of 2,499 fps or less.

LPA A U.S. Navy amphibious transport.

LPD A U.S. Navy amphibious transport dock.

LPH A U.S. Navy amphibious assault ship.

LPR A U.S. Navy amphibious transport, small.

LPSS A U.S. Navy amphibious transport submarine.

LS 7.7mm machine gun Model 26/32 A Finnish recoil-operated air-cooled machine gun with a rate of fire of 450 to 550 rounds per minute. It weighed 19.5 lb and was fed from 25- or 75-round magazines.

LSD Landing ship dock. The U.S. World War II versions were of 4,032 tons standard displacement. They had a length of 457 ft, a beam of 72 ft, a speed of 15.4 knots, and a complement of 240 men. They could carry three LSU's or eighteen LCM's.

LSFF A U.S. Navy flotilla flagship landing ship.

LSI A U.S. Navy giant Y boat.

LSIG A U.S. Navy landing craft, infantry (gunboat).

LSIL A U.S. Navy infantry landing ship, large.

LSIM A U.S. Navy landing craft, infantry (mortar).

LSIR A U.S. Navy landing craft, infantry (rocket).

LSM Medium landing ship. U.S. World War II versions had a displacement of 743 tons, a length of 203 ft, a speed of 12 knots, and a crew of 59; they carried five medium tanks.

LSMR A U.S. Navy medium landing ship (rocket).

LSSL A U.S. Navy support landing ship, large, Mk. III.

LST Landing ship tank. U.S. LST 1-1152 classes of World War II had a standard displacement of 1,653 tons, a length of 316 ft, a speed of 11 knots, and a complement of 211 men. They were armed with seven 40mm and two 20mm antiaircraft guns and had a cargo capacity of 2,100 tons. They were also nicknamed "Large Slow Targets."

LSTH A U.S. Navy landing ship, tank (casualty evacuation).

LSTS A U.S. Navy landing ship, utility.

LSU A U.S. Navy landing ship, utility.

LSV A U.S. Navy landing ship, vehicle. A roll-on, roll-off cargo ship.

LTA Lighter than air.

LTP-6 A U.S. Navy 5-ton personnel landing vehicle.

Lucerne hammer A fifteenth-century polearm with a hammerhead of four points opposite a single point and having a long, straight spike on the end.

Lufbery circle (After Raoul G. Lufbery, 1885–1918.) An aircraft formation in which two or more airplanes follow one another in a vertical spiral, or in a more or less horizontal circle, in order to protect one another and also to be in position to face attacking planes. R. G. Lufbery was French-

Lulu. (*U.S. Navy.*)

born and was an ace in the Lafayette Escadrille. He was, however, commissioned a major in the American Air Service in January 1918. He was killed in combat in May of that year.

Luftwaffe (Literally, "air weapon.") The name of the German air force from 1935 through World War II.

lug band Any of the bands on an aircraft rocket which, with the appropriate fittings, attach the rocket to a rail-type or post-type aircraft rocket launcher.

Luger automatic pistol An automatic pistol with a toggle-locked breech mechanism developed at the turn of the twentieth century from a Borchardt pistol design. Developed by the German engineer George Luger, the first model was called the "Pistole Parabellum Model 1900." It was in caliber 7.65 mm and was followed by the Model 1902, which was made in caliber 9 mm. This weapon has a detachable box magazine with a capacity of eight cartridges, a length of 8¾ in., and a barrel length of about 4 in. The total weight is about 30 oz. The Model 1904 was adopted by the German Navy in 1904. The Model 1908 was adopted for the German Army, as was the Long pistol Model 1908, a special model with an 8-in. barrel and a 32-round magazine. The Luger was the official military side arm in Germany until 1938 and was also adopted by other countries including Switzerland, Bulgaria, the Netherlands, and Portugal.

Lulu A U.S. Navy air-delivered atomic depth charge with a high radius of kill capability against submarines.

lunette 1. A towing ring in the trail plate or tongue of a towed vehicle, such as a gun carriage or trailer, used for attaching the

LST, the U.S.S. *Newport* (LST-1179). (*U.S. Navy.*)

Luger automatic pistol. (*The Smithsonian Institution, Department of Defense Collection.*)

towed vehicle to the prime mover or towing vehicle. **2.** In fortifications, a fieldwork consisting of two faces forming a salient angle and two flanks parallel to the capital or imaginary line bisecting the salient angle.

Lützow The name of three major German warships. The first *Lützow* was a battle cruiser completed in 1915. It had a displacement of 26,600 tons and main armament consisting of eight 12-in. guns, twelve

Lucerne hammer. (*The Metropolitan Museum of Art, gift of William H. Riggs, 1913.*)

LVT. (*U.S. Navy.*)

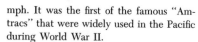

mph. It was the first of the famous "Amtracs" that were widely used in the Pacific during World War II.

LVT 2 An improved version of the LVT 1, it had a weight of 31,200 lb, a length of 26 ft 1 in., and a speed (on water) of 7.5 mph.

LVTE-1 A U.S. landing vehicle, tracked, engineer, Model 1.

LVTH-6 A U.S. Army and Marine Corps self-propelled amphibious 105mm howitzer. It has a speed of 30 mph on land and 7 mph on water. It weighs 41 tons and has a range of 190 mi.

LVTP Landing vehicle, tracked, personnel.

LVTP-5A1 A U.S. Marine Corps amphibious assault vehicle with a speed of 6.8 mph on water (30 mph on land), a weight of 44 tons, and a troop capacity of 34 men.

LVTP7 A U.S. Marine Corps amphibious assault vehicle with a speed of 8.4 mph on water (41.6 mph on land), a weight of 25 tons, and a troop capacity of 25 men.

LVTR Landing vehicle, tracked, recovery. A U.S. amphibious vehicle designed for vehicle recovery operations and maintenance.

LVW A U.S. 5-ton cargo landing vehicle with wheels for ground use.

LVXH-1 A U.S. Marine Corps amphibious support vehicle (hydrofoil) developed to operate from a mother ship 50 mi offshore to inland logistic-support areas. It has a payload of 10,000 lb and a speed of about 12 knots.

lyddite A British high explosive, mostly picric acid, once used as a shell explosive. The name derives from Lydd, England.

Lynx A full-track command and reconnaissance carrier based on the design of the U.S. armored personnel carrier M113. This FMC Corporation-produced vehicle is now in service with the Canadian and Royal Netherlands Armies. It is smaller, lighter, and more mobile than the M113 and is suitable for airlifting and paradropping. It has a crew of three, a weight of 8 tons, a road speed of 43 mph, and armament consisting of two machine guns (one .50 cal. and one .30 cal.).

lyonnois A machine mounted on wheels and used for the defense of a breach. It has a head with multiple sharp points or spikes.

Lyran A Bofors-built 71mm close-range illuminating system that projects a flare shell to a height of approximately 250 meters. The burning time of the parachute-borne flare is 30 seconds.

Lysander A two-place single-engine high-wing monoplane developed during World War II by the British firm of Westland and used as an Army cooperation airplane and also for such duties as target towing, training, air rescue, and other service.

Lyran. (*A. B. Bofors.*)

6-in. guns, and five 22-in. torpedo tubes. Sister ships included the *Derfflinger* and *Ersatz Hertha.* The second ship was a "pocket battleship" launched in 1931 and a sister ship of the **Admiral Graf Spee,** for details which see, and the *Admiral Scheer.* It was scuttled at Swinemunde in April 1945. The third vessel was a 13,900-ton heavy cruiser completed in 1939 and sold to the Soviet Union. It was a sister ship of the *Admiral Hipper* and was bombed in Leningrad early in World War II.

L.V.G. C types German (Luft-Verkehrs Gesellschaft) two-place single-engine observation and reconnaissance biplanes first introduced early in 1915. The C.I was the first two-place German aircraft provided with a Parabellum gun on a Schneider-ring mounting. Various models were used throughout World War I for artillery observation, photoreconnaissance, and light bombing. They had a top speed of about 105 mph and could carry 254 lb of bombs.

LVH A U.S. Navy hydrofoil landing craft.

LVT A U.S. Navy landing vehicle, tracked.

LVT 1 Landing vehicle, tracked, 1. A U.S. amphibious personnel carrier introduced in 1941. It had a weight of 21,800 lb, a length of 21 ft 6 in., and a speed (on water) of 6.1

LVTP-5, shown leaving an LSD, the U.S.S. *Alamo.* (*U.S. Navy.*)

M The following table lists current U.S. military designations. See also **MK** and **XM** tables.

M1	Bayonet. For .30 cal. M1, M1C, and M1D rifles.
M1	Cannon, 40mm.
M1	Carbine, .30 cal., semiautomatic.
M1	Cartridge, .30 cal., tracer and ball.
M1	Cartridge, .50 cal., incendiary.
M1	Cartridge, 105mm.
M1	Charge, propellant, 8-in., for M2A1E1, M47, and M110 howitzers.
M1	Gun, 90mm.
M1	Howitzer, 155mm.
M1	Mortar, 81mm.
M1A1	Cannon, 120mm.
M1A1	Howitzer (pack), 75mm.
M1A1	Howitzer, 155mm.
M1A2	Cannon, 120mm.
M1A2	Gun, 37mm.
M1A3	Cannon, 120mm.
M2	Armament subsystem, helicopter, 7.62mm machine gun, twin, used on the OH-13 and OH-23.
M2	Cannon, 40mm.
M2	Cannon, 90mm.
M2	Carbine, .30 cal., automatic.
M2	Cartridge, .30 cal., ball.
M2	Cartridge, .50 cal., four AP and one tracer.
M2	Cartridge, .50 cal., AP.
M2	Cartridge, 4.2-in.
M2	Charge, propellant, 8-in. For M2A1E1, M47, and M110 howitzers.
M2	Gun, 155mm. Fires M101 cartridge.
M2	Howitzer, 8-in.
M2	Howitzer, 105mm. Fires M327, M84, M60E1, M314A2, and M444 cartridges.
M2	Machine gun, .50 cal., Browning, heavy-barreled, fixed.
M2	Mine, AP.
M2	Mortar, 4.2-in. Fires M328A1, M335A2, and M328A1 cartridges.
M2	Mortar, infantry, 60mm. Fires M49A2E2, M50A2E1, M83A3, and M302E1 cartridges.

M2A1	Cannon, 40mm.
M2A1	Cartridge, 4.2-in.
M2A1	Gun, 155mm. Fires M101 cartridge.
M2A1	Howitzer, 105mm. Fires M67 and M444 cartridges.
M2A1	Howitzer, 8-in.
M2A1	Mine, AP.
M2A1E1	Howitzer, 8-in.
M2A2	Dummy cartridge, 75mm.
M2A2	Howitzer, 105mm. Fires M67, M395, and M84 cartridges.
M2A3	Mine, AP.
M2A3B2	Mine, AP.
M2A4	Mine, AP.
M3	Cannon, 75mm.
M3	Carrier, personnel, half-track.
M3	Cartridge, 4.2-in.
M3	Cartridge, grenade, rifle, .30 cal.
M3	Gun, 20mm. Fires M210 and M204 cartridges.
M3	Howitzer, 75mm. Fires M337 cartridge.
M3	Knife, trench.
M3	Mine, AP.
M3	Submachine gun, .45 cal.
M3A1	Carrier, personnel, half-track.
M3A1	Cartridge, 4.2-in.
M3A1	Cartridge, 40mm.
M3A1	Charge, propelling, 155mm. For M1, M1A1, M45, and M109 howitzers.
M3A1	Submachine gun, .45 cal.
M4	Bayonet knife. For M1, M1A1, M2, and M3 carbines.
M4	Howitzer, 105mm. Fires M327, M67, M84, M60E1, M314A2, M395, M444, and M413 cartridges.
M4	Tractor, full-track, high-speed, 18-ton.
M4A1	Howitzer, 105mm. Fires M67, M395, and M84 cartridges.
M4A1	Tractor, full-track, high-speed, 18-ton.
M4A1C	Tractor, full-track, high-speed, 18-ton.
M4A2	Charge, propelling, 155mm. For M1, M1A1, M45, and M109 howitzers.
M4A2	Tractor, full-track, high-speed, 18-ton.
M4A3	Tank, medium, full-track, 76mm.
M4C	Tractor, full-track, high-speed, 18-ton.
M5	Armament subsystem, helicopter, 40mm grenade launcher used on the UH-1B/C.

M5	Bayonet knife. For M1, M1C, and M1D rifles.
M5	Bulldozer, earthmoving, tractor mounting (mounted on the M8A2 tractor, full-track, high-speed).
M5	Cluster, practice bomb.
M5	Tractor, full-track, high-speed, 13-ton.
M5A1	Bayonet knife for M1, M1C, and M1D rifles.
M5A1	Tractor, full-track, high-speed, 13-ton.
M5A2	Tractor, full-track, high-speed, 13-ton.
M5A3	Tractor, full-track, high-speed, 13-ton.
M5A4	Tractor, full-track, high-speed, 13-ton.
M6	Armament subsystem, helicopter, 7.62mm machine gun, quad used on the UH-1B/C.
M6	Bayonet knife. For M14 rifle.
M6	Bulldozer, earthmoving, tank mounting (mounted on the M47 tank, combat, full-track, 90mm gun).
M6	Cartridge, grenade, carbine, .30 cal.
M6	Grenade, riot-control.
M6	Mine, antitank.
M6	Tractor, full-track, high-speed, 38-ton.
M6A1	Grenade, riot-control.
M7	Bayonet knife. For 5.56mm M16 and M16E1 rifles.
M7	Cartridge, 75mm.
M7	Grenade launcher.
M7	Grenade, riot-control.
M7	Mine, antitank.
M7	Rifle.
M7A1	Grenade, riot-control.
M7A1	Mine, antitank.
M7A1-6	Mechanized flamethrower.
M7A2	Mine, antitank.
M7A3	Hand grenade, riot-control.
M8	Bulldozer, earthmoving, tank mounting (mounted on tank, combat, full-track, 90mm gun, M48).
M8	Car, armored, light.
M8	Cartridge, .50 cal.
M8	Grenade launcher. For M1, M1A1, and M2 carbines.
M8	Hand grenade, smoke.
M8	Mine, practice, APERS.
M8A1	Bulldozer, earthmoving, tank mounting (mounted on tank, combat, full-track, 90mm gun, M48).

285

M8A1   Tractor, full-track, high-speed.
M8A2   Tractor, full-track, high-speed.
M9   Bulldozer, earthmoving, tank mounting (mounted on tank, combat, full-track, 105mm gun, M60).
M9   Rifle, .30 cal.
M9E1-7   Flamethrower, portable.
M9-7   Flamethrower, portable.
M10   Mine, antitank.
M10-8   Gun, flame, used on the M132 flamethrower, self-propelled, full-tracked.
M11   Personnel carrier.
M12   Cluster, incendiary bomb, 100-lb.
M12   Gun, subcaliber, 37mm.
M12   Mine, AT, practice, heavy.
M12   Rifle, .22 cal.
M12   Shotgun, 12-gauge Winchester riot type.
M12 SUU-16A   Vulcan pod for 20mm Gatling gun.
M12A1   Mine, AT, practice, heavy.
M12B1   Dummy cartridge, 90mm.
M12B2   Dummy cartridge, 90mm.
M13   Cluster, incendiary bomb, 500-lb.
M13   Gun, subcaliber, 37mm.
M14   Cartridge, 105mm.
M14   Gun, subcaliber, 37mm.
M14   Hand grenade, incendiary.
M14   Machine-gun pod, .50 cal.
M14   Projectile, 8-in.
M14   Rifle, 7.62mm.
M14E2   Rifle, 7.62mm. Weight, 8.7 lb; range, 3,500 yd.
M15   Gun, subcaliber, 37mm.
M15   Hand grenade, AT.
M15   Mine, AT.
M15   Projectile, 120mm.
M15A2   Tank transport semitrailer, 50-ton, eight-wheeled.
M16   Armament subsystem, helicopter, 7.62mm machine gun and 2.75-in. rocket launcher.
M16   Carriage, motor, multiple-gun.
M16   Dummy cartridge, 75mm.
M16   Mine, AP.
M16   Rifle, 5.56mm.
M16   Mine, AP, bounding fragmentation type.
M16A1   Rifle, 5.56mm, light, high-velocity.
M16E1   Rifle, 5.56mm.
M17   Cartridge, .50 cal., tracer.
M17   Dummy cartridge, 40mm.
M17   Standard protective mask.
M17 (T34)   Mine, AP.
M17A1   Signal, ground, pyrotechnic.
M17B1   Dummy cartridge, 40mm.
M18   Carriage, motor, 76mm.
M18   Hand grenade.
M18   Rifle, 57mm, recoilless.
M18 (T48)   Mine, AP.
M18A1   Cartridge, 40mm.
M18A1   Mine, claymore.
M18A1   Rifle, 57mm, recoilless.
M18A1   Signal, ground, pyrotechnic.
M18A2   Signal, ground, pyrotechnic.
M19   Cartridge, 12-gauge, shotgun.
M19   Cartridge, 75mm.
M19   Cluster, incendiary bomb, 500-lb.
M19   Mine, AT.
M19   Mortar, infantry, 60mm. Fires M49A2F2, M50A2E1, and M302E1 cartridges.
M19 (T18)   Mine, AT.
M19 (T18E4)   Mine, AT.
M19A1   Grenade, white phosphorous.
M19A1   Gun, antiaircraft, self-propelled, twin, 40mm.
M19A1   Signal, ground, pyrotechnic.
M19A2   Cluster, incendiary bomb, 500-lb.
M19A2   Signal, ILLUM, ground, parachute.
M19B1   Cartridge, 75mm.
M20   Cartridge, .50 cal.
M20   Cluster, incendiary bomb, 500-lb.
M20   Rifle, 75mm. Fires M320, M309, and M309A1 cartridges.
M20   Rocket launcher, 3.5-in.
M20 (T38)   Mine, AT.
M20A1   Cluster, incendiary bomb, 500-lb.
M20A1   Rocket launcher, 3.5-in.
M20A1   Signal, ground, pyrotechnic.
M21   Armament subsystem, helicopter, 7.62mm machine gun and 2.75-in. rocket launcher.
M21   Carrier, mortar, 81mm, half-track.
M21   Cluster, incendiary bomb, 500-lb.
M21   Dummy cartridge, 37mm.
M21   Mine, AT, HE.
M21A1   Signal, ground, pyrotechnic.
M22   Armament subsystem, helicopter, guided-missile launcher.
M22   Cluster, incendiary bomb, 500-lb.
M22   S-11 wire-guided missile.

M22A1   Cluster, incendiary bomb, 500-lb.
M22A1   Signal, ground, pyrotechnic.
M23   Armament subsystem, helicopter, 7.62mm machine gun, door-mounted.
M23   Cartridge, .30 cal.
M23   Cartridge, .50 cal.
M23   Mine, land.
M23A1   Grenade.
M24   Armament subsystem, helicopter, 7.62mm machine gun, door-mounted.
M24   Cartridge, .22 cal., long rifle.
M24   Gun, 20mm. Fires M99A1 and M97A2 cartridges.
M24   Mine, antitank.
M24   Protective mask for helicopters, with communications link.
M24   Tank, light.
M25   Adapter, cluster, 500-lb.
M25   Cartridge, .30 cal., tracer-linked.
M25   Cartridge, 40mm.
M25   Protective mask for tank crewmen, with communications link.
M25A2   Hand grenade, riot-control.
M26   Adapter, cluster, 500-lb.
M26   Hand grenade, fragmentation.
M26   Mine, AP.
M26   Tank, medium, 90mm.
M26A1   Cluster, fragmentation bomb, 500-lb.
M26A1   Grenade, fragmentation.
M26A1   Truck, tractor, 12-ton.
M26A2   Truck, tractor, 12-ton.
M27   Cartridge, .30 cal., carbine tracer.
M27   Guided-missile launcher for Corporal system.
M27   Rifle, 105mm. Fires M323 cartridge.
M27A1   Rifle, 105mm. Fires M323 cartridge.
M28   Cartridge, 75mm.
M28A2   Cluster, fragmentation bomb, 100-lb.
M28A2   Rocket, 3.5-in.
M29   Adapter, cluster, 1,000-lb.
M29   Carrier, cargo, 1/2-ton.
M29   Grenade, practice, rifle.
M29   Mortar, 81mm; range, 3,650 meters. Fires M43, M43A1, M57, M301, M362, M362A1, M370, M374, and M375 cartridges.
M29A2   Rocket, 3.5-in., practice.
M29C   Carrier, cargo, 1/2-ton amphibious.
M29E1   Mortar, 3.5-in.
M30   Adapter, cluster, 750-lb.
M30   Gun, 76mm. Fires M352A1 cartridge.
M30   Mortar, 107mm (formerly 4.2-in.). Range, 3,500 meters; weight, 1,565 lb. Fires M328A1, M335A2, and M328A1 cartridges.
M30   Rocket, 3.5-in.
M31   Cluster, incendiary bomb, 500-lb.
M31   Grenade.
M32   Cluster, incendiary bomb, 500-lb.
M32   Gun, 76mm. Fires M320, M331, M339, M340, M340A1, M352, M355, M361, and M363 cartridges.
M32A1B3   Recovery vehicle, full-track.
M33   Cartridge, .50 cal.
M33   Grenade, fragmentation.
M33   Rocket launcher and 7.62mm machine gun, helicopter.
M34   Cluster, gas bomb, nonpersistent, 1,000-lb.
M34   Grenade, hand and rifle.
M34   Truck, cargo, 2½-ton.
M34A1   Cluster, gas bomb, nonpersistent, 1,000-lb.
M35   Cartridge, .410 cal., shotgun.
M35   Cluster, incendiary bomb, 750-lb.
M35   Gun, AA, 75mm. Fires M334 cartridge.
M35   Truck, cargo, 2½-ton.
M35A1   Truck, cargo, 2½-ton.
M35A2   Truck, cargo, 2½-ton.
M35A2C   Truck, cargo, drop side.
M36   Cluster, incendiary bomb, 750-lb.
M36   Guided-missile launcher-loader semimobile unit for Nike-Hercules.
M36   Gun, 90mm. Fires M71A1, M313C, M318A1, M353A1, M36, and M431A1 cartridges.
M36   Truck, cargo, 2½-ton.
M36A2   Truck, cargo, 2½-ton.
M36C   Truck, cargo, 2½-ton.
M37   Gun, 165mm.
M37   Howitzer, light, self-propelled, full-track, 105mm.
M37   Machine gun, .30 cal. For tank and vehicle use.
M37   Truck, cargo, 3/4-ton.
M37B1   Truck, cargo, 3/4-ton.
M37C   Machine gun, .30 cal., tank.
M38   Truck, utility, 1/4-ton.

M38A1   Truck, utility, 1/4-ton.
M38A1C   Truck, utility, 1/4-ton.
M38A2   Bomb, practice, 100-lb.
M39   Gun, 20mm. Fires M563, M55A2, and M220 cartridges.
M39   Truck, 5-ton, 6 × 6.
M40A1   Bomb, fragmentation, 25-lb.
M40A1   Rifle, 106mm, recoilless (BAT), antitank.
M40A1C   Rifle, 106mm, recoilless.
M41   Gun, 90mm. Fires M71A1, M313C, M318A1, and M431A1 cartridges.
M41   Tank, combat, full-track, 76mm gun.
M41   Truck, cargo, 5-ton.
M41A1   Tank, combat, full-track, 76mm gun.
M41A2   Tank, combat, full-track, 76mm gun.
M41A3   Tank, combat, full-track, 76mm gun.
M42   Gun, antiaircraft artillery, self-propelled, twin 40mm.
M42A1   Gun, antiaircraft artillery, self-propelled, twin 40mm.
M43   Ambulance truck, 3/4-ton, 4 × 4.
M43   Cartridge, 81mm. For M1 and M29 mortars.
M43   Cluster, bomb, incapacitating agent, 750-lb.
M43A1   Cartridge, 81mm. For M1 and M29 mortars.
M43A1B1   Cartridge, 81mm.
M43B1   Truck, ambulance, 3/4-ton.
M44   Cluster, generator, incapacitating agent, 175-lb.
M44   Howitzer, medium, self-propelled, full-track, 155mm.
M44A1   Howitzer, medium, self-propelled, full-track, 155mm.
M44A2   Truck, 2½-ton.
M45   Howitzer, 155mm.
M45A2   Truck, 2½-ton.
M46   Gun, 155mm. Fires M101 cartridge.
M46   Tank, medium, 90mm gun.
M46   Truck, 2½-ton.
M46A1   Tank, medium, 90mm gun.
M47   Bomb, incendiary, 100-lb.
M47   Howitzer, 8-in.
M47   Tank, combat, full-track, 90mm gun.
M47   Truck, dump, 2½-ton.
M47A1   Bomb, incendiary, 100-lb.
M48   Cartridge, 75mm. For M1A1 and M5 howitzers.
M48   Flare, surface, trip, parachute.
M48   Gun, 76mm. Fires M320, M331, M339, M340, M340A1, M352, M352A1, M355, M361, and M363 cartridges.
M48   Tank, combat, full-track, 90mm gun.
M48   Truck, tractor, 2½-ton.
M48A1   Cartridge, .50 cal., spotter tracer.
M48A1   Tank, combat, full-track, 90mm gun.
M48A2   Tank, combat, full-track, 90mm gun.
M48A2C   Tank, combat, full-track, 90mm gun.
M48A3   Tank, combat, full-track, 90mm gun.
M48C   Tank, combat, full-track, 90mm gun.
M49   Flare, surface, trip.
M49   Howitzer, 105mm. Fires M327, M67, M60E1, M314A2, M395, M48, and M444 cartridges.
M49   Truck, tank, gasoline, 2½-ton.
M49A1   Flare, surface, trip.
M49A2   Cartridge, 50mm. For M2 and M19 mortars.
M49A2C   Truck, tank, fuel servicing, 1,200-gal, 2½-ton.
M49A2E2   Cartridge, 60mm. For M2 and M19 mortars.
M49A3   Cartridge, 60mm.
M49A4   Cartridge, 60mm.
M49C   Truck, tank, gasoline, 2½-ton.
M50   Rifle, self-propelled, full-track, multiple 106mm. Crew, three; speed, 30 mph; range, 150 mi.
M50A2   Truck, tank, water, 1,000-gal, 2½-ton.
M50A3   Cartridge, 60mm.
M51   Gun, antiaircraft artillery, towed, 75mm.
M51   Recovery vehicle, full-track, heavy. Crew, four; speed, 30 mph; range, 200 mi.
M51   Truck, dump, 5-ton.
M51A1   Signal, ground, pyrotechnic.
M52   Cartridge, 20mm. For M61 and M139 guns.
M52   Howitzer, 105mm.
M52   Howitzer, light, self-propelled, full-track, 105mm.
M52   Truck, tractor, 5-ton.
M52A1   Howitzer, light, self-propelled, full-track, 105mm. Crew, five; speed, 42 mph; range, 100 mi.
M52A1   Signal, ground, pyrotechnic.
M52A1   Truck, tractor, 5-ton.
M52A2   Signal, ground, pyrotechnic.
M53   Cartridge, 20mm. For M39 and M61 guns.
M53 (T97)   Gun, field artillery, self-propelled, 155mm, Long Tom. Crew, six.
M54   Cartridge, 20mm. For M39 and M61 guns.

M54 Cartridge, 37mm.
M54 Gun, 90mm. Fires M71A1, M313C, M318A1, M341A1, and M353A1 cartridges.
M54 Truck, cargo, 5-ton.
M54 (T125) Cannon, 90mm.
M54A1 Cartridge, 37mm.
M54A1 Truck, cargo, 5-ton.
M54A2 Truck, cargo, 5-ton.
M55 Howitzer, 8-in., full-track, self-propelled. Crew, six; speed, 30 mph; range, 160 mi.
M55 Rocket, gas, nonpersistent, 115mm.
M55 Rocket, gas, persistent, 115mm.
M55 Trailer mount, machine gun, .50 cal.
M55 Truck, cargo, 5-ton.
M55A1 Cartridge, 37mm.
M55A2 Cartridge, 20mm. For M39 and M61 guns.
M55A2 Truck, cargo, 5-ton.
M56 Cartridge, 20mm. For M61 and M139 guns.
M56 Cartridge, 81mm.
M56 Hand grenade.
M56 Gun, antitank, self-propelled, full-track. Crew, four.
M56A1 Cartridge, 81mm.
M56A3 Cartridge, 20mm. For M39 and M61 guns and VADS.
M56C Truck, ¾-ton.
M57 Cartridge, 81mm. For M1 and M29 mortars.
M57 Hand grenade.
M57A1 Cartridge, 81mm.
M58 Cannon, 37mm.
M58 Truck, 2½-ton.
M59 Carrier, personnel (2 crew, 10 troops), full-track, armored.
M59 Cartridge, 7.62mm, NATO ball. For M14 rifle and M60 and M73 machine guns.
M59 Cartridge, 37mm.
M59 Grenade.
M59 Gun, field artillery, towed, 155mm.
M59 Truck, dump, 2½-ton.
M59A1 Cartridge, 37mm.
M60 Cartridge, 7.62mm. For M14 rifle and M60 and M73 machine guns.
M60 Cartridge, 105mm.
M60 Machine gun, 7.62mm.
M60 Tank, combat, full-track, 105mm gun. Fires XM494E2 APERS cartridge.
M60 Truck, wrecker, light, 2½-ton.
M60A1 Tank, combat, full-track, 105mm gun.
M60A1E2 Tank, combat, full-track, 152mm. Crew, four; speed, 30 mph; range, 250 mi.
M60C Machine gun, 7.62mm. Weight, 23 lb; range, 3,500 yd.
M60D Machine gun, 7.62mm.
M60E1 Cartridge, 105mm. For M2, M4, and M49 howitzers.
M61 Cartridge, 7.62mm. For M60 machine gun.
M61 Cartridge, 75mm.
M61 Hand grenade, fragmentation.
M61A1 Cartridge, 75mm.
M61A1 Gun, automatic, six-barreled, 20mm. Vulcan aircraft Gatling gun, firing 100 rounds per second. Fires M56A3, M55A2, and M220 cartridges.
M61A2 Truck, 5-ton.
M62 Cartridge, 7.62mm tracer. For M14 rifle and M60 and M73 machine guns.
M62 Hand grenade, training.
M62 Signal, ground, pyrotechnic.
M62 Truck, wrecker, medium, 5-ton.
M62E1 Truck, wrecker, medium, 5-ton.
M63 Cartridge, 7.62mm, NATO blank.
M63 Cartridge, 37mm.
M63 Gun, recoilless, 120mm.
M63 Mod I Cartridge, 37mm.
M63C Truck, 5-ton.
M64 Cartridge, 75mm.
M64 Cartridge, grenade, rifle, 7.62mm. For M14 and M15 rifles.
M64 Gun, recoilless, 155mm.
M64 Signal, ground, pyrotechnic.
M65 Cartridge, .22 cal., ball (Hornet).
M65 Gun, heavy, motorized, 280mm.
M65 Signal, ground, pyrotechnic.
M66 Cannon, 280mm, truck-drawn.
M66 Cartridge, 75mm.
M66 Signal, ground, pyrotechnic.
M67 Cartridge, 105mm. For M2A1, M2A2, M4, M4A1, and M49 howitzers.
M67 Rifle, 90mm; effective range against armor, 450 meters. Fires M371, M371E1, and XM590 cartridges.
M67 Tank, combat, full-track, flamethrower.
M67A1 Tank, combat, full-track, flamethrower. Range, 200 meters; fuel capacity for flamethrower, 378 gal.

M68 Cartridge, 81mm, training.
M68 Gun, 105mm. Fires M392A2, M416, XM604, M456A1, M490, M456E1, XM494E3, and XM563 cartridges.
M69 Cartridge, 60mm, training.
M69X Bomb, incendiary, 6-lb.
M70 Bomb, gas, persistent, 115-lb.
M70A1 Bomb, gas, persistent, 115-lb.
M71 Cartridge, 90mm.
M71A1 Cartridge, 90mm. For M36, M41, and M45 guns.
M72 Rocket, light assault weapon (LAW), 66mm.
M72A1E1 Rocket, 66mm.
M73 Machine gun, 7.62mm. Weight, 28 lb; range, 3,500 yd.
M73 Projectile, 120mm.
M73C Machine gun, 7.62mm.
M74 Recovery vehicle, full-track, medium. Crew, four.
M74A1 Bomb, incendiary, 10-lb.
M75 Carrier, personnel, full-track, armored.
M75 Grenade launcher, 40mm. Fires M384 cartridge at the rate of 220 rounds per minute; range, 2,000 meters.
M76 Carrier, cargo, amphibious, tracked, 1½-ton (Otter).
M76 Grenade launcher. For 7.62mm M14 rifle.
M77 Cartridge, 90mm. For M1A2, M1A3, M2A1, and M2A2 rifles.
M79 Grenade launcher, 40mm. Fires M385, M386, M407A1, XM651, XM651E1, XM635, and M463 cartridges.
M80 Cartridge, 7.62mm, ball. For M14 rifle and M60 and M73 machine guns.
M81 Cartridge, 40mm. For M1, M2, and MK-I and Duster guns.
M81 Gun, 152mm.
M82 Bomb, fragmentation, 90-lb.
M82 Cartridge, 7.62mm. For rifle and machine guns.
M82 Cartridge, 90mm. For M36, M41, and M54 guns.
M83 Bomb, fragmentation, 4-lb.
M83 Cartridge, 60mm. For M2 and M19 mortars.
M83A1 Cartridge, 60mm.
M83A2 Cartridge, 60mm.
M83A3 Cartridge, 60mm.
M84 Cartridge, 105mm. For M2, M4, M49, and M102 howitzers.
M84 Cartridge, 105mm. For M2A1, M2A2, M4, M4A1, and M49 howitzers.
M84 Mortar, infantry, self-propelled, full-track, 107mm. (Formerly 4.2-in.)
M84A1 Bomb, target identification, 100-lb.
M84E1 Cartridge, 105mm.
M85 Machine gun, .50 cal., for tank turret use against ground and air targets.
M85 Tractor, 23-ton, full-track, for towing artillery.
M86 Bomb, fragmentation, 120-lb.
M86 Charge, propelling, 175mm. For M113 gun.
M88 Recovery vehicle for medium tanks, full-track. Crew, four.
M91 Cartridge, 40mm. For M1, M2, MK-I, and Duster guns.
M91 Rocket launcher, chemical, 115mm. Fired from ground or 2½-ton truck. Capacity of 45 rockets, each of which can cover 1 sq mi. Crew, six; airdroppable.
M97A2 Cartridge, 20mm. For M24 gun.
M99A1 Cartridge, 20mm. For M24 gun.
M101 Cartridge, 155mm, spotting.
M101 Cargo trailer, ¼-ton, 2-wheeled.
M101 Cargo trailer, ¾-ton, 2-wheeled.
M101 Howitzer, light, towed, 105mm.
M101 Projectile, 155mm. For M2, M2A1, and M46 guns.
M101A1 Howitzer, light, towed, 105mm.
M102 Howitzer, light, towed, 105mm. Airdroppable. Weight, 3,000 lb; range, 15,000 meters. Fires M84 and M444 cartridges.
M103 Bomb, semi-armor-piercing, 2,000-lb.
M103 Howitzer, 105mm. Fires M327 and M84 cartridges.
M103 Tank, combat, full-track, 120mm gun.
M103A1 Tank, combat, full-track, 120mm gun.
M104 Bomb, leaflet, empty, 100-lb.
M104 Howitzer, self-propelled, unarmored, 105mm.
M104 Projectile, 155mm.
M104A1 Cargo trailer, 1¼-ton, two-wheeled.
M105 Bomb, leaflet, empty, 500-lb.
M105 Projectile, 155mm.
M105A1 Cargo trailer, 1½-ton, two-wheeled.
M106 Dispenser, tear gas and/or smoke, Mity Mite.

M106 Mortar, self-propelled, full-track, 107mm.
M106 Projectile, 8-in. For M2A1E1 and M47 howitzers.
M106A1 Mortar, self-propelled, full-track, 107mm.
M107 Gun, field artillery, self-propelled, 175mm. Weight, 31 tons; air-transportable.
M107 Projectile, 155mm.
M107 (Comp B) Projectile, 155mm.
M107 (TNT) Projectile, 155mm.
M107B2 Projectile, 155mm, for howitzer.
M108 Howitzer, light, self-propelled, 105mm. Weight, 23 tons; range, 15,000 meters. Fires M444 cartridge.
M108 Truck, radio repair shop, 2½-ton.
M108 Truck, wrecker, crane, 2½-ton.
M109 Bomb, general-purpose, 12,000-lb.
M109 Howitzer, medium, self-propelled, 155mm. Amphibious and air-transportable. Weight, 26 tons; range, 18,500 meters.
M109A1 Truck, van, shop, 2½-ton.
M109C Truck, van, shop, 2½-ton.
M109D Truck, van, shop, 2½-ton.
M110 Bomb, general-purpose, 22,000-lb.
M110 Projectile, 155mm. For M1, M1A1, M45, and M109 howitzers.
M110 (T236E1) Howitzer, heavy, self-propelled, 8-in. Air-transportable; conventional and nuclear ammo.
M110E1 Projectile, 155mm.
M110E2 Projectile, 155mm.
M113 Bomb, gas, persistent, 125-lb.
M113 Carrier, personnel, full track, armored. Crew, 1 × 12; speed, 40 mph; range, 200 mi.
M113 Gun, 175mm.
M113A1 Carrier, personnel, full-track, armored. Range, 300 mi.
M114 Carrier, command and reconnaissance, armored. (Tracked, air-transportable and air-droppable.)
M114 Howitzer, medium, towed, 155mm.
M114A1 Carrier, command and reconnaissance, armored.
M114A1 Howitzer, medium, towed, 155mm.
M115 Howitzer, heavy, towed, 8-in. Air-transportable.
M116 Bomb, fire, external, 750-lb.
M116 Carrier, cargo, amphibious, tracked (T116E1).
M116 Howitzer, pack, 75mm.
M116 Projectile, 155mm.
M116A2 Bomb, fire, 750-lb.
M116B Projectile, 155mm. For M1, M1A1, M45, and M109 howitzers.
M116B1 Projectile, 155mm. For M1, M1A1, M45, and M109 howitzers.
M116E1 Projectile, 155mm. For M1, M1A1, M45, and M109 howitzers.
M117 Basic chassis for M118 and M119, semitrailers.
M117 Bomb, general-purpose, 750-lb.
M117 Gun, antiaircraft artillery, towed, 90mm.
M117 Simulators, booby trap, flash.
M118 Bomb, general-purpose, 3,000-lb.
M118 Cartridge, 7.62mm, match.
M118 Gun, antiaircraft artillery, towed, 90mm.
M118 Projectile, 155mm, illuminating.
M118A1 Semitrailer, 6-ton, two-wheeled stake.
M118A2 Projectile, 155mm, ILLUM. For M1, M1A1, M45, and M126 howitzers.
M118A2B1 Projectile, 155mm, illuminating.
M119A1 Semitrailer, 6-ton, two-wheeled van.
M120A1 Bomb, photoflash, 150-lb.
M121 Bomb, general-purpose, 10,000-lb.
M121 Projectile, 155mm, gas, nonpersistent.
M121A1 Projectile, 155mm. For M1, M1A1, M45, and M109 howitzers.
M121A1 Projectile, 155mm, gas, persistent.
M122 Bomb, photoflash, 100-lb.
M122 Projectile, 155mm, gas, nonpersistent.
M123 Truck, tractor, 10-ton.
M123A1 Cartridge, 165mm. For M37 gun.
M123A1 Howitzer, 155mm, towed.
M123A1 Howitzer, medium, towed, auxiliary-propelled, 155mm. Range, 18 kilometers.
M123A1C Truck, tractor, 10-ton.
M123C Truck, tractor, 10-ton.
M123D Truck, tractor, 10-ton.
M124 Bomb, practice, 250-lb.
M124 Truck, radio repair shop, 2½-ton.
M124 (T122E4) Projectile, 280mm.
M125 Signal, ground, pyrotechnic.
M125 Truck, cargo, 10-ton.
M125A1 Bomb, gas, nonpersistent, 10-lb.
M125A1 Carrier, 81mm mortar, full-track.

M125A1	Signal, illuminating, ground.
M126	Bomb, incendiary, 4-lb.
M126	Howitzer, 155mm.
M126	Signal, ground, pyrotechnic.
M126A1	Signal, illuminating, ground, pyrotechnic.
M127	Signal, ground, pyrotechnic.
M127A1	Cargo semitrailer, 12-ton, four-wheeled.
M127A1	Signal, illuminating, ground, pyrotechnic.
M128A1	Signal, smoke, ground, parachute.
M129	Bomb, leaflet, 750-lb.
M129	Grenade launcher, 40mm, helicopter suppressive fire system.
M129	Semitrailer supply van, 12-ton, 4-wheeled.
M129A1	Signal, smoke, ground, parachute.
M129E1	Bomb, leaflet, 750-lb.
M131A2	Semitrailer, gasoline tank, 5,000-gal, four-wheeled.
M132	Flamethrower, self-propelled, full-track.
M132A1	Flamethrower, self-propelled, full track.
M132E1	Flamethrower, self-propelled, full track. Range, 170 meters; crew, two; weight, 23,710 lb.
M133	Machine gun, 7.62mm, gas-drive Minigun; 6,000 rounds per minute.
M134	Machine gun, 7.62mm, electric-motor Minigun; 6,000 rounds per minute.
M135	Cannon, 165mm.
M135	Truck, cargo, 2½-ton.
M137	Howitzer, 105mm.
M139	Gun, 20mm, automatic, Hispano-Suiza. Fires M206, M599, and M601 cartridges.
M143A1	Trailer, bomb transport, 2-ton, four-wheeled.
M146C,D	Semitrailer, shop van, 6-ton, two-wheeled.
M147	Amphibious truck, 5-ton payload, 7 mph on water.
M147	Dummy cartridge, 20mm.
M149A1	Gun, 7.62mm.
M149E2	Trailer, water tank, 400-gal, two-wheeled.
M151	Truck, utility, ¼-ton (jeep). Speed, 65 mph; range, 300 mi.
M151	Warhead, 2.75-in. rocket, 10-lb.
M151A1C	Truck, utility, ¼-ton (jeep), with M40A1.
M156	Warhead, 2.75-in. rocket, chemical agent, 10-lb.
M158	Rocket launcher, 2.5-in.
M158	Signal, illuminating, ground.
M159	Signal, illuminating, ground.
M160	Cartridge, 7.62mm.
M162	Gun, 152mm.
M162	Semitrailer, 60-ton, six-wheeled, to transport engineer construction equipment.
M163	Vulcan air-defense system (VADS), 20mm.
M170	Truck, ambulance, ¼-ton.
M172A1	Semitrailer, 25-ton, four-wheeled, to transport heavy equipment and material.
M181	Cartridge, 14.5mm, trainer.
M185A3	Truck, repair shop van, 2½-ton.
M193	Cartridge, 5.56mm, ball. For M16 rifle.
M195	Cartridge, grenade, 5.56mm. For M16 rifle.
M195E1	Howitzer, self-propelled, full-track, 105mm.
M196	Cartridge, 5.56mm, tracer. For M-16 rifle.
M197	Cartridge, 5.56mm.
M198	Cartridge, 7.62mm, duplex ball.
M200	Cartridge, 5.56mm, blank.
M204	Cartridge, 20mm. For M3 gun series.
M206	Cartridge, 20mm. For M139 gun series.
M210	Cartridge, 20mm. For M3 gun series.
M211	Truck, cargo, 2½-ton.
M215	Truck, dump, 2½-ton.
M217	Truck, tank, fuel servicing, 2½-ton.
M217C	Truck, tank, fuel servicing, 2½-ton.
M219	Truck, tank, fuel servicing, 2½-ton.
M220	Cartridge, 20mm. For M39 and M61 guns and VADS.
M220	Truck, van, shop, 2½-ton.
M220C	Truck, van, shop, 2½-ton.
M220D	Truck, van, shop, 2½-ton.
M221	Truck, tractor, 2½-ton.
M222	Truck, tank, water, 2½-ton, 1,000-gal.
M246	Cartridge, 20mm. For M162 gun.
M246A	Truck, tractor, wrecker, 5-ton.
M249	Truck, gun-lifting, heavy. To lift and transport 280mm gun M56 and gun carriage M30. Crew, four.
M250	Truck, gun-lifting, heavy.
M258A1	Radar-tracking central van trailer, four dual wheels.
M259A1	Van trailer, Nike-Hercules director station.
M261A1	Guided-missile flatbed trailer, four dual wheels.
M268	Propellant servicing truck, 5-ton.
M269	Cargo semitrailer, 12-ton.
M274A1	Truck, platform, utility, ½-ton. For light infantry weapons and cargo. Speed, 25 mph; range, 151 mi.
M275	Truck, tractor, 2½-ton.
M275A2	Truck, tractor, 2½-ton.
M280	Truck-mounted servicing platform, 5-ton.
M292	Truck, van, shop, 2½-ton.
M301	Cartridge, 81mm, illuminating. For M1 and M29 mortars.
M301A1	Cartridge, 81mm, illuminating.
M301A2	Cartridge, 81mm, illuminating.
M301A3	Cartridge, 81mm, illuminating.
M302	Cartridge, 60mm. For M2 and M19 mortars.
M302A1	Cartridge, 60mm.
M302E1	Cartridge, 60mm. For M2 and M19 mortars.
M304	Cartridge, 90mm.
M306	Cartridge, 57mm. For M18 and M18A1 rifles.
M306A1	Cartridge, 57mm. For M18 and M18A1 rifles.
M307	Cartridge, 57mm. For M18 and M18A1 rifles.
M307A1	Cartridge, 57mm.
M308	Cartridge, 57mm. For M18 and M18A1 rifles.
M308A1	Cartridge, 57mm.
M309	Cartridge, 75mm. For M20 rifle.
M309A1	Cartridge, 75mm. For M20 rifle.
M310	Cartridge, 75mm. For M20 rifle.
M310A1	Cartridge, 75mm.
M311	Cartridge, 75mm. For M20 rifle.
M311A1	Cartridge, 75mm.
M313	Cartridge, 90mm.
M313C	Cartridge, 90mm. For M36, M41, and M54 guns.
M314	Cartridge, 105mm, illuminating.
M314A1	Cartridge, 105mm, illuminating.
M314A2	Cartridge, 105mm, illuminating. For M2, M4, M49, and M102 howitzers.
M314A3	Cartridge, 105mm, illuminating.
M3142B1	Cartridge, 105mm, illuminating.
M317A1	Cartridge, 90mm.
M318	Cartridge, 90mm. For M36, M41, and M54 guns.
M318A1	Cartridge, 90mm. For M36, M41, and M54 guns.
M318A1C	Cartridge, 90mm.
M319	Cartridge, 76mm.
M320	Cartridge, 76mm. For M32 and M48 guns.
M323	Cartridge, 105mm. For M27 and M27A1 rifles.
M323	Tracking station van semitrailer.
M324	Cartridge, 105mm.
M324	Doppler station van trailer.
M325	Cartridge, 105mm.
M326	Cartridge, 105mm. For M27 and M27A1 rifles.
M327	Cartridge, 105mm. For M2, M4, M49, and M103 howitzers.
M328	Cartridge, 4.2-in.
M328A1	Cartridge, 4.2-in. For M2 and M30 mortars.
M329	Cartridge, 4.2-in.
M329A1	Cartridge, 4.2-in.
M329B1	Cartridge, 4.2-in.
M331	Cartridge, 76mm. For M32 and M48 guns.
M331A1	Cartridge, 76mm.
M332	Cartridge, 90mm.
M332A1	Cartridge, 90mm.
M332B1	Cartridge, 90mm.
M333A1	Cartridge, 90mm.
M334	Cartridge, 75mm. For M35 AA gun.
M335A1	Cartridge, 4.2-in.
M335A2	Cartridge, 4.2-in. For M2 and M30 mortars.
M336	Cartridge, 90mm, canister.
M337	Cartridge, 75mm, blank. For M1A1 and M3 howitzers.
M337A1	Cartridge, 75mm, blank.
M337A2	Cartridge, 75mm, blank.
M338	Cartridge, 75mm.
M338A1	Cartridge, 75mm.
M339	Cartridge, 76mm.
M340	Cartridge, 76mm. For M32 and M48 guns.
M340A1	Cartridge, 76mm. For M32 and M48 guns.
M341	Cartridge, 76mm.
M342	Truck, cargo, dump, 2½-ton.
M344A1	Cartridge, 106mm.
M346A1	Cartridge, 106mm.
M348	Cartridge, 90mm.
M349	Cartridge, 75mm. For M20 rifle.
M351	Cartridge, 76mm, double pellet charge. For M1A1C and M1A2 guns.
M352	Cartridge, 76mm. For M32 and M48 guns.
M353	Cartridge, 90mm. For M36, M41, and M54 guns.
M353A1	Cartridge, 90mm. For M36 and M54 guns.
M353A2	Cartridge, 90mm.
M355	Cartridge, 76mm, blank. For M32 and M48 guns.
M356	Cartridge, 120mm.
M357	Projectile, 120mm.
M358	Projectile, 120mm.
M359A1	Electronic shop van trailer.
M359E2	Projectile, 120mm.
M360	Cartridge, 105mm, gas, nonpersistent.
M361	Cartridge, 76mm. For M32 and M48 guns.
M361A1	Cartridge, 76mm.
M362	Cartridge, 81mm. For M1 and M29 mortars.
M363	Cartridge, 76mm, canister. For M32 and M48 guns.
M370	Cartridge, 81mm, white phosphorous. For M1 and M29 mortars.
M371	Cartridge, 90mm. For M67 rifle.
M374	Cartridge, 81mm. For M1 and M29 mortars.
M375	Cartridge, 81mm. For M1 and M29 mortars.
M377	Cartridge, 90mm, canister.
M381	Cartridge, 40mm, high-explosive. For M79 grenade launcher.
M382	Cartridge, 40mm. For M79 grenade launcher.
M384	Cartridge, 40mm. For M75 grenade launcher.
M385	Cartridge, 40mm. For M79 grenade launcher.
M385	Rocket launcher (762mm), truck-mounted. For Honest John.
M386	Cartridge, 40mm. For M79 grenade launcher.
M392A2	Cartridge, 105mm. For M68 gun.
M393	Cartridge, 105mm.
M394	Cartridge, 90mm, blank. For M36, M41, and M54 guns.
M395	Cartridge, 105mm. For M2A1, M2A2, M4, M4A1, and M49 howitzers.
M397E2	Cartridge, 40mm. For M79 grenade launcher.
M404	Projectile, 8-in. For M2A1E1 and M47 howitzers.
M405	Rocket-handling unit (762mm), trailer-mounted. For Honest John.
M406	Cartridge, 40mm. For M79 grenade launcher.
M407	Cartridge, 40mm. For M79 grenade launcher.
M409	Cartridge, 152mm. For M81 and M162 guns.
M413	Cartridge, 105mm. For M2, M4, and M49 howitzers.
M415	Cartridge, 37mm, spotting.
M416	Cartridge, 105mm. For M68 gun.
M422	Truck, utility, ¼-ton, lightweight.
M424	Projectile, 8-in.
M426	Projectile, 8-in. For M2, M2A1, and M47 howitzers.
M431A1	Cartridge, 90mm. For M36, M41, and M54 guns.
M437	Cartridge, 175mm.
M444	Cartridge, 105mm. For M2, M4, M49, and M102 howitzers.
M445	Cartridge, 81mm.
M446	Cartridge, 37mm, spotting.
M449	Projectile, 155mm. For M109 and M114 howitzers.
M451	Dummy cartridge, 37mm.
M453	Cartridge, 4.2-in.
M453	Cartridge, 107mm. For M30 mortar.
M456	Cartridge, 150mm.
M458	Projectile, 175mm.
M463	Cartridge, 40mm. For M79 grenade launcher.
M467	Cartridge, 105mm.
M469	Projectile, 120mm.
M485	Projectile, 155mm, illuminating.
M488	Cartridge, 105mm.
M489	Cartridge, 105mm.
M490	Cartridge, 105mm. For M68 gun.
M494	Cartridge, 105mm.
M496	Cartridge, 76mm.
M512	Truck, van, shop, 2½-ton.
M520E1	Carrier, cargo, 8-ton.
M521A1	Howitzer, self-propelled, air-transportable, 105mm.
M523E2	Truck, tractor, 25-ton.
M543	Truck, wrecker, medium, 5-ton.
M548	Carrier, cargo, tracked, 6-ton.
M548	Cartridge, 105mm.
M551	Armored reconnaissance airborne assault vehicle (ARAAV, full-track, 152mm). Shillelagh surface-to-surface guided missile or 152mm conventional shell (General Sheridan).
M553E1	Wrecker, 10-ton.
M559E1	Tanker, 2,500-gal.
M561	Truck, cargo, 1½-ton, Gama Goat.
M576	Cartridge, 40mm.

M577	Carrier, command post, light-track.
M578	Recovery vehicle, full-track, light, armored.
M580	Cartridge, 90mm. For M36, M41, and M54 guns.
M581	Cartridge, 106mm.
M583	Cartridge, 40mm. For M79 grenade launcher.
M585	Cartridge, 40mm, white-star cluster. For M79 grenade launcher.
M590	Cartridge, 90mm.
M596	Cartridge, 152mm.
M599	Cartridge, 20mm. For M139 gun.
M601	Cartridge, 20mm. For M139 gun.
M601	Truck, special power wagon, 1-ton.
M602	Truck, cargo, 2½-ton.
M602E1	Cartridge, 20mm.
M604	Cartridge, 105mm.
M606	Truck, utility, ½-ton.
M615	Truck, ambulance, 1-ton.
M617	Cartridge, 152mm. For M81 gun.
M620A	Shotgun, 12 gauge, Stevens riot type.
M629	Cartridge, 105mm.
M651	Cartridge, 40mm.
M656	Truck, cargo, 5-ton. Air-transportable, floatable.
M657	Cartridge, 152mm.
M676	Cartridge, 40mm.
M684	Cartridge, 40mm.
M706	Armored car.
M715	Truck, cargo, 1¼-ton.
M718	Frontline ambulance, ¼-ton.
M725	Ambulance, 1¼-ton.
M728	Vehicle, combat, engineer, full-track.
M751A2	Truck, bolster, 2½-ton.
M792	Ambulance, 1¼-ton.
M1732	Signal, ground, pyrotechnic.
M1909	Cartridge, .30 cal., blank. For M1 rifles and machine guns.
M1911	Cartridge, .45 cal., ball.
M1911A1	Automatic pistol, .45 cal. Weight, 23 oz; range, 1,640 yd.
M1916	Gun, subcaliber, 37mm.
M1917	Bayonet. For riot-type shotgun.
M1917A1	Machine gun, .30 cal., Browning.
M1918A2	Browning automatic rifle (BAR). Weight, 19.4 lb; range, 3,500 yd.
M1919A4	Machine gun, .30 cal., Browning.
M1919A6	Machine gun, .30 cal., Browning.
M1928A1	Submachine gun, .45 cal., Thompson.

(End of **M** Table)

MAAG Military Assistance Advisory Group.

MAC The U.S. Navy designation for a mobile inshore underseas-warfare (MIUW) attack craft.

MAC 7.5mm aircraft machine gun Model 1934 A French gas-operated air-cooled machine gun with a rate of fire of about 1,300 rounds per minute. It was fed from a 500-round link belt.

Macchi C.200 Saetta See **Saetta.**

Macchi C.202 Folgore See **Folgore.**

Macchi C.205N Orione See **Orione.**

Macchi C.205V Veltro See **Veltro.**

Macchi series flying boats A series of Italian single-place single-engine (pusher) biplane flying boats introduced in mid-1915. Used variously for reconnaissance, bombing, escort, and ground-support duties, these aircraft had a speed of about 117 mph and were armed with a forward-firing Revelli machine gun and four 220-lb bombs.

mace A clublike weapon used in Europe mainly between the eleventh and the sixteenth centuries. It was made either of wood with a metal head or entirely of metal, and it had a spiked or flanged metal head. It was a common weapon in hand-to-hand fighting during the time that complete armor was worn.

MAC 7.5mm aircraft machine gun Model 1934. (*The Smithsonian Institution, Department of Defense Collection.*)

Mace An improved version of the MGM-1C Matador, differing primarily in its improved guidance system, longer range, low-level attack capability, and higher-yield nuclear or conventional warhead. The MGM-13A is guided by a self-contained radar guidance system. The CGM-13B is guided by an inertial guidance system. It is designated as MGM-13. It is 44 ft long and 54 in. in diameter and has a wingspan of about 23 ft. It is turbojet-powered and has a speed of about 650 mph and a range of 700 mi. Mace B has a range of 1,200 mi.

machete A knife with a large, heavy blade about 2 or 3 ft long. It resembles a broadsword.

machicolations The openings between the wall and the parapet made by extending the parapet out on corbels. Through the openings it was possible to drop missiles, boiling water, melted lead, and other objects on attackers.

machine cannon An automatic cannon.

machine gun 1. A weapon that automatically fires small-arms ammunition, caliber .60 or 15.24mm or under, and is capable of sustained rapid fire. It can be belt- or link-fed, air- or water-cooled, and recoil- or gas-operated, and it is usually fired from a mount. **2.** To riddle a target with machine-gun fire. (Picture, next page.)

machine gunner A soldier who serves a machine gun.

machine pistol 1. A pistol capable of full automatic fire. **2.** A **submachine gun,** which see. The application of the term in sense 2 has been in use since World War II, deriving from the German and Russian words for "submachine gun," *Maschinenpistole* (machine pistol) and *pistolyet-pulemyot* (pistol–machine gun), so called because the submachine gun ordinarily uses pistol-type ammunition.

machinist's mate In the U.S. Navy, a petty officer in the engineer's department.

Mach number The ratio of the velocity of a body to that of sound in the surrounding medium.

Macon A U.S. Navy dirigible that was wrecked off the coast of California in 1935. It was a sister ship of the **Akron,** which see.

Mad Bomber The code name for a U.S. Army weapon system used on helicopters. It dumps mortar shells and fragmentation bombs on enemy positions by tilting a trough.

Madge The NATO code name for the Soviet Beriev Be-6 twin-engine reconnais-

Mace. (*U.S. Air Force.*)

machete. (*U.S. Army.*)

mace. (*The Metropolitan Museum of Art, Rogers Fund, 1904.*)

machine gun. Shown is a Vickers twin .50 cal. machine gun of 1934. (*Vickers Ltd.*)

sance and transport flying boat in service with the Soviet Navy since about 1949. It has a range of 3,045 mi and a speed of 258 mph. It is armed with 23mm cannons in nose, dorsal, and tail gun turrets and has under-wing racks for bombs, mines, and depth charges.

MAD gear   Magnetic anomaly detection gear. Airborne magnetic equipment used for locating submerged submarines.

Madsen machine guns   The first Madsen design was the 8mm machine gun Model 1904. It was a recoil-operated air- or water-cooled weapon with a rate of fire of 500 to 650 rounds per minute. It weighed 21 lb and was fed from 25- or 40-round magazines. The Madsen was standard equipment for Danish and Norwegian forces, and over 100 variations (in numerous cartridge sizes) were sold to the military forces of other countries. In the early 1920s the basic design was altered to produce an aircraft version. It weighed 18.5 lb and had a cyclic rate of fire of 1,000 rounds per minute. Infantry, tank, and aircraft variations have been used by countries including Argentina, Brazil, Bulgaria, Chile, China, Czechoslovakia, Denmark, Great Britain, Finland, Holland, Italy, Portugal, Russia, Spain, Sweden, Turkey, and Thailand.

Madsen 8mm light machine gun   A Danish light machine gun weighing 21 lb. It has a length of 45.5 in., is recoil-operated, and

is fed by an overhead box magazine with a capacity of 30 rounds.

Madsen 9mm Parabellum submachine gun Model 1946   Introduced in 1946, this weapon carried the Madsen factory designation of P.16. It is a blowback-operated weapon utilizing the 9mm Parabellum cartridge and capable of full automatic fire only. It has a cyclic rate of fire of 480 rounds per minute and a muzzle velocity of about 1,250 fps. It is 21.60 in. long with stock retracted and has a barrel length of 7.80 in. With a 32-round magazine the weapon weighs 8.25 lb. The rear sight consists of a single aperture set for 100 meters. El Salvador, Paraguay, and Thailand were among the purchasers of this weapon.

Madsen 9mm Parabellum submachine gun Model 1950   This blowback-operated weapon, a slightly modified version of the Model 1946, is capable of automatic fire only and has a muzzle velocity of about 1,200 fps. The weight, without magazine, is 7.6 lb. It has an overall length of 30.71 in., with folding butt extended, and a barrel length of 7.87 in. The cyclic rate of fire is about 500 rounds per minute. It is reported to have been sold to Indonesia, Venezuela, Colombia, El Salvador, Guatemala, and several other nations.

Madsen 9mm Parabellum submachine gun M.53 and Mark II   New weapons similar in design to the Madsen Models

1946 and 1950, but with several improvements. They were introduced in 1953.

Madsen machine gun Model 1950   Usually found in .30/06 cal., it is advertised for any rifle cartridge. It is a recoil-operated weapon with selective automatic and semi-automatic fire. It has a weight of 22 lb, an overall length of 45.9 in., a barrel length of 18.8 in., a cyclic rate of fire of 400 rounds per minute, and a muzzle velocity of about 2,700 fps.

Madsen/Saetter machine gun   This weapon is manufactured for any military rimless cartridge from 6.5mm to 8mm and has undergone three basic model changes, the Marks I, II, and III. The Mark III was refined in 1959 and has a cyclic rate of fire of between 700 and 1,000 rounds per minute, a weight of 25.6 lb with heavy barrel, an overall length of 48 in., and a barrel length of 26 in. The weight of the tripod is 36.2 lb. The feed device consists of non-disintegrating metal belts of 50 rounds that can be joined to make any length and also joined with box magazines that fasten to the receiver.

Maestro   See **Firebar.**

Mae West   A yellow lifesaving jacket inflated by means of two carbon dioxide cartridges. It was named after the American actress Mae West, who was noted for her full figure.

magazine   1. A structure or compartment for storing ammunition or explosives. **2.** The part of a gun or firearm that holds ammunition ready for chambering. In sense 2, magazines for small arms may be detachable or nondetachable from the rest of the piece. A box magazine is a detachable magazine in the shape of a rectangular box; a drum magazine is a detachable magazine in the shape of a drum.

magazine area   An area specifically designed and set aside for the storage of explosives or ammunition.

Maginot Line   A line of defensive fortifications built in 1930–1934 by France on her border with Germany. It was named after André Maginot (1877–1932), a French minister of war.

Magis   Megawatt Air-to-Ground Illuminating System. The acronym for a powerful U.S. airborne searchlight system used on board Boeing C-96G transports to provide continuous nighttime illumination of Vietnam combat areas for up to 12 hours. The system, which consists of four 200-kilowatt searchlights and a turbine-driven power source, can illuminate 80 sq mi from an altitude of 20,000 ft.

magnesium bomb   An incendiary bomb in which the burning agent is magnesium. A magnesium flare bomb.

Magnet   The NATO code name for the Yak-17 two-place trainer version of the Feather.

magnetic anomaly detection gear See **MAD gear.**

magnetic mine An underwater mine detonated when the hull of a passing vessel causes a shift of the magnetic field at the mine.

Mahan A class of U.S. destroyers of about 1,500 tons standard displacement commissioned in 1936. They had a length of 334 ft, a beam of 34 ft, a speed of 36.5 knots, and a complement of 204 men. They were armed with five 5-in. guns and twelve 21-in. torpedo tubes.

mail Armor consisting of a flexible fabric of interlinked metal rings.

Mail The NATO code name for the Beriev Be-12 twin-turboprop maritime reconnaissance amphibian presently in service with the Soviet Naval Air Force and first seen in 1961. It can lift 10 tons and has a speed of 343 mph.

maillet, maillotin An ancient mallet-type weapon used to attack men wearing helmets and cuirasses.

main attack The principal attack or effort into which the commander throws the full weight of the offensive power at his disposal. An attack directed against the chief objective of the campaign or battle.

main battery On a warship, the guns of the largest size.

main deck On a warship, the uppermost complete deck that runs the entire length of the ship.

Maine Two battleships were named for the state of Maine. The first *Maine* (ex-ACRI) was commissioned in 1895. It had a normal displacement of 6,682 tons, a length of 319 ft, a beam of 57 ft, a speed of 17 knots, and a complement of 374 men. Main armament consisted of four 10-in. guns, six 6-in. guns, and four 14-in. torpedo tubes. It exploded in Havana harbor on February 14, 1898, and precipitated the Spanish-American War. The ship sank, and a total of 250 men were lost. The second *Maine* was a battleship of 12,500 tons standard displacement commissioned in 1902; it was a sister ship of the *Ohio* and the old *Missouri*. These ships had a length of 393 ft, a beam of 72 ft, a speed of 18 knots, and a complement of 561 men. Main armament consisted of four 12-in. guns, sixteen 6-in. guns, six 3-in. guns, and two submerged 18-in. torpedo tubes. *Maine* was used as a training ship during World War I.

main-gauche (Literally, *"left hand."*) A dagger to be held in the left hand to parry rapier thrusts; a rapier is held in the right hand. Usually applied to those daggers with knuckle guards produced in Spain and Italy. See **left-hand dagger.**

main guard The force of a garrison. Also, the keep of a castle.

main line of resistance A line at the forward edge of the battle position designated for the purpose of coordinating the fire of all units and supporting weapons, including air and naval gunfire. It defines the forward limits of a series of mutually supporting defensive areas, but does not include the areas occupied or used by covering or screening forces.

main road A road capable of serving as the principal ground line of communication to an area or locality. Usually it is wide enough and suitable for two-way all-weather traffic at high speeds.

main work The principal work of a fortification, as distinguished from the outworks.

Majestic **1.** A class of British aircraft carriers of about 15,000 tons standard displacement built in the 1940s. They have a length of 630 ft, a beam of 80 ft, and a speed of about 25 knots. They have a complement of about 1,300 men, carry 37 aircraft, and are armed with thirty 40mm antiaircraft guns. **2.** A class of British 14,900-ton battleships completed in 1895–1898. The class included *Majestic, Magnificent, Hannibal, Prince George, Victorious, Jupiter, Caesar,* and *Illustrious.* They had a length of 413 ft, a speed of 16 knots, a complement of 757 men, and main armament consisting of four 12-in. guns, twelve 6-in. guns, and five 18-in. torpedo tubes.

major An officer in the U.S. Army, Air Force, or Marine Corps who is next in rank below a lieutenant colonel and next above a captain. His insignia is a gold oak leaf. This rank corresponds with that of a lieutenant commander in the Navy.

major caliber In naval terminology, guns and ammunition 8 in. in caliber or larger. No longer used as an army classification.

major fleet A principal, permanent subdivision of the operating forces of the Navy with certain supporting short activities. Presently there are two such fleets: the Pacific Fleet and the Atlantic Fleet.

major general An officer in the U.S. Army, Air Force, or Marine Corps who is next in rank below a lieutenant general and next above a brigadier general. The insignia of this rank is two silver stars.

major port Any port with two or more berths and facilities and equipment capable of discharging 100,000 tons of cargo per month from oceangoing ships. Such ports are designated as probable nuclear targets.

major water terminal A water terminal with facilities for berthing numerous ships simultaneously at wharves and/or working anchorages, and located within sheltered coastal waters adjacent to rail, highway, air, and/or inland water transportation nets. It covers a relatively large area, and its scope of operation is such that it is designated as a probable nuclear target.

Makarov 9mm automatic pistol PM The official handgun of the Soviet military, this double-action blowback-operated weapon replaced the Tokarev 7.62mm Model 1933. It resembles the Walther PP but is somewhat larger. It has an overall length of 6.34 in. and a barrel length of 3.83 in. The weight of the pistol is 1.56 lb, and the capacity of the magazine is eight rounds. It fires the 9mm Makarov cartridge and has a muzzle velocity of 1,070 fps.

malabar guns Very long, heavy, and unwieldy pieces of ordnance made by joining iron bars together with loops.

Malaface A French surface-to-surface missile for use against small ships in support of landing craft. The solid-propellant missile has a weight of 1,545 lb and a range of 25 mi.

Malafon A French surface-to-surface or surface-to-underwater antisubmarine weapon with an airplane configuration that is ramp-launched with two solid-propellant boosters. It carries a 21-in. acoustic homing torpedo with a weight of 1,157 lb. The total system has a weight of 2,865 lb, a length of 19.75 ft, and a range of about 11 mi. Development began in 1956.

Malaya A British battleship of the **Queen Elizabeth** class, which see.

Malik-I-Mydan An Indian term meaning "master of the field" and referring to a large bronze gun in Bejapoor, India. It was cast in 1538, has a bore diameter of 28.5 in., and fired a stone ball weighing 1,000 lb.

malingerer A soldier or sailor who feigns illness to avoid duty.

Malkara An Australian Army surface-to-surface antitank missile with a range of about 2 mi.

malleolus A type of ancient fire arrow; it was hollow and was filled with combustible materials.

mallet An obsolete term for "mace."

Mallet's Mortar A built-up English mortar made of cast and wrought iron. It has a bore of 36 in. and fired a cast-iron shell weighing 2,986 lb. It was made in 1857–1858.

Mallow The NATO code name for the Beriev Be-10 twin-turbojet-engine recon-

Malkara. (*Australian Department of Supply.*)

Mannlicher 8mm rifle Model 1895. (*The Smithsonian Institution, War Department Collection.*)

naissance flying boat in service with Soviet forces. It has a crew of six and a speed of 570 mph.

man To assume station, as in "man your planes."

man-at-arms A heavily armed cavalry soldier.

Mandrake The NATO code name for the twin-turbojet high-altitude reconnaissance aircraft in service with Soviet forces. It is of Yakovlev design and has an estimated speed of 460 mph.

maneuver **1.** A movement to place ships, troops, materiel, or fire in a better location with respect to the enemy. **2.** A tactical exercise carried out at sea, in the air, on the ground, or on a map in imitation of war. **3.** The operation of a ship, aircraft, or vehicle to cause it to perform desired movements.

Mangler The shipboard version of the Army's Mauler surface-to-air solid-fuel missile.

mangonel A fourteenth-century weapon for throwing large stones, javelins, etc.

Mangrove The NATO designation for the tactical-reconnaissance version of the Yakovlev Yak-25. See **Flashlight.**

Manhattan Project A project of the Manhattan District, lasting from August 1942 to August 1946, that developed the U.S. atomic-energy program, with special reference to the atomic bomb. This secret project consolidated work begun in 1939–1940 under joint auspices of the War and Navy Departments.

manifest A document specifying in detail the passengers or items carried for a specific destination.

maniglions The two handles on the back of a piece of ordnance.

man-movable Said of items which can be towed, rolled, or skidded for short distances by an individual without mechanical assistance but which are of such size, weight, or configuration as to preclude being carried.

The upper weight limit is approximately 425 lb per individual.

Mannlicher 7.63mm automatic pistol Model 1900 This weapon was manufactured by Steyr Waffenfabrik in Austria and weighs 29 oz. It has a fixed box magazine with a capacity of eight cartridges. The overall length is 8¾ in., and the barrel length is 5½ in. The weapon and Spanish imitations of it require a special 7.63mm cartridge with a straight-side case. It should *not* be confused with the Model 1903, which uses a bottleneck case.

Mannlicher 7.63mm automatic pistol Model 1901 Like the Model 1900, this is a delayed-blowback automatic pistol made by Steyr Waffenfabrik. The weapon weighs 32 oz and has a fixed box magazine that holds eight cartridges. The overall length is 9⅝ in., and the barrel length is 6⁵⁄₁₆ in. This weapon was one of the earliest successful automatic pistols and was very popular throughout South America. Numerous Spanish copies of this design were manufactured.

Mannlicher 7.63mm automatic pistol Model 1903 This Austrian automatic pistol has a detachable box magazine with a capacity of six cartridges. It weighs 36 oz and has an overall length of 11 in. and a barrel length of 4½ in. The bottleneck cartridge originally issued for this weapon was described as "7.65mm Mannlicher 1903."

Mannlicher 7.65mm automatic pistol M1905 This blowback-operated pistol was developed at Steyr and introduced in 1901. It has an overall length of 9.62 in. and a barrel length of 6.31 in. It weighs 2 lb and has a nondetachable magazine with a capacity of eight cartridges. The muzzle velocity is about 1,025 fps. It was formerly the service pistol of Argentina.

Mannlicher 8mm carbine Model 1890 This was the first weapon featuring a straight-pull rotating bolt to enter the Aus-

trian service. The overall length is 39.5 in., and the barrel length is 19.5 in. It weighs about 6.9 lb and has a muzzle velocity of 1,900 fps and a five-round fixed box magazine.

Mannlicher 8mm carbine Model 1895 This Austrian bolt-action weapon has the same general characteristics as the 8mm short rifle Model 1895, but weighs ½ lb less, or about 7 lb.

Mannlicher 8mm rifle Model 1888 and Model 1888-90 This bolt-action rifle is the same as the Model 1886 rifle except that it has been chambered for the 8mm M88 black-powder cartridge and has had the rear sight altered for that round. It has a muzzle velocity of 1,750 fps. When smokeless powder was introduced in 1890, the new Austrian 8 × 50mm cartridge was developed, and the sights were once again modified. The rifle then became the M88-90, with a muzzle velocity of 2,115 fps.

Mannlicher 8mm rifle Model 1895 This Austrian weapon was made in tremendous quantities at Steyr and also in Budapest and was the principal bolt-action rifle for the Austro-Hungarians during World War I. After the war, great numbers of these weapons were turned over to other countries for war reparations. During World War II many of them were used by Italians, Bulgarians, Yugoslavs, and Greeks. It has an overall length of 50 in., a barrel length of 30.1 in., and a weight of 8.3 lb. It utilized a vertical-column box magazine with a capacity of five rounds.

Mannlicher 8mm short rifle Model 1895 A bolt-action rifle frequently confused with the Mannlicher 8mm carbine M95. It was designed for use by special troops. It has a bayonet lug and a stacking hook, while the carbine has neither. The weapon has an overall length of 39.5 in. and a barrel length of 19.65 in. It weighs 7.5 lb and has a muzzle velocity of 1,900 fps. Cartridges are contained in a fixed box magazine with a capacity of five rounds.

Mannlicher 11mm rifle Model 1886 An Austrian service rifle with an overall length of 52 in. and a barrel length of 31.75 in. It weighs 10 lb and has a muzzle velocity of 1,610 fps. It has a five-round fixed box magazine. Some 90,000 rifles of this model were manufactured by Steyr.

Mannlicher Berthier carbine See **French 8mm carbine M1890 (Mannlicher Berthier), French 8mm carbine 1892 (Mannlicher Berthier),** and **French 8mm carbine M1916.**

Mannlicher Carcano 6.5mm carbine Models 1891, 1891 TS, and 1891/24 These Italian weapons have an overall length of 36.2 in. and a barrel length of 17.7 in. They have a weight of 6.6 lb, a muzzle velocity of 2,297 fps, and a nondetachable box magazine with a capacity of six cartridges. The

Mannlicher Carcano 6.5 mm carbine Model 1891. (*The Smithsonian Institution, Treasury Department Collection.*)

weapons also have sights graduated from 500 to 1,500 meters and a permanently attached bayonet. The Model 1891 TS uses a knife-type bayonet that is removable. The Model 1891/24 is essentially the same as the 1891 TS except that the lower band is different. The Carcano rifles and carbines were developed at the Italian government arsenal at Turin by M. Carcano.

Mannlicher Carcano 7.35mm rifle Model 1938. (*The Smithsonian Institution, Treasury Department Collection.*)

Mannlicher Carcano 6.5mm carbine Models 1938 and 1938 TS The Italian 6.5mm version of the 7.35mm carbine Model 1938. The Model 1938 TS is the 6.5mm version of the 7.35mm carbine Model 1938 TS.

Mannlicher Carcano 6.5mm rifle Model 1891 This Italian rifle has an overall length of 50.8 in., a barrel length of 30.7 in., a weight of 8.6 lb, and a muzzle velocity of 2,395 fps. It has a six-round nondetachable box magazine. It has a straight bolt handle and sights graduated from 500 to 2,000 meters.

Mannlicher Carcano 6.5mm rifle Model 1938 This is the 6.5mm version of the 7.35mm rifle Model 1938. The decision had been made in 1938 to shift to the 7.35mm cartridge, but when the war broke out, it was decided to revert to the 6.5mm cartridge. All weapons made from 1940 onward were chambered for 6.5mm. Serial number C2766 of this weapon was manufactured in the Italian arsenal at Terni in 1940 and was sold in the United States as Italian Army surplus. On November 22, 1963, it was used in the assassination of President John F. Kennedy.

Mannlicher Carcano 7.35mm carbine Models 1938 and 1938 TS These are the 7.35mm versions of the Model 1891 carbine. They have a permanently attached folding bayonet and a bent bolt handle. The Model 1938 TS is the 7.35mm version of the Model 1891/24 carbine and uses a knife-type bayonet.

Mannlicher Carcano 7.35mm rifle Model 1938 In 1938 the 7.35mm cartridge was introduced in the Italian forces, and so a rifle and two carbines were developed to fire it. The Model 1938 has an overall length of 40.2 in., a barrel length of 20.9 in., a weight of 7.5 lb, and a muzzle velocity of 2,482 fps. Some are equipped with knife-type folding bayonets. With the outbreak of World War II, it was decided to revert back to the 6.5mm cartridge, and all Mannlicher Carcano weapons manufactured after 1940 were in that caliber.

man-of-war An armed vessel.

man-portable Said of items which are designed to be carried as a component part of the individual, crew-served, or team equipment of the dismounted soldier in conjunction with his assigned duties. The upper weight limit is approximately 30 lb.

man space The space and weight factor used to determine the combat capacity of vehicles, craft, and transport aircraft on the basis of the requirements of one man with his individual equipment. He is assumed to weigh between 222 and 250 lb and to occupy 13.5 cu ft of space.

mantlet, mantelet A protective shield or armor, e.g., in front of a gun or attached to the front of a tank. The term derives from a kind of movable shelter once used by the besiegers of a fortification. The mantlet afforded them a certain amount of protection while attacking.

manual An exercise whereby troops are taught the use of their rifles or other weapons.

manubaliste A type of crossbow or arbalest.

Manxman A class of British fast minelayers of 2,650 tons standard displacement completed in 1941–1943. They had a maximum speed of 40 knots and a complement of 246 men and carried 100 mines. Of six ships completed, three were lost to enemy action during World War II.

maquis A French guerrilla fighter who resisted the Germans in World War II. The term derives from the name of the scrubby brushland in which Corsican outlaws hid from the authorities.

Marauder The U.S. Martin B-26 Marauder was a twin-engine attack bomber first flown in 1940 and produced throughout World War II. It served in every theater of operations and was used by the forces of several countries. It had a speed of 283 mph and was armed with up to eleven .50 cal. machine guns; it carried a maximum bombload of 4,000 lb.

march The movement of personnel from one place to another; the advance of troops. Also, a measure of the marching done in a given time, such as a day's march.

Marder (German for "marten.") A German electrically propelled torpedo of World War II. It was steered by a human pilot who released it from its carrier body at short range of target. It was designed to be used from a beach against enemy landing vessels.

Marder-Schutzenpanzer Neu M-1966 A German (Federal Republic) armored personnel carrier that entered production in 1969. It has a crew of four, carries six infantrymen, weighs 26 tons, has a road speed of 43 mph, and carries one 20mm cannon and two 7.62mm machine guns. (Picture, next page.)

Mareszek antitank rifle A Polish antitank rifle of 1935. The Soviet Simonov 14.5mm AT rifle, the Soviet Degtyarov AT rifle M1941, and the German PzB38 and PzB39 were all patterned on this rifle. (Picture, next page.)

Marianas Turkey Shoot The nickname for a U.S. naval air victory in the Pacific during World War II. On June 19, 1944, 402 Japanese planes were destroyed during the Battle of the Philippine Sea.

marine A soldier who serves aboard ship. In the United States, a member of the U.S. Marine Corps, an organization authorized by act of Congress in 1775. Marines act as guards and orderlies aboard ship, operate gun batteries during battle, and are often used as landing forces.

Marine Corps air station A stopping place that provides operating, testing, overhaul,

Marauder. (*U.S. Air Force.*)

Marder-Schutzenpanzer Neu M-1966. (*Ministry of Defense, Federal Republic of Germany.*)

Mareszek antitank rifle. (*Defense Ministry, Polish People's Republic.*)

and personnel facilities for Marine aviation.

Marine Infantry rifle   See **French 11mm rifle Model 1878.**

Mariner   The Martin PBM-1/5 was a maritime reconnaissance flying boat developed for the U.S. Navy and first flown in 1939. It had a crew of seven or eight, was powered by two 1,900-hp engines, and flew at speeds up to 211 mph. It was armed with a total of eight .50 cal. machine guns and carried 8,000 lb of bombs. By the end of World War II, 1,289 aircraft of this type had been produced.

maritime operations   Actions performed by forces on, under, or over the sea to gain or exploit control of the sea or to deny its use to the enemy.

Mark   The term used to identify a specific type of weapon or equipment; it is always followed by a number to indicate the specific equipment and is frequently followed by a model number to indicate the variety of equipment, e.g., Torpedo Mark 46 Model 1. (The term derives from the German word *marke,* meaning "label" or "brand.") See also **MK,** a table of U.S. designations.

marker   A visual or electronic aid used to mark a designated point.

marker ship   In an amphibious operation, a ship which takes accurate station on a designated control point. It may fly identifying flags by day and show lights to seaward by night.

Market-Garden   A World War II Allied operation to establish a bridgehead across the Rhine in the Netherlands. It began on September 17, 1944.

Market Time   The code name of a U.S. sea surveillance program aimed at preventing infiltration in Southeast Asia from the South China Sea.

marking panel   A sheet of material displayed by ground troops for visual signaling to friendly aircraft.

Marlin   The Martin P5M Marlin is a twin-engine all-weather seaplane for long-range antisubmarine patrol and electronic reconnaissance. It was developed for the U.S. Navy and was first flown in 1951. It has a crew of 11, a speed of 365 mph, and a range of 2,000 nautical miles.

Marlin .30 cal. machine gun Model 1918   A U.S. gas-operated air-cooled machine gun with a rate of fire of 600 to 680 rounds per minute. It weighed 22 lb and was fed by 250- to 300-round link belts. Considerable numbers of this machine gun were used on various World War I fighter aircraft.

marshal   A general officer of the highest rank in certain foreign armies.

marshal of the royal air force   The highest commissioned rank in the RAF, equivalent to that of general of the air force in the USAF; a person holding this rank.

Martel   Missile *a*ntiradar and *tel*evision. A French-British guided air-to-surface missile with TV guidance or antiradar homing guidance.

martel, martel-de-fer   A war hammer. It was used in the Middle Ages and during the Renaissance to break armor.

Marten   The name of a German 75mm antitank gun mounted on a Czech 38 chassis. It was introduced in 1942 to serve with armored infantry and tank-destroyer units. It had a crew of four and was armed with one 75mm Pak 40 gun. It weighed 11.6 tons and traveled at speeds of about 30 mph on roads. The Marten II was a 75mm antitank gun mounted on a Panzer II chassis. It was also introduced in 1942 and had a crew of four.

martial law   The condition under which the laws of a country are administered by mili-

Mariner. (*U.S. Navy.*)

tary rather than civil authorities.

martinet A fourteenth-century weapon for throwing large stones.

Martini-Henry .45 cal. rifle This weapon was adopted by the British in 1871. It is a single-shot military rifle with a weight of 8 lb 10 oz and a barrel length of 33 in. It was replaced by the Lee-Metford in 1891.

Martinsyde F.4 Nicknamed the "Buzzard," this British single-seat single-engine fighter went into production in June 1918. It was armed with twin synchronized Vickers machine guns and flew at speeds up to about 133 mph. One of the fastest fighters of its day, it was produced too late for operational service in World War I.

Martinsyde G.100 and G.102 British single-seat single-engine biplanes designed as fighters. However, because of their size and unresponsive flying characteristics (earning the nickname "Elephant"), they were used as bombers and ground-attack aircraft. They had a speed of 95 mph, were armed with one forward-firing Lewis gun, and could carry two 112-lb bombs. They were in service from the beginning of 1916 until the end of 1917.

Martlet The British World War II name for the F4F Wildcat.

Martonite The French name for **bromacetone,** which see, a powerful tear gas of World War I.

Maruca A French Navy surface-to-air missile with a range of about 10 nautical miles.

Marut The Hindustan HF-24 Marut (Wind Spirit) is a single-seat jet fighter built in India and in service with the Indian Air Force. First flown in 1961, this airplane has a speed of Mach 1.02 and is armed with four 30mm Aden guns, forty-eight air-to-air rockets, and attachments for four 1,000-lb bombs.

Maryland A U.S. battleship of the **Colorado** class, which see. It was commissioned in 1921 and saw considerable service in the Pacific theater during World War II, during which time it was hit twice by Japanese kamikaze planes.

Masalca A French Navy surface-to-air missile with a range of about 65 nautical miles.

Mascot The NATO code name for a trainer version of the Soviet Ilyushin IL-28 bomber.

MASH Mobile Army surgical hospital. A U.S. Army field-hospital setup.

MAS Model 1938 submachine gun See **French 7.65mm Long submachine gun Mas Model 1938.**

Massachusetts Two battleships were named for the state of Massachusetts. The first *Massachusetts* was a ship of the old **Indiana** class, which see. It was commissioned in 1896 and saw action during the Spanish-American War (when it assisted in the sinking of the Spanish cruiser *Reina Mercedes*). The second *Massachusetts* was

Marlin. (*U.S. Navy.*)

Martel missiles, carried by a Buccaneer aircraft. (*Hawker Siddeley Aviation Ltd.*)

a ship of the new *Indiana* class. It was commissioned in 1942 and served both in North Africa and in the Pacific. It is presently at Fall River, Mass., where it serves as an official World War II memorial.

mass bombing 1. Bombing with a great quantity of bombs. **2.** Bombing by a concentration of many airplanes.

masse d'armes A weapon consisting of a

long pole with a large iron head affixed.

massed fire 1. The fire of the batteries of two or more ships directed against a single target. **2.** Fire from a number of weapons directed at a single point or small area.

master bomber During World War II mass-bombing attacks, any one of the bombers that circled over the target and directed other planes to their aiming points.

Martini-Henry .45 cal. rifle. (*The Smithsonian Institution, War Department Collection.*)

matchlock. (*The Smithsonian Institution, William C. Dodge Collection.*)

Matilda tank, flying a captured Italian flag. (*The Imperial War Museum.*)

Mauler. (*U.S. Army.*)

master gunner Formerly, a noncommissioned specialist rank in the U.S. Army Coast Artillery Corps. In the British artillery, a warrant officer.

masthead bombing Very low bombing, especially against shipping.

Masurca Mk2 A two-stage solid-propellant surface-to-air missile used for antiaircraft protection aboard certain vessels in the French Navy. It has a total length of about 28 ft, a weight of 4,080 lb, and a range of over 25 mi.

Matador The name applied to an Air Force surface-to-surface tactical missile, controlled electronically from the ground. It is powered by a jet engine, is rocket-boosted, and attains subsonic speed. It has a range of several hundred miles, can carry a conventional or atomic warhead, and has a combination radar and inertial guidance system. Takeoff weight for the Matador B was 14,000 lb.

matafunda An ancient weapon, possibly slinglike, used for throwing large stones.

match A chemically treated cord that burns at a uniform rate and was used for firing a powder charge in a matchlock or cannon. A slow match burns at a very slow rate. A quick match burns quite rapidly.

matchlock The earliest mechanical firearm ignition system, the matchlock consists of a slow match in a holder. When the trigger is pressed, the match is projected into a pan filled with priming powder, the burning of which ignites the main charge. It appeared in the last quarter of the fifteenth century.

mate A petty officer who serves as an assistant to a warrant officer in the U.S. Navy.

mategriffon A machine for throwing stones and darts; also, a kind of siege tower.

materiel All items of equipment necessary for the maintenance, operation, and support of military activities without distinction as to their application for administrative or combat purposes; the term excludes ships and naval aircraft.

Matilda The British tank, medium, MK II. It was introduced in 1939 for use as infantry support. It had a crew of four and was armed with one 2-pounder gun and one .303 tank machine gun. It weighed 29.7 tons and traveled at speeds up to 15 mph on roads.

M.A.T. Model 1949 submachine gun See **French 9mm Parabellum submachine gun M.A.T. Model 1949.**

Matra R.530 A French air-to-air missile with interchangeable semiactive radar and infrared homing heads. It has an overall length of 10.75 ft, a launching weight of 430 lb, a warhead weight of 60 lb, and a range of about 11 mi.

matross Formerly, a member of a cannon crew who assisted in loading, firing, and sponging the guns.

Matsu A class of Japanese 1,262-ton destroyers produced in the latter part of World War II. They had a speed of 27 knots and armament consisting of three 5-in. and twenty-four 25mm guns, four 24-in. torpedo tubes, and thirty-six depth charges. Of the approximately 40 ships produced, 10 were lost during the war.

Matterhorn   The code name for the World War II bombing of targets in Japan by B-29 aircraft of the U.S. XX Bomber Command based in Bengal, India, and staged through airfields at Chengu, China. The first mission was flown against Yawata, Japan, on June 14, 1944.

mattucashlash   A small dagger once used by Scottish Highlanders. It was also called an "armpit dagger" because it was worn under the armpit.

MAU-4 (12, 38A, 40A, and 50A)   U.S. Air Force designations for bomb racks.

Mauler   A mobile self-propelled-mount guided missile designed for providing all-weather air defense of forward ground-combat elements against low-flying aircraft and short-range rockets or missiles. Designated as XMIM-46A. It utilizes infrared guidance.

Mauritius   A class of British cruisers of 8,000 tons standard displacement completed in 1940–1942. Of eight in the class, two were lost in action during World War II. They had a length of 555 ft, a beam of 62 ft, a speed of 31.5 knots, and a wartime complement of 980 men. They were armed with nine 6-in. and eight 4-in. guns, plus two to sixteen 40mm, four to twelve 20mm, and eight to twenty-four 2-pounder antiaircraft guns. Six 21-in. torpedo tubes were carried.

Mauser   The first successful metallic-cartridge bolt-action rifle was invented by Paul Mauser, of Germany, the first designs having been patented in 1868.

Mauser 7.63mm (also 9mm and 9mm Parabellum) automatic pistol Military Model   This was one of the first successful automatic pistols. It first appeared in 1895 in the bottleneck 7.63mm cartridge. Winston Churchill credited this weapon with saving his life in the Sudan Campaign of 1898. Later it appeared in 9mm Mauser, and during World War I it was used by the German Army in 9mm Parabellum. The 1912 Mauser was issued in 9mm Parabellum during World War II and was called the "Model 1916." The 7.63mm Model 1932 was used by German security units during World War II. This model has detachable 10- and 20-round magazines and is a selective-fire version of the weapon. The Model 1932 has an overall length of 11.75 in. without stock, a barrel length of 5.63 in., and a weight (without stock) of 2.93 lb. It has a muzzle velocity of 1,575 fps.

Mauser 7.65mm (.32 ACP) automatic pis-

tol H.Sc   The H.Sc designation of this pistol means "hammer self-loading." It is, in other words, a double-action weapon. It has a magazine capacity of eight cartridges, an overall length of about 6½ in., a barrel length of 3⅜ in., and a weight of 20½ oz. This weapon was widely used during World War II by Germany's military and police units.

Mauser 7.65mm (.32 ACP) automatic pistol Model 1910   The M1910 pistol is one of the best-finished pistols ever made. It has a magazine capacity of eight cartridges, an overall length of 6.2 in., a 3.4-in. barrel, and a weight of approximately 20 oz. The M1934 version of this pistol is the same mechanically, but is slightly more streamlined. This weapon was used extensively by German troops in World War I and by SS police units during World War II.

Mauser 7.92mm carbine Models 98a and 98b   The Model 98a was the most popular carbine version of the Model 98 used by Germany in World War I. It also saw limited use in World War II. It was introduced in 1904 and was manufactured in large quantities until the end of World War I. The Model 98b was designated a carbine but was the same length as the Model 98 rifle. It has a turned-down bolt handle and a tangent sight like that of the Kar 98a. The Model 98a has an overall length of 43.3 in., a barrel length of 23.6 in., a weight of 8 lb, and a muzzle velocity of 2,853 fps. It utilizes a staggered-row fixed box magazine with a capacity of five cartridges.

Mauser 7.92mm rifle Model 33/40   This is the German version of the Czech Model 33 carbine. It is distinguished by its short length and light weight and was used by German mountain and paratroop divisions. Made in occupied Czechoslovakia, this weapon has an overall length of 39.1 in., a barrel length of 19.29 in., and a weight of 7.9 lb. It has a staggered-row fixed box magazine with a capacity of five cartridges and a muzzle velocity of about 2,400 fps.

Mauser 7.92mm rifle Model 98 (Gew 98)   This rifle (Gew or Gewehr 98) was the most successful bolt-action design ever produced and was the principal rifle of the German Army during World War I. It has an overall length of 49.2 in., a barrel length of 29.1 in., and a weight of 8.81 lb. It is equipped with a five-round staggered-row fixed box

Mauser 7.63mm automatic pistol Military Model. (*The Smithsonian Institution, G.S.A. Administration Collection.*)

Mauser 7.65mm (.32 ACP) automatic pistol Model 1910. (*The Smithsonian Institution, Post Office Department Collection.*)

magazine and has a muzzle velocity of 2,099 fps. The model 98/17 was manufactured with a bolt cover and had a square shoulder on the follower to prevent closing the bolt on an empty magazine.

Mauser 7.92mm rifle Model 98k (Kar 98k)   This was the standard bolt-operated rifle of the German Army during World War II. It was adopted in 1935 and was made in great quantities. It has an overall length of 43.6 in., a barrel length of 23.6 in., a weight of 8.6 lb, and a staggered-row fixed box magazine with a capacity of five cartridges. It has a muzzle velocity of 2,476 fps and an effective range of 800 yd. (Picture, next page.)

Mauser 11mm rifle Models 1871 and 1871/84   The first Mauser rifles to be adopted by any country, these were single-shot weapons that utilized a black-powder cartridge. They are called "Howth rifles"

Mauser 7.92mm rifle Model 98 (Gew 98). (*The Smithsonian Institution, War Department Collection.*)

Mauser 7.92mm rifle Model 98k (Kar 98k). (*The Smithsonian Institution, U.S. Senate Collection.*)

Mauser 11mm rifle Model 1871. (*The Smithsonian Institution, National Museum Collection.*)

Maxim machine gun, being held by its inventor, Hiram Maxim. (*Vickers Ltd.*)

in the Republic of Ireland. They were the principal weapon of the Irish rebels during the 1916 Easter Monday Rebellion and had been landed at the town of Howth, near Dublin, in a well-publicized gunrunning expedition. The Model 1871/84 is the same basic weapon but has provision for a nine-round tubular magazine.

Mauser 20mm aircraft cannon MG-151
See **MG-151 20mm aircraft cannon.**

Mauser 20mm antiaircraft cannon Flak 38 See **Flak 38 20mm antiaircraft cannon.**

Mavis The World War II Allied code name for the Japanese Kawanishi H6K1/5 four-engine long-range maritime reconnaissance-bomber flying boat. It had a crew of nine and was armed with four machine guns and one 20mm cannon, plus about 4,000 lb of bombs or torpedoes. It flew at speeds of 239 mph and had a range of 4,200 mi.

MAW Medium antitank assault weapon. See **Dragon.**

maximite A high explosive of the picric acid class once used in armor-piercing shells and named after Hudson Maxim, the inventor.

Maxim machine gun An automatic weapon developed by the American Hiram Maxim in England in 1883. It was a recoil-operated water-cooled machine gun with a

rate of fire of about 600 to 700 rounds per minute. Through a long association with Vickers in England, the weapon took the name of Vickers-Maxim, and was later referred to only as "Vickers." The Maxim was used by every major power, at one time or another, from 1900 until World War I. The first operational use of the weapon was made by the British in the Matabele War of 1893 in the northern Transvaal. A detachment of 50 British troops armed with four Maxim guns resisted the massed attacks of 5,000 warriors. At the end of 1½ hours, and after five charges, there were 3,000 dead in front of the British positions.

maximum depression The maximum vertical angle below the horizontal at which a piece can be laid and still deliver effective fire.

maximum effective range The maximum distance at which a weapon may be expected to deliver its destructive charge with the accuracy specified to inflict prescribed damage.

maximum elevation The greatest vertical angle at which a gun or launcher can be laid. It is usually limited by the mechanical structure of the piece.

maximum range The capability of an aircraft, gun, radar transmitter, or the like that expresses the most distant point to which the aircraft can fly, the gun can shoot, etc.

mayday The international distress call, from the infinitive of the French term for "help me" (*m'aider*).

MBL Motor lifeboat.

MBR Short-range reconnaissance seaplane (*Morskoi blizuii razvedchik*); used in the names of Russian aircraft from 1925 to 1945, as in MBR-2.

MBR-2 See **Beriev MBR-2 (Be-2).**

MCB A U.S. Navy motor cargo boat.

McCall and Craven Classes of U.S. destroyers (DD) of 1,500 tons standard displacement commissioned in 1937–1939. They had an overall length of 341 ft, a beam of 34 ft, a speed of 36.5 knots, and a complement of 200 men. They were armed with four 5-in. guns and sixteen 21-in. torpedo tubes.

M Class A class of Soviet submarines of 205 tons standard surface displacement launched in 1935–1940 (early Class M) and in 1940–1945 (later Class M). Large numbers were built. They had a speed of 8 knots submerged, a complement of 20 men, and armament consisting of two or four 21-in. torpedo tubes.

M Class A class of Goodyear dirigibles having a helium capacity of 725,000 cu ft.

MCS A U.S. Navy mine-countermeasures-support ship.

MD The U.S. military designation for the war gas **methyldichloroarsine,** which see.

M day The day on which mobilization be-

Mavis. (*The Smithsonian Institution, National Air Museum.*)

gins or is planned to begin.

MDR Long-range reconnaissance seaplane (*Morskoi dal'nii razvedchik*); used in the names of Russian aircraft from 1925 to 1945, as in MDR-6.

MDR-6 See **Beriev MDR-6 (Be-4).**

MDS A U.S. Navy minesweeper, drone.

Me Messerschmitt.

meaconing A system of receiving radio-beacon signals and rebroadcasting them on the same frequency to confuse navigation. The meaconing stations cause inaccurate bearings to be obtained by aircraft or ground stations.

meal powder An unglazed black powder of very fine granulation.

mean point of impact The point whose coordinates are the arithmetic means of the coordinates of the separate points of impact of a finite number of projectiles fired or released at the same aiming point under a given set of conditions.

maximum elevation. Shown are five French 105mm self-propelled guns at maximum elevation. (*French Ministry of Defense.*)

McCall. (*U.S. Navy.*)

M Class. (*Goodyear Aerospace Corporation.*)

Mechanical Mule. (*U.S. Army.*)

Medal of Honor. (*U.S. Army.*)

meatballs   The U.S. Navy World War II nickname for Japanese planes (from their circular red insignia).

Mechanical Mule   The popular name for U.S. ½-ton low-silhouette infantry light weapons carrier powered by a 17-hp engine. It travels at a speed of 25 mph and has a range of 151 mi.

medium artillery, a U.S. 155mm howitzer M1. (*U.S. Army.*)

mechanize   To equip a military force with armed and armored motor vehicles, such as tanks and combat vehicles. Mechanization differs from motorization in that the motorization of a unit provides a means of transportation only, whereas in mechanization the unit both travels in, and fights from, its vehicles.

mechanized   Of or pertaining to equipment or weapons operated or driven by some type of motor power, such as mechanized gear, mechanized force, etc.

mechanized gun   A gun mounted on, and fired from, a motor vehicle. It is usually an artillery gun mounted on an armored, wheeled, or tracklaying vehicle.

mechanized warfare   Warfare conducted by use of motored vehicles and weapons.

Médaille Militaire   A French silver medal for distinguished service in action. It is awarded to noncommissioned officers and men of the Army and Navy and to generals in command of armies. It was instituted in 1852 by Napolean III.

Medal of Honor (MH)   A U.S. military decoration awarded to a person who, while in the armed services of the United States and while engaged in conflict with an enemy of the United States, has distinguished himself conspicuously by gallantry and intrepidity at the risk of life above and beyond the call of duty.

MEDCOM   Mediterranean Communications. The U.S. Air Force 486L program that provides a troposcatter microwave communications system in the Mediterranean area and a link with other systems in Europe.

median lethal dose   **1.** *Nuclear:* The amount of radiation over the whole body which will be fatal to 50 percent of the

animals or organisms in question in a given period of time.   **2.** *Chemical:* The dose of a toxic chemical agent which will kill 50 percent of exposed unprotected personnel. It is expressed in milligram minutes per cubic centimeter.

medic   A combat medical orderly.

medium-altitude bombing   Horizontal bombing with the height of release between 8,000 and 15,000 ft.

medium-angle loft bombing   A type of loft bombing wherein weapon release occurs at an angle between 35° and 75° above the horizontal.

medium antiaircraft artillery   Conventional antiaircraft artillery pieces, 90mm or larger, the weight of which in a trailed mount, excluding on-carriage fire control, does not exceed 40,000 lb.

medium artillery   Guns and howitzers with calibers greater than 105mm but not greater than 155mm.

medium bomber   Any bomber considered to be intermediate in weight between the light and heavy bombers. In World War II, the B-25 and B-26 were considered medium bombers.

medium, or intermediate, caliber   In naval terminology, a caliber greater than 4 in. but less than 8 in.

medium-delay fuze   A type of delay fuze, especially in bombs, in which the fuze action is delayed for a period of time between that of short-delay fuzes and long-delay fuzes, normally 4 to 15 seconds.

medium machine gun   An automatic weapon of rifle caliber which is capable of sustained rapid fire and which is fired from a tripod or other form of mounting. Most medium machine guns are belt-fed. This enables them to carry out their sustained-fire tasks, which demand a comparatively high output in rounds per minute over a period of time.

medium-range ballistic missile A ballistic missile with a range capability of from 600 to 1,500 nautical miles.

megaton energy The energy of a nuclear explosion which is equivalent to that produced by the explosion of 1 million tons (or 1,000 kilotons) of TNT.

megaton weapon A nuclear weapon the yield of which is measured in terms of millions of tons of TNT explosive equivalents.

mehalla Formerly, mounted Moroccan troops, often under the leadership of foreign officers.

ME-IGOR A Soviet Army solid-propellant antitank missile.

Meiji 6.5mm rifle A bolt-action breech-loading rifle having a detachable magazine with a capacity of five cartridges. It was the principal Japanese infantry arm in the Russo-Japanese War. See **Japanese 6.5mm rifle Type 30.**

melee A confused fight or skirmish in which the combatants are closely mingled.

melt loading The process of melting solid explosive with heat and pouring it into bombs, projectiles, and the like to solidify. Also called "cast loading."

MEMS 9mm Parabellum submachine guns Produced in Argentina by the firm of Armas & Equipos S.R.L., these are lightweight, easily produced weapons with model designations of 52/58, 52/60, AR 163, and M 67. They are all blowback-operated, weigh on the order of $6\frac{1}{2}$ lb, and have a cyclic rate of fire of 750 to 800 rounds per minute and a muzzle velocity of about 1,200 fps. With stock extended, they are about 35 in. long and utilize staggered-row box magazines with a capacity of 40 rounds.

Mendoza 7mm light machine gun Model C1934 This weapon was standardized in the Mexican Army in 1934. It is a gas-operated selective-fire weapon with a cyclic rate of fire of 400 to 500 rounds per minute, a muzzle velocity of about 2,700 fps, an overall length of 46 in., a barrel length of about 25 in., and a weight of 18.5 lb. It is fed from a 20-round detachable box magazine.

Mendoza submachine gun A Mexican submachine gun developed in several variations to fire .45 cal. ACP, .38 cal. Super, and 9mm Parabellum cartridges. It is blowback-operated and has selective full automatic or semiautomatic fire, although the model with the 16-in. barrel fires full automatic only. The overall length is 25 in., and barrel lengths range from 10 to 16 in. The loaded weight is 6.25 lb with a 20-round magazine. The approximate muzzle velocity with .45 cal. ACP is 920 fps.

mention in despatch A British award, the

Mendoza 7mm light machine gun Model C1934. (*The Smithsonian Institution, Treasury Department Collection.*)

Mercator. (*U.S. Navy.*)

Messerschmitt Bf 109. (*The Smithsonian Institution, National Air Museum.*)

lowest in precedence.

Mercator A Martin-built long-range patrol aircraft developed for the U.S. Navy. It had a speed of 350 mph.

mercenary A paid soldier in the service of a foreign country.

merchant marine The commercial, as contrasted with the naval, vessels of a country.

mercury fulminate An explosive compound that is extremely sensitive to shock, spark, or friction and is used to set off other explosives.

merkin A mop used to clean a cannon.

merlon One of the solid portions separating the openings in the battlements of a fortification.

message Any thought or idea expressed briefly in a plain or secret language and prepared in a form suitable for transmission by any means of communication.

message center A communication agency charged with the responsibility for acceptance, preparation for transmission, receipt, and delivery of messages.

Messerschmitt Bf 109 This single-engine single-seat low-wing fighter, in all its variations, was manufactured in larger quanti-

Messerschmitt Bf 110. (*The Smithsonian Institution, National Air Museum.*)

Messerschmitt Me 262. (*U.S. Air Force.*)

Messerschmitt Me 323 transport. (*U.S. Air Force.*)

Meteor. (*The Imperial War Museum.*)

ties than any other World War II warplane. It accounted for 60 percent of all German single-seat fighter production between 1936 and 1945. The first models were flown in 1935, and certain types were flown operationally during the Spanish Civil War. The Bf 109G was powered by a 1,475-hp engine, flew at speeds of 387 mph, and was armed with two 13mm machine guns, one engine-mounted 20mm cannon, and two 20mm cannons mounted under the wing. It had a wingspan of 32.5 ft, a length of 29.75 ft, and a height of 8.5 ft.

Messerschmitt Bf 110 The Bf 110C-F versions of this twin-engine airplane were used as two-seat long-range day and escort fighters. The Bf 110G-H's were used as three-seat night fighters. First flown in the late 1930s, various versions were flown throughout World War II. The Bf 110G was powered by two 1,475-hp engines, flew at speeds up to 342 mph, and was armed with two forward-firing 30mm cannons, two forward-firing 20mm cannons, and two rearward-firing 7.9mm machine guns.

Messerschmitt Me 163 Komet See **Komet.**

Messerschmitt Me 210 A German two-seat twin-engine medium-range fighter first flown in 1939. Because of poor design and a high accident rate, the production was terminated in 1942. It had a speed of 385 mph and was armed with two forward-firing 20mm cannons, two forward-firing 7.9mm machine guns, and two remotely controlled rearward-firing 13mm machine guns. It could also carry two 1,100-lb bombs internally and two externally.

Messerschmitt Me 262 A German single-seat interceptor powered by two turbojet engines, and the first of its kind ever to fly operationally. The first prototype flew in 1942. A total of 1,433 airplanes were produced, but fewer than 15 percent were used operationally, and then in close-support operations, for which the aircraft was unsuited. It was powered by two turbojet engines with a thrust of 1,980 lb each. The maximum speed was 538 mph at 29,560 ft, and the armament consisted of four 30mm cannons and twenty-four unguided rockets. The fighter version was called the *Schwalbe* (Swallow), and the bomber version, the *Sturmvogel* (Stormbird).

Messerschmitt Me 321 glider The largest glider to see service during World War II. It had a wingspan of 181 ft and could carry 120 troops or a load of 40,000 lb of cargo. It proved to be difficult to fly, and this led to the development of a powered version (the Me 323). The popular name for this glider was the "Gigant."

Messerschmitt Me 323 transport Also called the "Gigant," this was a six-engine powered version of the Me 321 glider. It could carry 130 men or 18 tons of cargo, and it had a cruising speed of 129 mph. It had a crew of five and was armed with five 13mm machine guns. It was used to transport supplies and men to North Africa in the closing days of the Tunisian campaign.

Messerschmitt Me 410 Hornisse A German two-seat twin-engine heavy fighter-bomber and fighter-interceptor. It was powered by two 1,750-hp engines, flew at speeds of 388 mph, and was armed with four forward-firing 20mm cannons, two forward-firing 7.9mm machine guns, and two rearward-firing remotely controlled 13mm machine guns. Various versions of the aircraft were produced between 1943 and 1945.

mess kit A kit to hold a soldier's food.

messroom A dining room.

metal In gunnery, the substance forming the barrel. In naval terminology, the weight of projectiles that a warship can fire in a given broadside.

metal fouling Deposits of metal that collect in the bore of a gun. Metal fouling comes from the jackets or rotating bands of projectiles.

Meteor The British Gloster Meteor was the only Allied jet airplane to see service during World War II. A single-seat twin-jet fighter-interceptor, it was designed in 1940 and was first flown in 1943. The first operational squadron saw service in Europe in April 1945. Because the Luftwaffe was largely decimated by that time, the Meteor never had an opportunity to pit itself against German jet fighters, and was used largely for ground attack. Powered by two turbojet engines with 1,700 lb of thrust each, the aircraft was armed with four 20mm Hispano cannons and flew at a top speed of 493 mph.

methylchlorsulfonate A tear gas that is effective in concentrations as low as 1 part in 750,000. It was the first war gas to be successfully used in projectiles. The Germans used it in trench mortar bombs and hand grenades in June 1915. The German term for this material is *C-Stoff.*

methyldichloroarsine (MD) This war gas is one of the **blistering agents,** which see, and has a delayed-action casualty effect. Its blistering action is slightly less than that of HD (distilled mustard), and it has an effect on the eyes (corneal damage) similar to that of L (lewisite). It has an immediate irritation effect on the eyes and nose. Blistering is delayed several hours.

meurtrières Small loopholes through which a rifle or musket could be fired. Also, the cavities made in the walls of fortified towns or fortifications.

Mexican .30/06 rifle Model 1954 This weapon is patterned on the Springfield Model 1903A3, but features the Mauser-type action. It is about 48 in. long and has a barrel length of 24 in. and a weight of approximately 9 lb. The muzzle velocity is

MG-15 7.95mm aircraft machine gun. (*The Smithsonian Institution, Department of Defense Collection.*)

MG-34 7.92mm machine gun. (*The Smithsonian Institution, Treasury Department Collection.*)

MG-42 7.92mm machine gun. (*The Smithsonian Institution, National Museum Collection.*)

about 2,800 fps, and the weapon is fed from a five-round nondetachable box magazine.

Mexican Mauser 7mm rifle Model 1895 A rifle that is almost identical to the Spanish Mauser Model 1893.

Mexican Mauser 7mm rifle Model 1902 This rifle is quite similar to the Mauser Model 1895.

Mexican Mauser 7mm rifle Model 1912 This rifle is similar to the German Gewehr 98, the main differences being that the Mexican rifle has a longer handguard and uses a tangent-type rear sight.

Mexican Mauser 7mm rifle Model 1936 This is a Mauser of Mexican design. It bears an external resemblance to the Springfield Model 1930A1. It has an overall length of 42.9 in., a barrel length of 19.29 in., and a weight of 8.3 lb. The muzzle velocity is about 2,600 fps, and the rifle utilizes a five-round nondetachable box magazine.

mg Machine gun.

MG-1 machine gun The West German designation for the MG-42/59, a machine gun made by Rheinmettal in 7.62mm NATO. See **German 7.62mm machine gun MG-42/59.**

MG-08 machine gun See **German 7.92mm machine gun MG-08 (Maxim).**

MG-08/15 machine gun See **German 7.92mm machine gun MG-08/15.**

MG-08/18 machine gun See **German 7.92mm machine gun MG-08/15.**

MG-13 machine gun See **German 7.92mm machine gun MG-13.**

MG-15 and 17 machine guns See **Solothurn 8mm machine gun Model 30S.**

MG-15 7.95mm aircraft machine gun A German (Rheinmetall-built) recoil-operated air-cooled machine gun that appeared in 1932. It had a rate of fire of 750 to 1,000 rounds per minute, weighed 27.5 lb, and was fed from a 250-round link belt.

MG-17 7.92mm aircraft machine gun An improved version of the MG-15, but with essentially the same specifications.

MG-34 7.92mm machine gun A German (Mauser-built) recoil-operated air-cooled machine gun with a rate of fire of 750 to 800 rounds per minute. It weighed 24.5 lb and was fed from a 250-round link belt.

MG-42 7.92mm machine gun A German (Mauser-built) recoil-operated air-cooled machine gun with a rate of fire of 1,200 to 1,350 rounds per minute. It weighed 24 lb and was fed from a 75- to 250-round link-belt magazine.

MG-42/59 machine gun See **German 7.62mm machine gun MG 42/59.**

MG-81 7.92mm aircraft machine gun A German (Mauser-produced) recoil-operated air-cooled machine gun that was introduced in 1939. It had a rate of fire of 1,200 to 1,300 rounds per minute, weighed 13.75 lb, and was fed from a 250-round link belt. It was used on aircraft such as the JU-88,

MICV. (*U.S. Army.*)

FW-189, and ME-110.

MG-131 13mm aircraft machine gun A German belt-fed air-cooled weapon with a weight of 40 lb and a rate of fire of about 960 rounds per minute. It was the first heavy-caliber machine gun to be used in a German landplane (initially used in pairs in the power-driven turret of the DO-217E2).

MG-131 machine gun See **Solothurn 8mm machine gun Model 30S.**

MG-151 20mm aircraft cannon A German (Mauser-built) recoil-operated air-cooled cannon with a rate of fire of 700 to 750 rounds per minute. It weighed 93.5 lb and was fed by a 50-round link belt. This weapon was widely used during World War II. The Mauser Company alone made 29,500 in this caliber between 1940 and 1943.

MGM-5 See **Corporal.**

MGM-13 See **Mace.**

MGM-18 See **Lacrosse.**

MGM-21A See **Entac.**

MGM-29A See **Sergeant.**

MGM-31A See **Pershing.**

MGM-32 See **Entac.**

MGM-51A, B See **Shillelagh.**

MGR-1A, B See **Honest John.**

MGR-3A See **Littlejohn,** sense 1.

MHA A U.S. Navy mine hunter, auxiliary.

MHC A U.S. Navy mine hunter, coastal.

Mi The designation for Soviet aircraft designed by Mikhail L. Mil.

Mi-1 See **Hare.**

Mi-4 See **Hound.**

Mi-6 See **Hook.**

Mi-8 See **Hip.**

Mi-10 See **Harke.**

Mi 34 Schmeisser-Bayard See **Belgian 9mm submachine gun Model 34.**

Michigan A U.S. battleship of the **South Carolina** class, which see.

Mickey Mouse The World War II nickname for an early U.S. Army microwave radar that was used with antiaircraft-gun batteries in range finding. It was so named

because of its two-dish antennas, which were shaped like mouse ears.

Micon A Swiss land-based, mobile, medium-range surface-to-air guided weapon designed to combat airborne targets flying at speeds up to Mach 2. It has a length of 18 ft, a firing weight of 1,760 lb, and a range of from 1.8 to 21.7 mi (maximum).

MICV Mechanized infantry combat vehicle, a U.S. Army system for an 11-man rifle squad. It was designed for a top speed of 37 mph, a range of 400 mi, and armament consisting of a 20mm automatic gun and a 7.62mm coaxial light machine gun.

Midas Originally designated the U.S. Air Force Program 461, Midas was aimed at developing a satellite that would provide an additional 10 minutes' warning of ballistic-missile launches from the Soviet Union. The technology and sensors developed for Midas have since been incorporated into the **Integrated Satellite,** which see.

middle watch In naval terminology, the period from midnight to 4 A.M. Also, the men on that watch.

mid-range ballistic missile A ballistic missile with a range between 500 and 3,000 nautical miles.

midshipman A naval cadet in training to become a naval officer.

Midway A class of U.S. attack aircraft carriers (CVA) of about 51,000 tons standard displacement commissioned in 1945–1947. They have an overall length of 979 ft, an extreme flight-deck width of 222 ft, a top speed of 33 knots, and a complement of 4,000 men. In the World War II era they carried 137 aircraft and were armed with 108 antiaircraft guns (total barrels). There are three ships in the class: *Midway, Franklin D. Roosevelt,* and *Coral Sea.*

MiG The designation for Soviet aircraft designed by the team of Artem I. Mikoyan and Mikhail I. Gurevich.

MiG-1 A single-seat single-engine fighter-interceptor and fighter-bomber produced for the Soviet Air Force and first flown in March 1940. Designed by Artem I. Mik-

Midway. (*U.S. Navy.*)

oyan and Mikhail I. Gurevich, this airplane was equipped with a 1,200-hp engine and was armed with one 12.7mm machine gun, two 7.62mm machine guns, and six rockets or two 220-lb bombs.

MiG-3 A further development of the MiG-1, this aircraft carried basically the same armament, but flew at speeds of 407 mph (as compared with a top speed of 390 mph for the MiG-1).

MiG-5 A version of the MiG-3 with a radial engine. Produced in limited numbers, it is believed to have had armament consisting of four 7.62mm machine guns, six rockets, and two 220-lb bombs.

MiG-9 See **Fargo,** sense 2.

MiG-15 See **Fagot.**

MiG-17 See **Fresco.**

MiG-19 See **Farmer.**

MiG-21 See **Fishbed.**

MiG-23 See **Foxbat.**

MiG Alley The name given by UN aviators during the Korean conflict to the air space in northwest Korea from the Yalu River south of Pyongyang. The area was so called because it was defended by Soviet-built MiG-15 fighters.

Mighty Might A U.S. Army ¼-ton light-weight utility truck.

Mighty Mouse The popular name for a type of unguided 2.75-in. air-to-air folding-fin rocket developed by the U.S. Navy.

mil A unit of angular measurement defined by the Navy as the angle whose tangent is $\frac{1}{1,000}$ of the radius and equivalent to 3.44 minutes of arc. The Army defines the mil as $\frac{1}{6,400}$ part of the circumference of a circle. The Navy mil is 0.065 minute greater than the Army mil.

Milan A missile developed jointly by the French firm of Nord and the German firm of Bölkow GmbH. It is a wire-guided anti-tank weapon with an overall length of about 2.5 ft, a weight (missile and container-launcher) of 24.2 lb, and a range of 6,560 ft.

Military Assistance Advisory Group (MAAG) A joint service group normally under the military command of a commander of a unified command and representing the Secretary of Defense; primarily, it administers the U.S. military assistance planning and programming in the host country.

military attaché A military officer who serves with the diplomatic representative of his country in a foreign capital. He studies, in open ways, the military developments of the country.

military crest A position just behind the true crest of a hill such that the terrain offers some protection.

military currency Currency prepared by a power and declared by its military commander to be legal tender for use by civilian and/or military personnel as prescribed

military gliders, Waco CG-4's. (*U.S. Army.*)

in the areas occupied by its forces. It should be of distinctive design to distinguish it from the official currency of both the opposing powers, but it may be denominated in the monetary unit of either.

military flail See **morning star.**

military gliders A number of troop-carrying and cargo-carrying gliders saw service during World War II. They included the U.S. Waco gliders, the British Hamilcar and Horsa, the Soviet Anatonov A-7, and the German DFS-230A and Messerschmitt Me 321. The Me 321 was the largest glider to see service and could carry 40,000 lb of cargo or 120 troops.

military governor The military commander or other designated person who in an occupied territory exercises supreme authority over the civil population subject to the laws and usages of war and to any directive received from his government or his superior.

military intervention The deliberate act of a nation or a group of nations to introduce its military forces into the course of an existing controversy.

military mines Formerly, an important part of military engineering and used in the attack (and defense) of fortifications. A military mine consisted of a tunnel (called a "gallery") or tunnels in which powder could be exploded by besiegers to cause damage to the walls. The besieged could also use mines to set charges under the glacis over which the assaulting column had to charge. They could also use countermines to thwart the efforts of the besiegers. A "common gallery" was a tunnel having a height of 4 ft 6 in. and a width of about 3 ft.

military objective A place to be reached; a military target, as opposed to an industrial target. By extension, any target having direct or indirect military significance.

military occupation A condition in which territory is under the effective control of a foreign armed force.

military operation An action or series of

actions, either combat or noncombat, conducted by a military organization.

military pit See **trou-de-loup.**

military police The police force of an army charged with maintaining law, order, and security. They also arrest stragglers and take charge of prisoners during times of war.

Military Sea Transportation Service (MSTS) Ocean freight and passenger service, operated by the Navy, for all three services.

military service 1. The military establishment as a whole. 2. A branch of the military establishment, such as the Army, Navy, or Air Force. 3. Duty in a military service; a military activity.

military strategy The art and science of employing the armed forces of a nation to secure the objectives of national policy by the application of force or the threat of force.

military target 1. Any industrial plant, city, or other object or any person, group of persons, or force marked as a target for destruction, damage, injury, or capture because of its direct or indirect use in the conduct or support of an enemy's military endeavor. 2. In restricted usage, a military person, force, installation, or area marked as a target because of its use, or potential use, in direct military operations. It is distinguished from an industrial target.

military top Formerly, a lightly armored platform erected on the mast of a warship. It served as a vantage point for machine gunners, etc.

militia A military force that is trained and periodically drilled but not called into active military service except in emergencies.

milk run A slang term for a routine mission or flight flown repeatedly; also, mission involving little danger.

Millennium The code name for the first 1,000-bomber attack of World War II, a British air raid on Cologne, Germany, on May 30 and 31, 1942.

Mills grenade A high-explosive grenade

Mills grenade. (*The Imperial War Museum.*)

mine detector. (*U.S. Army.*)

weighing about 1½ lb and named after its British inventor, Sir William Mills (1856–1932).

Milne A class of British destroyers of 1,920 tons standard displacement completed in 1941–1942. They had a speed of 36 knots, a complement of 240 men, and armament consisting of six 4.7-in. guns, one 4-in. gun, four 2-pounders, ten 20-mm antiaircraft guns, and eight 21-in. torpedo tubes.

MIM-3 See **Nike-Ajax.**

MIM-14A and B See **Nike-Hercules.**

MIM-23A See **Hawk,** sense 1.

mine An explosive or other material, normally encased, designed to destroy or damage vehicles, boats, or aircraft or to wound, kill, or otherwise incapacitate personnel. It may be detonated by the action of its victim, by the passage of time, or by controlled means. The general types are land mines and underwater mines. See also **military mines.**

mine clearance The process of detecting and/or removing land mines by manual or mechanical means. Also, the specific procedures to rid an area of naval mines, including sweeping, disposal, and explosive clearance.

mine countermeasures All methods for preventing or reducing damage or danger to ships, personnel, aircraft, and vehicles from mines.

mine defense The defense of a position, area, etc., by land or underwater mines. A mine-defense system includes the personnel and equipment needed to plant, operate, maintain, and protect the minefields that are laid.

mine detector A complete set for the detection and indication of metallic and/or

nonmetallic mines buried in the ground, submerged in water, or placed on the surface of land or water within the operating range of the device.

mine dragging Minesweeping.

minefield The space either in water or on land in which mines have been placed.

minefield gap A portion of a minefield in which no mines have been laid; it is of specified width to enable a friendly force to pass through the minefield in tactical formation. It will seldom be less than 100 yd wide.

minefield lane An unmined (or demined) route through a minefield. The lane is normally 8 yd wide and suitably marked. The length of lanes through enemy minefields depends on the method of breaching and the purpose for which the lane is required.

mine hunting The branch of mine countermeasures based on determining the positions of individual mines and concentrating countermeasures on those positions, as opposed to techniques directed at a more extensive area suspected of containing mines. Mine hunting includes mine locating, clearance of located mines, and mine watching.

Minekaze A class of Japanese 1,215-ton destroyers built in the early 1920s. Thirteen ships of this class were constructed, of which eight were lost in action during World War II. They had a speed of 39 knots, a complement of 148 men, and armament consisting of four 4.7-in. and two 7.7mm guns, three 21-in. torpedo tubes, and depth charges.

minelayer A warship designed to lay underwater mines.

mine locating A hunting procedure for

minesweeper, of the U.S. AM type. (*U.S. Navy.*)

detecting mines, pinpointing their positions, and/or identifying them after they have been laid. It includes visual, photographic, electromagnetic, sonic, or other techniques which reveal the presence of mines without disturbing them.

Minenwerfer A German muzzle-loading trench gun used to destroy machine-gun nests. (The term means "mine thrower.")

mine row A single row of mine clusters laid in a generally straight line.

mine sterilizer A device to make a mine harmless after a preset number of days.

mine strip Two parallel mine rows laid simultaneously six paces apart.

minesweeper **1.** A heavy road roller pushed in front of a tank; it is used to destroy land mines by exploding them. **2.** A ship especially equipped for locating and removing or neutralizing underwater mines.

minesweeping The technique of searching for or clearing mines using mechanical or explosion gear which physically removes or destroys the mine or produces in the area the influence fields necessary to actuate it.

minesweeping boat (MSB) A specially constructed boat used for sweeping mines.

mine thrower A small trench mortar, such as a Minenwerfer, used to throw high-explosive projectiles to a distance of about 500 yd.

mine tracks Tracks fitted on the deck of a minelayer to permit mines to be dropped over the stern.

mine vessels Vessels designed to plant or sweep mines. The principal types are minelayer, destroyer minelayer, minesweeper, and destroyer minesweeper.

mine warfare The strategic and tactical use of mines and mine countermeasures.

mine-warfare forces, naval Navy forces charged with the strategic and tactical use of naval mines and mine countermeasures. Such forces are capable of offensive and defensive measures in connection with laying and clearing mines.

minibuoy An airdropped sonobuoy.

Minié ball A cylindroconical rifle ball with an expanding base. Some used iron or boxwood cones driven forward by the gas from the burning propellant charge. Others utilized the gas directly. Captain C. E. Minié, of the French Army, was among those who developed the design, and his name has been applied to this wide class of bullets. They were used extensively during the American Civil War.

Minié rifled musket A four-grooved muzzle-loading rifle adopted by the British in 1851. It is a .702 cal. weapon with a weight of 10 lb 8¾ oz and a barrel length of 39 in. It was replaced in 1853 by the .577 cal. Enfield.

Minigun The **U.S. 7.62mm aircraft machine gun M-133 and M-134,** which see. It fires at

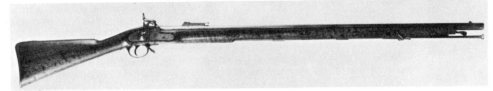

Minié rifled musket. (*The Smithsonian Institution, Military Service Institute Collection.*)

the rate of 6,000 rounds per minute.

Minilight A U.S. 20-lb searchlight with 1.5-million peak beam candlepower over a 1,000-yd range. It is used for ground battlefield illumination and aircraft lighting and as a rescue beacon.

minimum-altitude bombing Horizontal or glide bombing with the height of release under 900 ft. It includes masthead bombing, which is sometimes erroneously referred to as "skip bombing."

minimum normal-burst altitude The altitude above terrain below which air-defense nuclear warheads are not normally detonated.

minimum range **1.** The least range setting of a gun at which the projectile will clear an obstacle or friendly troops between the gun and the target. **2.** The shortest distance a gun can fire from a given position.

minimum safe altitude The altitude below which it is hazardous to fly, owing to the presence of high ground or other hazards.

minimum safe distance (MSD) In reference to an atomic explosion, the total distance from desired ground zero (DGZ) to

Minié ball. (*The Smithsonian Institution.*)

friendly positions required to ensure troop safety. The MSD is the sum of the radius of safety and the buffer distance.

minion An old four-pounder gun about 7 ft long. A sixteenth-century version was said to have a shot 3 in. in diameter.

MINISID Miniature Seismic Intrusion Detector. A U.S. hand-emplaced unattended ground sensor designed to detect seismic vibrations caused by troops and vehicles. Vibrations are transmitted to monitoring stations.

Minneapolis A class of U.S. 9,950-ton heavy cruisers completed between 1934

Minneapolis. (*U.S. Navy.*)

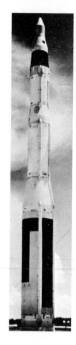

Minuteman. (*U.S. Air Force.*)

and 1937. It included *Minneapolis, Astoria, New Orleans, Tuscaloosa, San Francisco, Quincy,* and *Vincennes.* These ships had a length of 588 ft, a speed of 32.5 knots, a complement of 594 men, and main armament consisting of nine 8-in. and eight 5-in. guns, plus four aircraft. Three of these ships (*Astoria, Quincy,* and *Vincennes*) were sunk by the Japanese at the Battle of Savo Island on September 15, 1942.

Minnesota A U.S. battleship of the **Kansas** class, which see. It was commissioned in 1907.

Minnie Mouse A U.S. Navy antisubmarine rocket of World War II. It was launched from rails mounted on submarine chasers and cutters. The 2.5-in. rocket was launched in clusters.

minol A high-explosive mixture containing 40 percent TNT, 40 percent ammonium nitrate, and 20 percent powdered aluminum. It produces large blast effects and is suitable for melt loading.

minor caliber In naval terminology, guns and ammunition over .60 cal. and including 3 in. No longer used as an army classification.

minor port A port having facilities for the discharge of cargo from coasters or lighters only.

Minotaur A class of British 14,600-ton cruisers completed in 1908. They had a length of 525 ft, a complement of 755 men, and main armament consisting of four 9.2-in. and ten 7.5-in. guns. They had a speed of about 22 knots.

Minuteman A three-stage solid-propellant intercontinental ballistic missile developed for the U.S. Air Force by the Boeing Company and first fired in 1961. The latest version is the Minuteman III (LGM-30G), and it has an overall length of 59 ft 10 in., a launching weight of 76,000 lb, and a range of over 8,000 mi. Initial versions of this missile carried a 1-megaton thermonuclear warhead.

miquelet lock A form of flintlock developed by the Spanish. It has an externally mounted mainspring that fits on the lock plate in front of the cock. The sear operates horizontally through the lock plate to act on the base of the cock.

Mirage Several versions of the Dassault Mirage jet fighter, fighter-bomber, and strategic bomber have been developed since the prototype first flew in 1956. The Mirage F1 is a single-seat all-weather multipurpose fighter in service with the French Air Force. It has a speed of Mach 2.2+ and is armed with two 30mm cannons and two Sidewinder missiles. Various models have been provided to the forces of South Africa, Israel, Australia, Peru, Pakistan, Lebanon, Belgium, Iraq, and Switzerland. The Mirage III illustrated was built under license in Australia by the Government Aircraft Factories.

Mirka A class of Soviet escort vessels of about 900 tons standard displacement built in the early 1960s. They have a length of 262 ft, a beam of 29.5 ft, a speed of 28 knots, and a complement of 90 men. They are armed with four 12-barreled A/S rocket launchers, four 3-in. antiaircraft guns, and five torpedo tubes.

misericord A narrow-bladed, sharp-pointed medieval dagger that is believed to have been thrust between plates of armor to give the *coup de grâce* to a fallen adversary, although there is no proof of this assumption.

misfeed Failure to supply ammunition properly, especially to a magazine-fed or belt-fed automatic gun.

misfire **1.** Failure to fire or explode properly. **2.** The failure of a primer or the propelling charge of a projectile to function, wholly or in part.

missile Any object that is, or is designed to be, thrown, dropped, projected, or propelled, for the purpose of making it strike a target.

Missile A (division direct-support missile) A simple low-cost, lightweight, air-transportable mobile missile system providing sustained direct support for the battle group.

missile assembly-checkout facility A building, van, or other structure located near the operational missile-launching location and designed for the final assembly and checkout of the missile system.

Missile B (division support missile) A lightweight missile system utilizing a self-propelled launcher; it is air-transportable and capable of sustained ground combat in support of divisions.

missile launcher See **launcher.**

missile silo See **silo.**

mission **1.** The task, together with the

Mirage. (*U.S. Air Force.*)

Mirage III. (*Australian Department of Supply.*)

purpose, which clearly indicates the action to be taken and the reason therefor. **2.** In common usage, especially when applied to lower military units, a duty assigned to an individual or unit; a task. **3.** The dispatching of one or more aircraft to accomplish one particular task.

Mississippi Two battleships were named for the state of Mississippi. The first *Mississippi* was a sister ship of the **Idaho,** which see. It was commissioned in 1908 and was transferred to the Greek government in 1914, when it became the coastal-defense ship *Kilkis.* Both it and the *Lemnos* (ex-*Idaho*) were sunk by the German Luftwaffe in Salamis Harbor in April 1941. The second *Mississippi* was a ship of the *New Mexico* class and was commissioned in 1917. It saw extensive service in the Pacific theater during World War II.

Missouri Two U.S. battleships have been named for the state of Missouri. The first *Missouri* was commissioned in 1903 and was a sister ship of the *Maine* and the *Ohio.* (For details, see **Maine.**) The second *Missouri* was a battleship of the **Iowa** class, which see. It was commissioned in 1944 and served in the Pacific theater. On September 2, 1945, the formal surrender of the Japanese took place on the deck of the *Missouri* in Tokyo Bay. The *Missouri* later saw service in the Korean conflict.

Mistel See **composite aircraft** for definition and picture.

Mitchell The U.S. North American B-25 Mitchell was a five-place twin-engine attack bomber first flown in 1939 and produced throughout World War II, at the end of which time 9,816 had been manufactured. It served in every theater of war and was provided to several other countries under lend-lease. It had a speed of 274 mph, was armed with up to thirteen .50 cal. machine guns, and carried a maximum short-range bombload of 3,000 lb. In April 1942, sixteen Mitchells, under the command of Lieut. Col. James Doolittle, flew from the deck of the U.S.S. *Hornet* and successfully bombed Tokyo, Kobe, Nagoya, and Yokohama.

mitraille A cannon load consisting of bits of iron, heads of nails, grapeshot, etc.

mitrailleuse A weapon developed by the Frenchmen Faschamp and Montigny between 1851 and 1869. This 1-ton gun had 35 barrels and was mounted on a carriage that was pulled by four horses. It could fire the contents of 10 magazines (about 370 shots) in 1 minute and was very effective at close range.

Mitscher A class of U.S. warships of about 3,675 tons standard displacement first laid down as destroyers but reclassified as destroyer leaders (DL). Of the four built, two retained that classification, while the other two were converted to guided-missile de-

Mitchell. (*U.S. Air Force.*)

stroyers (DDG). They have a length of 493 ft, a beam of 50 ft, a speed of 35 knots, and a complement of 336 men. They are variously armed with two 5-in. guns, Tartar surface-to-air missiles, Asroc launchers, and torpedo launchers. (Picture, next page.)

Mitsubishi A5M4 See **Claude.**

Mitsubishi F1M2 See **Pete.**

Mitsubishi G4M Type 1 See **Betty.**

Mitsubishi J2M2-7 Raiden See **Jack.**

Mitsubishi Ki.21 Type 97 See **Sally.**

Mitsubishi Ki.67 Type 4 Hiryu See **Peggy.**

Mitsubishi Zero-Sen See **Zeke.**

Mity Mite A U.S. Army M106 tear-gas and/or smoke dispenser.

mixed minefield A minefield containing both antitank and antipersonnel mines.

mixed salvo A series of shots in which some fall short of the target and some fall beyond it. A mixed salvo differs from a bracketing salvo, in which the number of shots going over the target equals the number falling short of it.

MK The following table lists current U.S.

Missouri, of the *Iowa* class. (*U.S. Navy.*)

Mitscher. (*U.S. Navy.*)

military designations. See also **M** and **XM** tables.

MK-1	Cannon, 40mm.
MK-1	Grenade, illuminating.
MK-1	Projectile, dummy, 155mm.
MK-1	Projectile, dummy drill, 8-in.
MK-1	Projectile, dummy drill, 16-in.
MK-1	Warhead, practice, for 2.75-in. rocket.
MK-2	Cartridge, 40mm.
MK-2	Grenade, fragmentation.
MK-2	Projectile, dummy drill, 6-in.
MK-2	Projectile, dummy drill, 8-in.
MK-2	Projectile, dummy drill, 16-in.
MK-3	Cartridge, 40mm. For Duster system.
MK-3	Hand grenade, offensive.
MK-3	Projectile, 16-in.
MK-3A2	Grenade.
MK-4	Projectile, 5-in.
MK-4	Projectile, 6-in.
MK-4	Projectile, 12-in.
MK-5	Bomb, practice, miniature, 3-lb.
MK-5	Projectile, 16-in.
MK-5	Warhead, HEAT, practice, for 2.75-in. rocket.
MK-6	Projectile, 5-in.
MK-6	Projectile, 16-in.
MK-8	Projectile, 16-in.
MK-9	Projectile, 16-in.
MK-11	Cartridge, 40mm.
MK-14	Cartridge, 16-in.
MK-14	Cartridge, 40mm.
MK-14	Torpedo, 3,282-lb.
MK-15	Bomb, practice, 100-lb.
MK-16	Projectile, 14-in.
MK-16	Torpedo, 4,000-lb.
MK-17	Projectile, 12-in.
MK-18	Projectile, 12-in.
MK-18	Projectile, 16-in.
MK-19	Projectile, 12-in.
MK-19	Projectile, 14-in.
MK-21	Projectile, 8-in.
MK-22	Projectile, 8-in.
MK-22	Projectile, 12-in.
MK-22	Projectile, 14-in.
MK-24	Projectile, 8-in.
MK-25	Projectile, 8-in.
MK-26	Projectile, 8-in.
MK-27	Gun mount, 3-in., .50 cal.
MK-27	Projectile, 8-in.
MK-27	Torpedo, 1,174-lb.
MK-30	Projectile, 5-in.
MK-31	Projectile, 5-in.
MK-32	Projectile, 5-in.
MK-33	Bomb, armor-piercing, 1,000-lb.

MK-34	Projectile, 5-in.
MK-34	Projectile, 6-in.
MK-34	Torpedo, 1,154-lb.
MK-35	Projectile, 5-in.
MK-35	Projectile, 6-in.
MK-35	Torpedo, 1,800-lb.
MK-36	Projectile, 5-in.
MK-36	Projectile, 6-in.
MK-37	Projectile, 6-in.
MK-37	Torpedo, 1,690-lb.
MK-38	Projectile, 5-in.
MK-39	Projectile, 6-in.
MK-41	Projectile, 5-in.
MK-41	Projectile, 6-in.
MK-42	Gun mount, 5-in., .54 cal.
MK-42	Projectile, 5-in.
MK-42	Projectile, 6-in.
MK-43	Projectile, 6-in.
MK-43	Torpedo, 265-lb.
MK-44	Projectile, 5-in.
MK-44	Torpedo, 422-lb.
MK-45	Gun mount, 5-in., .54 cal.
MK-45	Projectile, 5-in.
MK-45	Torpedo, 2,400-lb.
MK-46	Projectile, 5-in.
MK-46	Torpedo, 575-lb.
MK-47	Projectile, 5-in.
MK-48	Projectile, 5-in.
MK-48	Torpedo, 3,600-lb.
MK-49	Projectile, 5-in.
MK-51	Projectile, 5-in., .38 cal.
MK-57	Projectile, 5-in., .38 cal.
MK-61	Warhead, inert. For 2.75-in. rocket.
MK-65	Bomb, practice, 500-lb.
MK-66	Bomb, practice, 1,000-lb.
MK-76	Bomb, practice, 25-lb.
MK-77 Mod 0	Bomb, fire, 750-lb.
MK-77 Mod 1	Bomb, fire, 500-lb.
MK-78	Bomb, fire, 750-lb.
MK-79	Bomb, fire, 1,000-lb.
MK-81 Mod 1	Bomb, low-drag, general-purpose, 250-lb, Snakeye I.
MK-82	Bomb, general-purpose, 500-lb.
MK-82 Mod 1	Bomb, low-drag, general-prupose, 500-lb, Snakeye I.
MK-82 Mod 2	Bomb, low-drag, 531-lb.
MK-83 Mod 3	Bomb, low-drag, 985-lb.
MK-84	Bomb, general-purpose, 2,000-lb.
MK-84 Mod 1	Bomb, low-drag, 1,970-lb.
MK-84 Mod 1	Projectile, 5-in., .54 cal.
MK-86	Bomb, practice, 250-lb.
MK-87	Bomb, practice, 500-lb.
MK-88 Mod 0	Bomb, practice, 1,000-lb.
MK-89 Mod 0	Bomb, practice, 56-lb.
MK-94 Mod 0	Bomb, gas, nonpersistent, 500-lb.

MK-106	Bomb, practice, 5-lb.
MK-122	Bomb, fire (also known as "Fireye").

(End of **MK** Table)

MK-101, MK-103, and MK-108 30mm aircraft cannons German aircraft cannons of World War II. See **Rheinmetall 30mm aircraft cannon MK-101**, **Rheinmetall 30mm aircraft cannon MK-103**, and **Rheinmetall 30mm aircraft cannon MK-108**.

MK-ST-5 and MK-ST-11 See **Rheinmetall 20mm aircraft cannon MK-ST-11** and **Rheinmetall 20mm antiaircraft cannon MK-ST-5**.

MLR See **main line of resistance**.

MM A U.S. Navy minelayer, fleet.

MMA A U.S. Navy minelayer, auxiliary.

MMC A U.S. Navy minelayer, coastal.

MMF A U.S. Navy minelayer, fleet.

moat A ditch around the ramparts of a fortress. It is deep (normally not less than 12 ft) and wide (usually not less than 24 ft). The moat is often filled with water, but may also be dry.

mobile artillery Artillery weapons designed for movement and ready conversion from traveling position to firing position. Wheels or other suspension devices are not ordinarily removed in the firing position.

mobility A quality or capability of military forces which permits them to move from place to place while retaining the ability to fulfill their primary mission.

mobilization 1. The act of preparing for war or other emergencies through assembling and organizing national resources. 2. The process by which the armed forces or part of them are brought to a state of readiness for war or other national emergency. This includes assembling and organizing personnel, supplies, and material for active military service.

mobilize 1. To convert an industry, economy, or country to a wartime basis; to call a person up to active duty under a mobilization plan. 2. To bring together the units or persons of a military force; to bring the force together.

mock-up A model, built to scale, of a machine, apparatus, or weapon. It is used to study construction, to test a new development, or to teach personnel how to operate the actual machine, apparatus, or weapon. Mock-ups or ships, landing craft, and aircraft are used in training personnel to load, embark, and debark.

Modified Centaur A class of British commando carriers of 23,300 tons standard displacement consisting of two former Hermes class aircraft carriers, *Albion* and *Bulwark*. They were completed in 1954, but were converted to their present role in 1959–1962. They have a length of 737.8 ft, a width of 123.5 ft, a speed of 28 knots, and a complement of about 1,900 men. They carry 16 helicopters and four LCVP (Landing craft, vehicle and personnel) and are armed with eight 40mm antiaircraft guns.

MOFAB Mobile floating assault bridge-ferry. A U.S. self-propelled amphibious transporter designed to carry superstructures that form a floating bridge or ferry across rivers. MOFAB units can be used to construct a bridge at the rate of 22 ft per minute, while a 60-ton-capacity ferry can be assembled from four MOFAB units in 6 minutes.

Mogami A class of Japanese 12,400-ton cruisers built in the late 1930s. The class consisted of *Kumano, Mikuma, Mogami,* and *Suzuya,* all of which were sunk by U.S. carrier aircraft during World War II. They had a speed of 34 knots, a complement of 850 men, and main armament consisting of ten 8-in. and eight 5-in. guns, four triple 24-in. torpedo tubes, and three aircraft.

mognions A type of armor for the shoulders.

Mohawk **1.** The Grumman OV-1 Mohawk is a two-place twin-engine high-performance observation aircraft developed for the U.S. Army and first flown in 1959. It has a top speed of 308 mph and a range of 1,330 mi and may be equipped with under-wing weapons. **2.** The British name for the Curtiss Hawk 75A, the export version of the P-36. See **Hawk,** sense 2.

moienne A piece of ordnance about 10 ft long, later called a "four-pounder."

moineau A small, flat bastion raised in front of an intended fortification to give protection from small-arms fire.

Mojave A twin-engine assault helicopter developed for the U.S. Marine Corps and first flown in 1953. It carries 36 fully equipped troops at a speed of 115 mph and has a range of 145 mi.

Molotov A name used in connection with certain World War II incendiary devices. The Molotov breadbasket is an adapter for holding 12 or more small incendiaries and scattering them over an area. A Molotov cocktail is a bottle containing a flammable liquid such as gasoline. These devices are named for V. M. Molotov, a Soviet foreign minister.

Moltke A German battle cruiser completed in 1911. It had a displacement of 23,000 tons, a speed of 27 knots, and a complement of 1,107 men. Main armament consisted of ten 11-in. guns, twelve 6-in. guns, and four 20-in. torpedo tubes. It had one sister ship, the *Goeben.*

Momi A class of Japanese 770-ton destroyers completed in the early 1920s. They had a speed of 36 knots, a complement of 110 men, and main armament consisting of three 4.7-in. guns, two 7.7mm guns, and two 21-in. torpedo tubes.

Mondragon 7mm semiautomatic rifle This weapon was invented by the Mexican General Mondragon in 1908. It is a gas-operated locked-breech rifle firing a 7mm cartridge. It is manufactured in Switzerland

Mondragon 7mm semiautomatic rifle. (*The Smithsonian Institution, War Department Collection.*)

at Neuhausen, and numbers of the rifle were used by Germany at the beginning of World War I. They did not hold up very well in trench service. They were among the earliest weapons carried by aerial observers (before the introduction of automatic weapons). In this role they were referred to as the "Model 1915."

monitoring **1.** The act of listening to, reviewing, and/or recording enemy communications, one's own communications, or those of friendly forces for the purpose of maintaining standards or improving communications or for reference, as applicable. **2.** The act of detecting the presence of radiation and the measurement thereof with radiation-measuring instruments.

Monmouth A class of British 9,800-ton cruisers completed in 1903–1904. They had a length of 440 ft, a complement of 678 men, and main armament consisting of fourteen 6-in. and eight 12-pounder guns. There were nine ships in this class. They had a speed of 24 knots.

monoplane An airplane having only one main lifting surface or wing, usually divided into two parts by the fuselage. It is distinguished from a biplane or triplane. (Picture, next page.)

Mons Meg A cannon in Edinburgh, Scotland, that was made around 1500 and

weighs 5 tons. It fired a 19½-in. iron ball a distance of 1 mi.

Montigny mitrailleuse A weapon developed by the Belgian, Joseph Montigny, in 1867. It consisted of 37 rifled barrels in a wrought-iron tube. It was operated by a hand crank, one turn of which fired 37 rounds in less than 1 second. An average crew could fire the weapon 12 times (444 rounds) in 1 minute.

moon In fortifications, a crescent-formed outwork.

Moon and Improved Moon Classes of Japanese destroyers of 2,350 (and 3,050) tons standard displacement completed in 1960–1969. The Moon class has a speed of 32 knots and a complement of 330 men and is armed with three 5-in. and four 3-in. guns, quadruple torpedo tubes, and antisubmarine weapons. The improved class has a speed of 32 knots and a complement of 270 men and is armed with two 5-in. guns, torpedo launchers, an octuple Asroc launcher, and a DASH helicopter. (Picture, next page.)

Moon Cone The NATO code name for a type of Chinese A-band early-warning and surveillance radar.

moonlight requisition A slang term for the surreptitious appropriation of equipment or supplies during hours of darkness.

Mohawk (OV-1). (*U.S. Army.*)

monoplane, an F4U Corsair fighter carrying the insignia of the French Navy. (*Vought Aeronautics Company.*)

Morane-Saulnier AI. (*The Smithsonian Institution, National Air Museum.*)

moored mine An underwater mine with a positively buoyant mine case. It is held at a predetermined depth beneath the surface by a cable or chain mooring attached to an anchor that rests on the bottom.

Mop The NATO code name for the Soviet version of the PBY Catalina as built under license in the U.S.S.R. during World War II.

mopping-up The liquidation of remnants of enemy resistance in an area that has been surrounded or isolated or through which other units have passed without eliminating all active resistance.

Morane-Saulnier AI A French single-place single-engine high-wing monoplane that first appeared early in 1917. It had a speed of 129 mph and was armed with one or two forward-firing Vickers machine guns. It had a very brief combat tour and was relegated to training duties.

Morane-Saulnier L, LA, and P A series of French single-place single-engine high-wing monoplane fighters, the first of which (L) was flown in 1913. They continued in production until 1917, the later versions being armed with a forward-firing Vickers machine gun, a bombload of six 25-lb bombs, and a speed of about 75 mph.

Morane-Saulnier M.S. 406 A French single-engine single-seat low-wing fighter designed in the late 1930s and produced until June 1940, by which time 1,037 had been manufactured. It was powered by an 860-hp engine, flew at speeds up to 302 mph, and was armed with one 20mm Hispano-Suiza cannon and two 7.5mm machine guns. At the beginning of World War II the French Air Force used these airplanes in four *escadres de chasse*, each of which comprised three *groupes* of 25 aircraft. Several foreign governments had also placed orders for this airplane.

Morane-Saulnier N A French single-place single-engine midwing monoplane that first

Moon. (*Japan Defense Agency.*)

appeared in 1914. It had a speed of about 130 mph and was armed with one synchronized forward-firing Vickers machine gun. Limited numbers were made.

Moray A U.S. two-man high-speed antisubmarine-warfare killer submarine.

Moreno A class of battleships (two in the class) formerly of the Argentine Navy. Completed in 1914–1915, their main armament consisted of twelve 12-in. and twelve 6-in. guns. They had a speed of 22.5 knots and a complement of 1,215 men.

morglay See **claymore.**

morion In the days of armor, an iron or steel high-crested helmet. Of Spanish origin, the helmet was visorless, and the edge was turned up like the brim of a hat.

morning report The daily record or log of any one of certain military units or unit sections required to keep records on the daily strength and official status of personnel assigned or attached to a command.

morning star A holy-water sprinkle. An iron ball with projecting spikes attached to a short staff by a length of chain.

mortar A complete projectile-firing weapon, rifled or smoothbore, characterized by shorter barrel, lower velocity, shorter range, and higher angle of fire than a howitzer or a gun. Like the howitzer, the mortar may be fired with any one of several propelling charges or zones, according to the trajectory desired. Most present-day mortars are muzzle-loaded and of simple construction for lightness and mobility.

mortar baseplate A circular or rectangular metal plate, with or without integral feet, designed to receive the spherical projection of the base cap of the cannon of an artillery or infantry mortar. It is used to absorb and spread the recoil force and to stabilize a mortar during firing.

mortar boat or vessel Formerly, a boat equipped for the firing of mortars and used for bombardment purposes.

mosaic An assembly of overlapping photographs which have been matched to form a continuous photographic representation of a portion of the earth's surface.

Moscow A class of Soviet cruiser helicopter ships of 15,000 tons standard displacement. *Moskva* and *Leningrad* are in the class, the former having run her sea trials in 1967. They have a length of 645 ft, a flight-deck capacity of 20 antisubmarine-warfare helicopters, and armament consisting of four 57mm guns, three twin launchers for surface-to-air missiles, two depth-charge mortars, and five trainable 21-in. torpedo tubes.

Mosin-Nagant 7.62mm carbine Model 1910 The first true Mosin-Nagant carbine, this weapon has an overall length of 40 in., a barrel length of 20 in., and a weight of 7.5 lb. It has a magazine with a capacity of five rounds. The muzzle velocity is 2,514 fps.

Mosin-Nagant 7.62mm carbine Model 1938 This weapon is similar, except for its length, to the Model 1891/30 rifle. It has a weight of 7.62 lb, a length of 40 in., and a barrel length of 20 in. It replaced the Model 1910 carbine and was the common carbine used by Soviet forces during World War II. It was also used later by Communist forces in Korea.

Mosin-Nagant 7.62mm carbine Model 1944 This weapon is the last of the

morning star. (*The Metropolitan Museum of Art, gift of William H. Riggs, 1913.*)

Mosin-Nagant designs. It is of basically the same design as the Model 1938 carbine except for a somewhat longer barrel (20.4 in.) and a permanently attached folding bayonet.

Mosin-Nagant 7.62mm Dragoon rifle Model 1891 This version of the Model 1891 rifle has a shorter barrel (28.8 in.) and

mortar. (*The Smithsonian Institution.*)

Mosin-Nagant 7.62mm carbine Model 1938. (*The Smithsonian Institution, War Department Collection.*)

Mosin-Nagant 7.62mm carbine Model 1910. (*The Smithsonian Institution, War Department Collection.*)

Moscow. (*U.S. Navy.*)

Mosin-Nagant 7.62mm rifle Model 1891. (*The Smithsonian Institution, War Department Collection.*)

was used by mounted troops before the development of the Mosin-Nagant carbine.

Mosin-Nagant 7.62mm rifle Model 1891
This bolt-action rifle was adopted by imperial Russia in 1891. The action was designed by Mosin, a Russian army colonel, and the magazine was developed by Nagant, a Belgian. The weapon had an overall length of 51.37 in., a barrel length of 31.6 in., a weight of 9.62 lb, and a magazine with a capacity of five rounds. During World War I, companies in the United States produced over 1½ million of these rifles for the imperial Russian and Kerensky governments.

Mosin-Nagant 7.62mm rifle Model 1891/30 This bolt-action weapon is about the same length as the Dragoon rifle but has many improvements. It was produced in 1930 and was used in large numbers. It was superseded at the end of World War II by the Model 1944 carbine. The Model 1891/30 has a weight of 8.7 lb, an

overall length of 48.5 in., a barrel length of 28.7 in., and a magazine capacity of five rounds. The sights are calibrated in meters rather than arshins. The muzzle velocity is 2,660 fps.

Mosin-Nagant 7.62mm sniper rifle Model 1891/30 This is the Model 1891/30 rifle adapted for use with a "PE" (four-power) or "PU" (3.5-power) telescopic sight. It is still used by the Soviet Union.

Mosquito 1. A wire-guided infantry anti-tank weapon developed jointly by Contraves (Italy) and Oerlikon (Switzerland). The missile has an overall length of 3 ft 7.7 in., a launching weight of 31 lb (with a 9-lb warhead capable of penetrating more than 26 in. of armor plate), and a range of 7,800 ft. **2.** This British de Havilland aircraft was a two-seat twin-engine night fighter and intruder first flown in 1941. It was one of the most successful Allied night fighters. It was powered by two 1,710-hp engines, had a maximum speed of 407 mph at 28,000

ft, and was armed with four 20mm Hispano cannons. A fighter-bomber version carried the four cannons plus four .303 cal. Browning machine guns and 2,000 lb of bombs.

mosquito boat A motor torpedo boat.

Mote The NATO code name for the Soviet MBR-2 single-engine (pusher) short-range reconnaissance flying boat used during World War II.

mothball fleet Ships out of commission, but maintained in good condition. The same as a reserve fleet.

mothballing The action or activity of treating equipment so as to protect it from the elements and prevent deterioration over a long period of time. Mothballing may include cocooning but is not neccessarily limited to this activity.

mother Used attributively to designate aircraft or ships that carry, launch, or direct other aircraft or ships. A naval vessel is also called a "tender."

moton In plate armor, small plates that covered the armpits.

motorize To equip a military force with motor-driven vehicles.

motorized artillery Artillery that is drawn by trucks or tractors or is self-propelled.

motorized heavy gun A mobile long-range artillery weapon of the double-recoil type, capable of firing conventional ammunition. It consists of a cannon, a gun carriage, a primary recoil mechanism, a secondary recoil mechanism, a projectile handcart, a front heavy gun-lifting truck, and a rear heavy gun-lifting truck.

motor torpedo boat A high-speed small vessel (100 ft) armed with torpedoes, mines, and automatic weapons. Also called a **PT boat,** which see.

motor transport Motor vehicles used for transporting military personnel, weapons, equipment, and supplies, excluding combat vehicles such as tanks, scout cars, and armored cars.

moulinet 1. A machine that bends a crossbow by winding it up. **2.** A circular movement with a saber.

mount A device to which, or upon which, something, such as a machine gun, camera, or searchlight, can be attached and supported in order to facilitate its installation, use, or accessibility or to protect it. A gun mount is the complete system of gun-supporting parts, elevating and training mechanism, and recoil and counterrecoil equipment.

mountain artillery Light artillery that can be carried on packhorses or mules; artillery designed for use in mountainous country.

mounting 1. All preparations made in areas designated for the purpose, in anticipation of an operation. It includes the assembly in the mounting area, preparation and maintenance within the mounting area, movement to loading points, and subse-

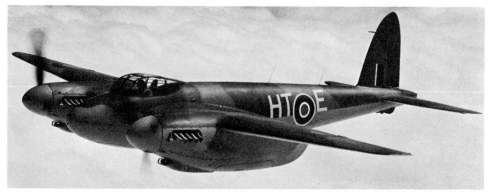

Mosquito. (*Hawker Siddeley Aviation Ltd.*)

motorized artillery, a U.S. 240mm howitzer. (*U.S. Army.*)

quent embarkation into ships, craft, or aircraft, if applicable. **2.** A carriage or stand upon which a weapon is placed.

mounting area An area where forces are assembled prior to an amphibious operation.

mounts 1. Metal blocks on a rifle barrel and receiver used for mounting a telescopic sight. **2.** Metal parts of a firearm used for protection and decoration and to affix the barrel, lock, and ramrod to the stock.

mourne The part of a lance or halberd to which the point or blade is fixed.

Mousetrap A U.S. Navy ahead-thrown antisubmarine weapon of World War II. It fired four or eight small rocket projectiles and was developed for those uses where Hedgehog was too large or powerful.

mousquetaire A musketeer, particularly a seventeenth- or eighteenth-century French royal musketeer.

mousqueton A variant of musketoon, a short smoothbore gun carried by cavalry and artillery forces. The term was occasionally used in the eighteenth century to designate a blunderbuss.

mouth 1. The opening of a piece of ordnance through which it is fired. **2.** An opening into a cavity or tube; the open end of a cartridge case is called the "mouth" of the case.

mouton A huge fourteenth-century machine for throwing large stones.

movable towers Towers, sometimes several stories high, were often employed in siege warfare to raise the attackers to the level of a fortification's walls. Once raised, bridges could be used to span the distance between the tower and the wall. Battering rams were sometimes mounted in the base of the towers, and the whole was covered with hides to prevent their being set on fire.

movement A part of a military or naval maneuver.

moving-target indicator A radar presentation which shows only targets which are in motion. Signals from stationary targets are subtracted out of the return signal by the output of a suitable memory circuit.

Möwe A class of German 924-ton torpedo boats produced in 1926–1928. They had a speed of 32 knots, a complement of 129 men, and main armament consisting of three 4.1-in. guns and six 21-in. torpedo tubes. All were lost in action during World War II.

MOX An explosive mixture containing a high explosive, plus powdered metal and an oxidizing agent. It is used in some antiaircraft projectiles.

moyenne, moyen An early type of cannon having a length of about 10 ft and firing a shot weighing 4 lb. By the latter part of the sixteenth century it was a 2¾-pounder.

MP 18,I submachine gun See **German 9mm Parabellum submachine gun MP 18,1.**

mount, a Bofors 40mm automatic gun on a field carriage. (A. B. Bofors.)

MP 18,II submachine gun See **German 9mm Parabellum submachine gun MP 18, II.**

MP 34 submachine gun See **Steyr-Solothurn 9mm Mauser submachine gun MP 34.**

MP 38 submachine gun See **German 9mm Parabellum submachine gun MP 38.**

MP 38/40 submachine gun See **German 9mm Parabellum submachine gun MP 38/40.**

MP 40 submachine gun See **German 9mm Parabellum submachine gun MP 40.**

MP 41/44 submachine gun See **Swiss 9mm Parabellum submachine gun Model 41/44.**

MP 3008 submachine gun See **German 9mm Parabellum submachine gun MP 3008.**

MPI Mean point of impact of a salvo of projectiles or bombs.

MPS A U.S. Navy multipurpose ship.

MR Reconnaissance seaplane (*Morskoi razvedchik*); used in the names of Russian aircraft from 1925 to 1945, as in MR-5.

MS A U.S. Navy motor ship.

MSA A U.S. Navy minesweeper, auxiliary.

MSB A U.S. Navy minesweeping boat.

MSBS (Mer-Sol-Ballistique-Stratégique) A French medium-range two-stage submarine-launched missile similar in concept to the U.S. Polaris, but of a somewhat greater size and weight. It has a length of 34 ft, a weight of about 39,600 lb, and a range of 1,200 nautical miles. A nuclear warhead is carried.

MSC A U.S. Navy minesweeper, coastal (nonmagnetic).

MSC. (U.S. Navy.)

multiple antiaircraft weapon. (U.S. Army.)

MSCO A U.S. Navy minesweeper, coastal (old).

MSF A U.S. Navy minesweeper, fleet (steel-hulled).

MSI A U.S. Navy minesweeper, inshore.

MSL A U.S. Navy minesweeping launch.

MSM A U.S. Navy minesweeper, river (converted LCM-6).

MSO A U.S. Navy minesweeper, ocean (nonmagnetic).

MSR A U.S. Navy minesweeper, patrol.

MSS A U.S. Navy minesweeper, special.

MSTS U.S. **Military Sea Transportation Service,** which see.

Muff Cob The NATO code name for a type of Soviet H-band antiaircraft artillery-fire-control radar.

Mug The NATO code name for the Soviet MDR-6, a twin-engine long-range reconnaissance flying boat equipped with bow and dorsal gun turrets. It was used by the Soviet Naval Air Force during World War II.

Mulberries Two artificial harbors built by the Allies off the Normandy beachhead during the invasion of June 1944. See also **Phoenixes.**

Mule The NATO code name for the Polikarpov Po-2 single-engine biplane trainer developed in the 1930s and used during World War II.

multiple antiaircraft weapon An antiaircraft weapon provided with more than one firing unit or barrel assembly.

multiple gun A group of guns emplaced and adjusted for firing as a unit; any group of guns mounted in one position and fired as a unit.

multiple lines In fortifications, several lines of detached walls for the defense of a position.

multipurpose close-support weapon A ground close-support weapon capable of defilade delivery of a variety of warheads, including nuclear.

multipurpose gun A weapon that can be used for a number of different purposes, such as against ground forces and against aircraft.

multipurpose projectile A projectile designed so that the type of payload can be changed. This is accomplished by using prepared loads in canister form and providing a removable base plug to permit change of canister. Thus a canister containing a colored smoke mixture can be replaced, for instance, by one containing leaflets.

munition Usually *pl.* **1.** In a broad sense, any and all supplies and equipment required to conduct offensive or defensive war, including war machines, ammunition, transport, fuel, food, and clothing, but ex-

MSF. (U.S. Navy.)

MSO. (U.S. Navy.)

cluding personnel and supplies and equipment for purposes other than direct military operations. **2.** In a restricted sense, ordnance.

Murata rifle See **Japanese 11mm rifle Type 13 (Model 1887).**

murderer An obsolete seventeenth- and eighteenth-century term usually indicating a wrought-iron breechloading swivel gun with an expanding bore.

murdresses A battlement with interstices to fire through. It was mounted on the tops of towers in fortifications.

musculus A seventh-century testudo containing a bore. Musculus means "mouse," and the object of this system was to gnaw a hole in the lower parts of a fortification.

musette bag A canvas or leather case carried by soldiers and containing provisions. It was suspended by a belt worn over the shoulder.

Mushroom The NATO code name for a type of Soviet airborne I-band radar.

musket In its earliest form, very heavy and clumsy smoothbore weapon of a large caliber. The first muskets were matchlocks, but these were followed by wheel locks, flintlocks, and lastly the percussion lock. The term first appeared in Spain (*mosquete*) in the 1530s and designated a shoulder arm requiring a forked rest, as distinct from the lighter arquebus.

musketade A fusilade of muskets.

musket arrow In the sixteenth century, an arrow fired from a musket or other firearm.

musketeer A soldier armed with a musket.

musketoon A short, light musket with a large bore, usually carried by cavalry or artillery forces. See **mousqueton.**

musket rest A forked rest for firing early heavy muskets.

mustang A slang term for an officer who was formerly an enlisted man.

Mustang The North American P-51 Mustang was a single-seat single-engine long-range fighter and fighter-bomber first flown in October 1940 and produced in various versions throughout World War II. Earlier types were used by the RAF early in the war. A total of 14,819 of all types were produced, and some 4,950 enemy aircraft were destroyed in combat by USAAF Mustangs in the European theater alone. (An additional 4,000 were destroyed on the ground.) It was equipped with a 1,695-hp engine and flew at speeds of 437 mph (P-51D). Armament consisted of six .50 cal. machine guns and two 500-lb or 1,000-lb bombs or six 5-in. rockets.

mustard gas A delayed-action casualty gas, this material acts as a cell irritant and cell poison. In addition to producing blisters, it causes eye irritation, conjunctivitis, and inflammation of the respiratory tract that can lead to pneumonia. It was first used by the Germans during World War I

musket. (*The Smithsonian Institution, National Museum Collection.*)

Mustang. (*U.S. Air Force.*)

in July 1917 at Ypres. The German designation was Yellow Cross (*gelb kreuz*). The French designation was Yperite. The British called it mustard gas because it has an odor like mustard, garlic, or horseradish. It was the most efficacious war gas of the war, causing some 400,000 casualties on both sides.

mustard-lewisite (HL) This war gas is one of the **blistering agents,** which see, and has a delayed-action casualty effect. The liquid causes severe damage to the eyes, and contamination of the skin is followed after a short time by reddening and then by blistering which tends to cover the entire area of the reddened skin. Liquid on the skin, as well as inhaled vapor, is absorbed and may cause systemic poisoning.

mustard-T mixture (HT) This war gas is one of the **blistering agents,** which see, and has a delayed-action casualty effect. It is a mixture of 60 percent HD (distilled mustard) and 40 percent T. The latter, a sulfur and chlorine compound similar in structure to HD, is a clear yellowish liquid with an odor similar to HD. HT has a strong blistering effect, irritates the eyes, and is toxic when inhaled.

muster To assemble troops or a ship's company for an inspection, parade, exercise, etc. Also, an assembly for roll call.

muster out To discharge or release from active duty.

mutiny A concerted, forcible resistance against constituted military or naval authority.

Mutsuki A class of Japanese 1,300-ton de-

Mutt. (*U.S. Army.*)

stroyers built in the mid-1920s. They had a speed of 37 knots, a complement of 150 men, and armament consisting of four 4.7-in. guns and six 24-in. torpedo tubes. All 12 ships of this class that entered World War II were lost (10 to aircraft, 1 to a submarine, and 1 to a PT boat).

Mutt A U.S. Army airdroppable ½-ton amphibious truck.

muzzle The end of the barrel of a gun from which the bullet or projectile emerges.

muzzle bell The bell-shaped built-up section at the muzzle of some types of cannons and blunderbusses.

muzzle blast Sudden air pressure exerted at the muzzle of a weapon by the rush of hot gases and air on firing.

muzzle brake. (*U.S. Army.*)

Myrt. (*U.S. Air Force.*)

muzzle brake A device attached to the muzzle of a weapon which utilizes escaping gas to reduce recoil and noise.

muzzle burst The explosion of a projectile at the muzzle of a weapon or at a very short distance from the muzzle.

muzzle compensator A device attached to the muzzle of a weapon which utilizes escaping gas to control muzzle movement.

muzzle flash A spurt of flame that appears at the muzzle of a gun when a projectile leaves the barrel.

muzzle-loader A weapon that is loaded from the muzzle.

muzzle plug A device that fits into the muzzle end of a cannon and serves as a protection to the cannon bore. A tompion.

muzzle ring A ringlike molding near the muzzle of a piece.

muzzle velocity The velocity of a projectile with respect to the muzzle at the instant the projectile leaves the weapon.

MWB A U.S. Navy motor whaleboat.

Mya The designation for Soviet aircraft designed by Vladimir M. Myasishchev.

Mya-4 See **Bison.**

Myoko A class of Japanese 13,000-ton cruisers completed in 1927–1928. Of the four ships in this class, three (*Myoko, Ashigara,* and *Haguro*) were sunk by British forces, and one (*Nachi*) was sunk by U.S. forces during World War II. They had a speed of 33 knots, a complement of 773 men, and main armament consisting of ten 8-in. and eight 5-in. guns, four torpedo tubes, and three aircraft.

Myrsky II A single-engine single seat low-wing fighter-interceptor developed in 1942 by the Valtion Lentokonetehdas (State Aircraft Factory) in Finland. The Myrsky (Storm) was powered by a 1,065-hp engine and flew at speeds of 329 mph. It was armed with four 12.7mm Browning machine guns.

Myrt The World War II Allied code name for the Japanese Nakajima C6N1 single-engine three-place carrier-borne reconnaissance aircraft. It flew at a speed of 390 mph, was armed with one 7.9mm machine gun, and could also be used as a torpedo carrier.

Mystère The French Dassault Mystère is a single-seat jet interceptor or ground-attack fighter first flown in the early 1950s. It is armed with two 30mm cannons.

mystery ship See **Q ship.**

NA Gasoline thickened with napalm and used in incendiary and fire bombs.

nab An obsolete term for the cock of a gun.

nacelle 1. Generally, a separate, streamlined enclosure on an airplane for sheltering or housing something. **2.** Specifically: **a.** A compartment for a crew. **b.** An engine nacelle.

Nachi A class of Japanese cruisers of about 10,000 tons standard displacement built in the late 1920s and used during World War II. They had a length of 640 ft, a beam of 62 ft, a speed of 33 knots, and a complement of 750 men. They were armed with ten 8-in. and eight 4.7-in. guns and were also equipped with twelve torpedo tubes and four seaplanes.

NACO Navy Cool. A new type of gunpowder developed by the Naval Ordnance Station, Indian Head, Md. It burns at temperatures 300° cooler than standard gunpowder, thereby reducing gun-barrel wear by more than 50 percent.

Nagant 7.62mm revolver This revolver was invented by the Belgian inventor Nagant and was adopted by the Russians in 1895. Manufactured as late as 1940, this weapon fires the 7.62mm Nagant cartridge and has a cylinder capacity of seven rounds. It weighs 1.65 lb and has an overall length of 9.06 in. and a barrel length of 4.3 in. A single-action model was once issued to enlisted men, and a double-action model to officers.

Nagara A class of Japanese 5,000-ton cruisers completed in 1921–1923. The class included *Nagara*, *Isuzu*, *Kinu*, *Abujuma*, *Natori*, and *Yura*, all of which were lost during World War II (three were sunk by U.S. submarines, and three by aircraft). They had a length of 535 ft, a beam of 46.5 ft, a speed of 36 knots, and a complement of 438 men. Main armament consisted of seven 5.5-in. and two 3-in. guns, four torpedo tubes, and one aircraft.

Nagato A class of Japanese battleships of about 32,720 tons standard displacement built between 1919 and 1921, reconstructed in 1936, and used during World War II. They had a length of 700 ft, a beam of 95 ft, a speed of 24 knots, and a complement of 1,304 men. They were armed with eight 16-in., twenty 5.5-in., and eight 5-in. guns, plus three seaplanes. There were two ships in the class, *Nagato* and *Mutsu*.

Nakajima A6M2-N A floatplane-fighter version of the Japanese Zero. See **Rufe.**

Nakajima B5N2 See **Kate.**

Nakajima B6N1 See **Jill.**

Nakajima J1N1-S Gekko See **Irving.**

Nakajima Ki.27 See **Nate.**

Nakajima Ki.43 Hayabusa See **Oscar.**

Nakajima Ki.44 Shoki See **Tojo.**

Nakajima Ki.49 See **Helen.**

Nakajima Ki.84 Hayate See **Frank,** sense 2.

Nambu 6.5 and 7.7mm light machine guns These machine guns resembled the Bren gun but were far lighter in weight.

Nagant 7.62mm revolver. (*The Smithsonian Institution.*)

The 6.5mm model weighed only 19 lb. (Picture, next page.)

Nambu 8mm automatic pistol Model 1904 An automatic weapon used extensively by Japanese troops but never a standard arm in the Japanese Army. The magazine capacity is eight cartridges, the overall length is 9 in., the barrel length is 4.7 in., and the weight is approximately 30 oz. It has a muzzle velocity of 1,065 fps. This pistol was developed by Col. Kijiro Nambu and was manufactured by the Kayoba Factory Co. Ltd. A smaller version of this pistol, in 7mm, was called the "Baby Nambu." It is 6.75 in. long and has a barrel length of 3.25 in. It weighs 1.43 lb and uses a detachable magazine with a capacity of seven rounds. (Picture, next page.)

Nambu 6.5mm light machine gun. (*The Smithsonian Institution, Treasury Department Collection.*)

Nambu 8mm automatic pistol Model 1904. (*The Smithsonian Institution, Department of Defense Collection.*)

Nancy A system of visual communications using a special light visible only by means of special equipment.

napalm A powder employed to thicken gasoline for use in flamethrowers and incendiary bombs. It is so named because it is made from the aluminum salts of *naph*thenic and *palm*itic acids.

Napier A class of British destroyers of 1,760 tons standard displacement completed in 1940–1942. They had a speed of 36 knots, a complement of 220 men, and armament consisting of six 4.7-in. guns, four 2-pounders, four 40mm and six 20mm antiaircraft guns, and ten 21-in. torpedo tubes.

Narval A class of French submarines that are essentially improved versions of the German XXI type. They have a standard surface displacement of 1,220 tons, a submerged speed of 18 knots, a complement of 68 men, and armament consisting of eight 21.7-in. torpedoes. They have a length of 256 ft and were completed in 1957–1960.

nasal The nose guard on early helmets.

Nasty A class of Norwegian motor gunboats.

Nate The code name for the Nakajima Ki.27 single-seat single-engine fighter-interceptor and fighter-bomber. It was the first low-wing fighter developed for the Japanese Army Air Force. Developed in 1936 and produced until mid-1940, this airplane flew at speeds of 286 mph and was armed with two 7.7mm machine guns plus four 55-lb bombs.

National Army In the military history of the United States, the divisions (number 76 and up) made up of men obtained through the Selective Service Act during World War I.

National Guard A militia force under the U.S. Army. A similar force, the Air National Guard, is under the U.S. Air Force. The term came into use in 1903. (During a period from 1824 to 1862 the New York Seventh Regiment called itself the National Guard. From 1862 to 1903 the term covered all New York State troops.)

NATO North Atlantic Treaty Organization.

NATO Sea Sparrow See **IPDSMS**.

Natori A class of Japanese cruisers of about 5,170 tons standard displacement built in the early 1920s and used during World War II. They had a length of 535 ft, a beam of 47 ft, a speed of 33 knots, and a complement of 450 men. They were armed with seven 5.5-in. and two 3-in. guns, plus four torpedo tubes and one seaplane.

Natter The Bachem BA 349A Natter (Adder) was developed in Germany in 1944 and consisted of a single-seat rocket-propelled target-defense interceptor. It was midway between a fighter aircraft and a guided missile, the human pilot being intended to have control only during the actual attack, after which he would bail out. The Natter utilized one rocket engine with 3,750 lb of thrust and four jettisonable 1,000-lb thrust rockets. Although never used operationally, this aircraft had a maximum speed of 560 mph, a powered flight time of 2 minutes, and an initial rate of climb of 25,800 ft per minute. It was armed with twenty-four 55mm unguided rockets.

nautical mile A measure of distance equal to 1 minute of arc on the earth's surface. The United States has adopted the international nautical mile, which is equal to approximately 6,076 ft, or 1.1508 statute miles. See **knot**.

Nautilus A U.S. nuclear-powered submarine that put to sea in January 1955. It was the world's first nuclear-propelled vessel and was the first submarine to pass from the Pacific to the Atlantic under the polar ice cap (August 3, 1958). The ship has a length of 323 ft, a speed of 20+ knots when submerged, and a complement of 105 men.

Navaho A supersonic cruise missile, the SM-64, said to have an operating range of 4,000 mi and to be powered by two ramjet engines. After launching, this missile is rocket-boosted to more than 50,000 ft and then continues to 100,000 ft on its own engines.

Natter. (*The Smithsonian Institution, National Air Museum.*)

Nautilus. (*U.S. Navy.*)

naval Pertaining to naval forces or warships.

naval air station A station that provides operating, testing, overhaul, training, and personnel facilities for naval aviation.

naval attaché A naval officer on duty at an embassy or legation abroad.

naval base A shore command in a given locality which includes and integrates all naval shore activities assigned for the more efficient support of the operating forces.

naval cadet A young man in training to become a naval officer. This term was used in the United States from 1882 to 1902, when it was replaced by the word "midshipman."

naval campaign An operation of a connected series of operations conducted essentially by naval forces, including all surface, subsurface, air, and amphibious troops, for the purpose of gaining, extending, or maintaining control of the sea.

naval district A geographically defined area in which one naval officer, designated commandant, is the direct representative of the Secretary of the Navy and the Chief of Naval Operations. The commandant has the responsibility for local naval defense and security and for the coordination of naval activities in the area.

naval gunfire liaison team Personnel and equipment required to coordinate and advise ground or landing forces on naval gunfire employment.

naval gunfire team A group of men organized to control and direct naval gunfire from the shore.

naval guns The following brief table expresses the effective gunnery ranges for naval guns developed over the period 1862 (the last of the muzzle-loading guns) to 1948 (the ultimate development of large naval ordnance):

1862	maximum 1 mi, average 100 yd
1905	4,000–6,000 yd
1910	12,000 yd
1915	18,000–20,000 yd
1918	24,000 yd
1948	40,000 yd

naval landing party Part of a ship's complement organized for ground-force operations ashore. Formerly called the "landing force."

naval mine See **underwater mine.**

naval operation A naval action, or the performance of a naval mission, the nature of which may be strategic, tactical, logistic, or training; the process of carrying on or training for naval combat to gain the objectives of any battle or campaign.

naval or marine (air) base An air base for support of naval or marine air units, consisting of landing strips, seaplane alighting areas, and all components of related facilities for which the Navy or Marine Corps has operating responsibilities, together with interior lines of communication and the minimum surrounding area necessary for local security. (Normally, it does not cover an area greater than 20 sq mi.)

naval reserve A force of qualified officers and men available, in an emergency, to meet the needs of an expanding navy while an adequate flow of new personnel is being established.

naval stores Any articles or commodities used by a naval ship or station, such as equipment, consumable supplies, clothing, petroleum, oils, and lubricants, medical supplies, and ammunition.

navigator An officer who is head of a ship's navigation department and is responsible for the safe navigation of the ship.

Navy Cross A naval decoration awarded for heroism in action against an enemy of the United States. In the order or precedence for U.S. decorations, the Navy Cross is between the Distinguished Service Cross and the Distinguished Service Medal.

Navy List An official quarterly publication listing the officers of the British Navy. Also, a bimonthly publication listing the officers of the U.S. Navy currently on active duty.

Navy Register An official annual publication listing the officers and ships of the U.S. Navy.

navy yard A naval shore station for the construction or repair of warships.

N class A class of Goodyear dirigibles having a helium capacity of 875,000 cu ft.

N Class 1. A class of Soviet nuclear-powered hunter-killer submarines of 3,500

Navaho. (*U.S. Air Force.*)

Nebelwerfer 150mm rocket launcher. (*The Imperial War Museum.*)

tons standard surface displacement. They have a length of 360 ft, a beam of 32 ft, a speed of 25 knots, and a complement of 88 men. They are armed with six 21-in. torpedo tubes. **2.** A class of U.S. submarines commissioned in 1930. They were armed with six 21-in. torpedo tubes and two 6-in. deck guns. They had a submerged speed of 8.5 knots.

NCO Noncommissioned officer.

near-miss The strike of an explosive missile, especially of an aerial bomb, that is near but not on the object of attack and usually close enough to it to cause effective damage.

Nebelwerfer (German for "smoke thrower.") A World War II German artillery piece that was originally designed to launch smoke shells, but was modified to launch rockets, including 150mm, 210mm, and 320mm rockets. As many as six launchers were mounted on one vehicle. The total weight of the 150mm unit was about 1,200 lb, and the rockets had a range of up to 7,750 yd. Nebelwerfers were first used on the Russian front in 1941.

Nebraska A U.S. battleship of the **New Jersey** class, which see. It was commissioned in 1907.

neck **1.** The open end of the cartridge case where the bullet is seated. **2.** The part of a cannon immediately behind the swell of the muzzle.

neckguard A piece of armor for the protection of the neck.

needle gun A gun that utilizes a needle-fire cartridge in which a needle penetrates through the base of the cartridge and strikes the primer within the case, thus setting off the charge. Needle guns were of muzzle-loading and breechloading types, and the best known of the latter was the **Dreyse rifle,** which see, which was first used by the Prussians in 1848. Other needle guns included the Chassepot, Needham, and Chatauvillard.

Negro A German manned torpedo of World War II. The pilot rode on a manually controlled electric torpedo with its warhead removed. He sat in a 20-in. plastic dome which rode just above the water. Attached beneath this vehicle was a regular electric torpedo with a live warhead. It could be launched by the pilot.

Nelson A class of British battleships completed in the late 1920s. They included *Nelson* and *Rodney.* They had a standard displacement of 33,950 tons, a length of 710 ft, a beam of 106 ft, a speed of 23 knots, and a complement of 1,361 men. Main armament consisted of nine 16-in. guns, twelve 6-in. guns, antiaircraft weapons, and two 24.5-in. torpedo tubes.

Nenohi A class of Japanese destroyers of about 1,368 tons standard displacement built in the mid-1930s and used during World War II. They had a length of 337 ft, a beam of 32 ft, a speed of 34 knots, and a complement of 220 men. They were armed with five 5-in. guns and six 21-in. torpedo tubes.

Neptune **1.** The Lockheed P2V Neptune is a twin-engine (piston) and twin-jet all-weather long-range land-based antisubmarine aircraft developed for the U.S. Navy and first delivered in 1945. It has a speed of about 300 mph, a range of 3,560 mi, and a crew of seven. It is armed with 20mm cannons and .50 cal. machine guns and can carry an 8,000-lb bombload. **2.** A British 19,900-ton battleship completed in 1911. It had a crew of 900 and main armament consisting of ten 12-in. guns, sixteen 4-in. guns, and three 21-in. torpedo tubes. It had

Neptune. (*Lockheed Aircraft Corporation.*)

Nevada. (*U.S. Navy.*)

a speed of 22 knots.

nerve agents War gases such as GA, GB, GD, and VX which upset the balance between the sympathetic and parasympathetic nervous systems, which together form the automatic nervous system. Individuals poisoned by nerve agents display approximately the same sequence of symptoms regardless of the route by which the poison enters the body (by inhalation, absorption, or ingestion). These symptoms, in normal order of appearance, are running nose; tightness of chest; dimness of vision and pinpointing of the eye pupils; difficulty in breathing; drooling and excessive sweating; nausea; vomiting, cramps, and involuntary defecation and urination; twitching, jerking, and staggering; and headache, confusion, drowsiness, coma, and convulsion. These symptoms are followed by cessation of breathing and death. Skin absorption great enough to cause death may occur in 1 to 2 minutes, although death may be delayed for 1 to 2 hours. Respiratory lethal dosages kill in 1 to 10 minutes, and liquid in the eye nearly as rapidly.

nerve gas See **nerve agents.**

nest Two or more ships moored together.

net An organization of stations capable of direct communications on a common channel or frequency.

netlayer A ship designed for laying and tending submarine or antitorpedo nets.

nets and booms A combination of underwater steel-mesh nets and surface floating booms used as a means of harbor defense against submarines, torpedoes, and small surface craft.

neutral Not involved in hostilities and not taking part either directly or indirectly in a war between other powers.

neutralization fire Fire which is delivered to cause casualties; to hamper and interrupt the enemy's movement, action, or firing of weapons; and to reduce the combat efficiency of enemy personnel.

neutralize 1. To destroy or reduce the effectiveness of enemy personnel and mate-

riel by gunfire, bombing, or any other means. **2.** To make a toxic chemical agent harmless by chemical action. **3.** To disarm or otherwise render safe mines, bombs, or other missiles and booby traps.

Nevada A class of U.S. battleships of about 29,000 tons standard displacement completed in 1916. The class included *Nevada* and *Oklahoma*. They had a length of 583 ft, a beam of about 108 ft, a speed of 20 knots, and a complement of 1,301 men. They were armed with ten 14-in. and twelve 5-in. guns, plus eight 5-in. guns for antiaircraft use. Three aircraft were carried. This class marked the first all-oil-burning battleships in the U.S. Navy. *Nevada* sustained heavy damage at Pearl Harbor on December 7, 1941. After being refloated and repaired, it served at the invasion of Attu and then was redirected to the European theater. It participated in the invasion of Normandy and of Southern France and then returned to the Pacific and operations against Iwo Jima and Okinawa. The Nevada had an astonishing end. A target ship for atomic-bomb tests at Bikini Atoll, it resisted both aerial and underwater nuclear explosions. It was towed back to Pearl Harbor. On July 26, 1948, an attempt was made to sink it with special explosive charges. Nothing happened. It then survived attempts to sink it with Navy radar-guided missiles, conventional gunfire from destroyers, and hundreds of rockets from Navy aircraft. The battleship *Iowa* was called in. The *Nevada* resisted the 16-in. gun salvos fired at it and then survived a shelling from the cruisers *Astoria*, *Pasadena*, and *Springfield*. It was finally sunk, on July 31, by a flight of Navy torpedo bombers.

Newcastle A class of British cruisers of 9,100 tons standard displacement completed in 1937. Of the five ships in the class, one was lost to action during World War II. They had a length of 584 ft, a beam of 61 ft, a speed of 32 knots, and a complement of 809 to 833 men. They were armed

with nine 6-in. and eight 4-in. guns, eight to twenty-four 2-pounder pompoms, six to twenty-four 40mm and four to seventeen 20mm antiaircraft guns, and six 21-in. torpedo tubes.

New Hampshire A U.S. battleship of the **Kansas** class, which see. It was commissioned in 1908.

New Jersey Two battleships have been named for the state of New Jersey. The first *New Jersey* was the name ship of a class that also included *Virginia*, *Georgia*, *Nebraska*, and *Rhode Island*, all of which were launched in 1904. They had a normal displacement of 14,948 tons, a length of 441 ft, a beam of 76 ft, a speed of 19 knots, and a complement of 812 men. Main armament consisted of four 12-in. guns, eight 8-in. guns, twelve 6-in. guns, and four 21-in. torpedo tubes. The *New Jersey* was sunk off Cape Hatteras, N.C., by Army aircraft serving under Gen. Billy Mitchell. These experimental bombing runs were conducted in September 1922. The second *New Jersey* was a battleship of the **Iowa** class, which see. It was commissioned in 1943 and saw service during World War II (in the Pacific), in Korea, and in Vietnam (where it was the last U.S. battleship to see service). (Picture, next page.)

New Mexico A class of U.S. battleships of about 34,400 tons standard displacement completed in 1917–1919. The class included *New Mexico*, *Mississippi*, and *Idaho*. They had a length of 624 ft, a beam of 106 ft, a speed of about 23 knots, and a complement of 1,323 men. They were armed with twelve 14-in. and twelve 5-in. guns, plus eight 5-in. guns for antiaircraft use. Three aircraft were carried. The *New Mexico* saw extensive service in the Pacific theater during World War II.

New Nambu 9mm Parabellum automatic pistol Model 57A A weapon similar in construction to the U.S. Colt M1911A1 and presently the standard handgun of the Japanese Self-Defense Forces. The overall length is 7.8 in., and the barrel length is

New Jersey (*Iowa* class). (*U.S. Navy.*)

4.6 in. It has a magazine capacity of eight cartridges, a weight of 2.12 lb, and a muzzle velocity of 1,148 fps.

New Nambu .32 cal. automatic pistol Model 57B A Japanese weapon based on the Browning 1910 pistol. It has an overall length of 6.3 in. and a weight of 1.3 lb and is fed by a detachable magazine with a capacity of eight cartridges.

New Orleans A class of U.S. heavy cruisers (CA) of about 9,950 tons standard displace-

ment completed in 1933–1934. The class consisted of *New Orleans, Minneapolis, Tuscaloosa,* and *San Francisco.* They had a length of 574 ft, a beam of 61 ft, a speed of 32.7 knots, and a wartime complement of 1,200 men. They were armed with nine 8-in. and eight 5-in. guns, plus twenty-four 40mm and nineteen 20mm antiaircraft guns. They carried four aircraft.

New York A U.S. battleship of the **Texas** class, which see. It was commissioned in

1914 and saw service during World War II, both in North Africa and in the Pacific.

Nick The code name for the Kawasaki Ki.45 Toryu (Dragon Killer) twin-engine two-seat night fighter developed for the Japanese Army Air Force and first delivered in 1939. It was equipped with two 1,080-hp engines and flew at speeds of 340 mph. Armament consisted of one 37mm cannon and two obliquely mounted 20mm cannons.

Nickels A World War II British Military slang term for propaganda and information leaflets dropped by Allied aircraft over enemy-occupied areas. "Nickeling" was the slang term for dropping such leaflets.

Nieuport 10 and 12 French two-place single-engine sesquiplane (a biplane with narrow lower wings) fighters. The Nieuport 10 entered service in the summer of 1915, and a number were converted to single-seat fighters by covering the front cockpit and mounting a forward- (and upward-) firing Lewis machine gun. The Nieuport 12 was an enlarged version with a more powerful engine. It flew at speeds of about 96 mph.

Nieuport 11 and 16 A French single-seat biplane fighter that entered service in mid-1915. Its small size earned it the nickname "Bébé" ("Baby"). It had a speed of about 97 mph. The Nieuport 16 had a more powerful engine than the 11 and mounted a synchronized Vickers gun instead of an over-wing Lewis.

Nieuport 17 One of the most popular and successful fighters of World War I. It entered service in May 1916 and was used by a number of countries. It had a speed of about 110 mph and was armed with a forward-firing synchronized Vickers machine gun.

Nieuport 24 and 27 The Nieuport 24 was an extension of the 17, and the Nieuport 27 differed from the 24 only in armament and undercarriage details. They had a speed of about 116 mph, but were used

New Orleans. (*U.S. Navy.*)

largely for training.

Nieuport 28 A continuation of the Nieuport series, this aircraft first flew on June 14, 1917. It had a speed of about 122 mph and was armed with either a Marlin or a Vickers machine gun. American pilots of this airplane included Capt. Eddie Rickenbacker and America's first World War I ace, Lieut. Douglas Campbell.

Nieuport-Delage 29 A French single-seat single-engine biplane fighter developed too late in 1918 to see operational service during World War I. It was the standard French fighter after the war and was one of the most outstanding fighters of the 1920s. Purchased by a number of foreign countries, they remained in service for some time. Japanese Nieuport 29's, for example, were used during the Sino-Japanese war in 1931–1932. They had a speed of about 143 mph and were armed with twin forward-firing Vickers machine guns.

night bomber A bomber designed, modified, or used for bombing at night. In World War II usage, this term ordinarily meant a slow-flying, lightly armed bomber carrying a heavier bombload than that carried by a day bomber.

night fighter A fighter that operates at night, especially a fighter provided with special equipment for detecting enemy aircraft at night. British fighters early in World War II were equipped with searchlights to operate as night fighters; later developments introduced radar as a means of locating enemy aircraft. Current aircraft development and production emphasize the more versatile all-weather fighter rather than the night fighter.

Nightingale The U.S. McDonnell Douglas-built C-9A Nightingale is an aeromedical airlift-transport version of the DC-9. It entered service with the U.S. Air Force in 1968 and can carry from 30 to 40 litter patients. It has a cruising speed of 565 mph. (Picture, next page.)

Nike The name applied to a system of U.S. Army surface-to-air guided missiles designed to seek out, intercept, and destroy enemy aircraft. Other weapons of the Nike system are **Nike-Ajax, Nike-Hercules, Nike-X,** and **Nike-Zeus,** which see.

Nike-Ajax This was the first U.S. operational supersonic antiaircraft guided missile. First deployed in 1953, it had a length of 31 ft (with booster), a launch weight of 2,300 lb, a ceiling of 60,000 ft, and a range of 25 mi.

Nike-Hercules A follow-on to the Nike-Ajax, this antiaircraft missile became operational in 1958. It had a length of 39 ft (with booster), a launch weight of 10,000 lb, a ceiling in excess of 150,000 ft, and a range of over 75 mi. (Picture, next page.)

Nike-X A U.S. antimissile-missile system for defense against ballistic missiles and a fol-

Nick. (*The Smithsonian Institution, National Air Museum.*)

Nieuport 17. (*The Smithsonian Institution, National Air Museum.*)

Nieuport 28. (*The Smithsonian Institution, National Air Museum.*)

low-on to Nike-Zeus. The system includes a multifunction array radar which performs target acquisition, discrimination, and tracking functions; a missile-site radar which performs missile command and track and target track and search functions; data processing equipment consisting of high-speed digital computers; and Sprint missiles.

Nike-Zeus A U.S. Army surface-to-air anti-

Nightingale. (*U.S. Air Force.*)

Nike-Hercules. (*U.S. Army.*)

Nike-Zeus. (*U.S. Army.*)

missile missile with a range of about 200 nautical miles and an estimated speed of Mach 4.

Nimrod The British Hawker Siddeley Nimrod is a long-range antisubmarine and maritime reconnaissance aircraft based on the de Havilland Comet. The Nimrod was first developed in 1967, carries a crew of 11, and is armed with various combinations of bombs, mines, depth charges, and torpedoes. It has a speed of about 540 mph.

nipple A hollow conical projection in the breech of a percussion gun. When a cap is exploded on its surface, a centrally located hole directs the flame to the main powder charge.

nipple pick A short metal pick for cleaning the vent of a percussion nipple that has been clogged with burnt gunpowder.

Nissen hut Named after its British designer, Lieut. Col. P. N. Nissen (1871–1930), this is a half-cylindrical metal structure of corrugated iron, similar in appearance to a Quonset hut.

niter, nitre Potassium nitrate (saltpeter), an ingredient in black powder.

nitrocellulose An explosive used in the manufacture of smokeless propellants. It is formed by the action of a mixture of nitric and sulfuric acids on cotton or some other form of cellulose. Guncotton is a nitrocellulose with a very high nitrogen content.

nitrogen mustard (HN-1, HN-2, and HN-3) These war gases are **blistering agents,** which see, and have a delayed action casualty effect. They have many of the same effects as HD (distilled mustard). Bronchopneumonia may appear after the first 24 hours.

nitroglycerin A colorless liquid at ordinary temperatures, this is a powerful and sensitive high explosive used in dynamite and in some propellant mixtures. It is eight times as powerful, weight for weight, as gunpowder.

Noah's Ark The World War II code name for operations against retreating German forces in Greece by guerrillas aided by Allied air forces in the Balkans in the fall of 1944.

nock 1. One of the notches on the ends of the bow for holding the string. **2.** The notch on the butt end of an arrow to hold the string. **3.** The notch in a crossbow nut for holding the string when the bow is bent.

no-fire line A line short of which artillery or ships may not fire except on request or with the approval of the supported commander, but beyond which they may fire at any time without danger to friendly troops.

no-man's-land The belt of land between the lines of battle.

nominal weapon A nuclear weapon producing a yield of approximately 20 kilotons.

noncombatant 1. A military person who does not ordinarily carry out combat duties. A cook or clerk is a noncombatant in this sense. **2.** A civilian, especially a civilian not serving in a military organization.

noncommissioned officer An officer less than a commissioned or warrant officer. In the U.S. Army, noncommissioned officers are corporals and sergeants.

nondelay fuze An inertia-type impact fuze that functions quickly, before penetrating or glancing off the target. A nondelay fuze is distinguished from a delay fuze, but its type of action is inherently slower than that of a superquick fuze.

nonpersistent war gas A chemical war agent that is normally effective in the open 10 minutes or less at the point of dispersion.

nonrigid In reference to lighter-than-air aircraft, having a gasbag, envelope, or skin that is not supported by any framework or reinforced by stiffening, maintaining its shape by internal pressure only.

nonrigid airship An airship without supports or framework in its gasbag. Distinguished especially from semirigid and rigid airships.

Nord 5210 (SS.11 and AS.11) A French line-of-sight wire-guided battlefield missile that can be fired from aircraft, vehicles, and ships. The SS.11 is a surface-to-surface version, and the AS.11 is a similar air-to-surface version. The missile has an overall length of about 4 ft, a launching weight of 66 lb, a warhead weight of 5.72 lb, and a range of 9,840 ft. The antitank warhead is capable of perforating 24 in. of armor plate. This missile is used by some 18 countries, including the United States (where it is designated AGM-22A).

Nord AS.20 A French surface-to-air missile developed for the French Air Force and Navy and also used by four other countries, including Germany and Italy. It has a launching weight of 315 lb, a warhead weight of 66 lb, an overall length of 8.5 ft, and an average range of 4.35 mi.

Nord AS.30 A French tactical air-to-surface missile which is virtually a scaled-up version of the AS.20. It has an overall length of 12.75 ft, a launching weight of 1,146 lb, a warhead weight of 510 lb, and a range up to 7.5 mi. It is used by the French Air Force and the forces of several other countries.

Nord AS.30L A lightweight version of the AS.30 intended for use in aircraft in the class of the Fiat G91 fighter. It has a launching weight of 838 lb, a warhead weight of 253 lb, and an overall length of 11.75 ft.

Norden bombsight (Named for its developer, C. L. Norden, A U.S. aeronautical consultant.) A gyroscopically stabilized synchronizing bombsight used mainly for synchronous bombing but useful for fixed-angle bombing. Utilizing preset data and manual operation by the bombardier, the Norden bombsight computes the correct dropping angle and, in connection with an automatic pilot or pilot direction indicator, determines the proper course of the aircraft required to maintain the necessary line of sight to the target.

Nordenfeld machine gun A machine gun, perfected in the 1870s, that utilized 10 stationary barrels mounted horizontally. (Picture, next page.)

Norfolk A class of U.S. frigates (DL) of 5,600 tons standard displacement produced in 1953. It has a length of 540 ft, a beam of 54.2 ft, a speed of 32 knots, and a complement of 411 men. It is armed with eight 3-in. guns, one Asroc eight-tube launcher, and two triple torpedo launchers.

normal barrage A standing artillery barrage (defensive artillery barrage) to be fired in case of an attack. The batteries are kept laid on the target line, and the barrage is fired on call. An emergency barrage is a standing barrage to reinforce the normal barrage of some other battery.

Northampton **1.** A class of U.S. tactical-command ships (CLC) developed from a

Nimrod. (*Hawker Siddeley Aviation Ltd.*)

Nord 5210 (SS.11 and AS.11). (*U.S. Army.*)

heavy cruiser of the *Baltimore* class. There is only one ship (*Northampton*) in the class. It has a standard displacement of 17,000 tons and was completed in 1953. It has a length of 676 ft, a beam of 71 ft, a speed of 33 knots, and a complement of 1,700 men. Armament consists of four 5-in. and eight 3-in. guns. **2.** A class of U.S. heavy cruisers of about 9,000 tons displacement completed in 1930–1931. There were six

nock. (*The Smithsonian Institution.*)

Nordenfeld machine gun. (*The Smithsonian Institution, War Department Collection.*)

ships in the class, and they had a length of 600 ft, a speed of 33 knots, a complement of 795 men, and main armament consisting of nine 8-in. and four 5-in. guns, plus four aircraft.

North Atlantic Treaty A treaty signed on April 4, 1949, by the United States, Canada, the United Kingdom, and nine Western European countries; it was the foundation for the North Atlantic Treaty Organization (NATO). The purpose of the treaty is to bind the members collectively to resist an armed attack on any one or more members.

North Carolina A class of U.S. battleships of about 35,000 tons standard displacement completed in 1941 and 1942. The class included *North Carolina* and *Washington*. They had a length of 729 ft, a beam of 108 ft, a speed of 28 knots, and a wartime complement of 2,500 men. They were armed with nine 16-in. and twenty 5-in. guns, plus sixty 40mm and fifty-six 20mm antiaircraft guns and three aircraft. The

Northampton (CLC). (*U.S. Navy.*)

North Carolina. (*U.S. Navy.*)

North Carolina, which served in almost every major Pacific campaign in World War II, is now a memorial in Wilmington, N.C.

North Dakota A U.S. battleship of the **Delaware** class, which see. It was commissioned in 1910 and served as a training ship during World War I.

Norwegian 6.5mm (and 7.9mm) machine guns Model 1898 (1898T) Machine guns of **Hotchkiss** design, which see.

Norwegian 7.9mm machine gun M1929 A machine gun of Browning design and manufacture.

Norwegian Krag (Jörgensen) rifle See **Krag-Jörgensen 6.5 × 55mm rifle Model 1894.**

nose 1. The forward point or section of an aircraft, especially of an airplane's fuselage. **2.** The foremost point or section of a bomb, guided missile, or the like. Although a bomb is said to have a "nose," a cannon shell has a "point."

nose fuze A fuze for use in the forward end or nose of a bomb or other missiles. The term is generally not applied to fuzes for use in artillery projectiles, where the term "point fuze" is more commonly used.

nose guard, nosepiece A piece of armor for the protection of the nose. It is often hinged or sliding.

nose spray Fragments of a bursting projectile that are thrown forward in the line of flight, in contrast to base spray, which is thrown to the rear, and side spray, which is thrown to the side.

notch To fit, or nock, an arrow into the bowstring.

Novgorod A remarkable *circular* armored coastal-defense battleship of the Russian Navy. Built in 1873, it had a speed of 8.5 knots and mounted an 11-in. 28-ton gun. A sister ship, *Vice-Admiral Popov*, mounted a 12-in. 40-ton gun. The circular shape provided a steady gun platform.

nozzle The exhaust duct of a rocket thrust chamber, designed to increase the velocity of the gas.

nuclear airburst The explosion of a nuclear weapon in the air at a height greater than the maximum radius of the fireball.

nuclear cloud An all-inclusive term for the volume of hot gases, smoke, dust, and other particulate matter from the nuclear bomb itself and from its environment which is carried aloft in conjunction with the rise of the fireball produced by the detonation of the nuclear weapon.

nuclear column A hollow cylinder of water and spray thrown up from an underwater burst of a nuclear weapon through which the hot, high-pressure gases formed in the explosion are vented to the atmosphere. A somewhat similar column of dirt is formed in an underground explosion.

nuclear damage There are three degrees of nuclear damage: (1) *Light damage:* Damage which does not prevent the immediate use of equipment or installations for which they were intended. Some repair by the user may be required to make full use of the equipment or installations. (2) *Moderate damage:* Damage which prevents the use of equipment or installations until extensive repairs are made. (3) *Severe damage:* Damage which prevents the use of equipment or installations permanently.

nuclear energy All forms of energy released in the course of a nuclear fission or nuclear transformation.

Nuclear Falcon The Hughes AIM-26A version of the USAF air-to-air missile which derived from the Falcon. It was the first guided air-to-air missile with a nuclear warhead to enter service. It has a length of 7 ft, a launching weight of 203 lb, and a range of 5 mi. The AIM-26B has a non-nuclear warhead.

nuclear radiation Particulate and electromagnetic radiation emitted from atomic nuclei in various nuclear processes. The important nuclear radiations, from the weapons standpoint, are alpha and beta particles, gamma rays, and neutrons. All nuclear radiations are ionizing radiations, but the reverse is not true; x-rays, for example, are included among ionizing radiations, but they are not nuclear radiations since they do not originate from atomic nuclei.

nuclear surface burst An explosion of a nuclear weapon at the surface of land or water, or above the surface, at a height less than the maximum radius of the fireball.

nuclear warfare Warfare involving the employment of nuclear weapons.

nuclear warhead A warhead with a fissionable or fusionable charge.

nuclear weapon A device in which the explosion results from the energy released by reactions involving atomic nuclei—fission, fusion, or both.

nuclear yields The energy released in the detonation of a nuclear weapon, measured in terms of the kilotons or megatons of trinitrotoluene (TNT) required to produce the same energy release. Yields are categorized as follows:

Very low	Less than 1 kiloton
Low	1 to 10 kilotons
Medium	Over 10 kilotons to 50 kilotons
High	Over 50 kilotons to 500 kilotons
Very high	Over 500 kilotons

nuisance minefield A minefield laid to

Nuclear Falcon. (*U.S. Air Force.*)

delay and disorganize the enemy and to hinder his use of an area or route.

nuisance raid An air raid to annoy or harass the enemy.

numbered fleet A major tactical unit of the Navy immediately subordinate to a major fleet command and comprising various task forces, elements, groups, and units for the purpose of prosecuting specific naval operations.

Nürnberg A German light cruiser launched in 1934 and used in World War II. It had a displacement of 6,710 tons, a speed of 32 knots, and a complement of 850 men. Main armament consisted of nine 5.9-in. and eight 3.5-in. guns, twelve 21-in. torpedo tubes, and two aircraft. After the war this ship was incorporated into the Soviet Navy as the *Admiral Makarov*.

Nussknacker The German World War II nickname for the MF-5 underwater-to-air missile under development for the German Navy. The two-stage solid-propellant missile was designed to be used against aircraft at low altitudes. Development was stopped in 1944.

O

O-1 See **Bird Dog.**

O-2 A U.S. Cessna-built two-place twin-engine light aircraft introduced in 1967 for use by the U.S. Air Force in a forward air-control function. The O-2A is equipped with four wing pylons for carrying rockets, flares, and other light ordnance including the 7.62mm Minigun.

O2U Corsair A biplane observation aircraft built by Chance Vought for the U.S. Navy in 1926. This was the first airplane to incorporate a fuselage with all-tubular construction, including engine mounts. It had

a top speed of 151 mph.

O3U Corsair A biplane observation aircraft built by Chance Vought for the U.S. Navy in 1931. Variations of this airplane could be operated from land, water, catapult (cruisers and battleships), and carriers. It had a top speed of 135 mph.

oak-leaf cluster A small emblem consisting chiefly of a number of bronze or silver oak leaves bunched together, representing an additional award or awards of the same kind.

Obdurate A class of British destroyers of

1,540 tons standard displacement completed in 1942. They had a speed of 31 knots, a complement of 200 men, and armament consisting of four 4-in. guns plus four 2-pounder and six 20mm antiaircraft guns.

Oberon A class of British patrol submarines of 1,610 tons standard surface displacement completed between 1960 and 1967. There are 13 in the class. They have a length of 295.2 ft, a beam of 26.5 ft, a speed of 17 knots submerged, and a complement of 68 men. They are armed with eight 21-in. torpedo tubes.

objective The physical object of the action taken, e.g., a definite tactical feature, the seizure or holding of which is essential to the commander's plan.

objective area A definite geographic area containing a military objective.

oblique To march at an angle of about 45° to the original front.

oblique fire Fire placed on a target from a direction diagonal to the long dimension of the target or on an enemy from a direction between his front and his flank.

Oboe (observer bombing over enemy) A system developed by the Allies early in World War II. It consisted of a radar navigation and blind-bombing system that used two ground stations which measured the distance to a radar beacon carried by an aircraft. The ground stations were desig-

O-2. (*Cessna Aircraft Company.*)

330

nated "Cat" and "Mouse" and served to keep the aircraft on a direct path to the target.

Obregon .45 cal. automatic pistol A Mexican pistol that has the outward appearance of the Colt U.S. M1911A1, but is internally quite different. It has an overall length of about 8.5 in. and a barrel length of 5 in. The capacity of the magazine is seven cartridges, and the overall weight of the pistol is approximately 2.5 lb. Although out of production for some time, it is still a standard arm of the Mexican Army (with the Colt .45 Model 1911A1).

observation aircraft A type of aircraft, usually light, for general observation use, artillery spotting, reconnaissance, etc. (Picture, next page.)

observation balloon A captive balloon used for purposes of aerial observation, artillery spotting, etc. (Picture, next page.)

observation kite A man-carrying kite that could be launched and towed by a warship or a submarine. The purpose was to gain sufficient altitude to materially increase the field of view.

observation mine A system in which a mine is moored below a contact buoy. If a ship strikes the buoy, a signal is displayed to an observer. If the observer identifies the ship as belonging to the enemy, he detonates the mine.

observation of fire The act of watching fire in order to locate the burst or impact of projectiles in respect to the target and to correct firing data. Observation of fire may be made from the ground or from the air.

observation post A position from which military observations are made, or fire directed and adjusted, and which possesses

O2U Corsair. (*Vought Aeronautics Company.*)

O3U Corsair. (*Vought Aeronautics Company.*)

Oberon. (*Vickers Ltd.*)

observation aircraft, the Cessna O-1 Birddog. (*Cessna Aircraft Company.*)

observation balloon, ascending to observe artillery fire, France, 1916. (*The Imperial War Museum.*)

appropriate communications. It may be airborne.

observation squadron Before 1943, in the air service of World War I, the Air Corps, and the AAF, an aviation squadron such as a balloon squadron that observed primarily for ground units. After 1943, the reconnaissance squadron observed for both ground and air units.

observe To watch and take notice of artillery fire, enemy movements, or the like.

observed fire Fire for which the points of impact or burst can be seen by an observer on the ground, in aircraft, or on a naval vessel. The fire can be controlled and adjusted on the basis of the observations.

observer A person who observes in one way or another. Specifically: (1) An aircraft observer. (2) An air observer, forward observer, ground observer, weather observer, or the like. Historically, the observer in

military operations has been essentially a person who was advantageously placed to overlook the battlefield, either from a high point on the ground or from a balloon. His normal function has been to note the accuracy and effects of friendly artillery fire and to spy upon enemy positions and movements. By the time of World War I, the airplane had brought him over and beyond enemy lines, giving emphasis to his duties; he was normally an extra man in an airplane and was called a "combat observer." In World War II, the rating of combat observer was separately retained, but the bombardier and navigator were also rated as observers. Since World War II, the term has tended to be disassociated from the action of observing and is indifferently applied to a gunner, bombardier, navigator, radarman, etc.

observer identification The first element

of a call for fire. It is used to establish communication and to identify the observer or spotter.

obstacles In fortifications, any materials or systems to obstruct the operations of an assaulting party. Abatis, crow's-feet (caltrops), palisades, etc., are examples of such systems.

obturation The act of, or means for, preventing the escape of gases. In explosives, the sealing of the breech of a gun to prevent the escape of propellant gases.

obturator 1. An assembly of steel spindle, mushroom head, obturator rings, and a gascheck or obturator pad of tough plastic material used as a seal to prevent the escape of propellant gases around the breechblock of guns using separate-loading ammunition and therefore not having the obturation provided by a cartridge case. **2.** A device incorporated in a projectile to make the tube of a weapon gastight, preventing escape of gas until the projectile has left the muzzle of the weapon.

obturator spindle Part of the breechblock assembly of a gun which fires separate-loading ammunition. It extends through the breechblock and holds in position the various parts of the obturator, while permitting the breechblock independent rotation about these parts.

obusier A type of small fifteenth-century mortar for delivery of high-angle fire.

oc A type of Turkish war arrow.

OC A U.S. Navy command ship.

occupation currency See **military currency.**

occupied territory Territory under the authority and effective control of a belligerent armed force. The term is not applicable to territory being administered pursuant to peace terms, treaty, or other agreement, express or implied, with the civil authority of the territory.

ocean convoy A convoy whose voyage, in general, lies outside coastal waters.

ocean station ship A ship assigned to operate within a specified area to provide several services including search and rescue, meteorological information, navigational aid, and communications facilities.

O-chlorobenzyl-malononitrile (CS) One of the **tear agents,** which see, with a very rapid irritating effect. It is effective even in low concentrations and incapacitates within 20 to 60 seconds, with a duration of effect of 5 to 10 minutes after the individual is removed to fresh air. During this time the affected individual is incapable of effective concerted action. The effects include extreme burning of the eyes accompanied by a copious flow of tears; coughing, difficulty in breathing, and chest tightness; involuntary closing of the eyes; stinging sensation of moist skin; running nose; and dizziness or swimming of the head. Heavier concentrations will cause nausea and vomiting in addition to the above effects.

O Class A class of U.S. submarines commissioned in 1918. They were armed with four 18-in. torpedo tubes and one 3-in. deck gun. They had a complement of 30 men and a submerged speed of 11 knots.

Oerlikon Any of certain Swiss-developed 20mm automatic aircraft or antiaircraft cannons shooting greased ammunition. These cannons have been used by various nations, including the United States, Great Britain, Germany, and Japan. The name derives from Oerlikon, Switzerland.

Oerlikon 20mm aircraft cannon A Swiss blowback-operated air-cooled cannon with a rate of fire of 280 rounds per minute. It weighed 136 lb and was fed from a 60-round drum magazine. Weapons of this type were used by Great Britain, France, the United States, Japan, and Germany. In Luftwaffe application a way was found to convert the feed system to metallic link belt.

off-carriage fire control A process of controlling fire on a target with the aid of a sighting device which is not mounted directly on the weapon.

offensive grenade A grenade having a light container, designed to kill or injure by blast and concussion, distinguished especially from a fragmentation grenade. The offensive grenade is so called because the thrower, being out of range of the grenade's effects, can continue to advance as he throws and does not have to take cover.

officer In a restrictive sense, a commissioned officer or warrant officer, as distinguished especially from a noncommissioned officer or enlisted person.

officer of the day A duty officer who represents the commander and is responsible, usually for a period of 24 hours, for the security of a base or other installation.

officer of the deck An officer taking his turn in charge of a naval vessel, during which time he is senior to all other officers except the captain and the executive. Previously he carried a spyglass or binoculars and wore white gloves.

offset bombing Any bombing procedure which employs a reference or aiming point other than the actual target. This type of bombing is employed when the target cannot be seen or is a poor reference point. When employed, the compensating factors are either set into the bombsight or computed by the bombardier.

offset distance (nuclear) The distance the desired ground zero or actual ground zero is offset from the center of an area target or from a point target.

offshore patrol A naval defense patrol operating in the outer areas of navigable coastal waters. It is a part of the naval local defense forces consisting of naval ships and aircraft and operates outside those areas assigned to the inshore patrol.

off-the-shelf items Those items required by the military services which are generally used throughout the civilian economy and which are available through normal commercial distribution channels.

ogee, ogive Formerly, an ornamental S-shaped molding on guns, mortars, and howitzers.

ogive The curved or tapered front of a projectile. With a bullet, shell, bomb, or other projectile having a fuze forming the nose, the ogive is included between the point where the projectile begins to curve or taper and the point on the line where fuze and body meet; in other types of projectiles, the nose of the projectile is included as a part of the ogive.

Ohio A U.S. battleship commissioned in 1904 and a sister ship of the new *Maine* and

the old *Missouri.* For details, see **Maine.**

oil buffer A mechanism on certain types of automatic weapons, especially the .50 cal. guns, for absorbing the shock of recoil and regulating the speed of firing.

oiler A naval or merchant tanker specially equipped and rigged for replenishing other ships at sea.

Oklahoma A U.S. battleship of the **Nevada** class, which see. It was commissioned in 1916 and was sunk at Pearl Harbor on December 7, 1941.

Oktyabraskaya Revolutsia A soviet battleship similar to the **Sevastopol,** which see.

Öland A class of Swedish destroyers of 2,000 tons standard displacement completed in 1947–1949 and modernized in 1960–1963. They have a speed of 35 knots, a complement of 210 men, and armament consisting of four 4.7-in. guns, six 40mm antiaircraft guns, one triple-barreled depth-charge mortar, and six 21-in. torpedo tubes. Sixty mines are also carried.

Old Faithful A World War II nickname for the U.S. 4.5-in. barrage rocket used in support of troops in amphibious operations. It proved very effective between the time naval and air bombardment ceased and troops actually landed. Between 1942 and the end of the war, some 1.6 million were delivered.

Old Ironsides See **Constitution,** sense 1.

olive drab (OD) 1. A standard olive-green color used to signify the U.S. Army. **2.** A material of this color used for Army uniforms.

Omaha A class of U.S. light cruisers (CL) of about 7,050 tons standard displacement completed between 1923 and 1925. There were 10 ships in the class. They had a length of 550 ft, a beam of 55 ft, and a speed of 35 knots. Main armament consisted of twelve 6-in. and four 3-in. guns.

Oklahoma. (*U.S. Navy.*)

Ontos. (*U.S. Marine Corps.*)

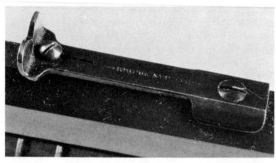

open sight. (*The Smithsonian Institution.*)

Two to four aircraft were carried.

onager An ancient weapon consisting of a slinglike catapult which threw stones from a bag or wooden bucket. It was so called after a mythological monster, Onager, which was said to throw stones at its pursuers with its feet.

on call The term used to signify that a prearranged concentration, air strike, or final protective fire may be called for.

on-carriage fire control A process of controlling fire on a target with the aid of a sighting device mounted directly on the weapon.

oncin A twelfth-century weapon having a hooked iron head resembling a one-sided pick.

one-day's supply A unit or quantity of supplies adopted as a standard of measurement and used in estimating the average daily expenditure under stated conditions. It may also be expressed in terms of a factor, e.g., rounds of ammunition per weapon per day.

One Eye The NATO code name for a type of Soviet C-band early-warning and surveillance radar.

one-pounder A gun firing a 1-lb shot or shell.

on the deck Said of an aircraft that is flying at minimum altitude.

on the way An expression that is sent over a communication system from the firing position to the observation position when a weapon is fired, thus warning the observers to be on the alert for spotting the impact.

on top Said of an aircraft that is flying above the overcast.

Ontos Designated as the M-50, this U.S. Marine Corps system is a full-track self-propelled direct-fire and antitank weapon. It is armed with six 106mm recoilless rifles, one .30 cal. machine gun, and four .50 cal. spotting rifles. It has a crew of three and a speed of 30 mph.

open bomb In intelligence usage, an undisguised or unconcealed sabotage explosive device, distinguished especially from an infernal machine.

open city, open town Formerly, a city or town that was unoccupied or undefended by military forces. Once so proclaimed and acknowledged, it was immune under international law from enemy bombardment.

open flank In fortifications, the part of the flank which is covered by the orillon.

open sight A rear gunsight having a notch. It is distinguished especially from a peep sight.

operating forces Those forces whose primary missions are to participate in combat and the integral supporting elements thereof.

operating handle A handle or bar with which the operating lever of a gun is operated to open and close the breech of the gun.

operating lever A lever device on a gun with which the breech of the gun is opened and closed.

operating slide A mechanism in a Browning machine gun that permits opening the breech for loading, unloading, and clearing out stoppages and closing the breech for firing.

operation A military action or the carrying out of a strategic, tactical, service, training, or administrative military mission; the process of carrying on combat, including movement, supply, attack, defense, and maneuvers needed to gain the objectives of any battle or campaign.

operational When used in connection with equipment such as aircraft, vehicles, etc., the term indicating that the equipment is in such a state of repair as to be immediately usable.

operational intelligence Intelligence needed by naval commanders in planning and executing operations.

operational missile A missile that, in contrast to a research and development missile, can be used against an enemy target; a "weaponized" system.

operational readiness The capability of a unit, a ship, a weapon system, or equipment to perform the missions or functions for which it is organized or designed. It may be used in a general sense or to express a level or degree of readiness.

opposite numbers Officers (including foreign) having corresponding duty assignments within their respective military services or establishments.

optical sight A sight with lenses, prisms, or mirrors that is used in laying weapons, for aerial bombing, or for surveying.

order A communication, written, oral, or by signal, which conveys instructions from a superior to a subordinate. In a broad sense, the terms "order" and "command" are synonymous. However, an order implies discretion as to the details of execution, whereas a command does not.

order arms A command to a soldier to bring his rifle to a vertical position at his side with the butt of the weapon on the ground. A similar order, once given to a cavalryman, directed him to drop his sword or saber to the front with the point of the weapon on or near the ground.

orderly A soldier or noncommissioned officer who attends an officer to carry out his orders and to render other services.

orderly officer The officer of the day.

orderly room An office or building where the commander and his assistants conduct the administrative affairs of the organization.

order of battle The identification, strength, command structure, and disposition of the personnel, units, and equipment of any military force.

order of the day Specific orders or notices issued by a commander to his troops.

ordnance Military weapons, ammunition, explosives, combat vehicles, and battle materiel collectively, together with the necessary maintenance tools and equipment.

Ordnance Corps A technical service of the U.S. Army, charged with the design, construction, testing, and supply of ordnance materiel. The Ordnance Corps provides guns, ammunition, missiles, armored and tracklaying vehicles, and apparatus for

Oregon City. (*U.S. Navy.*)

sighting and firing guns. It maintains arsenals and depots for the design, manufacture, testing, storage, and issue of such materiel; it also maintains an extensive research program.

ordnance depot A depot which contains reserve stocks of arms, ammunition, and equipment furnished by the Ordnance Corps.

Oregon A U.S. battleship of the old **Indiana** class, which see. Commissioned in 1896, it saw service in the Spanish-American War, assisting in the destruction of the Spanish fleet in Santiago Harbor.

Oregon City A class of U.S. heavy cruisers (CA) of about 13,000 tons standard displacement completed in 1946. The class consisted of *Oregon City, Albany,* and *Rochester.* They had a length of 673 ft, a beam of 71 ft, a speed of 33 knots, and a wartime complement of 1,700 men. They were armed with nine 8-in. and twelve 5-in. guns, plus fifty-two 40mm and twenty-four 20mm antiaircraft guns. One helicopter was carried.

oreillere The earpiece of an ancient helmet. It was often shaped like an oyster shell or a shield.

organ gun A piece of ordnance with numerous gun barrels arranged side by side and capable of being fired simultaneously. In the fourteenth to the seventeenth centuries as many as 160 barrels were sometimes so arranged.

orgue A former system of defense in which a quantity of musket barrels were arranged in a row and made to fire by a priming train of gunpowder.

orillon A seventeenth-century fortifications refinement that is a projection at the shoulder of a bastion beyond the ordinary flank of a curved portion of rampart and parapet, the curve being convex to the ditch.

Orion **1.** The Lockheed P-3 Orion is a four-engine (turboprop) antisubmarine patrol aircraft developed for the U.S. Navy from the Lockheed Electra and flown for the first time in 1958. The latest versions have a 12-man crew, a speed of 476 mph, a mission radius of about 2,500 mi, and a weapon load of almost 20,000 lb of tor-

pedoes, depth bombs, rockets, sonobuoys, underwater sound signals, marine markers, etc. **2.** A class of British battleships of 22,500 tons displacement completed in 1912. They had a length of 544 ft, a complement of 900 men, and main armament consisting of ten 13.5-in., sixteen 4-in., and four 3-pounder guns, plus three 21-in. torpedo tubes. The ships in this class included *Orion, Thunderer, Monarch,* and *Conqueror.* They had a speed of 22 knots.

Orione The Macchi C.205N was a single-seat single-engine fighter-interceptor used by the Italian Air Force. It was essentially a Folgore. The Orione (Orion) was equipped with a 1,475-hp engine and flew at speeds of 390 mph. It was armed with two 12.7mm Breda-SAFAT machine guns and one 20mm Mauser cannon.

Orita 9mm Parabellum submachine gun Model 1941 A Rumanian weapon developed to fire the 9mm Parabellum cartridge.

It was introduced in 1941 and produced during the early years of World War II. It is blowback-operated and has selective full automatic and semiautomatic fire. The cyclic rate of fire is 400 rounds per minute. It has an overall length, with a wooden stock, of 35.2 in. and a barrel length of 11.3 in. With a fully loaded 25-round magazine the weapon weighs 8.80 lb. It has a muzzle velocity of 1,280 fps and is equipped with a rear V notch sight that is adjustable from 100 to 500 meters.

Oscar The code name for the Nakajima Ki.43 Hayabusa (Peregrine Falcon) single-seat single-engine fighter-interceptor and fighter-bomber developed for the Japanese Army Air Force and first flown in 1939. Numerically the most important JAAF fighter of World War II (5,878 were produced), this airplane flew at speeds of 320 mph and was armed with two 12.7mm machine guns and two 550-lb bombs.

Orion. (*Lockheed Aircraft Corporation.*)

Oscar. (*The Smithsonian Institution, National Air Museum.*)

Oshio. (*Japan Defense Agency.*)

Oshio A class of Japanese submarines of 1,600 tons standard surface displacement completed in 1965–1969. They have a length of 288.7 ft, a beam of 27 ft, a speed of 18 knots submerged, and a complement of 80 men. They are armed with eight 21-in. torpedo tubes.

Oslo A class of Norwegian frigates of 1,450 tons standard displacement completed in 1966–1967. They have a length of 317 ft, a beam of 36.7 ft, a speed of 25 knots, and a complement of 151 men. They are armed with four 3-in. guns, two torpedo launchers, and Terne antisubmarine weapons.

Östergötland A class of Swedish destroyers of 2,150 tons standard displacement completed in 1958–1959. They have a speed of 35 knots, a complement of 244 men, and armament consisting of four 4.7-in. guns, four to seven 40mm antiaircraft guns, a tripled-barreled depth-charge mortar, and six 21-in. torpedo tubes.

Otter **1.** The de Havilland DHC-3 Otter is a single-engine (piston) utility aircraft used by Canadian forces, the U.S. Army, and the forces of at least eight other countries. It was first flown in 1951, flies at speeds up to 160 mph, and can carry nine passengers. **2.** A U.S. Army 1½-ton amphibious cargo carrier used to transport general cargo and personnel on either land or water. **3.** A paravane device used in naval minesweeping that keeps sweep wires extended laterally. **4.** A Canadian armored reconnaissance car produced during World War II. It had a crew of three, a weight of 9,070 lb, and armament consisting of a turret-mounted Bren machine gun and a Boys' .55 cal. antitank rifle firing from a front port.

OTTO A liquid monopropellant used in a hot gas generator to give increased speed, range, and depth to the U.S. Navy's Mark 48 torpedo.

outfit A slang term for a military unit or organization.

outflank To extend one's lines beyond or around those of the enemy.

outguard An advance guard or outpost.

outpost **1.** A military post, base, station, or other installation located at a remote place from its national homeland and having the primary responsibility of guarding the nation against surprise attack or protecting a territory or possession. **2.** A detachment of guards or sentries posted around a main body of men to protect it against surprise by the enemy when the main body is not moving.

outrigger Used mainly in antiaircraft artillery. An outrigger might be called a form of trail in that it aids in stabilizing the weapon. The outriggers are hinged, allowing them to be folded either horizontally or vertically for traveling and extended in a horizontal plane when the mount is emplaced. Four outriggers are usually attached to each mobile gun mount.

outsentry A sentry charged with guarding an outer approach.

outwall The exterior wall of a fortress or building.

outworks In fortifications, minor defenses constructed beyond the main body of the work. They are used to keep the enemy at a distance, and they consist of such works as ravelins, lunettes, demilunes, tenailles, rifle pits, etc.

OV-1 See **Mohawk,** sense 1.

Otter. (*U.S. Army.*)

Östergötland class, the *Södermanland.* (*Swedish Defense Staff.*)

OV-10 See **Bronco.**

over 1. A term used by a spotter or observer to indicate that a bomb or projectile has hit beyond or past the target. **2.** A code word in radio communications to signify that the speaker will temporarily cease speaking and that he expects a reply or confirmation.

over and out 1. A code phrase used in radio communications to signify that the speaker will break communication, provided the other party has nothing more to say.

overcast bombing The bombing of a target through an overcast above the target, using radar or other equipment to aid in sighting through the overcast.

overhead fire Fire that is delivered over the heads of friendly troops.

Overlord The World War II code name for the Allied cross-channel invasion of the continent of Europe on the Normandy coast of France. It commenced on D day, June 6, 1944.

overpressure The pressure resulting from the blast wave of an explosion. It is referred to as "positive" when it exceeds atmospheric pressure and "negative" during the passage of the wave when resulting pressures are less than atmospheric pressure.

overseas A place of service outside the continental limits of the United States.

overseas bar A strip of cloth worn on the sleeve for each full six months of overseas duty between December 7, 1941, and September 2, 1946.

overseas chevron A small chevron worn on the sleeve for each full six months of overseas duty in a theater of operations during World War I.

over-the-shoulder bombing A special case of loft bombing where the bomb is released past the vertical in order that it

Owen 9mm Parabellum submachine gun Mk 1/42. (*Australian Department of Supply.*)

may be thrown back to the target.

over the top In trench warfare going over the top of the parapet of a trench and advancing upon an enemy position or line.

Owen 9mm Parabellum submachine gun Mk 1/42 A weapon designed in Australia by Lieut. Evelyn E. Owen and officially adopted in 1941. Production totaled about 45,000 before terminating in late 1944. The weapon is blowback-operated and has selective full automatic and semiautomatic fire and a cyclic rate of fire of 800 rounds per minute. With a standard 33-round magazine the weight of the weapon is 10.7 lb. The length (without a stock) is 24 in., and the barrel length is 9.85 in.

Owl Screech The NATO code name for a type of Soviet I-band antiaircraft-artillery-fire-control radar.

oxygen equipment The equipment, including tanks, lines, regulators, connections, and masks, for use in the supply of oxygen to a person or persons in aircraft at high altitudes.

Oyster The name of a type of World War II German sea mine laid by aircraft.

P

P-1 A single-engine single-seat pursuit biplane built by Curtiss and used by the United States in the 1920s.

P2V See **Neptune**, sense 1.

P-3 See **Orion**, sense 1.

P4M-1 See **Mercator**.

P-5M See **Marlin**.

P-6 A single-engine biplane fighter developed by Curtiss-Wright and used by the United States in the 1930s. See **Hawk**, sense 2.

P-12 A U.S. single-seat single-bay biplane fighter developed by Boeing in the 1930s.

P-35A The Republic (Seversky) P-35A was a single-seat interceptor and fighter-bomber developed for the U.S. Army Air Corps and first flown in 1935. Also used by Sweden and Ecuador, this airplane had a speed of 310 mph and was armed with two .50 cal. machine guns and two .30 cal. machine guns.

P-36 See **Hawk**, sense 2.

P-38 See **Lightning**, sense 2.

P-39 See **Airacobra**.

P-40 See **Tomahawk** and **Warhawk**.

P-43 See **Lancer**.

P-47 See **Thunderbolt**.

P-51 See **Mustang**.

P-59 See **Airacomet**.

P-61 See **Black Widow**.

P-63 See **Kingcobra**.

P-66 See **Vanguard**, sense 2.

P-400 A World War II RAF designation for the Airacobra.

pace The regulated speed of a column or element as set by the pacesetter in order to maintain the average speed prescribed.

Packard-LePere LUSAC-II A U.S. two-place single-engine biplane escort and patrol fighter developed in 1918 but received too late to see service in World War I. It was armed with two synchronized forward-firing Marlin machine guns, plus twin Lewis guns on a Scarff ring in the rear cockpit. It had a speed of 136 mph.

pack artillery Artillery weapons designed for transport in sections by animals or delivery by parachute. The weapon and carriage are partially disassembled for transport and reassembled for firing from ground positions. When equipped with wheels, pack artillery may be used as towed artillery.

Packet See **Flying Boxcar**.

pack howitzer A complete projectile-firing weapon with a medium muzzle velocity and a curved trajectory. It is designed to be transported by animal or delivered by parachute. It may function as towed artil-

P-12. (*U.S. Air Force.*)

lery.

pack train Loaded pack animals, such as horses or mules, and their drivers.

PACV Patrol air-cushion vehicle. A designation applied to a U.S. patrol craft used on waterways and swamps and over inland terrain in Vietnam. The vehicle can carry a 4,300-lb load at speeds up to 55 knots.

painted ports Alternate black and white rectangles painted in a band along a ship's side in imitation of gunports. It was once a general practice to have painted ports on British sailing ships.

Pak The abbreviation for *Panzerabwehr-kanone,* German for "antitank gun."

palace guard Soldiers assigned to protect a castle or its occupants.

palander A type of fireboat or mortar boat.

palette In armor, one of the plates located at the armpits.

palikar Formerly, Greek or Albanian soldiers in the pay of the sultan of Turkey.

palisade A system of defense that uses long, pointed stakes arranged as a sort of fence. They may be mounted vertically or obliquely in rows.

pallasch A seventeenth-century European cavalry weapon; a broadsword with a saber hilt and a straight, single-edged blade.

Palldan A land-based Polaris missile.

pallet In armor, a headpiece.

paludamentum A military cloak once worn by a general.

pan **1.** The part of a matchlock, wheel lock, snaphaunce, or flintlock that holds the priming powder. **2.** In fortifications, the face or portion of a work forming one side of a salient angle.

panache A plume or feather worn on the crest of an ancient helmet.

pan coupé In fortifications, a straight line of parapet instead of a salient angle.

pan cover A protective plate over the pan to protect the priming powder from spilling or getting wet.

Pandora A World War II code name for the Long Aerial Mine, which consisted of an explosive charge attached to 2,000 ft of cable. The object of this RAF innovation was to tow the charge behind a Havoc aircraft and train it in the path of German bombers. It did not prove successful, and the idea was abandoned in November 1941.

panel **1.** A **marking panel,** which see, displayed on the ground as a means of signaling to aircraft. **2.** A type of carriage formerly used for transporting a mortar and its bed.

panel code A prearranged code designed for visual communications between ground units and friendly aircraft.

pannier **1.** A basketwork shield once used by archers. **2.** A basket filled with stones and used as an anchor for bridge and pontoon laying. **3.** Two boxes or packs carried on either side of a pack animal.

P-35A. (*U.S. Air Force.*)

They were once used especially for carrying medical supplies.

panoply **1.** A complete set of armor, as of a knight. **2.** An ornamental arrangement of arms and other military objects.

pansière In medieval armor, the piece of plate covering the lower front portion of the body.

Panther **1.** A single-seat single-engine jet carrier fighter developed for the U.S. Navy in the late 1940s. A sweptwing version was called the **Cougar,** which see. **2.** The name given to a series of U.S. bombers developed by Keystone in the late 1920s and early 1930s. The series included the B-3, B-4, B-5, and B-6, all of which were twin-engine biplanes.

Panther tank The German tank, heavy, PzKpfw V of World War II. This tank was introduced early in 1943 and was used in armored divisions. It had a crew of five, a weight of 50.2 tons, a length of 22.6 ft, and a speed of about 30 mph on roads. It was armed with one 75mm Kw.K. 42 gun and two 7.9mm MG-34 machine guns.

panzer A German term meaning "armor." It refers to a German tank or other armored

pansière. (*The Metropolitan Museum of Art, Rogers Fund, 1904.*)

vehicle and is used attributively to describe a panzer division, etc.

Panzerfaust A German hand-fired antitank rocket of World War II. It was modeled on the U.S. **bazooka,** which see.

Panther. (*U.S. Navy.*)

Panzerjäger K. (*Steyr-Daimler-Puch Akttengesellschaft.*)

Panzerjäger K An Austrian self-propelled antitank gun that consists of a French 105mm gun mounted on the chassis of a Saurer 4K armored personnel carrier. Development of this system began in 1965. It has a crew of three, a weight of 17 tons, and a road speed of 39 mph. The range of the 105mm gun is 2,000 meters.

Panzerkampfwagen German for "tank." It is abbreviated "PzKpfw."

paper-patched bullet A bullet patched with paper to produce a tighter fit in a rifled barrel and therefore provide a better spinning motion and improved accuracy. The patch also served as a gas seal and reduced lead fouling in the barrel.

parabellum A German term meaning "for war" and used to designate the German Luger pistol and also to differentiate 9mm Parabellum cartridges from 9mm Short cartridges.

Parabellum 7.92mm aircraft machine gun A German Maxim recoil-operated air-cooled machine gun with a rate of fire of 600 to 700 rounds per minute. It had a weight of 22 lb and was fed by a 250- to 350-round fabric belt. This weapon was the standard armament (rear-firing) for the observer on World War I aircraft.

parachute flare A pyrotechnic device attached to a parachute and designed to provide intense illumination for a short period. It may be discharged from aircraft or from the surface.

parachute fragmentation bomb A fragmentation bomb adapted for drop by parachute. Parachute fragmentation bombs are used in low-level bombing to give the bombing plane time to escape damage from the bomb explosion and to cause a bomb attitude which produces effective fragment distribution.

parachute troops Troops organized and trained to be carried into battle by transport aircraft and dropped by parachute, as distinguished especially from airborne infantry. Also called "paratroopers" or "paratroops."

parade **1.** A ceremonial procession of marching personnel, sometimes interspersed with vehicular equipment. **2.** The open field inside a fort or camp used for drill and reviews.

parados An elevation of earth behind a fortified place to protect against attack or fire in reverse.

parallel One of a series of long trenches prepared by the besiegers of a fortified place. The trenches are approximately parallel to the face of the works being attacked, and they provide cover for the attackers.

paramilitary forces Forces or groups which are distinct from the regular armed forces of any country but which resemble them in organization, equipment, training, or mission.

paramilitary operation An operation undertaken by a paramilitary force.

parang A short sword or knife of the Dyaks.

parapet The elevation of earth or material thrown up in front of a trench or emplacement to protect the occupants from fire and observation and over which fire may be delivered. In fortifications, parapets may consist of breastworks, walls, or bulwarks of earth, brick, wood, iron, stone, or other material.

pararaft A combination parachute and one-man life raft worn by Navy pilots.

pararescue team Specially trained personnel qualified to penetrate to the site of an incident by land or parachute, render medical aid, accomplish survival methods, and rescue survivors.

paratroops Parachute troops who are organized and trained to be carried into battle by transport aircraft and dropped by parachute.

paravane A protective underwater device which, when towed with a wire rope from a fitting on the bow of a ship, rides out from the ship's side and cuts the cables of anchored mines. The mines will then rise to the surface, where they can be seen and destroyed.

parazonium An ancient Greek dagger or small sword. Also, a similar weapon of medieval times.

Parca A French Army surface-to-air missile having a range of about 15 mi.

Paris guns Beginning on March 23, 1918, and continuing for 140 days, the Germans bombarded Paris with artillery pieces that were located 74.6 mi away. The 232mm *Parisgeschutz* (Paris gun) was developed from a German 380mm naval gun to which was added a 50-ft rifled extension plus another 28-ft extension that was not rifled. The overall length of the barrel was 128 ft, and the weight of an individual gun with mount was 308,000 lb. The projectile weight varied from 273.4 to 277.8 lb. Rounds were fired at an elevation of about 55°, reaching a zenith of 24 mi in their trajectory. Six guns of this type were used, and 256 Parisians were killed over the four-month bombardment period.

parkerize To impart a dull, relatively rough, rust-preventive finish to a firearm, using powdered iron and phosphoric acid.

parlementaire An agent employed by a commander of belligerent forces in the field to go in person within the enemy lines for the purpose of communicating or negotiating openly and directly with the enemy commander.

parma A round buckler used by the Romans. About 3 ft in diameter, it was made of leather-covered wood.

paroi A strong wooden frame with sharp stakes projecting horizontally from it. It was placed on the parapet of a fortified place to oppose scaling parties.

Parrott gun A type of muzzle-loading cast-iron rifled gun with a wrought-iron band shrunk around the breech for extra strength. It fired cylindroconical projectiles including shot, shell, case shot, and canister. Guns of this type, in various sizes, were used in the American Civil War era. They were invented by the American R. P. Parrott. Their calibers ranged from 2.9 to 10 in.

partisan **1.** Originally Russian, a member of an organized group of civilians who, in devoted adherence to a cause, work singly or in unison to sabotage or undermine an enemy's hold on the country in which they live. **2.** A partizan. **3.** The commander of a body of detached light troops who formerly were used to make forays and harass the enemy.

partizan A sixteenth- and seventeenth-century polearm with a long, tapering blade having two upturned lugs at its base. It is still used as a ceremonial weapon.

partridges, partridge mortars Large artillery mortars once used in sieges and in defensive fortifications. They had a central bore for a normal shell, which was ringed by 13 smaller bores for firing grenades.

pas-d'âne A seventeenth-century French term for one of the two lobes of a sword's shell guard. Since about 1850 it has been used to refer to the two branches between the quillons and the lower guard.

pas de sours Steps in the side of a ditch in a permanent fortification.

pass 1. A short tactical run or dive by an aircraft at a target; a single sweep through or within firing range of an enemy air formation **2.** A written leave of absence for a short period of time given a soldier.

passages In fortifications, openings cut in the parapet of the covered way.

passandeau An ancient cannon described as weighing 3,500 lb, having a length of 15 ft, and firing an 8-lb ball.

pass box A box, made of metal or wood, used to carry cartridge from a magazine or a caisson to a gun.

passegardes Ridges on the shoulder pieces of armor designed to turn the blow of a lance.

passe-mur An ancient cannon described as weighing 4,200 lb, having a length of 18 ft, and firing a 16-lb ball.

passive acoustic torpedo (PAT) A torpedo which homes on noise generated by its target.

passive air defense All measures, other than active defense, taken to minimize the effects of hostile air action. These include the use of cover, concealment, camouflage, dispersion, and protective construction.

passive defense Defense of a place without the employment of active weapons and without the expectation of taking the initiative.

passive electronic countermeasures The search, intercept, direction finding, range estimation, and signal analysis of electromagnetic radiations performed in

direct support of operations conducted for other than intelligence purposes.

passive homing guidance A system of homing guidance wherein the receiver in the missile utilizes natural radiations from the target.

password A secret word or distinctive sound used to reply to a challenge.

PAT **Passive acoustic torpedo,** which see.

patch 1. A piece of greased cloth or leather which was wrapped around the ball to make it fit the bore more tightly. It was commonly used with muzzle-loading rifles that fired spherical balls and in some dueling pistols. **2.** A small piece of cotton cloth used to clean the bore of small arms.

patch box A container for patches. In muzzle-loading rifles it usually consisted of a compartment in the butt. British riflemen called this a "butt trap" and carried small tools and extra flints in it.

Patchett submachine gun See **Sterling Mk II submachine gun.**

paté A horseshoe-shaped fortification sometimes used to cover the gate of a fortified town or place. Also, an iron or earthenware pot filled with powder and grenades and thrown at besiegers.

Pat Hand The NATO code name for a type of Soviet H-band surface-to-air missile (SAM) and surface-to-surface missile (SSM) acquisition and fire-control radar.

pathfinders 1. Experienced aircraft crews who lead a formation to the drop zone, release point, or target. **2.** Teams dropped or airlanded at an objective to establish and operate navigational aids for the purpose of guiding aircraft to drop and landing zones. **3.** A radar device used for navigating or homing to an objective when visibility precludes accurate visual navigation. **4.** Teams, air-delivered into enemy territory, for the purpose of determining the

partizan. *(The Metropolitan Museum of Art, gift of William H. Riggs, 1913.)*

best approach and withdrawal lanes, landing zones, and sites for helicopter-borne forces.

patrol A detachment of ground, sea, or air forces sent out by a larger unit for the purpose of gathering information or carrying out a destructive, harassing, mopping-up, or security mission. Formerly, a guard who went on rounds to ensure that sentinals were alert at their posts.

patrol bomber 1. A bomber used for patrol. **2.** A bomber specially suited to patrol duty; specifically, in the Navy, a bomber that strikes at targets of opportunity in the area being patrolled. In this sense, the patrol bomber of World War II was usually amphibious, like the PBY Catalina; the patrol bomber of the postwar period, like the P2V, is not necessarily amphibious, but it is equipped with electronic equipment for detection and attack. These patrol bombers usually fly singly.

patrol vessel A small warship used for general escort and patrol duties. The major types of U.S. Navy patrol vessels are escort vessel (DE), submarine chaser (PC), and escort (PCE).

pattern The distribution of a series of shots fired from one gun or a battery of guns under conditions as nearly identical as possible, the points of impact of the projectiles being dispersed about a point called the "center of impact." It is also called "dispersion pattern."

pattern bombing A method of bombing in which the bombs are made to strike the target in a certain pattern. Pattern bombing is done by a formation of planes acting as a single unit. The lead plane of a formation does the sighting for the entire formation, and the formation tries to release its bombs as simultaneously as possible. Pattern bombing, properly done, ensures an efficient distribution of bombs.

pattern harmonization The adjusting of a fighter's fixed guns so that they will produce the largest uniform pattern of lethal density possible at a given range.

pattern laying The laying of individual land mines in a fixed relationship to one another.

Patton tank The M-48A2, a full-track combat tank used by the U.S. Army and Marine Corps. It has a crew of four and is armed with a 90mm gun. It has a speed of 30 mph. (Picture, next page.)

Paul The Allied code name for the Japanese Aichi E16A1 Zui-un (Auspicious Cloud) two-seat single-engine reconnaissance and dive-bomber twin-float seaplane. It was first flown in 1942 and was armed with two 20mm cannons, one 12.7mm ma-

patrol bomber, the U.S. Navy Tracker. *(U.S. Navy.)*

Patton tank. (*U.S. Army.*)

chine gun, and one 550-lb bomb.

pauldron   A piece of armor for the protection of the shoulder at the point where the body piece and the arm piece join. It reached its highest development in the sixteenth century.

pavade   A short dagger once in use in Scotland.

pavis   A large shield used in the Middle Ages as a protection for archers and crossbowmen during siege operations. It was large enough for the protection of two men—the archer or crossbowman and the man (pavisor) who carried it. Shields of this type were made of wood covered with canvas or hide and painted.

pavisade   **1.** A defensive screen made up of pavises in a line.   **2.** A canvas screen along a ship's side.

pavisor   The soldier, varlet, or page who carried a pavis in front of an archer or crossbowman.

pavisses   Protection erected around a ship's rail against the boarding of an enemy.

payload   **1.** Generally, that part of a load which is expendable, deliverable, or ready for use in direct accomplishment of the mission.   **2.** In a guided missile or rocket, the warhead compartment and that which is carried in it.   **3.** In a projectile, the explosive or other filler.

PB   The abbreviation for "patrol bombing" or "patrol bomber," as used in the designation of certain Navy aircraft.

PB2Y   See **Coronado.**

PB4Y-1/2   U.S. Navy versions of the World War II B-24 **Liberator,** which see. The Navy designation was Privateer.

PBM   See **Mariner.**

PBR   River patrol boat. A type of lightweight, highly maneuverable, shallow-water boat developed to intercept and search enemy riverboats in the U.S. Navy's Operation Game Warden in Vietnam.

PBY   See **Catalina.**

PC   A U.S. Navy submarine chaser.

PCC   A U.S. Navy control submarine chaser.

PCE   A U.S. Navy escort vessel.

PCEC   A U.S. Navy control escort vessel.

PCER   A U.S. Navy rescue escort vessel.

PCF   A U.S. Navy patrol craft, inshore.

PCH   A U.S. Navy submarine chaser, hydrofoil. (Picture, p. 344.)

PCS   A U.S. Navy submarine chaser.

PCSC   A U.S. Navy control submarine chaser.

PD   The U.S. military designation for the war gas **phenyldichloroarsine,** which see.

PDR   Periscope depth range. The maximum range at which active sonar echoes can be made with a submarine at periscope depth.

PDSMS   Point Defense Surface Missile System. A U.S. Navy surface-to-air missile that provides relatively small craft with short-range defense against attacking aircraft. The system was built around a modified Sparrow 3 air-to-air missile.

PE   A U.S. Navy eagle boat.

pea jacket   A thick woolen jacket or coat worn by sailors in cold weather.

pea rifle   Formerly, a thick-barreled rifle firing a ball about the size of a pea.

pectoral   In armor, a breastplate.

Pedersen device   An invention of the American arms designer J. D. Pedersen, this was a noteworthy ordnance secret of World War I. It consisted of a receiver unit that could be locked into the receiver of a Springfield or Enfield rifle. Installed, it converted the rifle into a semiautomatic weapon that fired .30 cal. pistol-type cartridges from a 40-round box magazine. To hide its identity, the mechanism was officially listed as the U.S. .30 cal. automatic pistol Model 1918. The system was dropped after the war.

Paul, shown in U.S. markings. (*The Smithsonian Institution.*)

pavis. (*The Metropolitan Museum of Art, Rogers Fund, 1923.*)

pedestal The base or support of a fixed mount for a gun or other equipment about which the gun or equipment can be pivoted in traversing; hence, pedestal mount. (Picture, next page.)

pedestal sight In an aircraft gunnery system, a sight mounted on a pedestal for remote control of the guns.

PEDIN A U.S. Navy peapod dingy.

pedrero, pederero, peterero, patarero Formerly, a type of small breechloading swivel artillery used on ships and forts and for street defense.

pedro An early gun of large caliber used for throwing stone balls.

Peek Periodically elevated electronic kibitzer. The acronym for a radar-bearing low-altitude vertical takeoff and landing (VERTOL) drone developed to fly reconnaissance missions for the U.S. Army.

Peel Group The NATO code name for a type of Soviet I-band surface-to-air missile (SAM) and surface-to-surface missile (SSM) acquisition and fire-control radar. It is a shipboard system for use with naval **GOA** missiles, which see.

peel off To leave a formation of aircraft in flight.

Peeping Tom A U.S. Army reconnaissance drone developed by Beech Aircraft to be flown over enemy lines, snap photographs of battlefield operations, and return with intelligence data.

peep sight A rear gunsight having a small hole in which the front sight is centered in aiming. It is distinguished from an open sight. (Picture, next page.)

Peggy The Allied code name for the Mitsubishi Ki.67 Type 4 Hiryu (Flying Dragon) twin-engine bomber developed for the JAAF and first flown in 1943. It was the most successful Japanese bomber of World War II. It had a speed of 334 mph, a range of 2,360 mi, and armament consisting of one 20mm cannon and four 12.7mm machine guns, plus a bombload of 1,760 lb. (Picture, p. 345.)

Pelican **1.** A homing radar glide bomb developed by the U.S. Navy during World War II. It was discontinued in favor of the

PB4Y-2. (*U.S. Navy.*)

PCER. (*U.S. Navy.*)

PC. (*U.S. Navy.*)

PCH. (*U.S. Navy.*)

pedestal mount for twin .30 cal. machine guns. (*U.S. Air Force.*)

peep sight. (*The Smithsonian Institution.*)

Bat, sense 2, which see. **2.** The name of an ancient culverin that was 9 ft long and fired a 6-lb ball.

pellet The old name for a shot or bullet. In the Middle Ages it referred to a stone cannonball.

pellet lock See **pill lock.**

peloton A platoon or company of soldiers.

pelta A small, light shield made of wood or wickerwork and covered with hide.

pen A place for servicing submarines or torpedo boats, especially a dock or slip with an overhead concrete superstructure for protection against aerial bombs.

pencil See **banderolle.**

penetration **1.** A form of offensive maneuver which seeks to break through the enemy's defensive position, widen the gap created, and destroy the continuity of his positions. **2.** An intelligence term for the recruitment of agents within, or the planting of agents or technical monitoring devices in, a target organization for the purpose of gaining access to its secrets or of influencing its activities.

penetration fighter A long-range fighter designed primarily to penetrate deep into enemy territory against air or ground targets.

Penguin Mk 1 A Norwegian antiship missile with a length of 9.7 ft, a diameter of 0.9 ft, and a launching weight of 740 lb. It has an inertial/passive homing guidance system and a range of 11 + mi.

pennetière The pocket or bag used by slingers to carry stones and lead balls.

pennon A copper wing on a long, light arrow, used instead of a feather.

Pennsylvania A class of U.S. battleships of about 33,100 tons standard displacement completed in 1916. The class included *Pennsylvania* and *Arizona* (the latter was destroyed at Pearl Harbor on December 7, 1941). They had a length of 608 ft, a beam of 106 ft, a speed of 21 knots, and a complement of 1,385 men. They were armed with twelve 14-in. and twelve 5-in. guns, plus eight 5-in. guns for antiaircraft use. Three aircraft were carried. *Pennsylvania* saw considerable service in the Pacific theater during World War II.

Pennsylvania rifle See **Kentucky rifle.**

Pensacola A class of U.S. heavy cruisers (CA) of about 9,100 tons standard displacement completed in 1929–1930. There were two ships in the class, *Pensacola* and *Salt Lake City*. They had a length of 558 ft, a beam of 65 ft, and a speed of 32 knots. Main armament consisted of ten 8-in. and four 5-in. guns. Four aircraft were carried.

penstock A timber dam with a movable board which enables the defenders of a fortress to flood the ditch and destroy enemy positions in it.

pentagon In fortifications, a fort with five bastions.

Pentagon A relatively low, massive five-sided building on the Virginia side of the Potomac adjacent to Washington, D.C. Located in it are the principal executive offices of the U.S. Department of Defense, including those for the military departments of the USAF, the Army, and the Navy. Completed on January 15, 1943, the building contains over 17 mi of corridors and has space for as many as 32,000 workers.

penteconter In classical antiquity, a galley having decks fore and aft and carrying 50 rowers.

penthouse A kind of fixed or mobile shed for the protection of soldiers advancing on a fortified place. It could be moved to the wall, and soldiers could then safely try to create a breach in it.

pentolite An explosive consisting of a mixture of PETN and TNT. It can be melt-loaded.

pepperbox A firearm with a cluster of barrels, often a revolver, each barrel of which fires separately. Some weapons with fixed barrels and rotating hammers may also be classed as pepperboxes.

pepper pot An Allied World War II term for coordinated fire, sweeping enemy front lines at relatively short range. Such fire would include all available tank guns, antitank guns, light antiaircraft guns, medium machine guns, and heavy mortars.

Perafex An Allied mechanical deception device produced during World War II. They would be dropped from the air and, on hitting the ground, would imitate the sound of rifle fire and the explosion of hand grenades.

percussion A sharp blow, especially one for setting off an explosion.

percussion cap A small metal cap containing fulminating powder placed over the nipple on a percussion lock.

percussion lock A firearm mechanism in which a cap loaded with a detonating mixture is fitted over a pierced nipple and exploded by the blow of the falling hammer. The flash of the exploding cap is carried to the charge. Its development fol-

Peggy. (*The Smithsonian Institution, National Air Museum.*)

lowed that of the flintlock, and its use was widespread by the middle of the nineteenth century. By 1842 all British Brown Bess muskets were converted to percussion fire. The United States adopted percussion rifles and muskets in 1841 and 1842.

perdu An individual or group of soldiers doing extremely hazardous duty.

perimeter The whole outer edge of an area, object, etc.

perimeter defense A defense without an exposed flank consisting of forces deployed along the perimeter of the defended area.

periscope An optical instrument used to provide a raised line of vision in situations where direct vision may not be practical or possible, as in entrenchments, tanks, submarines, and the like. The raised line of vision is obtained by the use of mirrors or prisms within the structure of the device, maintaining a 180° line of vision for the eyes of the observer. It may have single or dual optical systems.

periscopic sight A gunsight made in the form of a periscope permitting a gunner to see over an obstacle.

Pennsylvania. (*U.S. Navy.*)

Pentagon. (*U.S. Army.*)

percussion lock. (*The Smithsonian Institution, H. Montague Collection.*)

Permit. (U.S. Navy.)

Pershing. (U.S. Army.)

Permit   A class of U.S. nuclear-powered attack submarines (SSN) formerly designated Thresher class, but renamed after the loss of the *Thresher* on April 10, 1963, with 129 men on board. The class has a displacement of 3,750 tons (standard), a length of 278.5 ft, a beam of 31.7 ft, a speed of 30+ knots submerged, and a complement of 107 men. They are armed with four 21-in. torpedo tubes and Subroc and antisubmarine-warfare torpedoes.

perrier, pierrier   A medieval device for throwing stones. The name was used later to describe a short shipboard mortar used for throwing stones and light shot. Likewise, a cannon perrier was one which fired stoneshot.

Pershing   A two-stage selective-range ballistic missile developed by Martin Marietta for the U.S. Army and first test-fired in 1960. It is deployed in Europe with U.S. and Federal German Republic forces. It has a length of 34.5 ft, a launching weight of 10,000 lb, and a range of 115 to 460 mi. It carries a nuclear warhead.

persistent war gas   A war gas that is normally effective in the open at the point of dispersion for more than 10 minutes. A moderately persistent war gas is one which is normally effective in the open at the point of dispersion for from 10 minutes to 12 hours.

personnel   Those individuals required in either a military or a civilian capacity to accomplish an assigned mission.

personnel carrier   A motor vehicle, sometimes armored, used for the transportation of troops and their equipment.

Perspex   The trade name for a British plastic similar to Plexiglas.

Perstoff   See **diphosgene.**

petard   An ancient device for bursting open gates, barricades, or doors to which it has been attached. Basically a case filled with explosives, a petard somewhat resembles a short mortar. A typical petard might weigh about 60 lb and have a mouth about 9 in. in diameter.

petardeer, petardier   A soldier who manages a petard.

Pete   The Allied code name for the Mitsubishi F1M2 two-seat single-engine general-purpose float seaplane. A biplane, this JNAF aircraft was first flown in 1936. It was used throughout World War II and was armed with three 7.7mm machine guns and two 132-lb bombs. Its top speed was 230 mph.

Peter Skram   A class of Danish fast frigates of 2,030 tons standard displacement completed in 1967–1968. They have a speed of over 30 knots, a complement of 112 men, and armament consisting of four 5-in. guns, four 40mm antiaircraft guns, and depth charges.

PETN   Pentaerythritol tetranitrate. One of the most powerful high explosives, it is used in detonating and priming compositions such as the base charge in antiaircraft shells and the high-explosive charge in sea mines, bombs, and torpedoes of the World War II era.

Petrel   A U.S. Navy air-to-surface tactical

personnel carrier, the British Alvis-built Saracin. (*Alvis Limited.*)

missile of the mid-1950s. It was launched from aircraft at distances beyond the target's defense range for attack of ships, other surface targets, or underwater targets. It employed radar homing.

petronel A sixteenth- and seventeenth-century short firearm with a sharply curved butt, falling somewhere between a short carbine and a long pistol. It was used mostly by cavalry and was originally designed to be braced against the chest in firing.

petty officer A U.S. Navy noncommissioned officer in the grades of chief, first, second, and third class.

Petya A class of Soviet escort patrol vessels with a standard displacement of 1,050 tons, the first example of which was completed in 1961. They have a length of 262 ft, a beam of 32 ft, a speed of 30 knots, and a complement of 100 men. They are armed with four 16-barreled A/S rocket launchers, four 3-in. guns, and five 21-in. torpedo tubes.

peytrel A variant of **poitrel**, which see.

PF A U.S. Navy patrol escort.

Pfalz D.III A German single-place single-engine biplane fighter, the prototype of which was tested in June 1917. It had a speed of 102.5 mph and armament consisting of twin Spandau machine guns buried in the front fuselage. Because they could dive faster than the Albatros, they were used extensively in antiballoon operations.

Pfalz D. XII A German single-place single-engine biplane fighter that entered service in September 1918. They had a speed of about 105 mph and were armed with twin forward-firing Spandau machine guns. A limited number had been produced by the end of the war.

PG A U.S. Navy gunboat.

PGH A U.S. Navy patrol gunboat, hydrofoil.

PGM A U.S. Navy motor gunboat.

PGM-11 See **Redstone.**

PGM-17 See **Thor.**

PGM-19 See **Jupiter.**

phalanx A unit of foot soldiers formed in close, deep ranks and files. The Macedonian phalanx was, in its later form, from 12 to 16 ranks deep. The men were armed with 18-ft lances.

Phalanx A code name for the U.S. Navy CIWS (Close-In Weapon System), consisting of radar-guided 20 to 25mm Gatling guns that provide a last-ditch defense against enemy antiship missiles. See also **CIWS.**

Phantom The McDonnell Phantom was a single-seat shipboard interceptor and the first jet designed for carrier operations. It first flew in early 1945, but was too late to see service in World War II. Equipped with two 1,600-lb-thrust engines, this aircraft flew at speeds up to 487 mph and was armed with four .50 cal. machine guns.

petronel. *(The Smithsonian Institution, R. G. Packard Collection.)*

(Picture, next page.)

Phantom II The McDonnell F-4 Phantom II is a two-seat twin-engine all-weather supersonic jet fighter-bomber used by the U.S. Air Force, Navy, and Marine Corps and first flown in 1958. It has a speed of 1,600 mph and a range of 1,500 mi. It may be armed with six Sparrow III or four Sparrow III and four Sidewinder air-to-air missiles. It can also carry up to 16,000 lb of nuclear or conventional bombs. This aircraft is also in service with the RAF and the Royal Navy and is designated Phantom. (Picture, next page.)

phases of military government (1) *Assault:* That period which commences with first contact with civilians ashore and extends to the establishment of military government control ashore by the landing force. (2) *Consolidation:* That period which commences with the establishment of military government control ashore by the landing force and extends to the establishment of control by occupation forces. (3) *Occupation:* That period which commences when an area has been occupied in fact and the military commander within that area is in a position to enforce public safety and order.

phenyldichloroarsine (PD) This war gas is both a blistering agent and a vomiting agent and has a delayed-action casualty effect. It has an immediate toxic effect on the eyes, with effects on the skin delayed $\frac{1}{2}$ hour to 1 hour. It also has an action similar to that of the vomiting agents. See **blistering agents** and **vomiting agents.**

Philippine Ribbon Any one of three decorations awarded by the Philippine Commonwealth government to U.S. military personnel who participated in the defense or liberation of the Philippine Islands dur-

Pfalz D.III *(The Smithsonian Institution, National Air Museum.)*

PG. *(U.S. Navy.)*

Phantom. (*McDonnell Douglas Corporation.*)

ing World War II.

Philippine Scouts At one time, a component of the U.S. Army stationed in the
Philippine Islands. The officers and men
were usually citizens of the Philippines.

PHM A U.S. Navy patrol hydrofoil guided
missile.

Phoenix A U.S. air-to-air missile developed
by Hughes and presently in production for
the U.S. Navy. This weapon has a length
of 13 ft, a diameter of 1.25 ft, and a launching weight of about 838 lb. It uses a semiactive radar-homing guidance system.

Phoenixes The Allied code name for concrete caissons or barges towed across the
English Channel to the Continent after the
Normandy landings and sunk to form main
breakwaters for artificial harbors.

Phönix C.I An Austro-Hungarian two-place
single-engine reconnaissance biplane that
entered service early in 1918. It had a top

speed of 110 mph and was armed with a
forward-firing Schwarzlose machine gun
and a free-firing Schwarzlose gun in the
rear cockpit. It could carry a 110-lb bombload.

Phönix D.I to D.III A series of Austro-
Hungarian single-place single-engine biplane fighters originally developed from the
Hansa-Brandenburg D.I, but with more
powerful engines. The first of the series
entered service in March, with others following through the end of the summer.
They had a speed of about 120 mph and
were armed with two forward-firing 8mm
Schwarzlose machine guns.

phony mine A harmless object used to
simulate a mine or to give false signals in
detectors; used in phony minefields.

phony minefield An area of ground used
to simulate a minefield with the object of
deceiving the enemy.

phony war A condition in which there are
declared hostilities between nations but
which is marked by the absence of any
armed conflict. In World War II the
months between September 1939 and April
1940 were a period of phony war.

phosgene (CG) This war gas is a choking
agent and has both an immediate- and a
delayed-action casualty effect. It exerts its
effect solely on the lungs and results in
damage to the capillaries. It causes seepage
of watery fluid into the air sacs. When a
lethal amount of CG is received, the air
sacs become so flooded that air is excluded
and the victim dies of anoxia. The severity
of poisoning cannot be estimated from the
immediate symptoms, since the full effect
is not usually apparent until 3 or 4 hours
after exposure. Most deaths occur within 24
hours. Called *D-Stoff* by the Germans, it
was first used by them in December 1915.
It is called *Collingite* by the French. It
became the principal war gas used by the
Allies and was delivered in trench mortars,
bombs, and projector drums. It is estimated
that 80 percent of chemical-agent fatalities
were caused by this gas. It has the odor of
new-mown hay or grass or of green corn.

phosgene oxime (CX) This war gas is one
of the **blistering agents,** which see, and has
a quick-acting casualty effect. It is a powerful irritant and produces immediate pain
varying from a mild prickling sensation to
a feeling resembling a severe beesting. It
causes violent irritation to the mucous
membrane of the eyes and nose.

phosphorus A chemical that ignites spontaneously in air and gives off a dense white
smoke. It is widely used as a smoke agent
and for incendiary bombs and shells.

phosphorus bomb An incendiary bomb
filled with phosphorus, especially white
phosphorus.

photoflash bomb A bomb designed to
produce a brief and intense illumination for
medium-altitude night photography.

photoflash cartridge A pyrotechnic cartridge designed to produce a brief and intense illumination for low-altitude night
photography.

photographic intelligence The collected
products of photographic interpretation,
classified and evaluated for intelligence use.

Phyllis Ann The code name for a U.S. Air
Force communication monitoring and
emitter-location system which was used on
retrofitted C-47 aircraft in Vietnam to track
movements of enemy forces.

physical security That part of security
concerned with physical measures designed
to safeguard personnel; to prevent unauthorized access to equipment, facilities,
materiel, and documents; and to safeguard
equipment, facilities, materiel, and documents against espionage, sabotage, damage,
and theft.

Phantom II. (*McDonnell Douglas Corporation.*)

Piaggio 108B. (*Rinaldo Piaggio Aircraft.*)

Piaggio 108 The only successful four-engine heavy bomber produced by the Axis in World War II was Italy's Piaggio 108. It had a crew of seven, a speed of 250 mph, and a range of 2,500 mi. It could carry a bombload of 22,000 lb. The P.108B (*bombardiere*) was first produced in 1938–1939 and is shown in Italian insignia. The P.108A (*artigliere*) was developed in 1943 to attack shipping. An example is shown in German insignia.

PIAT *P*rojector *i*nfantry *a*nti*t*ank. A British weapon of World War II. It fired a rocket-propelled charge weighing 3 lb. The projectile could pierce 4-in. armor.

pick An obsolete term for a pike or pike-staff. Also, the shrap point in the center of a buckler or the pointed end of a staff.

pickadills The fabric edging placed on armor parts to prevent clattering and scratching of the polished surfaces. Piccadilly Circus in London derives its name from the fact that craftsmen who lined armor once lived there.

picker A pointed brass instrument once used for cleaning the vent of a musket.

picket **1.** A ship or aircraft stationed in relation to a formation or in a geographic location for a specific purpose, such as air warning. **2.** Formerly, a detachment of soldiers serving to guard an army from surprise; a small outguard.

picket boat An outpost scouting or guard boat.

picket line A position held by a line of pickets.

pickle-barrel bombing The bombing of a very small target; highly accurate bombing.

pickup The general term used by the Allies in World War II for a landing operation by an aircraft behind enemy lines to bring out friendly agents.

picric acid Trinitrophenol. A high explosive slightly more powerful than TNT and used widely in the form of mixtures with other nitro compounds. It has found extensive use in some foreign countries and is also called "melinite" and "lyddite."

piece An artillery weapon, a machine gun, a rifle, or any firearm.

pier A structure for mooring vessels which is built out into the water perpendicular to

PIAT. (*The Smithsonian Institution, National Museum Collection.*)

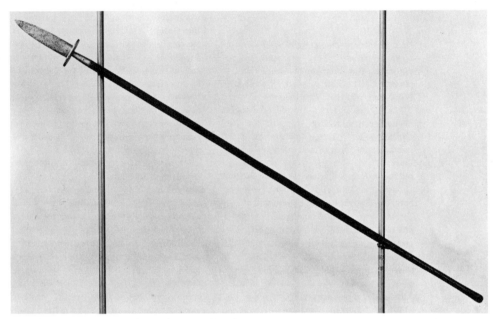

pike. (*The Smithsonian Institution, Library of Congress Collection.*)

the shoreline.

pig The float at the end of a minesweeping cable.

pigboat A slang term for a submarine.

pike Formerly, an infantry weapon consisting of a long wooden shaft with a pointed steel head, sometimes in the nineteenth century having also a hook or pick on the side. Most were protected with iron straps 3 or 4 ft from the head to prevent damage from swords, and they often had an iron-covered butt. The average length was 12 to 14 ft, but in the fifteenth and sixteenth centuries they often reached 16 to 22 ft. A shorter form of pike was used on shipboard as a weapon in boarding an enemy vessel or in repelling boarders. This type was normally 6 to 7 ft long.

Pike A class of U.S. submarines of 1,330 tons standard displacement commissioned in 1936–1937. They had a surface speed of 20 knots, a submerged speed of 10 knots,

Pike. (*U.S. Navy.*)

pistol, an American Savage .45 cal. automatic. (*The Smithsonian Institution.*)

and armament consisting of six 21-in. torpedo tubes and a 3-in. deck gun.

pikeman A soldier armed with a pike.

pikestaff The staff, or shaft, of a pike.

Pillar Box A British development of World War II, this system consisted of a rocket launcher mounted on ships to fire 2-in. surface-to-air barrage rockets. The 20-rocket launcher was used extensively in the war.

pillbox A small, low fortification that houses machine guns, antitank weapons, etc. A pillbox is usually constructed of concrete, steel, or filled sandbags.

pill lock An early percussion ignition system using a fulminate pellet or pill. Also called "pellet lock."

pilon A form of half-pike.

pilot A person who flies an airplane, an airship, or a balloon.

pilum An ancient Roman shafted weapon for throwing. It consisted of a stout iron head on an iron rod, the whole about 20 in. in length. It terminated in a socket for the wooden shaft, which was another 40 in. in length. When it struck a target, the soft iron rod would bend, making it difficult to extract and impossible to hurl back.

pincers A military movement in which two columns advance on either side of a stronghold and converge on it like the jaws of a pincers.

pineapple A slang term for a hand grenade.

pinfire A type of cartridge ignition system invented in about 1835. The cartridge had a detonating pin projecting outward from the base, and when this pin was struck with the hammer, the inner end struck a fulminate cap within the base of the cartridge.

ping The acoustic pulse signal of an echo-ranging indicator.

ping jockey A slang term for a sonarman.

Ping Pong A U.S. short-range front-line reconnaissance drone developed to be flown over a specific area, snap pictures automatically in flight, and then return to its launch area.

pinpoint **1.** A precisely identified point, especially on the ground, that locates a very small target; a reference point for rendezvous or for other purposes; the coordinates that define this point. **2.** The ground position of aircraft determined by direct observation of the ground.

pinpoint bombing Precision bombing.

pintle **1.** The vertical bearing about which a gun carriage revolves; a pin used as a hinge or axis. **2.** A hook for catching, sustaining, or pulling. It is mounted on a vehicle so that another vehicle can be attached.

pioneers From the fourteenth to the nineteenth centuries, soldiers detailed to clear forests, make roads, dig trenches, clear away obstructions before enemy forts, etc.

pip The visual indication of a target on an electronic indicator screen.

pipes Bagpipes. Still employed by Scottish regiments, bagpipe military music has been used since the sixteenth century.

pipper A small hole in the reticle of an optical sight or computing sight; a pipper image.

pipper image A spot of light projected through the pipper in an optical or computing sight and used in aiming.

piquier A pikeman; a soldier armed with a pike.

pistol **1.** In popular usage, any firearm, usually short-barreled, designed to be held and fired in one hand. Pistols came into use early in the sixteenth century, when the wheel lock first made them practical. **2.** More precisely, such a firearm in which the chamber is an integral part of the barrel, especially a self-loading pistol, as distinguished from a revolver.

pistol carbine A pistol equipped with a removable buttstock so that it can be used either as a shoulder weapon or as a handgun. Pistol carbines were first used in quantity early in the nineteenth century. The United States had an official model in 1855.

pistoleer A soldier armed principally with pistols.

pistol lanyard An assembly of a cord, slides, and a fastening device, generally used by military police. It is worn looped over the shoulder with the end attached to the pistol.

pivot gun An obsolete naval term for a gun capable of being fired on either side of a ship.

Pizarro A class of Spanish frigates of 1,924 tons standard displacement completed in 1947–1950. They have a speed of 18.5 knots, a complement of 291 men, and various armament combinations including 4.7-in. and 5-in. guns; 40mm, 37mm, and 20mm antiaircraft guns; hedgehogs; and racks for antisubmarine torpedoes.

place d'armes In fortifications, an enlarged space. It may serve as a rallying point for sortie groups, or it can be used

Pizarro. (*Spanish Ministry of Defense.*)

as a parade ground, station, or depot.

plane To ride on the step or the after section of the hull of a seaplane or boat.

plane of departure The vertical plane containing the path of a projectile as it leaves the muzzle of a gun.

plane of fire The vertical plane containing the axis of the bore of a gun when it is ready to be fired.

plane of position The vertical plane containing the gun and the target; the vertical plane containing a line of sight.

plane of site The plane made by two lines, one from the muzzle of the gun to the target, and the other horizontal but perpendicular to the first line at the muzzle of the gun.

plastic explosive An explosive which, within normal ranges of atmospheric temperature, is capable of being molded into a desired shape.

plasticized white phosphorus (PWP) A common ingredient in incendiary devices, PWP is produced by melting white phosphorus (WP) and stirring it into cold water. This produces small granules which are then mixed with a viscous solution of synthetic rubber. All the granules become coated with a film of rubber and thus are separated from one another. This rubbery mass is dispersed by an exploding munition, but does not break up to the extent that WP does.

plastron **1.** A metal breastplate worn under the hauberk in medieval armor. Later, the term for a pad or cushion worn at the shoulder to sustain the recoil of heavy muskets. **2.** A padded or canvas garment worn on the chest in fencing.

plate **1.** Armor made of broad pieces of metal, as distinguished from mail, scale, or other types of armor. **2.** Strong metal plates used to protect fortifications, warships, etc.

platform **1.** A temporary or permanent solid bed on which artillery pieces are supported to give greater stability. **2.** A metal stand at the base of some types of guns upon which the gun crew stands while serving the gun.

platform drop The airdrop of loaded platforms from rear-loading aircraft with roller conveyors.

platoon A subdivision of a tactical unit such as a company and usually commanded by a lieutenant. The term once referred to a body of men who fired together or to troops who drew up in a hollow square in order to strengthen the angles of a formation.

Plexiglas Often spelled, incorrectly, "plexiglass." A trade name for a clear, glasslike plastic made of acrylic resin. It is used especially in aircraft turrets, windows, and canopies.

plombée An ancient war club with a head loaded with lead.

plot **1.** A map, chart, or graph representing data of any sort. **2.** To represent on a diagram or chart the position or course of a target in terms of angles and distances from known positions; to locate a position on a map or chart. **3.** The visual display of a single geographic location of an airborne object at a particular instant in time. **4.** A position of a map or overlay on which are drawn the outlines of the areas covered by one or more photographs.

plotting board A device usually having a plane surface upon which data are compiled or recorded to serve as a basis for determining distances, ranges, velocities, and the like. It may be inscribed with predetermined data or may require the use of auxiliary items such as charts, maps, or patterns.

plunging fire An old term for a pitching discharge of shot from a higher level, at such an angle that the shot did not ricochet.

Plunkett guns U.S. 14-in. battleship guns that were mounted on railway carriages and placed in action on the Western Front during World War I. They were named after Rear Admiral C. P. Plunkett, who supervised the project.

pluteus An ancient wheeled device that provided shelter for advancing besiegers. Some were equipped with rams.

Pluto A code word for "pipeline under the ocean." Pluto was laid at the bottom of the English Channel during World War II for the supply of petroleum products.

pneumatic cannon See **dynamite gun.**

Po The designation for Soviet aircraft designed by Nikolai N. Polikarpov.

Po-2 See **Mule.**

pocket battleship A small battleship designed so as to stay within the treaty limitations established after World War I. It originally referred to German vessels of about 10,000 tons displacement and carry-

plastron. (*The Metropolitan Museum of Art, gift of William H. Riggs, 1913.*)

ing 6-in. and 11-in. guns.

pod **1.** A streamlined housing for something carried externally on an airplane or missile. **2.** A self-contained detachable compartment on an airplane. (The illustration shows the components of a Bofors 135mm air-to-ground rocket and the pod from which rockets of this type are fired.)

poignado, poinado A poniard.

point **1.** To aim a weapon; to lay a gun on a target. **2.** The tip or foremost part of a projectile. **3.** The man or group of men who precede an advancing force.

point-blank range A distance to a target that is so short that the trajectory of a bullet or projectile is practically a straight, rather than a curved, line.

point d'appui A basis of operations.

pointer The man who controls a gun in

pod. Shown in the background is a rocket pod for Bofors 135mm air-to-ground missiles. (*A. B. Bofors.*)

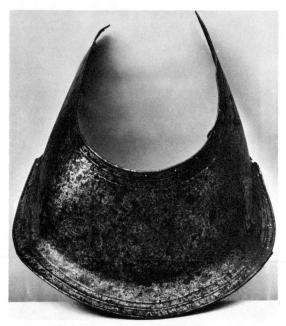

poitrel. (*The Metropolitan Museum of Art, Bashford Dean Memorial Collection.*)

elevation (range).

pointer board An obsolete term for a contrivance for training a ship's guns.

point fire Concentrated fire from a number of guns, directed at a single point or small area.

Polaris. (*Lockheed Aircraft Corporation.*)

point fuze A fuze for use in the forward end of a projectile or rocket warhead.

point of aim See **aiming point.**

point of burst The point at which a projectile bursts.

point of fall The point in the curved path of a falling projectile that is level with the muzzle of the gun. It is also called the "level point."

point of impact The point at which a bullet, bomb, projectile, or the like strikes.

point of no return A point along an aircraft track beyond which its endurance will not permit return to its own or some other associated base on its own fuel supply.

point of percussion The dividing line on a cutting sword blade where the forte joins the foible. Theoretically it is the spot where a blow should strike for maximum efficiency.

point-ring sight A front sight that consists of a ring with equidistant projections toward the center of the rim.

points See **arming points.**

point target A target which requires the accurate placement of bombs or fire.

poison gases See **war gases.**

poitrel In ancient armor, a breastplate for a horse.

Polaris A solid-propellant two-stage missile developed by Lockheed for the U.S. Navy and first fired in 1958. Designed to be launched from a submerged submarine, the latest version of the Polaris (A3) has a launching weight of about 30,000 lb, an overall length of 31 ft, and a range of 2,875 mi. The thermonuclear warhead has a yield of about 1 megaton.

polearm A weapon having a long handle, such as a poleax or a halberd.

poleax A weapon with a long handle and a head with an ax blade on one side and a hook, spike, or hammer on the other. In naval applications, they were used on board ship to cut away the rigging of an adversary. Also, in boarding an enemy ship whose hull was more lofty than that of the boarders, the blades or points of several poleaxes were driven into her side, one above the other, thus forming a kind of scaling ladder.

pole torpedo See **spar torpedo.**

poliabole A ballista capable of throwing both arrows and stones.

Polikarpov I-15 A single-seat single-engine biplane fighter that entered service with the Soviet Air Force in 1933. On November 21, 1935, a specially modified airplane of this type was flown by V. Kokkinaki to a world altitude record of 47,818 ft. Some 550 of these aircraft were used by the Republican forces in Spain, where they were nicknamed *Chato,* "The Flat-nosed One." Equipped with a 700 hp-engine, they flew at speeds of 224 mph. Armament consisted of four 7.62mm machine guns.

Polikarpov I-16 A single-seat single-engine fighter-bomber in service with the Soviet Air Force in 1934, and the world's first low-wing interceptor monoplane with retractable landing gear. Although it was obsolete at the beginning of World War II, it bore the brunt of early Luftwaffe attacks and remained in service until 1943. Used during the Spanish Civil War, it was called the *Mosca* (Fly) by its pilots and *Rata* (Rat) by its opponents. Equipped with a 1,000-hp engine, it had a maximum speed of 326 mph. It was armed with two 20mm cannons, two 7.62mm machine guns, and six rockets.

Polikarpov I-17 A single-seat single-engine interceptor and fighter-bomber first flown in September 1934. It had a speed of 305 mph and was armed with one 20mm cannons, two 7.62mm machine guns, and two 110-lb bombs.

Polikarpov I-135 A single-seat single-engine biplane fighter-bomber manufactured for the Soviet Air Force and first flown in 1935. It was equipped with retractable landing gear and was one of the fastest biplane fighters ever in service. It was used in the Spanish Civil War, where it was called the *Chaika* (Gull). It flew at speeds of 267 mph and was armed with four 7.62mm machine guns and six rockets.

Polish 7.62mm submachine gun Model 1943/52 A modification of the Soviet PPS M1943 submachine gun. It has a cyclic rate of fire of 600 rounds per minute and a muzzle velocity of 1,640 fps. It has an overall length of 32.72 in., a barrel length of 9.45 in., and a weight of 8 lb. It is fed from a 35-round detachable box magazine.

Polish 7.92mm carbine Model 98 Essentially the same as the German Kar 98a carbine.

Polish 7.92mm rifle Model 29 A variant of the Czech Model 24.

Polish 7.92mm rifle Model 91/98/25 This weapon was developed in Poland after World War I and contains features of Russian design (having a Russian Mosin Nagant action) and German design (having Mauser-type bands and fittings). This rifle has an overall length of 43.3 in., a barrel length of 23.6 in., a weight of 8.16 lb, and a muzzle velocity of 2,470 fps. It is fed from a 5-round nondetachable box magazine.

Polish 7.92mm rifle Model 98a This rifle is basically the same as the German rifle 98.

Polish 9mm automatic pistol Model 64 A double-action blowback-operated pistol chambered for the Soviet Makarov 9mm cartridge. It has an overall length of 6.1 in., a barrel length of 3.3 in., a weight of 1.5 lb, a muzzle velocity of 1,017 fps, and an eight-round detachable box magazine.

Polish 9mm machine pistol Model 63 A weapon similar in design to the Soviet 9mm

Polish 7.92mm rifle Model 91/98/25. (*Defense Ministry, Polish People's Republic.*)

Polish 9mm automatic pistol Model 64. (*Defense Ministry, Polish People's Republic.*)

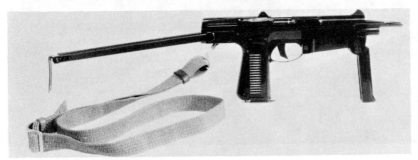

Polish 9mm machine pistol Model 63. (*Defense Ministry, Polish People's Republic.*)

poniard. (*The Smithsonian Institution, R. G. Packard Collection.*)

Stechkin and the Czech 7.65mm M61 Skorpion machine pistols. It is a selective-fire weapon that can be used as a pistol or a shoulder weapon. It has an overall length (with stock folded) of 13.1 in., a weight of 3.96 lb, a cyclic rate of fire of 600 rounds per minute, and a muzzle velocity of 1,065 fps. It is fed with 15- and 25-round detachable box magazines.

polygon The angular forms of the walls of fortified places.

pomerium In ancient fortified towns, the space between the walls and the houses.

Pomilio P types Italian two-place single-engine reconnaissance biplanes that first entered service in March 1917. The PC was subject to numerous accidents because of instability. The PD was developed to remedy the problem, and this led to the most successful variant, the PE (which went into service in February 1918). It had a speed of 120 mph and was armed with a forward-firing machine gun and one or two Lewis guns mounted in the rear cockpit. Total output of the three types was 1,616.

pommel The knob or cap at the end of a sword or dagger grip or on the butt of a pistol to counterbalance the weight of the weapon and give a more secure hold. Also, the cascabel of a cannon or the knoblike protuberance at the front of a saddlebow. The term derives from the Latin word for "apple," to which a pommel bears a resemblance.

pommelion An old name for the knob on the breech of a cannon.

pom-pom **1.** A rack of antiaircraft cannons, usually mounted in fours, as on the deck of a ship. **2.** An automatic cannon. The term "pom-pom" was first applied to an automatic cannon used by the Boers in the Boer War (1899–1902). This weapon, a 37mm Vickers-Maxim one-pounder automatic machine cannon, made a sound like

the beating of drums.

poniard A slender dagger with a triangular or square blade.

pontoon **1.** A float, such as a flat-bottomed boat or a metallic cylinder, used in building military bridges. **2.** The float of an airplane.

pontoon bridge A bridge with its deck supported on pontoons.

Pork Chop Hill The name for a topographical feature in the Yokkokchon Valley, Korea, and the scene of intense military action during the Korean conflict in the spring of 1953.

porpoise To break the surface of the ocean; to broach.

Porpoise A class of British patrol submarines of 2,030 tons standard surface displacement completed in 1958–1961. There are eight in the class. They have a length of 295.2 ft, a beam of 26.5 ft, a speed of

pontoon bridge. (*U.S. Army.*)

Portland. (*U.S. Navy.*)

Poseidon. The Poseidon is shown on the right. A Polaris A3 is shown on the left. (*Lockheed Aircraft Corporation.*)

17 knots submerged, and a complement of 71 men. They are armed with eight 21-in. torpedo tubes.

port 1. A harbor with its facilities, for example, a port of embarkation or debarkation. **2.** A slit or hole in an armored vehicle or fortification through which guns are fired. **3.** A small opening in some automatic guns through which the gas from the bore can escape. The escaping gas actuates a piston whose action prepares the gun for the next shot. **4.** The opening in a cylinder block or sleeve for intake, exhaust, water, oil, etc. **5.** A seagoing term for "left," as apposed to "starboard," which means "right." **6.** Carrying a rifle or saber in a position sloping across the body from right to left. **7.** A socket on a stirrup or saddle for the butt of a lance.

portable firearm A firearm that can be carried and fired by one man.

port capacity The estimated capacity of a port or an anchorage to clear cargo in 24 hours, usually expressed in tons.

port complex A port complex comprises one or more port areas of varying importance whose activities are geographically linked either because these areas are dependent on a common inland transport system or because they constitute a common initial destination for convoys.

portcullis A grating made of iron and heavy timbers that was hung over the gateway of a fortress or a fortified town. It ran in grooves and could be let down in case of a surprise attack, when there was too little time to close the gates.

Porter A class of U.S. destroyers (DD) of 1,850 tons standard displacement commissioned in 1936–1937. They had a length of 371 ft, a beam of 36 ft, a speed of 37 knots, and a complement of 230 men. They were armed with eight 5-in. guns and eight 21-in. torpedo tubes.

portfire A fire carrier. A paper case containing a composition of saltpeter, sulfur, and mealed powder. It burned with an intense flame that lasted about 10 minutes and was used to ignite primers, quick matches, etc., in firing guns.

Portland A class of U.S. heavy cruisers (CA) of about 9,800 tons standard displacement completed in 1933. There was only one ship (*Portland*) in the class. It had a length of 582 ft, a beam of 66 ft, a speed of 32.7 knots, and a wartime complement of 1,200 men. It was armed with nine 8-in. and eight 5-in. guns, plus twenty-four 40mm and sixteen 20mm antiaircraft guns. It was disabled off Guadalcanal in November 1942.

Port Said submachine gun An Egyptian-made 9mm Parabellum Carl Gustaf submachine gun.

Portuguese 7.65mm automatic pistols M/908 and M/915 Savage (.32 ACP) pistols M1908 and M1915. The M/908 weighs 1.2 lb, has an overall length of 6.5 in. and a barrel length of 3.8 in., and uses a 10-round staggered-row box magazine. The M/915 is generally the same.

Portuguese 7.69mm Madsen machine gun Portugal has used six models of the Madsen machine gun, ranging from Model 1930 to Model 1947. See **Madsen machine guns.**

Portuguese 7.92mm machine gun M/938 The same as the German MG 13.

Portuguese 9mm Parabellum submachine gun Model F.B.P. M/48 A weapon that derives its design from a number of other submachine guns, with particular emphasis on the best design features of the German MP-40 and the U.S. M3A1. It fires the 9mm Parabellum round and has a muzzle velocity of 1,280 fps. It is blowback-operated and operates on full automatic only, with a cyclic rate of fire of 500 rounds per minute. With stock retracted the weapon is 25 in. long, with a barrel length of 9.8 in. With a loaded 32-round magazine and a bayonet the weight is 10.70 lb.

Portuguese Mauser-Vergueiro 6.5mm rifle Model 1904 This is not a standard Mauser design. The bolt handle locks down in front of a split receiver bridge rather than behind it, as with most Mausers. This weapon has an overall length of 48 in., a barrel length of 29.1 in., and a weight of 8.4 lb. The staggered-column box magazine has a capacity of five rounds.

Poseidon A submarine-launched missile with about twice the payload of a Polaris A3. The Poseidon C3 is built by Lockheed and can be fired from existing Polaris launch tubes with very little modification to the tubes. It has a length of 34 ft, a launching weight of about 60,000 lb, and a range of 2,875 mi.

Posen A German battleship of 18,900 tons normal displacement completed in 1910. It had a length of 470 ft, a beam of 89 ft, a speed of 19.5 knots, and a complement of 963 men. Main armament consisted of twelve 11-in. guns, twelve 6-in. guns, and six 20-in. torpedo tubes. Sister ships (also completed in 1909–1910) included *Nassau, Rheinland,* and *Westfalen.*

position artillery Formerly, heavy artillery in fieldworks.

position defense The type of defense in which the bulk of the defending force is disposed in selected tactical localities where the decisive battle is to be fought. Principal reliance is placed on the ability of the forces in the defended localities to maintain their positions and to control the terrain between them. The reserve is used to add depth, to block, or to restore the battle position by counterattack.

position firing A method of defensive gunnery used by bombers, especially during World War II, in which definite amounts of deflection are prescribed for firing at attacking fighter planes.

post A place where a soldier is stationed, such as a place guarded or patrolled by a sentry or an outpost.

potato digger See **Colt .30 cal. machine gun M1917.**

Potez 63 Series A series of two-seat twin-engine light bombers and three-seat tactical-reconnaissance aircraft developed in France between 1935 and 1940. The 63.11

had a speed of 264 mph and was armed with up to eight 7.5mm machine guns plus four 110-lb bombs.

Potez 631 A French twin-engine two- or three-seat long-range night fighter first flown in 1936. It was powered by two 660-hp engines, flew at speeds up to 276 mph, and was armed with two forward-firing 20mm Hispano-Suiza cannons, six 7.5mm machine guns, and two flexibly mounted 7.5mm machine guns. At the time of the German invasion of France, a total of eight escadrilles were equipped with these airplanes.

potgun Formerly, a short, wide cannon formed like a pot.

Potvis and Dolfijm Similar classes of Dutch submarines of 1,494 tons standard surface displacement completed in 1960–1966. They have a submerged speed of 17 knots and a complement of 64 men and are armed with eight 21-in. torpedo tubes.

pouch A small leather bag for carrying ammunition or small implements.

pounder A term that refers to the weight, in pounds, of a projectile and is used as a measure of the size of the cannon from which it is fired. For example, a cannon firing a 6-lb projectile is called a "six-pounder."

POW Prisoner of war.

powder An explosive in powder form, that is, in small granules or grains, such as black powder or a smokeless propellant of fine granulation. No longer accepted as a general term for a propellant or propelling charge.

powder bag A propellant bag. See **powder silk.**

powder boy Formerly a boy employed on war vessels to carry powder to the guns.

powder charge The charge of powder for propelling a projectile.

powder chest An airtight box for the storage or transportation of powder.

powder flag A red flag hoisted aboard a ship when loading or carrying explosives.

powder flask A narrow-necked metal, wood, or hard leather case in which to carry gunpowder.

powderhorn A powder flask made from the horn of an animal such as an ox or a cow.

powder hoy An old naval term for an ordnance vessel expressly fitted to convey powder. It carried a distinguishing red flag, and the ships for which the powder was intended were warned to put out all fires before she came alongside.

powder keg A small barrel for storing or transporting gunpowder.

powder monkey Formerly, a powder boy on board a war vessel.

powder ring 1. A cloth bag in the shape of a ring that holds a section of the propelling charge in some types of ammuni-

tion. The number of rings used controls the strength of the charge and the range of the projectile. 2. A metal ring in which the powder train of black-powder time fuzes is loaded.

powder room A magazine or room for the storage of powder.

powder silk Also called "cartridge silk." Special silk fabric formerly used in making propellant bags. Powder silk leaves no burning residue when the propellant is burned. Silk has now been largely replaced by other materials, and the fabric is called "cartridge cloth."

powder train 1. A train, usually of compressed black powder, used to obtain time action in older fuze types. **2.** A train of explosives laid out for destruction by burning.

powered glider A modified glider having one or more engines. Usually, a powered glider performs as an ordinary powered airplane at certain loads less than maximum; with a maximum load, however, it cannot maintain air speed, and the engines serve merely to decrease its rate of descent.

PR A U.S. Navy river gunboat. (Picture, next page.)

practice ammunition Ammunition used for target practice or similar types of training. For gun- and rocket-type weapons, practice ammunition contains a propelling charge and either an inert filler or a spotting charge in the projectile. Other types of practice ammunition, such as bombs or mines, usually contain a spotting charge or some form of charge to indicate functioning.

prearranged fire Fire that is formally planned and executed against targets or target areas of known location. Such fire is usually planned well in advance and is executed at a predetermined time or during a predetermined period of time.

preassault operations Operations conducted in the objective area prior to the assault. They include reconnaissance, minesweeping, bombardment, bombing, underwater demolition, and destruction of beach obstacles.

precedence 1. In communications, a

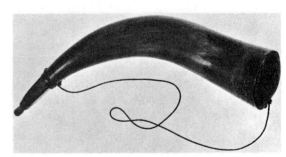

powderhorn. (*The Smithsonian Institution, National Museum Collection.*)

PR, the U.S.S. *Panay.* (*U.S. Navy.*)

designation assigned to a message by the originator to indicate to communications personnel the relative order of handling and to the addressee the order in which the message is to be noted. **2.** In reconnaissance a letter designation assigned by a unit requesting several reconnaissance missions to indicate the relative order of importance, within an established priority, of the mission requested.

precision bombing **1.** In a restricted sense, horizontal bombing done with the appropriate precision instruments and equipment so as to strike a target of comparatively small bulk or area. **2.** In a general sense (rare), any type of bombing against a small or restricted target. In sense 1, precision bombing is usually a strategic operation and is done either to achieve destruction of a target with a minimum expenditure of force or to hit a target near other areas or installations not considered desirable to hit. When the term is used in sense 2, it is usually applied to tactical attacks by dive bombers or fighter-bombers against tanks, etc.

precision fire Fire on which the center of impact is accurately placed on a limited target; fire based on precision adjustment. Usually precision fire is used to destroy enemy installations, such as gun emplacements, structures, and supply points. Pre-

pricker. (*The Smithsonian Institution, J. R. Awls Collection.*)

cision fire differs from area fire, which is directed against a general area rather than against a given objective in the area.

preemptive attack An attack initiated on the basis of incontrovertible evidence that an enemy attack is imminent.

preparation fire Fire delivered on a target or predetermined point preparatory to an assault on the target. It may be naval, ground, or air.

pre-position To place military units, equipment, or supplies at or near the point of planned use of at a designated location to reduce reaction time and to ensure timely support of a specific force during initial phases of an operation.

present arms A command which directs that a gun or other weapon be carried perpendicularly in front of the center of the body.

preset guidance A type of guidance for guided aircraft rockets or other guided missiles in which the path of the missile is determined by controls set before launching. The mechanism for this type of guidance usually consists of gyros, integrating accelerometers, and related devices.

President A class of South African antisubmarine frigates of 2,144 tons standard displacement completed in 1962–1964. They have a speed of over 30 knots, a complement of 203 men, and armament consisting of two 4.5-in. guns, two 40mm antiaircraft guns, and two Limbo three-barreled depth-charge mortars.

Presidential Unit Citation An honor accorded a unit for a distinguished combat

record.

presidio A Spanish term for a place of defense, such as a garrison or a guardhouse.

press gang Formerly, an English naval term for a party of seamen, under the command of a lieutenant, who were empowered, in time of war, to take seafaring men—on shore or afloat—and compel them to serve on board men-of-war.

pressures Pressures within a gun tube or barrel, as used in design practices.

preventive war A war initiated in the belief that military conflict, while not imminent, is inevitable and that to delay would involve greater risk.

pricker A thin, sharp tool used to clean powder residue from the touchhole or nipple of a firearm.

priestcap A type of fortification, so named because of its shape. It is also called "swallowtail."

primary blast injuries Those injuries incurred as a direct result of the pressures of the blast or shock wave.

primary gun The principal or main gun, especially of a tank or other armored vehicle.

primary target A target having the highest priority for attack.

primary weapon The principal arm of a combat unit. The rifle is the primary, or basic, weapon of an infantry rifle company, as compared with grenades or chemical projectiles, which are secondary, or auxiliary, weapons in such an organization.

prime To prepare a cannon, firearm, or other weapon for firing by providing a primer or priming.

prime mover A vehicle, including heavy construction equipment, possessing military characteristics; designed primarily for towing heavy, wheeled weapons; and frequently providing facilities for the transportation of the crew of, and ammunition for, the weapon.

primer A relatively small and sensitive initial explosive-train component which on being actuated initiates functioning of the explosive train and will not reliably initiate high-explosive charges. In general, primers are classified in accordance with the method of initiation, such as percussion, electric, friction, etc. "Primer" is also used to refer to the assembly which ignites propelling charges. The primer of a center-fire cartridge is a detonating mixture located in a small metal cup and exploded by the impact of a firing pin. In flintlock and earlier firearms the primer consisted of fine gunpowder placed in the flashpan and ignited by spark or flame.

primer cup A small cup holding a primer mixture and other components and used in small-arms cartridges and certain other ammunition.

primer detonator An element in a bomb

explosive train consisting of a primer and detonator combined and often incorporating a delaying element.

primer seat A chamber in the breech mechanism of a gun that uses separate-loading ammunition and into which the primer is set.

priming flask, priming horn A container for priming powder, usually finer-grained than the propellant charge, used to prime the pan or vent of prepercussion muzzle-loading shoulder arms and artillery.

priming wire A pointed wire once used to penetrate the vent of a piece and pierce the cartridge before priming.

principes The second line in the order of battle of a Roman army.

priority With reference to war plans and the tasks derived therefrom, an indication of relative importance rather than an exclusive and final designation of the order of accomplishment.

priority message A category of precedence reserved for messages which require expeditious action by the addressee or which furnish essential information for the conduct of operations in progress when routine precedence will not suffice.

prisoner-of-war cage A temporary construction, building, or enclosed area to which prisoners of war are evacuated for interrogation and temporary detention pending further evacuation.

prisoner-of-war camp A camp of a semi-permanent nature established in the communication zone, or zone of interior (home country), for the internment and complete administration of prisoners of war. It may be located on, or be independent of, other military installations.

prisoner-of-war collecting point A designated locality in a forward battle area where prisoners are assembled, pending local examination for information of immediate tactical value and subsequent evacuation.

prisoners of war Persons as defined in the Geneva convention relative to the treatment of prisoners of war (August 12, 1949, Part I, Article 4).

private A soldier below the grade of a noncommissioned officer.

Private A and Private F Solid-propellant rockets developed in 1944 and 1945; early missiles leading to the development of the WAC Corporal.

privateer Armed private vessels employed against enemy warships. Their use was abolished by the Declaration of Paris in April 1856.

Privateer See **Liberator.**

private, first class An enlisted man next below a corporal and above a private.

privy coat A light coat of mail worn under ordinary dress.

prize A merchant vessel captured during

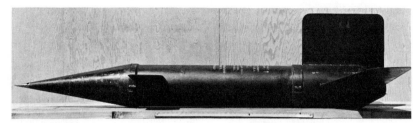

Private F. (*U.S. Army.*)

wartime and retained for legal prize proceedings.

prize crew A contingent of officers and men put aboard a captured ship.

prize master The officer placed in command of the prize to bring it into a port. He is provided with a prize crew.

prize money At one time, the proceeds of a captured vessel divided among officers and men of the capturing ship. Also, a sum awarded officers and men who participated in the destruction of an enemy vessel. No prize money of this type has been awarded by the U.S. Navy since March 3, 1899, when the practice was abolished by an act of Congress.

probably destroyed (aircraft) A damage assessment of an enemy aircraft seen to break off combat in circumstances which lead to the conclusion that it must be a loss, even though it is not actually seen to crash.

proclamation A document published to the inhabitants of an area which sets forth the basis of authority and scope of activities of a commander in a given area and which defines the obligations, liabilities, duties, and rights of the population affected.

prod, prodd A light crossbow with a double bowstring and a small central pouch used to shoot stones or bullets instead of quarrels.

production model A finished airplane or other object produced using particular production techniques. This term is applied especially to the first object to be turned out by a particular method of production, which serves as an example of the objects that will follow it. It differs from a prototype in that the latter is not necessarily, and usually is not, made by the same methods as those used in producing the objects that follow it.

program torpedo A torpedo that is designed to follow a preplanned course.

Project Anvil The code name for the Allied invasion of Southern France in August 1944.

projectile An object projected by an applied exterior force and continuing in motion by virtue of its own inertia, such as a bullet, bomb, shell, or grenade. Also applied to rockets and to guided missiles.

projectile cart A manually propelled two-wheeled vehicle used for transporting pro-

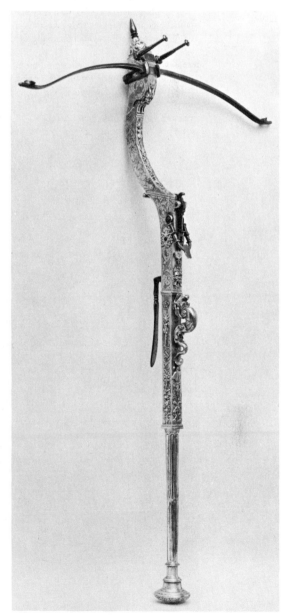

prod. (*The Metropolitan Museum of Art, Rogers Fund, 1965.*)

jectiles to a cannon.

projectile flat Storage space for projectiles in a turret.

projectile hoist A mechanism for lifting projectiles from a storage space or a projectile cart to guns.

projectile tracer A cylindrical item designed to contain tracer composition for the purpose of observation of fire. The projectile is equipped with the tracer element in its base. In most small-caliber antiaircraft projectiles, the tracer is used to ignite the filler and destroy the projectile should it miss the target.

projector **1.** In general, any apparatus for launching a projectile, such as a gun or rocket launcher. **2.** A smoothbore-type barrel or other unrifled weapon from which pyrotechnic signals, grenades, and certain mortar projectiles are fired. **3.** A rack for launching target rockets. **4.** A special type of gun for projecting antisubmarine projectiles.

Project Overlord The code name for the invasion of Normandy on June 6, 1944, by American, British, Canadian, and French forces.

proking spit A large Spanish rapier.

proof A ballistic test of weapons or ammunition to determine suitability. For propellants, proof also includes chemical and stability tests. For armor, it includes a test to indicate resistance to bullets. In the late sixteenth and throughout the seventeenth centuries, heavy breastplates were classed as pistol-proof or musket-proof.

proof charge A propellant charge used in the initial firing tests of a gun. For test purposes, it may sometimes exceed normal pressures intended for use in the gun.

proof dent The dent in a breastplate made by a bullet when the breastplate was tested to see whether it would withstand a musket shot.

proof firing The firing of certain rounds for the purpose of testing the serviceability of a weapon or its mounts.

proofmark A distinguishing mark on a weapon to indicate inspection and proof firing.

propaganda Any form of communication in support of national objectives designed to influence the opinions, emotions, attitudes, or behavior of any group in order to benefit the sponsor either directly or indirectly.

propellant That which provides the energy for propelling something. Specifically, an explosive charge for propelling a bullet, shell, or the like. Also, a fuel, either solid or liquid, for propelling a rocket or missile.

propellant bag A fabric container that holds the propelling charge for separate-loading or semifixed ammunition. It is usually made of cartridge cloth, a special fabric that is consumed without leaving a burning residue.

protective clothing Specially constructed or chemically treated clothing to protect individuals against liquid blister gas and blister-gas vapor and against certain biological agents. It includes permeable protective clothing and impermeable protective clothing.

protective deck A deck fitted with armor.

protective fire Fire delivered by supporting guns and directed against the enemy to hinder his fire or movement against friendly forces.

protective minefield A minefield employed to assist a unit in its local, close-in protection.

protectoscope A device in a tank or armored car, for example, similar to the periscope of a submarine. It enables a soldier to see around a shield without exposing himself to enemy gunfire directed at the ports of the tank or armored car.

prototype The first complete and working member of a class. The term is especially applied to the first aircraft made of a given model or model series or to the first specimen of a class of weapons or any other piece of equipment, such member or specimen serving, or intended to serve, as the pattern or guide for subsequently produced members of the same class.

Provider The Fairchild C-123 Provider is a twin-engine assault transport developed for the USAF and first flown in 1954. The C-123K version has two jet engines added to provide STOL performance. It has a speed of 173 mph and a range of 1,035 mi and can carry 61 troops.

proving ground An area or location where equipment, ammunition, or weapons are tested, or proved.

provost marshal An officer at a command or subordinate level who advises on, and exercises supervision and inspection over, the maintenance of discipline, the enforcement of security, and the confinement of prisoners.

proximity fuze A fuze designed to function under the influence of a target when close to or at the target. Also called an "influence fuze." It may be used to detonate a projectile, bomb, mine, or charge. Proximity fuzes may incorporate photoelectric cells, radar devices, or other devices as activating elements. The variable-time fuze is one type of proximity fuze.

PS The abbreviation for "passenger aircraft" (*Passazhirskii samolyot*) used in the

projectile hoist, seen raising the 600-lb projectile for a U.S. 280mm gun. (*U.S. Army.*)

names of Russian aircraft from 1925 to 1945, as in PS-84.

PSB A U.S. Navy port security boat, reserve.

psychological operations These operations include psychological warfare and, in addition, encompass those political, military, economic, and ideological actions planned and conducted to create in neutral or friendly foreign groups the emotions, attitudes, or behavior necessary to support the achievement of national objectives.

psychological warfare The planned use of propaganda and other psychological actions with the primary purpose of influencing the opinions, emotions, attitudes, and behavior of hostile foreign groups in such a way as to engender their support of the achievement of national objectives.

PT A U.S. Navy motor torpedo boat.

PT1 A mixture of magnesium with gasoline and other petroleum products thickened with isobutyl methacrylates and used in incendiary bombs.

PT boats A class of motor torpedo boats used by the United States during World War II. A total of 774 boats were completed, of which 70 were war losses. They had a standard displacement of 33 tons, a length of 80 ft, a beam of 20 ft, a draft of 5 ft, and a complement of 14 men. They were armed with one 40mm antiaircraft gun, two 20mm antiaircraft guns, and four torpedo tubes. They could make a speed of 41 knots.

PTC A U.S. Navy motorboat subchaser.

PTF A U.S. Navy fast patrol boat.

Puff Ball The NATO code name for a type of Soviet airborne I-band radar.

Puffin A U.S. Navy winged and fin-stabilized flying torpedo of World War II. It had a range of 10 to 20 mi and carried a 500-lb warhead.

Puff, the Magic Dragon See **Skytrain.**

pugio The short dagger carried by Roman legionnaires. It was carried on the left side, while the gladius was carried on the right.

pulse-jet A jet-propulsion engine, containing neither compressor nor turbine. Equipped with valves in the front which open and shut, it takes in air to create thrust in rapid periodic bursts rather than continuously.

Puma The French Sud-Aviation SA 330 Puma is a twin-engine assault helicopter developed by Sud-Aviation (France) and Westland (UK) and first flown in 1965. It has a speed of 165 mph and carries 16 troops.

Punchbowl A military name for a circular mountain-rimmed valley northeast of Yangu, Korea. It was the scene of military activity during the Korean conflict.

Purple Heart A U.S. decoration awarded to members of the armed forces and to civilians serving with the armed forces who

projector, for the Bofors 375mm antisubmarine rocket. (*A. B. Bofors.*)

PT boat. (*U.S. Navy.*)

PTF. (*U.S. Navy.*)

pusher, the Savoia S.16 Ter. (*Siai Marchetti.*)

PZL P.11. (*Defense Ministry, Polish People's Republic.*)

are wounded in action against an enemy of the United States. The Purple Heart was established by Gen. George Washington in 1782. It originally consisted of a heart-shaped piece of purple cloth edged with lace and was given for valor. The decoration later fell into disuse but was reestablished in 1932 as a bronze, enameled medal.

pusher Short for "pusher airplane," an airplane propelled by a pusher propeller or pusher propellers. The example shown is the Savoia S.16 Ter, an Italian amphibious reconnaissance bomber of 1919.

Puteaux 8mm machine gun Model 1905 A French gas-operated air-cooled machine gun with a rate of fire of 650 rounds per minute. It weighed 54 lb and was fed from a 25-round strip. It was issued to French troops in 1906, but was never as popular as the standard Hotchkiss. It was relegated

to reserve units and fortification, the latter giving rise to the erroneous designation "Fortification Model."

Puteaux 37mm aircraft cannon A French development of World War I, this weapon was a recoil-operated air-cooled cannon with a rate of fire of 60 rounds per minute. It weighed 198.5 lb and was fed from a five-round magazine. This weapon was fitted with two types of interchangeable barrels, a smoothbore and a rifled barrel. The smoothbore fired canister shot (and was actually an overgrown shotgun).

PV-1 See **Ventura.**

PV-2 See **Harpoon.**

PW White phosphorus, a standard filling for smoke bombs. Particles of white phosphorus ignite spontaneously by atmospheric oxygen and produce a dense white smoke.

PY A U.S. Navy patrol vessel–converted

yacht.

PYC A U.S. Navy patrol vessel–converted yacht, coastal.

pyrgi Greek movable towers on wheels used to scale the walls of besieged towns.

pyrotechnic code A significant arrangement of various colors and configurations of fireworks, signal lights, or signal smokes used for communication between units or between ground and air.

pyrotechnic pistol A pistol for firing flares or other firework signals.

pyrotechnics Ammunition, flares, or fireworks used for signaling, illuminating, or marking targets.

PzJäg The abbreviation for *Panzerjäger,* German for "self-propelled antitank gun" or "self-propelled tank hunter."

PzKpfw The abbreviation for *Panzerkampfwagen,* German for "tank."

PzKpfw I See **German tank, light PzKpfw I.**

PzKpfw II See **German tank, light, PzKpfw II.**

PzKpfw III See **German tank, medium, PzKpfw III.**

PzKpfw IV See **German tank, medium, PzKpfw IV.**

PzKpfw V See **Panther tank.**

PzKpfw VI See **Tiger tank.**

PzKpfw 38(t) See **German tank, TNHP, PzKpfw 38(t).**

PZL P.11 A Polish single-seat single-engine high-wing monoplane fighter-interceptor and fighter-bomber first flown in 1931. It was armed with four 7.7mm machine guns, two in the fuselage and two in the wing. It had a maximum speed of 242 mph.

PZL P.24 A Polish aircraft with most of the features of the PZL P.11, but built for export to such countries as Turkey, Bulgaria, Greece, and Rumania. It flew at speeds of 267 mph and was armed with two 20mm cannons and two 7.7mm machine guns, plus two 55-lb or 110-lb bombs. It, like the P.11, was virtually obsolete by the beginning of World War II.

PzSpähw The abbreviation for *Panzerspähwagen,* German for "armored reconnaissance car."

Q

Q boats Small Japanese plywood boats used during World War II. They carried two depth charges, which were released close to Allied ships (usually causing the death of the Japanese pilot).

QFB A U.S. Navy quiet, fast boat.

QH-50 See **drone antisubmarine helicopter (DASH).**

Q ship A disguised man-of-war used to decoy enemy submarines or merchant raiders. Originally a class of ships built in England during World War I and given the classification letter Q by the British Navy. They were also called "mystery ships" or "decoy ships." See also **Raider Cruisers.**

Q train The designation for a World War II German Flak train consisting of freight wagons which contained dozens of antiaircraft guns concealed in collapsible car bodies. They were used to fire on aircraft which followed railway tracks to targets (such as in the **Tidalwave** raid, which see, against Ploesti, Rumania, in August 1943).

quad mount Another name for the U.S. .50 cal. multiple machine-gun mount M55. It was developed during World War II and consisted of four heavy-barreled .50 cal. machine guns mounted in a power-operated turret.

Quail An air-launched decoy missile carried internally in the B-52 and used to degrade the effectiveness of enemy radar, interceptor aircraft, air-defense missiles, etc.

Designated as ADM-20, it has a length of 12.9 ft, a diameter of 2.5 ft, a launching weight of 1,230 lb, and a range of 345 mi.

Quaker guns Dummy pieces of ordnance made to resemble real artillery and used to deceive an enemy.

quarrel Specifically, a square-headed bolt or arrow shot from a crossbow or arbalest. In general use, any arrow fired by a crossbow.

quarter block See **block.**

quartermaster A staff officer of an army unit or post who is responsible for furnishing food, clothing, and certain other supplies and services.

quarters Lodgings or accommodations for one or more military persons.

quarterstaff A stout staff about 6 ft long, often shod with iron at both ends. It was so called because it was wielded with one

quad mount, the U.S. M-55 multiple antiaircraft missile. (*U.S. Army.*)

Queen Elizabeth. (*The Imperial War Museum.*)

Quonset hut. (*U.S. Army.*)

quillon. (*The Smithsonian Institution, C. Summerall Collection.*)

hand in the middle and the other between the middle and one end.

quay A wharf.

Queen A class of British 15,000-ton battleships completed in 1904. It and a sister ship, *Prince of Wales,* had a length of 430 ft, a complement of 750 men, and main armament consisting of four 12-in. guns and twelve 6-in. guns, plus four 18-in. torpedo tubes. They had a speed of 18 knots.

Queen Elizabeth A class of British battleships of about 31,000 tons standard displacement completed in 1913–1915. The class included *Queen Elizabeth, Warspite, Valiant, Malaya,* and *Barham.* They had an overall length of about 640 ft, a beam of 104 ft, a speed of 24 to 25 knots (after modernization in the mid-1930s), and a complement of 1,124 to 1,184 men. Their armament consisted of eight 15-in. guns, eight six-in. guns (twelve 6-in. guns on *Barham* and *Malaya*), eight 4-in. guns, and four 3-pounder guns, plus four aircraft.

Queen Mary A British 27,000-ton battle cruiser completed in 1914. It had one sister ship, *Tiger,* and they had a length of 725 ft and were armed with eight 13.5-in. guns, sixteen 4-in. guns, and three 21-in. torpedo tubes. They had a speed of 33 knots. In the Battle of Jutland in May 1916, the *Queen Mary* blew up after being hit in her main magazine.

Quick Look A Mohawk OV-1C aircraft carrying an electronic intelligence (ELINT) system. It is used in flights along the western edges of Warsaw Pact borders to keep tabs on radar activity.

quick match A fast-burning fuse made from a cord impregnated with black powder and alcohol.

Quicksilver A World War II deception scheme conducted by the Allies to mislead the Germans about the size and location of units in Operation Overlord and to make them believe that an attack on Pas de Calais, France, was being mounted.

quick time In the U.S. Army, a rate of marching in which 120 steps, each 30 in. in length, are taken per minute. In the British Army the steps are 33 in. in length.

quillon In sword and dagger guards, the element formed by a straight or recurved bar set at the base of the grip in the plane of the blade.

quilted armor Armor made from several thicknesses of cloth or quilted cloth and quite commonly used in Europe in the fourteenth century. It was also popular among Spanish explorers in America, who copied a form worn by the Aztecs.

quinquereme An ancient vessel with five banks of oars and carrying, according to Polybius, 300 seamen and 120 soldiers.

quiver A case or sheath for arrows.

quoin A wedge placed under the breech of a gun to elevate or depress it.

Quonset (Quonset hut) A half-cylindrical prefabricated structure of metal used to house personnel and as a warehouse or for other purposes. The Quonset hut is a modification of the Nissen hut.

R

R **1.** The abbreviation for "rigid," used in the names of certain airships, as in ZR-1, RS.1, R-34, etc. **2.** The abbreviation for "reconnaissance" (*Razvedchick*), used in the names of Russian aircraft from 1925 to 1945, as in R-6, R-10, etc.

R-422B3 A French Navy surface-to-air missile with a range of about 60 nautical miles.

R-440 See **Crotale.**

R-511 A French Engin Matra-produced air-to-air missile with a length of 10.5 ft, a diameter of 0.9 ft, and a range of 4+ miles. It utilizes semiactive radar homing.

R-530 A French Engin Matra-produced air-to-air missile with a length of 11.2 ft, a diameter of 0.9 ft, and a range of 6+ mi. It utilizes infrared and radar homing and is a follow-on to the R-511.

rabinet, robinet A small, obsolete piece of ordnance that weighed 300 lb and fired a ball about 1⅜ in. in diameter.

racer A turntable to which the chassis of a coast-artillery mount was secured and which was used for traversing the gun.

rack **1.** Short for "bomb rack." **2.** A frame holding two or more antiaircraft guns together to form a single weapon. **3.** A framework aboard ship from which depth charges are dropped. **4.** A slang term for "bunk" or "bed."

rad **1.** A unit of absorbed dose of radiation. It represents the absorption of 100 ergs of nuclear (or ionizing) radiation per gram of the absorbing material or tissue. **2.** On a ring sight, the space between two concentric circles, used to indicate both range of target and deflection of fire. A rad is equal to a 35-mil angle.

radar **1.** Any of certain methods or systems of using beamed and reflected radio-frequency energy (radio waves) for detecting and locating objects, for measuring distance or altitude, or for certain other purposes, such as navigating, homing, or bombing. **2.** The electronic equipment, sets, or devices used in any such system. The term derives from the words "*ra*dio *d*etection *and ra*nging."

radar bombing Any type of bombing in which radar is used to locate the target or aiming point or to aid in positioning the bombing aircraft at the proper release point for bombing, especially under conditions of poor visibility.

radar bombsight An airborne radar set used to sight the target, solve the bombing problem, and drop bombs.

radar clutter Unwanted signals, echoes, or images on the face of the display tube which interfere with observation of desired signals.

radar coverage The limits within which objects can be detected by one or more radar stations.

radar fire Gunfire aimed at a target which is tracked by radar.

radar frequencies The following are radar-band types, frequencies, and typical applications: (1) *L-band* (1,400 megahertz): Used for early-warning systems. (2) *S-band* (3,000 megahertz): Used for search, fighter direction, and missile acquisition. (3) *X-band* (10,000 megahertz): Used for gun laying, ground-to-air missile tracking, and ground-to-air missile guidance. (4) *KU-band* (14,000 megahertz): Used for airborne search, air-to-air missile tracking, air-to-air missile guidance, and blind bombing. (5) *KA-band* (35,000 megahertz): Used for airport ground surveillance, mortar locating, and mapping and reconnaissance.

radar gunlayer A radar device which tracks a target and aims a gun or guns automatically.

radar picket Any ship, aircraft, or vehicle stationed at a distance from the force protected for the purpose of increasing the radar-detection range.

radar picket escort ship A U.S. Navy escort ship modified to increase combat-information-center, electronic-countermeasure, and electronic-search facilities. Designated DER. (Picture, next page.)

radarscope The cathode-ray oscilloscope or screen in a radar set.

radar silence An imposed discipline prohibiting the transmission by radar of electromagnetic signals on some or all fre-

radar picket escort ship, the U.S.S. *Thomas* (DER-326). (*U.S. Navy.*)

quencies.

radial engine **1.** An engine with one or more stationary rows of cylinders arranged radially around a common crankshaft. **2.** In a more general sense, any engine having the cylinders arranged radially around the crankshaft.

radiated noise Underwater sound energy emitted by ships, submarines, and torpedoes.

radiation dose The total amount of ionizing radiation absorbed by material or tissues, commonly expressed in rads. The term "radiation dose" is often used in the sense of the exposure dose expressed in roentgens, which are a measure of the total amount of ionization that the quantity of radiation could produce in the air. This should be distinguished from the absorbed dose, also given in rads, which represents the energy absorbed from the radiation per gram of specified body tissue. Further, the biological dose, in rems, is a measure of the biological effectiveness of the radiation exposure.

radiation intensity (RI) The radiation-dose rate at a given time and place. It may be coupled with a figure to denote the radiation intensity at a given number of hours after a nuclear burst; e.g., RI3 is the radiation intensity 3 hours after the time of burst.

radiation sickness An illness resulting from excessive exposure to ionizing radiation. The earliest symptoms are nausea, vomiting, and diarrhea, which may be followed by loss of hair, hemorrhage, inflammation of the mouth and throat, and general loss of energy.

radioactivity The spontaneous emission of radiation, generally alpha or beta particles, often accompanied by gamma rays, from the nuclei of an unstable isotope.

radio beacon A radio transmitter which emits a distinctive or characteristic signal used for the determination of bearings,

courses, or location.

radio bomb A bomb provided with a radio bomb fuze.

radio bomb fuze An electronic bomb fuze that works in reaction to radio (i.e., radar) waves reflected from the target. This type of fuze may be set to detonate at any desired distance from the ground by use of the Doppler effect.

radio control A guidance system that uses radio-frequency energy to activate certain mechanisms or systems.

radio countermeasures (RCM) Actions taken to reduce the effectiveness of enemy radio.

radio deception The employment of radio to deceive the enemy. Radio deception includes sending false dispatches, using deceptive headings, employing enemy call signs, etc.

radio direction finder (RDF) A radio receiver with a directional antenna to determine bearings of radio signals.

radio fix **1.** The location of a friendly or enemy radio transmitter determined by finding the direction of the radio transmitter from two or more listening stations. **2.** The location of a ship or aircraft determined by finding the direction of radio signals coming to the ship or aircraft from two or more sending stations, the locations of which are known.

radio guard A ship, aircraft, or radio station designated to listen for and record transmissions and to handle traffic on a designated frequency for a certain unit or units.

radio-guided bomb A bomb, such as the azon bomb, guided by radio control from outside the missile.

radiological defense The means taken to minimize and control damage from radioactivity.

radiological warfare The employment of agents or weapons to produce residual radioactive contamination, as distinguished

from the initial effects of a nuclear explosion (blast, thermal, and initial nuclear radiation).

radio proximity fuze A proximity fuze that uses a radar antenna, the echoes triggering detonation at the right instant.

radio range finding Radio location in which the distance of an object is determined by means of its radio emissions, whether independent, reflected, or retransmitted on the same or other wavelength.

radio silence A period during which all or certain radio equipment capable of radiation is kept inoperative.

radio sonobuoy See **sonobuoy.**

radius of action The maximum distance a ship, aircraft, or vehicle can travel away from its base along a given course with normal combat load and return without refueling, allowing for all safety and operating factors.

radius of safety In reference to an atomic explosion, the horizontal distance from ground zero beyond which the weapon's effects on friendly troops are acceptable.

Radom 9mm Parabellum automatic pistol Model 35 A Polish variant of the original Browning-Colt Government Model 1911 automatic pistol. It was produced at the Radom arsenal in Poland. The pistol was used extensively by the Germans in World War II and was referred to as the "P.35." The overall length is 7.8 in., with a barrel length of 4.7 in. and a weight of 2.25 lb. It has a magazine capacity of eight cartridges.

radome A dome which encloses an antenna. It is specifically designed to permit maximum passage of radio-frequency energy through it, while providing protection to the antenna from weather.

RAF **Royal Air Force,** which see.

rafale A French expression of World War I to describe the massed fire of 75mm guns loaded with shrapnel. The French 75mm gun, Model 1897, fired a 16-lb shrapnel shell containing 300 lead balls weighing 12 grams each.

raid An operation, usually on a small scale, involving a swift penetration of hostile territory to secure information, to confuse the enemy, or to destroy enemy installations. It ends with a planned withdrawal upon completion of the assigned mission.

Raider Cruisers A class of ships developed by Germany for employment during World War II. They were essentially merchant ships converted to auxiliary cruisers with heavy concealed armament. Nine ships of this type were produced, the most successful of which was the *Atlantis*. It was a ship of 7,862 tons displacement and had a length of 488 ft, a beam of 61 ft, a speed of 16 knots, and a crew of 350 men. It was armed with six 5.9-in. and one 3-in. guns, plus two 37mm and two 20mm antiaircraft guns. It also carried four 21-in. torpedo tubes, two aircraft, and 92 mines. In a 622-day voyage it sank 22 ships totaling 145,697 tons.

railhead A point or place along a railroad line where supplies are unloaded for distribution or storage.

raillon A quarrel or short arrow.

Rail Rooter A German device to pull up railroad tracks. See also **Big Hook.**

railway artillery Heavy artillery given mobility by mounting on railway mounts or carriages. It is no longer in use by U.S. forces.

railway mount, railway carriage Railway mounts are classified, according to the method of absorbing recoil energy, as sliding mounts, rolling mounts, or platform mounts. In the first two types there is no recoil system, and the energy is absorbed by sliding or rolling with the brakes set. The platform mount is equipped with a recoil system and remains in place without movement.

Rain A class of Japanese antiaircraft destroyers of 1,800 tons standard displacement completed in 1959. They have a speed of 30 knots, a complement of 250 men, and armament consisting of three 5-in. guns, four 3-in. antiaircraft guns, tubes for short homing torpedoes, one hedgehog, a depth-charge rack, and one Y-gun.

Rainbow Division In World War I, a division (the Forty-second) composed of National Guard units from various parts of the United States.

rain cap A protective shield on artillery projectiles to desensitize the point-detonating fuze element while the projectile is in flight.

rainout Radioactive material in the atmosphere brought down by precipitation.

rake To sweep a target, especially a ship or a column of troops, with gunfire or cannon fire. Hence, raking fire. To enfilade.

Rakete M-1966 A German (Federal Republic) guided-weapon launcher developed in 1959–1960 and in service since 1963. It has a crew of four, a weight of 23 tons, a

Radom 9mm Parabellum automatic pistol Model 35. (*Defense Ministry, Polish People's Republic.*)

radome, carried by a U.S. Grumman Tracker. (*U.S. Navy.*)

road speed of 43 mph, and armament consisting of two SS-11 launchers and two 7.62mm machine guns. It carries a total of 14 SS-11 missiles (which have a maximum antitank range of 3,200 meters).

ram 1. The forward motion of an air scoop or air inlet through the air. **2.** To seat a projectile in the bore of a gun.

Ram A U.S. Navy rocket fired from airplanes during the Korean conflict. It was an antitank weapon and was equipped with a shaped charge.

rambade An elevated platform built across the prow of a galley and used for boarding.

ram bow A subsurface bow extension formerly used on certain warships to pierce

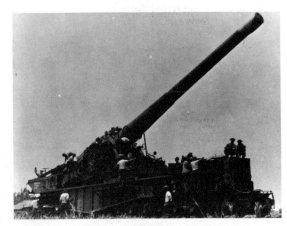

railway artillary, a U.S. 14-in. railroad gun. (*U.S. Army.*)

Rain. (*Japan Defense Agency.*)

ramp, showing a U.S. Navy FYU, yard freight utility boat. (*U.S. Navy.*)

rampart gun. (*The Metropolitan Museum of Art, Bashford Dean Memorial Collection.*)

the hull of an enemy vessel.

Ramillies A British battleship of the **Royal Sovereign** class, which see.

ramjet A jet-propulsion engine which contains neither compressor nor turbine and which depends for its operation on the air compression accomplished by the forward motion of the engine.

rammer The part of a gun mechanism that seats the projectile. It may be hand- or power-operated.

ramp 1. The hinged forward section of a landing ship or craft over which its cargo is unloaded when the craft is beached.

2. In fortifications, any inclined plane serving as a way between different interior levels.

rampart A broad embankment around a fortified place on which the parapet is raised. It is built immediately inside the ditch, often largely from earth taken from it. A rampart forms the *enceinte*, or body, of the place.

rampart grenade A large grenade thrown from the ramparts at attackers.

rampart gun A large gun fitted for rampart use and not used for field purposes.

ramp sight A type of metallic sight in

which the aperture is raised or lowered by moving it forward or backward on an inclined ramp.

ramrod The metal or wooden rod used to ram home the charge in muzzle-loading firearms. The term now refers chiefly to a cleaning rod for small arms.

ramrod pipes The short metal tubes which carry the ramrod under the stock when not in use.

R&R See **rest and recuperation.**

Randy The code name for the Kawasaki Ki.102 twin-engine two-seat attack fighter built for the Japanese Army Air Force and first flown in March 1944. It featured an armament system consisting of one 57mm cannon, two 20mm cannons, and one 12.7mm machine gun, plus a 1,100-lb bombload. It flew at speeds up to 360 mph.

range 1. The distance between any given point and an object or target. **2.** The extent or distance limiting the operation or action of something, such as the range of an aircraft, ship, or gun. **3.** The distance which can be covered over a hard surface by a ground vehicle, with its rated payload, using the fuel in its tank and in cans normally carried as part of the ground-vehicle equipment. **4.** An area equipped for practice in shooting at targets. In this meaning, also called "target range."

range angle The angle between the aircraft-target line and the vertical line from the aircraft to the ground at the instant a bomb is released. Also called "dropping angle."

range calibration The adjustment of a radar set so that when "on target," the radar set will indicate the correct range.

range correction A change of firing data necessary to allow for deviations of range

Ranger. (*U.S. Navy.*)

due to variations in weather, in materiel, or ammunition.

range-correction board A device with which the correction to be applied to a gun is computed mechanically. The correction that is obtained allows for all nonstandard conditions, such as variations in weather and ammunition, and is known as the "ballistic correction."

range determination The process of finding the distance between a gun and a target, usually by firing the gun, by estimating with the eye, by using a range-finding instrument, or by plotting.

range deviation The distance by which a projectile strikes beyond, or short of, the target. It is the distance as measured along the gun-target line or along a line parallel to the gun-target line.

range difference The difference between the ranges from any two points to a third point; especially, the difference between the ranges of a target from two different guns.

range finder An instrument used to measure range or distance to the target. Optical range finders are of either the stereoscopic or the coincidence type. Radar provides the most accurate range finding.

range ladder A naval term for a method of adjusting gunfire by firing successive volleys, starting with a range which is assuredly over or short and applying small, uniform range corrections to the successive volleys until the target is crossed.

ranger A soldier belonging to a specially selected group of soldiers in the U.S. Army, trained especially in raiding tactics. The British equivalent is a commando.

Ranger A U.S. aircraft carrier completed in 1933. It had a displacement of 14,500 tons, a length of 769 ft, a speed of about 30 knots, and a complement of 1,788 men. It carried about 80 aircraft.

range spotting Watching the burst or impact of shots to note their deviation beyond, or short of, the target.

range table A prepared table that gives elevations corresponding to ranges for a gun or other weapon under various conditions. A range table is part of a firing table.

ranging 1. Wide-scale scouting, especially by aircraft, designed to search an area systematically. 2. Locating an enemy gun by watching its flash, listening to its report, or using other, similar means. 3. Any process of establishing target distance, such as echo ranging, intermittent ranging, manual ranging, navigational ranging, explosive-echo ranging, optical ranging, radar ranging, etc.

rankling arrow An arrow with a loose barbed head that remains in the wound when the arrow is extracted.

RAP 14 A French short- to medium-range unguided spin-stabilized ground-to-ground artillery rocket system. The launcher holds 21 rockets, and they may be fired singly or in salvos of 7, 14, or 21. The individual rockets are of 138mm and have a length of 6.5 ft, a weight of 114 lb, and a range of about 9 mi.

rapid fire A rate of firing small-arms or automatic weapons that is faster than slow fire but slower than quick fire.

rapier A sword, particularly of the sixteenth and seventeenth centuries, with a long, narrow double-edged blade and a short grip. It was used chiefly for thrusting.

Rapier A low-level antiaircraft guided-weapon system produced by the British Aircraft Corporation for the British Army and the RAF. It has an overall length of 7.4 ft and a diameter of 6 in.

Rarden 30mm cannon A British weapon developed for vehicle armament and presently in service with the British Army. It has a length of 9 ft 9 in., a weight of 200 lb, and a range of about 10,000 meters. It is capable of firing automatically at a cyclic rate of about 120 rounds per minute. Since the gun holds two 3-round clips, any sustained burst would be limited to six rounds.

Rascal Formerly (1959), a U.S. Air Force guided aircraft missile. It was 32 ft in length and 4 ft in diameter and weighed about 13,000 lb. It was liquid-rocket-propelled and had a range of over 100 mi at a speed of about Mach 2.5.

Rast-Gasser 8mm (Gasser) revolver Model 1898 The earliest model of this basic revolver was introduced in 1870 for an 11.2mm black-powder cartridge. In the 1880s a 9mm version was produced, also with black powder. The Model 1898 (8mm) has a cylinder capacity of eight cartridges, an overall length of 9 in., a barrel length of 4½ in., and a total weight of 33 oz. It was used by the Austrians in World War I, during which considerable numbers of them were captured by the Italians. The Italians used these revolvers in World War II. They have a muzzle velocity of about 787 fps.

Rat A U.S. Navy *rocket-assisted torpedo.

rate of fire The number of rounds fired per weapon per minute.

rate of march The average number of miles or kilometers to be traveled in a given period of time, including all ordered halts. It is expressed in miles or kilometers per hour.

ration An allowance of provisions, especially food, for one person for one day.

RATO 1. A takeoff assist by an auxiliary rocket unit or units. 2. The auxiliary rocket unit or group of units used in such a takeoff. RATO is preferred to JATO (jet-assisted takeoff) when applied to a takeoff assist by a RATO unit.

ravelin In fortifications, formerly called a "demilune" or "half-moon." This is a detached work with two embankments that is raised before the curtain across the ditch at the top of the counterscarp of the place. It is intended to protect the space between two bastions.

Raven 1. A U.S. Navy long-range air-to-surface antisubmarine-warfare missile. 2. A British solid-propellant booster.

razon Range plus **azon,** which see. A kind of glide bomb having movable control surfaces in the tail adjusted by radio signals to control the bomb in range and in azimuth. Hence, razon bomb.

RB 08A A Swedish surface-to-surface long-range cruise missile developed for coastal-defense and ship-to-ship use. It has a wingspan of 10 ft, a length of 19 ft, and a total launching weight of 2,673 lb. It entered service with the Swedish forces in 1967.

R Class 1. A class of Soviet medium-range submarines with a standard surface displacement of 1,100 tons developed in the early 1960s. They have a length of 246 ft, a beam of 24 ft, a speed of 15 knots submerged, and a complement of 65 men.

RB 08A. (*Swedish Defense Staff.*)

R.E.8. (*The Imperial War Museum.*)

They are armed with six 21-in. torpedo tubes. **2.** A class of U.S. submarines commissioned in 1918–1919. They were armed with four 18-in. torpedo tubes and one 3-in. deck gun. They had a complement of 31 men and a submerged speed of 10 knots.

RCM See **radio countermeasures.**

RCN Royal Canadian Navy.

RCT Regimental Combat Team, a regiment of troops specially organized for an amphibious landing.

RDF See **radio direction finder.**

RDX **1.** Cyclonite. **2.** Any compound containing cyclonite. It is so called from British "*Research Department Formula X.*"

R.E.5 A British two-place single-engine reconnaissance biplane first flown in 1914. It was the first of the reconnaissance experimental biplanes produced by the Royal Aircraft Factory. Protected only by small arms in the hands of the observer, the aircraft flew at a maximum speed of 78 mph and could carry a bombload of 60 lb. Because of its slow speed and lack of maneuverability, its operational career was short-lived.

R.E.7 A modified R.E.5 designed to carry a newly designed 336-lb (152.4-kg) bomb. Deliveries of the aircraft began in late 1915, and some 200 were produced in all. They were used in France as reconnaissance aircraft and were not employed in the bombing role until mid-1916.

R.E.8 A British two-seat single-engine biplane in production in August 1916. The most widely used British two-seater on the Western front, some 4,099 were produced for such duties as observation, reconnaissance, ground-support patrols, ground attack, and night bombing. They had a speed of 102 mph and were armed with a synchronized front-firing Vickers gun and a ring-mounted Lewis gun in the rear cockpit. They carried a bombload of about 224 lb.

reaction time **1.** The elapsed time between the initiation of an action and the required response. **2.** The time required between the receipt of an order directing

an operation and the arrival of the initial element of the force concerned in the designated area.

ready **1.** The report made by a gun station when enough men are there to fire the guns. **2.** A position in the manual of arms or artillery drill at which the piece is cocked or otherwise made ready for immediate firing.

ready position (helicopter) A designated place where a number of paratroopers wait for the order to emplane in a helicopter.

ready service ammunition Ammunition at the gun and ready for use.

real time The absence of delay in acquisition, transmission, and reception of data.

rear admiral In the U.S. Navy, the rank next above a commodore and next below a vice admiral. The insignia of rank are two silver stars or, on the sleeves of blue uniforms, a two-in. stripe of gold lace with a $\frac{1}{2}$-in. stripe above it.

rear area The area in the rear of the combat and forward areas.

rear-area security The measures taken prior to, during, or after an enemy airborne attack, sabotage action, infiltration, guerrilla action, or initiation of psychological or propaganda warfare to minimize the effects thereof.

rear cover Cover provided by aircraft to the rear of the projected aircraft; the airplanes that give, or that are designated to give, this cover.

rear echelon The echelon charged with administrative and supply duties.

rear guard A security detachment that protects the rear of a column from hostile forces. During a withdrawal, it delays the enemy by using armed resistance, destroying bridges, and blocking roads.

rearming **1.** An operation that replenishes the prescribed stores of ammunition, bombs, and other armament items for an aircraft, naval ship, tank, or armored vehicle, including replacement of defective ordnance equipment, in order to make it ready for combat service. **2.** Resetting the fuze on a bomb, or on an artillery, mortar,

or rocket projectile, so that it will detonate at the desired time.

rearming boat A boat with padded gunwales used to service seaplanes.

rear sight An item attached to the breech end of, and integral to, a carbine, machine gun, pistol, rifle, or the like. It may be a fixed or adjustable cross blade with a U- or V-shaped notch or aperture, or it may have elevation- and windage-adjustment knobs, slides, and graduated scales and be provided with aperture disks.

Rebecca-Eureka A British development of World War II. It consisted of Rebecca, which was an airborne radar unit which transmitted pulses which were received and retransmitted by Eureka, a ground beacon which could be carried in a suitcase. It was used for directing aircraft to specific destinations and was employed for both dropping and landing operations behind enemy lines.

recall **1.** To call a person from a reserve component to active duty. **2.** A signal on trumpet, bugle, or drum calling soldiers to ranks. **3.** A signal to call a boat or vessel back to a parent ship or squadron.

recco, recce Short for "reconnaissance."

receiver **1.** The basic unit of a firearm, especially a small arm, which contains the operating mechanism of the weapon and to which the barrel and other components are attached. **2.** A component specifically designed to intercept and demodulate signals propagated by a transmitter. Short for "radio receiver" or "radar receiver."

rechamber To rebore or otherwise alter the chamber of a small arm, normally for the purpose of adapting it to cartridges for which it was not originally designed.

rechauds Large pans hung on the walls of a fortification, particularly during a siege. At night they were filled with burning materials to cast light into the ditches so that the enemy could not make a surprise attack.

reciprocal laying A method of making the planes of fire of two guns parallel by pointing the guns in the same direction. In reciprocal laying, the two guns sight on each other, and then swing out through supplementary angles to produce equal deflections from the base line connecting the two pieces.

recognition The determination by any means of the friendly or enemy character or the individuality of another; of objects such as aircraft, ships, or tanks; or of phenomena such as communications-electronics patterns.

recognition signal Any prearranged signal by means of which individuals or units may identify each other.

recoil The backward movement of a gun or part thereof on firing, caused by the backward pressure of the propellant gases;

the distance that a gun or part travels in this backward movement. Recoil, particularly as it pertains to small arms, is popularly called "kick."

recoil cylinder The part of a recoil mechanism that contains recoil oil and a recoil piston. The piston is forced through the oil-filled cylinder, forcing the oil through orifices and thus converting the recoil energy into increased temperature of the oil. The gun is returned to battery by a counterrecoil mechanism which stores energy for this purpose, usually in a pneumatic or spring mechanism.

recoilless Of a gun, built so as to eliminate or cancel out recoil.

recoilless ammunition Ammunition intended for use in recoilless rifles. Provision is made in the ammunition for release of propellant gases in the manner and quantity necessary to produce the recoilless action.

recoilless rifle A weapon consisting of a light-artillery tube of the recoilless type and a very light mount. For the 57mm caliber, the gun is fired from a shoulder mount, thus giving rise to the term "recoilless rifle." The larger calibers are fired from lightweight portable tripod mounts or from light vehicles such as the jeep. Ammunition for all calibers is termed "recoilless ammunition." Recoil is eliminated in these weapons by controlled escape of propellant gases to the rear through an opening in the breechblock.

recoilless rifle (heavy) A weapon which is capable of being fired from either a ground mount or a vehicle and which can destroy tanks.

recoil mechanism A hydraulic, pneumatic, or spring-type shock absorber that decreases the energy of the recoil gradually and so avoids violent movement of the gun or howitzer carriage.

recoil-operated Of an automatic or semiautomatic firearm, one that utilizes recoil to throw back or unlock the bolt or slide and actuate the loading mechanism. Applied especially to certain locked-breech firearms. Recoil-operated weapons are classified as "long-recoil" when the barrel and breechblock or bolt recoil the entire distance together and as "short-recoil" when the breechblock or bolt is unlocked and the barrel is stopped after only a short distance of recoil together.

recoil pit A pit dug near the breech of a gun to provide space for the breech when it moves backward during recoil.

reconnaissance An examination or observation of an area, territory, or airspace, now usually from the air, either visually or with the aid of photography or electronic devices, to secure information regarding the terrain, the strength and disposition of enemy troops, enemy resources or activi-

recoilless rifle, a U.S. 57mm recoilless rifle. (*U.S. Army.*)

ties, the location and layout of targets or of enemy installations and strongpoints, and the results of air operations or other operations.

reconnaissance patrol (ground) A small patrol used to gain information about the enemy, preferably without his knowledge.

reconnoiter To make a reconnaissance of an area, place, airspace, or the like.

recovery vehicle A special-purpose vehicle equipped with winch, hoist, or boom for recovery of vehicles. A full-track recovery vehicle is a self-propelled vehicle, usually armored, having boom and power-winch equipment and designed primarily to recover disabled tanks and other vehicles for combat areas. It may also be used for lifting engines, transmissions, and the like during repair of disabled vehicles. Recovery

vehicles may be equipped with armament or gun mounts.

recruit An enlisted person newly entered in military or naval service.

Recruit A scaled-down solid-propellant rocket similar to the Sergeant.

recurved Said of a blade or cross guard that curves first one way and then another, as in the shape of an S.

red alert An alert that exists when attack by enemy aircraft is, or seems to be, imminent.

redan A simple field fortification consisting of two parapets whose faces join to form a salient angle toward the enemy, much like the letter V, with the apex at the front. The gorge, being unfortified, is usually protected by being on the bank of a stream, at the head of a bridge, or in advance of

recovery vehicle. (*U.S. Army.*)

Redeye. (*General Dynamics.*)

a strong line. Redans joined by curtains constitute a simple form of fieldworks.

redcoat A soldier who wears a red coat. Formerly, a British soldier, so called because the typical uniform was red.

Reddy Fox A type of U.S. Navy bangalore torpedo used for blowing up obstacles during landing operations in World War II. It consisted of a long length of pipe filled with explosives.

redeployment The transfer of a unit, an individual, or supplies deployed in one area to another area, to another location within the area, or to the zone of interior for the purpose of further employment.

Redeye A U.S. portable shoulder-fired guided missile that employs infrared homing and was designed to destroy low-flying aircraft. Built by General Dynamics, it entered service in 1966. The total weight of the system is 29 lb, and the length of the launch tube is 4 ft. The diameter of the missile is 3 in.

red-hot shot Cannonballs heated until red hot and then fired at ships, buildings, etc.

Redstone. (*U.S. Army.*)

redoubt A roughly constructed fortification of varying shape, usually temporary and without flanking defenses.

RED SOD A U.S. *re*petitive *explosive* device for *so*il *d*isplacement.

Red Stocking The World War II code name for a series of flights by Allied Mosquito aircraft, equipped with recording devices, over specific areas behind enemy lines to pick up and record messages from agents on the ground.

Redstone A mobile liquid-propellant surface-to-surface guided missile with a nuclear-warhead capability, designed to support the field army by attacking targets up to a range of 175 nautical miles. Designated PGM-11.

Red Top A British air-to-air missile developed by Hawker Siddeley Dynamics as a follow-on to Firestreak. This missile has a length of 11.5 ft, a range of 7 mi, and a warhead weight of 68 lb. It is equipped with an infrared guidance unit.

reduit In fortifications, a central work within another work, representing the garrison's last retreat. It was often of circular shape, constructed of masonry, and equipped with loopholes.

reentering angle An angle in a line of

troops or of fortifications, with the apex turned away from the enemy.

reentering place of arms A place of arms within a reentering angle of the counterscarp.

reflex sight An optical or computing sight that reflects a reticle image or images onto a reflector plate for superimposition on the target by the eye.

reform To restore order in, and communications between, units after an attack.

reformado Formerly, an officer who is deprived of command because of reorganization but who retains rank. Also, a volunteer who serves with an officer's rank but who is without a commission.

refugee A civilian who by reason of real or imagined danger has left his home to seek safety elsewhere.

Regia Aeronautica (Royal Aeronautics.) The name of the Italian Air Force from 1923 through World War II.

Reggiane Re.2000 Falco I See **Falco I.**

Reggiane Re2001 Falco II See **Falco II.**

Reggiane Re.2002 Ariete See **Ariete.**

Reggiane Re.2005 Sagittario See **Sagittario.**

regiment In the U.S. Army and Marine Corps, an administrative and tactical unit larger than a battalion and smaller than a brigade.

regimental combat team (RCT) A task organization of troops for amphibious operations.

regimental landing team A task organization for landing comprised of an infantry regiment reinforced by those elements which are required for initiation of its combat function ashore.

register 1. To adjust fire on a visible point, called a "checkpoint," and compute accurate adjusted data so that firing data for later targets may be computed with reference to that checkpoint. 2. To adjust fire on several selected points in order that they may serve later as auxiliary targets.

registration fire Fire delivered to obtain accurate data for subsequent effective engagement of targets.

regular army The standing army of a state; regular troops, as opposed to militia or volunteers.

Regulus A surface-to-surface jet-powered guided missile. It is equipped with a nuclear warhead and is launched from surfaced submarines or cruisers. Designated RGM-6/15.

Reichswehr The military force organized in Germany in 1919 and at first numbering 500,000. It was reduced to 100,000 by 1921 under the terms of the Treaty of Versailles.

reinforce To strengthen by the addition of personnel or military equipment.

Reising .45 cal. submachine gun Models 50 and 55 American weapons designed to use the .45 cal. ACP cartridge and provided with selective full automatic and semiautomatic fire. They employ a retarded-blowback type of operation and have a cyclic rate of fire of 550 rounds per minute. They have an overall length of 35.75 in. and a barrel length of 11 in. With fully loaded 20-round magazines the weapons weigh 8.15 lb. (A 12-round magazine is also available.) They have a muzzle velocity of about 920 fps and a rear sight adjustable from 50 to 300 yd. The Model 55 is identical to the Model 50 in design and function except that the compensator has been omitted and a wire folding stock with a rear pistol grip has been substituted for a wood stock. Designed by Eugene G. Reising, the two models of this weapon were produced by Harrington and Richardson Arms. Between 1941 and 1945 a total of some 100,000 were made.

relais In fortifications, a space at the foot of the rampart and the scarp of the fosse. It is intended to catch any earth that washes or crumbles from the face of the rampart.

release altitude The altitude of an aircraft above the ground at the time of release of bombs, rockets, missiles, tow targets, etc.

reline To replace a worn liner of a gun to give it the ballistics of a new weapon.

relocator An instrument once used in seacoast fortifications to provide range and position data.

remblai The quantity of earth in the rampart, parapet, and banquette of a fortification.

remount To provide fresh horses to cavalry units.

removal liner, removable liner A rifled inner cylinder of a gun tube, made so that it can be taken out and replaced when it becomes worn.

Renault FT See **French tank, light, Renault FT.**

Renault R35 See **French tank, light, Renault R35.**

rendezvous An appointed place for troops, aircraft, or the ships of a fleet to assemble.

rendezvous area In an amphibious operation, the area in which the landing craft and amphibious vehicles rendezvous to form waves after being loaded and prior to moving to the line of departure.

Renown A class of British 32,000-ton battle cruisers completed in 1916 and refitted or reconstructed during the 1930s. There were two ships in the class, *Renown* and *Repulse,* each of which had a length of 794 ft, a beam of 102 ft, a speed of about 32 knots, and a complement of 1,200 men. Armament consisted of six 15-in., twenty 4-in., and four 3-pounder guns. *Renown* carried four aircraft, and *Repulse* was armed with eight 21-in. torpedo tubes. (*Repulse* was sunk by Japanese land-based aircraft near Singapore on December 10, 1941.)

Red Top, shown on BAC Lightning aircraft of the RAF. (*Hawker Siddeley Aviation Ltd.*)

repeater **1.** A repeating firearm; one capable of delivering several shots before reloading. **2.** In naval terminology, a flag used to repeat another in a hoist so that no two flags in one hoist are the same.

replacement A person who fills a vacancy created by a loss in order to bring an organization back to authorized strength.

replenishment The process of refueling, resupplying, and rearming naval ships, frequently completed under way with the support of specially configured ships.

report A sharp explosive sound, as of a shot, bursting bomb, or projectile.

Requa battery A .58 cal. weapon developed in 1861 and used during the American Civil War. It featured 25 barrels arranged horizontally and designed to fire volleys. It required a crew of three and could be fired at the rate of 7 volleys, or 175 shots, per minute. It had an effective range of 1,300 yd. It was sometimes called a "covered-bridge" gun, since it could effectively break up any charge across a bridge (many of which, at the time, were wooden bridges with roofs and sidewalls).

rerebrace In medieval and Renaissance armor, plate armor for the protection of the upper arm. (Picture, next page.)

reredos In ancient armor, a backplate.

Rescue Combat Air Patrol (RESCAP) Air patrols which cover rescue submarines and rescue aircraft.

reserve **1.** A force or forces kept out of action until needed for some contingency. **2.** An accumulation of supplies or equipment in excess of immediate needs. **3.** The military or naval forces of a nation in addition to the regular forces or other forces on active duty.

reserved demolition target A target for demolition, the destruction of which must be specifically controlled at whatever level of command, because it plays a vital part

Regulus. (*U.S. Navy.*)

rerebrace, the central portion for the protection of the upper arm. The large curved portion is the pauldron. (*The Metropolitan Museum of Art, gift of William H. Riggs, 1913.*)

in the tactical or strategic plan, because of the importance of the structure itself, or because the demolition may be executed in the face of the enemy.

reserve fleet   A group of naval vessels in an inactive status. Also called "mothball fleet."

Reserve Officers Training Corps (ROTC) A training corps with units established at civilian educational institutions to qualify students for appointment as reserve officers.

reservist   A member of the reserves of a military or naval organization.

resistance movement   An organized effort by some portion of the civil population of a country to resist the legally established government or an occupying power and to disrupt civil order and stability.

Resolution   1. A class of British nuclear-powered ballistic-missile submarines of 7,500 tons surface displacement accepted in 1967–1969. They have a length of 425 ft, a beam of 33 ft, a surface speed of 20 knots (25 knots submerged), and a complement of 141 men. They are armed with six 21-in. torpedo tubes and 16 tubes for Polaris A-3 ICBM's. There are four submarines in the class (*Renown, Repulse, Resolution,* and *Revenge*), and they represent the largest undersea craft ever built for the Royal

Navy.   **2.** A British battleship of the **Royal Sovereign** class, which see.

rest and recuperation   The withdrawal of individuals from combat or duty in a combat area for short periods of rest and recuperation. Commonly referred to as "R&R."

reticle image   A light image of the reticle in a computing gunsight or in certain types of optical gunsights and bombsights, cast on a reflector plate and superimposed on the target.

retirade   In fortifications, a retrenchment, usually of two faces which form a reentering angle.

retired flank   A flank bent inward toward the rear of the work.

retreat   1. The forced withdrawal from an enemy.   **2.** An evening signal for the lowering of the flag at a military installation.   **3.** A ceremony at the time the flag is lowered in the evening.

retreat gun   The firing of a gun as a signal for the lowering of the flag at retreat. The gun is fired after the sounding of the last note of the bugle call at retreat. Also called "evening gun."

retrenchment   A defensive work located inside another work to prolong the defense of the place. It usually consists of a simple traverse or parapet and ditch.

retrofit   (retroactive refit) A modification of equipment to incorporate changes made in later production of similar equipment. Retrofitting may be done in the factory or field.

retrograde movement   Any movement of a command to the rear, or away from the enemy. It may be forced by the enemy or may be made voluntarily. Such movements may be classified as withdrawal, retirement, or delaying action.

return load   The personnel or cargo to be transported by a returning carrier.

reveille   A signal, usually a bugle call or other music, for rousing persons at a mil-

itary post at the start of the day; a formation held at this time of the day.

reveille gun   The firing of a gun at the first note of reveille or at sunrise. Also called "morning gun."

Revelli 6.5mm aircraft machine gun Model 1914   A 29.5-lb air-cooled version of the 6.5mm Model 1914.

Revelli 6.5mm machine gun Model 1914 This was the first Italian machine gun to appear in any quantity. It was used in World War I. This weapon operates on a delayed-blowback system and is capable of selective fire. It has an overall length of 46.5 in., a barrel length of 25.75 in., and a weight (less water) of 37.5 lb. The weight of the tripod mount is 49.5 lb. The muzzle velocity is 2,080 fps, and the cyclic rate of fire is 450 to 500 rounds per minute. It is fed from 50 round spring-loaded magazine compartments.

Revelli 25.4mm aircraft cannon   A weapon developed for the Italian Air Force in World War I and used on some Caproni bombers. It was a recoil-operated air-cooled cannon with a rate of fire of 150 rounds per minute. It weighed 99 lb and was fed from an eight-round magazine.

Revelli submachine gun   See **Villar-Perosa 9mm (Glisenti) submachine gun Model 1915.**

Revenge   A British battleship of the **Royal Sovereign** class, which see.

revetment   A retaining wall faced with concrete, stone, etc., commonly used for fortifications or to protect against explosions. Also, a wall of earth, sandbags, or the like thrown up to protect aircraft, gun emplacements, storage areas, etc., against bombing, shelling, or strafing attacks.

review   1. A formal inspection of an organization during which a formation of the members of the organization is held.   **2.** A ceremony to honor a person or persons or to honor an event.

revolver   A firearm with a cylinder of several chambers so arranged as to revolve on an axis and be discharged in succession by the same lock.

Rex   The Allied code name for the Japanese Kawanishi N1K1 Kyofu (Mighty Wind) single-seat single-engine interceptor float seaplane first flown in 1942. It had a speed of 302 mph and was armed with two 20mm cannons and two 7.7mm machine guns.

Rexim F.V. Mk 4 submachine gun   A Swiss weapon introduced in 1953 by the firm of Rexim S.A. in Geneva. It is blowback-operated and has selective full automatic and semiautomatic fire. It uses the 9mm Parabellum cartridge and has an approximate muzzle velocity of 1,312 fps. The weight with a 32-round magazine is 10.29 lb. With stock retracted the length is 24.3 in., and the barrel length is 13.4 in. After Rexim went out of business, the weapon was manufactured in Spain as "La Coruña."

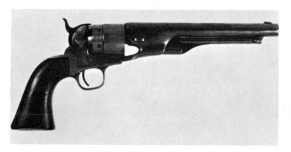

revolver, a .44 cal. Remington Model 1872. (*The Smithsonian Institution.*)

RGM-6 See **Regulus**.

Rheinbote (German for "Rhine maiden.") A German four-stage fin-stabilized surface-to-surface missile developed during World War II. It had an overall length of 37 ft, a range of about 135 mi, and a warhead weight of 88 lb. Over 60 of these missiles were fired against Antwerp in November 1944, but with little effect because of the small size of the explosive charge.

Rheinmetall 20mm aircraft cannon MK-ST-11 A German recoil-operated air-cooled cannon with a rate of fire of 280 rounds per minute. It weighed 118 lb and was fed from a 20-round magazine. An antiaircraft version was given the classification MK-ST-5. When used by German forces in the late 1930s, the MK-ST-5 was called the "Flak 30" and was used as an antiaircraft and tank gun.

Rheinmetall 20mm antiaircraft cannon MK-ST-5 See **Flak 30 20mm cannon**.

Rheinmetall (Solothurn) 20mm semiautomatic antitank cannon Model S18-1000 See **Tank Buchse**.

Rheinmetall 30mm aircraft cannon MK-101 A German recoil-operated air-cooled cannon with a rate of fire of 230 to 260 rounds per minute. It weighed 335 lb and was fed from a 30-round drum magazine. It was used chiefly in the Heinkel 129 for ground-attack duties on the Russian front in World War II.

Rheinmetall 30mm aircraft cannon MK-103 A German gas-operated air-cooled cannon with a rate of fire of 420 rounds per minute. It weighed 308 lb and was fed from a 25- or 100-round link belt. It was developed because the MK-101 did not deliver enough firepower.

Rheinmetall 30mm aircraft cannon MK-108 A German blowback-operated air-cooled cannon with a rate of fire of 400 to 500 rounds per minute. It weighed 135 lb and was fed from a 200-round link belt. It was first produced in 1944 and was designed for the specific purpose of air-to-air combat against large bombers. Later versions of the Messerschmitt Bf 109 (such as the Bf 109H) mounted a cannon of this type which operated through the hub of the propeller.

Rheintochter (German for "daughter of the Rhine.") A World War II nickname for a particular type of German antiaircraft rocket.

rhino barge, rhino ferry A self-propelled lighter made up of pontoons bolted together.

Rhinoceros A German tank destroyer of World War II, formerly called the "Hornet," developed by mounting an 88mm gun on a PzKpfw IV chassis. Built by Krupp, it was introduced in 1942. It had a crew of five and was armed with one 88mm Pak 43/1, caliber length 71. The weight of the

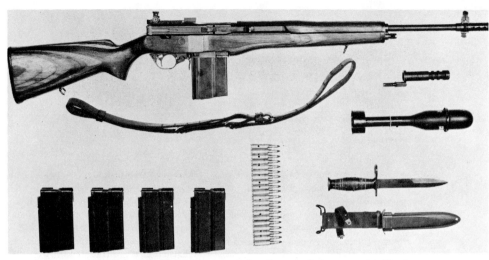

rifle, an experimental U.S. lightweight rifle, showing grenade launcher, grenade, bayonet and scabbard, cartridges, and magazines. (*U.S. Army.*)

vehicle was 26.5 tons, and it could make about 25 mph on roads. The 88mm gun represented the most powerful German antitank weapon.

Rhode Island A U.S. battleship of the **New Jersey** class, which see. It was commissioned in 1906.

rib A metal strip that unites the barrels of a double-barreled gun.

ribaudequin **1.** A protected elevated staging mounted on a wheeled cart and armed with spikes; a kind of movable fortification. After the fourteenth century it was armed with a small cannon. **2.** The name of the small cannon itself. **3.** A huge and powerful crossbow mounted on the wall of a fort and used for throwing heavy darts.

rib rifling Rifling with extremely wide grooves and very narrow lands.

ricasso The squared portion of a sword, dagger, or knife blade between the edge and the hilt.

Richelieu A French battleship of 35,000 tons standard displacement completed in 1940 and extensively refitted in 1951. It had a length of 794 ft, a beam of 108 ft, a speed of 30 knots, and a wartime complement of 1,946 men. It was armed with eight 15-in., nine 6-in., and twelve 4-in. guns, plus fifty-six 40mm and thirty-seven 20mm antiaircraft guns. An uncompleted sister ship, *Clemenceau*, was sunk by Allied bombers during World War II.

ricochet Of a bomb, bullet, or the like, to skip, bounce, or fly off at an angle after striking an object or surface.

ricochet burst The burst of a projectile in the air after it has hit and bounced. A ricochet burst is used effectively against enemy personnel.

ricochet fire The deliberate fire of a smoothbore cannon at a low angle of elevation so that the trajectory of the spherical cannonball will be a series of ricochets, thus

causing considerable damage.

ridge In fortifications, the highest portion of the glacis.

riding the city A fourteenth-century practice in which a cavalry charge was made through the streets of a captured city to prevent the inhabitants from erecting barricades.

rifle **1.** A firearm having spiral grooves upon the surface of its bore to impart rotary motion to a projectile, thereby stabilizing the projectile and ensuring greater accuracy of impact and longer range. It may fire projectiles automatically or semiautomatically, or successive rounds may be manually loaded. The operation may be gas, recoil or manual. It is provided with a stock for shoulder firing and may have a sling to aid in carrying and aiming. **2.** A recoilless breechloading single-shot artillery weapon with a manually operated vented breechblock and a rifle bore. It is fired from various types of ground or vehicular mounts. **3.** A rifled muzzle-loading cannon of any size. **4.** To cut spiral grooves (rifling) in the bore of a gun in order to give a spin to the projectile so that it will have greater accuracy of fire and longer range.

rifle grenade A grenade especially designed or adapted to be fired or launched from the muzzle of a rifle or carbine. (Picture, next page.)

rifle-grenade cartridge A specially loaded blank cartridge for firing a grenade from a rifle or carbine.

rifle-grenade launcher A special device that fits over the muzzle of a rifle or carbine and holds a grenade in position for launching.

rifleman A soldier armed with a rifle. Formerly, a special kind of light infantry consisting of superior marksmen armed with the most improved rifles.

rifle musket A muzzle-loading percussion

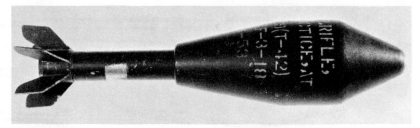

rifle grenade, U.S. M31. (*U.S. Army.*)

weapon of large caliber having musket features but with a rifled bore instead of a smooth bore.

rifle pit A short trench to protect riflemen.

rifles A body of riflemen.

rifling The helical grooves cut in the bore of a rifled gun tube, beginning at the front face of the gun chamber (origin of rifling) and extending to the muzzle; also, the operation of forming the grooves in the gun tube. The purpose of rifling is to impart spin to the projectile; if the spin is fast enough, the projectile will be gyroscopically stable and will travel approximately nose first.

Riga A class of Soviet destroyer escorts of 1,200 tons standard displacement produced in the early 1950s. They have a length of 295 ft, a beam of 31.5 ft, a speed of 28 knots, and a complement of 150 men. They are armed with three 3.9-in. guns, two 16-barreled A/S rocket launchers, four depth-charge projectors, and three 21-in. torpedo tubes.

rigging **1.** The system of bracing cables, control cables, lines, ropes, etc., with which an airplane, balloon, or other aircraft is rigged. **2.** The shroud lines attached to a parachute.

rigid airship A dirigible having several gasbags or cells enclosed in an envelope supported by an interior framework. Distinguished especially from nonrigid and semirigid airships.

Rikugun Ki.46-III-KAI A twin-engine two-seat fighter-interceptor developed for the Japanese Army Air Force and first flown in October 1944. Armed with two 20mm cannons and one 37mm cannon, it had a maximum speed of 379 mph. It was developed from the Mitsubishi Ki.46 Type 100 (Dinah).

RIM-2 See **Terrier**.

RIM-8 See **Talos**.

RIM-24 See **Tartar**.

RIM-50 See **Typhon**.

RIM 66A, RIM 67A See **Standard Missile**.

rimfire A cartridge having the primer in the rim of the head, or base.

rimless Said of a cartridge case in which the extracting groove is machined into the body of the case, with no part of the case extending beyond the body.

rimmed Said of a cartridge case in which an extractor rim projects beyond the body of the case.

ring-and-bead sight A type of gunsight in which the front sight is a bead or post and the rear sight is a ring.

ring armor Armor made of rings of metal.

ring mail A kind of mail made of small steel rings sewn on a leather or cloth garment. Sometimes the term is used to mean the standard mail made of interlinked rings.

ring sight A sight, especially a gunsight, in the shape of a ring or concentric rings, through which aim is taken and range is estimated. Ring sights include the iron type

(in which a simple ring or set of rings encloses a cross hair or the like) and the optical type (in which a system of lenses is used to show a series of concentric rings and the bead).

riot-control agent A chemical that produces temporary irritating or disabling effects when in contact with the eyes or when inhaled.

riot-control and miscellaneous agents See **vomiting agents**, **tear agents**, and **incapacitating chemical agents**.

riot grenade A grenade of plastic or other nonfragmenting material containing a charge of tear gas and a detonating fuze with short delay. The grenade functions and the gas is released by a bursting action.

riot gun Any shotgun with a short barrel, especially a short-barreled shotgun used in guard duty or to scatter rioters. A riot gun usually has a 20-in. cylinder barrel.

risban A fortification once used for the defense of a port or a harbor.

RITA Resistance in the Army. A data bank started at Fort Monroe, Va., by the U.S. Army to file intelligence information on soldiers considered to be possible dissenters.

River **1.** A class of Japanese frigates of 1,490 tons standard displacement completed in 1961–1964. They have a speed of 25 knots, a complement of 180 men, and armament consisting of four 3-in. guns, four 21-in. torpedo tubes, two triple torpedo launchers, one 4-barreled A/S rocket launcher, and one depth-charge rack. **2.** A class of British frigates of 1,370 tons standard displacement completed in 1942–1944. They had a speed of 20 knots, a complement of 140 men, and armament consisting of two 4-in. guns, ten 20mm antiaircraft guns, four depth-charge throwers, and two Squid depth-charge mortars.

RLT U.S. Army rolling liquid transport.

RO 35 Class A class of Japanese 960-ton submarines produced in 1942–1944. They

Riga. (*U.S. Navy.*)

River. (*Japan Defense Agency.*)

had a length of 264 ft, a submerged speed of 8 knots, a complement of 80 men, and armament consisting of four 21-in. torpedo tubes and one 3-in. deck gun. Of 18 produced, only one survived World War II.

RO 100 Class A class of Japanese 525-ton submarines produced in 1942–1943. They had a length of 199 ft, a submerged speed of 8 knots, a complement of 75 men, and armament consisting of four 21-in. torpedo tubes and one 3-in. gun. All 18 vessels in this class were lost in action during World War II.

roadblock A barrier or obstacle (usually covered by fire) used to block or limit the movement of hostile vehicles along a route.

robinet **1.** A light sixteenth-century cannon that fired a projectile weighing about ½ lb; a rabinet. **2.** An engine for throwing either stones or darts.

Robot 304 A Swedish Air Force air-to-surface missile with a range of about 3 mi.

Robot 315 A Swedish Navy surface-to-surface tactical missile with a range of 10 to 20 nautical miles.

robot bomb An explosive-carrying winged missile or rocket, such as the German V-1 or flying bomb of World War II, normally launched from the surface and directed in flight toward its target by an automatic pilot and other automatic devices.

Robot Rb 04 A Swedish Saab-built air-to-surface guided missile with a length of about 14.5 ft, a launching weight of 1,320 lb, and a warhead weight of approximately 660 lb. C, D, and E versions have been produced.

Roc **1.** A guided bomb with ring-shaped airfoils, controlled by radio in both azimuth and range, and equipped with a television camera in the nose as an aid to guidance. Developed by the United States during World War II, it was never used operationally. **2.** A British single-engine two-seat shipboard fighter first flown in late 1938 and produced only until 1940. Built by Blackburn, this airplane never operated from carriers, and was later used as a

trainer and as a target tug. It carried a power-driven turret armed with four .303 cal. Browning machine guns and could also carry eight 30-lb bombs.

Rochen A German experimental rocket developed during World War II and tested for ship-to-ship, ship-to-shore, and surface-to-surface operations. It was wire-guided, had a range of 4 mi, and carried a 220-lb high-explosive warhead. It never reached the production stage.

rochettes Fourteenth-century fire arrows thrown from ballistas.

rocket A missile or pyrotechnic device propelled by hot gases ejected rearward by a motor or burning charge. Such a motor or engine moves forward by ejecting a stream of hot gases to the rear, and because it carries its own oxidizer, it is independent of the atmosphere in which it operates. The first military rockets were the Congreve and the Hale.

rocket-assisted torpedo A torpedo de-

signed to be fired into the air by rocket and to drop into the water by parachute. Upon entering the water, the torpedo seeks its underwater target by a special homing device. (Picture, next page.)

rocket boat An old naval term for a flat-bottomed boat fitted with rocket frames from which Congreve rockets were fired during a naval bombardment.

rocket bomb An aerial bomb equipped with a rocket to give it added velocity and penetrating power after being dropped from an aircraft.

rocket launcher A device for launching rockets. Rocket launchers utilize rails, posts, tubes, or other devices to carry and guide the rocket. They are wheel-mounted, or motorized; aircraft-mounted; or, in the case of the bazooka, designed to be carried about by a man. In the nineteenth century they often consisted of light tripods. (Picture, next page.)

rocket propulsion Reaction propulsion

Robot Rb 04. (*Swedish Air Force.*)

rocket-assisted torpedo. (*U.S. Navy.*)

rocket launcher. Launchers for Nike-Hercules missiles. (*U.S. Army.*)

wherin both the fuel and the oxidizer, generating the hot gases expended through a nozzle, are carried as part of the rocket engine. Specifically, rocket propulsion differs from jet propulsion in that jet propulsion utilizes atmospheric air as an oxidizer, whereas rocket propulsion utilizes nitric acid or a similar compound as an oxidizer.

rocket ship (LSMR)   A landing ship used in close support of the leading assault waves during an amphibious landing. It is capable of heavy and rapid rocket firing. (Rocket ships were used by the British early in the nineteenth century, notably in the attacks on Copenhagen and Fort Mc-

Henry.)

Rockeye   A U.S. Navy general-purpose antiarmor cluster bomb designed for use against heavy tanks, trucks, and flak sites. It weighs 500 lb and has a mechanical time fuze which dispenses bomblets at a selected time, dispensing them over a wide area.

rod bayonet   A cylindrical bayonet, either sliding in a sleeve or hinged beneath a rifle barrel, fixed in position by a spring catch.

Rodman guns   Muzzle-loading cast-iron smoothbore guns of several large calibers used by the U.S. service during and after the Civil War. The 20-in. version (of which only two were cast) weighed about 117,000 lb and fired a cast-iron shot weighing about $\frac{1}{2}$ ton. See **columbiads.**

Rodney   A British battleship, sister ship of the **Nelson,** which see.

roger   Used in voice radio, a term meaning "I have received your transmission."

ROK   The abbreviation for Republic of Korea, and often pronounced as a word. In the Korean conflict it was used to refer to a South Korean soldier, air force, corps, division, or government.

Roland   A surface-to-air missile for protection against low-flying aircraft and helicopters. Built by the firm of Nord/Bölkow, this missile has a length of 7 ft 10½ in., a weight of 139 lb, and a maximum range of 19,700 ft.

Roland C.II   A German two-place single-engine observation biplane first flown in October 1915; it remained in service at the fronts until about mid-1917. It had a maximum speed of about 102 mph and was armed with one rearward-firing Parabellum gun in the observer's cockpit. When used for bombing, it carried four 28-lb bombs under the fuselage.

Roland D.I through D.III   German single-place single-engine biplane fighters, the first prototype of which was flown in July 1916. They had a speed of about 105 mph and standard armament consisting of one forward-firing Spandau machine gun.

Roland D.VI   A German single-place single-engine biplane fighter that first appeared

rocket ship, a U.S. Navy LSMR. (*U.S. Navy.*)

late in 1917. It had a speed of 113 mph and was armed with a pair of 7.92mm Spandau machine guns mounted in front of the cockpit. It saw limited operational service in the late spring and early summer of 1918.

roll call   The calling of a list of names. Also, the signal for this activity.

rolling barrage   An artillery barrage that precedes infantry troops at a predetermined rate in their advance during an attack to protect them and facilitate their advance. Also called a "creeping barrage."

rolling-block rifle   A breechloading rifle system in which a hinged block seals the breech for firing, but swings back and down for loading and unloading. It was developed in 1865 and manufactured by Remington Arms Co.

roll-in point   The point at which aircraft enter the final leg of the attack, e.g., dive or glide.

Roll-On/Roll-Off (LSV)   A U.S. Navy cargo ship specially built for rapid handling of wheeled or tracked vehicles.

Roman sword   The famous Roman infantry sword of the early empire was the gladius. It was made of bronze and iron and had a length of 22 to 24 in. The double-edged iron blade was obtusely pointed. A longer, single-edged blade was called a **spatha,** which see.

rondache   A seventeenth-century circular shield carried by foot soldiers and used for the protection of the upper part of the body. "Target" is another term for the same type of shield.

rondelle, rondel   **1.** In fortifications, a round tower that was sometimes located at the foot of a bastion.   **2.** A round plate for the protection of the openings in the joints of armor.   **3.** A roundel, or small shield.

ronfleurs   An eighteenth-century cannon weighing 3,200 lb and firing a 12-lb projectile.

Roon   A German armored cruiser of 9,050 tons displacement completed in 1905. It had a speed of 21 knots, a complement of 557 men, and main armament consisting of four 8.2-in. guns, ten 6-in. guns, and four 18-in. torpedo tubes.

rope   Electromagnetic-wave deflectors consisting of long strips of metal foil. It is similar to window or chaff, but longer. It is dropped from airplanes or shot into the air in projectiles. A small parachute or other device may be attached to each strip to reduce the rate of fall.

rope chaff   Chaff which contains one or more rope elements.

rorarii   Roman light infantry.

Ross .303 rifle   This rifle was developed in Canada by Sir Charles Ross and appeared in a wide variety of marks. The Mark II was introduced in 1905, and the Mark III in 1910, and these were the Canadian service rifles of World War I. Under actual trench-warfare conditions it was

rolling-block rifle. (*The Smithsonian Institution.*)

rondache. (*The Metropolitan Museum of Art, gift of William H. Riggs, 1913.*)

Ross .303 rifle. (*The Smithsonian Institution, War Department Collection.*)

found unsuitable. A serious problem with this weapon is the bolt. If reassembled wrong, it will permit firing in an unlocked position, resulting in serious injury or death to the shooter. The Mark III Ross has an overall length of 50.5 in., a barrel length of 30.5 in., and a weight of 9.75 lb. The magazine has a capacity of five cartridges.

rostrum   A ram attached to the prow of an ancient warship such as a **trireme,** which see. Rostrums sometimes protruded above the water line, but later they were fully submerged. They projected about 10 ft and consisted of a three-toothed spur of hardwood armored with iron or bronze.

rotate   To remove a person, crew, unit, or

the like from service in an overseas area, from combat service, or from service in a hardship environment and to return such person, crew, or unit to service in the zone of the interior or other less exacting environment.

rotating band   A band of soft metal, such as copper, ordinarily fitted around a projectile for a rifled cannon. It serves to engage the rifling in the gun barrel.

Rothesay   A class of British antisubmarine frigates of 2,200 tons standard displacement completed in 1960–1961. They have an overall length of 370 ft, a beam of 41 ft, a speed of 30 knots, and a complement of 235 men. They are armed with two 4.5-in.

Roth-Steyr 8mm automatic pistol M1907. (*The Smithsonian Institution, G. F. Gestering Collection.*)

guns and two Limbo three-barreled depth-charge mortars. They are in the process of being fitted for Seacat missile launchers in place of Bofors close-range antiaircraft guns. They also carry one helicopter armed with homing torpedoes.

Roth-Steyr 8mm automatic pistol M1907 The Austrian Roth-Steyr was designed around the turn of the century, was officially adopted by the Austro-Hungarian cavalry in 1907, and saw considerable service in World War I. It also saw wide use all over the Balkans and appeared in these areas during World War II. It has a nonremovable magazine with a capacity of 10 cartridges and a weight of about 36 oz. The overall length is about $9\frac{1}{8}$ in., and the barrel length is $5\frac{1}{8}$ in.

Rotte A German term for a two-ship (aircraft) formation. See also **Schwarm.**

Roughrider A member of the First U.S. Volunteer Cavalry during the Spanish-American War of 1898. This regiment was organized largely, and later led, by Teddy Roosevelt and was composed in large part of Eastern college athletes and sportsmen

and Western cowboys and hunters.

round A unit of gun ammunition consisting of a projectile, propellant, igniting charge, and primer. The term may also apply to a piece of rocket ammunition or to a bomb, especially in the phrases "complete round" and "bomb complete round."

round and grape Formerly, a naval term for a gun charged with a solid shot and grapeshot or canister and fired at close quarters.

roundel A small shield of the fourteenth and fifteenth centuries. It was circular and about 1 ft in diameter.

round shot A spherical projectile for ordnance.

rout The confused defeat or dispersion of an army or body of troops.

route army An army on the march or prepared to march.

route march An order of march in which the men maintain formation and distance but are not required to keep step, maintain silence, or hold their weapons in any particular position.

routine message A category of precedence to be used for all types of messages which justify transmission by rapid means unless of sufficient urgency to require a higher precedence.

Rover Joe A World War II system of forward air control used in close air support.

roving artillery Artillery withdrawn from its regular position and assigned to special missions. Roving artillery is usually moved about and fired from different positions to deceive the enemy as to position and strength.

roving gun A gun that is moved about and fired from different positions to mislead or harass the enemy. It is generally used for registration when the location of the battery position must remain secret.

row marker (land-mine warfare) A mark-

er—natural, artificial, or specially installed —located at the start and finish of a mine row where mines are laid by individual rows.

royal A small mortar, now obsolete, that fired a 5.5-in. shell.

Royal Air Force (RAF) An organization created in Great Britain in April 1918 by amalgamating the Royal Flying Corps and the Royal Navy Air Service.

royal artillery All Great Britain's army artillery forces.

Royal Flying Corps The name of the British air arm from 1912 to 1918. From 1912 to 1914 the Royal Flying Corps combined both Army and Navy units; from 1914 to 1918 the Royal Flying Corps was an Army corps responsible for military aeronautics.

Royal Marines An organization formed in Great Britain in 1923 by amalgamating the Royal Marine Light Infantry and the Royal Marine Artillery.

royal mortar An old brass mortar said to have a $5\frac{1}{2}$-in. bore, a weight of 150 lb, and the ability to throw a 24-lb shell up to 600 yd.

Royal Naval Air Service The name of the British naval air arm from 1914 to 1918. In 1918, the Royal Naval Air Service was combined with the Royal Flying Corps to form the RAF; the Navy regained control of the naval air arm (the Fleet Air Arm) in 1939.

Royal Oak A British battleship of the **Royal Sovereign** class, which see. It was torpedoed and sunk by a German submarine in Scapa Flow on October 14, 1939.

Royal Sovereign A class of British battleships of about 30,000 tons standard displacement completed in 1915–1916. There were five ships in this class: *Royal Sovereign, Resolution, Ramillies, Revenge,* and *Royal Oak.* These ships had an overall length of 620.5 ft, a beam of about 102 ft, a speed

Rudderow. (*U.S. Navy.*)

Rumanian Mannlicher 6.5mm rifle Model 1892. (*The Smithsonian Institution, Rumanian Government Collection.*)

runka. (*The Metropolitan Museum of Art, gift of William H. Riggs, 1913.*)

of 22 knots, and a complement of 1,000 to 1,150 men. Armament consisted of eight 15-in., twelve 6-in., eight 4-in., and four 3-pounder guns, plus two 21-in. torpedo tubes and one airplane.

RS-1 A semirigid airship built by Goodyear in 1925 for the U.S. Army. It was the first and largest semirigid airship built in the United States, having a length of 275 ft and a helium capacity of 710,000 cu ft. It was dismantled after two years because of deficiencies in construction.

RSD-58 A Swiss surface-to-air missile with a range of about 18 mi.

Ruby automatic pistol See **Alkartasuna .32 cal. ACP automatic pistol.**

RUC A U.S. Navy riverine utility boat.

Rudderow A class of U.S. escort ships (DE) of 1,450 tons standard displacement commissioned in 1944. Sixty-two ships were built, most of which were converted to high-speed transports (APD). They had a length of 306 ft, a beam of 37 ft, a speed of 24 knots, and a complement of 180 men. Armament consisted of two 5-in. guns, four 40mm antiaircraft guns, hedgehogs, and depth charges.

Rufe The Allied code name for the Nakajima A6M2-N floatplane version of the Mitsubishi A6M2 Zero-Sen (Zeke) fighter. This single-seat single-engine float seaplane flew at speeds of 270 mph and was armed with two 20mm cannons, two 7.7mm machine guns, and two 132-lb bombs. Production began in April 1942.

ruffles and flourishes The roll of the drum (ruffles) and short bursts of music (flourishes) that make up one of the honors rendered to high-ranking military and civil officials.

Rumanian 9mm Parabellum submachine gun Model 1941 (Orita) See **Orita 9mm Parabellum submachine gun Model 1941.**

Rumanian Mannlicher 6.5mm rifle Models

1892 and 1893 These weapons were adopted by Rumanian forces in 1892. They are bolt-operated and have an overall length of 48.3 in., a barrel length of 28.5 in., a weight of 8.9 lb, a muzzle velocity of about 2,400 fps, and a nondetachable box magazine with a capacity of five cartridges. The Model 1893 differs from the 1892 in sight graduations, position of the ejector, and a stacking rod. The Model 1893 is essentially the same as the Dutch Mannlicher Model 1895.

Rumpelkammer The code name for the German operation to bombard England by flying bombs during World War II. It began on June 12, 1944.

Rumpler 6B A German single-place single-engine biplane seaplane whose design was based on that of the Rumpler C.I two-place reconnaissance plane. It was first delivered in July 1916 and flew at speeds up to about 95 mph.

Rumpler C.I A German two-place single-engine reconnaissance biplane in service between 1915 and early 1918. It flew at speeds up to about 95 mph and was armed with a Parabellum gun in the observer's cockpit and with a synchronized Spandau machine gun mounted on the front fuselage. It could also carry 220 lb of bombs. It served on the Eastern and Western fronts and in Macedonia, Palestine, and Salonika.

Rumpler C.IV to C.VII German two-place single-engine reconnaissance biplanes developed in 1917. They had a speed of about 106 mph and were armed with a forward-firing synchronized Spandau gun and a ring-mounted Parabellum gun in the rear cockpit. The later version, the C.VII, was able to fly at an altitude of 23,950 ft, and at 20,000 ft it could fly as fast as the Allied S.E.5a. This version was equipped with oxygen breathing apparatus and electrically heated flying suits for the crew members.

runaway gun An automatic weapon that continues firing after the trigger is released, because of a defect in some part of its mechanism.

runka A fifteenth- and sixteenth-century polearm with a long, sharp blade and two short lateral blades at the base; a *chauve-souris* or corsesque.

runner A soldier who acts as a messenger between units, especially in battle.

running fight A battle which continues as one side retreats and the other advances.

running fire A technique once employed in which ranks of soldiers fired their weapons in rapid succession, right to left.

Ruptured Duck A World War II-era slang term for either a PBY Catalina or the Honorable Service Lapel Button.

RUR-4 See **Weapon Alpha.**

RUR-5A See **Asroc.**

Russian 7.62mm machine guns (Maxim) The Model 1905 and the Model 1910 were both basic Maxim-type machine guns. See **Maxim machine gun.**

Russian 7.62mm Madsen machine gun Russian forces used two models of the Madsen machine gun: the M1904 and the M1905. See **Madsen machine guns.**

Russian 76.2mm gun, Model 1902 This gun, produced by the French Schneider works, was the standard field gun used by the Russians in World War I. It fired a 14-lb shell 7,000 yd.

Ryuho A Japanese light aircraft carrier of 15,300 tons standard displacement commissioned in November 1942. It had a top speed of 26.5 knots and carried 36 planes.

Ryujo A Japanese aircraft carrier of 10,600 tons displacement completed in 1931. It had flight-deck dimensions of 513.5 by 75.5 ft, a speed of 29 knots, and a complement of 900 men. It carried 48 aircraft. It was sunk by U.S. carrier aircraft during the Battle of the East Solomon Sea in 1942.

S

S-2 **1.** See **Tracker.** **2.** The designation for the intelligence sections of battalions and regiments.

SA The U.S. military designation for the war gas **arsine,** which see.

S.A. See **Sturmabteilung.**

SA-1 A Soviet surface-to-air missile. See **Guild.**

SA-2 A Soviet surface-to-air missile. See **Guideline.**

SA-3 A Soviet surface-to-air missile. See **Coa.**

SA-4 A Soviet surface-to-air missile. See **Ganef.**

SA-5 A Soviet surface-to-air missile. See **Griffon.**

SA-6 A Soviet surface-to-air missile. See **Gainful.**

SA-7 A Soviet surface-to-air missile. See **Galosh.**

Saab-29 This Swedish aircraft was the first sweptwing jet fighter to be put into large-scale production in Western Europe and was first flown in 1948. It had a speed of 658 mph and was armed with four 20mm cannons and an air-to-air rocket load.

Saab-32 Lansen See **Lansen.**

Saab-35 Draken See **Draken,** sense 2.

Saab-37 Viggen See **Viggen.**

Saab-105 A Swedish two-seat jet basic trainer and light attack aircraft first flown in 1963. It has a speed of 478 mph and may be armed with a combination of 30mm gun pods, 13.5cm rockets, bombs, and missiles.

Saab Rb 05A A Swedish manually guided supersonic air-to-surface tactical missile with a length of about 11.5 ft and a launching weight of approximately 660 lb.

Saab Rb 08A A Swedish ship-to-ship or surface-to-ship missile developed from the French Nord CT.20 target drone. It has a length of 18.75 ft and a launching weight of 1,985 lb.

sabaton Armor for the protection of the foot.

saber A sword with a single-edged blade. It is designed primarily for cutting, but slightly curved or straight-bladed types may also be used for thrusting.

Saab-29. (*Swedish Air Force.*)

saber halberd A sixteenth-century pole-arm having a saber blade instead of a spike.

sabot In modern usage, a lightweight carrier in which a subcaliber projectile is centered to permit firing the projectile in the larger-caliber weapon. The sabot diameter fills the bore of the weapon from which the projectile is fired. One type of sabot is discarded a short distance from the muzzle and is known as a "discarding sabot." A sabot is also used with a hypervelocity armor-piercing projectile having a tungsten carbide core; in this case, the core may be considered the subcaliber projectile. In the muzzle-loading era, the sabot for smooth-bores was a wooden disk, slightly hollowed to receive a portion of the ball. It was usually attached to the ball by tinned iron straps. For rifled artillery the term "sabot" was applied to the papier-mâché or soft metal base used to engage the rifling.

sabotage An act with an intent to injure, interfere with, or obstruct the national defense of a country by willfully injuring or destroying, or attempting to injure or destroy, any national defense or war material, premises, or utilities.

Sabre The North American F-86 Sabre is a single-seat single-engine jet tactical fighter and fighter-bomber originally developed for the USAAF and first flown in 1947. It was the first American sweptwing fighter to see combat (in Korea). Numerous models were developed into the 1950s, and aircraft of this type are in service in about 20 countries. The F-86F has a speed of 687 mph, a range of about 1,000 mi, and armament consisting of six .50 cal. machine guns, plus attachments for two Sidewinder missiles or two 1,000-lb bombs.

SACCS SAC Control System. The operational system that transmits, collects, processes, and displays data to assist the commander in chief of the Strategic Air Command in the command and control of forces.

SACEUR The NATO abbreviation for Supreme Allied Commander Europe.

SACLANT The NATO abbreviation for Supreme Allied Commander Atlantic.

Saddler The NATO code name for a Soviet ICBM with a 5- to 10-megaton warhead.

Sadeye A U.S. cluster bomb used aboard high-performance aircraft.

sad sack A slang term used by U.S. forces in World War II to describe a soldier who, despite any good intentions, was completely ineffective.

Saetta The Macchi C.200 Saetta (Arrow) was an Italian Air Force single-seat single-engine fighter-interceptor and fighter-bomber first flown in December 1937. During the early part of World War II it saw service in Greece, Yugoslavia, Malta, and North Africa. In 1941–1942 it was used in the Russian campaign. Powered by an 870-hp engine, the airplane flew at speeds up to 312 mph and was armed with two 12.7mm Breda-SAFAT machine guns. (Picture, next page.)

SAFAT 7.7mm aircraft machine gun Model 1928 An Italian recoil-operated air-cooled machine gun with a rate of fire of 700 to 800 rounds per minute. It weighed 28 lb and was fed by a 250-round link belt.

safe Of a bomb or ammunition; so constituted and set as not to detonate or function accidentally; in a safe condition.

Safeguard A U.S. antiballistic-missile sys-

saber halberd. (*The Metropolitan Museum of Art, gift of George D. Pratt, 1925.*)

Saab Rb 05A. (*Swedish Air Force.*)

Saab Rb 08A. (*Swedish Defense Staff.*)

Sabre. (*U.S. Air Force.*)

Saetta. (*The Imperial War Museum.*)

tem employing **Spartan** and **Sprint** missiles, which see, and a variety of ground-based systems including a large long-range radar called the "Perimeter Acquisition Radar (PAR)," designed to detect and accurately track missiles at ranges of 1,500 to 3,000 kilometers.

safety A locking or cutoff device that prevents a weapon or missile from being fired accidentally.

safety factor **1.** An increase in range or elevation that must be set on a gun so that friendly troops, over whose heads fire is to be delivered, will not be endangered. **2.** An overload factor in design to ensure safe operation.

safety lanes Specified sea-lanes designated for use in transit by submarines and surface ships to prevent attack by friendly forces.

safety zone An area (land, sea, or air) reserved for noncombat operations of friendly aircraft, surface ships, or ground forces.

safing As applied to weapons and ammunition, the changing from a state of readiness for initiation to a safe condition.

SAGE Semi-Automatic Ground Environment System. The air-weapons control and

warning system for detecting, identifying, tracking, and carrying out interceptor control against air-breathing weapons posing a threat to the United States and Canada.

Sagger The NATO code name for a Soviet wire-guided solid-propellant antitank missile first seen in Moscow in May 1965. It has a length of 2 ft and a diameter of 6 in.

Sagittario The Reggiane Re.2005 Sagittario (Archer) was one of the best fighter aircraft built by Italy during World War II. First flown in 1942, this aircraft was equipped with a 1,475-hp engine and flew at speeds up to 390 mph. It was armed with one engine-mounted 20mm Mauser cannon, two wing-mounted 20mm Mauser cannons, and two 12.7mm Breda-SAFAT machine guns.

Saint A satellite inspector system designed to demonstrate the feasibility of intercepting, inspecting, and reporting on the characteristics of satellites in orbit.

Saint-Chamond 155mm G.P.F. See **French 155mm gun, Models 1917 and 1918.**

Saipan A class of U.S. light aircraft carriers (CVL) of 14,500 tons standard displacement commissioned in 1946–1947. The class included *Saipan* and *Wright.* They had an

overall length of 683 ft, an extreme flight-deck width of 115 ft, a top speed of 33 knots, and a complement of 1,763 men. They carried over 50 aircraft and were armed with forty 40mm and thirty-two 20mm antiaircraft guns.

saker A piece of fifteenth-century English ordnance. It weighed 1,400 lb and fired a projectile weighing 5.5 lb.

salade A fifteenth-century helmet, sometimes with a movable visor. It was put on over the head and did not close under the chin.

Saladin armored car A six-wheeled British vehicle developed from the **Saracen armored personnel carrier,** which see, and in service with British forces since 1955. It has a crew of three, a weight of 11.6 tons, a road speed of 45 mph, and armament consisting of one 76mm gun with a range (HE) of 5.000 yd and two .30 cal. Browning machine guns.

salient In fortifications, pointing away from the center.

Salisbury A class of British frigates designed primarily for the direction of carrier-borne and shore-based aircraft. They have a standard displacement of 2,170 tons, a length of 339 ft, a beam of 40 ft, a speed of 25 knots, and a complement of 207 men. They are armed with two 4.5-in. guns, two 40mm antiaircraft guns, and one Squid triple-barreled depth-charge mortar.

sallet A variant of **salade,** which see.

sally To make a sudden rush in a body from one part of a ship to another, a useful maneuver when a ship is aground forward or aft. Also, the effort of a body of men to clear a certain part of a deck of boarders lodged there.

Sally The Allied code name for the Mitsubishi Ki.21 Type 97 bomber, first flown by the Japanese in 1937 and manufactured until 1944. It was the mainstay of the JAAF heavy-bomber force during World War II. It had a speed of 297 mph and was armed with one 12.7mm machine gun and five 7.7mm machine guns. It could carry a bombload of 2,200 lb and had a range of

Saipan. (*U.S. Navy.*)

about 1,350 mi.

sally port **1.** A large gate or passage in a fortified place. **2.** A large port on each quarter of a fire ship, making possible the escape of the men when the train is fired. Also, a large port in a three-decker.

Salmon A class of U.S. submarines of 1,450 tons standard surface displacement commissioned in 1937–1938. They had a length of 298 ft, a beam of 26 ft, a surface speed of 20 knots (9 knots submerged), and a complement of 55 men. They were armed with eight 21-in. torpedo tubes and one 3-in. deck gun.

Salmson 2 A French two-place single-engine observation biplane that went into production near the end of 1917. It had a maximum speed of 115 mph and was armed with one forward-firing synchronized Vickers machine gun and a Scarff-mounted single Lewis gun or twin-yoked Lewis guns for the observer. A total of 3,200 aircraft of this type were built, serving with 22 French *escadrilles* on the Western front and in Italy and with 11 squadrons of the AEF. (Picture, next page.)

salt box An old English naval term for a case in which a temporary supply of cartridges for large guns was kept on deck.

salted weapon A nuclear weapon which has, in addition to its normal components, certain elements or isotopes which capture neutrons at the time of the explosion and produce radioactive products over and above the usual radioactive weapon debris.

saltpeter A popular name for potassium or sodium nitrate.

salute A greeting or sign of courtesy passed between parties; such as gesturing with the hand, firing a cannon, dipping a flag, dipping the wings of an aircraft, etc.

salvage **1.** Property which has some value in excess of its basic material content but which is in such condition that it has no reasonable prospect of use for any purpose as a unit and its repair or rehabilitation for use as a unit is clearly impractical. **2.** The saving or rescuing of condemned, discarded, or abandoned property and of materials contained therein for reuse, refabrication, or scrapping.

salvage procedure **1.** The recovery, evacuation, and reclamation of damaged, discarded, condemned, or abandoned allied or enemy materiel, ships, craft, or floating equipment for reuse, repair, refabrication, or scrapping. **2.** Naval salvage operations including harbor and channel clearance, diving, hazardous towing and rescue tug services, and the recovery of materiel, ships, craft, or floating equipment sunk offshore or elsewhere stranded.

salvo **1.** In naval gunfire support, a method of fire in which a number of weapons are fired at the same target simultaneously. **2.** In close air support–air inter-

diction operations, a method of delivery in which the release mechanisms are operated so as to release or fire all ordnance of a specific type simultaneously. (Picture, next page.)

salvo fire That method of fire in which weapons are discharged one after the other, usually at intervals of 2 seconds. Not to be confused with "salvo fire" in Navy usage, in which salvo is the equivalent of an artillery volley.

salvo latch A device to prevent the unintentional opening of the breech of a loaded gun until after the gun has been fired.

salvo point Formerly, in coast-artillery usage, a point with known range and azimuth on which the salvo fire of several batteries can be concentrated.

Samaritan The Convair C-131 Samaritan is a twin-engine (piston) military-transport

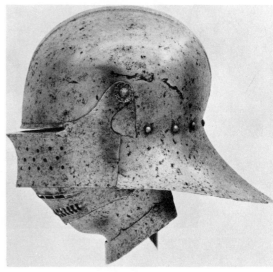

salade. (*The Metropolitan Museum of Art, gift of Edward S. Harkness, 1929.*)

Saladin armored car. (*Alvis Limited.*)

Sally. (*U.S. Air Force.*)

version of the Convair-Liner 240 and was first flown in 1947. It can carry up to 48 passengers and flies at a speed of 313 mph. (Picture, next page.)

SAM-D A solid-propellant air-defense rocket under development by the Army. It has a length of 17 ft and a diameter of 1.33

ft. (Picture, next page.)

Samlet The NATO code name for the Soviet surface-to-surface version of the Kennel air-to-surface missile. Used for coastal defense, it has a length of 26 ft, a wingspan of 14 ft, and a range of 50 mi.

S.A.M.L. S.1 and S.2 Italian (Società Aer-

Salmson 2. (*The Smithsonian Institution, National Air Museum.*)

Samaritan. (*U.S. Air Force.*)

SAM-D. (*U.S. Air Force.*)

onautica Meccanica Lombarda) two-place single-engine reconnaissance biplanes developed in 1917 from the Aviatik B.I design (being built under license). The S.1 was armed with a Revelli machine gun in the rear cockpit and carried up to 88 lb of small bombs. The S.2 had a more powerful engine and often carried camera equipment instead of a bombload. A total of 657 of both types were produced between 1916 and 1918.

Samos   A U.S. Air Force satellite and missile observation system of reconnaissance satellites. It can return definitive terrestrial photographs by electrical transmission or by capsule ejection.

Sandal   The NATO code name for a Soviet IRBM that was a follow-on to **Shyster,** which see. It has a length of 73.3 ft, a diameter of 5.4 ft, and a range of 1,100 mi.

This single-stage liquid-fueled missile was first seen in 1960.

sap   A trench or gallery dug by attackers either to gain entrance to a fortified place or to destroy it.

SAP   Semi-armor-piercing.

sapper   One who digs trenches or tunnels so as to undermine a fortification or to provide a place for the laying of a mine.

sap roller   A stiffly made gabion which a

salvo. A two-gun salvo from the 16-in. guns of the U.S.S. *New Jersey*. (*U.S. Navy.*)

sapper can roll ahead of him for protection from enemy fire.

sap shield A steel plate used for the protection of a sapper.

Saracen armored personnel carrier A British Alvis-built six-wheeled vehicle that was developed between 1950 and 1953. It has a crew of two (plus ten infantrymen), a weight of 10.4 tons, a road speed of 45 mph, and armament consisting of one .30 cal. Browning machine gun.

SARAC machine gun M1953 The MG42/59 made by the German firm of Rheinmettal and sold to Yugoslavia in 7.92mm.

Sarah The radar-guided version of Sidewinder.

Saratoga A U.S. aircraft carrier of 33,000 tons standard displacement commissioned in 1927. It had an overall length of 888 ft, a flight-deck width of 130 ft, a top speed of 33 knots, and a complement of 2,122 men. It carried 90 aircraft and was armed with over 100 antiaircraft guns (total barrels). It had one sister ship, *Lexington*.

Sargo A class of U.S. submarines of 1,450 tons standard displacement commissioned in 1939. They had a length of 310 ft, a beam of 27 ft, a surface speed of 20 knots (9 knots submerged), and a complement of about 55 men. They were armed with eight 21-in. torpedo tubes and one 3-in. deck gun.

sarin (GB) This war gas is one of the **nerve agents,** which see, and has a quick-acting casualty effect. Skin absorption great enough to cause death may occur in 1 to 2 minutes, although death may be delayed for 1 to 2 hours. Respiratory lethal dosages kill in 1 to 10 minutes, and liquid in the eye kills nearly as rapidly.

sarissa The Macedonian spear or pike. It had a length of 21 ft.

Sark The NATO code name for a Soviet two-stage solid-fueled submarine-launched (surface launch only) ballistic missile. It has a length of 45 ft and a diameter of 6 ft.

Saro London A British twin-engine biplane general-purpose coastal-reconnaissance flying boat first flown in 1934.

Sasin The NATO code name for a Soviet two-stage liquid-propellent (storable) ICBM with an estimated range of 6,500 mi. It has a length of 85 ft, a diameter of 9 ft, and a 5- to 10-megaton warhead.

satchel charge A number of blocks of explosive taped to a board fitted with a rope or wire loop for carrying and attaching. The minimum weight of the charge is usually about 15 lb.

saturation bombing Intense area bombing intended to leave no place in a given area free from destructive effects. Saturation bombing may be achieved by dropping many small bombs, by dropping a moderate number of large bombs, or by dropping a single massive bomb.

Saracen armored personnel carrier. (*Alvis Limited.*)

SAU See **search and attack unit.**

Sauer .32 ACP automatic pistol Model 38 A weapon designated as substitute standard for German forces and widely used by air and tank units during World War II. It has a magazine capacity of eight cartridges, an overall length of $6\frac{1}{4}$ in., a barrel length of $3\frac{1}{3}$ in., and a weight of about 20 oz.

Savage The NATO code name for a Soviet three-stage solid-propellant ICBM similar to the U.S. Minuteman. It has an overall length of 66 ft and a range estimated to be from 2,000 to 5,000 mi.

Savoia-Marchetti S.M.79 Sparviero See **Sparviero.**

Savoia-Marchetti SM.82 See **Canguru.**

Savoia-Marchetti SM.84 An Italian three-engine bomber and reconnaissance aircraft developed in 1939. It had a top speed of about 275 mph.

Sawfly The NATO code name for a Soviet third-generation submarine-launched IRBM. It is a two-stage solid-propellant missile considerably larger than the U.S.

Poseidon, and it probably has a range in excess of 2,000 mi. It has a length of 39 ft and a diameter of 6 ft and was first seen in 1967.

sax See **scramasax.**

SB The abbreviation for "medium bomber" (*Srednii bombovos*), used in the names of Russian aircraft from 1925 to 1945, as in SB-2.

SB2C-1 See **Helldiver.**

S-band radar See **radar frequencies.**

SBD-3 See **Dauntless.**

SC A U.S. Navy 110-ft submarine chaser.

scabbard A sheath with an open top. It is usually made of leather, metal, wood, or canvas and is designed to protect edged weapons, rifles, carbines, and submachine guns from the elements and rough usage.

scale **1.** To climb by a ladder, as to scale the ramparts of a fortification. **2.** In armor, the scales of armor collectively. **3.** To clean the inside of an old-time cannon by exploding a small quantity of powder in it.

scale armor Armor made of overlapping

Savoia-Marchetti SM.84. (*Siai Marchetti.*)

Schmidt-Rubin 7.5mm rifle Model 1889. (*Swiss Military Department.*)

metallic scales fastened on a base of leather or cloth.

Scaleboard The NATO code name for a Soviet surface-to-surface missile with a length of about 37 ft and an estimated range of about 450 mi. It was first seen in November 1967.

scaling ladder A ladder used in attacking fortifications and walled towns.

Scamp The NATO code name for a Soviet two-stage solid-propellant mobile strategic missile with a range of 2,500 mi. It has a length of 34 ft and was first seen in 1965.

scanning A sonar echo-ranging system employing a constantly transmitted outgoing signal over the angle of search.

Scapegoat The NATO code name for a Soviet two-stage solid-propellant IRBM having an overall length of about 35 ft. It was first seen in 1967.

Scarff mount A flexible gun mount for an open cockpit, consisting of a circular movable ring or track running around the cockpit, together with a swivel mounting device, by means of which a gun or guns can be swung through 360° and elevated or depressed at will. The scarff mount was used during World War I and after, especially with the Lewis gun. (It is named after Squadron Leader Frederick W. Scarff (d. 1931), of the Royal Naval Air Service and the RAF.)

scarp The side of a ditch next to the parapet.

Scarp The NATO code name for a Soviet two-stage liquid-fueled ICBM first seen in 1967. It is about 120 ft long and is believed to be capable of carrying a 7,700- to 12,100-lb (20-megaton) warhead over a distance of about 6,800 mi.

scatter bomb Any bomb that scatters its effects over a wide area. Fragmentation bombs or fragmentation clusters, as well as certain incendiary bombs equipped with bursters, are scatter bombs.

scattered laying (land-mine warfare) The laying of mines without regard to pattern.

SCC A U.S. Navy control submarine chaser.

Scharnhorst 1. A German battle cruiser completed in 1936 and a sister ship of the **Gneisenau,** for details which see. It was very active in the early part of World War II, sinking three British destroyers and (with the *Gneisenau* in Atlantic raiding forays) 22 other ships. It was sunk on December 26, 1943, by gunfire from the *Duke of York* and torpedoes from British destroyers.

2. *Scharnhorst* was also a class of German armored cruisers completed in 1907. There was one other ship in the class, the *Gneisenau.* These 11,600-ton ships had a length of 450 ft, a complement of 765 men, and main armament consisting of eight 8.2-in. and six 6-in. guns, plus four 18-in. torpedo tubes. Both *Scharnhorst* and *Gneisenau* were sunk by British cruisers in the Battle of the Falkland Islands in December 1914.

scheduled fire A type of prearranged fire executed at a predetermined time.

Schiesswolle 18 Aluminized hexanite, a high explosive, prepared by the Germans during World War II. Also designated as TWMV 1-101, it contained 60 percent TNT, 24 percent hexite, and 16 percent powdered aluminum. It had a large blast effect and was used in loading torpedo warheads.

Schmeisser See **German 9mm Parabellum submachine gun MP 18,II** and **German 9mm Parabellum submachine gun MP 28,II.**

Schmetterling (German for "butterfly.") A German surface-to-air missile developed in World War II. It had an effective range of 10 mi and a ceiling up to 6 to 7 miles. It was radio-command-guided and was to have been used against bomber formations. It never became operational.

Schmidt-Rubin 7.5mm carbine Model 1911 A shorter (43.4 in.) and lighter (8.6 lb) version of the Model 1911 rifle.

Schmidt-Rubin 7.5mm carbine Model 1931 This bolt-action rifle represents the last basic change in the design of Schmidt-Rubin weapons. It has a weight of 8.83 lb, an overall length of 43.5 in., and a barrel length of 25.67 in. It utilizes a six-round detachable box magazine, and the muzzle velocity is 2,560 fps.

Schmidt-Rubin 7.5mm rifle Model 1889 This bolt-action weapon was adopted by Switzerland in 1889. It has an overall length of 51.25 in., a barrel length of 30.7 in., and a weight of 9.8 lb. The muzzle velocity is 2,033 fps, and the detachable magazine has a capacity of 12 rounds. Modifications of this rifle include the M1889/96, which was slightly shorter; the M97 Cadet rifle, which is a single-shot variation; the Model 89/00 short rifle developed for use by various special troops; and the Model 1905 carbine, which is a 7.5-lb version of the rifle.

Schmidt-Rubin 7.5mm rifle Model 1911 This weapon was used by Switzerland and was the first of the Schmidt-Rubins made

for the 7.5mm Model 11 cartridge, which has higher pressures than earlier cartridges. It has an overall length of 51.6 in., a barrel length of 30.7 in., and a weight of 10.15 lb. The muzzle velocity is 2,640 fps, and the weapon utilizes a six-round detachable box magazine.

Schneider ordnance Ordnance originally manufactured at the Schneider works in France and used at times in the French, Russian, American, Japanese, and other armies.

schnorkel See **snorkel.**

Schrage Musik (German for "Jazz Musik.") The code name for a system of obliquely mounted armament on night-fighter aircraft. It was devised in 1943 by a Japanese naval commander, Yasuna Kozono, who applied it to the armament of Nakajima J1N1-C reconnaissance aircraft (later the Irving). First successes were recorded in May 1943, when two J1N1-C's destroyed two B-24 Liberators over Rabaul, New Britain. See **Irving.**

SchtzPzWg The abbreviation for *Schützenpanzerwagen,* German for "infantry armored vehicle."

Schultze powder The first successful smokeless powder. It was invented in about 1865 by the inventor J. F. E. Schultze and consisted of nitrated pellets of wood impregnated with barium and potassium nitrate.

Schützenpanzer German for "armored personnel carrier."

Schutzstaffel (SS) A Nazi organization created in 1923 as a bodyguard to Hitler. The members wore black uniforms with white or brown shirts and were later organized into military divisions (called "Waffen-SS").

Schwagen A German battleship of 11,800 tons displacement completed in 1902. Sister ships included the *Wittelsbach, Wettin, Zähringen,* and *Mecklenburg.* These had a length of 400 ft, a speed of 18 knots, a complement of 650 men, and main armament consisting of four 9.4-in. and eighteen 6-in. guns, plus six 17.7-in. torpedo tubes.

Schwalbe See **Messerschmitt ME 262,** the world's first operational jet fighter.

Schwarm The German designation for an operational flight of four or five airplanes in World War II. A *Schwarm* consisted of two *Rotten;* three *Schwarm* made up a *Staffel;* four *Staffeln* made a *Gruppe.*

Schwarzlose 7.63mm automatic pistol A pistol developed by the Austrian Andrea Schwarzlose in 1898; it saw very little military use. It was the first automatic weapon designed to have the action remain open when the magazine was empty.

Schwarzlose 7.92mm machine gun Model 1907 An Austrian blowback-operated water-cooled machine gun with a rate of fire of 400 to 450 rounds per minute. It weighed 46.5 lb and was fed from a 250-

round fabric belt.

Schwarzlose 8mm machine gun M 07/12 A machine gun used in several models by the Austro-Hungarian Empire and, often in other calibers, by Sweden, the Netherlands, Czechoslovakia, and Italy. It was used in both world wars. This weapon operates on the delayed-blowback principle and is water-cooled. It has an overall length of 42 in., a barrel length of 20.75 in., and a muzzle velocity of 2,000 fps. With a cyclic rate of fire of 400 rounds per minute, the weapon weighs 44 lb, and the tripod weighs 43.75 lb. Cartridges are fed by a canvas belt.

Schwimmwagen A German light 4 × 4 (four-wheeled, four-wheel drive) amphibious Kfz.1/20. This Volkswagen-produced vehicle was used in World War II and could make a speed of about 4 mph in water.

scimitar A sharply curved saber which was once much used by the Arabs and Persians. It is only a cutting weapon, the curve being too great to allow thrusting.

Scimitar The British Supermarine-built Scimitar was a single-seat twin-jet-engine naval carrier-borne fighter-interceptor and strike aircraft first flown in January 1956. It was originally armed with four 30mm Aden cannons.

S Class 1. A class of British submarines of 814 tons standard surface displacement completed in 1942–1945. They had a length of 217 ft, a beam of 23.75 ft, a speed of 10 knots submerged, and a complement of 44 men. They were armed with six 21-in. torpedo tubes and one 4-in. deck gun. **2.** A class of Soviet submarines of 780 tons standard surface displacement launched in 1937–1940. They had a speed of 8.5 knots submerged and armament consisting of six 21-in. torpedo tubes and one 3-in. deck gun. **3.** A class of U.S. submarines commissioned between 1920 and 1925. They were built in tonnage ranges between 790 and 1,000 tons standard surface displacement. Their top surface speed was about 14 knots (10 knots submerged), and they had a complement of about 38 men. They were armed with four or five 21-in. torpedo tubes and one 4-in. deck gun.

sconce In fortifications, a small redoubt or fort located away from the main works.

Scoop Pair The NATO code name for a type of Soviet E-band surface-to-air missile (SAM) and surface-to-surface missile (SSM) acquisition and fire-control radar.

scope 1. A cathode-ray screen or tube, such as the one used in a radar set. **2.** Short for "telescopic sight."

scorched earth A policy and process by which a retreating army destroys everything of any possible value to the enemy, such as food, fuel, equipment, buildings, railways, etc.

scorpion The name of various weapons

Schwarzlose 8mm machine gun M 07/12. (*The Smithsonian Institution, War Department Collection.*)

scimitar. (*The Smithsonian Institution, Patent Office Collection.*)

Scimitar. (*Vickers Ltd.*)

Scorpion. (*U.S. Air Force.*)

used at different times and places. **1.** A type of European halberd with a deep, narrow blade. **2.** A type of East Indian knife. **3.** An ancient instrument for grasping an enemy's battering ram. **4.** A type of ancient cannon. **5.** A small catapult operated by one man.

Scorpion 1. The Northrop F-89 Scorpion is a two-place twin-engine all-weather jet interceptor developed during the late 1940s for the USAF. It has a speed in excess of 600 mph and a range of about 2,000 mi.

Scorpion light tank. (*Alvis Limited.*)

One version was armed with one hundred and four 2.75-in. rockets, while others carried Falcon and Genie missiles. **2.** The name given to a full-track 90mm air-transportable self-propelled gun. It is a mobile antitank gun with a crew of four. It was replaced by the **General Sheridan,** which see.

Scorpion light tank A British tank developed in the late 1960s. It has a crew of three, a weight of 7.8 tons, a road speed of 50 mph, and armament consisting of one 76mm gun (with a range of about 5,000 meters) and a coaxial 7.62mm machine gun.

Scotti 7.7mm aircraft machine gun Model 1928 An Italian gas-operated air-cooled machine gun with a rate of fire of 450 to 500 rounds per minute. Used in limited numbers during World War II, it weighed 22 lb and was fed from a 250-round belt magazine.

scout 1. A soldier, vessel, or aircraft used to reconnoiter and gain information about the force and movements of the enemy. **2.** An early designation, chiefly British, for a lightly armed fighter aircraft. **3.** An aircraft used in search and rescue operations. **4.** Short for "scout bomber."

Scout See **ARSV.**

scout bomber A former Navy designation for a carrier-based airplane used as both a scout or reconnaissance plane and a bomber.

scout car A lightly armed and armored reconnaissance vehicle, either wheeled or half-track, without turrets, adapted for high-speed operation on hard roads and for cross-country missions.

scout cruiser Formerly, a high-speed vessel with moderate displacement and with heavier armament than a destroyer or light cruiser.

scouting In naval terminology, a mission involving search, patrol, tracking, or reconnaissance by a surface ship, submarine, or

scramasax. (*The Metropolitan Museum of Art, Bashford Dean Memorial Collection.*)

aircraft.

Scrag The NATO code name for a Soviet liquid-propellant three-stage ICBM first shown in 1965. It has a length of 120 ft and an estimated range of 5,000 mi.

Scram The NATO code name for a Soviet liquid-propellant three-stage ICBM first seen in 1965. It has a length of 124 ft, a diameter of 9 ft, and an estimated range of 5,000 mi.

scramasax An ancient short, single-edged knife with a broad blade about 5 to 15 in. in length. It was used by the Anglo-Saxons and Vikings. It was a shorter and later version of the sword-length sax.

scramble 1. The whole action involved in getting interceptors into the air in the shortest time possible, sometimes without adequate warmup. **2.** The complete action of a single interceptor pilot in climbing aboard his aircraft, starting his engine, taxiing, making the takeoff run, and getting into the air in the shortest time possible. **3.** To alter transmitted radio or telephone frequencies in order to make them unintelligible unless unscrambled.

screen Ships stationed to protect a unit, as an antisubmarine screen.

screening smoke A smoke cloud produced by chemical agents or smoke generators; used to conceal friendly troops and/or to deny observation by enemy troops.

screw The propeller of a ship.

Scrooge The NATO code name for a Soviet missile with an estimated range of 3,500 mi first seen in 1965.

scrub To cancel a plan, mission, or operation, especially after a long wait or psychological buildup; to cancel a planned attack on a target.

Scrubber The NATO code name for a Soviet cruise missile with a range of about 100 mi.

Scud-A and Scud-B The NATO code names for Soviet surface-to-surface missiles. Scud-B, first seen in 1965, is somewhat larger than Scud-A (which has a length of 35 ft, an estimated firing weight of 10,000 lb, and an estimated range of 50 mi).

Scud-C A Soviet medium-range missile with a length of 38 ft, a diameter of 3 ft, and a range of 450 mi.

Scunner The NATO code name for a single-stage liquid-fueled missile with a range of about 150 mi. It is a Soviet-built German V-2.

scuppet A variant of **escopette,** which see.

scutatus The heavily armed Byzantine foot soldier. He was armed with a lance, a sword, and an ax with a spike opposite the cutting edge.

scutum A shield carried by Roman heavily armed infantry. It was made of wood covered with leather and was sometimes bound with an iron rim. Rectangular in shape, the shield was about 4 ft long and $2\frac{1}{2}$ ft wide.

SD See **Sicherheitsdienst.**

SdKfz The abbreviation for *Sonderkraftfahrzeug*, German for "infantry armored vehicle."

SDV Swimmer delivery vehicle.

S.E.5 and S.E.5a British single-place single-engine biplane fighters first flown in November 1916. The first S.E.5's were delivered in March 1917. The S.E.5a, with a more powerful engine, began deliveries in June of that year. They had a speed of about 120 mph and were armed with two forward-firing machine guns, a Vickers and a Lewis. The S.E.5a gained a reputation for its flying qualities and performance and remained in service until the end of the war. Some were equipped with racks for four 25-lb bombs.

SE-4400 A French Air Force air-breathing surface-to-air missile with a range of about 25 mi.

SEA Southeast Asia.

Seabat A U.S. Navy antisubmarine-warfare-helicopter version of the Sikorsky S-58. See **Choctaw.**

Seabee From CB, or construction battalion. Any member of such a battalion formed as a volunteer branch of the U.S. Navy Civil Engineer Corps. During World War II, Seabees were responsible for building (and sometimes defending) aviation facilities and naval installations.

Seacat A short-range antiaircraft missile in use with the British Royal Navy. Built by Short, this weapon has been ordered by the navies of several other countries. It has an overall length of 4.9 ft and a diameter of 0.6 ft. The land-based version of this missile is designated **Tigercat,** which see.

seacoast artillery A class of artillery formerly used for seacoast defense. It consisted of fixed guns, howitzers, and mortars defending the harbors and manned by the former Coast Artillery Corps. As a class of artillery the term is now obsolete.

SeaCobra The Bell AH-1J SeaCobra is a twin-engine version of the HueyCobra. It has a range of 360 mi, a crew of two, a speed of 215 mph, and armament consisting of one General Electric XM-197 three-barreled turret-mounted 20mm cannon which fires 750 shots per minute. In wing pylons it may also carry Minigun pods and rocket pods.

Sea Dart A ship-to-air weapon system capable of intercepting aircraft and air- and surface-launched missiles. Built by Hawker Siddeley Dynamics, this missile has an overall length of 14.25 ft and a range of about 20 mi. (Picture, next page.)

Seafire This single-seat shipboard fighter-bomber was built by Supermarine for the British Royal Navy. It is the carrier version of the Spitfire. These aircraft saw considerable service during World War II, both in the Mediterranean and in the Far East. They flew at speeds up to 352 mph and were armed with two 20mm Hispano cannons and four .303 cal. Browning machine guns, plus one 500-lb or two 250-lb bombs.

Seafox This British single-engine two-seat biplane light reconnaissance twin-float seaplane was developed by Fairey and was first flown in 1936. It served as a catapult aircraft aboard various cruisers and armed merchant cruisers. It was armed with one .303 cal. machine gun and had a top speed of 124 mph.

Seagull The Curtiss SOC-1/4 was a single-engine two-seat biplane scout-observation seaplane first flown in 1934. It was adopted by the U.S. Navy as the standard scout-observation aircraft aboard battleships, cruisers, and aircraft carriers. It was widely used during World War II, outliving its intended replacement, the Curtiss SO3C-1/4 Seamew. The Seagull flew at a top speed of 168 mph and was armed with two .30 cal. machine guns and two 100-lb bombs.

Seahawk The Curtiss SC-1 was a single-engine single-seat shipboard scout and air-sea rescue float seaplane developed for the U.S. Navy and first flown in 1944. It was designed for use as standard equipment aboard battleships and cruisers. It had a speed of 313 mph and was armed with two .50 cal. machine guns and two 250-lb and two 100-lb bombs.

Sea Hawk A British single-seat naval jet fighter and fighter-bomber developed by Hawker in the early 1950s and produced by Armstrong Whitworth. It was armed with four 20mm cannons and carried bombs and rockets on under-wing racks.

Seahorse A U.S. Navy and Coast Guard utility transport-helicopter version of the Sikorsky S-58. See **Choctaw.**

Sea Killer Mk 1 A short-range surface-to-surface ship-based guided missile developed by the Italian firm of Contraves Italiana. It has an overall length of 12 ft 3 in., a weight of 370 lb, and a maximum effective range of 6.2 mi.

S.E.5a. (*The Smithsonian Institution, National Air Museum.*)

Seabat. (*U.S. Navy.*)

Sea Killer Mk 2 A surface-to-surface ship-based guided missile developed by Contraves Italiana. It has an overall length of 14.75 ft, a weight of 530 lb, and a maximum range of over 11.5 mi.

Sea King An antisubmarine and mine-countermeasure helicopter developed by Sikorsky for the U.S. Navy and built under license by Westland for the Royal Navy. It is also in use by several other countries. It has a speed of 166 mph and a range of about 670 mi. It carries 840 lb of homing torpedoes, depth charges, etc. A USAF version of this helicopter is called the "Jolly

Seacat. (*Short Brothers & Harland.*)

SeaCobra. (*Bell Helicopter Company.*)

Sea Dart. (*Hawker Siddeley Aviation Ltd.*)

Sea King. (*U.S. Navy.*)

Sea Knight. (*U.S. Navy.*)

Sea Otter. (*Vickers Ltd.*)

Green Giant" and can carry 26 passengers.

Sea Knight The Boeing Vertol CH-46 or UH-46 is a transport and utility helicopter used by the U.S. Navy and Marine Corps and first flown in 1958. It carries 25 troops and has a speed of 161 mph. The UH-46 version has a watertight hull for water landings and takeoffs.

Sea Lance A U.S. Navy shipboard version of **Lance,** which see.

sea-launched ballistic missile A missile launched from a submarine or surface ship.

Sea Lion The code name for the German plan to invade England in World War II. See **Seeloewe.**

Sea Mauler A sea-based version of the Army's Mauler surface-to-air missile.

Seamew The Curtiss SO3C-1/4 single-engine two-seat scout-observation and patrol float seaplane first flown in 1939 and intended as a replacement for the Curtiss SOC-1/4 Seagull. It was not a success, however, and saw limited operational service. It flew at a top speed of 182 mph and was armed with two .30 cal. machine guns and two 325-lb bombs.

Sea Otter A British Supermarine-built single-engine biplane amphibious flying boat that entered service in 1944. It carried three or four crew members, was armed with three Vickers machine guns, and had a speed of 150 mph. It was used for anti-submarine and air-sea rescue service.

seaplane **1.** An airplane designed or equipped to take off and alight on water only, i.e., either a floatplane or a flying boat, as distinguished from a landplane, carrier plane, or amphibian. **2.** In some contexts, a floatplane, as distinguished from a flying boat.

sear That part of the lockwork of a firearm that engages the hammer or striker to hold it in a cocked position.

search **1.** An operation to locate an enemy force known or believed to be at sea. **2.** A systematic reconnaissance of a defined area, such that all parts of the area pass within visibility. **3.** To distribute gunfire over an area in depth by successive changes in gun elevation.

search and rescue The use of aircraft, surface craft, submarines, and specialized rescue teams and equipment to search for and rescue personnel in distress on land or at sea.

search/attack unit (SAU) Two or more ships or aircraft teamed for coordinated search and attack on submarines.

searcher A long-handled tool used to check the bore of a muzzle-loading cannon for pits, cracks, or other defects.

searching fire Fire distributed in depth by

successive changes in gun elevation.

searchlight An apparatus for projecting a beam of light upon an object, especially on aircraft flying at night; the beam of light projected.

search mission (air) An air reconnaissance by one or more aircraft dispatched to locate an object or objects known or suspected to be in a specific area.

search pattern A pattern used in searching for something, as by aircraft in searching for lost personnel or equipment or by aircraft or radar in searching for an intruding force.

sea return An indication on a radarscope caused by the reflection of radio waves back from the surface of the sea.

Seaslug A surface-to-air shipboard guided missile built by Hawker Siddeley Dynamics and presently in service with the Royal Navy. It has a length of about 20 ft and an effective ceiling in excess of 50,000 ft.

Sea Sparrow A ship-launched version of the **Sparrow III** missile, which see. It is used for short-range point defense against enemy aircraft.

Seasprite This single-engine 14-place armed search and rescue helicopter was developed by Kaman for the U.S. Navy and was first flown in 1959. It has a range of 340 mi and a speed of about 156 mph. It is armed with a chin-mounted Minigun turret and waist-mounted machine guns.

Sea Stallion A Sikorsky heavy assault transport helicopter developed for U.S. forces and first flown in 1964. It has a cruising speed of 172 mph and a range of 258 mi and carries 38 passengers or 8,000 lb of cargo. It is designated the HH-65 or CH-65 and is called by the USAF the "Super Jolly Green Giant."

sea surveillance The systematic observation of surface and subsurface sea areas by all available and practicable means primarily for the purpose of locating, identifying, and determining the movements of ships, submarines, and other vehicles, friendly and enemy, proceeding on or under the surface of the world's seas and oceans.

seat 1. A support or holder for a mechanism or for a part of one. **2.** To fit correctly in or on a holder or in a prepared position, as to seat a fuze in a bomb, a projectile in the bore of a gun, or a cartridge in a chamber.

seating Specifically, the distance to which a projectile is rammed into the bore of a cannon, usually measured from the base of the projectile to the rear face of the breech.

SEATO Southeast Asia Treaty Organization.

Sea Vixen FAW Mk 1 and Mk 2 A two-seat carrier-based all-weather jet interceptor and ground-attack aircraft developed by Hawker Siddeley and currently in service with the Royal Navy. It has a speed of

Sea Sparrow. (*Raytheon.*)

Sea Stallion. (*Sikorsky Aircraft.*)

about 700 mph and is armed with twenty-eight 2-in. rockets, plus under-wing pylons for carrying bombs and rockets. (Picture, next page.)

seax A variant of "sax." See **scramasax.**

secondary armament In ships with multiple-size guns installed, that battery consisting of guns next largest to those of the main battery.

secondary blast injuries Those injuries sustained from the indirect effects of a blast, such as falling rubble from a collapsed building or missiles (debris or objects) which have been picked up by the winds generated and hurled against an individual. Also includes injuries resulting when individuals are hurled against stationary objects.

secondary mission Any mission assigned an organization, group of persons, or person that is deemed to be additional or supplementary to the primary mission.

secondary port A port with one or more berths, normally at quays, which can accommodate oceangoing ships for discharge.

secondary target A target having second priority in case the primary target cannot be attacked.

secondary weapon A supporting or auxiliary weapon of a unit, vehicle, position, or aircraft. It is generally a gun of smaller caliber than the primary weapon, and its purpose is to protect or supplement the fire of the primary weapon.

second front A term used extensively in World War II to designate a front opened

Sea Vixen. (*Hawker Siddeley Aviation Ltd.*)

up after a single front had been established.

second-in-command   The officer next in rank to the commanding officer.

second lieutenant   A commissioned rank in the U.S. Air Force, Army, or Marine Corps immediately below first lieutenant and the lowest of the commissioned ranks. The insignia of rank is a gold bar.

second strike   The first counterblow of a war. (Generally associated with nuclear operations.)

Second World War   A common name for the world war (1939–1945) that ended with the defeat of the Axis Powers.

secret   See **defense classification.**

secret weapon   A weapon closely guarded or kept under concealment so as to be used with advantage before countermeasures can be taken against it.

section   1.   As applied to ships or naval aircraft, a tactical subdivision of a division. It is normally one-half of a division in the case of ships, and two aircraft in the case of aircraft.   **2.**   A subdivision of an office, installation, territory, works, or organization; especially a major subdivision of a staff.   **3.**   A tactical unit of the Army and Marine Corps. A section is smaller than a platoon and larger than a squad and is the basic tactical unit.

sector   1.   A defense area designated by boundaries within which a unit operates and for which it is responsible.   **2.**   One of the subdivisions of a coastal frontier.

sector of fire   An area assigned to an individual, a weapon, or a unit to be covered by fire.

secure   1.   To get credit for a kill.   **2.**   To gain air superiority and take measures against its loss; to gain an objective and take measures against its loss.   **3.**   To close up a safe, office, or building so as to provide security for classified matter.   **4.**   In the Navy, to end or wind up an exercise or operation.

secure (operations)   To gain possession of a position or terrain feature, with or without force, and to make such disposition as will prevent, as far as possible, its destruction or loss by enemy action.

security   1.   Measures taken by a command to protect itself from espionage, observation, sabotage, annoyance, or surprise.   **2.**   A condition which results from the establishment and maintenance of protective measures which ensure a state of inviolability from hostile acts or influences.   **3.**   With respect to classified matter, the condition which prevents unauthorized persons from having access to official information which is safeguarded in the interests of national defense.   **4.**   The protection of supplies or supply establishments against enemy attack, fire, theft, and sabotage.

security patrol   An air patrol that warns against surprise activity on the part of the enemy.

Seehund   (German for "Seal.")   **1.**   A class of World War II German midget submarines (Type XXVIIB) of about 15 tons displacement. They had a length of 39 ft, a beam of 5.5 ft, a submerged speed of 6 knots, and a crew of two. They carried two 21-in. torpedoes.   **2.**   A German World War II glide bomb without propulsion. The bomb, weighing 2,000 lb (1,000 of which was high-explosive warhead), was flight-stabilized and equipped with a homing device.

Seeloewe   (German for "Sea Lion.")   The World War II code name for the German plan to invade the United Kingdom after the fall of France. It was not carried out.

seen fire   Fire which is continuously aimed at the future position of an aircraft, the aim being derived from visual observation.

selected mine   A controlled underwater mine which has been connected, through the selector assembly, to the control equipment at the shore station. A selected mine is exclusive of all other mines in its group and may be fired, tested, or disarmed independently of the remainder of the group.

selective service   Short for "Selective Service System." It also describes the service of a person in the armed forces in consequence of being inducted under the Selective Service System, as distinguished from "voluntary service."

Selective Service System   A system in the United States for selecting and inducting persons into the armed forces. This system was set up by the Selective Training and Service Act of 1940 and was reestablished by the Selective Service Act of 1948.

self-destroying fuze   A fuze designed to destroy itself (and the associated munition) after flight to a range greater than that to any probable target. It is employed in antiaircraft ammunition to avoid impact in friendly territory.

self-loading   Of a firearm or gun; utilizing either the explosive gases or recoil to extract the empty case and chamber the next round. Self-loading firearms or guns include both semiautomatic and full automatic types.

self-propelled   1.   Of a gun; mounted on a vehicle that has its own motive power.   **2.**   Of a missile; propelled by fuel carried by the missile itself, as in the case of a rocket.   **3.**   Of a military unit; having self-propelled guns.   **4.**   Of a vehicle; given motion by means of a self-contained motor.

self-propelled antiaircraft artillery gun   A complete projectile-firing weapon that is mounted on a self-propelled vehicle. It is designed for use as a mobile antiaircraft weapon.

self-propelled antitank gun   A complete projectile-firing weapon mounted on a self-propelled vehicle. It is designed for use against tanks or other armored vehicles.

self-propelled artillery   Artillery weapons permanently installed on vehicles which provide motive power for the piece. These weapons are fired from the vehicle.

self-propelled field-artillery gun.   A complete projectile-firing weapon mounted on a self-propelled vehicle. It is designed for use as a mobile artillery weapon.

self-propelled heavy howitzer   A complete projectile-firing weapon, with a medium muzzle velocity and a curved trajectory, mounted on a self-propelled vehicle. The bore diameter is larger than 200mm. It is designed for use as mobile artillery.

self-propelled light howitzer   A complete projectile-firing weapon, with a medium muzzle velocity and a curved trajectory, mounted on a self-propelled vehicle. The bore diameter is between 30 and 125 mm. It is designed for use as a mobile artillery or infantry weapon.

self-propelled medium howitzer   A complete projectile-firing weapon, with a medium muzzle velocity and a curved trajectory, mounted on a self-propelled vehicle. The bore diameter is between 126 and 200 mm. It is designed for use as mobile artillery.

self-propelled sled   A powered vehicle supported on pontoons with endless tracks, or runners and pontoons with endless tracks, deriving its traction power from the endless tracks. It is designed to transport personnel and/or cargo over snow-covered terrain.

self-sealing Of a fuel tank; lined with a substance, often a synthetic rubber, that closes immediately over any small rupture in the tank, such as a bullet hole.

Semag 20mm cannon A Swiss blowback-operated air-cooled cannon with a rate of fire of 350 rounds per minute. It weighed 94.6 lb and was fed from a 20-round magazine. It was used as both an aircraft and an antiaircraft weapon.

semaphore A rapid method of visual communications using handflags or lanterns.

semi-armor-piercing bomb A missile, designed for dropping from aircraft, which is capable of penetrating lightly armored ships' hulls and reinforced concrete. It usually contains an explosive charge weighing about 30 percent of the total weight of the bomb.

semiautomatic Of a firearm or gun, utilizing part of the force of an exploding cartridge to extract the empty case and chamber the next round, but requiring a separate pull of the trigger to fire each round. Hence, semiautomatic rifle; semiautomatic pistol; semiautomatic weapon; semiautomatic fire; etc.

semibastion Half of a bastion as measured by dividing the bastion at the salient angle.

semifixed ammunition Ammunition in which the cartridge case is not permanently attached to the projectile.

semimobile artillery Artillery weapons which are designed for movement but which require partial disassembly to place in firing position. Wheels or other suspension devices are removed from the mount to permit its resting on the ground. Examples are 90mm and 120mm antiaircraft weapons, 8-in. guns, and 240mm howitzers.

semirigid airship A dirigible having its main envelope reinforced by some means other than a completely rigid framework.

Sendai A class of Japanese cruisers of about 5,195 tons standard displacement built in the mid-1920s and used during World War II. They had a length of 535 ft, a beam of 48 ft, a speed of 33 knots, and a complement of 450 men. They were armed with seven 5.5-in. and two 3-in. guns, plus four torpedo tubes and one seaplane. The three ships in this class (*Sendai*, *Jintsu*, and *Naka*) were lost during World War II.

sensor A technical means to extend man's natural senses; a piece of equipment which detects and indicates terrain configuration, the presence of military targets, and other natural and man-made objects and activities by means of energy emitted or reflected by such targets or objects. The energy may be nuclear, electromagnetic (including the visible and invisible portions of the spec-

self-propelled artillery, the U.S. 90mm SP antitank gun M56. (*U.S. Army.*)

trum), chemical, biological, thermal, or mechanical, including sound, blast, and earth vibration.

sentinel A person charged with standing guard and giving notice of danger when it arrives.

sentry A guard, especially one who stands guard at a point where only properly authorized and identified persons are permitted to pass.

sentry box A place, such as a hut or box, to provide shelter for a sentry at his post.

separate-loading ammunition Ammunition in which the projectile, propellant charge (bag-loaded), and primer are handled and loaded separately into the gun. No cartridge case is utilized in this type of ammunition, though the powder is usually packaged in a bag or paper cartridge.

Serb The NATO code name for a Soviet underwater-to-surface Polaris-type missile designed for submarine launch. This two-stage solid-fueled IRBM has a length of 31 ft and a diameter of 4.5 ft.

SERE The acronym for "survival, evasion, resistance to interrogation."

sergeant The highest noncommissioned officer.

Sergeant A surface-to-surface missile system developed by Sperry Rand for the U.S. Army and deployed operationally in 1961. It is a medium-range field-artillery weapon utilizing a solid-propellant sustainer (and is a follow-on to the liquid-propelled Corporal). It has a length of 34.5 ft, a firing weight of 10,100 lb, and a range from 28 (minimum) to 85 (maximum) mi. Nuclear or conventional warheads may be used.

serial number Any number from a series used to identify a person, piece of equipment, or the like.

seriously wounded A stretcher case.

serpentine **1.** A type of cannon used in the fifteenth through the seventeenth centuries. It was produced in various calibers but was usually longer and lighter than a bombard. **2.** The S-shaped moving arm on the lock of a matchlock firearm. It is used to hold the slow match. **3. Serpentine powder,** which see.

Sergeant. (*U.S. Army.*)

Sharps .52 cal. carbine. (*The Smithsonian Institution.*)

Sharps .52 cal. rifle. (*The Smithsonian Institution.*)

serpentine powder   Black powder ground dry to a flourlike composition. At about the middle of the fifteenth century it was supplanted by corned powder.

service   The preparation, execution, and conduct of fire with service or target-practice ammunition.

service ammunition   Ammunition intended for combat, rather than for training purposes.

service award   An award for honorable service conferred upon an individual or unit, entitling a person or a member of the unit to wear a certain medal or device; a medal or device authorized by such an award. Service awards are distinguished from decorations and include various theater medals or ribbons, the American Campaign Medal, the Good Conduct Medal, and the overseas bar.

service marking   Symbols, numerals, or letters that are painted, stenciled, or stamped on supplies or ammunition to provide information needed for proper handling, storage, and use.

service medal   A medal for service in a specific campaign or theater of operations.

service of the piece   The operation and maintenance of a gun or other equipment by its crew.

service pistol   A standard handgun of a nation's military forces. In the United States, the .45 cal. automatic pistol Model 1911 or 1911A1.

service ribbon   A ribbon or ribbon bar of prescribed size, identical in color and design to a suspension ribbon, worn on the uniform in lieu of a decoration or medal.

service star   A small star-shaped piece of metal worn on a campaign ribbon or ribbon bar and signifying membership in a unit

shell case. (*The Smithsonian Institution.*)

that participated in a battle or campaign. Each bronze service star worn stands for a separate battle or campaign. Each silver service star signifies participation in five battles or campaigns.

service stripe   A sleeve mark worn on uniforms to denote length of service. The slang term for such a stripe is "hash mark."

service test   See **user test.**

setback   The force of inertia which tends to move certain fuze parts to the rear as a projectile is fired. It is used to arm a fuze.

settling rounds   Rounds fired at varying angles of elevation to seat the spade and baseplate of a gun mount firmly in the ground.

Sevastopol   A Soviet battleship of about 23,000 tons standard displacement completed in 1915. (Ships of the same design included *Oktyabraskaya Revolutsia*, *Petropavlovsk*, and *Poltava*.) *Sevastopol* was refitted and reboilered in 1936–1939. It had a length of 619 ft, a beam of 87 ft, a speed of 23 knots, and a complement of 1,087 men. Main armament consisted of twelve 12-in. and sixteen 4.7-in. guns.

Seydlitz   A German battle cruiser completed in 1913. It had a displacement of 25,000 tons and main armament consisting of ten 11-in. guns, twelve 6-in. guns, and four 20-in. torpedo tubes. It had a speed of 26.5 knots.

SF   A U.S. Navy fleet submarine.

Shackleton   A British Avro-built long-range maritime-reconnaissance aircraft with four piston engines and a crew of 10. First flown in 1949, this aircraft has a speed of about 300 mph and is armed with two 20mm cannons and antishipping weapons such as bombs, mines, and depth charges.

Shaddock   The NATO code name for a Soviet cruise missile with a range of about 200 mi. It has a length of 42 ft. In addition to a ground version, there is a naval version for deployment on surface ships and submarines.

SHAEF   In World War II, Supreme Headquarters, Allied Expeditionary Force.

shakedown   A period of adjustment, cleanup, and training for a ship after commissioning or a major overhaul. After commissioning, a ship also makes a shakedown cruise, usually including a visit to several foreign ports.

shako   A kind of tall military cap made of felt, leather, or fur.

shallow-fording ability   The ability of a vehicle or gun equipped with built-in waterproofing, with its suspension in contact with the ground, to negotiate a water obstacle without the use of a special waterproofing kit.

SHAPE   The NATO abbreviation for Supreme Headquarters Allied Powers Europe. A part of NATO established in December 1950 to execute its military plans.

shaped charge   An explosive charge so shaped as to have a hollow at one place, the hollow causing the blast to take a desired direction when the charge is detonated. It is also called "cavity charge" and, in Great Britain, "hollow charge."

Shark   A name given the P-40 by the Flying Tigers.

Sharps .52 cal. carbine   A breechloading single-shot carbine used during the American Civil War. It had a length of 37.5 in. and a weight of 8 lb.

Sharps .52 cal. rifle   A breechloading single-shot weapon used during the American Civil War. It had a length of 47 in. and a weight of 8.75 lb.

sharpshooter   **1.** A designation applied to one who has met a certain standard of excellence in marksmanship. The classification ranks above marksman and below expert.   **2.** A member of a specified regiment such as the First and Second U.S. Sharpshooters of the Civil War.

Sharps rifle   A percussion-lock breechloading weapon invented by the American gunsmith Christian Sharps in 1848. Many variations were made beginning with rifles that used paper or linen cartridges, with later use of metallic cartridges. A dropping-block breech action was used. This weapon was used by the U.S. Army in the West and also extensively during the Civil War.

shavetail   Formerly, an untrained mule and a slang term applied to a recently appointed second lieutenant.

Shawnee   The Boeing-built utility helicopter developed for the U.S. Army. It can carry up to 20 passengers and has a speed of 140 mph and a range of 450 mi. The USAF version is called "Workhorse."

Shch   A class of Soviet submarines of 620 tons standard surface displacement produced in large numbers between 1935 and 1947. They had a speed of 8.5 knots submerged and were armed with six 21-in. torpedo tubes.

sheaf Planned planes of fire which produce a desired pattern of bursts with rounds fired by two or more weapons.

sheaf arrow An old English military arrow.

sheaf of arrows Twenty-four arrows.

sheath A case or scabbard for a sword or knife blade.

Shed Light The overall U.S. Air Force designation for R&D and production effort in some 75 programs to develop nighttime sensor, illumination, and weapon systems to improve the capability of aircraft to find, target, and attack hostile forces or facilitate attack by ground forces.

shell 1. A hollow metal projectile designed to be projected from a gun, containing, or intended to contain, a high-explosive, chemical, atomic, or other charge. **2.** A shotgun cartridge or a cartridge for artillery or small arms. **3.** To shoot at with projectiles. In nomenclature, the term "projectile" is now used in sense 1, and the term "cartridge" in sense 2.

shell burst The bursting of a shell.

shell case That part of a cartridge or complete round for holding a charge, primer, and (usually) projectile; a case. The term "shell case" is applied to the cases of small-arms ammunition as well as to those of cannon ammunition.

shell-destroying tracer A tracer which includes an explosive element beyond the tracer element and which is designed to cause activation of the explosive by the tracer after the antiaircraft projectile has passed the target point, thus destroying the projectile to avoid impact in friendly territory.

shellfire The firing or shooting of shells; a bombardment by artillery.

shell hole, shell crater The cavity made by the explosion of a shell.

shell hooks A device used to hoist or move heavy projectiles.

shelling report Any report of enemy shelling containing information on caliber, direction, time, density, and area shelled.

shell room The projectile stowage area in a ship's turret.

shelter half One of the interchangeable halves of a two-man shelter tent, one such half being a part of each man's field equipment.

Shenandoah A U.S. Navy rigid airship destroyed in a line squall over Ohio in September 1925. It had been in service for 2 years at the time of its loss.

Sheridan The U.S. light tank M551 was introduced in limited service in 1967. It is air-transportable and can be dropped by parachute. It has a crew of four, a weight of 15 tons, and a road speed of 43 mph, and it is armed with a 152mm gun launcher that launches a Shillelagh missile or fires a conventional 152mm round. Secondary ar-

Sheridan. (*U.S. Army.*)

mament consists of two machine guns: one .50 cal. and one 7.62mm.

Sherman The U.S. tank, medium, M4A3E8, which was first introduced in 1944 and was employed in armored divisions. With a crew of five, this tank was armed with one 76mm gun M1A2, caliber length 53, plus one .50 cal. machine gun M2 for antiaircraft purposes and one .30 cal. machine gun M1919A4. It weighed 37.1 tons and traveled at speeds up to about 26 mph.

Sherman V C (M4A4) This was the British tank, medium, and was also called "Fire Fly." It was introduced early in 1944 and had a crew of five. The armament consisted of one 17-pounder (3-in.) gun, caliber length 60, plus a .50 cal. and a .30 cal. machine gun. With the addition of the 17-pounder, this tank became as effective as the German Panther. In combat, the Germans were ordered to destroy them before the regular Shermans armed with 75mm guns.

shield 1. Armor plate mounted on a gun carriage to protect the operating mechanism and gun crew from enemy fire. **2.** A broad piece of defensive armor usually carried in the left hand and used for protection in combat. Shields were used in ancient times and throughout the Middle Ages until the invention of firearms.

shielding 1. Material of suitable thickness and physical characteristics used to protect personnel from radiation during the manufacture, handling, and transportation of fissionable and radioactive materials. **2.** Obstructions which tend to protect personnel or materials from the effects of a nuclear explosion.

shifting fire Fire delivered at constant range at varying deflections; it is used to cover the entire width of a target.

Shillelagh A weapon system including gun launcher and fire-control system mounted on the main battle tank and assault reconnaissance vehicle for employment against enemy armor, troops, and field fortifications. It has a length of about 3 ft 9 in. and a firing weight of about 60 lb. Designated as XMGM-51, this missile has a range of 2.5+ mi. (Picture, next page.)

shimose See **trinitrophenol.**

Shinano A Japanese supercarrier of 64,800 tons standard displacement commissioned on November 19, 1944. It had a speed of 27 knots and carried 54 aircraft. It was sunk off the coast of Hunshu, Japan, by a *Balao* class submarine (the U.S.S. *Archerfish*) on November 29, 1944, only 10 days after commissioning. It was the largest warship ever sunk by a submarine.

Shin Chuo Kogyo 9mm Parabellum submachine gun Currently manufactured by the Shin Chuo Kogyo Company in Japan. It has a cyclic rate of fire of 600 rounds per minute, a muzzle velocity of about 1,200 fps, and sights graduated for 100 and 200 meters. It has an overall length with stock folded of 30 in., a barrel length of 6 or 7.3 in., and a weight of 8.8 lb.

Shin Meiwa PX-S A Japanese four-turboprop STOL maritime reconnaissance flying boat in service with the Japanese Maritime Self-Defense Force and first flown in 1967. It has a crew of 10 and a speed of 340 mph and carries a weapon load of 5,578 lb, including homing torpedoes, 5-in. rockets, and antisubmarine bombs. (Picture, next page.)

Shinyo 1. A Japanese aircraft carrier converted in 1942 from the former German

Shillelagh, as seen fired from a Sheridan light tank. (*U.S. Army.*)

Shin Meiwa PX-S. (*Shin Meiwa Industry Co. Ltd.*)

Shoho, the *Zuiho,* under attack by aircraft from the U.S.S. *Enterprise.*

liner *Scharnhorst.* It carried 33 aircraft and a crew of 948 and was sunk by a U.S. submarine in the South Yellow Sea in November 1944. **2.** A class of Japanese one-man suicide motorboats produced from 1943 onward during World War II. They had a weight of from 1.25 to 2 tons, a length of 16 to 18 ft, and a speed (provided by one or two automobile engines) of between 25 and 30 knots. They carried 4,406 lb of TNT or two depth charges in the bow. Designed to ram and sink ships, there is no record of an Allied ship being seriously damaged by one.

shipboard fire control The entire system of directing and controlling the offensive and defensive weapons of a ship.

ship of the line An armed vessel of the old Navy capable of taking a position in the first line of defense or offense. They were two-decked vessels carrying usually 74 or 86 guns. If of three decks they sometimes carried up to 120 guns, but never less than 60.

shipping A term applied collectively to those ships which are used to transport personnel, cargo, or both; often modified to denote type, use, or force to which assigned.

ship's company All hands; everyone on board.

ship-to-shore movement That portion of the assault phase of an amphibious operation which includes the deployment of the landing force from the assault shipping to designated landing areas.

Shiratsuyu A class of Japanese 1,580-ton destroyers produced in the mid- to the late 1930s. They had a speed of 34 knots, a complement of 180 men, and armament consisting of five 5-in. guns, four 25mm guns, and eight 24-in. torpedo tubes. All 10 ships of this class were lost during World War II.

shock action A method of attack by mobile units in which the suddenness, violence, and massed weight of the first impact produce the main effect. Tank attacks usually rely on shock action. The same was formerly true of cavalry attacks.

shock front The boundary between the pressure disturbance created by an explosion (in air, on water, or on earth) and the ambient atmosphere, water, or earth.

shock tactics Tactics that employ shock action.

shock troops Well-trained, well-disciplined troops with high morale who are specially suited for offensive work.

shock wave The continuously propagated pressure pulse formed by the blast from an explosion in air by the air blast, underwater by the water blast, and underground by the earth blast.

shoe A fitting on the stem of a ship, from which paravanes are towed. More generally, a protecting member under the keel or bottom of a ship.

Shoho A class of Japanese aircraft carriers of about 11,262 tons displacement launched in 1935–1936. There were two ships in the class, *Shoho* (sunk by U.S. carrier aircraft during the Battle of the Coral Sea in May 1942) and *Zuiho* (sunk by U.S. carrier aircraft during the Battle of Leyte Gulf in October 1944). They had flight-deck dimensions of 590 by 75 ft and a speed of 28 knots, and they carried a force of 30 aircraft.

Shokaku A class of Japanese aircraft carriers of 25,675 tons displacement commissioned in 1941. There were two ships in the class, *Shokaku* (sunk by an American submarine during the Battle of the Philippine Sea in 1944) and *Zuikaku* (sunk by U.S. carrier planes during the Battle of Leyte Gulf in 1944). They had flight-deck dimensions of 795 by 95 ft, a speed of 34 knots, a complement of 1,660 men, and a force of 84 aircraft.

shoot 1. To project a missile with force; to fire a weapon, as a gun or cannon; to strike or hit something with a missile. **2.** To shoot down; to cause an aircraft to fall by hitting it with missiles. **3.** To shoot something up; to strike something with several missiles.

Shooting Star The Lockheed P-80 (F-80) Shooting Star was a single-seat fighter-interceptor and fighter-bomber developed for the USAAF and first flown in January 1944. It was the first jet flown operationally by the United States, but was too late to see action in World War II. It was equipped with a turbojet engine with 3,850 lb of thrust and flew at speeds up to 558 mph. It was armed with six .50 cal. machine guns, plus two 500-lb or 1,000-lb bombs or ten 5-in. rockets. The designation Shooting Star was subsequently given to the two-place training version of the P-80, the Lockheed T-33. It has a speed of 580 mph and is armed with two .50 cal. machine guns.

shoran A precise short-range electronic navigation system which uses the time of travel of pulse-type transmission from two or more fixed stations to measure slant-range distance from the stations. Also, in conjunction with a suitable computer, used in precision bombing. (This term is derived from the words *short-range* navigation.)

shore bombardment lines Groundlines established to delimit bombardment by friendly surface ships.

shore party A task organization of the landing force, formed for the purpose of facilitating the landing and movement off the beaches of troops, equipment, and supplies; for the evacuation from the beaches of casualties and prisoners of war; and for facilitating the beaching, retraction, and

Shooting Star. (*Lockheed Aircraft Corporation.*)

Shorland armored car. (*Short Brothers & Harland Ltd.*)

salvaging of landing ships and craft. It comprises elements of both the naval and landing forces.

shore patrol (SP) The military police of the U.S. Navy.

shore-to-shore movement The assault movement of personnel and materiel directly from a shore staging area to the objective, involving no further transfers between types of craft or ships incident to the assault movement.

Shorland armored car A British Short-built four-wheeled vehicle developed between 1965 and 1966 and essentially a long-wheelbase Landrover chassis clad in 8mm armor plate. It has a crew of three, a weight of 7,400 lb, a road speed of 50 mph, and armament consisting of one .30 cal. (or 7.62mm) machine gun.

short A spotting, or an observation, used

by an observer to indicate that a burst (or bursts) occurred short of the target in relation to the spotting line.

Short 184 A British two-place single-engine twin-float torpedo bomber first flown in early 1915. It was armed with one ring-mounted Lewis machine gun in the rear cockpit and carried one torpedo or four 100-lb bombs. On August 12, 1915, an aircraft of this type flown by Flt. Cmdr. C. H. K. Edmonds sank a Turkish merchantman. It represented the first sinking of a ship by means of an air-launched torpedo. About nine-hundred 184's were built, and about one-third were still in service at the end of the war.

Short Bomber A land-based version of the **Short 184,** which see. It could carry four 230-lb bombs or eight 112-lb bombs beneath the lower wings.

Shrike. (*U.S. Navy.*)

short-delay fuze A type of delay fuze in both bombs and artillery projectiles in which the fuze action is delayed for a short period of time, normally 0.01 to 0.24 seconds.

Shorthorn See **Farman MF.11.**

Short Horn The NATO code name for a type of Soviet airborne J-band radar.

short-range ballistic missile A ballistic missile with a range capability up to about 600 nautical miles.

short round 1. The unintentional or inadvertent delivery of ordnance on friendly troops, installations, or civilians by a friendly weapon system. 2. A defective cartridge in which the projectile has been seated too deeply.

short takeoff and landing (STOL) The ability of an aircraft to clear a 50-ft obstacle within 1,500 ft of commencing takeoff or, in landing, to stop within 1,500 ft after passing over a 50-ft obstacle.

Shorty A U.S. Colt-developed gas-operated air-cooled 5.6mm submachine gun with an 11.5-in. barrel. It also permits attachment of the 40mm grenade launcher.

shot 1. **a.** A solid projectile for cannon, without a bursting charge. **b.** A mass or load of numerous, relatively small lead pellets used in a shotgun, as birdshot or buckshot. 2. That which is fired from a gun, as "the first shot was over the target." In sense 1a, the term "projectile" is preferred for uniformity in nomenclature. 3. The flight of a missile, as of a rocket.

shot crossbow A crossbow having a barrel through which bullets could be shot. Also a **prod**, which see.

shotel An Abyssinian sword with a guardless hilt and a double-edged blade with a pronounced curve.

shot flask A bag, often made of leather, for holding lead shot.

shotgun A smoothbore shoulder weapon that fires shot pellets or slugs. The usual classes are riot gun, skeet gun, and sporting gun.

shotgun shell 1. A container or capsule, usually made of stiff paper with a brass base, containing primer, powder, wadding, and shot for use in a shotgun. 2. A blank shell of this type for use in a cartridge starter.

shot locker An old naval designation for the strong compartment in a ship's hull used for storing shot and shell.

shot tongs A device used to lift and convey heavy projectiles in a horizontal position.

shot truck In loading heavy artillery, a small truck or cart on which heavy projectiles are loaded to be run up to the breech. It is adjusted to the height of the breech so that the projectile can be rammed into the breech.

shoulder 1. In a cartridge case, the tapered portion between the body and the neck. 2. The upper part of a sword blade. 3. The angle of a bastion between the face and the flank. Also called an "epaule." 4. To bring a weapon to the shoulder or to place it aslant on the shoulder, as a pike or a rifle. 5. Formerly, to arrange troops shoulder to shoulder.

shoulder arm A shoulder weapon.

shoulder arms A command to bring weapons to the shoulder.

shoulder guard Any shield over the firing mechanism of a gun designed to protect the gunner from contact; particularly, such a shield on cannons mounted in tanks, armored vehicles, and other cramped quarters.

shoulder weapon Any firearm designed to be braced on or against the shoulder when firing, as a rifle, carbine, automatic rifle, bazooka launcher, etc.

shrapnel 1. Strictly speaking, small lead or steel balls contained in certain shells, which are discharged in every direction upon explosion of the shell. The system was invented by Lieut. (later Gen.) Henry Shrapnel in 1784. 2. A popular term for munition fragments.

shrapnel balls A type of shell fired from U.S. 155mm and 203mm guns. When these shells explode, they project 104 small balls that are 3.7cm in diameter, each of which is equipped with fins. Each bounces on the ground and explodes at a height of about 5 ft, projecting 600 small fragments.

Shrike An air-to-surface missile developed by the U.S. Naval Ordnance Test Station (NOTS) in China Lake, Calif. Formerly called "ARM" (antiradar missile), this weapon is intended to home in on enemy radar installations. Operational in 1964, it has an overall length of 10 ft, a launching weight of 390 lb, and a range of 10 mi.

Shropshire An Australian heavy cruiser of 9,830 tons standard displacement completed in 1929. It had a length of 633 ft, a speed of 32 knots, a complement of 650 men, and armament consisting of eight 8-in. and eight 4-in. guns, sixteen 2-pounders, and three 40mm and twenty-one 20mm antiaircraft guns. It was lost in action off Savo Island on August 9, 1942.

Shu mine A German mine of World War II that consisted of ½ lb of TNT in a small wooden box. The lid was held open with a stick. If the stick was disturbed, the lid was snapped shut, detonating the mine. It could not be detected by electromagnetic mine detectors. It injured more frequently than killed, often blowing off a foot when stepped on.

shuttered fuze A fuze in which inadvertent initiation of the detonator will not initiate either the booster or the burst charge.

shuttle bombing 1. The technique of bombing a target by taking off from a base, bombing the target, continuing on to another base, reloading, and bombing a target again on return to the home base. 2. The bombing of a target so nearby that a bomber makes two or more round trips to the target in a single day of operations.

Shyster The NATO code name for a Soviet single-stage liquid-fueled missile. A first-generation IRBM, it has a length of 70 ft, a diameter of 5 ft, and a range of 750 mi. It was first seen in 1957.

S.I.A. 6.5mm aircraft machine gun Model 1918 An Italian recoil-operated air-cooled machine gun with a rate of fire of 650 to 700 rounds per minute. It weighed 25.5 lb and was fed from a 50- or 100-round magazine.

S.I.A. 7 and 9 (and Fiat R-2) Italian (Società Italiana Aviazione) two-place single-engine reconnaissance biplanes first flown

Shropshire. (*Royal Australian Navy.*)

in 1917. The 7B had a speed of 124 mph and was armed with two Revelli machine guns, one in the rear cockpit and the other mounted on the top wing to fire over the propeller arc. It could carry 132 lb of bombs. The 9B was a larger version and carried a 772-lb bombload. An improved version of this type was made when S.I.A. became Fiat Aviazione. The Fiat R-2 was used by the Italian Air Force through the end of World War I and until 1925 as a standard reconnaissance and bomber type.

Sibling The NATO code name for a Soviet follow-on to the German V-2 missile.

Sicherheitsdienst (SD) The security service of the Nazi SS. See **Schutzstaffel.**

SID Seismic intrusion detector. A device used by U.S. Army and Marine Corps personnel in Vietnam for acoustic detection. By monitoring the "phones" which were placed in the ground, an operator could sense the earth noises made by enemy tunnel construction and movements of troops by foot or by vehicle.

side arms Weapons that are worn at the side or in the belt when not in use. The sword, bayonet, automatic pistol, revolver, etc., are side arms.

side boys Men standing at the gangway of a naval vessel to salute visiting officers of rank.

side-looking airborne radar An airborne radar, viewing at right angles to the axis of the vehicle, which produces a presentation of terrain or moving targets. Commonly referred to as "SLAR."

side spray Fragments of a bursting projectile thrown sidewise from the line of flight, in contrast with base spray, which is thrown to the rear, and nose spray, which is thrown to the front.

Sidewinder An air-to-air missile developed by the U.S. Naval Ordnance Test Station (NOTS) in China Lake, Calif., and first fired in September 1953. It has been produced in great numbers by Philco and General Electric and is in service with the U.S. Navy and Air Force, plus the forces of numerous other countries. It has an overall length of 9 ft 2 in., a launching weight of 159 lb, and a range of 2 mi (at a speed of

Sidewinder. (*U.S. Air Force.*)

Mach 2.5). It is a solid-propellant missile that utilizes an infrared homing guidance system and a conventional high-explosive warhead. It is also designated as AIM-9.

Sidewinder 1C An advanced Sidewinder, with higher speed capabilities and greater range.

siege The placing of an army around a fortification or fortified town to compel its surrender or to reduce it by assault. From the French word *siège*, meaning "a seat, a sitting down."

siege artillery Heavy ordnance used generally for sieges or stationary operations. The counterpart in modern armies is heavy field artillery.

siege howitzer A short, heavy gun of large caliber, used for destruction of fortresses. Such a weapon was the German 11-in. (28cm) howitzer.

siege train See **battering train.**

siegeworks The works erected by a besieging force for either offense or defense.

Siegfried See **German 380mm (38cm) railroad gun Siegfried.**

Siegfried Line See **Westwall.**

Siemens-Schuckert D.III and D.IV A German single-place single-engine biplane fighter first tested in June 1917. It had a speed of about 115 mph and was armed with two forward-firing machine guns.

SIG 9mm Parabellum automatic pistol P210 (SP47/8) Model 49 This weapon has been the standard pistol of the Swiss forces since 1948. It has an overall length of 8.5 in. and a barrel length of 4.75 in. The total weight of the pistol is 2.18 lb, and the magazine capacity is eight cartridges.

sight 1. A mechanical or optical device for aiming a firearm or for laying a gun or launcher in position. It is based on the principle that two points in fixed relation to each other may be brought in line with a third. Sights are classified as fixed or adjustable depending on the provision made for setting windage and range, and also according to type. Glass sights comprise all sights which include an optical element, such as a collimator, telescope, periscope, etc. Iron sights are classified as either open or aperture. Aperture sights are those that are sighted through, such as peep, ring, etc. Open sights are all those that are sighted over or at, such as post, bead, notch, etc. Leaf sights are those which can be folded down for protection. **2.** To aim at a target or aiming point. **3.** To look through a

SIG 9mm Parabellum automatic pistol P210 (SP47/8) Model 49. (*Swiss Military Department.*)

Sikorsky Grand. (*The Smithsonian Institution, National Air Museum.*)

sighting device to determine the angular direction of a point, either horizontal or vertical, in surveying or navigation, especially the angular position of the sun, a star, or a planet in navigation. **4.** In armor, an obsolete term for a slit in a visor to permit vision.

sighting Actual visual contact. It does not include other contacts, which must be reported by type, e.g., radar and sonar contacts.

sighting angle See **range angle.**

sighting hood An armored hood with viewing slits in the sides, as on the top of a turret, a submarine, etc.

sighting shot A trial shot, fired to find out whether the sights are properly adjusted.

sighting system A mechanical or optical device for aiming a firearm or for laying a gun in position; all such devices required for a specific weapon or group of weapons.

sight leaf The movable hinged part of a rear sight of a gun that can be raised and set to a desired range or snapped down when not in use.

sight setter The gun-crew member who sets the range and deflection data ordered by the officer controlling the fire.

signal **1.** As applied to electronics, any transmitted electrical impulse. **2.** Operationally, a type of message, the text of which consists of one or more letters, words, characters, signal flags, visual displays, or special sounds with prearranged meanings and which is conveyed or transmitted by visual, acoustical, or electrical means.

Signal Corps A corps of the U.S. Army, charged with the development, maintenance, and operation of communications systems within the Army.

signal flags Colored flags including international alphabet flags, used for visual communications.

signal pistol A pistol designed to fire pyro-

technic signals such as flares.

signal rocket A rocket that gives off some characteristic color or display which has a meaning according to an established code. It is usually fired from a signal pistol or a ground signal projector.

signal security A generic term which includes both communications security and electronic security.

signature (target) The characteristic pattern of the target displayed by detection and classification equipment.

significant tracks Tracks of aircraft or of missiles which, if hostile, would pose a threat to a defended area.

SIG submachine gun Model 1920 (Brevet Bergmann) A weapon manufactured by SIG (Swiss Industrial Company) in Switzerland from 1920 to 1927. It is a copy of the German M.P. 18,1, which had been produced by the Bergmann factories in Gaggenau and Suhl. Because of restrictions placed on Germany by the Versailles Treaty, Bergmann ceased production of this submachine gun and offered manufacturing rights to SIG. Models were produced to fire the 7.65mm Parabellum and the 7.63mm Mauser cartridges, and quantities were sold to Finland, China, and Japan.

Sigure A class of Japanese destroyers of about 1,368 tons standard displacement built in the mid-1930s and used during World War II. They had a length of 335 ft, a beam of 32 ft, a speed of 34 knots, and a complement of 220 men. They were armed with five 5-in. guns and eight 21-in. torpedo tubes.

Sikorsky Grand The first four-engine aircraft ever flown (May 13, 1913), this biplane bomber was designed by the aviation pioneer Igor Sikorsky. It had a 92-ft wingspan, a length of 65.8 ft, and a height of 12 ft. It was powered by four 100-hp Argus engines and had a loaded weight of approximately 9,000 lb. It led to the development

of the **Ilya Mourometz,** which see.

siladar Formerly, in the Anglo-Indian Army, an irregular cavalry soldier who provided his own horse and equipment.

silence Formerly, to silence an enemy battery by an intensive barrage.

silencer A device specifically designed to silence the explosive report caused by the discharge of cartridges by a small-arms weapon. It incorporates integral chambers or baffles which allow the gases to expand gradually.

silent running A condition of quiet operation of machinery in a submarine to deny detection by listening.

silo An in-ground hardened missile base; an ICBM launching base that is protected against a nuclear explosion.

Silver Star A military decoration awarded any person (military, civilian, or foreign) who, while serving in any capacity, distinguished himself by gallantry in action against an enemy of the United States.

Simonov 7.62mm automatic rifle Model 1936 (AVS) This was the first automatic rifle developed by the Soviets in 7.62mm. It has a length of 48.6 in., a barrel length of about 24 in., and a weight of 8.93 lb. The capacity of the magazine is 15 rounds.

Simonov 14.5mm antitank rifle A Soviet weapon that saw considerable service in World War II. It is about 7 ft long overall and fires one round of armor-piercing high-explosive ammunition. It can penetrate 1.2 in. of armor at ranges up to about 500 yd.

Sims A class of U.S. destroyers of 1,570 tons standard displacement completed in the late 1930s. They had a speed of 37 knots and main armament consisting of four 5-in. guns and eight 21-in. torpedo tubes.

single action A method of fire in some revolvers and shoulder arms in which the hammer must be cocked by hand, in contrast to double action, in which a single pull of the trigger both cocks and fires the weapon.

single-base powder A propellant that contains only one explosive ingredient, normally nitrocellulose. A double-base propellant contains two explosive ingredients, commonly nitrocellulose and nitroglycerin.

single-engine Of an aircraft: having only one engine, especially a propeller-driven engine.

single float A single central float fitted under a floatplane and usually requiring two stabilizing floats to give adequate stability and to complete the float system.

single-loader Single shot.

single-seater A single-seat aircraft or other vehicle.

single-shot **1.** Of a firearm, loaded by hand for each shot. **2.** Semiautomatic operation of an automatic gun, in which the trigger must be pulled for each shot fired.

single-shot weapon A gun, such as an

old-style rifle, that is loaded by hand for each shot.

sinuating See **evasive steering.**

siren A high-pitched noisemaking device used aboard ship when an emergency, collision, or grounding, for example, is imminent.

sister ships Those built on the same lines.

site 1. The position of anything, for example, the position of a gun emplacement. **2.** The vertical angle between the horizontal and a line joining the target and the muzzle of a weapon. In this meaning, it is usually called "angle of site."

situation map A map showing the tactical or the administrative situation at a particular time.

situation report A report giving the situation in the area of a reporting unit or formation.

six-by-four As applied to motor vehicles, one having six wheels, four of which are driving wheels, dual wheels being considered one wheel. It is usually written "6 × 4."

six-by-six As applied to motor vehicles, one having six wheels, all of which are driving wheels, dual wheels being considered one wheel. It is usually written "6 × 6."

six-gun, six-shooter A common term for revolvers; most are chambered for six cartridges.

six-pounder A cannon firing a 6-lb solid ball.

sixteen-pounder A cannon firing a 16-lb projectile.

Sjölejonet A class of Swedish submarines of 650 tons standard surface displacement built in 1936–1940. They had a speed of 10 knots submerged, a complement of 32 men, and armament consisting of four 21-in. torpedo tubes.

Sjöormen A class of Swedish submarines of 800 tons standard surface displacement completed in 1967–1969. They have a length of 167 ft and are armed with four 21-in. torpedo tubes.

Skate A class of U.S. nuclear-powered attack submarines (SSN) of 2,570 tons standard displacement commissioned in 1957–1959. These were the first U.S. production-model nuclear-powered submarines. They have a length of 267.7 ft, a beam of 25 ft, a speed of about 25 knots submerged, and a complement of 95 men. They are armed with six 21-in. torpedo tubes and antisubmarine-warfare torpedoes.

skate mount A mounting for a machine gun that permits it to travel on a continuous track extending around the inside of the body of a vehicle. The gun can be locked in any position for use.

SKB A U.S. skiff, large.

skean A Gaelic word meaning "knife."

single float, showing three Kingfishers. (U.S. Navy.)

Sjölejonet. (Swedish Defense Staff.)

Skate. (U.S. Navy.)

Skean The NATO code name for the Soviet IRBM that is a later development of the Shyster-Sandal series of missiles. First seen in 1964, Skean has a length of 80 ft, a diameter of 8 ft, and a range of 2,000 mi. It has been shown in underground silos in official Soviet films.

skean dhu Literally, black knife. A kind of small dagger often worn by Scottish Highlanders in the top of the stocking.

Skeleton See **U.S. tank, light, 8-ton.**

skelp Strips of iron or steel used in the manufacture of Damascus barrels. The strips are fashioned into tubes by bending them around a cylindrical form and then welding them.

SKI A U.S. skiff, large.

skip bombing A method of aerial bombing in which the bomb is released from such a low altitude that it slides or glances along the surface of the water or ground and strikes the target at or above water level or ground level.

Skipjack A class of U.S. nuclear-powered

attack submarines (SSN) of 3,075 tons standard displacement commissioned in 1959–1961. They have a length of 251.7 ft, a beam of 31.5 ft, a submerged speed of 30+ knots, and a complement of 93 men. They are armed with six 21-in. torpedo tubes and antisubmarine-warfare torpedoes. (Picture, next page.)

Skip Spin The NATO code name for a type of Soviet airborne I-band radar.

skirmish A light combat between armies at a considerable distance or between small parties.

skirmisher A soldier sent forward in advance to discover or intercept hostile forces.

skirmish line A line of skirmishers in advance of a line of battle.

skirting plate A thin plate which is spaced a considerable distance in front of the main armor plate and which acts as a passive form of resistance to the jet of shaped-charge ammunition.

SKL A U.S. skiff, light.

Skipjack. (*U.S. Navy.*)

Skycrane. (*Sikorsky Aircraft.*)

SKM A U.S. skiff, medium.

Skoda 8mm machine gun Model 1902 An Austrian retarded-blowback-operated water-cooled machine gun with a rate of fire of 300 to 400 rounds per minute. It weighed 38.5 lb (without water or loaded hopper) and was fed from a 25-, 50-, or 75-round hopper.

Skoda machine gun The first Skoda machine gun appeared in 1888 and was a delayed-blowback weapon. It was adopted in Austria in 1893 and saw some service during the Boxer Rebellion in the hands of the Austro-Hungarian detachment defend-

ing their legation in Peking. The original hopper feed of this weapon was changed to a belt feed by design changes in 1909. It weighed about 25 lb and was made in rifle calibers ranging from 6.5 to 11mm.

Skory A class of Soviet destroyers of 2,600 tons standard displacement produced in the early 1950s. They have a length of 420 ft, a beam of 41 ft, a speed of 36 knots, and a complement of 260 men. They are armed with four 5.1-in. guns, two 3-in. and seven 37mm antiaircraft guns, four depth-charge throwers, ten 21-in. torpedo tubes, and eighty mines.

Skybolt A U.S. Air Force air-to-surface ballistic missile with a range of 1,000 nautical miles. Production ceased in 1962.

Skycrane This flying crane helicopter was developed by Sikorsky for the U.S. Army and was first flown in 1962. It can carry a load of 22,890 lb and has a speed of 129 mph and a range of 253 mi. It can also carry 45 fully equipped troops.

sky glow Illumination caused by a weapon firing from a defiladed position.

Skyhawk The Douglas A-4 Skyhawk is a single-seat lightweight attack bomber developed for U.S. Navy carrier use and first flown in 1954. It has a top speed of 675 mph and a range of 2,000 mi with external tanks, and it can carry up to 8,200 lb of weapons. It can also operate from short, unprepared fields.

Skymaster The Douglas C-54 Skymaster is a four-engine military transport developed from the DC-4 and first flown in 1939. It was widely used during World War II and is still in service with the U.S. Air Force and the U.S. Navy. The Navy designation is R5D. This airplane has a top speed of 250 mph and a normal range of 1,500 mi. It can carry about 30,000 lb of cargo.

Skyraider The Douglas A-1 (formerly AD) Skyraider is a single-engine (piston) single-seat attack aircraft developed for the U.S. Navy and first flown in 1945. It was produced in several versions and during the Korean conflict operated with bombloads totaling 10,500 lb (more than the four-engine Flying Fortress of World War II). It has a speed of 365 mph and a combat radius of 1,500 mi. It is armed with two 20mm cannons, plus various combinations of rockets and missiles.

Skyray A U.S. Douglas-built single-engine single-seat, supersonic jet fighter developed for the U.S. Navy and first flown in 1951. It is armed with four 20mm cannons, plus two 1,000-lb bombs.

Sky Spot A ground-based radar-controlled bombing system which permits pinpoint accuracy, night operations, and all-weather delivery. Controlled almost exclusively from the ground, the only aircraft equipment necessary is a rapid-response radar beacon. It was used in Vietnam, mainly in conjunction with U.S. Air Force B-52 raids.

Skysweeper A U.S. 75mm radar-equipped automatic antiaircraft weapon. It fires 11.5-lb high-explosive projectiles to an effective ceiling of about 4 mi. The weapon, which has a weight of 10 tons, can also be directed against ground targets at ranges up to about 8 mi. It fires at the rate of 45 projectiles a minute.

Skytrain The Douglas C-47 is a twin-engine military transport version of the DC-3 and was first flown in December 1935. It was the most commonly used transport in the Allied Air Forces during

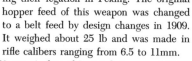

Skyhawk. (*U.S. Navy.*)

World War II and operated in every theater of war. Called the "R4D" by the USN, "Dakota" by the British, and generally nicknamed "Gooney Bird," this airplane flew at speeds up to 229 mph and carried 8,000 lb of cargo or 28 fully equipped troops. It is still operational with the U.S. Air Force, the U.S. Navy, and the forces of no fewer than 73 other countries. As used in Vietnam, the USAF AC-47 (nicknamed "Puff, the Magic Dragon" or "Spooky") was a close-support aircraft armed with three side-firing 7.62mm Miniguns.

Skytrooper An aircraft similar to the Douglas C-47 Skytrain but without the facilities for carrying heavy cargo.

Skywarrior The Douglas A-3 Skywarrior is a three-seat carrier-based twin-jet attack bomber developed for the U.S. Navy and first flown in 1952. It is armed with two radar-directed 20mm cannons in a rear turret and can carry large bombs and nuclear weapons in a bomb bay. It has a speed of 630 mph and a range of over 2,000 mi. (Picture, next page.)

slant range The line-of-sight range between two points not at the same elevation. Used as a distinguishing term. This term is used in reference to range between an airborne gun or radar set and a ground target or other target not at the same elevation, between an antiaircraft gun and the future position of a target, between a bomber and a target, etc. In operations, slant range includes the range between objects vertical to one another.

SLAR Side-looking airborne radar.

slew To rotate rapidly, as a gun director slews to get on a new target.

slide 1. The sliding part of the receiver of certain automatic weapons. **2.** The sliding catch on the breech mechanism of certain weapons.

slightly wounded A casualty that is a sitting or a walking case.

Slim The Allied code name for the Watanabe E9W1 single-engine two-seat submarine-borne observation twin-float seaplane. First flown in 1935, this aircraft was transported in a watertight compartment on the deck of a submarine and was assembled prior to launching. It was armed with one 7.7mm machine gun and had a maximum speed of 144 mph. This biplane was replaced for submarine use by the Yokosuka E14Y1, code name "Glen."

Slim Net The NATO code name for a type of Soviet E-band early-warning and surveillance radar.

sling 1. An item made of leather, webbing, or the like, designed to be attached to a carbine, mortar, musket, rifle, rocket launcher, shotgun, submachine gun, or the like. Used as a means of carrying a small-arms weapon and also to steady the weapon for firing. **2.** A weapon consisting of a

Skyraider. (*U.S. Air Force.*)

piece of leather with a round hole in the middle and two pieces of cord about 1 yd long. When a smooth stone is placed in the leather pouch and the cords are swung rapidly around, the stone attains considerable speed. When one of the cords is let go, the stone travels with a greater force than could be imparted by merely throwing it. **3.** An obsolete term for a small swivel gun with a long barrel.

sling cart A kind of cart once used to transport cannons.

slinger A soldier armed with a sling.

slit trench A narrow trench in which persons may take refuge in case of air attack.

sloop of war A light cruiser that ranked below a frigate and carried guns on one deck—18 to 32 in number.

Slot, The A World War II Japanese shipping lane between Bougainville and Guadalcanal.

Skysweeper. (*U.S. Army.*)

Skytrain. (*McDonnell Douglas Corporation.*)

Skywarrior. (*U.S. Navy.*)

slow fire　Gunfire in which all guns of a battery fire together at regular intervals.

slow match　A slow-burning match or fuse used for firing blasting charges and fireworks and, formerly, used in matchlock muskets and cannons.

slung shot　A striking weapon that consists of a stone or a small mass of metal on a flexible handle or strap.

SM　A U.S. Navy minelaying submarine.

small arms　All arms, including automatic weapons, up to and including those of .60 cal. and shotguns.

small-arms ammunition　Ammunition for small arms, i.e., all ammunition up to and including those of .60 cal. and all gauges of shotgun shells.

smallsword　A light, tapering sword with a triangular or hexagonal blade, used only for thrusting.

S mine　A small antipersonnel mine of the "bounding" type, employed by the Germans during World War II.

Smith & Wesson .38 cal. British service pistol (Revolver No. 2 S&W)　Approximately 890,000 of these weapons were produced between 1940 and 1945 for British forces. It was an official British service revolver and, like the British-made Enfield revolver, shoots .38 S&W Regular cartridges. It has an overall length of $10\frac{1}{8}$ in., a barrel length of 5 in. (although earlier models had 4- and 6-in. barrels), and a weight of 31 oz. The cylinder capacity is six cartridges.

Smith & Wesson .44 cal. S&W Russian　Between 1870 and 1878 about 215,000 of these weapons were produced, most of them for the Russian Imperial Army. Smith & Wesson facilities were tied up for five years making guns to fill the Russian order.

smallsword. (*The Smithsonian Institution, H. Wells Collection.*)

This weapon has a barrel length of $6\frac{1}{2}$ in. (although some were made in 6-, 7-, and 8-in. lengths).

Smith & Wesson .45 cal. revolver Model 1917　This weapon is a double-action revolver with an overall length of 10.8 in., a barrel length of 5.5 in., and a weight of 2.25 lb. It has a cylinder with a capacity of six cartridges. Smith & Wesson made 153,311 of this model revolver.

S.M.L.E.　Short magazine Lee-Enfield rifles. See **British .303 S.M.L.E. rifle** in various rifle numbers and Mark numbers.

smoke and flash defilade　**1.** A condition in which the smoke and flash of a gun are concealed from enemy observation by an intervening obstacle, such as a hill or ravine. **2.** The vertical distance by which the smoke and flash of a gun are concealed from enemy observation.

smoke ball　Formerly, a ball or case filled with a composition that, when burned, emitted thick smoke. In addition to concealing operations, they were once used to suffocate an enemy's miners.

smoke blanket　A dense concentration of smoke established over and around friendly areas to protect them from observation and precision bombing and over enemy areas to protect attacking aircraft from antiaircraft fire.

smoke bombs　Smoke bombs have a three-fold purpose: They are used for screening the movement of troops and ships in combat areas; for creating an antipersonnel effect on troops in the open or in dug-in positions; and for marking targets. They also have an incendiary effect in that they will set fire to materials which are easily ignited such as clothing, dry brush, canvas, etc. The bodies are filled with plasticized white phosphorus (PWP) or white phosphorus (WP). The functioning of a fuze and burster shatters the bomb on impact, dispersing the filler over a wide area. Atmospheric oxygen ignites the particles,

which produce a dense white smoke.

smoke boxes　Receptacles containing phosphorus which were once carried by merchant ships; they were used to make a smoke screen to enable the ship to escape from an attacking submarine.

smoke canister　A chemical fill encased in ogival or cylindrical containers for loading into projectiles of chemical shells. When ignited, a colored or white smoke is produced.

smoke curtain　A vertical smoke screen placed between friendly and hostile troops or installations to prevent enemy ground observation.

smoke generator　A device on the stem of a ship for making smoke screens.

smoke grenade　A hand grenade or rifle grenade containing a smoke-producing mixture and used for screening or signaling. It is sometimes charged with colored smoke, such as red, green, yellow, or violet.

smokeless　When used in cartridge or propelling-charge nomenclature, the term indicates that the ammunition is relatively smokeless when used in the weapon for which it is intended.

smokeless propellant　The term used to distinguish the relatively "smokeless" propellants from black powder, which produces a heavy smoke and which they have supplanted as a propellant.

smoke screen　A screen of smoke used to hide a maneuver, force, place, or activity. Smoke screens may be generated on the ground by use of a smoke generator, a smoke grenade, or a smoke pot. They may also be laid down by ships, by aircraft using smoke tanks, or by artillery fire.

Smokey Bear　A U.S. system developed for use in Vietnam; it consists of a helicopter smoke-screen generator that employs a 16-gal tank of fog oil to lay a dense screen lasting 40 seconds.

smoking lamp　Formerly, aboard ship, a lamp that was kept lighted during the hours when smoking was permitted. Men could light their pipes at it. It is now used only in phrases to announce that smoking is allowed.

smoothbore　Having a bore that is smooth and without rifling. Shotguns and mortars are commonly smoothbore.

snafu　A military slang term of World War II meaning "*s*ituation *n*ormal: *a*ll *f*ucked *u*p." Related terms were "tarfu" ("things are *really* fucked up") and "fubar" ("fucked up beyond all recognition").

snake　**1.** A mine-clearing device developed by the Allies during World War II. It consisted of a long pipe or tube filled with explosives which would be pushed onto a minefield and there exploded. **2.** A post-World War II refinement in which a 100-ft-long raillike device is propelled across a minefield by a 4.5-in. rocket. On the rail are mounted high explosives which, as they are detonated, clear a path.

Snakeye I An attachment to U.S. low-drag general-purpose bombs. It consists of a flight-retarding tail-fin assembly of four blades which open like an umbrella to decelerate the bomb. It provides aircraft with a high-speed, low-altitude bombing capability. It is used chiefly with 250- and 500-lb bombs.

snap cap A small cover to protect the nipple of a percussion musket. It is usually made of leather with a metal top.

snaphance, snaphaunce A type of muzzle-loader with a lock in which a cock, holding a piece of flint, strikes a steel anvil that hinges vertically over the pan. Later, the flintlock combined the steel with the pan cover. The snaphance first appeared toward the middle of the sixteenth century.

Snapper The NATO code name for a Soviet wire-guided antitank missile similar in configuration to the **Cobra** or **Mosquito,** sense 1, which see. It has a length of 3 ft 8½ in., a launching weight of 49 lb, and a range of from 1,650 (minimum) to 7,650 (maximum) ft. The 11.5-lb warhead is said to be capable of penetrating 13.7 in. of armor.

snap report A preliminary report of observations by air crews rendered by intelligence personnel immediately following interrogation and dispatched prior to compilation of a detailed mission report.

Snare The nickname for a type of surface-to-air antiaircraft missile used with some success during World War II by both British and Soviet forces. Rockets trailed quantities of wire, which would foul airplane propellers.

Snark The first intercontinental missile in service with U.S. forces. It was a subsonic system that became operational in 1959. It resembled an aircraft and had a length of 69 ft, a wingspan of 42 ft, and a launching weight of 59,936 lb. It had a ceiling of above 50,000 ft and a range of 5,500 nautical miles. It carried an all-inertial guidance system and a nuclear warhead.

sneak attack An attack made before a declaration of war or before hostilities are mutually recognized to exist.

sneeze gas A gas that causes sneezing, specifically, **diphenylchloroarsine,** which see.

Snider rifle The name of the Enfield muzzle-loaders converted to breechloaders by a system invented by the American Jacob Snider and adopted by the British in 1867. The brass cartridge system of the Snider was successful in providing a breech seal when fired.

Sniffer Airborne equipment for detection of exhaust gases from a snorkeling submarine.

sniper An especially skilled rifleman, usually having special equipment for shooting at long range, whose mission is to kill key

smoke screen. (*U.S. Army.*)

Snider rifle. (*The Smithsonian Institution, W. H. Carter Collection.*)

sniperscope. (*U.S. Army.*)

enemy personnel.

sniperscope **1.** A **snooperscope,** which see, for use on a carbine or rifle. An electronic device that permits a rifleman to aim at a target at night without himself being seen. Infrared rays illuminate the target, which is then viewed through a combination telescope sight and fluorescent screen (in which all objects appear as various shades of green). The system was developed by the U.S. Army during World War II. It weighs 32 lb and has an angle of view of 14° and a range of 125 yd. **2.** A device developed during World War I for firing a rifle from a trench parapet without exposing the shooter. It consisted of a periscope attached near the rifle's rear sights and projecting downward into the trench.

snooper An aircraft that is shadowing or observing.

snooperscope A hand-carried device combining a source of infrared rays with a viewer; it enables the operator to see in the dark.

snorkel A tube or pair of tubes for air intake and exhaust that can be extended above the surface of the water for operating submerged submarines. The term is now also applied to almost any tube which similarly supplies air for underwater operation, whether it be for materiel or personnel. This system was developed by Germany in World War II, and the name derives from the German word *Schnorchel,* meaning "snout."

Snowflake The World War II nickname for a type of flare used by the Allies in antisubmarine warfare.

sofar *S*ound *f*ixing *a*nd *r*anging. The technique of fixing an explosion at sea by time

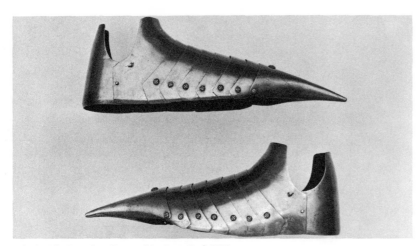

solerets. (*The Metropolitan Museum of Art, Rogers Fund, 1904.*)

difference of arrival of sound energy at several separate geographic locations.

soften To weaken the resistance of the enemy by an attack or attacks in preparation for a major assault; to bomb or strafe enemy positions or locations in preparation for another attack or assault.

soft missile base A launching base that is not protected against a nuclear explosion.

soldier **1.** A male person in the army. **2.** A male enlisted person, as distinguished from an officer.

solerets Armor for the feet. Specifically, the long pointed variety of the fifteenth century.

Solothurn 7.92mm machine gun Model 29 A German recoil-operated air-cooled machine gun with a rate of fire of 400 to 500 rounds per minute. It weighed 17 lb and was fed by a 25- or 50-round magazine.

Solothurn 7.92mm machine gun Model 30 A German recoil-operated air-cooled machine gun with a rate of fire of 450 to 500 rounds per minute. It weighed 18.5 lb and was fed from a 25- or 50-round maga-

zine.

Solothurn 8mm machine gun Model 30S A weapon adopted by the Austrians in 1930 and, with modifications (the Model 31), by Hungary in 1931. In addition to its use as a ground gun, the Germans used it in 7.92mm as a fixed aircraft gun (the MG 15) and as a flexible aircraft gun (the MG 17). It is a recoil-operated weapon with selective-fire capability, a cyclic rate of fire of 450 to 500 rounds per minute, and a muzzle velocity of 2,395 fps. It has an overall length of 46.25 in., a barrel length of 23.6 in., and a weight of about 18½ lb. The ground version used a 25-round magazine, while the MG 15 used a 75-round drum magazine. The MG 17 had solenoids for remote firing. A heavy model of the same type, the MG 131, used a 13mm cartridge with a muzzle velocity of 2,560 fps.

Solothurn 9mm submachine gun A British version of the Solothurn, this weapon has a weight of about 9.5 lb, a length of 32.25 in., and a rate of fire of 700 rounds per minute. It has selective-fire capability

and a magazine capacity of 30 or 32 rounds.

Solothurn 20mm cannon A German recoil-operated air-cooled cannon with a rate of fire of 280 rounds per minute. It weighed 142 lb and was fed from a 20-round magazine. It was used as both an aircraft and an antiaircraft cannon.

Solothurn submachine gun SI-100 See **Steyr-Solothurn 9mm Mauser submachine gun MP 34.**

soman (GD) This war gas is one of the **nerve agents,** which see, and has a quick-acting casualty effect. Skin absorption great enough to cause death may occur in 1 to 2 minutes, although death may be delayed for 1 to 2 hours. Respiratory lethal dosages kill in 1 to 10 minutes, and liquid in the eye kills nearly as rapidly.

Somers A class of U.S. destroyers (DD) of 1,850 tons standard displacement commissioned in 1937–1938. They had a length of 371 ft, a beam of 36 ft, a speed of 37 knots, and a complement of 198 men. They were armed with eight 5-in. guns, twelve 21-in. torpedo tubes, and depth charges.

Somua S35 See **French tank, cavalry, Somua S35.**

sonar *S*ound *n*avigation *a*nd *r*anging. A method system, analogous to radar, in which high-frequency sound waves are emitted so as to be reflected back from objects of interest; it is used especially by ships for detecting underwater objects, such as submarines or mines. Also, an apparatus used for this purpose. This system is called "asdic" by the British.

sonar receiver A single component designed to be used in conjunction with a hydrophone or transducer for the specific purpose of intercepting underwater sounds. Facilities for presenting intelligence may be provided.

sonic Of or pertaining to sound or the speed of sound. This is approximately 1,087 fps, or about 738 mph.

Somers. (*U.S. Navy.*)

Sonnenblume (German for "Sunflower.") The World War II German code name for the movement of German forces to North Africa in February 1941. These forces, led by Field Marshal Erwin Rommel, were the beginning of the Deutsches Afrika Korps.

sonobuoy A sonar device used to detect submerged submarines. When activated, they relay information by radio. They may be active directional or nondirectional, or they may be passive directional or nondirectional. The first sonobuoys were developed by the Allies for antisubmarine operations in World War II.

Sopwith 1½-Strutter A British two-place single-engine biplane that entered production in 1916 and was used for reconnaissance, bombing, coastal patrol, ground strafing, and antisubmarine duties. Armed with a synchronized front-firing Vickers gun and a Lewis gun in the rear cockpit, it could also carry four 65-lb bombs. Some 1,500 aircraft of this type were produced, a number of which served aboard naval vessels.

Sopwith Baby A British single-place single-engine floatplane (biplane) delivered in 1915. It was armed with one forward-firing machine gun, and for bombing or antisubmarine work it carried two 65-lb bombs under the fuselage. It operated in a number of theaters during World War I. It had a top speed of 98 mph.

Sopwith Camel A British single-seat single-engine biplane fighter first flown in December 1916. It had a speed of about 115 mph and was armed with twin Vickers machine guns synchronized to fire forward. Some 5,490 aircraft of this type were built, a number of which were carried aboard aircraft carriers and other warships.

Sopwith Cuckoo A British single-place single-engine biplane torpedo bomber produced in 1918, but too late to see service during World War I. It carried one torpedo and had a speed of about 103 mph.

Sopwith Dolphin Also designated the Sopwith 5F.I, this was a British single-seat single-engine biplane fighter that was first flown in May 1917. It was armed with two Lewis machine guns and had a speed of 119 mph. It could also carry four 25-lb bombs.

Sopwith Pup A single-seat single-engine biplane fighter that resembled a scaled-down version of the earlier 1½-Strutter. It had a speed of about 112 mph and was armed with one forward-firing synchronized Vickers machine gun. In addition to their application in squadrons, Pups were carried by five aircraft carriers and seven Royal Navy cruisers between 1916 and 1918.

Sopwith Salamander A British single-seat single-engine biplane fighter first flown in April 1918. It had a speed of 125 mph and was armed with two forward-firing Vickers

Sopwith 1½-Strutter. (*The Smithsonian Institution, National Air Museum.*)

machine guns.

Sopwith Snipe A British single-seat single-engine biplane fighter that went into production in the spring of 1918; it was designed to replace the Camel. It had a speed of about 121 mph and was armed with two forward-firing Vickers machine guns. It was generally used for escort work, but could carry four 20-lb bombs.

Sopwith Tabloid A British single-seat single-engine biplane scout made in limited numbers and first flown in late 1913. It had a speed of 92 mph.

Sopwith Triplane A British single-seat single-engine triplane fighter, an unarmed prototype of which first flew in May 1916. Operational late in 1916, this airplane had a speed of 102 mph and was armed with a forward-firing Vickers machine gun.

sortie **1.** A sudden attack made from a defensive position. In this meaning, it is sometimes called a "sally." **2.** An operational flight by one aircraft. **3.** To depart from a port or anchorage, with an implication of departure for operations or maneuver.

Soryu A class of Japanese aircraft carriers of 16,000 to 17,000 tons displacement produced between 1935 and 1937. There were two in the class, *Soryu* and *Hiryu*. They had flight-deck dimensions of 711.5 by 85.5 ft,

a speed of 34 knots, and a complement of 1,101 men. They carried 73 aircraft. Both were lost in the Battle of Midway in 1942.

SOSUS *S*ound *s*urveillance *u*ndersea. The U.S. Navy's antisubmarine-warfare systems, on which development began in 1956. A number of systems are included, the major ones being **Caesar, Colossus,** and **Barrier,** which see.

sound and flash ranging Two distinct and separate but supplementary systems of locating enemy weapons and, secondarily, adjusting friendly counterfire by (1) observation by sonic devices on the sound produced by the enemy weapon in firing or by the friendly projectile in exploding or (2) visual observation of the flash produced or of the point of burst of the enemy weapon or friendly projectile.

sound locator A device formerly used to detect aircraft in flight by sound. A sound locator comprised four horns, or sound collectors (two for azimuth detection and two for elevation), together with their associated mechanisms and controls, which enabled the listening operators to determine the position and angular velocity of aircraft.

sound ranging A method of locating the source of a sound, such as that of a gun report or a projectile burst, by calculations based on the intervals between the recep-

Sopwith Camel. (*The Smithsonian Institution, National Air Museum.*)

South Carolina. (*U.S. Navy.*)

Soviet 7.62mm AK assault rifle. (*The Smithsonian Institution, War Department Collection.*)

Soviet 7.62mm carbine SKS. (*U.S. Army.*)

tion of the sound at various previously oriented microphone stations.

South Carolina A class of U.S. battleships of 16,000 tons standard displacement commissioned in 1910. There were two ships in the class, *South Carolina* and *Michigan*. These ships had a length of 452 ft, a beam of 80 ft, a speed of 18.5 knots, and a complement of 869 men. Main armament consisted of eight 12-in. guns, twenty-two 3-in. guns, and two submerged 21-in. torpedo tubes.

South Dakota A U.S. battleship of the new **Indiana** class, which see. Commissioned in 1942, it saw intensive service in the Pacific theater during World War II.

Southhampton An eight-ship class of British 9,100-ton cruisers completed in the late 1930s. They had a length of 591 ft, a speed of 32 knots, a complement of 700 men, and main armament consisting of twelve 6-in. guns, eight 4-in. guns, six 21-in. torpedo tubes, and three aircraft.

Soviet 7.62mm aircraft machine gun (Shkas) A weapon with a weight of about 23 lb, a length of 37 in. (turret- or wing-mounted), and a rate of fire of 1,500 to

1,800 rounds per minute. It used a belt and revolving-cage system of feeding.

Soviet 7.62mm AK assault rifle This weapon has been called a submachine gun and, indeed, replaced two submachine guns (the PPsh M1941 and PPS M1943) in the Soviet service. However, it fires rifle-type cartridges instead of pistol cartridges and has greater accuracy over longer ranges. The AS (also called the "AK-47") is a gas-operated selective-rifle weapon with a cyclic rate of fire of 600 rounds per minute and a muzzle velocity of 2,330 fps. It has an overall length of 34.25 in., a barrel length of 16.34 in., and a weight of 10.58 lb. It uses a 30-round detachable box magazine. (AK stands for "Automat Kalashnikov.")

Soviet 7.62mm assault rifle AKM This weapon is an improved version of the AK assault rifle.

Soviet 7.62mm automatic pistol (Tokarev) TT Model 1933 See **Tokarev 7.62mm automatic pistol TT Model 1933.**

Soviet 7.62mm automatic rifle Model 1936 See **Simonov 7.62mm automatic rifle Model 1936 (AVS).**

Soviet 7.62mm carbine SKS This semi-automatic weapon was introduced to Soviet forces in 1946. It is a gas-operated weapon with an overall length of 40.16 in., a barrel length of 20.47 in., and a weight of 8.8 lb. It is fed from a 10-round nondetachable box magazine and has a muzzle velocity of 2,410 fps. It was replaced by the Soviet 7.62mm AK assault rifle.

Soviet 7.62mm heavy machine gun Model 1939 DS (Degtyarev) A heavy machine-gun version of the 7.62mm light machine gun Model DP. Because of manufacturing shortcomings, it was not successful.

Soviet 7.62mm heavy machine gun SG43 (Goryunov) This very successful weapon was developed during World War II and replaced the 1939 DS (Degtyarev). It is gas-operated and fires on automatic only. The cyclic rate of fire is 600 to 700 rounds per minute, and the muzzle velocity is 2,832 fps. It is air-cooled and utilizes a 250-round drum magazine holding a metallic link belt. It has an overall length of 44.09 in., a barrel length of 28.3 in., and a weight of 30.42 lb. The mount weighs an additional 59.3 lb.

Soviet 7.62mm heavy machine gun SGM (Goryunov) This weapon, the Heavy Modernized Goryunov, is a modification of the SG43 heavy machine gun. It is a gas-operated weapon with an overall length of 44.09 in., a barrel length of 28.3 in., and a weight of 29.76 lb. The mount weighs 50.9 lb. The cyclic rate of fire is 600 to 700 rounds per minute, and the muzzle velocity is 2,870 fps. It is fed by a 250-round metallic link belt.

Soviet 7.62mm light machine gun DP (Degtyarev) This was the first Soviet-developed machine gun and was invented by Degtyarev in 1926. It is a gas-operated air-cooled weapon capable of full automatic fire only. It has a cyclic rate of fire of 500 to 600 rounds per minute, a muzzle velocity of 2,756 fps, a weight of 26.23 lb (loaded), and an overall length of 50 in. It utilizes a 47-round drum magazine.

Soviet 7.62mm light machine gun DPM (Degtyarev) This weapon is a modification of the DP. It is basically the same, the major difference being the design of the recoil spring.

Soviet 7.62mm light machine gun RP46 This weapon is basically a post-World War II modification of the DPM (which was itself a modification of the DP). It has an overall length of 50 in., a barrel length of 23.8 in., and a weight of 28.7 lb. It has a cyclic rate of fire of 600 to 650 rounds per minute and a muzzle velocity of 2,750 fps. It utilizes a 250-round metallic link belt.

Soviet 7.62mm light machine gun RPD (Degtyarev) This is the standard squad automatic weapon in the Soviet Army. It is bipod-mounted and about equivalent to the U.S. Browning automatic rifle or the British Bren gun. It is gas-operated and has a cyclic rate of fire of 650 to 750 rounds per minute and a muzzle velocity of 2,410 fps. It has an overall length of 40.8 in., a barrel length of 20.5 in., and a weight of 15.6 lb. It utilizes a 100-round metallic link belt in a drum magazine.

Soviet 7.62mm light machine gun RPK This weapon is basically the same as the AKM assault except that it has a longer barrel and a tripod. It utilizes 30- and 40-

Soviet 7.62mm light machine gun DPM (Degtyarev). (*The Smithsonian Institution.*)

round box magazines and also a 75-round drum magazine.

Soviet 7.62mm machine gun DP (Degtyarev) A gas-operated air-cooled weapon with a rate of fire of 500 to 600 rounds per minute. It has a weight, with bipod, of 20 lb and is fed by a 47-round drum magazine. It has a range of about 880 yd. (DP designates "Degtyarev Infantry.") Other models have the same or similar characteristics. They include DA (Degtyarev Aircraft), DT (Degtyarev Tank), DPM (Degtyarev Infantry Modified), and DTM (Degtyarev Tank Modified). They saw considerable service during World War II.

Soviet 7.62mm machine gun DS (Degtyarev Medium) A gas-operated air-cooled weapon with a rate of fire of 500 to 600 (normal) or 1,000 to 1,200 (fast) rounds per minute. It has a length of 46 in. and a weight (gun only) of 26.4 lb and is capable of automatic fire only. It is fed by a 250-round canvas belt or a 50-round metallic link belt.

Soviet 7.62mm machine gun (Maxim) This particular model features a wheel mount. With very little modification, this pattern was used by the Russians in both world wars and was also used by the Chinese during the Korean conflict. It has a cyclic rate of fire of 450 to 550 rounds per minute.

Soviet 7.62mm machine gun Model 1910 (Maxim) A recoil-operated water-cooled weapon with a rate of fire of 300 to 500 rounds per minute. It weighed 145 lb on a mount (with the water jacket filled) and was fed by a fabric belt.

Soviet 7.62mm machine gun (Maxim). (*U.S. Army.*)

Soviet 7.62mm submachine gun PPS-43. (*The Smithsonian Institution.*)

Soviet 7.62mm machine gun PK/PKS
This gas-operated weapon was developed as a general-purpose machine gun. PK is used to designate the bipod-mounted version, while PKS refers to the tripod-mounted version. Designed by Mikhail Kalashnikov, this weapon has a cyclic rate of fire of 650 to 700 rounds per minute, a muzzle velocity of 2,700 fps, an overall length of 47.2 in., a barrel length of 25.9 in., and a weight of 19.8 lb (with bipod). It utilizes 100-, 200-, and 250-round metallic link belts.

Soviet 7.62mm machine gun SG-43 (Stankovaya Goryunov 1943) A gas-operated air-cooled weapon with a rate of fire of 500 to 700 rounds per minute. It has a length of 44.75 in. and a weight of about 78 lb and is fed by a 250-round canvas belt or multiples of 50-round metallic link belts.

Soviet 7.62mm semiautomatic and automatic rifles (Tokarev) Models 1938 and 1940 See **Tokarev 7.62mm semiautomatic and automatic rifles Model 1940** and **Tokarev 7.62mm semiautomatic rifle Model 1938.**

Soviet 7.62mm sniper rifle SVD The SVD (self-loading rifle, Dragunov) was developed to replace the Model 1891/30 Mosin-Nagant sniper rifle. It uses a 7.62mm rimmed cartridge and is fitted with a Model PSO-1 telescopic sight (four-power). It is a gas-operated semiautomatic rifle with an overall length of 48.2 in., a barrel length of 24 in., and a weight of 9.5 lb. It uses a 10-round detachable box magazine and has a muzzle velocity of 2,720 fps.

Soviet 7.62mm submachine gun Model PPD-1940 Designed by V. A. Degtyarov, this weapon was a modification of the earlier PPD-1934/38 submachine gun.

Soviet 7.62mm submachine gun PPD 1934/38 A blowback-operated submachine gun with selective full automatic and semiautomatic fire. It has a cyclic rate of fire of 900 rounds per minute and a muzzle velocity of about 1,600 fps. It utilizes 7.62mm cartridges and a 7.63mm Mauser. Available for use are 25- and 71-round magazines. The weight of the weapon with a 71-round drum magazine is 11.5 lb. It is 30.63 in. long and has a barrel length of 10.75 in. The general design of the PPD series is similar to that of the Schmeisser-designed MP-28II.

Soviet 7.62mm submachine gun PPS-43 A modified and improved version of the PPS-42, which was produced in limited numbers in 1942. Both were designed by A. I. Sudarev. The PPS-43 was manufactured from 1943 until some time after World War II and could be easily mass-produced. It is blowback-operated and operates on full automatic only. Its cyclic rate of fire is 700 rounds per minute, and the muzzle velocity is about 1,600 fps. The length with the stock retracted is 24.25 in., and the length of the barrel is 9.45 in. With a 35-round magazine the weight of the weapon is 8.65 lb. Rear sights are adjustable to 100 and 200 meters.

Soviet 7.62mm submachine gun PPSh-41 This weapon, designed by George S. Shpagin, was officially adopted by the Soviet Army in 1941. By the late 1940s over 5 million had been produced. It is blowback-operated and has selective full automatic and semiautomatic fire. The approximate muzzle velocity is 1,600 fps, and the cyclic rate of fire is 900 rounds per minute. The weapon employs a 35-round box magazine and a 71-round drum magazine. The weight of the weapon with the drum magazine is 12 lb. The overall length is 33.10 in., with a barrel length of 10.60 in.

Soviet 7.62mm tank machine gun DT (Degtyarev) This weapon is the tank version of the DP and may still be found on older Soviet armored vehicles.

Soviet 7.62mm tank machine gun DTM (Degtyarev) A machine gun that is the tank version of the DPM. It may still be found on Soviet armored vehicles manufactured before 1949.

Soviet 9mm automatic pistol PM (Makarov) See **Makarov 9mm automatic pistol PM.**

Soviet 9mm machine pistol APS (Stechkin) A Soviet weapon designed after World War II. It is capable of full automatic and semiautomatic fire. It fires the 9mm Makarov cartridge and has an overall length of 8.85 in. (with shoulder stock the length is 21.25 in.). With shoulder-stock holster the weight of the weapon is 3.92 lb. Without it the weight is 1.7 lb. It is equipped with a 20-round staggered-row magazine and has a cyclic rate of fire of 750 rounds per minute.

Soviet 12.7mm aircraft machine gun (Beresin) A weapon with a weight of about 47 lb, a length of 55 in., and a rate of fire of 800 to 1,000 rounds per minute.

Soviet 12.7mm heavy machine gun DShK M1938/46 (Degtyarev) This weapon is gas-operated and has a cyclic rate of fire of 540 to 600 rounds per minute. It has an overall length of 62.5 in., a barrel length of 42.1 in., a weight of 78.5 lb (the mount weighs 259 lb), and a muzzle velocity of 2,822 fps. It utilizes a 50-round metallic link belt. For ground use it is mounted on a wheeled mount which can be converted into a tripod mount for AA fire. This weapon is also used as antiaircraft armament on tanks and armored personnel carriers.

Soviet 12.7mm machine guns DK (Degtyarev Heavy) and DShK (Degtyarev-Shpagin Heavy) Gas-operated air-cooled weapons with a rate of fire of 550 to 600 rounds per minute. They have a length of about 62 in., a weight of about 73 lb, and a maximum effective range of 3,792 yd. They are fed by a metallic link belt.

Soviet 14.5mm antitank rifle See **Simonov 14.5mm antitank rifle.**

Soviet 14.5mm heavy machine gun KPV This weapon is recoil-operated and has a cyclic rate of fire of 600 rounds per minute. It has a muzzle velocity of 3,280 fps, an overall length of 78.7 in., a barrel length of 53.2 in., and a weight of 107.9 lb. It feeds from a metallic link belt. This weapon is mounted on a series of towed antiaircraft mounts designated the ZPU1, ZPU2, and ZPU4. The ZPU1 is a two-wheeled mount with one gun, the ZPU2 is a two-wheeled mount with two guns, and the ZPU4 is a four-wheeled mount with four guns.

Soviet 20mm aircraft cannon (Shvak) A weapon with a weight of 88 to 97 lb, a length of 66 to 83 in., and a rate of fire of 700 to 850 rounds per minute.

Soviet 23mm aircraft cannon NS 23 A recoil-operated air-cooled cannon with a rate of fire of 600 to 700 rounds per minute. Introduced in 1947, it has a length of 78.75 in., a weight of 121 lb, and a pneumatic feed system.

Soviet 23mm aircraft cannon (VYa) A weapon with a weight of 467 lb, a length of 84 in., and a rate of fire of 550 to 650 rounds per minute. It was adopted early in World War II.

Soviet 37mm aircraft cannon NS 37 A recoil-operated air-cooled cannon with a rate of fire of 300 to 350 rounds per minute. Introduced in 1943, it had a length of 134 in., a weight of 375 lb, and a pneumatic/spring feed system.

Soviet 45mm antitank gun M1942 A World War II weapon with a weight of 1,257 lb and a projectile weight of 4.7 lb. It fired fixed ammunition and had a range of 5,000 yd.

Soviet 57mm antiaircraft gun S-60 (ZSU 57) The S-60 is the towed version of the gun, while the ZSU 57 is a self-propelled version mounting twin guns. Both are in service with Soviet forces, Warsaw Pact nations, the Chinese People's Republic, and Indonesia. The gun has a rate of fire of 120 rounds per minute and a range of 16,000 ft vertically. It was developed in the late 1940s, possibly from German designs.

Soviet 57mm antitank gun M1943 A World War II weapon with a weight of 1.2 tons and a projectile weight of 8.3 lb. It fired fixed ammunition and had a range of 7,700 yd.

Soviet 57mm antitank gun MO1943 (ZIS-2) A gun with a firing weight of 2,535 lb and a crew of seven. It is also used by Warsaw Pact countries and the Chinese People's Republic. It fires fixed ammunition and has a projectile weight of 8.3 lb and a range of 7,700 yd. It was used during World War II.

Soviet 75mm antiaircraft gun M1938 A World War II weapon with a weight of 4.7 tons and a projectile weight of 15 lb. It fired fixed ammunition and had an effective ceiling of 25,000 ft.

Soviet 76mm divisional gun M1942 (ZIS-3) A weapon that is presently in service with Soviet forces and also with the forces of Warsaw Pact countries, Indonesia, Cuba, and the Chinese People's Republic. The gun has a weight of 5,513 lb, a crew of six, and a range of 14,500 yd.

Soviet 76mm gun M1936 A World War II weapon with a weight of 1.8 tons and a projectile that weighed 14 lb. It fired fixed ammunition and had a range of 15,260 yd.

Soviet 76mm gun M1939 A World War II weapon with a weight of 2.6 tons and a projectile weight of 14 lb. It fired fixed ammunition and had a range of 12,200 yd.

Soviet 76.2mm gun M1942 This weapon fired 25 rounds per minute at ranges up to 14,500 yd. Using high-velocity armor-piercing ammunition, it could penetrate 3.62 in. of armor at 550 yd.

Soviet 76.2mm self-propelled gun SU-76 This system was introduced in 1943 and used with infantry tank-destroyer units. It had a crew of four and was armed with one 76.2mm gun Model 42/43, caliber length 41.5. It weighed 12.3 tons and could travel at speeds of about 28 mph.

Soviet 85mm antiaircraft gun M1939 A World War II weapon with a weight of 4.7 tons and a projectile weight of 20 lb. It fired fixed ammunition and had an effective ceiling of 27,500 ft.

Soviet 85mm antiaircraft gun M1944 A World War II weapon with a weight of 5.3 tons and a projectile weight of 20 lb. It fired fixed ammunition and had an effective ceiling of 32,000 ft.

Soviet 85mm antiaircraft gun M44 A gun that is similar to the D48 antitank gun, but with different mountings. It fires a 21-lb

projectile to an effective altitude of 34,500 ft.

Soviet 85mm antitank gun D48 A weapon that is similar in some ways to the German 88mm (8.8cm) gun of World War II. It has a range of 17,100 yd and fires a 12-lb projectile.

Soviet 100mm antitank gun M1944 The main armament on the T54/55 tanks, and also as a towed piece and on naval mountings, this gun has a barrel length of 17 ft 6.5 in. and a range of 22,960 yd. The weight of the fixed ammunition is 66 lb.

Soviet 100mm self-propelled gun SU-100 A T34 tank outfitted with a 100mm gun. It was introduced in 1944 and had a crew of four, a combat weight of 31.6 tons, and a road speed of 35 mph.

Soviet 122mm gun M1937 A World War II weapon with a weight of 7.8 tons and a projectile weight of 55 lb. It fired fixed ammunition and had a range of 22,900 yd.

Soviet 122mm howitzer M1938 Large numbers of these weapons have been produced and are in the service with Soviet, Chinese, and Warsaw Pact forces. They have a weight of 4,961 lb, a barrel length of 8 ft 10 in., a range of 12,903 yd, a rate of fire of five to six rounds per minute, and a projectile weight (HE) of 48 lb.

Soviet 122mm self-propelled gun JSU-122 A JS-1 tank outfitted with a 122mm gun (and a 12.7mm machine gun for antiaircraft protection). It was introduced in 1944 and had a crew of five, a combat weight of 46 tons, and a road speed of 23 mph.

Soviet 122mm self-propelled howitzer SU-122 A World War II system introduced in 1941–1942. It has a weight of 31 tons and was based on a T34 tank chassis.

Soviet 132mm rocket launcher M13 See Katyusha rocket launcher.

Soviet 152mm gun Three separate versions of the 152mm gun were used. The 152mm gun had a range of 28,600 yd, the gun-howitzer had a range of 18,900 yd, and the simple howitzer had a range of 13,500 yd.

Soviet 152mm gun-howitzer M37 (ML-20) This weapon has a barrel length of 13 ft 10 in., an overall weight of 15,717 lb, and a range of 19,275 yd. It uses separate-loading ammunition, and the weight of

the projectile is 95.7 lb (HE).

Soviet 152mm gun M1935 A World War II weapon with a weight of 20 tons and a projectile weight of 108 lb. It fired fixed ammunition and had a range of 24,800 yd.

Soviet 152mm howitzer M1938 A World War II weapon with a weight of 4.5 tons and a projectile weight of 88 lb. It fired fixed ammunition and had a range of 14,100 yd.

Soviet 152mm self-propelled gun JSU-152 A JS-2 tank outfitted with a 152mm gun-howitzer (and one 12.7mm machine gun for antiaircraft protection). It was introduced in 1944 and had a crew of five, a combat weight of 46 tons, and a road speed of 23 mph.

Soviet 210mm gun M1939 A World War II weapon with a weight of 47.6 tons and a projectile weight of 297 lb. It fired separate-loading ammunition and had a range of 30,100 yd.

Soviet 302mm gun-howitzer M55 This is the largest weapon presently in use by Soviet forces. It has an overall weight of 44,970 lb and a maximum range of 31,700 yd. The projectile weight is 300 lb (conventional or nuclear), and the gun fires at the rate of about one round every 2 minutes.

Soviet aircraft machine guns Numerous aircraft weapons have been made in 7.62mm, 12.7mm, 20mm, 23mm, 30mm, and 37mm calibers. The 12.7mm UB was introduced during World War II.

Soviet amphibious tank PT-76 This tank was introduced in 1955 and is employed with reconnaissance units. It has a crew of three, a combat weight of 14 tons, and a road speed of 27 mph (6.2 mph on water). It is armed with one 76mm gun and one 7.62mm tank machine gun.

Soviet antiaircraft gun carrier SU-37 A 37mm gun mounted on a T70 light tank. It was introduced in 1943 and had a crew of six and a combat weight of 10.5 tons.

Soviet armored car BA-10 (GAZ) A six-wheeled vehicle developed in the mid-1930s and used extensively during World War II. It had a weight of about 6 tons, a crew of four, and armament consisting of one 45mm gun and two 7.62mm machine guns.

Soviet armored car BA-64 A four-

Soviet 7.62mm submachine gun PPSh-41. (*The Smithsonian Institution.*)

Soviet tank, medium, T34. (*U.S. Army.*)

wheeled vehicle introduced in 1943 and used with reconnaissance and signal units. It had a crew of two, a combat weight of 2½ tons, a road speed of 50 mph, and armament consisting of one 7.62mm DT tank machine gun. It was the most widely used Soviet armored car in World War II.

Soviet armored personnel carrier AAICV 67   First seen in 1967, this full-track armored vehicle has a crew of three (plus eight infantrymen), a weight of 12 tons, a road speed of 32 mph, and estimated armament of one 76mm gun, one Sagger anti-tank missile, and one 7.62mm machine gun.

Soviet armored personnel carrier BTR50P   This amphibious full-track vehicle belongs to a family which includes the Soviet light tank PT-76, and it has similar performance. It has a crew of three (plus twelve infantrymen), a weight of 14 tons, and a road speed of 26 mph (a water speed of 6 mph) and is armed with up to four machine guns (14.5mm, 12.7mm, or 7.62mm).

Soviet armored personnel carrier BTR-60   An eight-wheeled vehicle first seen in 1961. It has a crew of two (plus ten infantrymen), a weight of 10 tons, and a road speed of 50 mph and is armed with a 14.5mm and a 7.62mm machine gun, and sometimes with an antitank rocket launcher.

Soviet assault gun ASU-57   This full-track system has been in service since 1957. It has a crew of four and a weight of 5.4 tons and is armed with one 57mm high-velocity antitank gun.

Soviet assault gun ASU-85   The chassis of this air-transportable amphibious full-track vehicle is the same as that of the **Soviet light amphibious tank PT-76,** which see, and has similar mobility. It has a crew of three and a weight of 14 tons and is armed with an

85mm high-velocity gun. It has been in service with Soviet Army antitank battalions since 1962.

Soviet assault gun Su-85   A T34 tank outfitted with an 85mm gun. It was introduced in 1943 and had a crew of four, a combat weight of 29.6 tons, and a road speed of 35 mph.

Soviet light amphibious tank PT-76   The main reconnaissance vehicle of the Soviet Army and Warsaw Pact forces, this tank was first seen in about 1950. It has a crew of four, a weight of 14 tons, a road speed of 25 mph (a water speed of 7 mph), and armament consisting of one 76mm low-velocity gun and one 7.62mm machine gun.

Soviet main battle tanks T54 and T55   The T55 is essentially a later variation of the T54, and the following specifications refer to both. The system has a crew of four, a weight of 35.7 tons, a road speed of 32 mph, and armament consisting of a 100mm high-velocity gun and two 7.62mm machine guns. Some 30,000 tanks of this description are estimated to have been built between 1948 and 1963. Warsaw Pact countries are equipped with this tank, as are the United Arab Republic and Cuba. The Soviet Army has largely reequipped with T62's.

Soviet main battle tank T62   First seen in 1963, this tank resembles the T54 and T55 but incorporates a 115mm smoothbore gun in a newly designed turret. It has a crew of four, a weight of 36.5 tons, and a road speed of 31 mph. The 115mm gun is thought to fire a spin-stabilized round with a range of about 1,500 meters.

Soviet reconnaissance car BRDM-1   Also known as the "BTR40P," this vehicle relates to the BTR-40 of 1945–1948, itself almost a direct copy of the U.S. **White scout car** (M3A1), which see. BRDM-1 was man-

ufactured in large quantities between 1960 and 1966 and continues in service with Warsaw Pact forces and also in the United Arab Republic and Cuba. It has a crew of five, a weight of 6.5 tons, a road speed of 50 mph, and armament consisting of one 7.62mm machine gun.

Soviet reconnaissance car BRDM-2   A four-wheeled amphibious vehicle also designated as BTR40PB. First seen in 1966, it has a crew of three to four, an estimated weight of 7 tons, a road speed of 50 mph (a water speed of 7 mph), and armament consisting of a 14.5mm machine gun.

Soviet tank, heavy, JS-III   See **Stalin tank.**

Soviet tank, heavy, KV-1 C   This tank was introduced in 1939 and was used in armored divisions. It had a crew of five and was armed with one 76.2mm gun Model 1940, caliber length 41.5, and three 7.62mm machine guns DT. The weight of the tank, a forerunner of the JS III, was 52 tons, and its maximum speed was 22 mph.

Soviet tank, heavy, KV-2   This tank was introduced in 1942 for use in heavy-tank battalions. It had a crew of six, a combat weight of 52 tons, a road speed of 15 mph, and armament consisting of one 152mm howitzer and three 7.62mm DT machine guns. It mounted the heaviest gun ever used on a mass-produced tank.

Soviet tank, heavy, T10   This tank is a direct descendent of the Joseph Stalin III of World War II. In operation since the mid-1950s, it has a crew of four, a weight of 50 tons, a road speed of 31 mph, and armament consisting of one 122mm gun and two 12.7mm machine guns. Although being replaced by the T62 in the Soviet Army, it is still in broad use with the forces of the Warsaw Pact nations.

Soviet tank, light, T60   A tank introduced in 1941 and made only in small numbers. It had a crew of two, a combat weight of 6 tons, and armament consisting of one 20mm automatic gun and one 7.62mm machine gun.

Soviet tank, light, T70   This tank was introduced in 1942 and was employed in reconnaissance units. It had a crew of two, a combat weight of 10.1 tons, a road speed of 21 mph, and armament consisting of one 45mm gun and one 7.62mm machine gun.

Soviet tank, medium, T34   Introduced in 1940, this tank was used in armored divisions. It had a crew of four and was armed with one 76.2mm gun Model 40, caliber length 41.5, and two 7.62mm machine guns DT. It had a weight of 32 tons and could travel at speeds of 33 mph. It was one of the best tanks of World War II, as it combined low silhouette, good mobility, and good firepower. The gun's 14.3-lb AP projectile could penetrate 3 in. of armor at 100 yd at 0°.

Soviet tank, medium, T34-84   This tank

was introduced in 1944 and was used in armored divisions. With a crew of four to five, it was armed with one 85mm gun Model 1944, caliber length 53, and two 7.62mm machine guns DT. The weight was 34.4 tons, and the speed was about 33 mph. As compared with the T34, this tank achieved a tremendous increase in fire-power with very little weight penalty. The gun's 20.3-lb AP projectile could penetrate 4.7 in. of armor at 100 yd at 0°.

Soviet tank, medium, T54 This tank was introduced in 1954 and was the standard medium tank of the Soviet Army until the late 1960s. It is still the major tank of most Warsaw Pact countries. It has a crew of four, a combat weight of 40 tons, a road speed of 30 mph, and armament consisting of one 100mm gun, one 12.7mm heavy machine gun, and two 7.62mm tank machine guns.

sowar Formerly, an Anglo-Indian native cavalryman.

SP **1.** A U.S. Navy motor patrol boat. **2.** The U.S. Navy Shore Patrol. **3.** Self-propelled.

spaced armor An arrangement of armor plate using two or more thicknesses, each thickness being spaced from the adjoining one. It is used as a protective device, particularly against shaped-charge ammunition.

Spacetrack A global system of radar, optical, and radiometric sensors linked to a computation and analysis center in the North American Air Defense Command combat-operations-center complex. The Spacetrack mission is detection, tracking, and cataloging of all man-made objects in orbit of the earth. It is the Air Force portion of the North American Air Defense Command Space Detection and Tracking System.

Spad VII A French single-seat single-engine biplane fighter first flown in April 1916. It had a speed of 119 mph and was armed with one forward-firing synchronized Vickers machine gun. Some 5,600 aircraft of this type were built by eight French manufacturers. The VII's remained in service until mid-1917, when they were replaced with Spad VIII's.

Spad XI A French two-seat single-engine biplane that first appeared in September 1916, had a speed of about 109 mph, and was armed with one forward-firing synchronized Vickers machine gun and one or two Lewis guns on a ring mounting in the rear cockpit. It could carry a 154-lb bombload. It was used during 1917 and until the Armistice in 1918.

Spad XIII A further development of the Spad VII, this French single-seat single-engine biplane fighter first flew on April 4, 1917. Between that time and the end of World War I, 8,472 Spad XIII's were built.

Spad XIII. (*The Imperial War Museum.*)

Flown by every leading French pilot of the period, this aircraft had a speed of about 137 mph and armament consisting of two forward-firing Vickers guns.

Spad A2 A two-place single-engine biplane fighter first flown in May 1915. It was essentially a tractor biplane with an additional nacelle attached to the front (ahead of the propeller). It flew at speeds up to about 94 mph.

Spadats A *space detection and tracking* system capable of detecting and tracking space vehicles from the earth and of reporting the orbital characteristics of these vehicles to a central control facility.

spade bayonet A bayonet with a blade broad enough to be used for digging.

spade grip A D-shaped handle for pointing a gun, fastened on the rear of the receiver of certain flexible automatic weapons.

spadroon A light cutting and thrusting sword used by officers of the British infantry in the late eighteenth and early nineteenth centuries.

spall Fragments torn from either surface of armor plate, such as might result from the impact of **kinetic-energy ammunition,** which see, or the functioning of **chemical-energy ammunition,** which see.

Spanish 7mm Mauser Carbine Model 1895 This is the carbine version of the 7mm rifle Model 1893. It has an overall length of 37 in., a barrel length of 17.56 in., and a weight of 7.5 lb.

Spanish 7mm (Mauser) machine guns Models 1907 and 1914 Machine guns of

Hotchkiss design, which see.

Spanish 7mm Mauser rifle Model 1893 This Mauser design introduced the staggered-row integral box magazine that is flush with the stock. This bolt-action rifle has an overall length of 48.6 in., a barrel length of 29.1 in., a weight of 8.8 lb, and a nondetachable box magazine with a capacity of five cartridges. The muzzle velocity is 2,650 fps. A short rifle version of this weapon was also produced.

Spanish 7mm Mauser short rifle Model 1916 Called a "mosqueton" by the Spanish, this bolt-action weapon was made in very large quantities during the Spanish Civil War. It has an overall length of 40.9 in., a barrel length of 23.6 in., and a weight of 8.4 lb. It has a muzzle velocity of about 2,625 fps.

Spanish 7.92mm Mauser rifle Model 1943 This weapon is much the same as the German Kar 98k, but with a straight-bolt handle.

Spanish 7.92mm Mauser rifle Standard Model This weapon was procured by Spain during the Spanish Civil War. It is a bolt-action rifle with an overall length of 43.6 in., a barrel length of 23.62 in., and a weight of 8.8 lb. It has a nondetachable box magazine with a capacity of five rounds. The muzzle velocity is about 2,360 fps.

Spanish 11mm Remington rifle Model 1871 This single-shot rolling-block rifle was used in Spain in the 1870s and 1880s. It has an overall length of 50.3 in., a barrel

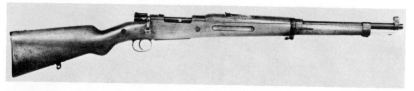

Spanish 7.92mm Mauser rifle Standard Model. (*Spanish Ministry of Defense.*)

Spanish 11mm Remington rolling block rifle Model 1871. (*Spanish Ministry of Defense.*)

Sparrow III. (*Raytheon Company.*)

Spartan. (*U.S. Army.*)

Sparviero. (*Siai-Marchetti.*)

length of 35.2 in., and a weight of 9.3 lb.

spanner In British terminology, a wrench. Specifically used in arms references to the key or wrench used to wind the wheel of a wheel-lock firearm.

Spanner-Anlage A type of infrared spotlight used by German night-fighter aircraft during World War II. A sighting screen (called "Q-Rohr") was used in conjunction with a special gunsight. The system was later replaced with radar.

Spar A member of the Women's Reserve of the U.S. Coast Guard Reserve. This organization was created on November 23, 1942, and the word "spar" is derived from "Semper *Par*atus—Always Ready," the motto of the Coast Guard.

Sparrow The name applied to a series of U.S. Navy and Air Force air-to-air solid-propellant-powered supersonic missiles. They are used against high- or low-altitude targets and employ evasive tactics. A beam rider with homing radar, Sparrow III has a range of 5 nautical miles.

Sparrow IIIB A radar-homing air-to-air missile developed by Raytheon for the U.S. Navy and operational since the mid-1950s. It has an overall length of 12 ft, a launching weight of 400 lb (of which 60 lb is high-explosive warhead), a speed of Mach 2.5, and a range of over 8 mi.

Spartan A U.S. command-guided antimissile missile carrying a nuclear warhead and powered by a three-stage solid-propellant rocket. Developed under a prime contract to Western Electric Company, this system has a range of several hundred miles and was first successfully test-fired in 1968. It is designated as the long-range element of the Safeguard missile defense system.

spar torpedo Formerly, a high explosive mounted on the end of a spar that projected from the bow of a vessel and was intended to be thrust against the target and exploded.

Sparviero The Italian Savoia-Marchetti S.M. 79 Sparviero (Hawk) was a five-place three-engine low-wing monoplane bomber first flown in 1935. It had a speed of 270 mph and a range of 1,243 mi. It was armed with three 12.7mm Breda machine guns and one 7.7mm Lewis machine gun, plus a bombload of 2,755 lb. It was one of the most successful airplanes used by Italy during World War II.

Spasur An operational space-surveillance system with the mission to detect and determine the orbital elements of all man-made objects in orbit of the earth. The mission is accomplished by means of a continuous fan of continuous-wave energy beamed vertically across the continental United States and an associated computational facility. It is the Navy portion of the North American Air Defense Command–Continental Air Defense Command Space Detection and Tracking System.

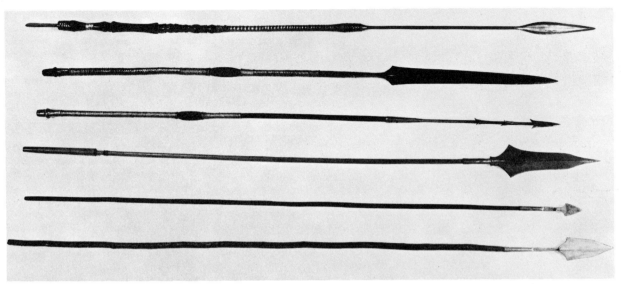

spears. (*The Smithsonian Institution.*)

Spat See **Scorpion light tank.**

spatha A long Roman sword of the fourth century.

spaulder An Old English word for armor for the protection of the shoulder.

spear A lance or long weapon with a sharp, pointed head and no auxiliary blades or points.

spearhead Any force that precedes others in an attack; the leading or most advanced element of an attacking force.

spear javelin A framea.

spearman A soldier who is armed with a spear.

special atomic demolition munition A small, lightweight atomic demolition munition.

special-equipment vehicle A vehicle consisting of a general-purpose chassis with a special-purpose body and/or mounted equipment designed to meet a specialized requirement.

Special Forces Military personnel with cross training in basic and specialized military skills, organized into small multiple-purpose detachments with the mission to train, organize, supply, direct, and control indigenous forces in guerrilla warfare and counterinsurgency operations and to conduct unconventional warfare operations.

special operations Secondary or supporting operations which may be adjuncts to various other operations and for which no one service is assigned primary responsibility.

special-purpose vehicle A vehicle incorporating a special chassis and designed to meet a specialized requirement.

special weapon Any out-of-the-ordinary modern weapon, such as an atomic, radiological, or biological weapon.

speed of sound The speed at which sound travels in a given medium under specified conditions. The speed of sound at sea level in the International Standard Atmosphere is 1,108 fps, 658 knots, or 1,215 kph (kilometers per hour).

Spencer .52 cal. repeating carbine This weapon was the first successful breechloading magazine rifle and was patented by Christopher M. Spencer in the United States in 1860. It was a seven-shot carbine with a tubular magazine in the stock. During the Civil War it was considered that one man armed with a Spencer was equal to seven using muzzle-loaders. The Spencer could be fired about seven times in 9 seconds and could maintain a sustained rate of 15 aimed shots a minute. It had a length of 39 in. and a weight of 8.25 lb.

Spencer .52 cal. rifle A seven-shot repeating rifle used during the American Civil War. It had a length of 47 in. and a weight of 10 lb.

spetum A sixteenth-century polearm with a long, narrow blade with curved lateral projections at the base.

S phone A radio telephone used by Resistance forces during World War II for talking an aircraft down to the right place.

spiculum A light Roman javelin.

spider mine A U.S. antipersonnel device about the size of a Ping-Pong ball. It is airdropped, and upon touching the ground, it throws out eight nylon threads a distance of about 8 meters. Disturbing any of the threads causes the mine to explode.

spigot mortar A mortar which propels a warhead larger than the bore of the mortar by means of a closed tube (spigot) attached to the warhead and extending into the mortar. The force of the propellant within the mortar acts upon the tube, thus propelling the warhead toward the target.

spike To disable a cannon by driving a spike in the vent or, in a modern weapon, by breaking or removing part of the breech mechanism.

spiked armor Armor with spikes on the

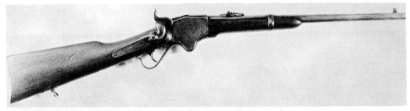

Spencer .52 cal. repeating carbine. (*The Smithsonian Institution, War Department Collection.*)

Spencer .52 cal. rifle. (*The Smithsonian Institution, War Department Collection.*)

spinning bombs. (*Vickers Ltd.*)

Spitfire. (*Vickers Ltd.*)

face, used as active resistance to the penetrating jet of shaped-charge ammunition.

spin The rotation of a projectile or missile about its longitudinal axis to provide stability during flight.

spingard A kind of small cannon.

spingarda A large fourteenth-century crossbow mounted on wheels.

spinning bombs Barrel-shaped bombs or mines developed during World War II for the British forces by Sir Barnes Wallis. When dropped from an altitude of 60 ft, they would skid or skip across the surface of a lake or reservoir until they reached a dam, at which point they would sink and explode far beneath the water. They were carried by Lancaster bombers and were successfully used against the Moehne, Eder, and Sorpe dams in the Ruhr during a night attack on May 17, 1943.

spin-stabilized projectile Any projectile, such as a bullet, shell, or rocket, that is steadied in flight by a rotating motion about its longitudinal axis. A projectile fired from a gun has spin imparted to it by the rifling in the gun barrel; on a rocket, a ring of nozzles may be used with each nozzle slanted sidewise so that the escape of the

exhaust gases through them will impart spin to the rocket.

Spitfire The Supermarine Spitfire was a British single-seat single-engine fighter-interceptor (and later fighter-bomber) that had the distinction of being the only Allied fighter in continuous production throughout the whole of World War II. Many models were produced, from the prototype, which first flew on March 5, 1936, to the Spitfire Mk 22, the last of which was delivered in 1947. Some 20,334 aircraft of all types were delivered to the RAF. The first Spitfires were armed with eight .303 cal. Browning machine guns. Powered by 1,030-hp engines, they flew at speeds of 365 mph. The wingspan was 36 ft 10 in., the length was about 30 ft, and the height was 11 ft 5 in. Later versions flew at speeds up to 454 mph.

splash 1. The term used to indicate enemy aircraft shot down, usually over water. **2.** The word transmitted by a firing ship or artillery-fire direction center to the spotters 5 seconds before the estimated time of the impact of a salvo or a round.

splint armor Armor produced with thin overlapping metal plates.

splinter bulkhead A heavy bulkhead on the gun deck of a warship. The purpose of the bulkhead is to localize damage from shell splinters.

splinter deck A deck fitted with armor.

splinter screen Also called "splinter shields," these are light metal armor placed around the bridge and gun stations on a ship. They provide moderate protection against bomb and shell fragments.

split trail In modern times, an artillery weapon trail composed of two rigid members hinged at the carriage. They are together in the traveling position and spread apart in the firing position. In the muzzle-loading era, the split trails were rigid, being prolongations of the cheeks.

spoiling attack A tactical maneuver employed to seriously impair a hostile attack while the enemy is in the process of forming or assembling for an attack. Usually employed by armored units in defense by an attack on enemy assembly positions in front of a main line of resistance or battle position.

sponge 1. A long-handled brush or mop used to clean the bore of muzzle-loading cannons between shots and also to put out sparks or smoldering remnants of the previous round. Often the same staff had a ramming head on the other end and was thus called a "sponge-rammer." **2.** To swab a cannon bore.

sponson 1. A projection from the side of an aircraft used for housing some part or for other purposes; specifically, a protuberance on either side of a flying-boat hull near the water line, used to give the plane sta-

split trail, on a Vickers 105mm long-range gun. (*Vickers Ltd.*)

bility in the water. **2.** A hollow enlargement on the side of the hull of a tank, used for storing ammunition or as a space for radio equipment or guns. **3.** A projecting structure, platform, or short wing on the hull of a ship, often used as a gun platform. It provides a greater arc of fire.

spontoon, espontoon A type of half-pike or partisan, usually having a lobed, leaf-shaped blade. It was the badge of rank and the principal weapon for some officers of infantry, especially in the eighteenth century.

Spooky See **Skytrain.**

spot 1. To determine, by observation, deviations of ordnance from the target for the purpose of supplying necessary information for adjustment of fire. **2.** To place in a proper location.

spot jamming The jamming of a specific channel or frequency.

spot net A radio communication net used by a spotter in calling fire.

spotter An observer stationed for the purpose of observing and reporting results of naval gunfire to the firing agency. He also may be employed in designating targets.

spotting A process of determining, by visual or electronic observation, deviations of artillery or naval gunfire from the target in relation to a spotting line for the purpose of supplying necessary information for the adjustment or analysis of fire.

spotting pistol A short automatic or semi-automatic firearm mounted coaxially on a larger-caliber gun and designed to conserve and to increase the first-round-hit probability of the ammunition used in the larger weapon. It employs a magazine and fires a spotter-tracer projectile which is ballistically matched with the trajectory of the projectile of the gun on which it is mounted.

spotting rifle An auxiliary firearm mounted coaxially on a larger-caliber gun used to assist a gunner in determining range. It is usually a magazine-fed semiautomatic gun with a rifled barrel that utilizes ammunition incorporating a tracer element providing a smoke puff on impact.

spread A multiple salvo of torpedoes fired ahead of, at, and astern of a target to ensure a hit.

spreading A maneuver of moving ships out from a formation to stations on a scouting line.

Sprengmunition-02 A German military term for "trinitrotoluene" (TNT).

spring bayonet A spring-loaded bayonet hinged to the barrels of certain weapons. They could be flipped forward and locked into position for use by releasing a catch.

Springfield .30 cal. rifle Model 1903 See **U.S. .30 cal. rifle Model 1903 (Springfield).**

Springfield .45 cal. rifle A single-shot breechloading rifle in use in the U.S.

services from about 1868 until 1893 and employed by volunteers in the war with Spain in 1898. It was equipped with a triangular bayonet.

Springfield .58 cal. musket A single-shot muzzle-loading weapon used during the American Civil War. It had a length of 56 in. and a weight of 9.9 lb.

Sprint A U.S. radar-command-guided antimissile missile propelled by a two-stage solid-propellant rocket motor. It has a nuclear warhead, a length of 8.2 meters, and a range of about 40 kilometers. It is designated as the closer-range element of the Safeguard missile defense system.

spud An obsolete name for a type of dagger or short knife.

spur 1. In fortifications, a wall that crosses a part of a rampart and joins to an inner wall. **2.** A tower or blockhouse used to form a salient in the outworks.

SPz The abbreviation for *Schützenpanzer,* German for "armored personnel carrier."

spontoon. (*The Metropolitan Museum of Art, Rogers Fund, 1931.*)

spotting rifle, 15mm to match the characteristics of a U.S. 152mm gun cannon. (*U.S. Army.*)

spring bayonet. (*The Smithsonian Institution.*)

Springfield .45 cal. rifle. (*The Smithsonian Institution.*)

Sprint. (*U.S. Army.*)

SPZ 12-3. (*Ministry of Defense, Federal Republic of Germany.*)

SR-71. (*Lockheed Aircraft Corporation.*)

stacking swivel. (*The Smithsonian Institution.*)

SPZ 11-2 (Hotchkiss SPIA)   A French-produced light tank developed from a German Army specification issued in 1956. It has a crew of four, a weight of 8.3 tons, a road speed of 36 mph, and armament consisting of one 20mm cannon. Variants include the SPZ 22-2 (an eight-man troop carrier with a roof-mounted 7.62mm machine gun), the SPZ 31-2 (a command and control vehicle), and the SPZ 51-2 (a mortar vehicle for an 81mm mortar).

SPZ 12-3 (HS-30)   A German (Federal Republic) armored personnel carrier that has been standard equipment in the German Army since 1960. It carries a driver plus seven infantrymen and has a weight of 14 tons and a road speed of 32 mph. It is armed with one 20mm cannon. Variations of this system include the SPZ 21-3 (command vehicle), the SPZ 51-3 (81mm mortar vehicle), the SPZ 52-3 (120mm mortar vehicle), and the SPZ 81-3 (artillery-fire-control vehicle).

squad   A small party of soldiers grouped for drill, inspection, or other purpose.

squadron   1. An organization consisting of two or more divisions of ships or two or more divisions (Navy) or flights of aircraft. It is normally, but not necessarily, composed of ships or aircraft of the same type.

2. The basic administrative aviation unit of the Army, Navy, Marine Corps, and Air Force.   **3.** Formerly, a U.S. Army unit composed basically of a headquarters and two or more troops of cavalry. It was normally commanded by a major.

squadron leader   1. The pilot in command of a squadron of aircraft.   **2.** A commissioned rank in the RAF or RCAF corresponding to major in the U.S. Air Force.

squash head   A term used, especially by the British, for a high-explosive plastic (HEP) projectile.

Squat Eye   The NATO code name for a type of Soviet C-band early-warning and surveillance radar.

squawk box   An interoffice of interstation voice communication unit; intercom.

squib   1. Used in a general sense to mean any of various small pyrotechnic or explosive devices.   **2.** Specifically, a small explosive device, similar in appearance to a **detonator,** which see, but loaded with low explosive, so that its output is primarily heat (flash). It is usually electrically initiated and is provided to initiate action of pyrotechnic devices and rocket propellants.

Squid   A British shipborne surface-to-subsurface medium-range antisubmarine mortar system. A triple-barreled mortar fires a pattern of three mortar bombs which are programmed to give a three-dimensional explosive pattern ahead of the target. The system has a range of 2,000 meters, a missile length of 5.75 ft, and a missile weight of about 440 lb. It became operational in about 1948.

SR-71   A U.S. Lockheed-built high-speed high-altitude reconnaissance aircraft. It has a crew of two and is powered by twin jets to speeds up to Mach 3+ and altitudes up to about 100,000 ft (approximately 19 mi).

SRAM   A U.S. air-to-surface missile developed by Boeing and presently in production for the U.S. Air Force. It is a short-range attack missile with a length of 14 ft, a diameter of 1.46 ft, a launching weight of 2,240 lb, and a range of 120 mi.

SS   1. A U.S. Navy submarine.   **2.** The abbreviation for "single shot."   **3.** The abbreviation for **Schutzstaffel,** which see.

SS-10 and AS-11   See **Nord 5210 (SS.11 and AS.11).**

SSA   A U.S. Navy submarine cargo.

SSB   A U.S. Navy fleet ballistic-missile submarine.

SSBN   A U.S. Navy nuclear-powered fleet ballistic-missile submarine. These submarines are equipped with Polaris missiles.

SSBS   Sol-Sol-Balistique-Stratégique. A French medium-range two-stage solid-propellant missile with a nuclear warhead, stored in, and launched from, an underground silo. It has an overall length of 58.5 ft, a launching weight of 70,180 lb, and a range of better than 1,863 mi. It was first test-fired in 1965.

SSC A U.S. Navy cruiser submarine.

SSG A U.S. Navy guided-missile submarine.

SSGN A U.S. Navy nuclear-powered guided-missile submarine.

SSK A U.S. Navy antisubmarine submarine.

SSM A surface-to-surface missile.

SSN A U.S. Navy nuclear-powered attack submarine.

SSO A U.S. Navy submarine oiler.

SSP A U.S. Navy submarine transport.

SSR A U.S. Navy radar picket submarine.

SSRN A U.S. Navy nuclear-powered radar picket submarine.

SST **1.** A U.S. Navy target and training submarine. **2.** Supersonic transport (aircraft).

STAB A U.S. Navy strike assault boat.

stack To **stack arms,** which see.

stack arms To put a number of rifles in a group, upright, with their butts on the ground. Three of them are linked together with the stacking swivels. Additional rifles are stacked leaning against this group.

stacking swivel An elongated C-shaped part usually mounted on an axis to permit partial rotation and with facilities for attachment near the muzzle end of a rifle or other shoulder-fired gun. It is used for attachment to two or more other, similar items to form a gun stack.

staff **1.** A quarterstaff; a cudgel or club. **2.** A selected group of officers, or officers and civilians, who assist the commander in his exercise of command.

Staffel The German designation for an air squadron, usually having from nine to twelve airplanes. The plural is *Staffeln*. See **Gruppe.**

stage **1.** To process, in a specified area, troops which are in transit from one locality to another. **2.** An element of the missile of propulsion system that generally separates from the missile at burnout or cutoff. Stages are numbered chronologically in order of burning.

Staghound An antiaircraft armored car produced in the United States for British lend-lease during World War II. Introduced in 1943, it had a crew of three, and was armed with twin .50 cal. machine guns. It was also designated as the T17E2.

staging area An area or general locality where troops, units, forces, equipment, or the like are staged during movement or before an operation.

Stalag From the German *Stammlager*. In World War II a permanent German prisoner-of-war camp, especially for enlisted men. A *Stalagluft* was a POW camp for airmen.

Stalin Organ The nickname for a Soviet mobile rocket launcher of World War II. It fired 30 to 48 rockets with a range of

Standard Missile. (*General Dynamics.*)

about 3 mi.

Stalin tank The Soviet tank, heavy, JS (Joseph Stalin) I, II, and III. The latest version, the III, went into action in Poland in 1945. It had a crew of five and was armed with one 122mm gun 1944, one 7.62mm machine gun, and one 12.7mm machine gun. The weight of the tank was about 57 tons, and the top speed was about 20 mph.

standard An organizational flag.

Standard ARM A U.S. air-to-surface antiradiation missile (ARM) developed by General Dynamics for the U.S. Navy. It has a length of 14 ft, a diameter of 1 ft, and a launching weight of 1,300 lb. It utilizes a radar-homing guidance system. (This missile is similar in appearance to the Standard Missile.)

standard arrow The old English clothyard shaft of 37 in.

standard-bearer The soldier who bears a standard.

Standard E.I A British single-seat single-engine biplane that was designed as a fighter, but was eventually used as an advanced trainer. It had a speed of 100 mph and was first flown early in 1918.

Standard Missile U.S. General Dynamics-produced surface-to-air missiles of two types: MR (medium-range) and ER (extended-range). Both are in service with the U.S. Navy. MR has a length of 14 ft, a launching weight of 1,300 lb, and a range in excess of 10 mi. ER has a length of 27 ft, a launching weight of 3,000 lb, and a range of over 30 mi. MR and ER are also designated RIM 66A and RIM 67A.

standard muzzle velocity The velocity at which a given projectile is supposed to leave the muzzle of a gun. The velocity is calculated on the basis of the particular gun, the propelling charge used, and the type of projectile fired from the gun. Firing tables are based on standard muzzle velocity. Also sometimes called "prescribed muzzle velocity."

standby A condition or state of preparedness in which aircraft, with aircrews on board, remain ready for a combat flight.

standing barrage A defensive artillery barrage. See also **normal barrage.**

standing order Promulgated orders which remain in force until amended or canceled.

standing patrol A patrol which will be of a strength decided by the commander allotting the task. Its task may be reconnaissance, listening, fighting, or a combination of these. It differs from a reconnaissance, fighting, or listening patrol in that, having taken up its allotted position, it is not free to maneuver in the performance of its task without permission.

stand of arms Originally, the complete set for one soldier, including a musket and its bayonet and sometimes a cartridge box and its belt. Later it designated the rifle alone.

stang ball Formerly, a type of bar shot; two half-balls connected by a bar.

star See **battle star** and **service star.**

Star .32 ACP Military automatic pistol A Spanish pistol, manufactured by Echeverria. The magazine has a capacity of nine cartridges, and the overall length is about 7.5 in. The barrel length is 4.8 in., and the weight is about 30 oz. This was one of the

Star .32 ACP Military automatic pistol. (*Spanish Ministry of Defense.*)

Star 9mm (Largo) submachine gun Z-45. (*Spanish Ministry of Defense.*)

Star 9mm (Largo) submachine gun Z-62. (*Spanish Ministry of Defense.*)

Starfighter. (*Lockheed Aircraft Corporation.*)

weapons used by the French Army in World War II.

Star .45 ACP automatic pistol A Spanish modification of the Colt Government Model M1911A1. In one version, the weapon becomes a full automatic pistol. In this configuration it is impossible to fire fewer than six shots at a single pull of the trigger, and it is likewise impossible to control the aim of the weapon.

Star 9mm (Largo) submachine gun Z-45 A Spanish copy of the German MP-40 submachine gun, except produced for the 9mm Bergmann Bayard cartridge (called the "9mm Largo cartridge" in Spain). Other modifications resulted in a selective semi-

automatic or full automatic fire control and the use of a compensator.

Star 9mm (Largo) submachine gun Z-62 This weapon has been adopted by the Spanish Army and has the following characteristics: an overall length of 27.6 in., a barrel length of 18.9 in., and a weight of 6.3 lb. It is blowback-operated and has selective-fire capability. At full automatic the cyclic rate of fire is 550 rounds per minute with a muzzle velocity of about 1,200 to 1,800 fps.

star bomb A **star shell,** which see.

Starfighter The Lockheed F-104 Starfighter is a single-seat single-engine all-weather tactical strike and reconnaissance jet fighter developed for the USAF and first flown in 1954. It is presently in service with many NATO forces and with the JASDF. It has a range of about 1,500 mi, a speed of Mach 2.2, and armament consisting of Sidewinder missiles, rocket pods, and bombs.

Starfire The U.S. Lockheed F-94 Starfire was a two-place single-jet tactical fighter developed for the U.S. Air Force from the basic F-80 design. First flown in 1949, later models carried forty-eight 2.75-in. rockets and flew at speeds up to 646 mph.

star fort An enclosed fieldwork in the shape of a star with four or more salients and no curtain walls.

StarLifter The Lockheed C-141 StarLifter is a long-range transport powered by four turbofan engines. It was developed for the USAF and was first flown in 1963. It carries 154 troops, has a range of 6,140 mi, and flies at a speed of about 570 mph.

Starlight Scope A U.S. system which may be mounted on individual or crew-served weapons or may be hand-held for night viewing. Using ambient night skylight and an image intensifier, the device permits the individual to observe and fire accurately at targets with complete security.

star shell A projectile that detonates in the air and releases an illuminating parachute flare.

state of readiness—armed (demolition) Demolition is ready for immediate firing.

state of readiness—safe (demolition) A demolition target upon or within which the demolition agent has been placed and secured. The firing or initiating circuits have been installed, but not connected to the demolition agent. Detonators or initiators have not been connected or installed.

static line A line attached to a parachute pack and to a strop or anchor cable in an aircraft so that when the load is dropped, the parachute is deployed automatically.

static weapon A weapon which is used in place, such as a chemical cylinder that is used to release chemical agents from the point where it is located.

station 1. A general term meaning any

military or naval activity at a fixed land location. **2.** A particular kind of activity to which other activities or individuals may come for a specific service, often of a technical nature, e.g., aid station. **3.** An assigned or prescribed position in a naval formation or cruising disposition or an assigned area in an approach, contact, or battle disposition. **4.** Any place of duty or post or position in the field to which an individual, a group of individuals, or a unit may be assigned. **5.** One or more transmitters or receivers or a combination of transmitters and receivers, including the accessory equipment, necessary at one location for carrying on radio communication service. Each station is classified by the service in which it operates permanently or temporarily.

staves An old English term for staff weapons or polearms in general.

Stechkin 9mm machine pistol APS See **Soviet 9mm machine pistol APS (Stechkin).**

stellar guidance A system wherein a guided missile may follow a predetermined course with reference primarily to its relative position and that of certain preselected celestial bodies.

Sten 9mm submachine gun Marks I, II, III, IV, and V British weapons introduced in 1941 and named from the initials of the two designers, R. V. Sheppard and H. J. Turpin, plus the first two letters of Enfield, where they were developed. During World War II, approximately $3\frac{3}{4}$ million weapons and 34 million magazines were produced. They were designed for rapid manufacture and utilized welding, rivets, and pins. All were designed for the 9mm Parabellum cartridge, were blowback-operated, and had selective full automatic and semiautomatic fire. The cyclic rate of fire is 550 to 600 rounds per minute. The weight is from 8.5 to 9.5 lb, and the capacity of the magazines is 32 rounds. The Mark V was related in design to the Mark II and was the standard submachine gun for the British Army from 1945 until 1953. A Mark VI weapon was produced in limited quantities. It consists of a short-barreled Mark V with a silencer.

sterilizer (mine) A device incorporated in a mine to detonate or make the mine inactive after a certain preset period of time.

Sterling 9mm Parabellum submachine gun L2A3 The standard submachine gun of the British forces, this weapon has a cyclic rate of fire of 550 rounds per minute, an overall length of 19 in. (with stock folded), a barrel length of 7.8 in., a loaded weight of 7.65 lb, and a muzzle velocity of 1,280 fps. The magazine has a capacity of 34 cartridges. Accepted in 1953, this weapon is a development of the Patchett submachine gun designed during World War II. Built by Sterling engineering, there were earlier versions of the same weapon,

Starfire. (*Lockheed Aircraft Corporation.*)

StarLifter. (*U.S. Air Force.*)

Sten 9mm submachine gun Mk IV. (*The Smithsonian Institution, G.S.A. Administration Collection.*)

Sterling 9mm Parabellum submachine gun L2A2. (*The Imperial War Museum.*)

Stirling III. (*Short Brothers & Harland Ltd.*)

St. Laurent. (*Canadian Armed Forces Photograph.*)

Stoner system. (*U.S. Army.*)

the L2A1 and the L2A2.

sternutators See war gases.

St. Étienne 8mm machine gun Model 1907 A French gas-operated air-cooled machine gun with a rate of fire of 500 rounds per minute. It weighed 46 lb and was fed from a 25-round strip.

Steyr 9mm automatic pistol M12 A pistol using the 9mm Steyr cartridge, once the official Austrian pistol cartridge. The weapon is often referred to as the "Steyr-Hahn" (hammer Steyr). Introduced in 1911 it was the official pistol of the Austrians in World War I and was also widely used in the Balkans. It was the official pistol of the Rumanian and Chilean governments of that era. The pistol measures 8½ in. overall and has a 5-in. barrel. The weight is about 33 oz. The magazine is built into the butt and has a capacity of eight cartridges. During World War II a number of these weapons were converted to shoot the standard German P-08 (9mm Luger) cartridge.

Steyr 9mm Parabellum submachine gun A modern weapon developed by Steyr Daimler Puch in Austria and representing the first military weapon developed in that country since the 1930s. It is a compact submachine gun somewhat resembling the Israeli UZI. It has an overall length, with stock retracted, of 18 in. and a barrel length of 10.2 in. It has a weight of 6 lb and a cyclic rate of fire of 550 rounds per minute. It has selective semiautomatic and full automatic fire, magazines with capacities of 25 and 32 cartridges, and a muzzle velocity of about 1,350 fps.

Steyr-Solothurn 9mm Mauser submachine gun MP 34 This weapon was designed in Germany, but was manufactured outside the country because German military arms development was restricted by the Versailles Treaty. This submachine gun is blowback-operated and has selective full-automatic and semiautomatic fire. With a cyclic rate of fire of 500 rounds per minute, it has an overall length of 33.5 in., a barrel length of 7.8 in., and a loaded weight of 9.87 lb. It was adopted by the Austrian Army in 1934 and continued to be manufactured until 1940. It was also used (sometimes in other calibers) by Chile, El Salvador, Bolivia, Uruguay, and, in limited quantities, Japan. When the Germans took over Austria, they took over production of the weapon, chambering it for 9mm Parabellum. It was known commercially as the "Solothurn" or "Steyr-Solothurn SI-100." An earlier model was the Steyr-Solothurn Model 1930.

stick 1. A number of aerial bombs released from an aircraft so as to fall or strike in train. When the bombs are stacked one above the other inside the aircraft, they are ordinarily released simultaneously in close train. **2.** A number of paratroopers jumping singly and in succession in one pass over the drop zone. **3.** A number of aerial mines, flares, or the like released singly and in succession. **4.** A series of rounds fired in an automatic firearm or gun in one burst.

sticky grenade A small explosive charge covered with an adhesive and intended to be thrown or placed by hand where the adhesive will hold the charge in place until detonated by a time fuze. Also called "sticky charge."

stiletto A small dagger with a slender three- or four-sided pointed blade and no edge, used exclusively for stabbing.

stink bomb A small bomb that gives off a foul odor when exploded.

stinkpot Formerly, an earthenware shell or jar filled with materials, often flammable, that produced a foul and suffocating smell or smoke. They have been used during sieges to drive defenders from their garrisons, in boarding ships, etc.

Stirling The British Short Stirling was a seven-place four-engine heavy bomber first flown in 1939 and produced throughout World War II (2,375 having been manufactured). It flew at a maximum speed of 260 mph, was armed with eight .303 cal. machine guns, and could carry a bombload of seven 2,000-lb bombs or eighteen 500-lb bombs. Fully loaded it had a range of 740 mi.

St. Laurent A class of Canadian destroyer escorts of 2,263 tons standard displacement completed in 1955–1957. They represent the first major warship class to have been designed entirely in Canada. They have a length of 366 ft, a beam of 42 ft, a speed of 28.5 knots, and a complement of 250 men. Armament consists of two 3-in. guns and two Limbo three-barreled depth-charge mortars.

St. Louis A class of U.S. 10,000-ton cruisers completed in 1905–1906. They had a length of 426 ft, a speed of 22 knots, a complement of 727 men, and main armament consisting of fourteen 6-in. and eighteen 3-in. guns.

stock 1. A store on hand of materiel, equipment, or other supplies. **2.** The wooden part of a firearm, especially of a shoulder arm.

stockade 1. A type of fortification built by planting a line of strong posts or timbers to form a barrier. Stockades were usually equipped with loopholes. **2.** A guardhouse where military prisoners are confined.

stockpile A reserve stock of materiel, equipment, raw material, or other supplies; specifically, a stock of an important or critical product or article stored for use in time of emergency.

stock-trail carriage A carriage for muzzle-loading field artillery with a one-piece trail (as contrasted to a split-trail carriage).

Stokes bomb See **Stokes trench mortar.**

Stokes trench mortar Named after the inventor, Sir Wilfrid S. Stokes, this is a British light 3-in. muzzle-loading mortar that fires a projectile (Stokes bomb) weighing 11 lb.

STOL See **short takeoff and landing.**

stonebow A crossbow or catapult for shooting or throwing stones. A prod.

stone fougasse A natural mortar formerly made by digging an excavation in the ground, setting a large explosive charge, and covering the whole with several yards of stones. If the excavation were made in the shape of a frustrum of a cone, with angles of about 40°, the exploded charge would throw 1-lb rocks to a range of about 120 yd in all directions. See also **fougasse.**

Stoner system A U.S. 5.56mm (.233 cal.) small-arms weapons system consisting of a carbine, an assault rifle, and light and medium machine guns.

stoneshot Cannonballs made of stone. Many of the earliest cannons used stoneshot.

stoppage A jam in an automatic weapon; the condition of being jammed.

storage life The length of time in storage, under stated conditions, during which an item will remain in serviceable condition. For small items the term "shelf life" is frequently used.

Storch The German Fieseler Fi 156 Storch (Stork) was a three-place single-engine high-wing light monoplane of World War II. It was used for staff transport, reconnaissance, and other general purposes.

stores Any articles or commodities used by a naval ship or station, such as equipment; consumable supplies; clothing; petroleum, oils, and lubricants; medical supplies; and ammunition.

Stormovik See **IL-2.**

straddle In range, or in deflection, when projectiles from a salvo fall both over and short of, or to both the left and right of, the target, a straddle is obtained.

strafe (German for "punish.") To rake a body of troops or other persons with gunfire

Storch. (*The Smithsonian Institution, National Air Museum.*)

or rocket fire at close range and from a flying aircraft; to attack a roadway, railyard, factory, or other installation with bullets, projectiles, or rockets fired from a low-flying airplane.

strategic air warfare Air combat and supporting operations designed to effect, through the systematic application of force to a selected series of vital targets, the progressive destruction and disintegration of the enemy's war-making capacity to a point where he no longer retains the ability or the will to wage war. Vital targets may include key manufacturing systems, sources of raw material, critical material, stockpiles, power systems, transportation systems, communications facilities, concentrations of uncommitted elements of enemy armed forces, key agricultural areas, and other such target systems.

strategic bomber A bomber, usually a long-range bomber, used in strategic air operations.

strategic bombing The bombing of a selected target or targets vital to the war-making capacity of a nation.

strategic intelligence Intelligence which is required for the formation of policy and military plans at national and international levels.

strategic material A material needed for the industrial support of a war effort.

strategic minefields Minefields calculated to reduce and impede the enemy's war-making ability by destroying his seaborne communications.

strategic missile Specifically, a missile designed for use in a strategic attack.

strategic mission A mission directed

against one or more of a selected series of enemy targets with the purpose of progressive destruction and disintegration of the enemy's war-making capacity and his will to make war. Targets include key manufacturing systems, sources of raw material, critical material, stockpiles, power systems, transportation systems, communications facilities, and other such target systems. As opposed to tactical operations, strategic operations are designed to have a long-range rather than an immediate effect on the enemy and his military forces.

strategic target Any installation, network, group of buildings, or the like considered vital to a country's war-making capacity and singled out for attack.

strategy The art and science of developing and using political, economic, psychological, and military forces as necessary during peace and war to afford the maximum support to policies in order to increase the probabilities and favorable consequences of victory and to lessen the chances of defeat.

Stratofortress The U.S. Boeing-built B-52 (Models F, G, and H) is an eight-jet swept-wing long-range heavy bomber developed for the U.S. Air Force and first flown in March 1952. It has a crew of six and a speed of over 650 mph and is armed with four .50 cal. machine guns in a rear turret. It can carry a bombload of 60,000 lb or various combinations of bombs, Hound Dog missiles, and Quail decoy missiles. It has a range of 12,500 mi. (Picture, next page.)

Stratofreighter The Boeing C-97 Stratofreighter is a four-engine (piston) military transport with a large two-deck fuselage. It was developed during World War II and

Stratofortress. (*U.S. Air Force.*)

Stratofreighter. (*U.S. Air Force.*)

Stratotanker. (*U.S. Air Force.*)

could carry 134 troops over a range of 4,300 mi. Its maximum speed was 375 mph. (The postwar civilian designation of this airplane was "Stratocruiser.") An aerial-tanker version is designated the KC-97. The last airplane of this type was produced on July 18, 1956, and marked the end of Boeing's production of piston-engine aircraft.

Stratojet The U.S. Boeing B-47 all-weather strategic medium bomber developed for the USAF and first flown in December 1947. It has a crew of three (five in reconnaissance versions) and flies at a top speed of about 630 mph. Its maximum bomb capacity is 20,000 lb, and two radar-directed 20mm cannons are mounted in the tail.

Stratolifter See **Stratoliner.**

Stratoliner The Boeing Model 707 Strato-

liner was the first American four-jet transport to be completed and was first flown in July 1954. Military versions of this aircraft have included the USAF C-135 long-range transport (Stratolifter), which can carry 75 troops or 50,000 lb of cargo, and the KC-135 tanker (Stratotanker), which carries 31,000 gal of fuel. The airplane has a speed of about 605 mph.

Stratotanker See **Stratoliner.**

strength of enemy forces The description of an enemy unit or force in terms of men, weapons, and equipment.

stretcher See **litter.**

strike An attack which is intended to inflict damage on or to seize or destroy an objective.

strike force A force composed of appropriate units necessary to conduct strikes or attack or assault operations.

striker A firing pin or a projection on the hammer of a firearm which strikes the primer to initiate a propelling charge, explosive train, or fuze explosive train.

striker plate A plate in the breech of a firearm or gun which supports the base of the cartridge and which is pierced with a hole through which the striker or firing pin hits the primer.

striking plate The frizzen or upright metal piece in a flintlock against which the pyrites or flint strikes a spark.

string A given number of shots fired within a certain time interval.

strip **1.** To disassemble a piece of equipment, such as a gun, in order to clean, repair, or transport it. **2.** An **airstrip,** which see.

stripes Chevrons.

strip marker (land-mine warfare) A marker, natural, artificial, or specially installed, located at the start and finish of a mine strip.

stripper clip See **charger clip.**

stripping **1.** Disassembling a weapon for cleaning and care. **2.** The condition in which parts of the bullet jacket are stripped off and left in the bore. **3.** Loading a magazine weapon with a charger clip.

stronghold A fort or fortified place.

strongpoint A key point in a defensive position, usually strongly fortified and heavily armed with automatic weapons, around which other positions are grouped for its protection.

STRV 103 (S tank) A Swedish main battle tank that has been in full production since 1966. It has a crew of three, a weight of 37.5 tons, a road speed of 31 mph, and main armament consisting of one 105mm gun. Secondary armament consists of two 7.62mm machine guns. This tank is unusual in that there is no turret on it; the gun is fixed to the hull and is aimed in elevation by a hydropneumatic suspension system and in traverse through an advanced steering system.

Stuart tank MK IV See **Honey.**

Stuka The German Junkers Ju 87 Stuka was a two-seat single-engine dive bomber and close-support aircraft first flown in 1935 and produced in various models until 1943. It was powered by one 1,400-hp engine and flew at a speed of about 255 mph. Armament consisted of four 7.9mm machine guns and a bombload of about 2,000 lb. (In a short-range overload condition it could carry a 3,968-lb bomb.) Stukas were the first aircraft to fly bombing missions during World War II, attacking Polish targets some 11 minutes before the official declaration of war.

Sturgeon A class of U.S. nuclear-powered attack submarines (SSN) of 3,860 tons standard displacement, the first of 37 built in 1966. This is the largest class of nuclear-powered ships of the same design in the U.S. Navy. They have a length of 292.2 ft, a beam of 31.7 ft, a surface speed of 20 knots (30 knots submerged), and a complement of 107 men. They are armed with four 21-in. torpedo tubes and Subroc and anti-submarine-warfare torpedoes.

Sturmabteilung (S.A.) (German for "storm section.") Also known as "Brownshirts" or "storm troopers," these were the shock troops of the Nazi party and were formed privately in 1923 by Adolph Hitler. They were organized into a national militia about 1934.

Sturmpanzer III A **German tank, medium, PzKpfw III,** which see, with a 75mm low-velocity gun.

Sturmpanzer 43 See **Grizzly Bear.**

Sturmvogel See **Messerschmitt Me 262.**

St. Vincent A class of British 19,250-ton battleships completed in 1910. The class included *St. Vincent, Collingwood,* and *Vanguard.* They had a length of 536 ft, a crew of 670, and main armament consisting of ten 12-in. and eighteen 4-in. guns, plus three 18-in. torpedo tubes. They had a speed of 22 knots.

stylet A small poniard or dagger; a **stiletto,** which see.

Styx The NATO code name for a Soviet naval surface-to-surface cruise missile with a cropped-delta-wing aircraft configuration. Launched from patrol boats, it has a length

Stratojet. (*U.S. Air Force.*)

Stuka. (*The Smithsonian Institution, National Air Museum.*)

of 15 ft, a wingspan of 2 ft, and a range of 20 mi.

Su The designation for Soviet aircraft designed by Pavel Osipovich Sukhoi.

Su-7B See **Fitter.**

Su-9 See **Fishpot.**

subahdar Formerly, in the Anglo-Indian Army, the chief native officer in charge of a native company. His rank was about equivalent to that of a captain.

subaltern A commissioned officer below the rank of captain. A subaltern officer.

subaqueous ranging Detecting and locating invisible marine targets, such as enemy vessels at night or enemy submarines, by means of sound detectors placed below the surface of the water. These instruments

Sturgeon. (*U.S. Navy.*)

STRV 103 (S tank). (*Swedish Defense Staff.*)

submarine chaser, the U.S.S. *Peoria.* (*U.S. Navy.*)

Subroc. (*Goodyear Aerospace Corporation.*)

Sunderland. (*Short Brothers & Harland Ltd.*)

Super Constellation. (*U.S. Air Force.*)

pick up sound vibrations and automatically register the distance and direction from which they come.

subarmor Armor worn under the outer armor.

subcaliber Pertaining to a much smaller-caliber gun mounted on or in a larger gun for practice purposes.

subcaliber ammunition Ammunition used with a gun or launching tube, usually in practice firing, of a smaller caliber than that which is standard for the weapon used. Subcaliber ammunition is adapted for firing in weapons of larger caliber by subcaliber tubes, interchangeable barrels, sabots, or other devices.

subcaliber firing Practice firing of sub-caliber ammunition, in connection with drills in elevating, traversing, or aiming guns of larger caliber.

subcaliber gun A gun mounted on the outside and above the tube of a larger gun. It is used in practice firing of subcaliber ammunition, in connection with aiming drills with the larger gun.

SUBCAP Rescue Combat Air Patrol.

subcloud car On an airship, a car designed to be lowered by cable to a position beneath the clouds. It was used for aerial observation, and a telephone system connected the observer with the airship.

subkiloton weapon A nuclear weapon producing a yield below 1 kiloton.

sublieutenant In the British service, an officer ranking next below a lieutenant.

submachine gun A type of machine gun. A short-barreled shoulder firearm using pistol-type ammunition and capable of full automatic fire. It is sometimes called a "machine pistol."

submarine A warship designed for under-the-surface operations with the primary mission of locating and destroying ships, including other submarines. It is also capable of various other naval missions. The U.S. Navy designations include SS, SSN, etc.

submarine base A base providing logistic support for submarines.

submarine chasers (PC) A class of U.S. ships of 280 tons standard displacement completed in 1942–1944. They had a length of 173 ft, a beam of 23 ft, a speed of 20 knots, and a complement of 80 men. They were armed with one 3-in. gun, one 40mm and two to five 20mm antiaircraft guns, and four depth-charge throwers.

submarine emergency identification signals (1) *Black or green smoke:* Torpedo has been fired. (2) *Yellow smoke:* Submarine is coming up. (3) *Red smoke:* Submarine is in danger.

submarine havens Specified sea areas for

submarine noncombat operations including: (1) Submarine sanctuaries announced by the area, fleet, or equivalent commander. (2) Areas reserved for submarine operations and training in noncombat zones. (3) Moving areas, established by "submarine notices," surrounding submarines in transit and extending 50 nautical miles ahead, 100 nautical miles behind, and 15 nautical miles on each side of the estimated position of the submarine along the stated track.

submarine-launched missile A missile launched from a submarine or surface ship at sea.

submarine patrol zones Restricted sea areas established for the purpose of permitting submarine operations and unrestricted by the operations or possible attack of friendly forces.

submarine rocket (Subroc) A submerged surface-to-surface rocket, launched from a submarine, with a nuclear-depth-charge or homing-torpedo payload, primarily antisubmarine. Designated as UUM-44A.

submarine striking forces Submarines having guided- or ballistic-missile launching and/or guidance capabilities formed to launch offensive nuclear strikes.

Subroc A tactical weapon developed for the U.S. Navy by Goodyear and designed to be launched from a submarine against another submarine. It is fired from the torpedo tubes of a submerged submarine and is propelled upward and out of the water. It is then directed toward the target area, where the nuclear-depth-bomb warhead separates, sinks, and explodes. It has a length of 21 ft, a launching weight of 4,000 lb, and a range of 25 to 30 mi. The Navy designation is UUM-44A.

subsidiary demolition belt A supplement to the primary belt to give depth in front or behind or to protect the flanks. See also **demolition belt.**

subsidiary troops Formerly, mercenaries or hired troops who were subjects of another power.

subsonic Of or pertaining to speeds less than the speed of sound.

subversion Action designed to undermine the morale or the military, economic, psychological, or political strength of a regime.

Sud-Est LeO 45 Series A series of four-seat twin-engine medium bombers developed by France between 1937 and 1942. The LeO 451 flew at a top speed of 307 mph and was armed with one 20mm cannon and two 7.5mm machine guns; it carried a bombload of about 4,500 lb.

Suffren A class of French guided-missile frigates of 4,700 tons standard displacement commissioned in 1968–1969. They have a length of 518.4 ft, a speed of 34 knots, and a complement of 446 men. They are armed with Masurca antiaircraft missiles, Malafon rocket-torpedoes, two 3.9-in. guns, two

30mm guns, and four torpedo launchers for antisubmarine torpedoes.

suicide bomb See **Baka bomb.**

suicide motorboat See **Shinyo,** sense 2.

suicide torpedo See **Kaiten 1.**

SUM A surface-to-underwater missile.

Sunderland A British Short-built four-engine long-range maritime reconnaissance-bomber flying boat first flown in 1937. This aircraft had a crew of 10 and was armed with 10 machine guns in various positions. It also carried approximately 5,000 lb of bombs, mines, or depth charges. This airplane saw considerable antisubmarine duty during World War II. Its armament earned it the German Luftwaffe nickname of *Fliegendes Stachelschwein* (Flying Porcupine).

sunken battery A battery that is protected by being sunk below the surface of the ground.

Suomi 9mm Parabellum submachine gun M/1931 A submachine gun designed by Aimo Johannes Lahti and adopted by the Finnish armed forces in 1931. It is blowback-operated and has selective full automatic and semiautomatic fire with a cyclic rate of fire of 900 rounds per minute. With a 71-round drum magazine the weight of the weapon is 15.65 lb. There are also a 40-round drum magazine and 20- and 50-round box-type magazines for use with this weapon. The length is 34.25 in., and the barrel length is 12.50 in. This weapon was adopted by Finland, Sweden, Norway, and Switzerland and was also used by the Polish police before World War II. It was also manufactured under Suomi license by Madsen in Denmark, Hispano-Suiza in Switzerland, and Husqvarna in Sweden.

Superb A British cruiser of 8,000 tons standard displacement completed in 1945.

It had a speed of 31.5 knots, a complement of 867 men, and armament consisting of nine 8-in. and ten 4-in. guns, plus antiaircraft protection from eighteen 2-pounders and four 40mm guns. Six 21-in. torpedo tubes were also carried.

super bazooka A 3.5-in. rocket launcher.

Super Constellation The U.S. Lockheed-built C-121 Super Constellation is quite similar to the C-69 Constellation, but has a longer fuselage and other modifications to improve both payload and performance. It has four piston engines and was first flown in 1950. As used by the U.S. Air Force, it carries 106 passengers or 40,000 lb of cargo. It has a speed of 375 mph and a range of 4,800 mi.

Super Duck The U.S. Army amphibious truck M-147. It has a 5-ton payload and a speed of 7 mph on water.

Superdumbo A slang term for B-17's and B-29's converted to rescue work.

Super Falcon The Hughes AIM-4E and 4F versions of the USAF air-to-air missile which derived from the Falcon. AIM-4E has semiactive radar, and AIM-4F has infrared homing guidance. Both were introduced in 1959. They have a length of about 7 ft, a weight of about 150 lb, and a range of 7 mi.

Superfortress The U.S. Boeing B-29 Superfortress was a heavy bomber first flown in 1942 and produced until 1945, by which time 3,970 had been manufactured. The first aircraft to feature remotely controlled armament, the Superfortress had a speed of 357 mph and armament consisting of twelve .50 cal. machine guns and one 20mm cannon. It carried a 20,000-lb bombload and had a range (with 10,000 lb) of 3,250 mi. The greatest destruction of any

Superfortress. (*U.S. Air Force.*)

Super Sabre. (*U.S. Air Force.*)

Super Star 9mm (Largo) automatic pistol. (*Spanish Ministry of Defense.*)

single raid of the war was caused by 334 Superfortresses when, on the night of March 9, 1945, they dropped incendiary bombs that destroyed 16 sq mi in the center of Tokyo and killed 80,000 people. Superfortresses also dropped the atomic bombs on Hiroshima and Nagasaki.

Super Frelon   The French Sud-Aviation SA 321 was developed as a heavy assault helicopter and was first flown in 1962. It has a speed of 152 mph and can carry 30 troops. Another version is used as a naval antisubmarine helicopter.

superheavy tank   The heaviest type of tank for military use; a tank weighing over 75 tons.

superior slope   The upper surface of a parapet.

Super Jolly Green Giant   See **Sea Stallion.**

Superlite   See **diphosgene (DP).**

Super Mystère   A French Dassault single-seat interceptor and tactical strike fighter developed in several versions and first flown in 1955. Used by the French Air Force and the Israeli Air Force, the airplane flies at a speed of Mach 1.13 and is armed with two 30mm cannons and a pack of 55 air-to-air rockets.

superquick fuze   A type of impact fuze using a nose striker to cause the fuze to function almost instantaneously upon impact. Also called an "instantaneous fuze."

Super Sabre   The North American F-100 Super Sabre is a single-seat single-engine interceptor and fighter-bomber developed for the USAF and first flown in 1953. It was the first supersonic operational fighter in service with the USAF. It has a speed of Mach 1.3, a range of 1,500 mi with external tanks, and armament consisting of four 20mm cannons and under-wing points for bombs, rockets, and missiles. It is presently in service with several countries.

supersensitive fuze   A fuze that will set off a projectile dependably when it strikes a very light target, such as a fabric airplane wing.

supersonic   Of or pertaining to speed in excess of the speed of sound. See also **speed of sound.**

Super Star 9mm (Largo) automatic pistol   A Spanish pistol similar in design and operation to the U.S. Colt .45 M1911A1. It is the standard handgun of the Spanish forces. It has an overall length of 8.03 in. and a barrel length of 5.25 in. The magazine has a capacity of nine cartridges, and the pistol's total weight is 2.21 lb.

supplies   All items necessary for the equipment, maintenance, and operation of a military command, including food, clothing, equipment, arms, ammunition, fuel, materials, and machinery of all kinds.

support   1. The action of a force which aids, protects, complements, or sustains another force in accordance with a directive requiring such action.   **2.** A unit which helps another unit in battle. Aviation, artillery, or naval gunfire may be used as a support for infantry.   **3.** A part of any unit held back at the beginning of an attack as the reserve.   **4.** An element of a command that assists, protects, or supplies other forces in combat.

supporting arms   Air, sea, and land weapons of all types employed to support ground units.

supporting artillery   Artillery which executes fire missions in support of a specific unit, usually infantry, but which remains under the command of the next higher artillery commander.

supporting fire   Fire delivered by support-

Sverdlov. (*U.S. Navy.*)

ing units to assist or protect a unit in combat.

supporting weapon Any weapon that is used to assist or protect a unit of which it is not an organic part.

Supreme War Council In World War I, a committee formed of political and military representatives of the Allied Powers to coordinate military affairs. It was formed on November 9, 1919.

surcoat A thirteenth- and fourteenth-century cloak worn over armor and often emblazoned with arms.

Surcouf A class of French destroyers of 2,750 tons standard displacement completed in 1955–1957. They have a length of 421 ft, a beam of 42.6 ft, a speed of 35 knots, and a complement of 293 men. They are armed with six 5-in. guns, six 57mm and six 20mm antiaircraft guns, and twelve 21.7-in. torpedo tubes. Some are equipped with Tartar missiles.

surface burst See **nuclear surface burst.**

surface-to-air missile A surface-launched missile designed to operate against a target above the surface.

surface-to-surface missile A surface-launched missile designed to operate against a target on the surface.

surface-to-underwater missile A missile launched from the ground or a surface ship and designed to operate against an underwater target.

surveillance The systematic observation of aerospace, surface, or subsurface areas, places, persons, or things by visual, aural, electronic, photographic, or other means.

SUU A U.S. prefix designation for bomb, flare, and grenade dispensers.

Sverdlov A class of Soviet cruisers of 15,450 tons standard displacement, with 14 ships completed between 1951 and 1960. They have a length of 689 ft, a beam of 70 ft, a speed of 34 knots, and a complement of 1,050 men. Armament consists of twelve 5.9-in. guns, twelve 3.9-in. guns, thirty-two 37mm antiaircraft guns, ten 21-in. torpedo tubes, 140 to 250 mines, and a twin launcher for Guideline (the latter on some ships).

swab A long-handled brush used for cleaning the bore of a cannon.

Swatter The NATO code name for the Soviet wire-guided solid-propellant antitank missile having a length of 3 ft and a diameter of 6 in.

Swedish 6.5mm automatic rifle Model 37 A modification of the Browning automatic rifle as developed by the Swedish government arsenal.

Swedish 6.5mm Madsen machine gun Sweden used three models (1906, 1914, and 1921) of the Madsen machine gun. See **Madsen machine guns.**

Swedish 6.5 × 55mm Mauser carbine

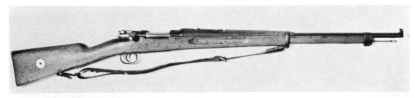

Swedish 6.5 x 55mm Mauser rifle Model 96. (*Swedish Defense Staff.*)

Swedish 9mm Parabellum submachine gun Model 45. (*Swedish Defense Staff.*)

Model 94 This bolt-action weapon has the same action as the Model 96 rifle. It was introduced in 1894 and has an overall length of 37.6 in., a barrel length of 17.7 in., and a weight of 7.6 lb. It utilizes a five-round nondetachable box magazine and has a muzzle velocity of 2,313 fps.

Swedish 6.5 × 55mm Mauser rifle Model 38 This bolt-action rifle is a conversion of the Model 96 to make a shorter, lighter weapon. The weight has been reduced to 8.5 lb, and the overall length is 44.1 in.

Swedish 6.5 × 55mm Mauser rifle Model 41 This weapon is a sniper version of the Model 96 rifle. It is fitted with a 3× or 4× telescopic sight that is also referred to as a "Model 41." The entire system weighs 11.1 lb.

Swedish 6.5 × 55mm Mauser rifle Model 96 This bolt-action rifle has an overall length of 49.6 in., a barrel length of 29.1 in., and a weight of 9.1 lb. It has a muzzle velocity of 2,625 fps and utilizes a five-round nondetachable box magazine.

Swedish 8 × 63mm Mauser rifle Model 40 This is a bolt-action rifle and is a German-produced Mauser Kar 98k which has been rebarreled for the Swedish 8 × 63mm Bofors M1932 machine-gun cartridge.

Swedish 9mm Parabellum submachine gun Model 45 A weapon developed in Sweden in 1944 and in production for the Swedish Army since that time. It is a blowback-operated weapon that fires on full automatic only and has a cyclic rate of fire of 600 rounds per minute. With the stock retracted the length is 21.7 in., and the barrel length is 8 in. The weapon used a 50-round Suomi-type magazine and a 36-round magazine. A special high-velocity 9mm Parabellum cartridge was developed

for use with this weapon and is reportedly capable of piercing steel helmets at ranges up to 400 meters. The M/45B is the latest model of this submachine gun and is sold commercially under the trade name "Carl Gustaf." The weapon is produced in Egypt for use by Egyptian forces, and large numbers have been sold to Indonesia.

Swedish 40mm automatic gun L/70 See **Bofors 40mm automatic gun L/70.**

Swedish 57mm automatic gun L/60 A Bofors-built weapon with a total weight of 17,900 lb and a maximum horizontal range of 15,860 yd. The weight of the projectile is 5.75 lb. (Picture, next page.)

Swedish 90mm recoilless antitank gun A current Bofors-built weapon with an overall weight of 572 lb and a projectile weight of 6.8 lb. It is operated by two men. The projectile has a time of flight to 1,000 meters of 1.9 seconds. (Picture, next page.)

Swedish 105mm howitzer L/32 A Bofors-built weapon with a total weight of 3 tons, a crew of four, and a rate of fire of 25 rounds per minute. The high-explosive shell weighs 33.6 lb; the range of the weapon is 15,300 meters. (Picture, next page.)

Swedish 155mm self-propelled gun L/50 A Bofors-built system with a weight of 48 tons, a crew of four to six, and main armament consisting of one 155mm gun (which can be fired at the rate of 15 rounds per minute at ranges up to 25,000 meters). (Picture, next page.)

Swedish 375mm antisubmarine rocket launcher A Bofors-built four-tube system that fires rockets with a weight of about 550 lb (of which about 235 lb consists of explosive charge). The longest range of the three types fired is 2,230 meters. (Picture, p. 431.)

Swedish 57mm automatic gun L/60. (A. B. Bofors.)

Swedish 90mm recoilless antitank gun. (A. B. Bofors.)

Swedish 105mm howitzer L/32. (A. B. Bofors.)

Swedish armored personnel carrier PBV 302 A vehicle that was developed between 1961 and 1966. It carries a crew of two (plus ten infantrymen) and has a weight of 13.5 tons, a road speed of 41 mph, and armament consisting of one 20mm automatic gun.

Swedish main battle tank STRV 103 See **STRV 103 (S tank).**

Swedish Rb 27 and Rb 28 missiles Swedish Air Force designations for the HM-55 and HM-58 Falcon. See **Falcon.**

sweep **1.** A swift flight of a formation of combat airplanes over enemy territory.

Swedish 155mm self-propelled gun L/50. (A. B. Bofors.)

2. To cover a wide area with gunfire. **3.** A trace produced on the screen of a cathode-ray tube by linear deflection of the electron beam; time base; base line. **4.** To drag a body of water to find and remove or explode mines. **5.** To pass a mine detector over an area to detect any mines that may be contained therein. **6.** An ancient engine for throwing stones.

sweep jamming The action of jamming a radarscope by sweeping space with electronic impulses of the same frequency at those received by the radarscope.

swept channel An area that is kept clear of mines.

Swift A British single-engine (jet) interceptor and ground-attack fighter first flown in 1951. It was developed by Supermarine.

Swiftsure **1.** A British cruiser of 8,000 tons standard displacement completed in 1944. It had a speed of 31.5 knots, a complement of 960 men (wartime), and armament consisting of nine 6-in. and ten 4-in. guns, plus seventeen 40mm antiaircraft guns and six 21-in. torpedo tubes. **2.** A British 11,800-ton battleship completed in 1904. It and its sister ship, *Triumph*, had a length of 470 ft, a complement of 700 men, and main armament consisting of four 10-in. guns, fourteen 7.5-in. guns, and two 18-in. torpedo tubes. They had a speed of 19 knots.

Swingfire A wire-guided antitank missile built by British Aircraft Corporation and presently in service with the British Army. It has an overall length of 3.5 ft and a range of more than 9,800 ft.

swinging traverse A type of fire used against dense troop formations moving toward a machine-gun position or rapidly moving targets; the traversing clamp is loosened so that a gunner makes rapid changes by exerting pressure against the pistol grip.

swing-out cylinder A revolver cylinder that swings out for loading.

Swiss 7.45mm machine guns (Maxim) Swiss Models 1894, 1900, and 1911 were all basic Maxim machine-gun types. See **Maxim machine gun.**

Swiss 7.5mm assault rifle Model 57 This weapon was adopted in 1957 by the Swiss forces. It is a delayed-blowback-operated selective-fire weapon with a cyclic rate of fire of 450 to 500 rounds per minute. It has a muzzle velocity of 2,493 fps, an overall length of 43.4 in., a barrel length of 23 in., and an empty weight of 12.32 lb. It utilizes a 24-round detachable box magazine.

Swiss 7.5mm carbines See **Schmidt-Rubin 7.5mm carbine Model 1911** and **Schmidt-Rubin 7.5mm carbine Model 1931.**

Swiss 7.5mm heavy machine gun Model 11 A Maxim design. Switzerland first adopted the Maxim gun in 1894.

Swiss 7.5mm light machine gun Model 25 This weapon was designed by Colonel

Swedish 375mm antisubmarine rocket launcher. (*A. B. Bofors.*)

Swedish armored personnel carrier PBV-302. (*Swedish Defense Staff.*)

Swift. (*Vickers Ltd.*)

Swiss 7.5mm assault rifle Model 57. (*Swiss Military Department.*)

Swiss 7.5mm light machine gun Model 25. (*Swiss Military Department.*)

Furrer, of the Swiss arms plant at Bern. Also known as the "Fusil Furrer," this weapon has a toggle-joint action similar to that of the Luger, but breaks at the side rather than at the top. It has a cyclic rate of fire of about 450 rounds per minute, a weight of 23.69 lb (with bipod), an overall length of 45.8 in., and a barrel length of 23 in.

Swiss 7.5mm rifles See **Schmidt-Rubin 7.5mm rifle Model 1889** and **Schmidt-Rubin 7.5mm rifle Model 1911.**

Swiss 9mm Parabellum submachine gun Model 41/44 This is a recoil-operated selective-fire weapon with a cyclic rate of fire of 900 rounds per minute, a weight of 11.4 lb, an overall length of 30.5 in., and a barrel length of 9.8 in. It features a 40-round detachable box magazine.

Swiss 9mm Parabellum submachine gun Model 43/44 A blowback-operated selective-fire weapon with a cyclic rate of fire

Swiss 9mm Parabellum submachine gun Model 41/44. (*Swiss Military Department.*)

of 800 rounds per minute, a weight of 10.5 lb, an overall length of 33.9 in., and a barrel length of 12.4 in. It utilizes a 50-round detachable box magazine and has a muzzle velocity of about 1,350 fps.

Swiss main battle tank PZ 61 A tank developed in 1961 that utilizes a crew of four and has a weight of 37 tons and a road speed of 34 mph. Main armament consists

of one 105mm gun; secondary armament consists of one 20mm cannon and one 7.5mm machine gun. (Picture, next page.)

swivel gun A gun mounted on an oarlock-type swivel or on a pedestal so that it can be turned from side to side or up and down.

swivel musket An **amusette** or **jingal,** which see.

sword A general term for a weapon with

Swiss main battle tank PZ 61. (*Swiss Military Department.*)

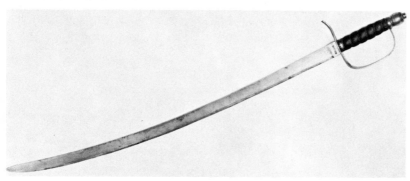

sword. (*The Smithsonian Institution, E. H. Wilkins Collection.*)

a long blade and, usually, a sharp point. It may have a cutting edge on one or both sides. It includes such forms as the smallsword, cutlass, saber, scimitar, and rapier.

sword bayonet A bayonet which resembles, and can be used like, a sword.

sword breaker A notch, hook, or other piece on a sword, dagger, or buckler designed to catch an enemy's sword blade and break it.

Swordfish A single-engine biplane two- or three-seat torpedo bomber and reconnaissance twin-float seaplane developed by Fairey and first flown in 1933. Nicknamed "Stringbag" by its pilots, this aircraft was obsolete before the beginning of World War II, but remained operational throughout. It flew at a top speed of 134 mph and was armed with two .303 cal. machine guns. It could carry a torpedo, a sea mine, or up to 1,500 lb of bombs. It served as a catapult aircraft aboard British battleships and cruisers.

sword-pistol A combination weapon having a pistol action mounted in the hilt of a sword. The barrel lies alongside the blade.

sympathetic detonation An explosion caused by the transmission of a detonation wave through any medium from another explosion.

synchronize To cause certain functions, events, or movements to occur simultaneously in the cycle of operations of a machine or of a mechanical apparatus or arrangement, as a machine gun, so as to allow the firing mechanism to function only when the propeller is within certain degrees in its rotation.

synchronous bombing Bombing done with certain bombsights, such as the Norden bombsight, in which the travel of the telescope, focused upon the target, is synchronized with the ground speed of the airplane and the course flown is determined by manual adjustment of the bombsight, the two together determining the dropping angle and correcting for drift so that the release occurs at the right instant.

synchronous radar bombing A kind of radar bombing in which special airborne radar equipment containing rate and steering mechanisms is used to control the direction of flight of the bombing aircraft, solve the bombing problem, and automatically drop bombs at the proper release point. The radar equipment used in synchronous radar bombing is an independent unit; i.e., it is not used in conjunction with an optical bombsight.

T

T-12 The designation for a U.S. 44,000-lb general-purpose bomb.

T-33 See **Shooting Star.**

T-38 See **Talon.**

TAAM-1D A Japanese Air Force air-to-air missile with a range of about 1.5 mi.

tables of fire See **firing table.**

taborite A Roman soldier armed with a double-edged ax.

tabun (GA) This war gas is one of the **nerve agents,** which see, and has a quick-acting casualty effect. Skin absorption great enough to cause death may occur in 1 to 2 minutes, although death may be delayed for 1 to 2 hours. Respiratory lethal dosages kill in 1 to 10 minutes, and liquid in the eye kills nearly as rapidly.

Tack The code name of an operation carried out during the Korean conflict (February 4, 1951) in which C-47 aircraft of the U.S. Third Bombardment Wing dropped 8 tons of roofing nails on highways south of Pyongyang, Korea.

tactical **1.** Of or pertaining to tactics, i.e., to the arranging, positioning, or maneuvering of forces in contact or near contact with the enemy so as to achieve an objective or objectives in a campaign or battle. **2.** Often used in sense 1 to distinguish between "tactical" and "strategic" considerations. **3.** Of or pertaining to combat operations, as distinguished from administrative, technical, or logistical operations. **4.** Restrictively, applied to activities of surface battle-line areas only.

tactical air command **1.** A U.S. Air Force organization designed to conduct offensive and defensive air operations in conjunction with land or sea forces. **2.** A designation of one of the subordinate commands of the Air Force.

tactical air force An air force charged with carrying out tactical air operations in coordination with ground or naval forces.

tactical air operation An air operation involving the employment of air power in coordination with ground or naval forces to: (1) Gain and maintain air superiority. (2) Prevent movement of enemy forces into and within the objective area and to seek out and destroy these forces and their supporting installations. (3) Join with ground or naval forces in operations within the objective area in order to assist directly in the attainment of their immediate objective.

tactical air reconnaissance The use of air vehicles to obtain information concerning terrain, weather, and the disposition, composition, movement, installations, lines of communications, and electronic and communication emissions of enemy forces. Also included are artillery and naval gunfire adjustment and systematic and random observations of ground battle area, targets, or sector of airspace.

tactical air support Air operations carried out in coordination with surface forces which directly assist the land or naval battle.

TAAM-1D. (*Japan Defense Agency.*)

433

tactical command ship, the U.S.S. *Wright* (CC-2). (*U.S. Navy.*)

Talon. (*U.S. Air Force.*)

tactical atomic demolition munition An atomic demolition munition which provides a capability for the execution of a wide variety of demolition missions on the tactical battlefield.

tactical bomber Any airplane designed or used for tactical bombing, especially a bomber with relatively short range and light bombload.

tactical bombing Bombing conducted, usually by tactical air units, in support of surface forces. Bombing to achieve air superiority or to carry out interdiction is a part of tactical bombing, although the term tends to be restricted to battle-area operations.

tactical command ship A warship, converted from a light cruiser and designed to serve as a command ship for a fleet or force commander. It is equipped with extensive communication equipment. Designated as CC.

tactical control The detailed and, usually, local direction and control of movements or maneuvers necessary to accomplish missions or tasks assigned.

tactical diversion (naval) A modification for operational reasons in the route, or the rate of progress along the route, including waiting periods in a holding anchorage, of a ship or convoy without alteration of its ultimate destination.

tactical intelligence Intelligence which is required for the planning and conduct of tactical operations. Essentially, tactical intelligence and strategic intelligence differ only in scope, point of view, and level of employment.

tactical reserve A part of battalion, regiment, or similar force held initially under the control of the commander as a maneuvering force to influence future action.

tactical target Any physical object, person, group of persons, or position singled out for attack during the course of battle or tactical operations in order to reduce or to destroy the enemy's ability to sustain his combat operation.

tactical troops Combat troops, together with any service troops required for their direct support, who are organized under one commander to operate as a unit and engage the enemy in combat.

tactical unit An organization of troops, aircraft, or ships which is intended to serve as a single unit in combat. It may include service units required for its direct support.

tactical vehicle A vehicle having military characteristics and designed primarily for use by forces in the field in direct connection with, or support of, combat or tactical operations or the training of troops for such operations.

tactical warning A notification that the enemy has initiated hostilities. Such a warning may be received any time from the launching of the attack until it reaches its target.

tactics **1.** The employment of units in combat. **2.** The ordered arrangement and maneuver of units in relation to one another and/or to the enemy in order to utilize their full potentialities.

Taifun A German surface-to-air missile of World War II. It weighed about 43 lb and had a length of about 6 ft. It attained a velocity of from 3,000 to 3,500 fps and an altitude of about 50,000 ft.

Taiho A Japanese aircraft carrier of 29,300 tons standard displacement completed in March 1944. It had flight-deck dimensions of 844 by 98 ft, a speed of 33 knots, and a complement of 1,751 men. It carried 53 aircraft. It was sunk by an American submarine in the Battle of the Philippine Sea in June 1944.

tail assembly See **empennage.**

tail fuze A fuze designed to be inserted in the after end of a bomb.

tail gun The flexible gun mounted in the tail of an aircraft.

tail hook The hook that, lowered below a carrier aircraft, engages the arresting gear upon landing aboard the carrier.

Taiyo A class of Japanese aircraft carriers originally laid down as ocean liners. There were three ships in this class, and they were completed in 1939–1940. *Taiyo* was sunk by an American submarine northwest of Luzon in August 1944. *Chuyo* was sunk by an American submarine off the coast of Honshu in December 1944. *Unyo* was sunk by an American submarine in the South China Sea in September 1944. They had flight-deck dimensions of 564 by 77 ft, a speed of 21 knots, and a complement of 850 men. They carried 27 aircraft.

Takao A class of Japanese 13,000-ton cruisers completed in the early 1930s. The class included *Takao*, *Maya*, *Chokai*, and *Atago*, all of which were lost during World War II. They had a speed of 34 knots, a complement of 773 men, and main armament consisting of ten 8-in. guns, eight 5-in. guns, four quadruple torpedo tubes, and three aircraft.

takedown The process of taking a gun apart.

takel An ancient Anglo-Saxon name for the arrows which were supplied to ships.

Tallboy A British 12,000-lb aircraft bomb developed in 1945. It was a relatively heavy-walled bomb with approximately 43 percent explosive and was designed for use against heavily fortified targets such as U-boat pens and underground factories.

Tall King The NATO code name for a type of Soviet A-band early-warning and surveillance radar.

tallyho The call transmitted by a fighter pilot when he sights his target.

Talon The U.S. Northrop-built T-38 Talon is a two-seat supersonic basic jet trainer developed for the U.S. Air Force and first flown in 1959. It has a maximum level speed of above Mach 1.3.

Talos A surface-to-air and surface-to-surface guided missile developed by Bendix for the U.S. Navy. It has a length of 31.25 ft, a weight of 7,000 lb, and a slant range of over 65 mi. Either a high-explosive or a nuclear warhead may be carried.

talus In fortifications, the slope of the face of a work.

tampion See **tompion,** sense 2.

tang The portion of a sword, dagger, or knife blade that passes through the hilt.

Tang A class of U.S. attack submarines (SS) of 2,100 tons standard displacement commissioned in 1951–1952. They have a length of 287 ft, a beam of 27.3 ft, a speed of 18 knots submerged, and a complement of 83 men. They are armed with eight 21-in. torpedo tubes.

tank A self-propelled, heavily armored offensive vehicle having a fully enclosed revolving turret with one major weapon. It may mount one or more machine guns. The term excludes self-propelled weapons. Tanks were first used by the British during World War I in the advance on the Somme in September 1916. The name of the system arose from the fact that the hull was called "a water carrier for Mesopotamia" in the English factories where they were being produced. In this effort to conceal their purpose, the name was soon shortened to "tank."

Tank Buchse The nickname given by German soldiers of World War II to the Rheinmetall (Solothurn) 20mm semiautomatic antitank cannon Model S18-1000. It was recoil-operated, clip-fed, and air-cooled, and its high-velocity projectile could penetrate $1\frac{1}{2}$ in. of armor plate at a range of 350 yd. (The term means, literally, "tank rifle.")

tank buster A slang term for an airplane designed for, or considered effective in, operations against tanks or other armored vehicles. The Hawker Hurricane was so called during World War II.

tank commander's cupola A turret-type steel rotatable dome mounted on the turret roof of a combat tank. It has facilities for mounting a gun and is designed to protect the commander or gunner from enemy fire.

tank ditch See **antitank ditch.**

tanker A ship that transports fuel to a base or service squadron. An oiler fuels other ships at sea or at an anchorage.

tank gun A gun mounted in a military tank.

tank, main battle A tracked vehicle pro-

viding heavy armor protection and serving as the principal assault weapon of armored and infantry troops.

tank obstacle See **antitank obstacle.**

tank periscope A rectangular or cylindrical periscope, usually positioned in a holder or mount within an armored vehicle. It is used to observe terrain, near and distant targets, and the like. It may also be linked to gun training mechanisms for integration of movement for fire-control purposes.

tannoy The loudspeaker system of RAF stations.

tape lock A lock using a tape primer which consists of percussion pellets sandwiched between two strips of paper and resembling the rolls of caps used in toy cap pistols.

tapered bore A term applied to a gun with a tapered bore and also to its ammunition. The gun bore may be tapered throughout its length or only in the muzzle section. The projectile which starts out as a lightweight projectile of the larger caliber may

Talos. (*U.S. Navy.*)

Tang. (*U.S. Navy.*)

be projected at hypervelocity in the form of a smaller-caliber projectile of normal or heavy weight. The smaller caliber maintains a higher velocity than the larger caliber would (for equal-weight projectiles) because of lowered air resistance. For this reason the tapered bore is sometimes used for antitank weapons. Sometimes referred to as "squeeze bore" or "Gerlich gun," after its originator.

tapul In sixteenth- and seventeenth-century armor, a vertical ridge down the center of the breastplate.

tarfu See **snafu.**

targe, target A small, round shield most often made of wood covered with leather and often studded with patterns of nails or bosses. Targets might also be made of iron or steel or of several layers of leather. (Picture, next page.)

target 1. A geographic area, complex, or installation planned for capture or destruction by military forces. **2.** In intelligence usage, a country, area, installation, agency, or person against which intelligence operations are directed. **3.** An area designated and numbered for future firing. **4.** In

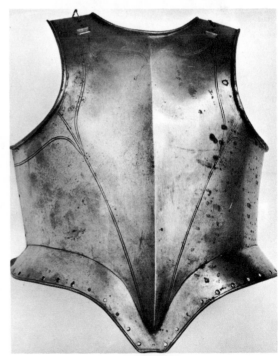

tapul. (*The Metropolitan Museum of Art, Bashford Dean Memorial Collection.*)

targe, target. (*The Metropolitan Museum of Art, gift of William H. Riggs, 1913.*)

Tartar. (*General Dynamics.*)

gunfire-support usage, an impact burst which hits the target.

target analysis   An examination of potential targets to determine military importance, priority of attack, and weapons required to obtain a desired level of damage or casualties.

target angle   The relative bearing of the firing ship from the target measured from the bow of the target to the right through 360°.

target approach point   In air transport operations, a navigational checkpoint over which the final turn-in to the drop zone or landing zone is made.

target aquisition   The detection, identification, and location of a target in sufficient detail to permit the effective employment of weapons.

target array   A graphic representation of enemy forces, personnel, and facilities in a specific situation, accompanied by a target analysis.

target bearing   **1.** True. The true compass bearing of a target from a firing ship. **2.** Relative. The bearing of a target measured in the horizontal from the bow of one's own ship clockwise from 0 to 360° or from the nose of one's own aircraft in hours of the clock.

target combat air patrol   A patrol of fighters maintained over an enemy target area to destroy enemy aircraft and to cover friendly shipping in the vicinity of the target area in amphibious operations.

target complex   A geographically integrated series of target concentrations.

target discrimination   The ability of a guidance system to lock on and home on any one target when multiple targets are present.

target dossiers   Files of assembled target intelligence about a specific geographic area.

target folders   The folders containing target intelligence and related materials pre-

pared for planning and executing action against a specific target.

target grid   A device for converting the observer's target locations and corrections with respect to the observer target line to target locations and corrections with respect to the gun-target line.

target-grid method   A standard shore-bombardment procedure.

target identification   The technique (usually electronic) used to determine whether a target is friend or foe.

target-identification bomb   A missile designed to be dropped from aircraft. Upon impact it produces a relatively prolonged and conspicuous effect, such as a brightly colored light, which provides other aircraft with a means of locating and identifying the target.

target intelligence   Intelligence which portrays and locates the components of a target or target complex and indicates its vulnerability and relative importance.

target marking   The marking of a target with smoke or incendiary bombs or rockets, with airdropped beacons, or with radar systems.

target number (artillery)   The reference number given to the target by the fire-control unit.

target of opportunity   A target visible to surface or air sensor or observer which is within range of available weapons and against which fire has not been scheduled or requested.

target priority   A grouping of targets with the indicated sequence of attack.

tariere   An ancient sharp-pointed battering ram.

tarmac   A British expression for a paved apron or runway for aircraft. It is derived from the two words "tar" and "macadam."

Tartar   A solid-propellant ship-to-air missile developed by the U.S. Bureau of Naval Weapons and in full production for the U.S. Navy since 1960. It has an overall length

task force. (*U.S. Navy.*)

of 15 ft, a launching weight of slightly over 1,200 lb, a range of over 10 mi, and an effective ceiling of 40,000 ft. It is also used by the navies of several other countries. The U.S. Navy designation is RIM-24.

tarzon   A 6-ton razon bomb.

task element   A subdivision of a task group; one or more ships with a specific common mission.

task fleet   A mobile command consisting of ships and aircraft necessary for the accomplishment of a specific major task or tasks, which may be of a continuing nature.

task force   **1.** A temporary grouping of units under one commander formed for the purpose of carrying out a specific operation or mission.   **2.** A semipermanent organization of units under one commander formed for the purpose of carrying out a continuing specific task.   **3.** A component of a fleet organized by the commander of a task fleet or higher authority for the accomplishment of a specific task or tasks.

task group   A subdivision of a task force; a group of ships with a specific common mission.

task unit (TU)   A component of a task group or a task element.

tasset   In armor, a metal plate or plates attached to the breastplate for the protection of the thigh.

tatoo   The call preceding taps, giving notice to repair to quarters.

Taube   A German single-place single-engine high-wing monoplane aircraft used for observation and training and first flown in prototype form in 1910. The Taube (Dove) had a speed of about 71 mph.

TB   **1.** U.S. Navy torpedo boat.   **2.** Torpedo bombing, in designations of U.S. Navy aircraft, as in TBF.   **3.** Heavy bomber (*Tyazhelii bombovoz*), used in the names of Russian aircraft from 1925 to 1945, as in TB-3, TB-7, etc.

TBD-1   See **Devastator.**

TBF-1   See **Avenger.**

T-boat   The U.S. Army designation for a 65-ft vessel used for carrying passengers or freight. It had a displacement of about 95 tons.

Tchapayev   A class of Soviet cruisers of 10,000 tons standard displacement completed in the late 1940s. They have a speed of 35 knots, a complement 834 men, and main armament consisting of twelve 6-in. and eight 4-in. guns.

T Class   1. A class of British submarines of 1,090 tons standard displacement completed in 1942–1946. They had a length of 265 ft, a beam of 26.5 ft, a speed of 9 knots submerged, and a complement of 59 men. They were armed with eleven 21-in. torpedo tubes and one 4-in. deck gun.   **2.** A class of British antisubmarine frigates of 1,710 tons standard displacement. They had a speed of 34 knots, a complement of 200 men, and armament consisting of two 4-in. guns, seven 40mm antiaircraft guns, four 21-in. torpedo tubes, and two Squid depth-charge systems. They were completed in 1943–1944.   **3.** A former class of U.S. submarines of 1,475 tons standard displacement commissioned in 1940–1941. They had a surface speed of 21 knots and a submerged speed of 9 knots and were armed with ten 21-in. torpedo tubes.

TDC   The torpedo firing-data computer in a submarine.

tear agents   Tear gases such as **CN, CNC, CNS, CNB, BBC,** and **CS,** which see, are used for training and riot control. They cause a flow of tears and irritation of the skin, but rarely produce casualties.

tear gas   A substance, usually liquid, which when atomized and of a certain concentration causes temporary but intense eye irritation and a blinding flow of tears in anyone exposed to it. Also called a "lacrimator."

tasset. (*The Metropolitan Museum of Art, Bashford Dean Memorial Collection.*)

Taube. (*The Smithsonian Institution, National Air Museum.*)

Tchapayev. (*U.S. Navy.*)

Tempest. (*Hawker Siddeley Aviation Ltd.*)

tebet A kind of Turkish battle-ax.

technical sergeant The rank higher than staff sergeant but lower than master sergeant.

TEDS A U.S. Navy turbine electric-drive submarine.

telecommunication Any transmission, emission, or reception of signs, signals, writing, images, and sounds or information of any nature by wire, radio, visual, or other electromagnetic systems.

telemetry The science involving the taking of measurements and their transmission to detached stations where they can be displayed, interpreted, or recorded.

telescopic sight A telescope used on a firearm as a sight.

Tellebomb The name of an Italian guided bomb developed in the 1920s. It had a weight of 175 lb (of which 130 lb was payload), a range of 6 mi, and a speed of 250 mph.

teller mine A large land antitank mine employed by the Germans during World War II. It weighed about 15 lb, was shaped like a large plate, and was frequently booby-trapped. The name derives from the German word *Teller*, meaning "plate."

Téméraire A class of British 18,600-ton battleships completed in 1909. They had a length of 526 ft, a complement of 850 men, and main armament consisting of ten 12-in. and sixteen 4-in. guns, plus three 18-in. torpedo tubes. The class included *Téméraire*, *Bellerophon*, and *Superb*. They had a speed of 22 knots.

Tempest A British single-engine single-seat interceptor and fighter-bomber built by Hawker Siddeley and first flown in 1942. One version was the most powerful piston-engine fighter in the RAF, being equipped with a 2,520-hp radial engine. It flew at speeds up to 440 mph and was armed with four 20mm Hispano cannons and two 1,000 lb bombs or eight 60-lb rockets. The Tempest represented the principal fighter defense against German V-1 flying bombs, accounting for 638 of the 1,771 missiles destroyed by the RAF between June 13 and September 5, 1944.

tenaille In fortifications, an outwork located in the main ditch between two bastions.

tenaillon In fortification, works constructed on each side of the ravelin. They were used for added strength or to cover the shoulders of the bastions.

Tench A class of U.S. attack submarines (SS) of 1,840 tons standard displacement

Tennessee. (*U.S. Navy.*)

commissioned in 1944–1946. They had a length of 312 ft, a beam of 27.2 ft, a speed of 20 knots on the surface (10 knots submerged), and a complement of about 85 men. They were armed with ten 21-in. torpedo tubes, one 5-in. gun, and one 40mm antiaircraft gun.

tender A logistical support and repair ship such as a destroyer tender.

Tennessee A class of U.S. battleships of about 32,000 tons standard displacement completed in 1920 and 1921 and rebuilt in 1942. The class included *Tennessee* and *California*. They had a length of 624 ft, a beam of 114 ft, a speed of 21 knots, and a wartime complement of 2,200 men. They were armed with twelve 14-in. and sixteen 5-in. guns, plus forty 40mm and forty-two to fifty 20mm antiaircraft guns and four aircraft. After repairs from the damage sustained at Pearl Harbor, the *Tennessee* saw considerable service during World War II in the Pacific theater.

Tenryu A class of Japanese light cruisers of 3,230 tons displacement completed in 1919. There were two ships in the class, *Tenryu* and *Tatsuta*, both of which were lost during World War II. They had a speed of 33 knots, a complement of 332 men, and main armament consisting of four 5.5-in. guns, one 3-in. gun, and six 21-in. torpedo tubes.

tercio In the sixteenth and seventeenth centuries, a Spanish or Italian infantry regiment.

terebra A ninth-century device for boring holes into the walls of fortresses. It consisted of a pole or beam having a sharp iron point.

TERI Torpedo effective range indicator.

terminal guidance **1.** The guidance applied to a guided missile between mid-course guidance and arrival in the vicinity of the target. **2.** Electronic, mechanical, visual, or other assistance given an aircraft pilot to facilitate arrival at, operation within or over, landing upon, or departure from an air-landing or airdrop facility.

terminal phase The period of flight of a missile between the end of mid-course guidance and impact.

terminal velocity **1.** The hypothetical maximum speed a body could attain along a specified flight path under given conditions of weight and thrust in diving through an unlimited distance in air of specified uniform density. **2.** The remaining speed of a projectile at the point in its downward path where it is level with the muzzle of the weapon.

Terne Mk 8 A Norwegian rocket-propelled depth charge with a length of 6 ft 4¾ in., a weight of 298 lb, and a warhead weight of 110 lb.

terrain intelligence Processed information on the military significance of the natural

Terne Mk 8. (*Norwegian Defense Department.*)

and man-made characteristics of an area.

terrain study An analysis and interpretation of the natural and man-made features of an area, their effects on military operations, and the effect of weather and climate on these features.

Terrapin A British eight-wheeled amphibious vehicle of World War II. It had a weight of about 7 tons and was powered by twin Ford V8 engines of 85 bhp (brake horsepower) each.

terreplein **1.** The level country around a fieldwork. **2.** A rampart's rear talus. **3.** The top of a rampart where a cannon is located behind the parapet.

terrestrial reference guidance The technique of providing intelligence to a missile from certain characteristics of the surface over which the missile is flown, thereby enabling it to achieve flight along a predetermined path.

Terrier A U.S. Navy surface-to-air missile with a solid-fuel rocket motor. It is equipped with radar-beam rider or homing guidance and a nuclear or nonnuclear warhead. Produced by General Dynamics, it has a length of 26.5 ft, a launching weight of 3,070 lb, and a range in excess of 20 mi. It is also designated RIM-2. (Picture, next page.)

Terrier land weapon system A surface-to-air missile system, utilizing the Terrier RIM-2B and Terrier TIM-2C missiles with ground-launching and guidance equipment, developed specifically for amphibious operations. This equipment is a lighter and

land-mobile version of the U.S. Navy system.

Terry and the Pirates A World War II organization, officially called "Air Commandos," which flew out wounded men belonging to long-range penetration groups from behind Japanese lines in Burma. It was under the command of U.S. Col. Philip Cochran.

Teryu A class of Japanese cruisers of about 3,000 tons standard displacement built around 1920 and used during World War II. They had a length of about 465 ft, a beam of 40 ft, a speed of 31 knots, and a complement of 328 men. They were armed with six 5.5-in. guns and one 3-in. gun, plus two torpedo tubes and thirty-four mines.

testudo A penthouse with a rounded upper surface that resembled a tortoise and was used in the Middle Ages for the protection of soldiers trying to enter a fortified place. Also, a defensive system in which soldiers joined their shields over their heads, thus providing a solid protective cover.

tetrahedron **1.** A pyramid-shaped underwater beach obstacle. **2.** A type of anti-tank obstacle. **3.** A four-pronged device dropped on enemy roads or airfields to puncture tires. See **caltrop.**

Texas Two battleships were named for the state of Texas. The first *Texas* was also the first battleship commissioned in the U.S. Navy. Launched in 1892, it had a normal displacement of 6,315 tons, a length of 308 ft, a beam of 64 ft, a speed of 17 knots, and a complement of 392 men. Main armament

Terrier. (*General Dynamics.*)

Texas. (*U.S. Navy.*)

consisted of two 12-in. guns, six 6-in. guns, and four 14-in. torpedo tubes. The second *Texas* was the name ship of a class of battleships of 27,000 tons standard displacement commissioned in 1914. The class consisted of *Texas* and *New York.* They had a length of 573 ft, a beam of 106 ft, a speed of 19 knots, and a complement of 1,314 men. They were armed with ten 14-in. guns, sixteen 5-in. guns, and eight 3-in. antiaircraft guns. They carried three aircraft. *Texas* saw considerable action during World War II in the invasions of Africa and Europe and also in the Pacific. The ship is now moored in the San Jacinto State Park in Houston, Tex., as a state memorial.

TF Task force.

TG **Task group.**

theater of operations That portion of a theater of war which is necessary for military operations, either offensive or defensive, pursuant to an assigned mission, and for the administration incident to such military operation; theater limits are designated by competent authority.

theater of war That area of land, sea, and air which is, or may become, involved directly in the operations of war.

theater ribbon A ribbon worn for service in a particular theater or war.

thermal radiation **1.** The heat and light produced by a nuclear explosion. **2.** Electromagnetic radiations emitted from a heat or light source as a consequence of its temperature; it consists essentially of ultraviolet, visible, and infrared radiations.

thermate This material, also called "TH3," is a standard metallic filling used in incendiary bombs. It is a mixture of **thermite** (which see), barium nitrate, and sulfur in an oil binder.

thermite A mixture of powdered aluminum and powdered iron oxide which, when ignited by black powder, burns at a temperature of about 4000°F. White-hot molten iron is released when thermite burns, and it acts as a heat reservoir to prolong and spread the incendiary effect. When used as a filler for incendiary munitions, thermite is called "THI."

thermonuclear Pertaining to the process (or processes) in which very high temperatures are used to bring about the fusion of light nuclei, such as those of the hydrogen isotopes (deuterium and tritium), with the accompanying liberation of energy.

Thetis A German World War II code name for spar buoys which supported reflecting material. They were released by U boats to confuse Allied radar operations.

THI See **thermite.**

Third Reich The German dictatorship of Adolph Hitler between 1933 and 1945.

thirty The popular term for ".30 cal. machine gun." Usually used in the plural in reference to two or more such guns mounted on an aircraft or in a multiple mount.

Thomas-Morse S-4 A U.S. single-seat single-engine biplane trainer first flown in June 1917. Nicknamed "Tommy," it had a speed of about 95 mph.

Thompson submachine gun A weapon designed by Gen. John T. Thompson (1860–1940), Director of Arsenals in the United States during World War I. The first prototypes were developed in 1918. There are several models of the Thompson, with the Models 1921 and 1928 manufactured by Colt, and the M1928A1 and the M1 series manufactured by Auto-Ordnance and Savage. The Model 1921 is a retarded-blowback-operated weapon with selective full automatic and semiautomatic fire. The cyclic rate of fire is 800 rounds per minute, and the .45 cal. ACP cartridge provides muzzle velocities of about 920 fps. The length of the weapon (with stock and compensator) is 33.75 in., and it has a barrel length of 10.50 in. without compensator. Available for use with this weapon are 18-, 20-, and 30-round box magazines and 50- and 100-round drum magazines. The weapon weighs 12 lb with a 20-round magazine. The Model 1927 is a Model 1921 with an action that permits semiautomatic fire only. The Model 28 is basically a Model 1921 with provisions to reduce the rate of fire from 800 rounds per minute to less than 700 and with simplifications to allow mass production. When this weapon was adopted as standard with U.S. forces, it became known as the "Thompson .45 cal. submachine gun M1," and finally as the "M1A1."

Thor A U.S. liquid-propellant one-stage, rocket-powered intermediate-range ballistic missile equipped with a nuclear warhead. It was also equipped with an all-inertial guidance system. It had a range of 250 to 300 mi.

thorax The bronze cuirass used by the ancient Greeks.

three-cocked hat An old style of hat once worn by naval officers.

three-decker Formerly, a warship fitted for carrying guns on three decks.

Thresher See **Permit.**

throat **1.** The tapered portion of the bore

Thomas-Morse S-4. (*U.S. Air Force.*)

Thompson submachine gun M1A1. (*U.S. Army.*)

forward of the chamber where it diminishes in cross section to meet the rifling. In a revolver it is the enlargement of the bore at the breech to facilitate the centering of the bullet in the barrel when it jumps from the cylinder into the bore. Also may be referred to as "leade." **2.** In a sword or dagger scabbard, the metal reinforcement around the mouth.

throwing knife, throwing iron A device made like a knife, sometimes with several sharp blades set at different angles, and used for throwing at an enemy.

Thunder A class of Japanese frigates of 1,070 tons standard displacement completed in 1956. They have a speed of 25 knots, a complement of 160 men, and armament consisting of two 3-in. guns, two 40mm antiaircraft guns, one hedgehog, eight K-guns, and two depth-charge racks.

Thunderbird A solid-propellant surface-to-air missile with semiactive radar homing.

It is built by the British Aircraft Corporation and has a length of 20 ft 10 in.

Thunderbolt The Republic P-47 Thunderbolt was a single-seat single-engine long-range fighter developed for the USAAF and first flown in May 1941. It was the largest and heaviest single-seat single-piston-engine fighter ever built. During World War II 15,660 Thunderbolts of various types were produced. In the European theater this airplane accounted for 3,752 enemy aircraft destroyed in the air and 3,315 on the ground. The P-47N had a speed of 470 mph with a 2,800-hp radial engine. Armament consisted of six or eight .50 cal. machine guns, plus two 1,000-lb bombs or ten 5-in. rockets. (Picture, next page.)

Thunderchief The Republic F-105 Thunderchief is a single-seat single-engine long-range jet tactical fighter-bomber developed for the USAF and first flown in 1955. It has a speed of Mach 2.1, a range of 2,070 mi,

Thunder. (*Japan Defense Agency.*)

Thunderbolt. (*U.S. Air Force.*)

Thunderchief. (*U.S. Air Force.*)

Thunderjet. (*U.S. Air Force.*)

and armament consisting of a 20mm Vulcan cannon plus other weapon loads, including Bullpup or Sidewinder missiles and various combinations of bombs and rockets.

Thunderflash See **Thunderstreak**.

Thunderjet The original model of this aircraft was first flown in 1946; there were

subsequent design improvements into the 1950s. The F-84G is a single-seat jet fighter-bomber in service with the air forces of Iran, Portugal, Thailand, and Yugoslavia. It has a speed of 622 mph, a range of 2,000 mi, and armament consisting of six .50 cal. machine guns, plus under-wing attach-

ments for four 1,000-lb bombs or thirty-two 5-in. rockets.

Thunderstreak The Republic F-84F is a single-seat jet fighter, fighter-bomber, and tactical-reconnaissance aircraft developed from the F-84 Thunderjet and first flown in 1951. It is in service with the USAF and several NATO countries. It has a speed of 695 mph and a range of about 2,000 mi and is armed with six .50 cal. machine guns, plus attachments for four 1,000-lb bombs or twenty-four 5-in. rockets. The reconnaissance version of the airplane is designated "Thunderflash."

Ticonderoga A class (modified Essex class) of U.S. aircraft carriers (CV) of 27,100 tons standard displacement commissioned in 1944–1945. They had an overall length of 888 ft, an extreme flight-deck width of 147.5 ft, a top speed of 33 knots, and a complement of 3,448 men. They carried 100 aircraft and were armed with over 85 antiaircraft guns (total barrels).

Tidalwave The World War II code name for the U.S. low-level attack on oil refineries at Ploesti, Rumania, by B-24 bombers based in Libya. It took place on August 1, 1943.

tier A row of guns or gun portholes in a warship or a fort.

Tiger **1.** A class of British cruisers of 9,500 tons standard displacement completed in 1959–1961. They have a length of 566 ft, a beam of 64 ft, a speed of 31.5 knots, and a complement of 885 men. They are armed with four 6-in. and six 3-in. guns. **2.** The Grumman F11 Tiger is a follow-on development of the Panther and Cougar aircraft. The Tiger is a single-engine single-seat supersonic jet fighter with armament consisting of Sidewinder missiles, cannons, and rocket packs.

Tigercat **1.** A land-based version of the Short-built Seacat ship-to-air missile. **2.** The Grumman F7F Tigercat was a twin-engine two-seat night fighter (or one-seat day fighter) developed for U.S. Marine Corps shore-based operations. It was deployed too late to see service in World War II. It flew at a maximum speed of 435 mph and was armed with four 20mm cannons and four .50 cal. machine guns.

Tiger Moth The British de Havilland D.H. 82 single-engine biplane which first appeared in 1931 and was built in large numbers as a trainer for the RAF.

Tiger tank The German tank, heavy, PzKpfw VI, of World War II. It was introduced in 1943 and was used by armored battalions. It had a crew of five and armament consisting of one 88mm KwK 36 gun, caliber length 56, and two 7.9mm machine guns MG 34. It weighed 62.8 tons and could travel on roads at speeds of 23 mph.

tiller The wooden stock of a crossbow.

timed run A bomb run in which the moment of bomb release is determined by timing the run from a given known point.

time fuze A fuze which contains a graduated time element to regulate the time interval after which the fuze will function.

time of attack The hour at which an attack is to be launched. If a line of departure is prescribed, it is the hour at which the line is to be crossed by the leading elements of the attack.

time of flight The elapsed time in seconds from the instant a projectile or other missile leaves the gun or launcher until the instant it strikes or bursts.

time on target **1.** The method of firing on a target in which various artillery units and naval gunfire ships so time their fire as to assure that all projectiles will reach the target simultaneously. **2.** The time at which aircraft are scheduled to attack or photograph the target. **3.** The actual time at which aircraft attack or photograph the target.

tin can A slang term for a destroyer.

tin case shot Another term for canister shot.

tinclad A river steamer converted to a gunboat by the application of light armor. Tinclads were used by the Union forces during the American Civil War.

tin fish A slang term for a torpedo.

tin hat A slang term for a steel helmet.

Tiny Tim The nickname for an 11.75-in. aircraft rocket developed by the United States in World War II. It had an overall weight of 1,200 lb, a warhead weight of 150 lb (TNT), and a range of 1 mi. It was used in the Battle of Okinawa and was later employed with great effectiveness in the Korean conflict.

tirailleur Formerly, in the French Army, an infantry skirmisher.

Tirpitz A German battleship completed in 1939 and a sister ship of the **Bismark,** for details which see. In Norway it was attacked by British midget submarines, three air strikes by British carrier aircraft, and two air strikes by RAF Lancaster bombers. It capsized off Tromso on November 11, 1944.

Titan A liquid-propellant two-stage rocket-powered intercontinental ballistic missile

equipped with a nuclear warhead. Designated as HGM-25, it is guided by radio-inertial guidance; the LGM-25C, an improved version of the HGM-25, is guided by all-inertial guidance and is equipped with a higher-yield warhead. The system is for deployment in a hardened and dispersed configuration. Titan II (LGM-25C) has a length of 103 ft, a diameter of 10 ft, and a launching weight of 330,000 lb. It has a range of 6,300 mi. (Picture, next page.)

titanium tetrachloride A liquid which causes formation of a screening smoke when it is dispersed in air. It may be dispersed by explosive effect or as a mechanically produced spray. The smoke is corrosive and irritating to the nose and throat,

Tigercat. (*Grumman Aerospace Corporation.*)

Tigercat. (*Short Brothers & Harland Ltd.*)

Tiny Tim. (*U.S. Navy.*)

Tirpitz. (*The Imperial War Museum.*)

Titan. (*U.S. Air Force.*)

but not serious in effect in the concentration usually present in a smoke cloud.

TNT   The abbreviation for **trinitrotoluene** and **trinitrotoluol,** which see.

TNT equivalent   A measure of the energy release from the detonation of a nuclear weapon or from the explosion of a given quantity of fissionable or fusionable material, in terms of the amount of TNT (trinitrotoluene) which would release the same amount of energy if exploded.

toggle   To release a bomb or bombs by the use of a toggle switch without benefit of the automatic release system of the bombsight.

TOG method   Target observer gun method. A method of pointing a gun by indirect laying, using the angle at the observer between a line to the target and a line to the gun.

Tojo   The code name for the Nakajima Ki.44 Shoki (Demon) single-seat single-engine fighter-interceptor developed for the Japanese Army Air Force and first flown in August 1940. It had a maximum speed of 376 mph and was armed with four 12.7mm machine guns and two 220-lb bombs.

Tokarev 7.62mm automatic pistol TT

Tojo. (*The Smithsonian Institution, National Air Museum.*)

Tokarev 7.62mm automatic pistol TT Model 1933. (*The Smithsonian Institution.*)

Model 1933   A weapon introduced in 1930 and a Russian modification of the original Colt-Browning design. While designed for the Russian 7.62mm cartridge (officially adopted for both automatic pistols and submachine guns in 1930), it was found during World War II that it would as easily shoot the German Mauser 7.63mm pistol cartridge. It has a magazine capacity of eight cartridges. It weighs 29 oz and has an overall length of 7.68 in. and a barrel length of 4.57 in. This pistol has been produced in Hungary as the Model 48 and in the Chinese People's Republic as the Type 51.

Tokarev 7.62mm semiautomatic and automatic rifles Model 1940   These weapons were introduced to Soviet forces in 1940. The semiautomatic version (SVT) and the automatic version (AVT) are both gas-operated weapons with a length of 48.1 in. and a barrel length of 24.6 in. The semiautomatic version (at about 9.5 lb) is about ¼ lb heavier than the automatic version. These weapons saw considerable service in World War II, but were difficult to repair and maintain.

Tokarev 7.62mm semiautomatic rifle Model 1938   This weapon (also called the "SVT-38") has a weight of 8.70 lb, an overall length of 48.1 in., a barrel length of 25 in., and a magazine capacity of 10 rounds. It is very lightly built.

Token   The NATO code name for a type of Soviet E/F-band ground-controlled interception radar.

Tokkatai   World War II Japanese Army Air Force suicide pilots who volunteered to fly aircraft into targets. Suicide pilots of the Japanese Naval Force were called "*kamikaze.*"

tolenon   The ancient equivalent of a modern-day "cherry picker," a tolenon consisted of a long arm mounted on a pivot and carrying a box large enough to hold 20 men. It was raised to a firing position level with the loopholes or the top of the wall of a fort.

tolite   A French term for TNT.

tomahawk   The fighting hatchet of the North American Indians. Tomahawks were first made of wood, or wood and stone, but later of steel, the heads of which were sometimes combined with a tobacco pipe. The metal types were provided by traders. American colonial troops often carried tomahawks instead of swords, and riflemen continued to carry them into the nineteenth century.

Tomahawk   The Curtiss P-40A/C Tomahawk was first flown in 1938 and consisted of a P-36 reworked to incorporate a 1,150-hp Allison liquid-cooled engine. It represented the only relatively modern fighter in service when the United States entered World War II. It was used by the United States, the RAF (which designated it "Hawk"), and the American Volunteer Group in China. The airplane had a speed of 352 mph and was armed with two .50 cal. machine guns and two .30 cal. machine guns. It had a wingspan of 37.25 ft, a length of 31.75 ft, and a height of about 10.5 ft. Later versions (P-40D through Q) were called "Warhawks." See **Warhawk.**

Tomcat   The U.S. Grumman-built two-place twin-jet fighter with a speed of Mach 2+, in service with the U.S. Navy. It is armed with Sparrow, Sidewinder, and Phoenix missiles and with M-61 rapid-fire 20mm aircraft cannons.

Tom Cat   A special picket destroyer that operates with a fast carrier task force.

Tommy   A British soldier. It derives from "Thomas Atkins," a fictitious name used as a sample on official blank forms used by soldiers in the British Army.

tommy gun   A **Thompson submachine gun,** which see.

tompion   **1.** A wooden plug or cover, especially for the muzzle of a gun.   **2.** A cover for the sight bracket of a gun when the sight is not in place. Also called "tampion."

Tone   A class of Japanese 11,000-ton light cruisers produced in the late 1930s. The two ships of the class, *Tone* and *Chikuma,* were sunk by U.S. carrier aircraft during World War II. They had a speed of 35 knots, a complement of 850 men, and main armament consisting of eight 8-in. and eight 5-in. guns, four triple 24-in. torpedo tubes, and five aircraft.

Tony   The code name for the Kawasaki Ki.61 Hien (Swallow), a single-seat single-engine fighter-interceptor and fighter-bomber developed for the Japanese Army Air Force and first flown in December 1941. It was the only Japanese fighter powered by a liquid-cooled engine to see active service in World War II. It flew at speeds up to 348 mph and was armed with two 20mm cannons and two 12.7mm machine guns, plus two 550-lb bombs.

top A platform once located on the masts of war vessels which served as an observation and antiaircraft position for certain crew members.

top secret See **defense classification.**

torch pot The energy-releasing unit in an air-steam torpedo where combustion takes place.

tormentum An ancient device for throwing stones.

Tornado The first American four-jet bomber to fly. Designated the B-45, it was developed by North American and was first flown in 1947. It had a speed of 580 mph and could carry a short-range bombload of 22,000 lb.

torpedo 1. In current usage, a missile designed to contain an explosive charge and to be launched into water, where it is self-propelling and usually directable. It is launched from ships, submarines, or aircraft against ships or other targets in the water. When designed for launching from aircraft, it is sometimes called an "aerial torpedo." **2.** In earlier times, a metal case containing explosives and anchored in a channel (underwater or on the surface) or set adrift. Such torpedoes would explode on contact with a vessel. They are now called "naval mines." (During the American Civil War, Adm. David Farragut led a squadron of 18 ships into Mobile Bay and there issued his famous order, "Damn the torpedoes, full speed ahead!" He was proceeding through what today would be called a minefield.)

torpedo battery Formerly, in certain coastal-defense works, a land installation for discharging torpedoes.

torpedo boat A small, fast vessel armed with torpedo tubes and carrying only light guns.

torpedo bomber An aircraft designed or equipped to carry and launch torpedoes. (Picture, next page.)

torpedo bombing The launching of a torpedo or torpedoes from an aircraft against a target in the water.

torpedo defense net A net employed to close an inner harbor to torpedoes fired from seaward or to protect an individual ship at anchor or under way.

torpedo net, torpedo netting A strong steel-link underwater netting stretched around a ship by booms and intended to protect it from torpedoes.

torpedo range The distance a torpedo can run with its available fuel supply.

torpedo run The actual distance a torpedo travels to a target.

torpedo tube A device for launching torpedoes from a ship or submarine.

torpedo-tube shutters Movable fairings on the outboard end of submarine torpedo tubes whose closure preserves the streamlined form of the hull.

torpex A high explosive consisting of TNT,

Tomahawk. (*U.S. Air Force.*)

Tony. (*The Smithsonian Institution, National Air Museum.*)

Tornado. (*U.S. Air Force.*)

torpedo. (*U.S. Navy.*)

torpedo bomber, the Vickers Vildebeest of 1926. (*Vickers Ltd.*)

TOW (*U.S. Army.*)

towed antitank gun, a U.S. 57mm gun. (*U.S. Army.*)

towed light howitzer, a U.S. 150mm howitzer. (*U.S. Army.*)

cyclonite, and aluminum powder, used especially in torpedoes, mines, and depth bombs.

tortoise In military antiquity, the form of battle adopted by the Greeks in besieging fortified towns. It served to protect the besiegers in their approach to the walls. The soldiers placed their shields over their heads in a sloping position, similar to the tiles of a house. The first rank stood erect, the second stooped a little, the third stooped still more, and the last rank knelt. They were thus protected from the enemy's missile weapons as they advanced or stood under his walls. The chelone was similar to the testudo of the Romans. See **testudo.**

toss bombing A method of bombing in which an aircraft flies on a line toward the target and pulls up in a vertical plane, releasing the bomb at an angle that will compensate for the effect of gravity drop on the bomb. Similar to loft bombing. It is unrestricted as to altitude.

Toti A class of Italian submarines of 460 tons standard surface displacement completed in 1968–1969 (and Italy's first native-built submarines since World War II). They have a length of 153.2 ft, a beam of 15.4 ft, a submerged speed of 14 knots, and a complement of 24 men. They are armed with four 21-in. torpedo tubes.

touchbox The box in which lighted tinder was formerly carried by soldiers armed with matchlocks.

touchhole The opening in the breech of early firearms that provided a pathway for fire to ignite the powder charge.

touman A Mongol division of 10,000 men. These troops were armed with scimitars, bows, and lances (some of which were equipped with hooks for pulling an enemy out of his saddle). A light bow was used on horseback, but a more powerful bow, reinforced with horn or steel, was used for siege operations.

TOW An acronym for "*t*ube-launched *o*ptically tracked *w*ire-guided missile," a U.S. battlefield-support missile developed by Hughes. It has a launching weight of about 48 lb and is propelled by a two-stage solid-propellant motor to an estimated range of 25 meters.

towed antiaircraft-artillery gun A complete projectile-firing weapon designed to fire on and destroy enemy aircraft. It does not have facilities for self-propulsion.

towed antitank gun A complete projectile-firing weapon designed for use against tanks or other armored vehicles. It does not have facilities for self-propulsion.

towed artillery Artillery weapons designed for movement as trailed loads behind prime movers or draft animals. Some adjustment of the weapon is necessary to place it in firing position.

towed field-artillery gun A complete projectile-firing weapon mounted on a carriage and mobile enough to accompany infantry or armored units in the field. It is used for long-range fire or for the delivery of fire requiring a flat trajectory and high velocity. It does not have facilities for self-propulsion.

towed heavy howitzer A complete projectile-firing weapon with a medium muzzle velocity and a curved trajectory. The bore diameter is larger than 200mm. It does not have facilities for self-propulsion.

towed light howitzer A complete projectile-firing weapon with a medium muzzle velocity and a curved trajectory. The bore diameter is over 30mm through 125mm. It does not have facilities for self-propulsion.

towed medium howitzer A complete projectile-firing weapon with a medium muzzle velocity and a curved trajectory. The bore diameter is 126mm through 200mm. It does not have facilities for self-propulsion.

tower From ancient through medieval times multistoried towers were constructed in order to attack fortifications. The towers, mounted on wheels, were sometimes as high as 20 stories and were covered with raw skins to prevent their being set on fire by the besieged. The upper parts contained archers, and the bottom was often occupied by a battering ram. In 309 B.C. at the siege of Rhodes, a tower was produced which required 3,400 men to move it to the walls. Another 1,000 men operated a 180-ft battering ram.

toxic attack An attack directed at man, animals, or crops, using injurious agents of radiological, biological, or chemical origin.

Tracer The U.S. Grumman-built E-1 Tracer is a four-place twin-engine (reciprocating) early-warning aircraft developed for the U.S. Navy. It has a speed of 265 mph and may also be used in the role of a fighter direction aircraft. Its design was based on that of the Grumman C-1 Trader.

tracer bullet A bullet containing a pyrotechnic mixture that is ignited by the exploding powder charge in the cartridge to make the flight of the projectile visible both by day and by night. Tracer bullets may be spaced at intervals in a machine-gun load of ball ammunition either (as formerly done) to allow the gunner to follow the path of the stream of fire and thus improve accuracy or to serve as a psychological deterrent to the enemy, who may hesitate to press home against the tracer.

track **1.** A series of related contacts displayed on a plotting board. **2.** To display or record the successive positions of a moving object. **3.** To lock onto a point of radiation and obtain guidance therefrom. **4.** To keep a gun properly aimed or to point a target-locating instrument at a moving target continuously. **5.** The actual path of an aircraft above, or a ship on, the surface of the earth. The course is the path which is planned; the track is the path which is actually taken. **6.** One of the two endless belts on which a full-track or half-track vehicle runs. **7.** A metal part forming a path for a moving object, e.g., the track around the inside of a vehicle for moving a mounted machine gun.

track angle The angle between the target course and the reciprocal of the torpedo course measured from the bow of the target

Tracer. (*U.S. Navy.*)

tracer bullet. (*U.S. Army.*)

Tracker. (*U.S. Navy.*)

to the right through 360° or to port or starboard through 180°.

Tracker The Grumman S-2 Tracker is a twin-engine (piston) carrier-based antisubmarine search and attack aircraft developed for the U.S. Navy and first flown in 1952. It is presently in the service of several countries. It has a speed of 263 mph and a ferry range of 1,300 mi, and it may be armed with 5-in. rockets, 25 echo-sounding

depth charges, and one nuclear depth bomb.

tracklaying vehicle A vehicle which travels upon two endless tracks, one on each side of the machine. A tracklaying vehicle has high mobility and can maneuver, is usually armed and frequently armored, and is intended for tactical use. Tanks are one type of tracklaying vehicle. (Picture, next page.)

tracklaying vehicle, an Austrian Panzerjäger K. (*Austrian Ministry of Defense.*)

Trackmaster   A U.S. Army two-passenger tracked resupply vehicle that can carry a cargo of 1,500 lb.

tractor group   A group of landing ships in an amphibious operation which carry the amphibious vehicles of the landing force.

Trader   The Grumman C-1A Trader is a twin-engine nine-passenger transport version of the **Tracker,** which see.

trail   **1.** In bombing, the line between the point of impact of the bomb and a point on the ground directly beneath the aircraft at the moment of impact, assuming that the aircraft stays on course after release and maintains a constant speed.   **2.** The rear part of a gun carriage which connects the piece with a limber or tractor. When the gun is unlimbered, the trail rests on the ground and stabilizes the piece in firing position.   **3.** A series of bombs dropped one after the other, instead of in a group.   **4.** To attach the trail of a gun to the limber.   **5.** To carry a firearm at trail arms.

trail angle   In bombing, the angle, measured in mils, between a vertical line from the aircraft to the trail at the moment of the bomb's impact and a line from the aircraft to the point of impact.

trail arms   The command to carry a rifle so that the butt is raised a few inches from the ground and the muzzle is inclined forward.

trail formation   Vehicles proceeding one behind the other at designated intervals. Also called "column formation."

trail handspike   A long, stout handspike used in moving the trail of a gun carriage, especially in aiming.

trail support   A log or other object placed under the trail spade of an artillery piece to provide additional resistance to recoil.

train   **1.** A service force or group of service elements which provide logistic support, e.g., the vehicles and operating personnel which furnish supply, evacuation, and maintenance services to a land unit.   **2.** To bring something to bear upon an object, as to train a gun upon a target; also, to aim or direct a radar antenna in azimuth.   **3.** Bombs dropped in short intervals or sequence.   **4.** Formerly, a powder train to lead fire to an explosive charge.

train bombing   Bombing by releasing two or more bombs in succession from the same airplane in a single sighting operation so as to make the bombs fall or strike in train.

training level   Formerly, an English term for a level used in estimating the elevation or depression of a gun.

training pendulum   Formerly, an English term for an instrument having a pendulum and a level attached and used in pointing guns.

trajectory   The curve traced by a bullet, projectile, missile, bomb, or other object thrown, launched, or trajected by an applied exterior force, the projectile continuing in motion after separation from the force.

transfer area   In an amphibious operation, the water area in which the transfer of troops and supplies from landing craft to amphibious vehicles is effected.

transient   **1.** Personnel, ships, or craft stopping temporarily at a post, station, or port to which they are not assigned or attached and having destination elsewhere.   **2.** An individual awaiting orders, transport, etc., at a post or station to which he is not attached or assigned.

transitory attrition minefields   A small number of mines laid in areas where sufficient enemy traffic will give a reasonable probability of a casualty but which could be easily swept or avoided and would be unprofitable to replenish.

transponder   A transmitter-receiver capable of accepting the electronic challenge of an interrogator and automatically transmitting an appropriate reply.

transport   A vehicle, aircraft, or vessel used to convey cargo or personnel. A transport aircraft may carry cargo, passengers, troops, or supplies. The illustration shows the off-loading of a British Short Belfast transport. A Saladin armored car is followed by an Abbot self-propelled gun and a Ferret scout car.

transport area   A station area for the transports that debark troops during an amphibious assault.

transport division (squadron)   The attack transports and cargo ships that carry and land a regimental combat team. Several divisions organized to carry a reinforced infantry division constitute a transport squadron.

transport group   The subdivision of an amphibious attack force comprising the assault transports and cargo ships.

traphole   A pit with a sharpened stake in

transport, a Belfast aircraft unloading a Saladin armored car, an Abbot self-propelled gun, and a Ferret scout car. (*Short Brothers & Harland Ltd.*)

the bottom of it. See **trou-de-loup.**

trap mine A land mine designed to explode unexpectedly when enemy personnel attempt to move an object. A form of booby trap.

traverse 1. A movement to the right or left on a pivot or mount, as of a gun, launcher, or radar antenna. **2.** To move or point a gun, launcher, radar antenna, or the like to the right or left on its pivot. **3.** A bank of earth in a trench to protect the occupants from enfilade fire and to localize the effect of shell bursts.

tread In fortifications, the surface of the banquette on which a soldier stands to fire over a parapet.

trebuchet, trebucket A machine used in the Middle Ages for throwing large stones. It consisted of a great weight attached to the short arm of a lever. The long arm was fitted with a box or basket to hold stones. When the weight was permitted to fall, the long arm was raised with great velocity and hurled the stone a considerable distance.

trench A ditch to protect soldiers from gunfire.

trench artillery Artillery placed in trenches and designed to throw projectiles at high angles in order to attack targets at fairly short range.

trench bomb An old term for a hand grenade.

trench burial A method of burial resorted to when casualties are heavy. A trench is prepared, and the individual remains are laid in it side by side, thus obviating the necessity of digging and filling in individual graves.

trench knife A knife for hand-to-hand fighting. United States models have combined a stabbing blade with a set of knuckles.

trial An action or process by which some piece of equipment is tested.

trial fire Deliberate gunfire laid on a fixed point or target to determine the corrections for firing data. Trial fire is used to prepare for fire for effect.

triangulation A method of finding a position or location by means of taking bearings with reference to two fixed points a known distance apart, thus obtaining the values of one side and all the angles of a triangle, from which the position can be computed.

triarii The third line in the Roman order of battle.

Tribal 1. A class of British general-purpose frigates of 2,300 tons standard displacement completed in 1961–1964. They have a length of 360 ft, a beam of 42.3 ft, a speed of 28 knots, and a complement of 253 men. They are armed with two 4.5-in. guns, two 40mm antiaircraft guns, one Limbo three-barreled depth-charge mortar, and one helicopter. **2.** A class of British 1,870-ton destroyers completed in 1939. They had a

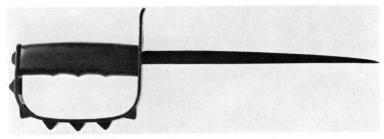

trench knife. (*The Smithsonian Institution.*)

length of 355 ft, a speed of 36.5 knots, a complement of 190 men, and armament consisting of eight 4.7-in. guns and four 21-in. torpedo tubes.

Trident The code name for the overall program to establish a long-range deep-water ocean surveillance system using a variety of active and passive systems. Begun in late 1959, it includes at least three major efforts—Artemis, Caesar, and Colossus—which are highly classified.

trigger A metallic item, part of the firing mechanism of a crossbow or a firearm, designed to release a firing pin or the bow-string by the application of pressure by the finger.

trigger guard A protective device consisting of a curved framework, usually of metal, on a gun or rocket launcher within which a trigger is located.

trigger housing An item, usually of metal, designed to fit into the framework of a carbine, machine gun, pistol, rifle, or the like. It is used to provide a mounting for a trigger.

trigger pull The resistance offered by the trigger of a rifle or other weapon; the force which must be exerted to pull the trigger. Usually expressed in pounds.

trigger squeeze A method of firing a rifle or similar weapon in which the trigger is not pulled, but is squeezed gradually by an independent action of the forefinger.

trimethylene trinitramine Another word for "cyclonite," a powerful high explosive. During World War II it was used in mixture with TNT as a bursting charge for bombs, sea mines, and torpedoes.

trinitrophenol Picric acid. An explosive that was one of the most important of the shell fillers during World War I. It was first used by the Japanese in the Russo-Japanese War and was called by them *shimose*. It is the British lyddite, the French *melinite*, and the Italian *pertite*.

trinitrotoluene TNT, a widely used high-explosive material for bombs, shells, torpedo warheads, etc. It has been an important military explosive since 1904 and is called *trotyle* by the British, *tolite* by the French, and *Sprengmunition-02* by the Germans.

Trinity bomb The Alamogordo bomb.

tripantum A special type of trebuchet having two weights, one fixed and the other adjustable.

trip flare A surface flare which is actuated by, and thus serves as a warning of the approach of, infiltrating enemy troops. It is booby-trapped and, in one type, is attached to a parachute which is projected into the air.

trireme An ancient warship so called because of its three banks of oars. The Athenian trireme had a length of 140 ft, a beam of 20 ft, and a crew of about 225, including 174 rowers, 20 sailors, and a small force of hoplites. It was further armed with a rostrum, a 10-ft ram that protruded from the prow. See **hoplite.**

tritonal An explosive composed of 80 percent TNT and 20 percent powdered aluminum. It was developed and standardized in the United States during World War II. It can be melt-loaded and is used in bombs for its blast effect.

tromblon A French term for a type of blunderbuss.

Tromp A Dutch light cruiser of 3,350 tons standard displacement completed in 1938. It had a speed of 32 knots, a complement of 334 men, and main armament consisting of six 5.9-in. and four 3-in. guns.

troop 1. Troops, or a collective term for soldiers. **2.** Specifically, in the parlance of cavalry, a part of a cavalry squadron. A troop corresponded to an infantry company and was commanded by a captain.

troop-carrying gliders See **military glider.**

trooper A cavalryman.

troops A collective term for uniformed military personnel (usually not applicable

trigger guard. (*The Smithsonian Institution.*)

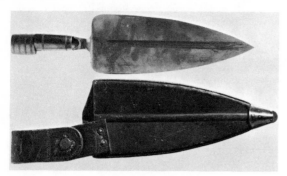

trowel bayonet. (*The Smithsonian Institution.*)

to naval personnel afloat).

troop test See **user test.**

trotyle A British term for TNT.

trou-de-loup A pit, also called a "trap-hole," that is about 6 ft deep and is pointed at the bottom like an inverted cone. Rising from the bottom is a pointed stake.

trowel bayonet A bayonet so made as to be used as an entrenching tool.

true airspeed See **airspeed.**

true altitude The height of an aircraft as measured from mean sea level.

truncheon A short staff or cudgel used as a weapon. It was also a staff of command.

trundleshot A type of old-time ordnance projectile that consisted of a sharpened iron bar with a lead ball toward each end. It turned end over end while in flight.

trunnion One of the two pivots supporting a piece of artillery on its carriage and forming the horizontal axis about which the piece rotates when it is elevated.

trunnion band A metal band provided with trunnions, the band being bolted about some object, especially about an aerial bomb that requires being swung down to clear an obstacle on release from an airplane.

trunnion cradle A part of the carriage of certain cannons; it has branching arms, in the ends of which the trunnions of the gun rest.

trunnion ledge A small shelf on the trun-

nion of a heavy cannon.

trunnion support A supporting pivot for holding a piece of artillery on its carriage and forming the horizontal axis about which the barrel rotates when it is elevated.

Truxton A U.S. nuclear-powered guided-missile frigate (DLGN) of 8,200 tons standard displacement completed in 1967. It has a length of 564 ft, a beam of 58 ft, a speed in excess of 30 knots, and a complement of about 500 men. It is armed with one 5-in. and two 3-in. guns, one twin Terrier or Asroc launcher, two triple torpedo launchers, and two fixed torpedo tubes. It also has facilities for helicopters.

TS The U.S. Army designation for a small tug, variously 65 and 85 ft in length.

T Series During World War II Germany utilized a series of large torpedo boats (*Tor-pedoboote*). They consisted of the following classes: T1-T8, T9-T12, T13-T21, T22-T36, T37-T51, T52-T60, and T61-T72. These ships, produced from 1939 to 1944, ranged in size from 844 to 1,931 tons, with crews from 119 to 223 men. They were typically armed with four 4.1-in. or 5-in. guns and three to eight 21-in. torpedo tubes. Some 20 were lost in action during World War II.

Tsibin KTS-20 A single-wing troop or general transport glider used in World War II by the Soviet Union. Named after P. V. Tsibin, a Russian aircraft designer.

Tu The designation for Soviet aircraft designed by Andrei Nikolaevich Tupolev.

Tu-2 A three- or four-seat twin-engine attack bomber developed for the Soviet Air Force at the end of World War II. It was armed with two 20mm cannons and four machine guns and flew at a maximum speed of 348 mph. Later it was given the NATO code designation "Bat."

Tu-4 See **Bull.**

Tu-7 A four-engine heavy bomber developed at the end of World War II. It was armed with one 20mm cannon and six machine guns and carried a bombload of about

8,000 lb. It had a speed of 280 mph and a range of 2,500 mi.

Tu-14 See **Bosun.**

Tu-16 See **Badger**, sense 1.

Tu-20 See **Bear.**

Tu-22 See **Blinder.**

Tu-70 See **Cart.**

Tu-114 See **Cleat.**

Tu-124 See **Cookpot.**

Tu-134 See **Crusty.**

Tuba A World War II development that consisted of a powerful radar jammer installed on the south coast of England in the spring of 1944. It was aimed at the coast of France and successfully jammed the radar sets (Lichtenstein) of German night fighters.

tube The main part of a gun; the cylindrical piece of metal surrounding the bore. The term "tube" is frequently used in referring to artillery weapons, and "barrel" is more frequently used in referring to small arms.

tuck A thrusting sword with a stiff blade, usually triangular in section.

T.u.F. (Maxim) 12.7mm aircraft machine gun A German recoil-operated air- or water-cooled machine gun with a rate of fire of 400 to 450 rounds per minute. It weighed 84 lb and was fed from a 100-round fabric belt.

TUG A U.S. Army towed universal glider built by Ryan and designed to deliver 4,000-lb payloads into combat areas.

tuille In armor, one of the hinged plates over the thigh.

tulwar, talwar A kind of curved saber or scimitar used in India.

tumbling Concerning missiles and projectiles in flight, turning end over end about the transverse missile axis.

tumbrel A kind of two-wheeled cart once transported with troops and used to carry tools, ammunition, etc.

Turbinlite The World War II British name for a searchlight fitted to an air interceptor aircraft.

turbojet A jet engine whose air is supplied

Truxton. (*U.S. Navy.*)

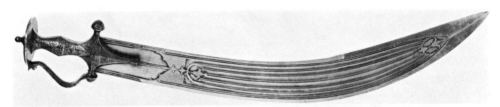

TUG. (*U.S. Army.*)

by a turbine-driven compressor, the turbine being activated by exhaust gases.

turbojet engine A continuous-combustion-type power unit designed to exert thrust; its prime physical characteristics include an air compressor, a combustion chamber or chambers, and a gas turbine. The operating principle is as follows: Atmospheric air is inducted into the unit at its front; the air is then compressed, heated by combustion of a fuel, expanded through the gas turbine, and ejected at high velocity at its rear.

Turkish Mauser 7.65mm rifle Model 1890 This rifle is essentially the same as the Belgian Mauser 7.65mm rifle Model 1889.

Turkish Mauser 7.65mm rifle Model 1893 A slightly modified version of the Spanish Mauser Model 1893. It differs in caliber and in having a magazine cutoff.

Turkish Mauser 7.65mm rifle Model 1903 This rifle is essentially the same as the German Mauser rifle Model 98.

turma A subdivision of the cavalry in a Roman legion. It consisted of 30 men, and later of 32 men. There were 10 turmas in every legion.

turnaround The length of time between arriving at a point and departing from that point. The term is used in this sense for the turnaround of shipping in ports and for aircraft that are refueling and rearming.

turnaround cycle Used in conjunction with vehicles, ships, and aircraft. It comprises the following: loading time at home, time to and from destination, unloading and loading time at destination, unloading time at home, planned maintenance time, and, where applicable, time awaiting facilities.

turn-in point The point at which an aircraft starts to turn from the approach direction to the line of attack.

turnpike A revolving frame with pikes projecting from it; used as a cheval-de-frise.

turret 1. A dome-shaped or cylindrical armored structure containing one or more

tulwar. (*Smithsonian Institution, R. G. Packard Collection.*)

turret, of a Martin B-26 Marauder. (*U.S. Air Force.*)

guns located on forts, warships, airplanes, and tanks. Most turrets are built so that they can be revolved. **2.** In ancient times, a movable tall building used for attacking fortified places. See **tower.**

turret guns Guns 6 in. and larger mounted in a turret or mount.

Twin Mustang The North American F-82 Twin Mustang is a two-seat twin-engine long-range escort fighter and fighter-bomber that consists basically of two Mustang fuselages on a single wing. First flown on April 15, 1945, this aircraft had a maximum speed of 482 mph and was armed with six .50 cal. machine guns and two

2,000-lb bombs or twenty-five 5-in. rockets. (Picture, next page.)

twist (of rifling) The inclination of the spiral grooves (rifling) to the axis of the bore of a weapon. It is expressed as the number of calibers of length in which the rifling makes one complete turn.

two-decker Formerly, a warship with guns on two decks.

Two Spot The NATO code name for a type of Soviet I-band early-warning and surveillance radar.

two-up A formation with two elements disposed abreast; the remaining element or elements are in the rear.

Type IXC40. (*The Imperial War Museum.*)

Twin Mustang. (*U.S. Air Force.*)

Typhoon. (*Hawker Siddeley Aviation Ltd.*)

37mm and one or two 20mm guns. The IXC40 differed in that it had a somewhat greater radius of action and carried snorkel equipment.

Type IXD2 A class of German submarines of 1,616 to 1,804 tons displacement. They had a submerged speed of 7 knots, a complement of 57 men, and armament consisting of six 21-in. torpedo tubes, plus one 4.1-in. deck gun and two antiaircraft guns (one 37mm and one 20mm).

Type XXI A German submarine class of about 1,612 to 1,819 tons displacement. About 140 were produced during World War II. They had a length of 251 ft, a beam of about 22 ft, a surface speed of 15.5 knots (16 knots submerged), and a complement of 57 men. They were armed with six 21-in. torpedo tubes and four 30mm (or 20mm) antiaircraft guns.

Type XXIII A German coastal submarine of 232 to 256 tons displacement, about 50 of which were produced during World War II. They had a length of 112 ft, a beam of 9.75 ft, a surface speed of 9 to 12 knots, and a complement of 14 men. They were armed with two 21-in. torpedo tubes.

Type XXVIIA See **Hecht,** sense 2.

Type XXVIIB See **Seehund,** sense 1.

Typhon A U.S. Navy surface-to-air missile of advanced design for installation on carriers, cruisers, frigates, and destroyers and for use against high-performance aircraft and short-range tactical missiles. It will be equipped with either a nuclear or nonnuclear warhead. Designated as RIM-50/RIM-55.

Typhoon A British single-seat single-engine fighter-bomber developed by Hawker. It was designed in 1938 and was flown operationally in 1941. It was used in a number of roles, the most successful of which was as a rocket-carrying low-level attack aircraft. It was particularly successful in knocking out armor. Powered by a 2,180-hp engine, it flew at a speed of 405 mph. It was armed with four 20mm Hispano cannons and eight 60-lb rocket projectiles.

Type IIA (B, C, and D) A series of German submarine classes used during World War II. They had a displacement of from 254 to 364 tons, a speed of 7 knots submerged, a complement of 25 men, and armament consisting of three 21-in. torpedo tubes and one 20mm antiaircraft gun.

Types VIIC and VIIC41/42 By far the largest classes of submarines developed by Germany for use during World War II, approximately 700 having been produced. They had a displacement of 769 to 871 tons, a length of 220 ft, a beam of 20 ft, a surface speed of 17 knots (7.5 knots submerged), and a complement of 44 men. They were

armed with five 21-in. torpedo tubes and one 3.5-in. deck gun, plus one 37mm and two 20mm antiaircraft guns. The VIIC41/42's differed only in that they had strengthened pressure hulls for deeper diving and carried snorkel equipment.

Types IXC and IXC40 Classes of German World War II submarines built in substantial numbers (over 140) and having a displacement from 1,120 to 1,247 tons. They had a length of 252 ft, a beam of about 22 ft, a surface speed of 18 knots (7 knots submerged), and a complement of 48 men. They were armed with six 21-in. torpedo tubes, plus one 4.1-in. deck gun and one

U-1 through U-12 German coastal-type submarines of 370 tons standard surface displacement built in 1961–1968. They have a length of 142 ft, a beam of 15 ft, a submerged speed of 17 knots, and a complement of 21 men. They are armed with eight torpedo tubes.

U-2 A U.S. high-altitude reconnaissance aircraft. See **WU/U-2A.**

U-6A See **Beaver.**

UAM Underwater-to-air missile.

U-boat From the German *U-boot,* short for *unterseeboot.* A German submarine.

UET A U.S. universal engineering tractor.

Ufag C.I An Austro-Hungarian (Ungarische Flugzeugfabrik A.G.) two-place single-engine observation biplane that went into service early in 1918. It had a speed of 118 mph and was armed with one Schwarzlose machine gun in the rear cockpit.

UGM-27 See **Polaris.**

uhlan Formerly, a skirmisher or scout armed with a lance, pistol, saber, or carbine.

ULMS U.S. Undersea Long-range Missile System.

Ulster A class of British destroyers (later antisubmarine frigates) of 1,710 tons standard displacement completed in 1943. They had a speed of 34 knots, a complement of 180 men, and armament consisting of four 4.7-in. guns, four 40mm and four 20mm antiaircraft guns, and eight 21-in. torpedo tubes.

umbrella A protective cover of airplanes.

umbro The central metal boss of a shield.

unarmed The condition of a fuze (or other firing device) in which the necessary steps to put it in condition to function have not been taken. It is the condition of the fuze when it is safe for handling, storage, and transportation. The fuze is "partially armed" if some, but not all, of the steps have been taken.

unclassified Pertaining to official matter which does not require the application of security safeguards, but the disclosure of which may be subject to control for other reasons.

unconventional warfare Includes the three interrelated fields of guerrilla warfare, evasion and escape, and subversion. Unconventional-warfare operations are conducted within enemy or enemy-controlled territory by predominantly indigenous personnel, usually supported and directed in varying degrees by an external source.

undercarriage A fixed or movable base on which the top carriage of a weapon moves. Also, a landing gear.

underground An organized group of people who carry on some regular operation without effective discovery by those in authority; the network to which these people belong.

undermine Formerly, the process of digging under a fort or other structure with the purpose of causing it to fall down or of setting charges to blow it up.

underwater demolition Destruction or neutralization of underwater obstacles (near a landing beach) which can affect the approach of landing craft. The destruction is normally accomplished by an underwater demolition team.

underwater demolition unit (UDU) Frogmen who do the necessary reconnaissance and demolition work along an enemy beach prior to an amphibious assault.

underwater mine An item designed to be located underwater and exploded by means of propeller vibration, magnetic attraction,

underwater mine, a 1,000-lb Russian-made contact mine. (*U.S. Navy.*)

453

underwater-to-surface missile, the Poseidon. (*U.S. Navy.*)

contact, or remote control.

underwater-mine ship counter A device designed to count the number of ships passing over an underwater mine. It is set to allow detonation after a predetermined number of ships have passed.

underwater obstacle A natural or artificial obstacle located to seaward of the high-water line and wholly or partly submerged. It acts as a barrier or obstruction to the passage of ships, landing ships, craft, vehicles, or torpedoes.

underwater ordnance Munitions designed for use underwater, e.g., torpedoes, underwater mines, and depth charges.

underwater-to-surface missile (USM) A missile designed for launch from a submerged submarine to a surface target.

underwater-to-underwater missile (UUM) A missile launched from a submarine at another submarine.

underway replenishment forces A task force of fleet auxiliaries (consisting of oilers, ammunition ships, stores issue ships, etc.) adequately protected by escorts furnished by the responsible operational commander. The function of this force is to provide underway logistic support for naval forces.

unexploded ordnance An object containing explosives which did not function as intended or an object which contains some type of delayed-action device.

unicorn An old name for a howitzer.

uniform Military uniforms were developed in the seventeenth century and were originally of bright colors so that friend and foe could be distinguished in a battlefield nearly obscured with black-powder smoke.

unit **1.** Any military element whose structure is prescribed by competent authority, such as a table of organization and equipment; specifically, part of an organization. **2.** An organizational title of a subdivision of a group in a task force. **3.** A standard or basic quantity into which an item of supply is divided, issued, or used.

unit aircraft Those aircraft provided an aircraft unit for the performance of a flying mission.

United Nations Service Medal A United Nations decoration awarded military personnel for service in the Korean theater under certain specified conditions.

unit of fire A unit of measure for ammo supply representing a specified number of rounds per weapon.

unload through the muzzle To fire in a safe direction in order to empty a gun of its charge.

unobserved fire Fire for which the points of impact or burst are not observed.

Unryu A class of Japanese aircraft carriers of 17,150 tons displacement completed in 1943. There were to have been six ships in the class, but only two (*Unryu* and *Amagi*) were commissioned and saw service. *Unryu* was sunk by an American submarine in the East China Sea in December 1944. *Amagi* was sunk by U.S. carrier aircraft in Kure dockyard in July 1945. They had flight-deck dimensions of 711.5 by 88.5 ft, a speed of 32 knots, and a complement of about 1,100 men. They carried 65 aircraft.

unseen fire Fire which is continuously aimed at the future position of an aircraft, the aim being derived from radar sources.

unthickened fuel A blend of gasoline and light fuel oils or lubricating oils (without thickener) used as an incendiary fuel in portable flamethrowers.

up **1.** A correction used by an observer or a spotter in time fire to indicate that an increase in height of burst is desired. **2.** A term used in a call for fire to indicate that the target is higher in altitude than the point which has been used as a reference point for the target location.

Uritski A class of Soviet destroyers of 1,150 to 1,417 tons standard displacement completed between 1914 and 1928.

U.S. ¾-ton weapons carrier T124 See **Dodge weapons carrier.**

U.S. 2.36-in. antitank rocket launcher See **bazooka.**

U.S. 2.75-in. aircraft rocket (FFAR) This folding-fin high-explosive rocket has a length of 48.7 in., a weight of 18.65 lb, and a velocity of 2,300 fps. This model is for air-to-air use. The FFAR AT M1 model is designed for air-to-ground used against tanks and other armored vehicles.

U.S. 3-in. antiaircraft gun M3 A World War II weapon with a weight of 8.3 tons and a projectile weight of 15.5 lb. It fired fixed ammunition and had an effective ceiling of 27,900 ft.

U.S. 3-in. antiaircraft gun Model 1918 A World War I weapon with an effective ceiling of about 36,500 ft.

U.S. 3-in. antitank gun M5 A World War II weapon with a weight of 2.4 tons and a projectile weight of 12.65 lb. It fired fixed ammunition and had a range of 15,400 yd.

U.S. 3-in. antitank gun M5. (*U.S. Army.*)

U.S. 3-in. gun T12 This weapon was developed before World War II for use as a tank armament. It fired a projectile weighing 15 lb and had a muzzle velocity of about 2,600 fps.

U.S. 3-in./50 naval gun A U.S. Navy antiaircraft weapon that is typically used in twin mounts. It fires a round that is about 35 in. long and weighs 24 lb (of which the projectile weight is 13 lb). It has a horizontal range of about 14,000 ft and an effective ceiling of 30,200 ft.

U.S. 3.5-in. rocket M28 The M28 and the M28A2 AT rockets have approximately the same specifications. They have a length of 23.6 in., a weight of about 9 lb (1.9 lb of warhead explosive), a velocity of about 325 fps, and a range of 945 yd. They are fixed-fin-stabilized and are used against armored targets.

U.S. 3.5-in. rocket M35 The M35 and the M35A1 AT rockets have approximately the same specifications. They have a length of 23.5 in., a weight of about 7.5 lb (1.6 lb of warhead explosive), a velocity of about 485 fps, and a range of 1,300 yd. They are fixed-fin-stabilized and are used against armored targets.

U.S. 3.5-in. rocket launcher Also called a **bazooka,** which see, this weapon has a length of 60 in., a weight of 12 lb, and a range of 900 yd.

U.S. 4-lb bomb, fragmentation, M83 A small barrel-shaped bomb loaded with about 0.5 lb of explosive filler. It is equipped with spring-loaded propeller blades that deploy and slow the descent of the bomb.

U.S. 4-lb bomb, incendiary, AN-M50A3 This bomb has a length of 21.34 in. It is hexagonal in cross section and measures 1.63 in. across opposite faces of the hexagon. It consists of a magnesium body that is ignited by 10 oz of thermate (which is a mixture of thermite, barium nitrate, and sulfur in an oil binder).

U.S. 4-lb bomb, incendiary, M126 This bomb is identical to the AN-M50A3, except that it has a retractable fin assembly.

U.S. 4.2-in. mortar cannon M30 This is a rifled-bore muzzle-loading weapon intended for high-angle fire; it fires a projectile weighing 29 lb. It has a maximum range of about 6,000 yd and a weight of about 639 lb. The World War II version of the 4.2-in. mortar fired a 24-lb shell up to 4,500 yd.

U.S. 4.5-in. gun This World War II gun had a range of 12 mi and a projectile weight of about 55 lb.

U.S. 4.5-in. multiple rocket launcher A current system consisting of a light, mobile cluster of 25 tubes, each of which fires a 39-lb rocket. It can be hauled by a $\frac{1}{4}$-ton or 4 × 4 truck and has a total weight of 1,530 lb. It is generally followed by a 2½-

U.S. 3-in./50 naval gun. (*U.S. Navy.*)

U.S. 3.5-in. rocket launcher. (*U.S. Army.*)

U.S. 4.2-in. mortar cannon M30. (*U.S. Army.*)

U.S. 4.5-in. multiple rocket launcher. (*U.S. Army.*)

U.S. 5-in./54 antiaircraft gun Mk 45 Mod 0. (*U.S. Navy.*)

U.S. 7.62mm machine gun M60. (*U.S. Army.*)

ton truck carrying ammunition. The range of the rockets is from 2,400 to 9,000 yd.

U.S. 4.5-in. rocket M8 A U.S. aircraft rocket of World War II. It weighed 40 lb and had a maximum velocity of 865 fps. It had a maximum accurate range of about 800 yd, and the weight of its high explosive was 5.1 lb.

U.S. 4.5-in. rocket M16 The M16 and the M16A1 high-explosive rockets have approximately the same specifications. They have a length of 27.81 in., a weight of about 41 lb (5.1 lb of TNT for the M16 warhead and 4 lb of composition B for the M16A1 warhead), a velocity of 940 fps, and a range of 6,000 yd. These rockets, similar in shape to artillery projectiles, are spin-stabilized and are fired from multiple launchers.

U.S. 4.5-in. rocket M20 A spin-stabilized high-explosive rocket similar to the M16 but designed to be fired from expendable rocket launchers.

U.S. 4.5-in. rocket M32 This high-explosive rocket has a length of 30.22 in., a weight of 42 lb (6.1 lb of warhead explosive), a velocity of 1,250 fps, and a range (at 45° elevation) of 9,100 yd. This rocket, similar in shape to an artillery projectile, is spin-stabilized and is fired from a multiple launcher.

U.S. 4.7-in. antiaircraft gun Model 1918 A World War I development with an effective ceiling of 10,000 meters.

U.S. 4.7-in. gun Model 1906 A gun that had a maximum range of about 12,000 yd. It fired a 45-lb high-explosive shell or a 60-lb shrapnel shell.

U.S. 5-in. aircraft rocket (HVAR) This folding-fin high-explosive rocket has a length of 68.6 in., a weight of 134 lb, and a velocity of 1,360 fps. See also **Holy Moses.**

U.S. 5-in./54 antiaircraft gun Mk 42 Mod 9 A U.S. Navy weapon with a weight of 60.4 tons, a maximum rate of fire of 40 rounds per minute, and a projectile weight of 70 lb.

U.S. 5-in./54 antiaircraft gun Mk 45 Mod 0 A U.S. Navy weapon with a weight of 22.1 tons, a maximum rate of fire of 20 rounds per minute, and a projectile weight of 70 lb.

U.S. 5-in. high-velocity rocket (HVAR) An aircraft rocket that has a 7.9-lb TNT burster charge. It can be used effectively against ships, locomotives, light tanks, and pillboxes (it can penetrate 6 ft of concrete).

U.S. 5-in./38 naval gun A weapon that is used in the main batteries aboard destroyers and as an antiaircraft weapon on cruisers and aircraft carriers. It has a range of about 18,000 yd and a rate of fire of 15 to 18 rounds per minute.

U.S. 5-in./54 naval gun A weapon with a horizontal range of about 26,000 yd and an effective ceiling of about 49,000 ft. It fires a 70-lb projectile and has a sustained firing rate of 15 to 18 rounds per minute.

U.S. 5.5-lb antiaircraft bomb See **antiaircraft bomb.**

U.S. 5.56mm rifle M16 An air-cooled gas-operated magazine-fed automatic or semiautomatic shoulder- or hip-fired weapon used by all U.S. services. It has a weight of 7.4 lb, an overall length of 39 in., and a maximum effective range of 460 meters. It has a cyclic rate of fire of 650 to 850 rounds per minute.

U.S. 6-in. coast and railroad gun M1905 A weapon with a weight of 21.2 tons and a projectile weight of 90 lb. It fired separate-loading ammunition and had a range of 14,800 yd.

U.S. 6-in. naval gun A weapon of 47 cal. length that serves in the main batteries of light cruisers. It has a range of 26,100 yd and a rate of fire of 10 rounds per minute.

U.S. 7.2-in. ahead-thrown rocket   An antisubmarine missile with a range of about 200 yd. It was designed for use in a Mark 20 launcher (which launches four) and the Mark 10 (which throws 24 charges ahead of the attacking vessel).

U.S. 7.62mm aircraft machine guns M133 and M134 (Miniguns)   Lightweight aircraft machine guns used by the U.S. Army and Air Force. The M133 is a gas-driven version, and the M134 is electric-motor-driven. It fires 6,000 rounds per minute.

U.S. 7.62mm machine gun M6   M60 machine guns mounted on attack aircraft. In the M6E3 versions, for example, four machine guns are mounted on two power-operated flexible gun mounts for helicopter weaponization. They have a capacity of 2,200 rounds per minute.

U.S. 7.62mm machine gun M60   This weapon is used on a tripod as a heavy machine gun and on a bipod as a light machine gun. The design dates back to the end of World War II and incorporates the belt-feed mechanism of the German MG42 and the operating mechanism of the German FG42 automatic rifle. Although it does not have selective-fire capabilities, it has a low cyclic rate which permits firing single rounds. It is gas-operated and has a cyclic rate of fire of 600 rounds per minute and a muzzle velocity of 2,800 fps. It has an overall length of 43.73 in., a barrel length of 25.6 in., and a weight of 23.05 lb. The mount (M122) weighs 15 lb. The weapon is fed from a disintegrating link belt. The M60C has a maximum range of 3,500 yd.

U.S. 7.62mm rifle M14   This weapon was developed to replace the M1 rifle, the M3A1 submachine gun, the M2 carbine, and the Browning automatic rifle. It is an evolution of the M1, but with many improvements. It has selective semiautomatic or full automatic fire and a cyclic rate of fire of 750 rounds per minute. The overall length is 44.14 in., and it has a barrel length of 22 in. and a weight of 8.7 lb. The weapon utilizes a 20-round detachable box magazine and has a muzzle velocity of 2,800 fps. The M14E2 is a variation produced for use as a squad automatic weapon. It features a full pistol grip and a folding handgrip on the forestock.

U.S. 7.62mm tank machine gun M73   This weapon was developed specifically for use in tanks. Browning-type machine guns were unsatisfactory because of problems with feed mechanisms and long receivers. The M73 is a shorter weapon, has a quick-change barrel, and can be fed from either side. It is recoil-operated with gas assist and has a muzzle velocity of 2,800 fps and a cyclic rate of fire of 450 to 500 rounds per

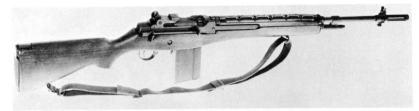

U.S. 7.62mm rifle M14. (*U.S. Army.*)

U.S. 8-in. coast and railroad gun MkVIM3A2. (*U.S. Army.*)

U.S. 8-in. howitzer cannon M2. (*U.S. Army.*)

minute. It weighs 28 lb and has an overall length of 34.75 in. and a barrel length of 22 in. It is fed by a disintegrating link belt and has a range of 3,500 yd.

U.S. 8-in. coast and railroad gun MkVIM3A2   A weapon with a weight of about 51.5 tons and a projectile weight of 240 lb. It fired separate-loading ammunition and had a range of 35,635 yd.

U.S. 8-in. gun M1   A World War II weapon with a weight of 34 tons and a projectile

weight of 240 lb. It fired separate-loading ammunition and had a range of 35,635 yd. The gun was transported in two sections and assembled by cranes at the firing site.

U.S. 8-in. howitzer M1   A World War II weapon with a weight of 16 tons and a projectile weight of 200 lb. It fired separate-loading ammunition and had a range of 18,500 yd.

U.S. 8-in. howitzer cannons M2, M2A1, M2A1E1, and M47   These are mobile field

U.S. 8-in. naval gun, aboard the heavy cruiser U.S.S. *Newport News.* (*U.S. Navy.*)

U.S. 8-in. self-propelled howitzer M110. (*U.S. Army.*)

weapons used to provide heavy, long-range artillery fire. The M2 and M2A1 are mounted on towed carriages; the M2A1E1 and M47 are mounted on self-propelled full-track vehicles. These weapons fire a high-explosive projectile to ranges up to 16,000 yd. The projectiles are loaded with 36.75 lb of TNT or a nuclear warhead. (Picture, preceding page.)

U.S. 8-in. howitzer Model 1918M3 A U.S. howitzer of British design; it fired a 200-lb projectile and had a range of 11,750 yd.

U.S. 8-in. naval gun A weapon of 55 cal. length (440 in.) commonly used in the main batteries of heavy cruisers. It fires an armor-piercing projectile weighing 335 lb, with a powder charge of 78 lb. It has a rate of fire of 10 rounds per minute and a range of 30,000 yd.

U.S. 8-in. self-propelled howitzer M55 A U.S. Army full-track self-propelled howitzer served by a crew of six and having a speed of about 30 mph.

U.S. 8-in. self-propelled howitzer M110 This weapon was introduced in 1962 as a

replacement for the M55. It utilizes the same chassis as the 175mm self-propelled gun M107, and both were introduced at the same time. The M110 has a crew of 13, an overall length of 24 ft 7 in., a total weight of 58,500 lb, and a maximum range of 18,370 yd. It fires separate-loading ammunition (high-explosive, high-explosive spotting, and nuclear). The M110 travels at a top speed of 34.4 mph.

U.S. 8-in. self-propelled howitzer M115 A U.S. Army air-transportable 8-in. howitzer.

U.S. 9mm Parabellum submachine gun UD M. '42 An American weapon manufactured by the Marlin Firearms Company for the United Defense Supply Corp., a U.S. government corporation. It uses a 9mm Parabellum cartridge and is provided with selective full automatic and semiautomatic fire. It is blowback-operated and has a cyclic rate of fire of 700 rounds per minute. It has an overall length of 32.30 in. and a barrel length of 11 in. With a fully loaded 20-round clip the weapon weighs 10 lb. It

has a muzzle velocity of about 1,312 fps. It was designed before World War II by Carl G. Swebilius, the founder of High Standard. An estimated 15,000 were produced during the war years.

U.S. 9.2mm howitzer A British-made weapon used during World War I. It had a range of 13,000 yd.

U.S. 10-in. coast and railroad gun M1900 A weapon with a weight of 245.2 tons and a projectile weight of 617 lb. It fired separate-loading ammunition and had a range of 16,300 yd.

U.S. 10-lb bomb, gas (incapacitating), M138 A small bomb filled with BZ incapacitating gas. See **BZ**.

U.S. 10-lb bomb, gas (nonpersistent), GB, M125A1 This bomb has a length of 12 in. and a diameter of 3.63 in. It is filled with 2.6 lb of GB (sarin), an extremely quick-acting nerve gas.

U.S. 10-lb bomb, incendiary, M74, M74A1 This bomb has a length of 19.5 in. It is hexagonal in cross section and measures 2.9 in. across opposite faces of the hexagon. It is loaded with a 6-oz white phosphorus igniting charge and 2.75 lb of PT1 (a mixture of magnesium with gasoline and other petroleum products thickened with isobutyl methacrylates).

U.S. 11.75-in. rocket (Tiny Tim) This system is essentially a rocket-propelled 500-lb bomb with an armor-piercing head containing 150 lb of TNT.

U.S. 12-gauge shotgun M12 A U.S. Army Winchester riot-type shotgun.

U.S. 12-in. coast and railroad gun M1895 A weapon with a weight of 203.8 tons and a projectile weight of 1,070 lb. It fired separate-loading ammunition and had a range of 27,600 yd.

U.S. 12-in. coast and railroad mortar A weapon with a weight of 82.8 tons and a projectile weight of 700 lb. It fired separate-loading ammunition and had a range of 17,900 yd.

U.S. 12.75-in. rocket-propelled depth charge Also called "Weapon Alpha," this antisubmarine surface-to-underwater system has a range of about 1,000 yd.

U.S. 14-in. coast and railroad gun M1909 A weapon with a weight of 1,108.3 tons and a projectile weight of 1,660 lb. It fired separate-loading ammunition and had a range of 22,800 yd.

U.S. 16-in. coast and railroad gun MkIIM1 A weapon with a weight of 800.8 tons and a projectile weight of 2,240 lb. It fired separate-loading ammunition and had a range of 45,100 yd.

U.S. 16-in. coast gun Model 1919 A barbette-carriage-mounted gun with a barrel length of 70 ft, a projectile weight of 2,340 lb, and a range of 31 mi.

U.S. 16-in. howitzer Model 1920 A weapon that was barbette-carriage-mounted and had a range of over 15 mi.

U.S. 16-in. naval gun A weapon with a typical length of 50 cal. (about 800 in.) that fired a 2,700-lb projectile and utilized a 650-lb powder charge.

U.S. 20-lb bomb, fragmentation, M41A1 This bomb is constructed of a thin tubular sleeve holding a steel fragmenting coil. It has a length of 22.4 in. and a diameter of 3.64 in. It contains 2.7 lb of TNT or 2.57 lb of amatol.

U.S. 20-lb bomb M41 The standard U.S. 20-lb fragmentation bomb used in World War II.

U.S. 20mm aircraft gun AN-M2 A weapon whose operation is similar to that of the M3.

U.S. 20mm automatic aircraft gun AN-M2 The Hispano-Suiza Birkigt 20mm aircraft cannon Type 404 as manufactured in the United States during World War II.

U.S. 20mm automatic aircraft gun M3 A blowback- and gas-operated weapon with a weight of 95.5 lb, an overall length of 77.7 in., a cyclic rate of fire of 650 to 800 rounds per minute, and a range of 5,900 yd.

U.S. 20mm Gatling gun M12 SUU-16A The U.S. Army and Air Force Vulcan pod for the 20mm Gatling gun.

U.S. 20mm Gatling gun M61 The rapid-fire 20mm Vulcan aircraft gun. This electrically driven rotating six-barreled weapon fires 100 rounds a second. The weight of the weapon is 300 lb, and the length is about 72 in. It has a range of about 4 mi.

U.S. 20mm gun Mk 11 Mod 5 A twin 20mm gun system for use on aircraft and also on ground vehicles. Introduced in 1966, it has a firing rate of either 700 rounds per minute or 4,200 rounds per minute and a range of 950 meters.

U.S. 20mm gun pod Mk 4 Mod 0 A self-contained and self-powered 20mm gun system that utilizes twin guns. They have a firing rate of either 700 or 4,200 rounds per minute and a range of 950 meters. They are used on various aircraft of the U.S. Navy and Marine Corps and were introduced in 1966.

U.S. 20mm naval gun The Navy typically uses 20mm antiaircraft guns in twin mounts. The gun fires from a magazine containing 60 rounds and has a cyclic rate of fire of 450 rounds per minute. It has a range of about 2,000 yd.

U.S. 21-in. torpedo A World War II torpedo with a weight of 2,215 lb, a warhead weight of 600 lb (TNT), a speed of 46 knots, and a range of 4,500 yd.

U.S. .22 cal. rifle M12 M12 is used throughout the U.S. services to refer to a .22 cal. rifle.

U.S. 23-lb bomb, fragmentation, M40A1 This is a parachute-type bomb designed for assembly in clusters. It has a length of 30.15 in. and a diameter of 4.37 in. It contains

U.S. 12-in. coast gun, destroyed at Corregidor at the beginning of World War II. (*U.S. Army.*)

U.S. 14-in. coast and railroad gun M1909. (*U.S. Army.*)

U.S. 16-in. coast gun Model 1919. (*U.S. Army.*)

U.S. 20mm Gatling gun M61. (*U.S. Army.*)

U.S. .30 cal. aircraft machine gun M2 (Browning). (*U.S. Air Force.*)

U.S. .30 cal. carbine M1. (*U.S. Army.*)

U.S. .30 cal. machine gun M1917A1 (Browning). (*U.S. Army.*)

2.7 lb of explosive.

U.S. 23-lb bomb M40 The standard U.S. 23-lb fragmentation bomb used in World War II.

U.S. .30 cal. aircraft machine gun M2 (Browning) This weapon is recoil-operated and has a cyclic rate of fire of 1,000 to 1,350 rounds per minute. It has an overall length of 39.9 in. and a barrel length of 23.9 in. The fixed-gun version weighs 21.5 lb, and the flexible-gun version weighs 23 lb. It utilizes a disintegrating link belt and has a muzzle velocity of 2,800 fps. It is air-cooled.

U.S. .30 cal. automatic pistol Model 1918 See **Pedersen device.**

U.S. .30 cal. Browning machine guns Numerous models of Browning machine guns in this caliber have been employed by U.S. forces for infantry, tank, cavalry, general-purpose, and aircraft uses. A few of the model numbers have included the M1918,

the M1919 and its numerous variations, the M1921, M1922, and the M2. There were both air-cooled and water-cooled models.

U.S. .30 cal. carbine M1 This weapon was developed to replace the pistols in use by noncommissioned officers, special troops, and company-grade officers. Over 7 million of these weapons were produced during World War II, more than any other U.S. weapon. The carbine fires a different cartridge from that fired by the M1 rifle. Also, none of its parts are interchangeable. The weapon is gas-operated and semiautomatic and utilizes 15- or 30-round detachable box magazines. It has an overall length of 35.6 in., a barrel length of 18 in., and a weight of 5.5 lb. It has a muzzle velocity of 1,970 fps and an effective range of 300 yd.

U.S. .30 cal. carbine M1A1 The paratrooper model of the M1 carbine, this weapon is equipped with a folding-type metal buttstock. With the stock folded, the carbine has an overall length of 25.4 in. The weight is 6.19 lb.

U.S. .30 cal. carbine M2 This weapon has the same characteristics as the M1 carbine, but it is capable of both semiautomatic and full automatic fire. It has a cyclic rate of fire of 750 to 775 rounds per minute.

U.S. .30 cal. carbine M3 This weapon is an M2 carbine with a special receiver designed to be used with an infrared sniperscope.

U.S. .30 cal. machine gun (Benét-Mercié) Model 1909 See **Benét-Mercié 8mm machine gun Model 1909.**

U.S. .30 cal. machine gun Model 1904 The American designation for the **Maxim machine gun,** which see.

U.S. .30 cal. machine gun Model 1915 (Vickers) An American designation for a type of **Maxim machine gun,** which see.

U.S. .30 cal. machine gun Model 1917 For details of this weapon see **Lewis machine gun.** The United States used three ground models and four aircraft models of the Lewis in caliber .30/06.

U.S. .30 cal. machine gun M1917A1 (Browning) This is a recoil-operated machine gun with an overall length of 38.5 in., a barrel length of 24 in., and a weight of 41 lb (with water). The mount weighs 53.15 lb. The weapon has a cyclic rate of fire of 450 to 600 rounds per minute and a muzzle velocity of about 2,800 fps. It is fed by a 250-round fabric belt or disintegrating link belt. This weapon is an improved version of the Model 1917, which was invented by John Browning in 1917 and used by American forces in World War I. The M1917A1 was the standard battalion-level rifle caliber machine gun used by the United States in World War II.

U.S. .30 cal. machine gun Model 1918 (Chauchat) See **Chauchat 8mm machine gun Model 1915.**

U.S. .30 cal. machine gun M1919A4 (Browning) This weapon evolved from a design developed after World War I. It is most often used in two roles, as a flexible gun and as a fixed gun. The flexible gun was used mostly as an infantry company-level gun. The fixed gun was widely used on World War II armored vehicles. It is recoil-operated and has a cyclic rate of fire of 400 to 500 rounds per minute, a muzzle velocity of 2,800 fps, and a feed device consisting of a fabric belt or disintegrating link belt. It is 41 in. long and has a barrel length of 24 in. and a weight of 31 lb.

U.S. .30 cal. machine gun M1919A6 (Browning) A modification of the M1919A4 made during World War II in an effort to evolve a weapon with more tactical flexibility. The tripod mount was eliminated, and a bipod, shoulder stock, and carrying handle were added. The 1919A6 also has a lighter barrel and a higher cyclic rate of fire.

U.S. .30 cal. machine gun M37 A U.S. Army machine gun for tank and vehicle use. See **U.S. .30 cal. tank machine gun M37 (Browning).**

U.S. .30 cal. machine guns Model 1909 and Model 1910 and Mark I and Mark I Mod I Machine guns of the **Hotchkiss** design, which see, as used in caliber .30/06 by the U.S. Army (Models 1909 and 1910) and the U.S. Navy (Mark I and Mark I Mod I).

U.S. .30 cal. rifle (Johnson M1941) This is a recoil-operated semiautomatic rifle with an overall length of 45.87 in., a barrel length of 22 in., and a weight of 9.5 lb. It uses a 10-round rotary-type nondetachable magazine and has a muzzle velocity of about 2,770 fps. Quantities of this weapon were used by the U.S. Marines for a limited period of time during World War II.

U.S. .30 cal. rifle M1 (Garand semiautomatic rifle) This rifle was standardized in the United States in 1936. A total of 4,040,000 were manufactured during World War II, and some 600,000 were made after the war. It is a gas-operated semiautomatic rifle with an overall length of 43.6 in., a barrel length of 24 in., and a weight of 9.5 lb. It has a muzzle velocity of 2,805 fps and an effective range of 500 yd and uses an eight-round nondetachable box magazine. The M1C version was a sniper rifle adopted in 1944. The M1D was also a sniper version. The M1 was replaced by the M14 in 7.62mm caliber.

U.S. .30 cal. rifle Model 1903 (Springfield) This rifle, often known as the "03 Springfield," has an action that is basically a modification of the Mauser Model 98 action. It is a bolt-action rifle with an overall length of 43.2 in., a barrel length of 24 in., and a weight of 8.69 lb. It has a muzzle velocity of 2,805 fps and

U.S. .30 cal. machine gun M1919A6 (Browning), on bipod mount. (*U.S. Army.*)

U.S. .30 cal. rifle M1 (Garand semiautomatic rifle) shown with the inventor, John C. Garand. (*U. S. Army.*)

U.S. .30 cal. rifle Model 1903 (Springfield). (*U.S. Army.*)

utilizes a five-round nonremovable magazine. It remained standard until the Model 1903A1 was adopted in 1929.

U.S. .30 cal. rifle Model 1903A1 This version of the Model 1903 rifle was adopted in 1929. It has a pistol-grip stock and a few other minor modifications. A total of 1,295,000 of the Models 1903 and 1903A1 were produced at Springfield, Rock Island, and Remington Arms.

U.S. .30 cal. rifle Model 1903A3 A version of the Model 1903 that was designed to simplify production. It was adopted in

1942, and a total of 945,846 were manufactured.

U.S. .30 cal. rifle Model 1903A4 The sniper version of the M1903A3. This rifle was adopted in 1942, and some 26,500 were produced. It utilized the M73B1 (Weaver 330C) 2.5-power telescopic sight.

U.S. .30 cal. rifle Model 1917 (Enfield) This weapon has an overall length of 46.3 in., a barrel length of 26 in., and a weight of 8.18 lb. It has a five-round nonremovable box magazine and a muzzle velocity of 2,830 fps. The design originated from the

U.S. 37mm antiaircraft gun M1A1. (*U.S. Army.*)

U.S. 37mm antitank gun M3. (*U.S. Army.*)

British-designed .303 cal. P14 Enfield rifle, and the weapon was produced in quantity when the United States entered World War I.

U.S. .30 cal. tank machine gun M37 (Browning)   During World War II the need for an improved tank machine gun was recognized. The 1919 Browning fed only from one side and had a receiver that was too long. Modifications were made in the feed mechanism, and the resulting weapon was called the "T153." In 1953 this was standardized as the M37. This weapon has an overall length of 41.75 in., a barrel length of 24 in., and a weight of 31 lb. It has a cyclic rate of fire of 400 to 500 rounds per minute and is fed from a disintegrating link belt.

U.S. .30/40 rifles Krag-Jörgensen M1892, M1896, and M1898   The U.S. versions of the Norwegian military rifle. The M1892 had an overall length of 49.14 in., a barrel length of 30 in., and a weight of 9.35 lb. The M1896 had the same overall length, but the weight was 9.94 lb. The Model 1898 differed only in the bolt-handle seat and the rear sight.

U.S. 37mm aircraft cannon M9   See **Browning 37mm aircraft cannon M9.**

U.S. 37mm antiaircraft gun M1A1   A World War II weapon with a weight of about 2.5 tons and a projectile weight of 1.34 lb. It fired fixed ammunition and had an effective ceiling of 12,000 ft.

U.S. 37mm antitank gun M3   This gun, developed in the late 1930s, was 6 ft 10.5 in. long, weighed 191 lb (912 lb with carriage), and had a range of about 8,000 yd. It fired fixed ammunition (with a projectile weight of 1.61 lb) at the rate of 25 rounds per minute.

U.S. 37mm antiaircraft gun M1A1   A rapid-fire weapon mounted on a combination gun and motor carriage. Although it can be employed against ground targets, it is designed primarily for antiaircraft fire. The HE-T round (high-explosive with tracer) has a muzzle velocity of 2,600 fps and a range of 3,500 yd and is used for antiaircraft fire. The APC-T round (armor-piercing capped with tracer) has a muzzle velocity of 2,050 fps and a range of 5,790 yd and is used against light armor and similar targets.

U.S. 37mm gun M5   A pre-World War II weapon that fired a projectile weighing 1.91 lb and had a muzzle velocity of about 2,550 fps. It was employed on the T1E2 light tank.

U.S. 37mm gun M6   A tank weapon of World War II, this gun fired an armor-piercing projectile weighing 1.9 lb and had a muzzle velocity of 2,600 fps.

U.S. 40mm antiaircraft gun (Bofors)   Originally produced by the Swedish firm of Bofors, this was an automatic gun that fired a 2-lb projectile at the rate of 120 rounds per minute to altitudes up to 3 mi. There were both air-cooled and water-cooled models.

U.S. 40mm antiaircraft gun carriage M5   A weapon designed specifically for air transport during World War II. It consisted of a redesigned 40mm antiaircraft gun carriage M2A1. It weighed considerably less, and its width was decreased to permit passage through the doorways of the transport aircraft (C-46, C-47, and C54).

U.S. 40mm antiaircraft gun M1   A World War II weapon with a weight of 2.8 tons and a projectile weight of 2.06 lb. It fired fixed ammunition and had an effective ceil-

U.S. 40mm grenade launcher M79 This weapon is capable of destroying bunkers, machine-gun nests, and small troop concentrations at ranges up to 400 meters. It fires a 9-oz high-explosive shell and has a length of 28.6 in. and a weight of 6 lb 2 oz. It is a break-open-type weapon similar to a shotgun.

U.S. 40mm grenade launcher M75 A U.S. Army grenade launcher that fires 220 rounds per minute at ranges up to 2,000 meters. It is often mounted in remote-control turrets (M5) for helicopter use.

U.S. 40mm gun cannons M1, M1A1, M2, M2A1, and Mk1 These 40mm guns are rapid-fire recoil-operated automatic weapons intended primarily for antiaircraft fire. They may also be used against ground targets. The weapons fire fixed ammunition in rapid bursts of automatic fire at the rate of 120 rounds per minute. They can also operate on single fire. The HE-T round (high-explosive with tracer) has a muzzle velocity of 2,870 fps and a range to tracer burnout of 4,300 yd and is used for firing against aircraft. The HEI-T round (high-explosive incendiary with tracer) has a muzzle velocity of 2,890 fps and a range to tracer burnout of 4,300 yd and is used for firing against aircraft. The AP-T round (armor-piercing with tracer) has a muzzle velocity of 2,870 fps and a range of 9,600 yd and is used for firing against armored and similar targets.

U.S. 40mm naval gun The Navy typically uses 40mm antiaircraft guns in twin mounts or in quad mounts. A complete round for this weapon weighs about 5 lb, with the projectile itself weighing about 2 lb. Projectiles with self-destructive mechanisms have a range of 5,000 yd; without self-destructive mechanisms, they have a range of 11,000 yd.

U.S. 40mm self-propelled antiaircraft weapon M42 A twin 40mm weapon developed for use against low-flying aircraft. Also called "Duster." It was replaced by Mauler.

U.S. 40mm self-propelled twin antiaircraft gun M42 This system entered service in 1953 and consists of a full-track armored vehicle mounting two 40mm Bofors guns. The system has an overall length of 20 ft 9 in., a weight of 49,500 lb, a road speed of 45 mph, a crew of four, and a range of 9,000 yd.

U.S. .44 cal. pistol Model 1847 This pistol, also called the "Walker-Colt Dragoon," was a six-shot percussion revolver that utilized a combustible envelope cartridge.

U.S. .45 cal. automatic pistol M1911A1 See **Colt .45 cal. Government Model 1911, 1911A1.**

U.S. .45 cal. flare projector This was a single-shot smoothbore pistol produced

from stampings and having a barrel made of seamless steel tubing. By August of 1942 the Guide Lamp Division of General Motors had produced 1 million of these. The weapon was chambered for the .45 cal. M1911 automatic pistol cartridge, and after firing, the empty case was extracted with a wooden rod or a pencil. Designed to be dropped into enemy-occupied Allied countries, the pistol was packed with a wooden rod, 10 cartridges, and an instruction sheet. The entire waterproofed kit cost the U.S. $2.10.

U.S. .45 cal. pistol Model 1874 A six-shot revolver manufactured by Colt. It utilized metallic cartridges.

U.S. .45 cal. pistol Model 1875 A pistol that was also called the "Smith & Wesson Schofield revolver." It utilized reloadable brass cartridges. The cylinder held six cartridges.

U.S. .45 cal. rifle Model 1873 This was a Springfield-built breechloading rifle in general use during the Indian wars.

U.S. .45 cal. submachine guns M3 and M3A1 American weapons designed to use the .45 cal. ACP cartridge and capable of

U.S. 40mm antiaircraft gun (Bofors). (U.S. Army.)

U.S. 40mm grenade launcher M79. (U.S. Army.)

U.S. 40mm self-propelled twin antiaircraft gun M42. (U.S. Army.)

U.S. .45 cal. submachine gun M3. (*U.S. Army.*)

U.S. .50 cal. antiaircraft machine gun M2. (*U.S. Army.*)

U.S. .50 cal. multiple machine-gun mount M55. (*U.S. Army.*)

full automatic fire only. They are blow-back-operated and have a cyclic rate of fire of 350 to 450 rounds per minute. With the wire stock extended they have a length of 29.80 in. The barrel length is 8 in. With a fully loaded 30-round magazine the weapons weigh 10.25 lb. The approximate muzzle velocity is 920 fps. They were introduced in 1942. The M3A1 is a simplified, improved version of the M3 and was adopted as standard in December 1944. The weapon is all metal, fabricated mainly of stamped parts, and could be produced cheaply and quickly. Approximately 646,000 of the M3 and M3A1 submachine guns were produced during World War II. During the period of the Korean conflict another 33,200 were produced. They were nicknamed "grease gun" because of their similarity to one.

U.S. .50 cal. aircraft machine gun M2
This weapon was standardized in 1933 and has the feature that it can be fed from either side. It is recoil-operated and has a cyclic rate of fire of 750 to 850 rounds per minute and a muzzle velocity of 2,840 fps. It has an overall length of 56.25 in., a barrel length of 36 in., and a weight of 61 lb. It is fed from a disintegrating link belt. This weapon had a level of reliability and performance unmatched by any foreign machine gun. Nearly 2 million M2 machine guns of all types (i.e., aircraft, heavy-barrel, and water-cooled antiaircraft) were manufactured.

U.S. .50 cal. aircraft machine gun M3   A modification of the M2 to achieve a higher rate of fire. It has a cyclic rate of fire of 1,150 to 1,250 rounds per minute and a muzzle velocity of 2,840 fps. It has an overall length of 57.25 in., a barrel length of 36 in., and a weight of 68.75 lb. It utilizes a disintegrating link belt and has an effective range up to about 1,000 yd.

U.S. .50 cal. antiaircraft machine gun M2   Adopted in 1933, this weapon is an improved version of the 1921A1. It was used throughout World War II on various single and double antiaircraft mounts. It has an overall length of 66 in., a barrel length of 45 in., and a weight (with water) of 121 lb. The M3 antiaircraft mount weighs 401 lb. The cyclic rate of fire of this machine gun is 500 to 650 rounds per minute, and the muzzle velocity is 2,930 fps. It is fed from a disintegrating link belt.

U.S. .50 cal. antiaircraft machine gun M1921A1   This weapon is a modification of the M1921, a scaled-up version of the Browning Model 1917 water-cooled gun. It has an overall length of 56 in., a barrel length of 36 in., and a weight (without water) of 79 lb. It has a cyclic rate of fire of 500 rounds per minute and is fed from a 250-round fabric belt or disintegrating link belt. This weapon was declared obsolete in 1944.

U.S. .50 cal. heavy machine gun M2 A variation of the .50 cal. aircraft and antiaircraft M2 machine guns. During World War II, some 2 million M2's were produced.

U.S. .50 cal. multiple machine-gun mount M55 A weapon designed specifically for air transport during World War II. It consisted of four heavy-barreled .50-cal. machine guns in a power-operated turret. It was mounted on a two-wheeled trailer and could be carried in either a CG-4A glider or a C-47 plane.

U.S. .50 cal. tank machine gun M85 A U.S. Army tank machine gun for turret use against ground and air targets.

U.S. 50-lb gas (incapacitating) generator M16 This unit consists of 42 incapacitating BZ canisters M6 packaged in a pail and provided with a fuse and a parachute assembly. Each M6 canister is a cylindrical sheet-metal container approximately $2\frac{1}{2}$ in. in diameter and $4\frac{1}{2}$ in. high. It is filled with a solid mixture of incapacitating BZ. A central cylindrical hole in the mixture is coated with a starter mixture.

U.S. .54 cal. pistol Model 1805 The first pistol to be produced by a U.S. government establishment (the National Armory at Harpers Ferry). It was a single-shot flintlock pistol that fired a $\frac{1}{2}$-oz ball.

U.S. .54 cal. pistol Model 1842 A percussion-lock pistol designed at Springfield Armory. Henry Aston, of Middletown, Conn., received a contract in 1845 to produce 30,000 of these pistols. It fired a ball weighing $\frac{1}{2}$ oz.

U.S. 57mm antitank gun M1 A World War II weapon with a weight of 1.3 tons and a projectile weight of 6.28 lb. It fired fixed ammunition and had a range of 10,000 yd.

U.S. 57mm gun M3 A World War II gun used for tank armament. The muzzle velocity was about 2,800 fps, and the projectile weight was about 6.25 lb.

U.S. 57mm gun motor carriage T48 A World War II self-propelled gun that was produced exclusively for Russia under lend-lease. It was introduced in 1942, had a crew of five, and was armed with one 57mm gun M1.

U.S. 57mm recoilless rifle A World War II weapon with a weight of 45 lb and a projectile weight of 2.75 lb. It fired fixed ammunition and had a range of 4,350 yd.

U.S. 57mm recoilless rifles M18, M18A1, and T15E16 These weapons are designed for direct fire from a tripod mount or the shoulder. They are equipped with a manually operated breech mechanism and a percussion firing mechanism. They fired a canister cartridge that has a range of 175 ft. The high-explosive cartridge has a range of 4,930 yd, while the HEAT (high-explosive antitank) round has a range of 4,860 yd. The weapons have a weight of 44 lb 7 oz

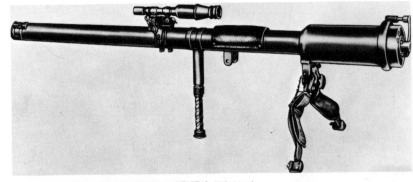

U.S. 57mm recoilless rifles M18, M18A1, and T15E16. (*U.S. Army.*)

and a length of 62 in.

U.S. .58 cal. musket Model 1861 A muzzle-loading percussion musket in general use during the Civil War.

U.S. .58 cal. rifled carbine Model 1855 A percussion carbine developed at Springfield Armory to use the minié bullet.

U.S. 60mm mortar M2 A weapon with a length of $28\frac{5}{8}$ in., a weight of 42 lb (including mount), and a maximum range of 1,990 yd. It has a sustained rate of fire of 18 rounds per minute. (For short periods it can be rapid-fired at the rate of 35 rounds per minute.)

U.S. 60mm mortar M19 A weapon with a length of $32\frac{1}{4}$ in., a weight of about 46 lb, and a range of 2,350 yd. It has a sustained rate of fire of 18 rounds per minute.

U.S. 66mm antitank missile Also called "Law," this is an antitank rocket with a range of 500 to 600 yd.

U.S. .69 cal. musket Model 1763 A muzzle-loading flintlock musket of French design. It was in general use during the Revolutionary War. The total length of this weapon is 5 ft (with bayonet, 6 ft).

U.S. .69 cal. pistol Model 1799 A single-shot flintlock pistol made by Simeon North of Berlin, Conn., and copied from the French Model 1799 pistol.

U.S. 75mm antiaircraft weapon See **Sky-sweeper.**

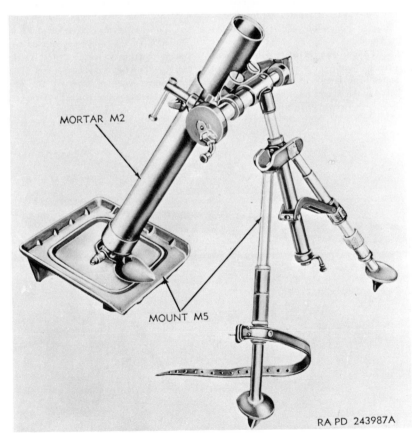

MORTAR M2

MOUNT M5

RA PD 243987A

U.S. 60mm mortar M2. (*U.S. Army.*)

U.S. 75mm pack howitzer M1. (*U.S. Army.*)

U.S. 75mm field gun Model 1916 The first attempt to improvise an antiaircraft gun resulted when this gun was mounted on a 2½-ton White truck (designated "antiaircraft truck mount 1917"). This weapon fired a 15-lb projectile to an effective altitude of 6,000 meters.

U.S. 75mm gun M2 A World War II-era tank gun with a projectile weight of 14.4 lb and a muzzle velocity of about 1,850 fps.

U.S. 75mm gun M6 A World War II gun that was specially developed for tank use. The projectile weight is 14.4 lb, and the muzzle velocity is about 2,000 fps. It uses the same ammunition as the M2 and M3 tank guns.

U.S. 75mm gun M1897 The famous French 75mm gun as used by the United States. The length of the gun was 34.5 cal., and the weight was 1,015 lb. This light field-artillery piece had a range of 13,500 yd.

U.S. 75mm gun cannon M3 The 75mm gun cannon M3 is a tank-mounted low-trajectory-type weapon. The breechblock opens automatically during recoil and closes automatically when a cartridge is loaded into the weapon. The high-explosive cartridge is used primarily for fragmentation, blast, and mining. The projectile has a bursting charge consisting of 1.49 lb of TNT. It has a muzzle velocity of 1,500 fps and a range of 11,285 yd. The reduced-charge high-explosive round has a range of 6,990 yd, and a supercharged high-explosive round has a range of about 14,000 yd. The APC-T (armor-piercing capped with tracer) cartridge is used against ground targets, primarily armored materiel. It has a maximum range of 4,250 yd. The AP-T (armor-piercing with tracer) has a range of 5,000 yd.

U.S. 75mm gun cannon (T83E1) This is an autoloading gun cannon which is used primarily as an antiaircraft weapon. It can be utilized, however, against ground targets. Because the chamber of this weapon differs from that of other 75mm weapons, the ammunition for it is not interchangeable with that for other types of 75mm weapons. The high-explosive cartridge is intended principally for fragmentation, blast, or mining effect against both air and ground targets. It has a muzzle velocity of 2,800 fps, a maximum horizontal range of 14,415 yd, and a maximum vertical range of 10,000 yd.

U.S. 75mm howitzer M1 A World War II weapon with a weight of 1,340 lb and a projectile weight of 14.6 lb. It fired fixed ammunition and had a range of 9,600 yd.

U.S. 75mm howitzer M1897A4 A World War II weapon with a weight of 1.7 tons and a projectile weight of 14.6 lb. It fired fixed ammunition and had a range of 13,600 yd.

U.S. 75mm pack howitzer M1 This howitzer, standardized in 1927, had a range of 9,760 yd, weighed 1,269 lb in firing position, and fired a projectile weighing 14 lb. It was widely used in World War II.

U.S. 75mm pack howitzer cannon M1A1 This is a general-purpose towed light field-artillery weapon that can be used for either direct or indirect fire. The weapon can be readily disassembled into major components either for packing by animal or for airborne operations. The high-explosive round has a range of 9,620 yd. The HEAT-T (high-explosive antitank with tracer) round has a range of 3,000 yd.

U.S. 75mm radar-equipped automatic antiaircraft gun See **Skysweeper.**

U.S. 75mm recoilless rifle A World War II weapon with a weight of 115 lb and a projectile weight of 14.4 lb. It fired fixed ammunition and had a range of 7,000 yd.

U.S. 75mm recoilless rifles M20 and T21E12 These are air-cooled single-loading weapons designed for direct fire from a tripod mount. The high-explosive cartridge has a range of 6,960 yd, and the HEAT (high-explosive antitank) cartridge has a range of 7,300 yd. The weapon has a weight of 114 lb and a length of 6 ft 10 in.

U.S. 76mm gun cannons M32 and M48 These are lightweight high-velocity tank and antitank weapons. The gun cannon M32 provides the major armament for 76mm full-track combat tanks M41 and M41A1. The gun cannon M48 is employed on a two-wheeled gun carriage. Cartridges include canister (which fires a cone-shaped pattern of steel balls) with a range of 170 yd, HVAP-T (hypervelocity armor-piercing antitank with tracer) with a range of 2,190 yd, AP-T (armor-piercing with tracer) with

U.S. 75mm recoilless rifle. (*U.S. Army.*)

a range of 16,080 yd, HE (high-explosive) with a range of 15,680 yd, and HVAP-T (hypervelocity armor-piercing with tracer) with a range of 23,630 yd. The gun has a weight of 1,425 lb and a length of 192 in.

U.S. 76mm gun motor carriage See **Hell-cat**, sense 3.

U.S. 81mm mortar M1 This weapon has a length of about 50 in., a weight (with baseplate) of 89 lb 8 oz, and a maximum range of 3,300 yd. It can be fired at the rate of 30 rounds per minute.

U.S. 81mm mortars M29 and M29E1 Weapons with a length of 51 in., a weight of 76 lb, and a maximum range of 3,885 yd. They have a normal rate of fire of 18 rounds per minute (and a maximum rate of 30 rounds per minute).

U.S. 81mm mortar Stokes-Brandt M1 A mortar adopted in the late 1930s. It had a total weight of 91.5 lb and a maximum range (with a 7.5-lb shell) of 3,250 yd.

U.S. 90-lb bomb, fragmentation, M82 This bomb is constructed of spirally wound wire. It has a length of 28 in. and a diameter of 6.06 in. It contains approximately 87 lb of explosive.

U.S. 90mm antiaircraft gun M1A1 This weapon, developed during World War II, fires a 24-lb projectile to an effective ceiling of about 40,500 ft. It is mounted on an outrigger platform and weighs 2,370 lb. It has a length of 192 in. and fires at the rate of 23 to 28 rounds per minute.

U.S. 90mm gun cannons M36, M41, M54, M1, and M2 series The 90mm gun cannons M36 and M41 are used as tank weapons, and the M54 is employed as an antitank weapon on a self-propelled vehicle. The ammunition for all three of these weapons is interchangeable. All rounds authorized for the M1 and M2 series gun cannons (except antiaircraft rounds) can be fired in the M36, M41, and M54 weapons. The M1 and M2 weapons are used primarily as antiaircraft weapons, and the ammunition for the M36, M41, and M54 *cannot* be used in them. The APERS-T cartridge is intended for antipersonnel use at both close and long range. It is also effective against personnel in dense foliage. The projectile body is loaded with 4,100 light-grain steel fléchettes and has an effective range of 328 yd. There is a canister round with a range of 440 yd, a high-explosive round with a range of 19,375 yd, an HE-T (high-explosive with tracer) round with a range of 16,800 yd, a HEAT (high-explosive anti-tank with tracer) round with a range of 13,010 yd, an AP-T (armor-piercing with tracer) round with a range of 21,400 yd, and an HVAP-T (hypervelocity armor-piercing with tracer) round with a range of 15,130 yd.

U.S. 90mm gun T-7 A World War II tank weapon with a muzzle velocity of 2,800 fps

and a projectile weight of 24.1 lb.

U.S. 90mm recoilless rifle M67 This weapon is designed for direct fire from the ground or the shoulder. It employs a percussion-type firing mechanism. The projectile, fin-stabilized in flight, has a range of 438 yd (HE) and 440 yd (HEAT). The weapon has a length of 4 ft and a weight of 35 lb.

U.S. 90mm self-propelled gun M36 This system was introduced in 1943. It had a crew of five and was armed with one 90mm gun M3, caliber length 53, and one .50 cal. machine gun M2. It was the only Allied vehicle to carry a 90mm gun into action during World War II.

U.S. 90mm self-propelled gun M56 A U.S. Army self-propelled full-track 90mm gun that is air-transportable and provides troops with a mobile antitank weapon. It has a crew of four. It was replaced by the **General Sheridan**, which see.

U.S. 100-lb bomb, fragmentation cluster, AN-M1A2 A bomb consisting of six 20-lb fragmentation bombs AN-M4A1 in a special cluster adapter.

U.S. 100-lb bomb, fragmentation cluster, AN-M4A2 A bomb consisting of three 23-lb fragmentation bombs M40A1 in a special cluster adapter.

U.S. 100-lb bomb, fragmentation cluster, M28A2 A bomb consisting of twenty-four 4-lb fragmentation bombs M83 in a special cluster adapter.

U.S. 100-lb bomb, general-purpose, M30 The standard U.S. 100-lb demolition bomb used in World War II.

U.S. 100-lb bomb, general-purpose, AN-M30A1 This bomb has a length of 40.26 in. and a diameter of 8.18 in. and is loaded with about 57 lb. of TNT, amatol, or tritonal.

U.S. 100-lb bomb, incendiary, AN-M47A4 A bomb designed for use against combustible land targets and for use in igniting oil slicks on water. It is 51.7 in. long and 8.1 in. in diameter and is filled with 40 lb of NP (gasoline thickened with napalm).

U.S. 100-lb bomb, smoke, AN-M47A4 A bomb with a length of 52.6 in. and a diam-

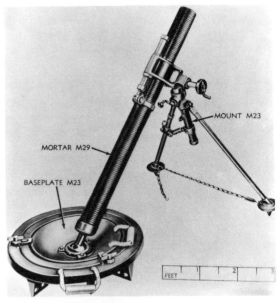

U.S. 81mm mortar M29. (*U.S. Army.*)

U.S. 90mm antiaircraft gun M1A1. (*U.S. Army.*)

U.S. 90mm self-propelled gun M56. (*U.S. Army.*)

U.S. 105mm howitzer M2A1. (*U.S. Army.*)

U.S. 105mm howitzer M3. (*U.S. Army.*)

eter of 8.0 in. It is filled with 74 lb of plasticized white phosphorus. When exploded, it creates a dense white smoke.

U.S. 105mm antiaircraft gun M1 A World War II weapon with a weight of 16.8 tons and a projectile weight of 33 lb. It fired fixed ammunition and had an effective ceiling of 50,000 ft.

U.S. 105mm gun cannon M68 This is used as a tank weapon primarily against armored targets. It has an APDS-T (armor-piercing discarding-sabot with tracer) cartridge with a range of 40,162 yd and a HEAT-T (high-explosive antitank with tracer) cartridge with a range of 8,975 yd. It has a length of 218.5 in.

U.S. 105mm howitzer M2 This weapon was first developed in 1928 and had a range of about 12,000 yd. Its weight was on the

order of 3,750 lb, and the weight of the projectile was about 33 lb. More ammunition was fired from this weapon than from any other piece of artillery in World War II.

U.S. 105mm howitzer M2A1 The original version of this weapon (the M1) was introduced in 1938. After the United States entered World War II, it was improved and designated the M2A1. It was used in World War II, in Korea, and in Southeast Asia. It is a standard U.S. weapon and is also used by numerous other countries. It has a weight of 4,980 lb, a six-man crew, and a range of 15,300 yd. The weight of the projectile (HE) is 33 lb.

U.S. 105mm howitzer M3 This howitzer and its carriage M3A1 were designed specifically for air transport during World War

II. The M3 fires the same 33-lb shell as the original 105mm M2 model, but maximum range was reduced from 12,000 yd to just over 7,000 yd. Howitzer and carriage weighed only 2,500 lb. Two completed, assembled units could be transported in a C-47 (as compared with only one M2 model and carriage disassembled into five major units).

U.S. 105mm howitzer M102 This U.S. Army 105mm howitzer is a towed, air-droppable weapon with a weight of 3,000 lb and a range of 15,000 meters. It has a length of 8 ft 5 in. and fires a projectile weighing 33 lb.

U.S. 105mm howitzer cannons M2A1, M4, M4A1, M49, M103, and M137 The 105mm howitzer cannons are used as field-artillery pieces and are mounted on towed carriages or self-propelled vehicles. Ammunition for the various models is interchangeable. The antipersonnel cartridge has a range of 328 yd, and the high-explosive cartridge has a range of 12,330 yd and is loaded with 4.8 lb of composition B explosive. (Another high-explosive cartridge is the HE, RA, XM548. This is actually an artillery projectile with a built-in rocket motor. The rocket motor adds thrust to the projectile in flight and extends the range to 15,000 yd.) A total of about 13 different cartridges are available.

U.S. 105mm recoilless rifles M27 and M27A1 These are antitank and antipersonnel weapons designed for direct fire from a special mount which may be employed on a rifle carriage or adapted for use on trucks and jeeps. The high-explosive cartridge has a range of 9,367 yd, with the projectile containing a bursting charge of 4.38 lb of TNT. The HEAT-T cartridge (high-explosive antitank with tracer) has a range of 9,280 yd. The weapon has a weight of 365 lb and a length of 134 in.

U.S. 105mm self-propelled gun M7 A World War II weapon, also called a "gun motor carriage," that was introduced in 1942 for use in artillery battalions, armored divisions, infantry regiments, and howitzer companies. It had a crew of seven and was armed with one 105mm howitzer M2A1, caliber length 24, and one .50 cal. machine gun M2 (for antiaircraft use).

U.S. 105mm self-propelled gun M37 (T76) This weapon was introduced in 1945. It had a crew of seven and was armed with one 105mm howitzer M4 and one .50 cal. machine gun M2.

U.S. 105mm self-propelled gun M104 A U.S. Army self-propelled unarmored 105mm howitzer.

U.S. 105mm self-propelled gun M108 A U.S. Army self-propelled howitzer with a total weight of about 23 tons and a range of 15,000 meters.

U.S. 105mm self-propelled howitzer

M52A1 A self-propelled full-track weapon served by a crew of five. It has a 500-hp engine and a speed of 42 mph.

U.S. 105mm self-propelled howitzer M108 This system entered service in 1964. It has the same chassis as the 155mm self-propelled howitzer M109, a crew of five, a total weight of 45,000 lb, and a speed of 37 mph. The howitzer has the same specifications as the **U.S. 105mm howitzer M2A1,** which see.

U.S. 105mm self-propelled howitzer T98E1 A self-propelled weapon with a crew of five and armed with a 155mm howitzer and a .30 cal. machine gun. The weight of the system is about 27 tons. The T98 was introduced in 1946.

U.S. 106mm recoilless rifle M40A1, M40A1C An air-cooled breechloading portable weapon designed for the defeat of heavy armor. Depending on rifle mount, it may be used as a ground weapon or mounted on utility trucks. It fires a HEAT (high-explosive antitank) projectile up to 10,000 yd. It is also called "Bat." The weapon has a weight of 251 lb.

U.S. 106mm self-propelled recoilless rifle M50 Also called "Ontos," this is a self-propelled full-track vehicle used to mount six 106mm recoilless rifles.

U.S. 107mm mortar (howtar) A Marine Corps modification mounting of a 4.2-in. mortar tube on a 75mm pack-howitzer carriage.

U.S. 107mm mortar M30 This weapon, formerly designated the "4.2-in. mortar," has a weight of about 321 lb and a range of about 6,000 yd. It has a normal rate of fire of 5 rounds per minute (and a maximum rate of 20 rounds per minute).

U.S. 107mm self-propelled mortar carrier U.S. Army 107mm self-propelled air-transportable full-track armored mortar carrier.

U.S. 115mm rocket M55 A U.S. Army surface-to-surface chemical-warfare rocket having a relatively short range.

U.S. 115mm rocket launcher M91 A U.S. Army chemical rocket launcher that can be fired from the ground or from a 2½-ton truck. It has a capacity of 45 chemical-warfare rockets, one of which can cover 1 sq mi. It is airdroppable and is served by a crew of six. (Picture, next page.)

U.S. 120mm antiaircraft gun This World War II gun fired a 50-lb projectile to a height of 50,000 ft.

U.S. 120mm antiaircraft gun M1 A World War II weapon with a weight of 30.8 tons and a projectile weight of 50 lb. It fired fixed ammunition and had an effective ceiling of 48,000 ft.

U.S. 120mm gun cannons M1A1, M1A2, and M1A3 These weapons are designed for use against aircraft at medium altitudes. They may also be used against ground and

U.S. 105mm howitzer M102. (*U.S. Army.*)

U.S. 105mm self-propelled howitzer M108. (*U.S. Army.*)

U.S. 106mm recoilless rifle M40A1. (*U.S. Army.*)

U.S. 115mm rocket launcher M91. (*U.S. Army.*)

U.S. 120mm gun cannon M1A2. (*U.S. Army.*)

U.S. 155mm howitzer cannon M1A1. (*U.S. Army.*)

waterborne targets. They are single-fired, recoil-operated, semiautomatic weapons. The HE-T (high-explosive with tracer) round has a range of 10,910 yd, the HEAT-T (high-explosive antitank with tracer) round has a range of 25,290 yd, and the AP-T (armor-piercing with tracer) round has a range of 25,290 yd. These weapons have a rate of fire of 15 rounds per minute, and the weight of the projectile is about 50 lb.

U.S. 120mm recoilless gun A recoilless gun designed for firing from a tripod ground mount or from a mount on a self-propelled vehicle.

U.S. 152mm gun cannon M81 This weapon is a versatile, lightweight gun-launcher capable of firing both missiles and the conventional ammunition. It is the main armament of the airborne reconnaissance combat vehicle M551 and may also be tank-mounted. It has a range of 9,850 yd.

U.S. 155mm gun M1A1 A World War II weapon with a weight of about 15 tons and a projectile weight of 95 lb. It fired separate-loading ammunition and had a range of 25,400 yd.

U.S. 155mm gun M2 A gun that was first introduced in the late 1930s (to replace a 1917 155mm gun of French design). The M2 serves with the forces of many countries and has an overall weight of 30,100 lb, a barrel length of 23 ft 2 in., and a range of 25,715 yd. It uses separate-loading ammunition, with a powder charge of about 30 lb and a projectile weight of 95 lb (HE).

U.S. 155mm gun cannons M2 and M46 The M2 version of this weapon is a towed field-artillery piece. The M46 provides the major armament for the full-track self-propelled gun M53. The ammunition for the two weapons is interchangeable. They have a range of 25,715 yd, a rate of fire of 40 rounds per hour, and a projectile weight of 95 lb. The barrel length is 23 ft. The M2 was given the nickname "Long Tom" during World War II.

U.S. 155mm howitzer M1 A World War II weapon with a weight of about 6 tons and a projectile weight of 95 lb. It fired separate-loading ammunition and had a range of 16,355 yd.

U.S. 155mm howitzer M123 This weapon, in service for several years, is used by the U.S. Army and the forces of a number of other countries. It has an overall weight of 12,700 lb and a range of 16,000 yd. It uses separate-loading ammunition, and the projectile weight is 97 lb.

U.S. 155mm howitzers M1917 and M1918 These weapons are very similar, the M1917 being of French manufacture and the M1918 of American manufacture. The total weight of the weapons is 2,740 lb, the length of the barrel is 92 in., and the weight of the projectile is 95 lb. The M1918 had a range of 12,530 yd (over 7 mi).

U.S. 155mm howitzer cannons M1, M1A1, M45, and M126 The M1 and M1A1 howitzer cannons are towed field-artillery pieces. The M45 and the M126 are self-propelled. All four weapons have similar gun tubes and fire the same ammunition. The high-explosive cartridge has a range of 15,958 yd. The projectile is loaded with 14.61 lb of TNT.

U.S. 155mm self-propelled gun M12 Also called a "gun motor carriage," this weapon was introduced in 1942, had a crew of five, and was armed with one 155mm gun M1917A1. It saw service in Italy, Germany, and France.

U.S. 155mm self-propelled gun M40 Also called a "gun motor carriage," this weapon was developed during World War II and was used in the European theater of operations. It had a crew of eight and was armed with one 155mm gun M2, caliber length 45, "Long Tom."

U.S. 155mm self-propelled gun M53 This system has a maximum speed of 30 mph and is served by a crew of six. The gun has a range of about 13 mi.

U.S. 155mm self-propelled howitzer M44A1 A U.S. Army self-propelled 155mm howitzer with a crew of five and a speed of about 35 mph.

U.S. 155mm self-propelled howitzer M109 This is a U.S. Army and Marine Corps self-propelled amphibious air-transportable howitzer with a range of about 18,500 meters and a weight of 26 tons. It is practically identical to the 105mm self-propelled howitzer M108, and its performance is about the same as that of the U.S. 155mm howitzer M123.

U.S. 165mm gun cannon XM315 This weapon is the main armament on the full-track combat engineer vehicle T118E1. It is designed to fire demolition-type projectiles at short range with a high degree of accuracy.

U.S. 175-lb gas (incapacitating) generator cluster M44 This cluster consists of three 50-lb incapacitating-gas (BZ) generators M16. The cluster is dropped from an aircraft as a single unit. The three generators separate and land by parachute.

U.S. 175mm gun cannon M113 This weapon is used for general artillery support of ground troops and armored columns. It constitutes the main armament on the full-track field-artillery gun M107, a highly mobile self-propelled weapon capable of being air-transported in large cargo aircraft. It fires separate-loading ammunition. At full charge the weapon has a range of 35,740 yd. The projectile is loaded with 30 lb of TNT.

U.S. 175mm self-propelled gun A U.S. Army full-track self-propelled gun with a

U.S. 155mm self-propelled gun M12. (*U.S. Army.*)

six-man crew, a weight of 31 tons, and a range of about 32,000 meters.

U.S. 175mm self-propelled gun M107 This system entered service in 1962 and uses the chassis of the 8-in. self-propelled howitzer M110. The M107 has a crew of 13, an overall length of 37 ft 1 in., a total weight of 62,100 lb, and a range of 35,760 yd. The weight of the (HE) projectile is 147 lb. The system travels at a top speed of 34.4 mph.

U.S. 220-lb bomb, fragmentation, AN-M88 This bomb has a body constructed of spirally wound 13/16-in. square steel wire over a seamless steel tube. It has a length of 43.7 in. and a diameter of 8.12

in. It contains about 216 lb of composition B or TNT.

U.S. 240mm howitzer M1 This World War II weapon had a weight of 25.5 tons overall and normally fired about 30 rounds per hour (although it could perform rapid-fire missions at the rate of one round per minute for a maximum of 30 minutes). It fired separate-loading ammunition and had a projectile weight of 360 lb. It had a range of 25,250 yd (about 14.25 mi). (Picture, next page.)

U.S. 240mm howitzer M1918M1 This weapon was used by the United States in World War I. It was a French (Schneider-designed) howitzer that fired a 356-lb pro-

U.S. 175mm self-propelled gun M107. (*U.S. Army.*)

U.S. 240mm howitzer M1. (*U.S. Army.*)

U.S. 280mm gun cannon M66. (*U.S. Army.*)

jectile to a range of about 17,000 yd.

U.S. 250-lb bomb, fire, BLU-10B   An antipersonnel and materiel fire bomb with a length of 88 in. and a diameter of 12.5 in. It is filled with 33 gal of napalm.

U.S. 250-lb bomb, general-purpose, AN-M57A1   This bomb has a length of 47.8 in. and a diameter of 10.9 in. and is loaded with 261 lb of TNT, amatol, or tritonal.

U.S. 250-lb bomb, general-purpose, low-drag, Snakeye I   This bomb is equipped with a retarding fin assembly that opens like an umbrella to decelerate the bomb, thus providing aircraft with a high-speed low-altitude bombing capability. It has a length of 75 in. and a diameter of 9 in. and is loaded with 100 lb of explosive.

U.S. 260-lb bomb, fragmentation, AN-M81   This bomb has a body constructed of spirally wound 1-in. square steel wire. It has a length of 43.7 in. and a diameter

of 8.13 in. It contains approximately 262 lb of composition B or TNT.

U.S. 280mm gun cannon M66   This mobile long-range heavy-artillery weapon has been popularly called the "atomic cannon," even though the design predates the use of tactical nuclear warheads. It is based closely on the World War II German 21cm (210mm) gun. It has a weight of about 83.5 tons, a range of 31,400 yd, and a separate-loading round which weighs 750 lb. The length of the gun is 42 ft 9 in.

U.S. 300-lb bomb, depth, AN-MK54 Mod 1   This bomb is designed for underwater targets, particularly submarines. It has a length of 54.6 in. and a diameter of 13.5 in. and contains 225.5 lb of TNT (or 248 lb of HBX or HBX-1).

U.S. 300-lb bomb M31   The standard U.S. 300-lb demolition bomb used in World War II.

U.S. 500-lb bomb, fire, BLU-11/B   A modification of the 750-lb fire bomb M116A2. It is filled with 65 gal of napalm.

U.S. 500-lb bomb, fire, BLU-23/B   A smaller version of the BLU-1/B (750-lb fire bomb). It has a length of 119 in. and a diameter of 15.75 in. and is filled with 67 gal of napalm.

U.S. 500-lb bomb, fire, MK77 Mod 1   A 500-lb modification of the MK77 Mod 0 750-lb fire bomb. It is loaded with 72 gal of gasoline gel.

U.S. 500-lb bomb, gas (nonpersistent), AN-M78   This bomb is 59 in. long and about 19.25 in. in diameter. It is loaded with CG or CK, which see.

U.S. 500-lb bomb, gas (nonpersistent), GB, MK94 Mod 0   This bomb has a length of 88.8 in. and a diameter of 10.8 in. and is loaded with 108 lb of GB (sarin), an extremely quick-acting nerve gas.

U.S. 500-lb bomb, general-purpose, AN-

M64A1   This bomb has a length of 59.16 in. and a diameter of 14.18 in. and is loaded with about 265 lb of explosive.

U.S. 500-lb bomb, general-purpose, low-drag, Snakeye I   This bomb is equipped with the retarding fin assembly described above. It has a length of 89.5 in. and a diameter of 10.8 in. and is loaded with 192 lb of explosive.

U.S. 500-lb bomb, incendiary cluster, M31   A bomb consisting of 38 incendiary bombs M74 in a special cluster adapter.

U.S. 500-lb bomb, incendiary cluster, M32   A bomb consisting of one hundred and eight 4-lb incendiary bombs AN-M50A3 in a special cluster adapter.

U.S. 500-lb bomb M43   The standard U.S. 500-lb demolition bomb used in World War II.

U.S. 750-lb bomb, fire, BLU-1/B   A bomb with a length of 130 in. and a diameter of 18.5 in. It is filled with approximately 95 gal of napalm.

U.S. 750-lb bomb, fire, M116A2   This bomb, designed to be carried externally on high-performance aircraft, has a length of 137 in. and a body diameter of 18.63 in. and is loaded with 100 gal (approximately 615 lb) of thickened fuel.

U.S. 750-lb bomb, fire, MK77 Mod 0   A bomb somewhat similar in appearance to the M116A2, but carrying 110 gal of thickened fuel.

U.S. 750-lb bomb, fire, MK78 Mod 2   A bomb with a length of 89.12 in. and a diameter of 26.4 in. It is filled with 110 gal of gasoline gel.

U.S. 750-lb bomb, gas (incapacitating) cluster, M43   A bomb consisting of fifty-seven 10-lb gas bombs M138 (filled with BZ incapacitating gas, which see) in a special cluster adapter.

U.S. 750-lb bomb, gas (nonpersistent) GB, MC-1   This bomb is designed for internal or external carriage on bomber and fighter-bomber aircraft. It has a length of 90 in. and a diameter of 16 in. and is loaded with 220 lb of GB (sarin), an extremely quick-acting nerve gas.

U.S. 750-lb bomb, general-purpose, M117   This bomb has a length of 89.43 in. and a diameter of 16.1 in. It is loaded with 386 lb of tritonal.

U.S. 750-lb bomb, incendiary cluster, M35   A bomb consisting of fifty-seven 10-lb incendiary bombs M74A1 in a special cluster adapter.

U.S. 750-lb bomb, incendiary cluster, M36   A bomb consisting of one hundred and eighty-two 4-lb incendiary bombs M126 in a special cluster adapter.

U.S. 914mm mortar   See Little David.

U.S. 1,000-lb bomb, fire, MK79 Mod 1   A bomb with a length of 167.96 in. and a diameter of 19.6 in. It is filled with 112 gal of napalm.

U.S. 1,000-lb bomb, gas (nonpersistent), AN-M79 This bomb is 69.5 in. long and 18.75 in. in diameter. It is loaded with **CG, AC,** or **CK,** which see.

U.S. 1,000-lb bomb, gas (nonpersistent) cluster, M34A1 A bomb consisting of seventy-six 10-lb gas bombs M125A1 (filled with GB nerve gas) in a special cluster adapter.

U.S. 1,000-lb bomb, general-purpose, AN-M65A1 This bomb has a length of 69.5 in. and a diameter of 18.8 in. and is loaded with about 555 lb of explosive.

U.S. 1,000-lb bomb M44 The standard U.S. 1,000-lb demolition bomb used in World War II.

U.S. 1,000-lb bomb, semi-armor-piercing, AN-M59A1 This bomb has a thick metal body designed to give greater penetration than a general-purpose bomb of comparable weight. It has a length of 70.38 in. and a diameter of 15.09 in. It contains 310 lb of TNT and penetrates 37 to 45 in. of concrete.

U.S. 2,000-lb bomb, general-purpose, AN-M66A2 This bomb has a length of 92.63 in. and a diameter of 23.29 in. and is loaded with about 1,097 lb of explosive.

U.S. 4,000-lb bomb M56 The standard U.S. 4,000-lb light-case bomb used in World War II.

U.S. 44,000-lb bomb The largest bomb employed in World War II was the British 22,000-lb Grand Slam. Under development, however, was a U.S. bomb weighing about 44,000 lb, of which 17,600 lb was high explosive. It was loaded with tritonal and had a tail assembly that took up 122 in. of its total 322-in. length. At war's end several experimental models were ready for testing whenever the B-36 bomber became available.

usable rate of fire The normal rate of fire of a gun in actual use, measured in units of shots per minute. The usable rate of fire is considerably less than a gun's maximum rate of fire, which is a theoretical value based on the purely mechanical operation of the weapon.

U.S. aircraft mine Mark 12 Mod 1 A mine that is similar to the U.S. naval mine Mark 12 Mod 0, but is 130 in. long to incorporate parachute gear.

U.S. Air Force (USAF) The official name given the air arm of the United States military forces. According to the Air Force Organization Act of 1951, the USAF shall consist of the Regular Air Force, the Air Force Reserve, the Air National Guard of the United States, and the Air National Guard while in the service of the United States.

U.S. amphibious cargo carrier M116 An airdroppable full-track vehicle developed in

U.S. amphibious cargo carrier M116. (*U.S. Army.*)

the late 1950s as a replacement for the earlier Weasel and Otter vehicles that cross mud and snow.

U.S. antipersonnel mine M2A4 This is a mine of the "bounding" type. A pressure of 8 to 20 lb causes it to fire, projecting the bursting charge (consisting of .34 lb of TNT) several feet in the air for a more effective fragmentation pattern. It has a casualty radius of 10 meters, but is dangerous up to 150 meters.

U.S. antipersonnel mine M3 This fragmentation mine consists of a high-explosive charge in a heavy cast-iron case. A pressure of 8 to 20 lb detonates the charge of 0.90 lb of flake TNT. It has a casualty radius of 10 meters, but fragments may be thrown up to 100 meters.

U.S. antipersonnel mine M14 This small mine is a nonmetallic blast-type high-explosive device consisting of a main charge of tetryle (1 oz) in an all-plastic body. The total weight is only 3⅓ oz. It is capable of inflicting a serious casualty since it explodes in direct contact with the enemy.

U.S. antipersonnel mine M18A1 This mine is a direction-fixed fragmentation mine that is used primarily for defense of bivouac areas and outposts and against infiltration tactics. It is also effective against thin-skinned vehicles such as jeeps, automobiles, trucks, etc., readily perforating the outer body and injuring or killing the occupants. The fragments also puncture tires, gas tanks, crankcases, radiators, and engine accessories. When detonated, a fan-shaped pattern of spherical steel fragments is projected in a 60° horizontal arc covering a casualty area of 50 meters to a height of 2 meters. The explosive charge consists of 1.5 lb of composition C-4. It is dangerous to a range of 250 meters.

U.S. antitank mine M19 (T18E4) This mine is intended for use against heavy tanks and other types of heavy-tracked and wheeled vehicles. Being of nearly all-plastic construction, it is nondetectable by mag-

U.S. antitank mine M603. (*U.S. Army.*)

netic mine detectors. The mine contains 21 lb of composition B explosive. When buried 1½ in. deep, the mine will completely immobilize light and heavy tanks by track damage. The mine is two to three times as effective in water as it is on land because water tends to amplify the shock waves. Vehicles which strike mines implanted in water not only have their tracks or wheels destroyed but also have their support members destroyed as well. Smaller vehicles are flipped over on their backs and are almost completely destroyed.

U.S. antipersonnel mine M19A1 This is a mine of the "bounding" variety. It detonates about 3 ft above the ground. Weighing about 7⅞ lb, the bursting charge consists of 1 lb of TNT. It has a casualty radius of 30 meters and is dangerous up to 200 meters.

U.S. antitank mine M603 This mine is intended for use against heavy tanks. The weight of the explosive charge (composition B) is 22 lb. If buried 3 in. deep, this mine will disable a tank by breaking the track. If laid flush with the ground, it will disable a tank by breaking the track and bogies (road wheels and other parts of the suspension system).

U.S. armored car, light, M8 (T22E2) A

U.S. armored car, light, M8 (T22E2). (U.S. Army.)

U.S. armored car, utility, M20 (T26). (U.S. Army.)

U.S. armored personnel carrier M113. (U.S. Army.)

six-wheeled armored car developed by Ford and produced between 1942 and 1945. A total of 8,523 were produced. It had a weight of 17,200 lb and was powered by a six-cylinder engine of 112 bhp (brake horsepower). It was armed with one 37mm gun and one .30 cal. machine gun. It was designated "Greyhound" by the British.

U.S. armored car M6 (T17E1)   This Chevrolet-produced four-wheeled vehicle was produced between 1942 and 1944. It had a weight of 29,100 lb and was powered by twin six-cylinder engines of 104 bhp (brake horsepower) each. Called "Staghound" by the British, it was armed with one 37mm gun, three .30 cal. machine guns, and one .45 cal. submachine gun.

U.S. armored car M706   See **Armored Commando V-100**. This is the only armored car presently in the U.S. inventory.

U.S. armored car, utility, M20 (T26)   A Ford-built vehicle produced between 1942 and 1945, during which time 3,791 were produced. It had a weight of 15,650 lb and was powered by a six-cylinder engine of 112 bhp (brake horsepower). It was used as an armored cargo and personnel carrier and field commander's car. This six-wheeled vehicle was armed with one ring-mounted .50 cal. machine gun.

U.S. armored personnel carrier M113   The current APC in service with the U.S. Army, this tracked vehicle entered production in 1959. Since that time some 30,000 vehicles have been produced, a number of which are in service with the military forces of 13 other countries. It has a crew of two (plus ten infantrymen), a weight of 10 tons, a road speed of 39 mph, and armament consisting of one .50 cal. machine gun. Inherently amphibious, it has a water speed (propulsion by tracks) of 3.5 mph.

U.S. armored personnel carrier XM 706   See **Commando**, sense 1.

U.S. Army (USA)   The land military forces of the United States, including the Regular Army, the National Guard of the United States, and the Army Reserve. Often shortened to "Army." In general the U.S. Army shall include land combat and service forces and such aviation and water transport as may be organic therein. It shall be organized, trained, and equipped primarily for prompt and sustained combat incident to operations on land.

U.S. Army Special Forces   Military personnel with cross training in basic and specialized military skills, organized into small multiple-purpose detachments with the mission to train, organize, supply, direct, and control indigenous forces in guerrilla warfare and counterinsurgency operations and to conduct unconventional-warfare operations.

U.S. bayonet knife M4   A bayonet knife for carbines used by U.S. forces.

U.S. breechloading flintlock and percussion carbines

Model	Manufacturer	Caliber	Total length	Average weight
1833	Hall-North	.58	45 in.	8 lb 4 oz (with bayonet)
1837	Hall	.64	43 in.	8 lb 7 oz (with bayonet)
1839	Jenks (musketoon)	.64	42¼ in.	7 lb
1840	Hall-North	.52	40 in.	8 lb
1843	Hall-North	.52	40 in.	8 lb 1 oz
1845	Jenks	.54	41¼ in.	6 lb
1852	Sharps	.52	37½ in.	8 lb
1855	Colt (five-shot revolving cylinder)	.56	21-in. barrel	9 lb 8 oz
1856	Burnside	.54	39½ in.	6 lb 12 oz
1856	Gibbs	.54	39 in.	7 lb 6 oz
1856	Greene	.53	34¾ in.	7½ lb
1856	Maynard	.50	36⅞ in.	6 lb
1857	Smith	.50	39½ in.	7½ lb
1858	Merrill	.54	37⅜ in.	6½ lb
1858	Starr	.54	37⅝ in.	7 lb 6 oz
1859	Lindner	.58	38¾ in.	6 lb
1860	Gallaher	.52	39$\frac{3}{16}$ in.	7½ lb
1862	Gwyn & Campbell	.52	39⅛ in.	6½ lb

U.S. breechloading percussion rifles

Model	Manufacturer	Caliber	Total length	Average weight
1843	Jenks	.54	52½ in.	7½ lb (with bayonet)
1852	Sharps	.52	53 in.	8 lb 12 oz (without bayonet)
1855	Colt	.44	31-in. barrel	9 lb
1857	Greene	.54	52¾ in.	10 lb (without bayonet)
1858	Merrill	.54	48½ in.	9 lb (without bayonet)

U.S. cartridge revolvers

Date	Manufacturer	Caliber	Total length	Weight
Pat. 1864	Bacon	.38	12¾ in.	2 lb 2 oz
Model 1872	Colt	.45	13 in.	2 lb 7 oz
Model 1878	Colt	.45	12½ in.	2 lb 7 oz
Model 1892 94, 96 Army	Colt	.38	11½ in.	2 lb 1 oz
Model 1901 1903 Army	Colt	.38	11½ in.	2 lb 1 oz
Model 1889 1895 Navy	Colt	.38	11½ in.	2 lb 1 oz
Model 1907	Colt	.38	10¾ in.	2 lb ½ oz
Model 1909	Colt	.45	10⅝ in.	2 lb 8 oz
Model 1917	Colt	.45	10¾ in.	2 lb 8 oz
Pat. 1877	Forehand & Wadsworth	.44	13⅛ in.	2 lb 8 oz
Pat. 1871	Hopkins & Allen	.38	11 in.	1 lb 10 oz
Model 1876	Merwin & Hulbert	.44	12 in.	2 lb 9 oz
Pat. 1859	Plant	.42	10¾ in.	2 lb
Pat. 1862	Pond	.44	12¾ in.	2 lb 8 oz
Pat. 1860	Prescott	.38	12½ in.	1 lb 13 oz
Model 1872	Remington	.44	12⅞ in.	2 lb 11 oz
Pat. 1855	Smith & Wesson	.32	10¾ in.	1 lb 8 oz
Model 1869	Smith & Wesson	.44	13½ in.	2 lb 10 oz
Model 1875	Smith & Wesson	.45	12½ in.	2 lb 8 oz
Model 1881	Smith & Wesson	.44	11½ in.	2 lb 5 oz
Model 1899	Smith & Wesson	.38	11 in	1 lb 15 oz
Model 1917	Smith & Wesson	.45	10¾ in.	2 lb 4 oz

U.S. combat engineer vehicle T-118E1. (*U.S. Army.*)

U.S. Coast Guard (USCG) A military or police force responsible for certain duties along the coasts of the United States, especially in enforcing customs, immigration, and navigational laws, and for maintenance of the International Ice Patrol. Usually shortened to "Coast Guard."

U.S. combat engineer vehicle T-118E1 This is a 57-ton vehicle equipped with an A-frame boom with 30,000 lb capacity and armed with a 165mm assault gun. It is somewhat similar to the U.S. M-60A1 tank.

U.S. combat engineer vehicle T-120E1 A U.S. Army armored full-track recovery vehicle that is designed for the repair and recovery of vehicles in the 15- to 30-ton range.

U.S. command and reconnaissance carrier M114 A full-track amphibious vehicle introduced to the U.S. Army in 1962 and produced in very large numbers. It has a crew of three or four, a weight of 6¾ tons, a road speed of 35 mph (a water speed of 2.9 mph), and armament consisting of one .50 cal. machine gun and one 7.62mm machine gun. (Picture, next page.)

U.S. depth bomb Mark 53 An antisubmarine depth bomb designed to be dropped from aircraft. The weight of the TNT burster charge is 350 lb.

U.S. depth bomb Mark 54 A depth bomb with an HBX burster charge weighing 325 lb. (Picture, next page.)

U.S. depth charge Mark 6 A depth charge, previously used, that was about 28 in. long and 18 in. in diameter and contained 300 lb of TNT.

U.S. depth charge Mark 7 A depth charge, previously used, that was cylindrical in shape and considerably larger than the Mark 6. It contained 600 lb of TNT.

U.S. depth charge Mark 9 A teardrop-shaped depth charge with a diameter of 18 in. It has a weighted nose that increases its sinking rate and carries an explosive charge of 200 lb of TNT or HBX.

U.S. depth charge Mark 14 A depth charge similar to the Mark 9 depth charge.

U.S. depth charge Mark 57 A nuclear depth charge.

U.S. depth charge Mark 101 A nuclear depth charge.

U.S. depth-charge projector Mark 6 Mod 1 Commonly called the "K-gun," this device utilizes various black-powder charges to launch Mark 6 depth charges (to ranges of 50, 75, and 120 yd) or Mark 9 and Mark 14 depth charges (to ranges of 60, 90, and 150 yd).

user test An evaluation test conducted on materiel under development following a satisfactory **engineering test,** which see. It is performed by the using agency to determine the suitability of the developmental materiel for military use. User tests are of two types: (1) *Service test:* A test under

U.S. command and reconnaissance carrier M114. (*U.S. Army.*)

U.S. depth bomb Mark 54. (*U.S. Navy.*)

U.S. flamethrower tank M67. (*U.S. Army.*)

simulated operational conditions to determine to what degree the item meets the military requirement as expressed in the military characteristics. (2) *Troop test:* A test in which a troop unit, equipped with appropriate numbers of the item, operates under actual or simulated field conditions to test the suitability of the item and also the adequacy of the organization, doctrine, technique, training, and logistic support required for its use.

U.S. flamethrower M2A1-7   A multishot portable flamethrower used by the U.S. Army and Marine Corps. It has a capacity of 4.75 gal of thickened fuel, weighs 69 lb, and has a range of 40 to 50 meters.

U.S. flamethrower M4A2   A U.S. Army truck-mounted flamethrower, replaced by the M132.

U.S. flamethrower M7A1-6   A U.S. Army mechanized flamethrower with a range of 200 meters.

U.S. flamethrower M9-7(ABC)   A U.S. Army lightweight multishot portable flamethrower with a weight of 50 lb and a range of 40 to 50 meters. It contains 4 gal of thickened fuel.

U.S. flamethrower M132E1   A U.S. Army lightweight amphibious air-transportable self-propelled mechanized flamethrower mounted on an M113. It has a weight of 23,710 lb, a crew of two, and a capacity of 200 gal. It is also armed with a 7.62mm machine gun.

U.S. flamethrower tank M67   A U.S. Army weapon combining an M48A2 tank and an M7A1-6 mechanized flamethrower. The flamethrower has a range of 200 meters and a capacity of 378 gal.

U.S. flintlock carbines   See table on next page.

U.S. flintlock muskets   See table on next page.

U.S. flintlock pistols   See table on next page.

U.S. flintlock rifles   See table on next page.

U.S. half-track personnel carrier M3   A World War II vehicle with a weight of 14,800 lb. It carried a crew of 13 and was armed with one .50 cal. machine gun.

U.S. hand grenade M26   This grenade replaced the Mk2 "pineapple" grenade of World War II and later. It has a larger explosive charge and a more effective casualty radius and produces more fragments (which, although smaller, have a higher initial velocity). The grenade weighs 16 oz and has an explosive charge of 5.5 oz of composition B. The average soldier can throw this grenade about 40 meters. The effective casualty radius is 15 meters, although fragments will be thrown much further.

U.S. hand grenade Mk2   This is the grenade from which the term "pineapple" originated because of its deeply serrated

U.S. flintlock carbines

Model	Manufacturer	Caliber	Total length	Average weight
1807	Springfield	.54	48½ in.	5 lb
1839	Springfield (musketoon)	.69	41 in.	7 lb 3 oz
1847	Springfield (musketoon)	.69	41 in.	6 lb 6 oz
1855	Springfield (pistol-carbine)	.58	17¾ in. (pistol)	3 lb 13 oz (pistol)
1855	Springfield (rifled carbine)	.54	36¾ in.	6 lb 8 oz

U.S. flintlock muskets

Model	Manufacturer	Caliber	Total length	Average weight
1795	Springfield Armory and others	.69	59½ in.	8 lb 14 oz
1808	Springfield Armory and others	.69	59 in	10 lb (with bayonet)
1812	Springfield Armory and others	.69	57 in.	9 lb 6 oz (with bayonet)
1816	Springfield Armory and others	.69	57¹¹⁄₁₆ in.	9 lb 5½ oz (with bayonet)
1835	Springfield Armory and others	.69	57¹³⁄₁₆ in.	9 lb 12 oz (with bayonet)

U.S. flintlock pistols

Model	Manufacturer	Caliber	Total length	Weight
1799	North & Cheney	.69	14½ in.	3 lb 4 oz
1806	Harpers Ferry	.54	16 in.	2 lb 9 oz
1808	S. North	.64	16¼ in.	2 lb 14 oz
1810	S. North	.69	15 in.	2 lb 11 oz
1813	S. North	.69	15¼ in.	3 lb 6 oz
1816	S. North	.54	15¼ in.	3 lb 3 oz
1818	Springfield Armory	.69	17¾ in.	3 lb 3 oz
1819	S. North	.54	15½ in.	2 lb 10 oz
1826	W. L. Evans	.54	13⅜ in.	2 lb 4 oz
1826	S. North	.54	13¼ in.	2 lb 4 oz
1836	R. Johnson	.54	14 in.	2 lb 10 oz
1836	A. Waters	.54	14 in.	2 lb 10 oz

U.S. flintlock rifles

Model	Manufacturer	Caliber	Total length	Average weight
1803	Harpers Ferry Armory	.54	47 to 49½ in.	
1817	Harpers Ferry Armory	.54	51¼ in.	10 lb (without bayonet)
1819	J. H. Hall	.52	52¾ in.	10 lb 12 oz (with bayonet)

U.S. magazine rifles

Model	Manufacturer	Number of shots	Caliber	Total length	Average weight
1882	Chaffee-Reese	5	.45	49 in.	
1892	Krag-Jörgensen	5	.30	49⅛ in.	9 lb 5 oz
1896	Krag-Jörgensen	5			
1898	Krag-Jörgensen	5			
1903	Springfield	5	.30	43½ in.	9 lb 8 oz
1917	Enfield	5	.30	45⅜ in.	10 lb 5 oz (with bayonet)
M1	(Garand)	8	.30	43½ in.	9½ lb
M14		20	7.62mm	44.14 in.	8.7 lb
M16		20	5.56mm	39 in.	6.3 lb

U.S. hand grenade M26. (*U.S. Army.*)

U.S. hand grenade Mk2. (*U.S. Army.*)

ters and has an effective casualty radius in open terrain of about 2 meters. Inside a closed room, case, or bunker, the radius is much greater.

U.S. landing vehicle, tracked, Mk 3 (LVT3) A World War II vehicle with a payload of 6,000 lb and powered by two Cadillac V8 engines.

USM An underwater-to-surface missile.

U.S. magazine rifles See table at the left.

U.S. main battle tank M47 The design of this tank stemmed from that of the M26,

body. These deep serrations delineate the fragmentation of the body when the grenade explodes. The grenade weighs 21 oz and has an explosive charge of 2 oz of flaked TNT. An average soldier can throw this grenade about 30 meters. The casualty radius is 10 meters, but fragments may be thrown up to 185 meters. This grenade was replaced by the M26 series fragmentation grenade.

U.S. hand grenade Mk3A2 This grenade is called an "offensive" hand grenade. It consists of a cylindrical body made of pressed fiber, weighs about 15.6 oz, and contains 8 oz of flaked TNT as filler. This grenade depends on concussion to produce casualties. It can be thrown about 40 me-

U.S. main battle tank M47. (*U.S. Army.*)

U.S. main battle tank M60. (*U.S. Army.*)

U.S. naval mine Mark 12 Mod 0. (*U.S. Navy.*)

U.S. muzzle-loading percussion rifles and rifle muskets

Model	Manufacturer	Caliber	Total length	Average weight
1841	Harpers Ferry Arsenal and others	.54	48¾ in.	9¾ lb
1842	Springfield Arsenal	.69	57¹³⁄₁₆ in.	9 lb 12 oz (with bayonet)
1855	Harpers Ferry Arsenal	.58	49⅜ in.	10 lb (without bayonet)
1855	(Rifle and musket) Springfield	.58	56 in.	9 lb 2 oz (without bayonet)
1861	(Rifle and musket) Springfield and others	.58	56 in.	9 lb 6 oz (without bayonet)
1862	Remington	.58	49 in.	9 lb 6 oz (without bayonet)
1863	Lindsay	.58	56 in.	9 lb (without bayonet)

which entered service in 1945 (and which, with minor improvements, became the M46, or Patton, in 1948). The M47 has a crew of five, a weight of 44 tons, a road speed of 25 mph, and armament consisting of one 90mm gun, two .50 cal. machine guns, and one .30 cal. machine gun. It is still in service in a number of countries.

U.S. main battle tank M48 A redesigned and stretched version of the U.S. M47 that was developed in 1953 and is still in service with the forces of Belgium, Greece, Turkey, and Israel. It has a crew of four, a weight of 47.6 tons, a road speed of 30 mph, and armament consisting of one 90mm gun and two machine guns (one .50 cal. and one 7.62mm).

U.S. main battle tank M60 The current main battle tank in service with the U.S. Army, this system entered service in 1959. It is also used by the Austrian and Italian Armies. It has a crew of four, a weight of 48 tons, a road speed of 30 mph, and armament consisting of one 105mm high-velocity gun and two machine guns (one .50 cal. and one 7.62mm).

U.S. Marine Corps (USMC) A corps of soldiers in the U.S. Navy. Also shortened to "Marine Corps." The USMC includes land combat and service forces and organic aviation units. It is responsible for service with the fleet in the seizure or defense of advanced naval bases and for the conduct of such land operations as may be essential to the prosecution of a naval campaign.

U.S. muzzle-loading percussion rifles and rifle muskets See table at left, below.

U.S. naval mine Mark 6 A contact mine with a spherical steel case 34.25 in. in diameter and loaded with 300 lb of TNT.

U.S. naval mine Mark 12 Mod 0 A mine that has been designed for deployment from submarine torpedo tubes. It is a magnetic mine and has an explosive charge of about 1,200 lb of TNT or HBX.

U.S. naval mine Mark 25 Mod 0 A magnetic mine that is designed to be dropped from airplanes. It has a total weight of about 1,930 lb, of which 1,200 lb is the main explosive charge (TNT or HBX).

U.S. naval mine Mark 25 Mod 1 A mine that is essentially the same as the Mod 0, but with an acoustic (rather than a magnetic) firing mechanism.

U.S. naval mine Mark 25 Mod 2 A mine that is essentially the same as the Mod 0, but which also responds to changes in pressure (caused by a passing vessel).

U.S. Navy (USN) The naval establishment of the United States. Often shortened to "Navy." The Navy includes seagoing fleets, aviation units, the U.S. Coast Guard when operating as a part of the Navy under the provisions of law, and the U.S. Marine Corps. In general the U.S. Navy shall include naval combat and service forces and such aviation as may be organic therein. It shall be organized, trained, and equipped primarily for prompt and sustained combat incident to operations at sea.

U.S. percussion muskets See table on next page.

U.S. percussion pistols See table on next page.

U.S. percussion revolvers See table on next page.

U.S. repeating and magazine carbines See table on next page.

U.S. repeating rifles See table on next page.

U.S. percussion muskets

Model	*Manufacturer*	*Caliber*	*Total length*	*Average weight*
1841	Springfield Armory and others	.57	$55\frac{1}{4}$ in.	
1842	Springfield Armory and others	.69	$57\frac{3}{4}$ in.	9 lb 3 oz (without bayonet)
1851	(Similar to 1841)			

U.S. percussion pistols

Model	*Manufacturer*	*Caliber*	*Total length*	*Weight*
1842	H. Aston	.54	14 in.	2 lb 12 oz
1842	I. N. Johnson	.54	14 in.	2 lb 12 oz
1842	Palmetto Armory	.54	14 in.	2 lb 12 oz
1843	N. P. Ames	.54	$11\frac{5}{8}$ in.	2 lb
1843	Deringer	.54	$11\frac{5}{8}$ in.	2 lb
1855	Springfield	.58	$17\frac{3}{4}$ in.	3 lb 13 oz

U.S. percussion revolvers

Date	*Manufacturer*	*Caliber*	*Total length*	*Weight*
Pat. 1853	Adams	.36	$11\frac{1}{2}$ in.	2 lb 9 oz
1856–1865	Allen & Wheelock	.44	$13\frac{1}{4}$ in.	2 lb 14 oz
Pat. 1857	Allen & Wheelock	.36	$13\frac{3}{8}$ in.	2 lb 10 oz
Pat. 1861	Alsop	.36	$9\frac{7}{8}$ in.	1 lb 4 oz
Pat. 1858	Beals	.36	$13\frac{3}{8}$ in.	2 lb 10 oz
Pat. 1855	Butterfield	.41	$13\frac{3}{4}$ in.	2 lb 10 oz
Model 1847	Colt	.44	$15\frac{1}{2}$ in.	4 lb 9 oz
Model 1848	Colt	.44	14 in	4 lb 1 oz
Model 1851	Colt	.36	13 in.	2 lb 10 oz
Model 1855	Colt	.44	$15\frac{1}{8}$ in.	4 lb $2\frac{1}{2}$ oz
Model 1860	Colt	.44	14 in.	2 lb 11 oz
Model 1861	Colt	.36	13 in.	2 lb 10 oz
Model 1862	Colt	.36	$11\frac{1}{2}$ in.	1 lb 10 oz
Pat. 1851	Cooper	.36	$10\frac{3}{4}$ in.	1 lb 12 oz
Pat. 1862	Freeman	.44	$12\frac{1}{2}$ in.	2 lb 13 oz
Pat. 1858	Joslyn	.44	$14\frac{3}{8}$ in.	3 lb
1837–1839	Leavitt	.40	$13\frac{7}{8}$ in.	3 lb 10 oz
Pat. 1859	Manhattan	.36	$11\frac{1}{2}$ in.	2 lb
Pat. 1862	Metropolitan	.36	13 in.	2 lb 8 oz
Pat. 1856	Pettingill	.44	14 in.	3 lb
Model 1861	Remington	.44	$13\frac{3}{4}$ in.	2 lb 14 oz
Pat. 1858	Remington-Rider	.36	$11\frac{1}{2}$ in.	2 lb 1 oz
Pat. 1865	Rogers & Spencer	.44	$13\frac{3}{8}$ in.	3 lb 2 oz
Pat. 1856	Savage	.36	$14\frac{1}{4}$ in.	3 lb 6 oz
Pat. 1856	Savage-North	.36	14 in.	3 lb 7 oz
Pat. 1856	Starr	.44	$11\frac{5}{8}$ in.	2 lb 15 oz
Pat. 1861	Union	.36	$13\frac{1}{2}$ in.	2 lb 8 oz
Pat. 1859	Walch	.36	$12\frac{1}{4}$ in.	2 lb 4 oz
Pat. 1851	Warner	.36	$12\frac{1}{2}$ in.	2 lb 2 oz
1849–1851	Wesson & Leavitt	.40	15 in.	4 lb 6 oz
Pat. 1854	Whitney	.36	$13\frac{1}{8}$ in.	2 lb 9 oz

U.S. repeating and magazine carbines

Model	*Manufacturer*	*Number of shots*	*Caliber*	*Total length*	*Average weight*
1860	Spencer	7	.52	39 in.	8 lb 4 oz
1863	Ball	7	.50	$37\frac{1}{2}$ in.	7 lb 6 oz
1866	Winchester	12	.44	39 in.	7 lb 12 oz
1874	Remington-Keene	7	.45	$39\frac{1}{2}$ in.	8 lb
1879	Hotchkiss	5	.45	44 in.	8 lb 4 oz
1896	Krag-Jörgensen	5	.30	$40\frac{7}{8}$ in.	8 lb 1 oz
M1	Semiautomatic	30	.30	$35\frac{5}{8}$ in.	5 lb 3 oz
M2	Automatic	30	.30	$35\frac{5}{8}$ in.	5 lb 3 oz

U.S. repeating rifles

Model	*Manufacturer*	*Number of shots*	*Caliber*	*Total length*	*Average weight*
1860	Henry	12	.44	$43\frac{1}{2}$ in.	$9\frac{1}{4}$ lb
1860	Spencer	7	.52	47 in.	10 lb
1866	Winchester (similar to Henry Model 1860)				
1874	Remington-Keene	8	.45	$48\frac{1}{2}$ in.	9 lb
1882	Lee	5	.45	52 in.	

U.S. rifle grenade M31 This is a fin-stabilized point-initiated high-explosive antitank grenade. It weighs 1.56 lb and has an explosive charge weighing 9.92 oz (composition B). It is capable of penetrating in excess of 10 in. of armor plate or 20 in. of reinforced concrete. The maximum range is approximately 185 meters at a 45° angle of elevation.

U.S. scout car M3A1 An armored car introduced in 1939 and employed by reconnaissance platoons. It had a crew of eight and was armed with one .50 cal. machine gun and one .30 cal. machine gun. It weighed 13,000 lb and had a road speed of 55 mph.

U.S. rifle grenade M31. (*U.S. Army.*)

U.S. single-shot cartridge carbines See table on next page.

U.S. single-shot cartridge pistols See table on next page.

U.S. single-shot cartridge rifles See table on next page.

U.S. six-pounder field gun Model 1840 A bronze muzzle-loading gun that was in general use throughout the American Civil War.

U.S. tank M41 A full-track vehicle with light armor protection against small-arms fire and shell fragments. Used primarily for armored reconnaissance, it is armed with a 76mm gun. (Picture, next page.)

U.S. tank M47 A tank with a crew of five and armament consisting of one 90mm gun, two .50 cal. machine guns M2, and one .30 cal. machine gun M1919A4. It weighed 48.6 tons.

U.S. tank M48 This series of combat tanks has the following general characteristics: a weight of 52 tons, a maximum speed of about 30 mph, and armament consisting of one 90mm gun (with a range in excess of 19,000 meters), a cupola-mounted .50 cal.

U.S. single-shot cartridge carbines

Model	Manufacturer	Caliber	Total length	Average weight
1860	Gallager	.50	39³⁄₁₆ in.	7½ lb
1862	Joslyn	.52	38¾ in.	6 lb 10 oz
1862	Peabody	.50	39 in.	6½ lb
1863	Palmer	.52	36 in.	6 lb 8 oz
1863	Remington	.50	33½ in.	6 lb
1863	Sharps	.50	39 in.	8 lb
1864	Warner	.50	36 in.	7 lb
1867	Ballard	.54	38 in.	7 lb
1870	Springfield	.50	41⅜ in.	7 lb 15 oz
1873	Springfield	.45	41⅜ in.	7 lb 12 oz
1879	(Progressive			
1884	variations of			
1890	Model 1873)			

U.S. single-shot cartridge pistols

Model	Manufacturer	Caliber	Total length	Weight
1866	Remington	.50	13¼ in.	2 lb 4 oz
1867	Remington	.50	11¾ in.	2 lb
1869	Springfield	.50	18¼ in.	4 lb 8 oz
1871	Remington	.50	12 in.	2 lb

U.S. single-shot cartridge rifles

Model	Manufacturer	Caliber	Total length	Average weight
1868	Springfield	.50	52 in.	9¼ lb
1868	Springfield (Cadet rifle)	.50	51⅞ in.	7½ lb
1870	Remington (U.S. Navy rifle)	.50	48⅝ in.	
1871	Remington (similar to 1870)	.50	51¾ in.	
1871	Ward-Burton	.50	51⅞ in.	
1873	Springfield	.45	52 in.	8¼ lb

machine gun, and a coaxially mounted .30 cal. machine gun.

U.S. tank M60A1E1/A1E2 This is the main battle tank of the U.S. Army and Marine Corps. It has a crew of four and is armed with Shillelagh missiles. It was previously armed with a 105mm gun. It is also equipped with one .50 cal. machine gun and one .30 cal. machine gun.

U.S. tank T9E1 The airborne version of the M22.

U.S. tank, heavy, M6A2 This tank was introduced in 1941. It had a crew of six, and was armed with one 3-in. gun T12, caliber length 50; one 37mm gun M6, cali-

ber length 53; three .50 cal. machine guns; and one .30 cal. machine gun M1919A4. It had a weight of 60 tons and could travel, on roads, at speeds up to about 27 mph.

U.S. tank, heavy, M103 This tank has a crew of five and is armed with one 120mm gun, one .50 cal. machine gun, and one .30 cal. machine gun. It has a weight of about 60 tons.

U.S. tank, heavy, Mark VIII This tank was designed by the British and called by them the "Allied" tank. It was built in the United States, but was armed with British guns. It was designed for use against highly organized defensive works, had a crew of

11 and a weight of 43.5 tons, and was armed with two 6-pounder guns and two Hotchkiss machine guns. Designed in England in 1917, it was not introduced until 1919.

U.S. tank, light, 3-ton A tank developed in 1918 by the Ford Motor Company. It weighed about 3.4 tons, had a crew of two, and was armed with one .30 cal. machine gun.

U.S. tank, light, 8-ton This tank was developed in 1918 and had an open, skeletal design so that it could cross wide trenches. It had a crew of two and was armed with one .30 cal. machine gun. It could travel 2 to 5 mph cross-country.

U.S. tanks, light, M2A2E3 and M2A3 Tanks introduced in 1938. They had a crew of four and were armed with one .50 cal. machine gun M2 and two .30 cal. machine guns M1919A4. Their weight was about 10 tons, and they could travel from 30 to 38 mph on roads.

U.S. tank, light, M2A4 A tank introduced in 1940 for use with light tank companies. It had a crew of four and was armed with one 37mm gun M5 and four .30 cal. machine guns M1919A4. It weighed 24,125 lb and could travel 35 mph on roads.

U.S. tank, light, M3A3 This tank was introduced in 1942 and had a crew of four, a speed (on roads) of 31 mph, a weight of 29,700 lb, and armament consisting of one 37mm gun M6 and three .30 cal. machine guns M1919A4.

U.S. tank, light, M5A1 A tank introduced in 1942 for use with armored divisions and armored reconnaissance cavalry. It had a crew of four and was armed with one 37mm gun and two .30 cal. machine guns M1919A4. It had a weight of 16.9 tons and could travel at speeds up to 36 mph on roads.

U.S. tank, light, M22 This tank was introduced in 1943 and was intended for airborne operations (and in that configuration designated T9E1). Called "Locust" by the British, it had a crew of three and was armed with one 37mm gun M6, caliber length 53, and one .30 cal. machine gun M1919A4. It had a weight of 8.5 tons and could make a speed of 40 mph on roads. The British forces used this tank in the Normandy landings on June 6, 1944.

U.S. tank, light, M24 A tank introduced in 1943 and used with armored divisions. It had a crew of four and was armed with one 75mm gun M6, caliber length 40; one .50 cal. machine gun M2 (antiaircraft); and two .30 cal. machine guns M1919A4. It had a weight of 20.3 tons and could travel at a speed of 34 mph on roads. It was the first tank of its weight class to mount a specially designed 75mm gun. It saw service in Europe and the Pacific during World War II and was also used later in Korea.

U.S. tank M41. (U.S. Army.)

U.S. tank, light, M551 See **Sheridan.**

U.S. tank, light, T1E2 A tank introduced in 1929. It had a crew of two and armament consisting of one 37mm gun M5, caliber length 50, and one .30 cal. machine gun M1919A4. It weighed 8.8 tons and could travel at a speed of 18.2 mph on roads.

U.S. tank, medium, M2A1 A tank introduced in 1939 for use with armored battalions. It had a crew of six and was armed with one 37mm gun M6, caliber length 53, and eight .30 cal. machine guns M1919A4. The weight of this tank was 19 tons, and it had a road speed of about 30 mph.

U.S. tank, medium, M3A1 The General Stuart or Stuart MK IV as provided to the British through lend-lease. See **Honey.**

U.S. tank, medium, M3A5 A tank introduced in 1942 for use with armored divisions. It had a crew of six and was armed with one 75mm gun M2, caliber length 31; one 37mm gun M6, caliber length 53; and three .30 cal. machine guns. The weight of the tank was 32.5 tons, and the speed, on roads, was about 25 mph. As used by the British, this tank was called the "General Lee."

U.S. tank, medium, M4A4 See **General Sherman.**

U.S. tank, medium, M7 This tank was introduced in 1941 for use with armored divisions. It had a crew of five and was armed with one 57mm gun M3 and two .30 cal. machine guns M1919A4. It had a weight of about 20 tons and could travel at speeds up to approximately 30 mph on roads.

U.S. tank, medium, M26 See **General Pershing.**

U.S. tank, medium, M46 This tank has a crew of five and is armed with one 90mm gun, two .50 cal. machine guns, and two .30 cal. machine guns. It has a weight of 48.5 tons.

U.S. tank, medium, T5 This basic design was introduced in 1938 to be employed with armored divisions. The T5 was equipped with the long 37mm gun, the T5E1 had two short 37mm guns, and the T5E2 had a pack howitzer in the hull. All models additionally carried six .30 cal. machine guns M1919A4. This tank weighed 15 tons and could make a speed of about 30 mph on roads.

U.S. tank recovery vehicle M31 This system was introduced in 1942. It carried a crew of six in basic recovery operations in the field. In order to confuse the enemy, it carried a dummy 75mm gun. Its only armament consisted of two .30 cal. machine guns. It weighed 32.8 tons and could travel at speeds up to 25 mph on roads.

U.S. torpedo Mark 13 This torpedo was designed for aircraft and PT-boat use. It is 22.42 in. in diameter and has a speed of 33 knots, a range of from 4,000 to 5,500 yd,

U.S. tank, medium, M3A1. (*U.S. Army.*)

a warhead weight of 600 lb, and a length of 13.5 ft.

U.S. torpedo Mark 14 A torpedo of the Mark 15 type, but with a length of 20.5 ft, which enables it to fit submarine tubes. It has two speeds: At 32 knots it has a range of 9,000 yd, and at 46 knots it has a range of about 4,500 yd. The warhead contains 700 lb of high explosive.

U.S. torpedo Mark 15 U.S. Navy three-speed steam-driven torpedo. It is 24 ft long and 21 in. in diameter. It weighs over 3,500 lb and carries a 600-lb explosive charge of torpex. It travels 6,000 yd at 46 knots, 10,000 yd at 34 knots, and 15,000 yd at 28 knots.

U.S. torpedo Mark 16 A torpedo with a diameter of 21 in., a length of 21.5 ft, and a warhead weight of 800 lb of high explosive. It is a single-speed torpedo with a speed of 46 knots and a range of 11,000 yd.

U.S. torpedo Mark 18 An essentially wakeless torpedo for submarine use. It has a length of 20.5 ft, a diameter of 21 in., and a warhead weight of 600 lb. A single-speed torpedo, it has a range of 4,000 yd at 29 knots.

U.S. torpedo Mark 23 A single-speed Mark 14 torpedo.

U.S. torpedo Mark 37 An electrically propelled torpedo launched from surface ships or submarines. Mod 0 is an antisubmarine-warfare and antishipping torpedo with passive or active homing guidance, a length of

U.S. tank, medium, M46. (*U.S. Army.*)

U.S. torpedo Mark 45. (*U.S. Navy.*)

U.S. torpedo Mark 48. (*U.S. Navy.*)

11.25 ft, a diameter of 19 in., and a weight of 1,430 lb. Mod 1 is a wire-guided antisubmarine-warfare torpedo with a weight of 1,690 lb and a length of 13.5 ft.

U.S. torpedo Mark 43   A lightweight homing antisubmarine-warfare torpedo for surface ships and aircraft. It has a weight of 265 lb.

U.S. torpedo Mark 44   An electrically propelled torpedo with active homing guidance. It is launched from surface ships or from DASH. Mod 0 has a length of 8.33 ft, a diameter of 12.75 in., and a weight of 422 lb. Mod 1 has a length of 8.5 ft, a diameter of 12.75 in., and a weight of 433 lb.

U.S. torpedo Mark 45   The ASTOR (*anti*submarine *tor*pedo) is an electrically propelled torpedo with a nuclear warhead. Both the Mod 0 (wire-guided antisubmarine-warfare torpedo) and the Mod 1 (antishipping or antisubmarine-warfare torpedo) are launched from submarines. Both have a length of 19.9 ft, a diameter of 19 in., a weight of 2,400 lb, and a range in excess of 10 mi.

U.S. torpedo Mark 46   A torpedo that is launched from surface ships or aircraft, and the successor to the Mark 44. Mod 0 is a solid-propellant torpedo with a length of 8.4 ft, a diameter of 12.75 in., and a weight of 570 lb. Mod 1 is a monopropellant fuel torpedo with the same basic specifications. This lightweight homing torpedo is designed to destroy fast, deep-diving, highly maneuverable submarines. The maximum estimated speed is 45 knots, the maximim operating depth is about 2,500 ft, and the maximum operating range is probably 15 to 20 mi.

U.S. torpedo Mark 48   A torpedo that is launched from surface ships or submarines, and the successor to the Mark 37. It is designed for use against high-speed, deepdiving submarines and utilizes a liquid monopropellant fuel. It has a weight of about 3,600 lb and a diameter of 21 in. It is wire-guided.

USW   Undersea warfare.

Utah   A class of U.S. battleships of 21,825 tons standard displacement. Two ships were in the class, *Utah* and *Florida*, both of which were commissioned in 1911. They had a length of 521 ft, a beam of 88 ft, a speed of 20.75 knots, and a complement of about 1,000 men. Main armament consisted of ten 12-in. guns, sixteen 5-in. guns, and two 21-in. torpedo tubes. *Florida* was decommissioned in 1931, and *Utah* was sunk by the Japanese at Pearl Harbor on December 7, 1941.

UTD   A U.S. utility boat, large.

UTL   A U.S. utility boat, light.

UTM   A U.S. utility boat, medium.

UUM   An underwater-to-underwater missile.

UUM-44A   See **Subroc.**

Utah. (*U.S. Navy.*)

UZI 9mm submachine gun. (*The Smithsonian Institution, Treasury Department Collection.*)

UXB An unexploded bomb.

UXO Unexploded ordnance.

UZI 9mm submachine gun A weapon designed by Uziel Gal, an officer in the Israeli Army. It is produced both in Israel and, under UZI license, by Fabrique Nationale in Belgium. It is a blowback-operated weapon with a cyclic rate of fire of 650 rounds per minute and selective full automatic and semiautomatic fire. The approximate muzzle velocity is 1,310 fps. With the stock retracted, the length is 17.9 in., and it has a barrel length of 10.20 in. It utilizes 25-, 32-, and 40-round magazines and weighs 8.80 lb with a 25-round magazine. This is one of the most widely distributed weapons in the Western World. It has been adopted by Israel, the Netherlands, and West Germany and has been purchased by numerous other European, African, and South American countries.

V

V-1 The abbreviation for *Vergeltungswaffe eins*, German for "Revenge Weapon One." A German robot bomb provided with wings, a horizontal stabilizer, a vertical stabilizer, a rudder, and elevators; it was used in World War II. Also called the "FZG-76" by the Germans and the "buzz bomb" by the British. The V-1, first landed across the English Channel on June 13, 1944, was powered by a pulse-jet engine mounted on its back. Its overall length was 25 ft 4 in., and its greatest diameter was 2 ft 7 in. This missile was provided with complicated control devices and was kept on course by an automatic pilot. It had a speed of about 360 mph and a range of 150 mi, and it flew at a height between 2,000 and 3,000 ft. Some 2,000 of these robot bombs were directed against England in World War II, most of them against London.

V-2 The abbreviation for *Vergeltunswaffe zwei*, German for "Revenge Weapon Two." A large German liquid-fueled rocket developed as a ballistic missile in World War II. Also called the "A-4" by the Germans. The V-2, first launched against England on September 8, 1944, developed 60,000 lb of thrust from its rocket engine. From nose to exhaust tail, it measured 46 ft, and its diameter was about 5 ft. Shaped like an artillery projectile, it was without wings, but was subject to some guidance through movable panels built into the four tail fins and through graphite vanes extending into the exhaust stream. Launched vertically, it quickly reached a speed of 3,600 mph and then was tilted in the direction of its target. It exhausted its fuel supply of 9 tons in 60 seconds, but reached an altitude of 60 mi with a range of 200 mi and plunged earthward at about 1,500 mph. Some 1,115 V-2's were sent across the Channel in the last months of World War II.

VADS Vulcan Air Defense System.

Val The Allied code name for the Aichi D3A2 Type 99 single-engine carrier-based dive bomber used by the JNAF during World War II. It had a speed of 266 mph,

V-1. (*The Imperial War Museum.*)

a range of 838 mi with an 823-lb bombload, and armament consisting of three 7.7mm machine guns.

Valentine A British infantry tank (Mark III) that entered production in 1940. It had a crew of two, a weight of 16 tons, a length of about 18 ft, and a speed of 15 mph. It was originally armed with one 2-pounder gun and one machine gun (6-pounder guns being installed in later models). It saw considerable service during World War II, particularly in the Western Desert of Africa. Some 8,275 tanks of this type were produced.

Valetta A British Vickers-built twin-engine transport developed from a design (the commercial *Viking*) first flown in June 1945. It had a maximum speed of 263 mph and carried 27 passengers.

Valiant 1. A class of British nuclear-powered fleet submarines (SSN) of 3,500 tons standard surface displacement, the first of which were commissioned in 1966–1967. They have a length of 285 ft, a beam of 33.2 ft, a speed of approximately 30 knots, and a complement of 103 men. They are armed with six 21-in. torpedo tubes. **2.** A British battleship of the **Queen Elizabeth** class, which see. It was completed in 1914. **3.** A British four-engine (turbojet) bomber first flown in 1952. Developed by Vickers, this aircraft had a crew of five and carried a 10,000-lb bombload.

vambrace In armor, the defensive system for the entire arm below the shoulder. (Picture, next page.)

Vampire This de Havilland single-seat fighter-interceptor was Britain's second jet fighter (the other having been the Gloster Meteor) and was first flown in September 1943. Powered by a turbojet engine with 3,100 lb of thrust, this airplane flew at a maximum speed of 531 mph and was armed with four 20mm Hispano cannons. A version of this aircraft was the first pure jet to operate from a carrier deck, those trials having taken place on December 3, 1945. This airplane was not used operationally during World War II. (Picture, next page.)

vamplate In the sixteenth and seventeenth centuries, the round piece of metal fitted on the shaft of a lance to protect the user's

Valentine. (*Vickers Ltd.*)

Valetta. (*Vickers Ltd.*)

Valiant. (*Vickers Ltd.*)

Valiant. (*Vickers Ltd.*)

vambrace. (*The Metropolitan Museum of Art, John Stoneacre Ellis Collection.*)

Vampire. (*Hawker Siddeley Aviation Ltd.*)

hand.

van 1. The forward portion of a formation of ships—the opposite of rear. **2.** Formerly, the front of an army or other advancing body.

Vandenberg volley gun A weapon used in limited numbers by Confederate forces during the American Civil War. It had from 85 to 451 barrels and was made to fire .45 cal. bullets. It was invented by the American Gen. O. Vandenberg.

vanguard An element of the advanced guard.

Vanguard 1. A British battleship of 44,500 tons standard displacement and the largest warship ever built in Great Britain. Completed in 1946, this ship had a length of 814 ft, a beam of 108 ft, and a speed of 29.5 knots. It had a complement of 1,600 men and was armed with eight 15-in. guns, sixteen 5.25-in. guns, and seventy 40mm anti-aircraft guns. **2.** The Vultee P-66 Vanguard was a single-seat single-engine interceptor first flown in 1939. Limited numbers were produced, with the majority (124) going to China under lend-lease. It flew at a speed of 331 mph and was armed with two .50 cal machine guns and four .30 cal. machine guns.

Van Speijk A class of Dutch frigates of 2,200 tons standard displacement completed in 1967–1968. They have a speed of 28.5 knots, a complement of 254 men, and armament consisting of two 4.5-in. guns, one three-barreled depth-charge mortar, two quadruple launchers for Seacat, and one lightweight helicopter armed with homing torpedoes.

vapor trail See **condensation trail.**

variability The manner in which the probability of damage to a specific target decreases with the distance from ground zero. In damage assessment, a mathematical factor introduced to average the effects of orientation, minor shielding, and uncertainty of target response to the effects considered.

variable time fuze A fuze designed to detonate a projectile, bomb, mine, or charge when activated by external influence other than contact in the close vicinity of a target.

Vautour The French Sud-Aviation SO 4050 two-seat jet bomber and all-weather fighter used by French and Israeli forces. It has a speed of Mach 0.9 and is armed with four 30mm cannons and two packs containing 232 rockets. It can also carry four Matra R 511 air-to-air missiles. It was first flown in 1952.

V.B. rifle grenade A grenade adopted by the United States in 1917. Invented by the Frenchmen Viven and Bessière, it had a length of 2.5 in., a diameter of 2 in., and a range of about 300 yd.

vectored attacks Attacks in which a weapon carrier (air, surface, or subsurface) not holding contact on the target is vectored to the weapon delivery point by a unit (air, surface, or subsurface) which holds contact on the target.

V-E Day In World War II, the day of victory in Europe. The Germans surrendered on May 8, 1945.

Vega A French surface-to-air missile with

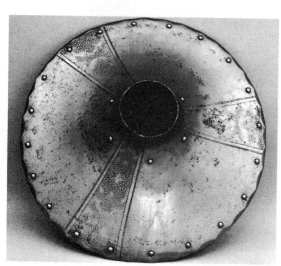

vamplate. (*The Metropolitan Museum of Art, gift of William H. Riggs, 1913.*)

Venom. (*Hawker Siddeley Aviation Ltd.*)

a range of about 115,000 ft.

vehicle A self-propelled, boosted, or towed conveyance for transporting a burden on land, on sea, or through air or space.

Vela This U.S. program provided research in advanced sensors for the detection and evaluation of nuclear tests in underground, underwater, atmosphere, and space environments.

Vela Hotel A U.S. satellite program for the detection of nuclear detonations in space, a role now absorbed by the **Integrated Satellite,** which see.

velocity The speed of a projectile. It is usually measured in feet per second (fps).

Veltro The Macchi C.205V Veltro (Greyhound) was a single-seat single-engine fighter-interceptor and fighter-bomber developed for the Italian Air Force and first flown in April 1942. A progressive development of the Folgore, this airplane was powered by a 1,475-hp engine and flew at speeds up to 399 mph. It was armed with two 20mm Mauser cannons and two 12.7mm Breda-SAFAT machine guns, and it also carried two 110-lb, 220-lb, or 353-lb bombs.

Vengeance A single-engine two-place aircraft used during World War II. Produced in the United States, it was used mostly by RAF and Royal Indian Air Force units in the India-Burma theater. It had a speed of 279 mph and armament consisting of four to six .50 cal. machine guns and two 500-lb bombs.

Venom 1. A British single-place single-engine jet fighter and fighter-bomber with twin tail booms. It was a further development of the de Havilland **Vampire,** which see. 2. A British (Vickers-built) low-wing single-engine fighter of the 1930s.

vent The aperture at the rear of a muzzle-loading cannon that communicates fire to the main charge.

Ventura A U.S. twin-engine light bomber first produced in 1941 by the firm of Lockheed-Vega and designated B-34 and, with modifications, B-37. (The U.S. Navy designation was PV-1.) It flew at a top speed of 298 mph and could carry 2,000 lb of bombs.

verat An ancient twelve-pounder gun weighing about 2,300 lb.

verification fire Preparatory fire to test the mechanical adjustment of guns and fire-control equipment and to measure the accuracy of corrections determined by calibration and trial fire.

verify 1. To ensure that the meaning and phraseology of the transmitted message convey the exact intention of the originator. 2. A request from an observer, a spotter, or a fire-control agency to reexamine firing data and report the results of the reexamination.

Vermont A U.S. battleship of the **Kansas** class, which see. It was commissioned in

Ventura. (*Lockheed Aircraft Corporation.*)

1907.

vertical bomb A bomb that has no wings, but is sometimes provided with control surfaces, such as in the azon or razon bomb. It is distinguished from a glide bomb or robot bomb such as the V-1.

vertical envelopment A tactical maneuver in which troops, either airdropped or air-landed, attack the rear and flanks of a force, in effect cutting off or encircling it.

vertol Vertical takeoff and landing.

Very pistol Named after its inventor, USN Lieut. Edward W. Very (1847–1910). A flare pistol used for signaling; specifically, a flare pistol of a type designed by Very having a relatively short barrel. The original Very system consisted of firing various combinations of red and green fireballs, the arrangement having a code significance.

vesicants Chemical agents that injure the flesh by inflammation, burns, or blister production.

Vetterli 10.4mm rifle Model 1869–81 Various Vetterli rifles were used by Switzerland during a period from 1869, when they were first introduced, until 1889, when the first Schmidt-Rubin rifles were adopted. They featured a bolt action but a tubular magazine. The Model 1881, for example, had a tubular magazine with a capacity of 12 cartridges. It had an overall length of 52 in., a barrel length of 33.2 in., and a weight of 9.75 lb.

Vetterli 10.4mm rifle Model 1871 This weapon was designed by the Swiss engineer F. Vetterli. A single-shot rifle, it was adopted by Italy in 1871. In 1887 this rifle was adapted to handle a box magazine (see **Vetterli-Vitali 10.4mm rifle Model 1871–87**).

Very pistol. (*The Smithsonian Institution.*)

Rifles of these patterns were used by the Italians in both world wars. The overall length of the rifle, without bayonet, is 53.5 in., and the barrel has a length of 34 in. The weight is 9.56 lb.

Vetterli-Vitali 10.4mm rifle Model 1871–87 This is the Vetterli M1871 single-shot rifle modified to receive the Vitali single-column box magazine. The capacity of the magazine is four rounds.

veuglaire A type of small sixteenth-century breechloading cannon.

Vickers .30 cal. aircraft machine gun M1918 This weapon is recoil-operated with gas assist. It has a cyclic rate of fire of 800 to 900 rounds per minute, a muzzle velocity of 2,800 fps, and a feed device consisting of a 250-round fabric belt or disintegrating link belt. It has a length of 44.19 in., a barrel length of 28.4 in., and a weight of 25 lb. (Picture, next page.)

Vickers .303 medium machine gun Mk I Also called the "British .303 medium machine gun Mk I," this weapon is recoil-operated and has a cyclic rate of fire of 500 rounds per minute. The length of the gun is 3.6 ft, and the weight of the gun, with

Vetterli 10.4mm rifle Model 1878/81. (*Swiss Military Department.*)

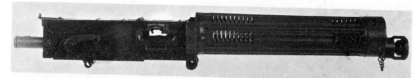

Vickers .30 cal. aircraft machine gun M1918. (*The Smithsonian Institution, Treasury Department Collection.*)

Vickers .303 medium machine gun Mk I. (*Vickers Ltd.*)

water, is 40 lb. The gun is fed by a fabric belt holding 250 rounds. At one time called the "Vickers Maxim," this weapon was adopted by the British in 1912 and was used in both world wars.

Vickers-Armstrong 6-ton tank Type A and Type B These tanks were first produced in 1928 and set new standards in track life. Old-style plate tracks rarely lasted more than 20 mi, but the manganese-steel skeleton-type tracks of these tanks could travel for about 3,000 mi. The Type A carried two machine guns in the turret, while the Type B carried a machine gun and a three-pounder gun. Tanks of this type were exported to Russia, Japan, Poland, Siam, China, Finland, and Bulgaria.

Vickers-Armstrong 37mm aircraft cannon This British weapon was a further development of the C.O.W. 37mm aircraft cannon and was produced in the 1920s and 1930s. A limited number were used to arm flying boats. They were recoil-operated and air-cooled and had a rate of fire of 150 rounds per minute. They weighed 150 lb and were fed from six-round magazines.

Vickers-Berthier .303 cal. aircraft machine gun Mk I A British World War I gas-operated air-cooled machine gun with a rate of fire of 750 to 900 rounds per minute. It weighed 31.5 lb and was fed from a 97-round flat drum.

Vickers-Berthier .303 light machine gun Also called the "British .303 light machine gun (Vickers-Berthier)," this gas-operated weapon has a cyclic rate of fire of 500 to 600 rounds per minute and selective-fire capabilities. It has a weight of 22 lb and a length of 45.5 in. and utilizes a vertical box magazine with a capacity of 30 cartridges.

Vickers-Berthier .303 machine gun Mark III The Berthier light machine gun was first introduced in 1908, and the Vickers Company purchased the manufacturing rights in 1925. For details of this weapon, see **Indian .303 cal. Vickers-Berthier machine gun.** The Indian Army was the only one to adopt this weapon officially.

Vickers F.B.5 A British two-place single-engine biplane (pusher) fighter that became operational early in 1915. It was armed with a front-firing Lewis gun and had a speed of 70 mph. It was nicknamed "Gunbus."

Vickers F.B.9 This aircraft, called the "Streamline Gunbus," was a follow-on to the F.B.5 and appeared in December 1915. It had shorter wings and a rotatable Lewis machine gun on a ball-and-socket mounting in the prow of the nacelle. Its operational career ended in the fall of 1916.

Vickers F.B.19 A British single-seat single-engine biplane fighter first flown in August 1916. It had a speed of about 98 mph and was armed with a single front-firing synchronized Vickers machine gun. It was produced in limited numbers.

Vickers machine guns A Maxim-type (see **Maxim machine gun**) series of weapons used by Great Britain and various other countries, including France, Japan, the United States, Portugal, Switzerland, Chile, China, Turkey, and Czechoslovakia.

Vickers main battle tank A British-built tank developed between 1958 and 1963 and presently in service in Kuwait and India. It has a crew of four, a weight of 38 tons, a road speed of 33 mph, and main armament consisting of one British 105mm gun (equipped with a ranging .50 cal. machine gun). Secondary armament consists of an additional .50 cal. machine gun and one .30 cal. machine gun.

Vickers-Maxim machine guns Maxim machine guns produced by the British firm of Vickers. See **Maxim machine gun.**

Vickers Vimy A British twin-engine bomber first flown in August 1917, but produced too late for operational service during World War I. It had a speed of 103 mph, armament consisting of four Lewis machine guns, and a bombload of 4,408 lb. These planes were used in British bombing squadrons from 1919 to 1924, but continued in service as trainers until the early 1930s.

Vickers-Armstrong 6-ton tank Type A. (*Vickers Ltd.*)

Vickers-Berthier .303 cal. aircraft machine gun Mk I. *(Vickers Ltd.)*

Vickers F.B.9. *(Vickers Ltd.)*

Vickers main battle tank. *(Vickers Ltd.)*

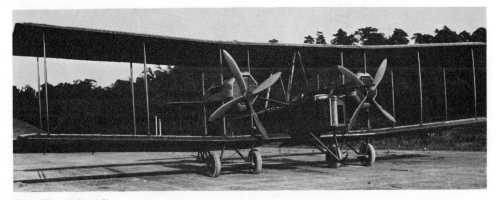

Vickers Vimy. *(Vickers Ltd.)*

A Vimy made the first nonstop transatlantic crossing in April 1919, flying between St. Johns, Newfoundland, and Clifden, Northern Ireland. It was piloted by Capt. John Alcock and Lieut. Arthur Whitten-Brown.

Victor A British four-jet medium bomber developed by Handley Page and first flown in 1952. It had a five-man crew and a speed of 655 mph.

Victoria Cross A British decoration consisting of a bronze Maltese cross awarded a member of the British armed services for remarkable valor. First bestowed in 1857, it is the most highly prized of British military decorations. The abbreviation is V.C.

Viggen The Saab-37 Viggen (Thunderbolt) is a single-seat multimission jet combat aircraft in service with the Swedish Air Force and first flown in 1967. It has a speed above Mach 2 and is armed with a variety of systems that attach to three positions under the fuselage and one under each wing. Typical packages are 30mm gun pods, Saab Rb 05 rockets, bombs, and mines. (Picture, next page.)

Vigilant 1. A wire-guided antitank missile built by the British Aircraft Corporation and in service with the British and Finnish Armies. It has a length of 3.5 ft, a launching weight of 31 lb, a warhead weight of 13.2 lb, and a range of 1 mi. The hollow-charge warhead can penetrate 22 in. of armor plate. This man-portable solid-propellant missile is launched from its carrying case. **2.** A single-engine liaison and observation monoplane developed for the USAAF during World War II by Vultee. (Picture, next page.)

Vigilante A supersonic twin-engine (turbojet) tactical all-weather attack aircraft designed to be operated from carriers and developed for the U.S. Navy by North American. First flown in 1958, this aircraft has a speed of Mach 2.1 and a range of 2,650 mi and can carry a variety of weapons, including nuclear weapons, in a large internal weapons bay and on under-wing attachments. (Picture, next page.)

Vigneron 9mm Parabellum submachine gun M2 A Belgian weapon with selective full automatic and semiautomatic operation. It is blowback-operated and has a cyclic rate of fire of 620 rounds per minute. With its stock telescoped, it is about 24 in. long. The barrel length is 12 in., and the weight of the weapon, with a fully loaded 32-round magazine, is 8.74 lb. It was adopted by the Belgian Army, Navy, and Air Force in 1953. (Picture, next page.)

Vijayanta (Victorious) An Indian tank manufactured in Madras, India, to a design by the Vickers Engineering Company of

Viggen. (*Swedish Air Force.*)

Vigilant. (*Vickers Ltd.*)

Vigilante. (*U.S. Navy.*)

Vigneron 9mm Parabellum submachine gun M2. (*Belgian Ministry of Defense.*)

England. Production started in 1967. It has a crew of four, a weight of 37.5 tons, a road speed of 35 mph, and main armament consisting of a British 105mm QF gun with a range of 1,800 meters (APDS) or 6,400 meters (HESH). The gun is ranged with a .50 cal. machine gun. Secondary armament consists of two .30 cal. machine guns.

Vildebeest A single-engine three-place biplane designed by Vickers in 1926 as a torpedo-carrying and bombing landplane. At that time, torpedo bombers were regarded as a frontline weapon for coastal defense.

Villar-Perosa 9mm aircraft machine gun (double-barreled) An Italian recoil- and blowback-operated air-cooled machine gun with a rate of fire of 1,500 rounds per minute (per barrel). It weighed 14.75 lb and was fed from 50-round magazines.

Villar-Perosa 9mm (Glisenti) submachine gun Model 1915 The Italian Villar Perosa (V.P.) was the first known weapon to fire pistol ammunition automatically and is therefore rated as the first submachine gun. It is sometimes referred to as the "Revelli," from the name of its designer, Abiel Betel Revelli. The first version, the Model 1915, was a retarded-blowback-operated weapon. It was originally produced with no stock and was mounted in dual sets. It was used on aircraft, on motorcycle sidecars, and on various bipods and tripods. The twin-gun version had an overall length of 21 in., a barrel length of 12.56 in., and a weight of about 16 lb. The cyclic rate of fire was about 1,200 rounds per minute, and it operated at full automatic only. The weapon utilized a 25-round detachable box magazine.

Villar-Perosa 9mm (Glisenti) submachine gun O.V.P. This was the version of the Villar-Perosa Model 1915 with stock attached and with provisions for selective fire.

Vindicator The Vought-Sikorsky SB2U-3 was a single-engine two-seat scout and dive bomber developed for the U.S. Navy and used during the early part of World War II. It had a speed of 257 mph and was armed with four .30 cal. machine guns in the wings, a single .30 cal. machine gun in the rear cockpit, and a 1,000-lb bombload. The British version was called the "Chesapeake."

vireton Also called "vire," this was a long, light arrow with the feathers arranged so that the arrow revolved around its axis and provided more stability in flight. It was often used in crossbows.

Virginia A U.S. battleship of the **New Jersey** class, which see. It was commissioned in 1906.

visibility range The horizontal distance (in kilometers) at which a large, dark object can just be seen against the horizon sky in daylight.

visor   That part of a helmet which covered the face. Visors were usually arranged so as to lift or pivot to open, and they had holes in them for seeing and breathing.

visual bombing   Bombing done by sighting on an aiming point or points, under conditions where the aiming point or points are visible from the bombing aircraft.

visual bombsight   A bombsight designed for aiming a bomb when the aiming point is visible.

visual signaling   Any system of signaling that depends on visual contact, such as lights, flags, panels, flares, smoke, etc.

vital area   A designated area or installation to be defended by air-defense units.

vital ground   **Key terrain,** which see.

Vittorio Veneto   An Italian guided-missile cruiser of 8,850 tons displacement completed in 1969. It has a speed of 32 knots, a complement of 550 men, and armament consisting of eight 3-in. antiaircraft guns, two triple torpedo tubes, and one Terrier-Asroc twin launcher.

V-J Day   During World War II, the day of victory in the war against Japan. Hostilities ceased on August 14, 1945, and the formal surrender took place aboard the battleship *Missouri* on September 2, 1945.

voider   In armor, a covering of mail over any part of the body not protected by plate armor.

Voisin 5   A French two-place single-engine (pusher) biplane bomber introduced in 1915. It had a speed of 65 mph and was armed with one Hotchkiss machine gun for use by the observer and 132 lb of bombs.

Voisin 8   A French two-place single-engine biplane night bomber introduced in 1916. It was armed with one or two machine guns and 396 lb of bombs. A later version, the Voisin 10, appeared in 1918 and could carry about 660 lb of bombs.

volant piece   In the sixteenth century, a reinforcing piece of armor that protected the lower face, neck, and upper chest.

Volksjäger   See **Heinkel He 162A Salamander.**

Volkssturm Gewehr 1 7.92mm rifle   A last-ditch weapon made in Germany at the end of World War II. This was a poorly made rifle that used the magazine of the semiautomatic Model 43 rifle. It fired the standard 7.92mm cartridge and had an overall length of 43 in., a barrel length of 23.2 in., and a weight of 8.3 lb. It utilized a 10-round staggered-row detachable box magazine.

Volkssturm Karabiner 98 7.92mm rifle   A weapon fabricated in the closing days of World War II. It combined the Model 98 rifle action with miscellaneous barrels from old German and foreign Mausers. For the most part these were single-shot weapons and had an overall length of 40.6 in., a barrel length of 20.8 in., and an overall

Vildebeest. (*Vickers Ltd.*)

Vindicator. (*Vought Aeronautics Company.*)

Volkssturm Gewehr 1 7.92mm rifle. (*The Smithsonian Institution, William Penn Memorial Museum Collection.*)

weight of 6.9 lb.

volley   **1.** A method of artillery firing in which each piece fires the specified number of rounds without any attempt to synchronize with the other pieces.   **2.** A burst of fire, especially a salute fired by a detachment of riflemen.   **3.** The simultaneous discharge of a large number of muskets, arrows, etc.

volley bombing   A simultaneous or nearly simultaneous release of a number of bombs.

volley fire   In modern usage, artillery fire

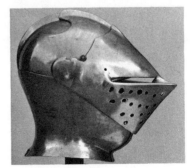

visor. (*The Metropolitan Museum of Art, Bashford Dean Memorial Collection.*)

Voodoo. (*U.S. Air Force.*)

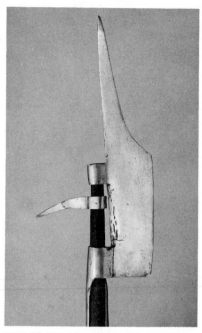

vouge. (*The Metropolitan Museum of Art, gift of William H. Riggs, 1913.*)

Vulcan. (*Hawker Siddeley Aviation Ltd.*)

in which each piece fires a specified number of rounds without regard to the other pieces and as fast as accuracy will permit. In the days of linear tactics, the term referred to the simultaneous discharge of all the muskets in a unit of men.

volley gun   A gun or rifle with multiple barrels, all of which discharge simulta-

neously.

vomiting agents   War gases and mob- and riot-control gases, such as **DA, DM,** and **DC,** which see. These three vomiting agents are normally solids which, when heated, vaporize and then condense to form toxic aerosols. Under field conditions, vomiting agents cause great discomfort to their vic-

tims; when released indoors, they may cause serious illness or death. The vomiting agents are also used for mob and riot control.

vomiting gas   See **vomiting agents.**

Von der Tann   A German battle cruiser completed in 1910. It had a normal displacement of 19,400 tons, a speed of 25 knots, and a complement of 910 men. Main armament consisted of eight 11-in. guns, ten 6-in. guns, and four 18-in. torpedo tubes.

Von Roeder   A class of German 2,400-ton destroyers of World War II. They had a speed of 38 knots, a complement of 313 men, and main armament consisting of five 5-in. guns and eight 21-in. torpedo tubes. There were six ships in this class, five of which were lost during the war.

Voodoo   The McDonnell F-101 is a twin-jet supersonic fighter-interceptor developed for the U.S. Air Force and first flown in 1954. There are different versions of this aircraft (single-place and two-place) and both nuclear and nonnuclear armament systems. A typical armament package consists of four 20mm cannons, three Falcon missiles, and twelve rockets. It has a speed of Mach 1.7+.

vouge, voulge   A type of polearm of the twelfth to the sixteenth centuries. The example shown is Swiss and is dated 1380.

VRFWS   Vehicle Rapid Fire Weapon System. This U.S. system, also designated M139, is a 20mm weapon with a weight of about 145 lb, a length of 101 in., and a maximum range of 7,200 meters (an effective fighting range of 1,500 meters). It has a rate of fire of 800 to 1,050 rounds per minute.

VSTOL Vertical and/or short takeoff and landing capability for aircraft.

VT fuze See **proximity fuze.**

VTOL A type of aircraft having a vertical takeoff and landing capability.

Vulcan The British Hawker Siddeley Vulcan (originally developed by Avro) was the first jet bomber to employ a delta-wing configuration and was first flown in 1952. It has a speed of Mach 0.94 and may be armed with a weapon load consisting of a Blue Steel air-to-surface missile, free-fall nuclear weapons, or twenty-one 1,000-lb bombs.

Vulcan automatic gun A very fast-firing machine gun of the Gatling type. It is made in 20mm and 30mm calibers. The U.S. Air Force M61 consists of a cluster of six electrically driven rotating barrels firing about 100 rounds a second. For more information see **U.S. 20mm Gatling gun M61.** The illustration shows a Vulcan mounted on a U.S. Army M114A1 vehicle. This version fires an average of 3,202 rounds per minute from a linkless ammunition feed system which stores 1,200 rounds of ammunition in a ready-to-fire condition.

vulnerability The susceptibility of a nation or military force to any action by any means through which its war potential or

Vulcan automatic gun. (*U.S. Army.*)

combat effectiveness may be reduced or its will to fight diminished.

vulnerable area Specifically, the product of (1) the probability that a projectile which strikes an armored vehicle will cause disabling damage and (2) the presented area of the vehicle.

VX This war gas is one of the **nerve agents,** which see, and has a quick-acting casualty effect with a normally long duration of effectiveness. Skin absorption great enough to cause death may occur in 1 to 2 minutes, although death may be delayed for 1 to 2 hours. Respiratory lethal dosages kill in 1 to 10 minutes, and liquid in the eye kills nearly as rapidly.

W

WAAC A member of the Women's Auxiliary Army Corps, an organization formed in England in 1917.

WAAPM Wide-*area* *a*ntipersonnel *m*ine. The BLU-54/B antipersonnel bounding mine which is dropped by USAF aircraft.

WAC A member of the Women's Army Corps of the U.S. Army, first established by an act of Congress on July 1, 1943.

Waco CG-4 glider This U.S. glider was developed during World War II, had a wingspan of 83.6 ft, and could carry 13 troops. It was used in the invasion of Sicily and also in northern and southern France. With British Horsa gliders, CG-4's were used in the largest glider operation of World War II, the abortive attempt to seize the Rhine crossing at Arnheim in September 1944. The CG-4 was also nicknamed "Hadrian."

Waco CG-13 A U.S. glider of World War II. It had a wingspan of 85.5 ft and a speed of about 190 mph. It could carry 8,000 lb of cargo or 42 troops. It had a crew of two.

wad A felt or cardboard pad used to secure the propellant in place in cartridges. It was formerly used in muzzle-loading cannons and other firearms to retain a charge of powder or to keep the powder and host close.

wad cutter A bullet designed for target shooting and shaped to cut a clean hole in a paper target.

wad hook A screw or hook formerly used to draw wadding from a muzzle-loading gun.

WAF A member of the women's component of the U.S. Air Force.

Waffen-SS See **Schutzstaffel (SS)**.

WAGB A U.S. Navy icebreaker.

Wager A class of British destroyers of 1,710 tons standard displacement completed in 1943–1944. They had a speed of 33 knots, a complement of 186 men, and armament consisting of four 4.7-in. guns, five 40mm and four 20mm antiaircraft guns, four depth-charge throwers, and eight 21-in. torpedo tubes.

WAGO A U.S. Navy oceanographic cutter.

WAK A U.S. Navy cargo cutter.

Wakatake A class of Japanese 820-ton destroyers completed in the mid-1920s. They had a speed of 35 knots, a complement of 110 men, and main armament consisting of three 4.7-in. guns, two 7.7mm guns, and two 21-in. torpedo tubes. Five ships of this class were in service during World War II, and all were lost.

walkie-talkie A two-way voice radio set, normally carried on the back with the receiver and microphone on a cord, used either while in motion or while at rest. The World War II versions were powered by dry batteries and had a range of 1 to 2 mi.

Walleye A 1,100-lb glide bomb developed for the U.S. Navy by the Naval Ordnance Test Station, China Lake, Calif. It carries a television camera which transmits a picture of the target to a monitor aboard the launch aircraft. Once the pilot centers the Walleye on target, it automatically homes

Waco CG-4 glider. (*U.S. Air Force.*)

494

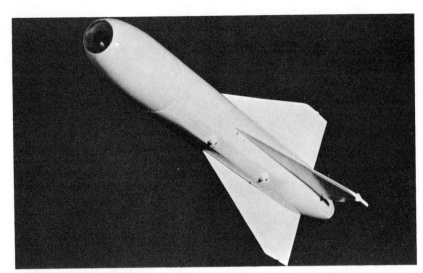

Walleye. (*Martin Marietta Aerospace Group.*)

on it, leaving the pilot free to take any necessary evasive action. The weapon has an overall length of 11 ft 3 in., a diameter of 1.3 ft, and a range of 3 to 5 mi. It entered production in 1966.

wall grenade Formerly, a grenade larger than a hand grenade that was thrown from a wall of a fortified place.

wall-piece A small cannon or large musket (or rifle) mounted on the wall of a fortress. It was usually supported on a swivel and was sometimes also called a "rampart gun" or "swivel gun." See **amusette.**

Walrus A British Supermarine-built single-engine biplane amphibious flying boat used prior to, and during, World War II for reconnaissance, training, and air and sea rescue. First flown in 1935, it had a speed of 135 mph and was armed with two machine guns.

Walther .25 ACP pistol Model 8 A .25 cal. automatic pistol with a magazine capacity of eight rounds. It weighs 12.83 oz and has an overall length of 5.12 in., with a barrel length of 2.92 in. It was carried by German ranking officers during World War II as an auxiliary arm.

Walther 7.65mm automatic pistols PP and PPK The Model PP (Police Pistol)

was introduced in Germany by the firm of Karl Walther in 1929. It is a double-action pistol with an overall length of about 6.8 in., a barrel length of 3.9 in., a magazine capacity of eight cartridges, and a total weight of about 23 oz. It was later manufactured for the .22 Long Rifle and the .380 ACP cartridges. The Model PPK (Police Pistol "Kriminal") was developed in 1931 as a smaller model of the PP. It has an overall length of 6.1 in., a barrel length of 3.4 in., and a weight of about 18½ oz. The magazine has a capacity of seven cartridges. These weapons were widely used by German forces in World War II. A copy of the PP, made by the Turkish government arms plant at Kirikkale, was a standard handgun of the Turkish forces.

Walther 9mm (Luger) automatic pistol P-38 When introduced by Walther, this pistol was designated the H.P. model. During World War II the official designation became P-38. The weapon has an overall length of 8.6 in., a barrel length of 4.9 in., and a weight of about 34 oz. The capacity of the magazine is eight cartridges. The P-38 as developed for use with the 9mm Parabellum cartridge is now the standard side arm of the West German Army. It is

called the "P1" in that army.

wambais A gambeson, or quilted protective covering for the body. It is composed of layers of cloth or other material quilted onto a foundation of canvas or leather. The outer covering may be of linen or silk. They were commonly found in twelfth-century Europe.

Wampum A U.S. Army anti-intrusion device consisting of 3,200 yd of thin double-strand wire which is strung about an area. When the wire is tripped, a buzzer or light, activated by a battery, signals enemy penetration in the area. The entire unit weighs only ½ lb and is the size of a cigarette pack.

wanigan A house or shelter, usually mounted on a vehicle or sled, which may be placed on the ground. It is used for sleeping, cooking and eating, storage, first aid, and machine-shop or other special purpose so it is particulary adapted for use in arctic regions.

war bow The English longbow. Cloth yard arrows were used with such bows.

war cart A four-wheeled wagon with a protective covering. It mounted two small cannons. A larger version of a war cart carried a number of men and represented

Walther 7.65mm automatic pistol PPK. (*The Smithsonian Institution, Treasury Department Collection.*)

Walrus. (*Vickers Ltd.*)

Walther 9mm (Luger) automatic pistol P-38. (*The Smithsonian Institution, Treasury Department Collection.*)

war hammer. (*The Metropolitan Museum of Art, Rogers Fund, 1904.*)

Warning Star. (*U.S. Navy.*)

Warwick. (*Vickers Ltd.*)

a small movable fortress.

war club Any type of club used by warriors or soldiers.

war cry A cry used by warriors or soldiers to raise their own morale and also to terrify an enemy.

wardroom Living quarters for the commissioned officers of a ship.

war drum A drum that is beaten on the march or in battle.

war game A simulation, by whatever means, of a military operation involving two or more opposing forces and using rules, data, and procedures designed to depict an actual or assumed real-life situation.

war gases Any chemical agent (liquid, solid, or vapor), used in war, which produces poisonous or irritant effects on the human body. War gases can be subdivided into the following categories, which see: **blistering agents, blood agents, choking agents, incapacitating chemical agents, nerve agents, tear agents,** and **vomiting agents.**

war hammer A hammer with a heavy head, often having a blunt or cusped face side and a spiked poll. In the fifteenth and sixteenth centuries war hammers were much used for breaking armor.

Warhawk The Curtiss P-40D/Q single-seat fighter-bomber developed as a follow-on to the **Tomahawk,** which see. A number of these aircraft were allocated to Great Britain (where the fighter was called "Kittyhawk"), China, the Soviet Union, and Australia. Powered by a 1,300-hp engine, the aircraft flew at speeds up to 365 mph and was armed with six .50 cal. machine guns, plus a bombload weighing up to 1,000 lb.

warhead That part of a missile, projectile, torpedo, rocket, or other munition which contains either the nuclear or thermonuclear system, the high-explosive system, chemical or biological agents, or inert materials intended to inflict damage.

warhead compartment The section of a missile in which the warhead installation is mounted. In some cases the warhead compartment may be part of the adaptation kit.

warhead mating The act of attaching a warhead section to the rocket or to the missile body, torpedo, airframe, motor, or guidance section.

warhead section A completely assembled warhead including appropriate skin sections and related components.

warning piece A gun that fires a warning signal.

warning red See **air-defense warning conditions.**

Warning Star A variation of the Lockheed Super Constellation used by the Air Force as the RC-121 and by the Navy as the WV-2. It was developed to patrol the U.S. coasts on an "always-on-station" basis for high-altitude radar picket duties.

warning white See **air-defense warning conditions.**

warning yellow See **air-defense warning conditions.**

war potential The capacity and capability of a country to conduct a war, with respect to political, economic, industrial, social, psychological, and military factors.

warrant officer An officer who receives his rank by warrant rather than by commission. The rank is intermediate between that of noncommissioned and commissioned officers.

war reserves Stocks or material amassed in peacetime to meet the increase in military requirements consequent upon an outbreak of war. War reserves are intended to provide the interim support essential to sustain operations until resupply can be effected.

Warrior **1.** A class of British 13,550-ton cruisers completed in 1907–1908. They had a length of 480 ft, a complement of 704 men, and main armament consisting of six 9.2-in. and four 7.5-in. guns. They had a speed of 23 knots. **2.** A British warship launched in 1860. It was the first iron-hulled armored warship. It and a sister ship, *Black Prince*, had a displacement of 9,210 tons, a speed of 14.5 knots, and armament consisting of nine smoothbore cannons.

war scythe   An ancient weapon with a scythe-like blade in line with the handle.

warship   A naval vessel equipped for war purposes, particularly an armed vessel.

Warspite   A British battleship of the **Queen Elizabeth** class, which see.

Warwick   A British (Vickers-Armstrong-built) twin-engine aircraft used during and after World War II for general transport, reconnaissance, and air rescue duties.

war zone   Designated areas in which the rights of neutrals are not respected by a belligerent nation at war.

Washing-machine Charlie   The nickname for a Japanese plane that made nightly nuisance raids over Henderson Field, Guadalcanal, early in World War II (October 1942). Also called "Maytag Charlie."

Washington   A U.S. battleship of the **North Carolina** class, which see. Commissioned in 1942, this ship saw service during World War II, in both the North Atlantic and the Pacific. *Washington* was also the name of a class of 16,000-ton armored cruisers completed in 1907–1908. It included *Washington*, *North Carolina*, *Montana*, and *Tennessee*. They had a length of 504 ft, a speed of 20 knots, a complement of 990 men, and main armament consisting of four 10-in. and sixteen 6-in. guns.

Wasp   **1.** A U.S. aircraft carrier of 14,700 tons displacement completed in 1939. It had an overall length of 739 ft, a speed of 30 knots, a complement of 1,800 men, and armament consisting of eight 5-in. guns and forty smaller antiaircraft guns. It carried 72 aircraft. The *Wasp* was sunk at the Battle of Santa Cruz in October 1942. **2.** A second *Wasp* entered service during World War II. Of the **Essex** class, which see, this ship was commissioned on November 24, 1943. **3.** A German self-propelled 105mm howitzer mounted on a PzKpfw II chassis and used in World War II. Introduced in 1942, it had a crew of five and was armed with one 105mm howitzer and one 7.9mm machine gun. It weighed 12.1 tons and traveled at speeds up to 25 mph on roads.

water jacket, on a machine gun (*U.S. Army.*)

4. A World War II Allied system which was comprised of a flamethrower mounted on an armored personnel carrier.

WASP   Women's Air Force Service Pilots of the U.S. Army Air Forces. Pilots of this organization ferried aircraft. It was disbanded in December 1944.

Wasserfall   A German radio-controlled rocket designed toward the end of World War II. It had a length of 25 ft, a range of about 30 mi, and a 200-lb high-explosive warhead. This surface-to-air guided rocket used liquid propellant.

Wassermann   The German code name for **chimney,** which see.

Watanabe E9W1   See **Slim.**

watch   The duty period at sea, normally 4 hours long.

Watchdog   A special picket destroyer with a carrier task force.

Water Buffalo   A nickname for U.S. LVT's (landing vehicle, tracked) during World War II.

Water Bug   A World War II Allied nickname for LCVP (landing craft, vehicle and personnel) and LCM (landing craft, mechanized) landing craft.

water chest   A box containing water for a water-cooled machine gun; a water box.

water jacket   The casing about the barrel of a water-cooled machine gun.

wave   A formation of forces, landing ships, craft, amphibious vehicles, or aircraft required to beach or land about the same time. They can be classified as to type, function, or order as follows: (1) Assault wave. (2) Boat wave. (3) Helicopter wave. (4) Numbered wave. (5) On-call wave. (6) Scheduled wave.

Wave   A class of Japanese antisubmarine destroyers of 1,700 tons standard displacement completed in 1958–1960. They have a speed of 32 knots, a complement of 230 men, and armament consisting of six 3-in. guns, two hedgehogs, two Y mortars, and torpedo launchers.

WAVES   Women Accepted for Voluntary Emergency Service. Commissioned and enlisted women serving in the Navy.

way of the rounds   In fortifications, a narrow covered way between the rampart and the wall of a fortified town.

W Class   A class of Soviet patrol-type submarines of 1,030 tons standard surface dis-

W Class. (*U.S. Navy.*)

Weapon Alpha. (*U.S. Navy.*)

placement built from 1950 to 1957. Some 150 are in this class. They have a length of 240 ft, a beam of 22 ft, a speed of 15 knots submerged, and a complement of 60 men. Originally designed for six 21-in. torpedo tubes, some have been converted to Shaddock missile-launching types.

weapon An instrument of combat, either offensive or defensive, used to destroy, injure, defeat, or threaten an enemy, e.g., a gun, a bayonet, a bomb, or a missile.

Weapon A class of British antisubmarine destroyers of 1,980 tons standard displacement completed in 1947–1948. They had a speed of 34 knots and a complement of 234 men and were armed with four 4-in. guns, six 40mm antiaircraft guns, two Squid depth-charge systems, and ten 21-in. torpedo tubes.

Weapon Alpha A U.S. Navy 12.75-in. rocket-propelled depth charge with a range of about 1,000 yd. Designated as RUR-4.

weapons carrier Any vehicle used to carry light weapons such as rifles, mortars, or recoilless weapons. A particular vehicle may or may not be also adapted to carrying personnel or equipment.

weapons list A list of weapons authorized and on hand within tactical or other units employed in a combat role. It includes hand-carried weapons, towed artillery, and weapons mounted on wheeled or tracked vehicles.

weapons of mass destruction In arms-control usage, weapons that are capable of a high order of destruction and/or of being used in such a manner as to destroy large numbers of people. The term includes nuclear, chemical, biological, and radiological weapons, but excludes the means of transporting or propelling the weapon where such means is a separable and divisible part of it.

weapon system An instrument of combat with all the related equipment, operating skills, and direct supporting facilities and services required to enable the instrument of combat to operate as a single unit of striking power.

weapon-target line An imaginary straight line from a weapon to a target.

wear tables Tables indicating the decrease of muzzle velocity expected as the result of firing a certain number of equivalent rounds. Although tubes may vary considerably from the wear rate indicated in such tables, the tables may be used to correct calibration data between periods of calibration.

Weary Willie A name applied to any of certain B-17 or B-24 bombers loaded with TNT and piloted by radio control after becoming airborne. Weary Willies were tried out operationally in World War II, but without any notable success. They were taken aloft by a human pilot, who later bailed out, leaving the craft to be flown into the target by remote control.

Weasel The popular name for the U.S. cargo carrier M29 of World War II. It was a tracked vehicle for use over snow and ice and across fields or poor trails. It carried a crew of two and about 1,000 lb of cargo.

weather central An organization which collects, collates, evaluates, and disseminates meteorological information in such a manner that it becomes a principal source of such information for a given area.

weather forecast A prediction of weather conditions at a point, along a route, or within an area for a specified period of time.

weather map A map showing the weather conditions prevailing, or predicted to prevail, over a considerable area. Usually, the map is based upon weather observations taken at the same time at a number of stations.

weaving See **evasive steering.**

web belt A broad belt made of cotton khaki and fitted with eyelets for carrying a canteen, pistol holster, first-aid pouch, etc.

Webley .380 pistol No. 2 Mark I A British service pistol with a weight of 1.75 lb, a length of 9.5 in., and a cylinder with a capacity of six cartridges.

Webley .455 revolvers Weapons used by the British forces for 60 years. The Mark I was adopted in 1887, and the No. 1 Mark VI was declared obsolete in 1947. The first five models have "bird's-head" grips, and the Mark VI has a square grip. The Mark VI was adopted in May 1915, and some 300,000 were made during World War I. It has an overall length of 11.25 in. and a barrel length of 6 in. It weighs 38 oz and has a cylinder with a capacity of six cartridges.

Webley .455 self-loading pistol An automatic pistol that was the official arm of the British Royal Navy from 1912 until 1945.

Weasel. (*U.S. Army.*)

It has an overall length of 8½ in. and a barrel length of 5 in. It weighs about 39 oz and has a magazine capacity of seven cartridges. There are two models of this weapon, the Mark 1 and the Mark 1 No. 2. The difference between the two is that the Mark 1 No. 2 has a different type of manual safety and an adjustable rear sight. During World War I a number of these pistols were fitted with shoulder stocks and used by the Royal Flying Corps.

Weed The code name for an intrusion-detection set used in an anti-intrusion barrier across the DMZ in Vietnam. It was a two-part system consisting of a sensor and transmitter which could detect a man-sized object with a 100- to 200-ft radius.

Wegmann rocket launcher A German Federal Republic 36-tube rocket launcher mounted on cross-country trucks and organized in division artillery battalions.

Wehrmacht (German for "defense force.") The German armed forces of the Third Reich, 1934 to 1945. Sometimes used restrictively to refer only to German ground forces.

weight of metal Formerly, the weight of the projectiles that a warship could fire at one round from all her guns.

weight zone A weight range having specified minimum and maximum limits. Artillery projectiles of 75mm caliber and larger are sometimes grouped into weight zones and marked with appropriate symbols. The selection of the projectiles of a single weight zone for a specific firing problem results in improved ballistic uniformity.

Weiss Operation (German for "White Operation.") The World War II code name for the German invasion of Poland. Also called *Fall Weiss*, it began on September 1, 1939.

Welkin The Westland Welkin was a single-seat high-altitude day or night interceptor developed for the RAF and first flown in November 1942. It was armed with four 20mm Hispano cannons and had a maximum speed of 382 mph.

Wellington The Vickers-Armstrong Wellington was a British six-place twin-engine bomber first flown in 1937 and manufactured until 1945, by which time 11,461 had been produced. Nicknamed "Wimpy" by its crews (after the portly hamburger-eating character in the "Popeye" comic strip), the Wellington was used to a great extent in the RAF's night-bombing offensive. It had a speed of 255 mph, a range of 1,325 mi. (with a 4,500-lb bombload), and armament consisting of six .303 cal. machine guns and a maximum bombload of 6,000 lb.

Wellington Minesweeper A specialized version of the World War II Wellington bomber in service with the RAF. It carried a 48-ft-diameter circular degaussing belt. This electrically controlled loop was used to explode naval mines from an average

Webley .455 revolver Mark VI. (*The Smithsonian Institution, War Department Collection.*)

Wegmann rocket launcher. (*Ministry of Defense, Federal Republic of Germany.*)

Wellington. (*Vickers Ltd.*)

Wellington Minesweeper, (*Vickers Ltd.*)

wheel lock. (*The Smithsonian Institution, R. G. Packard Collection.*)

altitude of about 60 ft over the water.

Werfgerat   A German rocket launcher of World War II. It fired a 320mm rocket weighing about 300 lb to a range of about 1 mi.

Weserübung   (German for "Weser Exercise.") The World War II German code name for the occupation of Denmark and Norway. Also called *Fall Weserübung*, it began on April 8, 1940.

Wessex   The British Westland Wessex is a utility and antisubmarine helicopter in service with the Royal Navy and first flown in 1957. It is armed with various antisubmarine strike weapons.

West Virginia   A U.S. battleship of the **Colorado** class, which see. It was commissioned in 1923 and was one of the warships sunk at Pearl Harbor on December 7, 1941. Subsequently refloated and repaired, it saw considerable service in the Pacific theater during the balance of World War II.

Westwall   In World War II, the official German name for the fortified belt along the Western German frontier. It was also known as the "Siegfried Line." It ran parallel to the Rhine, extending from the Swiss border to Cleve.

wet dock   See **dock.**

Weteye   A U.S. Navy 500-lb nonlethal chemical bomb.

Whales   The Allied code name for flexible steel roadways made of bridge spars resting on pontoons (Beetles) and connecting pierheads of artificial harbors (Mulberries) with the shore. Such systems were used in June

1944 in Operation Overlord, the invasion of the European continent in World War II.

WHEC   A U.S. Navy high-endurance cutter.

wheel lock   A type of gunlock in which sparks are produced from a piece of iron pyrites by a spring-wound wheel made of steel. It was first developed in the early sixteenth century and continued to be made until the eighteenth century.

Whiff   The NATO code name for a type of Soviet E-band antiaircraft-artillery-fire-control radar.

whip   The transverse vibration of the muzzle end of long guns.

Whippet   Also called the "British tank, medium, MK A," this tank was first introduced in 1917 and was used in battalions for cavalry support. It had a crew of three and was armed with four .303 cal. Hotchkiss machine guns. It had a weight of 15.7 tons and could travel at a speed of about 8 mph.

Whirlwind   **1.** A British single-seat twin-engine escort fighter and fighter-bomber built by Westland for the RAF. It was the first twin-engine fighter used by the RAF and was first flown in October 1938. It remained in production until early 1942. It had a maximum speed of 360 mph and was armed with four 20mm Hispano cannons plus two 250-lb or 500-lb bombs.   **2.** A German antiaircraft tank that consisted of a PzKpfw IV chassis on which were mounted quadruple 20mm antiaircraft guns. These guns were designated "Flakvierling 38" and had a rate of fire of 450

rounds per minute per gun. The projectile weight was .3 lb. They were introduced late in 1943 and carried a crew of five.

Whispering Death   A U.S. air-deliverable quad .50 cal. machine gun capable of firing 2,400 rounds per minute.

Whitby   A class of British antisubmarine frigates of 2,150 tons standard displacement completed in 1956–1958. They have a length of 369 ft, a beam of 41 ft, a speed of 31 knots, and a complement of 221 men. They are armed with two 4.5-in. guns, two 40mm Bofors antiaircraft guns, and two Limbo three-barreled depth-charge mortars.

white flag   A plain white flag is recognized as a flag of truce or as a token of surrender when flown over a place, position, or body of men. See also **black flag.**

Whitehead torpedo   Named after Robert Whitehead, who invented the locomotive torpedo in 1866. The first torpedo was driven by a compressed-air engine and had a speed of 6 knots, a range of a few hundred yards, and a warhead weight of 18 lb of dynamite. By 1900 the torpedo in general use was about 16.5 ft in length and had a weight of 1,200 lb, a range of 800 yd, and a top speed of 30 knots.

White Igloo   An early name for the Igloo White system, the Air Force segment of the overall anti-infiltration system managed by the Defense Communications Planning Group. Igloo White supported the U.S. Army's Commando Hunt operations aimed at reducing the flow of supplies through Laos into South Vietnam. The system utilized ground sensors, aircraft, and ground assessment facilities.

white phosphorus   See **phosphorus.**

white phosphorus grenade   A hand grenade or rifle grenade containing a main charge of white phosphorus and a small explosive burster charge for scattering the main charge. It is used for smoke and some incendiary effect.

White scout car   The U.S. scout car M3A1 was made by White and produced between 1937 and 1943. Some 20,000 were manufactured and used by the U.S., Soviet, British, and Canadian forces. It had a weight of 8,900 lb and a six-cylinder engine of 110 bhp (brake horsepower).

Whitley   The British Armstrong Whitworth Whitley was a five- or six-place twin-engine bomber first flown in 1936 and manufactured until 1943, by which time 1,824 had been produced. It had a speed of 228 mph and a range of 1,650 mi (with a 3,000-lb bombload). It was armed with five .303 cal. machine guns and could carry a maximum bombload of 7,000 lb. On March 19 and 20, 1940, it became the first Allied aircraft to drop bombs on German soil.

Whiz Bang   The World War II nickname for the U.S. Army 20-tube rocket launcher

White scout car. (*U.S. Army.*)

which fired the 7.2-in. demolition rocket.

whole block See **block.**

whole cannon By the terms of some sixteenth- and seventeenth-century ordnance classifications, a cannon firing a projectile weighing from 70 to 120 lb.

Whoofus The U.S. Army World War II nickname for landing vessels equipped with banks of as many as 1,000 rockets, which could be fired in groups or discharged simultaneously.

WIA Wounded in action.

Wichita A class of U.S. heavy cruisers (CA) of about 10,000 tons standard displacement completed in 1939. There was only one ship (*Wichita*) in the class. It had a length of 600 ft, a beam of 61 ft, a speed of 32.5 knots, and a wartime complement of 1,200 men. It was armed with nine 8-in. and eight 5-in. guns, plus twenty 40mm and twelve 20mm antiaircraft guns. Four aircraft were carried.

wicket The small door in the main gate of a fortified place. It afforded passage without opening the large gate.

Widgeon See **Grumman G-44 Widgeon.**

wigwag A system of signaling wherein flags or lights are waved according to some prearranged code.

wilco A term indicating receipt and understanding of a voice radio message. Used only when asked to acknowledge. Not to be confused with "Roger."

Wildcat The Grumman F4F Wildcat was a single-seat single-engine shipboard fighter developed for the U.S. Navy and first flown in September 1937. It was also used by France, Greece, and the United Kingdom (where it was nicknamed "Martlet"). It was the only American shipboard fighter in service for the first half of World War II. When the Japanese attacked Wake Island on December 8, 1941, eight of twelve Wildcats (of Marine Squadron VMF-211) were destroyed. The other four were flown continuously until the Japanese occupied the island on December 22. During the interval they broke up innumerable air attacks and sank a cruiser and a submarine with 100-lb bombs. The Wildcat had a speed of 318 mph and was armed with six .50 cal. machine guns and two 100-lb bombs.

Wildcat, in Royal Air Force markings. (*Grumman Aerospace Corporation.*)

wildfire A flammable substance, such as Greek fire, used in warfare and discharged against an enemy.

Wild Weasel The McDonnell Douglas F-4D aircraft with the primary mission of seeking out and destroying radar-directed weapon systems with the use of antiradar missiles and conventional ordnance.

Wild Weasels A U.S. Air Force group that began flying antiradar missions in Vietnam in November 1965. Initially it used North American Rockwell F-100F aircraft, and later Republic F-105 and McDonnell Douglas F-4 aircraft.

Williams machine gun The first machine gun to be successfully used in battle was that invented by Capt. D. R. Williams of the Confederate Army during the early part of the American Civil War. His crank-operated weapon was a one-pounder, with a bore of 1.57 in. and a rate of fire of 65 shots per minute. It had an extreme range of 2,000 yd and caused considerable consternation among Union forces when first used against them at the Battle of the Seven Pines, Va., on May 3, 1862.

Wimpy (Wimpey) The popular World War II name for the British Wellington bomber.

Wind A class of Japanese destroyers of 1,700 tons standard displacement completed in 1956. They have a speed of 30 knots, a complement of 240 men, and armament consisting of three 5-in. guns, eight 40mm antiaircraft guns, tubes for short homing torpedoes, two hedgehogs, one depth-charge rack, and four K-guns.

windage **1.** The deflection of a bullet or other projectile due to wind. **2.** The cor-

rection made for such deflection. **3.** In ordnance terminology, the space between the projectile of a smoothbore gun and the surface of the bore.

winder The mechanism for bending certain types of crossbows.

wind-gauge rule A simple, practical rule used to allow for wind in firing the M1 or M1903 rifle. The rule is as follows: Four clicks, or one point of windage, moves the impact of the bullet 4 in. for each 100 yd of range.

windlass The apparatus used to draw the stronger crossbows.

window Strips of frequency-cut metal foil, wire, or bars usually dropped from aircraft or expelled from shells or rockets as a radar countermeasure.

wing **1.** An Air Force unit composed normally of one primary mission group and the necessary supporting organizations, i.e., organizations designed to render supply, maintenance, hospitalization, and other services required by the primary mission group. Primary mission groups may be functional, such as combat, training, transport, or service. **2.** A fleet air wing is the basic organizational and administrative unit for naval land and tender-based aviation. Such wings are mobile units to which are assigned aircraft squadrons and tenders for administrative control. **3.** A balanced Marine Corps task organization of aircraft groups or squadrons together with appropriate command, air-control, administrative, service, and maintenance units. A standard Marine Corps aircraft wing contains the aviation elements normally re-

Wind. (*Japan Defense Agency.*)

Wirraway. *(Australian Department of Supply.)*

worm. *(The Smithsonian Institution, R. G. Packard Collection.)*

quired for the air support of a Marine division. **4.** A flank unit; that part of a military force to the right or left of the main body. **5.** In fortifications, the large sides of hornworks or other outworks.

wing commander An RAF rank equivalent to that of a lieutenant colonel in the U.S. Air Force.

wing gun A fixed gun mounted in the wing of an airplane.

wingman A pilot who furnishes protection to the leader of a flying formation by flying outside and behind him.

wings The insignia worn by pilots, bombardiers, etc.

Winnie and Pooh The World War II nicknames for two large 14-in. guns on the South Foreland, east of Dover, England, which fired at the European continent.

Winter Line A German defensive line across the Italian peninsula from Ortona to Gaeta in World War II (1943–1944). It was also known as the "Bernhard Line."

wire entanglement Barbed wire strung on supports to impede assaulting troops.

wire-wrapped The term applied to guns manufactured by wrapping wire under tension on a central tube. The wire puts the metal of the tube under compression. An outer cylinder or jacket is generally shrunk on over the wire. This method of manufacture was formerly used on many major-caliber guns as it made possible a savings in weight.

Wirraway A single-engine two-place general-purpose low-wing military airplane, like the T-6, built by the Commonwealth Aircraft Corporation of Australia and used during World War II.

Wisconsin Two battleships have been named for the state of Wisconsin. The first *Wisconsin* was a sister ship of the old **Alabama,** which see. Commissioned in 1901, it was used during World War I for training purposes. The second *Wisconsin* was a ship of the **Iowa** class, which see. It was commissioned in 1944 and saw considerable wartime service, both in the Pacific theater during World War II and in Korea.

withdrawal action A maneuver whereby a force disengages from an enemy force in accordance with the will of the commander.

WIX A U.S. Navy training cutter, sail.

WLB A U.S. Navy tender, seagoing.

WLI A U.S. Navy tender, inland (large and small).

WLIC A U.S. Navy tender, inland construction.

WLM A U.S. Navy tender, coastal.

WLR A U.S. Navy tender, river (large and small).

WLV A U.S. Navy lightship, miscellaneous.

WMEC A U.S. Navy medium endurance cutter, oceangoing tug.

Wolf A class of German 933-ton torpedo boats produced in 1928–1929. They had a speed of 33 knots, a complement of 129 men, and main armament consisting of three 5-in. (or 4.1-in.) guns and six 21-in. torpedo tubes. All were sunk during World War II.

wolf pack Submarines operating and attacking together.

Worcester A class of U.S. light cruisers (CL) of about 14,700 tons standard displacement completed in 1948. The class consisted of *Roanoke* and *Worcester*. They had a length of 668 ft, a beam of 70 ft, a speed of 32 knots, and a wartime complement of 1,700 men. They were armed with twelve

6-in. guns and twenty 3-in. guns. They carried one helicopter.

Workhorse See **Shawnee.**

works The fortifications made around the body of a place.

World War I (WW I) A war (July 28, 1914, to November 11, 1918) between the Central Powers and the Allies. The Central Powers consisted of Germany, Austria-Hungary, Turkey, and Bulgaria. The Allies consisted of the British Commonwealth, France, Russia, Italy, the United States, Japan, Rumania, Serbia, Belgium, Greece, Portugal, and Montenegro. The United States entered the war on April 6, 1917.

World War I Victory Medal A U.S. service medal for military service between 1917 and 1920.

World War II (WW II) A war (September 1, 1939, to September 2, 1945) between the Axis Powers and the Allies. The Axis Powers consisted of Germany, Italy, Japan, Rumania, Bulgaria, Hungary, Finland, and Siam. The Allies consisted of 46 nations, chief among which were the United Kingdom, France, the U.S.S.R., China, the United States, India, Poland, Turkey, Canada, Australia, Belgium, Greece, Norway, the Netherlands, and Yugoslavia. The United States entered the war on December 8, 1941.

World War II Victory Medal A U.S. military decoration awarded for any period of service between December 7, 1941, and December 31, 1946.

worm An attachment on the end of a ramrod. It was shaped something like a corkscrew and was used to withdraw a wad or soft lead bullet from a muzzle-loading firearm. The expression "to worm something out of someone" derives from this early firearms term.

WU/U-2A. (*Lockheed Aircraft Corporation.*)

wound chevron In World War I, a decoration given a person who was wounded in action.

wounded in action Pertaining to a battle casualty, other than one who has been killed in action, who has incurred an injury as a result of an external agent or cause. The term encompasses all kinds of wounds and other injuries incurred in action, whether there is a piercing of the body, as in a penetrating or perforated wound, or not, as in a contused wound; all fractures, burns, and blast concussions; all effects of biological- and chemical-warfare agents; and the effects of exposure to ionizing radiation or any other destructive weapon or agent.

WPB A U.S. Navy patrol craft (large and small).

WRAC The Women's Royal Army Corps, formerly the Auxiliary Territorial Service (ATS).

WRAF The Women's Royal Air Force, formerly the Women's Auxiliary Air Force (WAAF).

WREN A member of the Women's Royal Naval Service, an auxiliary of the British Navy.

WTR A U.S. Navy reserve training cutter.

Wurger (German for "Butcher Bird.") The nickname for the German **Focke-Wulf FW 190,** which see. Over 20,000 were produced for the Luftwaffe during World War II.

Wurzburg A highly accurate radar set for directing fighter aircraft and pointing antiaircraft guns. It was developed by Germany during World War II, and there were 4,000 of these sets in France alone (controlling some 20,000 antiaircraft guns). Bomber losses were so high over the French coast, because of the radar-controlled flak, that Allied pilots called it the "Iron Hump." The effectiveness was later reduced by the use of chaff and jammers.

WU/U-2A A U.S. Lockheed-built high-altitude reconnaissance aircraft. It carries a crew of one or two, is powered by a single-jet engine, and has a wingspan of 80 ft and an overall length of 49.6 ft. It carries out photoreconnaissance missions at altitudes up to 90,000 ft (about 17 mi).

Wyoming A U.S. battleship of the **Arkansas** class, which see. It was commissioned in 1912 and was used in World War II as a training ship.

WYTL A U.S. Navy harbor tug, small.

WYTM A U.S. Navy harbor tug, medium.

X A U.S. Navy submersible craft.

x axis A horizontal axis in a system of rectangular coordinates; that line on which distances to the right or left (east or west) of the reference line are marked, especially on a map, chart, or graph.

XB The abbreviation for "experimental bomber." Used in aircraft designations, as in XB-29, XB-36, XB-46, etc.

X-band radar See **radar frequencies.**

XBG An air-to-surface glider loaded with explosives. It was developed during World War II but was never used.

X craft A class of British miniature submarines developed during World War II. They measured 48 ft in length and were armed with limpet mines. They were transported to their target area by larger submarines. Frogmen from submarines of this class succeeded in placing mines under the German battleship *Tirpitz* (causing severe damage) and the Japanese cruiser *Tokao* (sinking it).

XM The following table lists current U.S. military designations. See also **M** and **MK** tables.

XM1	Armament subsystem, helicopter, twin .30 cal. machine guns.
XM1E1	Armament subsystem, helicopter, twin .30 cal. machine guns.
XM3	Dispenser for gravel mine (XM27).
XM3E1	Armament subsystem, helicopter, 2.75-in. rocket launcher.
XM4	Ground dispenser, mine, for XM27 AP mine.

XM6E3	Armament subsystem, helicopter, 7.62mm quad machine gun.
XM8	Armament subsystem, helicopter, 40mm grenade launcher.
XM11	Armored personnel carrier, bulldozer.
XM13	Dispenser and destructive chemical agent.
XM14	Armament pod, aircraft, .50 cal. machine gun.
XM15	Aircraft dispenser and flare.
XM15	Canister, cluster.
XM16	Armament subsystem, helicopter, 7.62mm machine gun and 2.75-in. rocket launcher.
XM16E1	Rifle, 5.56mm.
XM18	Dispenser for six-tube 2.75-in. rockets.
XM18E1	Armament pod, helicopter, 7.62mm machine gun.
XM19	Flare, aircraft, parachute.
XM19	Special-purpose individual weapon (SPIW).
XM20	Dispenser, grenade, smoke.
XM21	Armament subsystem, helicopter, 7.62mm machine gun and 2.75-in. rocket launcher.
XM22	Stoner weapons system.
XM23	Stoner weapons system.
XM25	Dispenser and bomb, aircraft.
XM25	Vulcan gun pod, 20mm.
XM26	Armament subsystem, helicopter, guided-missile launcher, TOW.
XM27	Armament subsystem, helicopter, 7.62mm machine gun.
XM27	Dispenser and grenade, helicopter.
XM27E1	Armament subsystem, helicopter, 7.62mm machine gun.
XM28	Dispenser, helicopter.
XM28E1	Armament subsystem, helicopter, 7.62mm machine gun and 40mm grenade launcher.
XM30	Armament subsystem, helicopter, 30mm automatic gun.
XM30	Dispenser and riot-control agent, hand.
XM32	Dispenser and riot-control agent.
XM34	Rocket launcher for Little John 318mm weapon system.
XM35	Armament subsystem, helicopter, 20mm

	automatic gun.
XM35	Mine, practice, APERS.
XM37	Mine, practice, APERS.
XM41	Armament subsystem, helicopter, 7.62mm gun.
XM42	Mine, adapter-projector, pop-up.
XM45	Flamethrower, service unit, track-mounted.
XM45E1	Flamethrower, service unit, track-mounted on M548 vehicle.
XM47	Grenade, nonhazardous, riot-control.
XM47	Mine-dispensing subsystem, aircraft.
XM48	Armored personnel carrier, launcher for Chaparral.
XM51	CB pressurized pod.
XM52	Smoke-generating subsystem, helicopter.
XM54	Pop-up grenade, flame.
XM59	Armament subsystem, helicopter, 7.62mm and .50 cal. machine guns.
XM63	Hand grenade, floating.
XM64	Hand grenade, floating.
XM65	Hand grenade, floating.
XM70	Main battle tank, MBT70/XM803.
XM70	Rocket-boosted artillery weapon, 115mm.
XM74	Rocket, incendiary, 66mm.
XM78E3	Missile launcher, trailer-mounted, for Hawk missile.
XM80	Rocket, 2.75-in.
XM81E2	Gun, 152mm. Fires XM409E5 and XM410 cartridges.
XM81E3	Gun, 152mm. Fires XM409E5 and XM410 cartridges.
XM123	Charge, propelling, 155mm.
XM124	Howitzer, self-propelled, 105mm.
XM128	Grenade launcher, 40mm. automatic and semiautomatic.
XM129	Grenade launcher, 40mm.
XM130	Gatling-type gun, 20mm.
XM134	Automatic gun, 7.62mm.
XM138	Howitzer, 155mm.
XM140	Automatic gun, 30mm.
XM148	Grenade launcher, 40mm.
XM152	Warhead, 2.75-in. rocket, 6-lb.
XM153	Warhead, 2.75-in. rocket, 6-lb.
XM156	Mount, multiarmament, helicopter.
XM157	Warhead, 2.75-in. rocket.

X craft. (*The Imperial War Museum.*)

XM157B	Rocket launcher, aircraft, for 2.75-in. FFAR. (Seven-tube reusable pod.)
XM158	Warhead, 2.75-in. rocket.
XM158A1	Rocket launcher, aircraft, 2.75-in. FFAR.
XM159C	Rocket launcher, aircraft, 2.75-in. FFAR.
XM162	Cannon, 152mm.
XM162	Cartridge, 12-gauge, shotgun, #00 buckshot.
XM163	Armored personnel carrier, weapons system, Vulcan.
XM164	Gun, 105mm, air-transportable. Weight, 3,500 lb.
XM165	Canister, cluster, tactical, 130 lb.
XM166	Armored personnel carrier, twin 40mm guns.
XM166	Signal, ground.
XM167	Vulcan air-defense system, 20mm, towed.
XM169	Signal, ground.
XM174	Grenade launcher, 40mm.
XM175	Grenade launcher, 40mm.
XM176	Launcher and grenades for Sheridan vehicle.
XM177E2	Submachine gun, 5.56mm, commando.
XM179	Howitzer, 155mm.
XM191	Flamethrower.
XM195	Cartridge, 5.56mm, grenade.
XM195	Gun, 20mm, automatic.
XM198	Howitzer, 155mm, towed.
XM200	Cartridge, 5.56mm, blank.
XM200	Rocket launcher, aircraft, 2.75-in. FFAR. (Nineteen-tube repairable and reusable.)
XM202	Launcher, multishot weapon.
XM207	Stoner weapons system, 5.56mm machine gun.
XM220E1	Cartridge, 20mm.
XM221E1	Projectile, 20mm.
XM229	Warhead, 2.75-in. rocket, 17-lb.
XM232	Warhead, practice, for 2.75-in. rocket.
XM236	Warhead, for 2.75-in. rocket.
XM246	Cartridge, 20mm, for VADS.
XM246E1	Projectile, 20mm.
XM257	Cartridge, 12-gauge, shotgun.
XM260	Cartridge, .38 cal., multishot.
XM261	Cartridge, .45 cal., multishot.
XM314A2E1	Projectile, 105mm.
XM387E4	Projectile, 40mm.
XM388	Semitrailer, 3,000-gal, two-wheeled.
XM396	Projectile, 155mm (beehive).
XM403	Projectile, 175mm.
XM408	Truck, utility, 3/4-ton.
XM409E5	Cartridge, 152mm. For XM81E2 and XM81E3 guns.
XM409E8	Truck, cargo, 8-ton.
XM410	Cartridge, 152mm. For XM81E2 and XM81E3 guns.
XM410E1	Truck, cargo, amphibious, 2½-ton.
XM411E1	Cartridge, 152mm.
XM411E2	Cartridge, 152mm.
XM411E3	Cartridge, 152mm.
XM411E4	Cartridge, 152mm.
XM416	Projectile, 105mm.
XM428	Cartridge, 40mm, practice and spotting charge.

XM428E1	Cartridge, 40mm, practice. For M5 system.
XM429	Cartridge, 40mm (anti-light armor–anti-personnel).
XM430	Cartridge, 40mm.
XM433	Cartridge, 40mm.
XM433E1	Truck, 3/4-ton, dual-purpose.
XM434	Cartridge, 40mm.
XM437E1	Truck, cargo, 16-ton, GOER.
XM438	Fuel tank, 5,000-gal.
XM449	Rocket trailer, 318mm, for Little John.
XM453	Truck, cargo, 5-ton.
XM474E2	Carrier, guided-missile equipment, for Pershing.
XM483	Projectile, 155mm. For M109 and M114 howitzers.
XM484E1	Projectile, 175mm. For M113 gun.
XM494E3	Cartridge, 105mm. For M68 gun and M60 tank.
XM501E2	Loader-transporter, guided-missile, Hawk.
XM509	Projectile, 8-in. For M2A1E1 and M47 howitzers.
XM510E1	Projectile, 175mm. For M113 gun.
XM520E1	Cargo carrier, 8-ton.
XM533E1	Wrecker, 10-ton.
XM533E2	Heavy equipment transporter (HET).
XM541	Projectile, 155mm. For M109 and M114 howitzers.
XM546	Cartridge, 105mm, APERS. For M103 howitzer.
XM548	Cartridge, 105mm.
XM549	Projectile, 155mm. For M1, M1A1, M45, M109, and XM138 howitzers.
XM551	Armored reconnaissance airborne assault vehicle (ARAAV), full-track, 152mm.
XM552	Cartridge, 30mm (anti-light armor–anti-personnel).
XM553	Cartridge, 30mm.
XM554	Cartridge, 30mm, practice.
XM559E1	Tanker, 2,500-gal.
XM563	Cartridge, 105mm. For M68 gun.
XM566	Cartridge, 105mm.
XM571	Carrier, utility, articulated.
XM571E1	Carrier, utility, articulated.
XM574	Cartridge, 40mm.
XM576E1	Cartridge, 40mm.
XM577E1	Cartridge, 40mm.
XM578	Cartridge, 152mm discarding sabot.
XM580E1	Cartridge, 90mm.
XM581	Cartridge, 105mm.
XM583	Cartridge, 40mm, white star cluster, parachute, ILLUM.
XM585	Cartridge, 40mm, white star cluster.
XM590	Cartridge, 90mm, APERS. For M67 howitzer.
XM590E1	Cartridge, 90mm, canister.
XM591	Cartridge, 90mm.
XM604	Cartridge, 105mm. For M68 gun.
XM617	Cartridge, 152mm, beehive.
XM622	Cartridge, 105mm.
XM625	Cartridge, 152mm, canister.
XM629	Cartridge, 105mm.
XM630	Cartridge, 4.2-in.
XM631	Projectile, 155mm.

XM635	Cartridge, 40mm. For M79 grenade launcher.
XM639	Cartridge, 30mm.
XM640	Cartridge, 30mm.
XM651	Cartridge, 40mm. For M79 grenade launcher.
XM651E1	Cartridge, tactical, 40mm.
XM656	Cartridge, 152mm.
XM657E2	Cartridge, 152mm.
XM667E1	Armored personnel carrier, basic vehicle, Lance.
XM674	Cartridge, 40mm, riot-control.
XM674	Semitrailer for Nike-Hercules power plants.
XM675	Cartridge, 40mm.
XM676	Truck, cargo, 1-ton.
XM677	Truck, cargo, 1-ton.
XM678	Carryall, 1-ton.
XM679	Ambulance, 1-ton.
XM683	Cartridge, 40mm.
XM684	Cartridge, 40mm.
XM688E1	Armored personnel carrier, loader, transporter, Lance.
XM696	Recovery vehicle.
XM701	Mechanized infantry combat vehicle.
XM705	Truck, 1¼-ton.
XM706	Car, armored, light.
XM706E1	Car, armored, light, with 7.62mm machine gun.
XM727	Armored personnel carrier, basic vehicle for Hawk.
XM729	Armored reconnaissance scout vehicle.
XM730	Armored personnel carrier, basic vehicle for Chaparral.
XM733	Low-silhouette amphibious assault vehicle.
XM734	Armored personnel carrier.
XM740	Lightweight launcher for Lance.
XM741	Armored personnel carrier, basic vehicle, Vulcan.
XM746	Tractor for HET.
XM747	Semitrailer for HET 70.
XM752	Launcher for Lance.
XM754	Armored personnel carrier for Hawk.
XM759	Cargo carrier.
XM765	Armored personnel carrier.
XM791	Firing battery control central van for Pershing 1A.
XM800	Vehicle, armored, tracked, amphibious, armored reconnaissance scout vehicle (ARSV) scout.
XM803	Tank, combat, full-track, 152mm, main battle tank.
XM806	Vehicle, recovery.
XM808	Twister.

Xylophone The World War II nickname for the U.S. Army eight-tube rocket launcher which fired 4.5-in. rockets at intervals of ½ second. It was also designated M8.

Y

YAG A U.S. Navy miscellaneous auxiliary ship.

YAGR A U.S. Navy ocean radar station ship. (Converted to radar picket ship, AGR.)

Yak The designation for Soviet aircraft designed by Aleksandir Sergievich Yakovlev.

Yak-1 This was the first fighter to be designed by Alexander S. Yakovlev for the Soviet Air Force. Also dubbed the *Krasavec* (Beauty), this aircraft was a single-seat single-engine general-purpose fighter and fighter-bomber that was first flown in mid-1940. It was equipped with a 1,100-hp engine and flew at speeds up to 364 mph. It was armed with one 20mm cannon, two 7.62mm machine guns, and six rockets.

Yak-3 A fighter developed in parallel with the Yak-9 and introduced in 1943 as a single-seat close-support fighter. It had a maximum speed of 403 mph and was armed with one 20mm cannon and two 12.7mm machine guns.

Yak-7 A Yak-1 fighter modified by cutting down the rear fuselage and providing a more powerful engine.

Yak-9 A follow-on to the Yak-1 and Yak-7 program, this aircraft had larger fuel cells and a longer range. It was used to escort USAAF heavy bombers on the shuttle raids between England, the Soviet Union, and Italy. It represented the larger part of the 30,000 Yakovlev fighters produced during World War II. Equipped with a 1,260-hp engine, it flew at speeds up to 363 mph and was armed with one 37mm cannon and one 12.7mm machine gun. It was later given the NATO code name "Frank."

Yak-9U The first of a second generation of fighters in production at the end of World War II, but delivered too late to see operational service. It was used by the Soviet Air Force and certain Eastern European countries until the fifties. It was armed with one 20mm cannon, two 12.7mm machine guns, and two 220-lb bombs. It flew at speeds up to 415 mph.

Yak-15 A Soviet single-seat jet fighter from which the Yak-17 (Feather) and the Yak-23 (Flora) were derived.

Yak-17 See **Feather** or **Magnet.**

Yak-23 See **Flora.**

Yak-24 See **Horse.**

Yak-25 See **Flashlight** and **Mangrove.**

Yak-28 See **Firebar.**

Yamato A class of Japanese battleships of about 64,000 tons standard displacement completed in 1940. They had an overall length of 863 ft, a beam of 127 ft, a speed of 27.5 knots, and a complement of 2,500 men. Their main armament consisted of nine 18.1-in., twelve 6.1-in., and twelve 5-in. guns, plus six aircraft. There were three ships in the class, *Yamato, Musashi,* and *Shinano,* but the latter was completed in 1944 as an aircraft carrier. Both of the battleships were sunk by carrier aircraft late in World War II, and the *Shinano* was sunk by a U.S. submarine only 10 days after commissioning.

yatagan **1.** A short, curved saber used by the Mohammedans. **2.** A bayonet with a double curved blade, developed in the first half of the nineteenth century.

y axis A vertical axis in a system of rectangular coordinates; that line on which distances above or below (north or south) the reference line are marked, especially on a map, chart, or graph.

YBR A U.S. Navy sludge-removal barge.

YC A U.S. Navy open lighter.

YCD A U.S. Navy fueling barge.

YCK A U.S. Navy open cargo lighter.

YCV A U.S. Navy aircraft transportation lighter.

YD A U.S. Navy floating derrick.

YDF A U.S. Navy car float.

YDG A U.S. Navy district degaussing vessel.

YDT A diving tender.

YE A U.S. Navy ammunition lighter.

yellow alert A term applied to the circumstance existing when hostile or apparently hostile aircraft are over, or en route to, a defended territory. See also **red alert.**

Yellow Cross (Gelb Kreuz) See **mustard gas.**

Yellow Devil See **Deacon.**

YF A U.S. Navy covered lighter, self-

Yamato. (*U.S. Navy.*)

propelled.

YFB A U.S. Navy ferryboat or launch.

YFD A U.S. Navy yard floating dry dock.

YFN A U.S. Navy covered lighter, non-self-propelled.

YFNB A U.S. Navy large covered lighter.

YFND A U.S. Navy dry-dock companion craft.

YFNX A U.S. Navy special-purpose lighter.

YFP A U.S. Navy floating power barge.

YFR A U.S. Navy refrigerated covered lighter, self-propelled.

YFRN A U.S. Navy refrigerated covered lighter, non-self-propelled.

YFRT A U.S. Navy covered lighter, range tender.

YFT A U.S. Navy torpedo transportation lighter.

YFU A U.S. Navy harbor utility craft.

YG A U.S. Navy garbage lighter, self-propelled.

YGN A U.S. Navy garbage lighter, non-self-propelled.

Y-gun A two-barreled antisubmarine gun, shaped like the letter Y, used to throw depth charges to either side of the stern of the vessel on which the gun is mounted. (Picture, next page.)

YH A U.S. Navy ambulance boat.

YHB A U.S. Navy houseboat.

yield A measure of the energy of a nuclear weapon. It is expressed in kilotons or megatons of equivalent TNT.

YM A U.S. Navy dredge.

YMP A U.S. Navy motor mine planter.

YMS A U.S. Navy auxiliary motor minesweeper.

YMT A U.S. Navy motor tug.

YN A U.S. Navy net tender (boom).

YNG A U.S. Navy gate craft.

YNT A U.S. Navy district net tender (tug class).

YO A U.S. Navy self-propelled fuel-oil barge.

YO-3A A U.S. Lockheed-built observation aircraft developed for use by the U.S. Army. It carries a crew of two and is essentially a modified Schweizer SGS 2-32 sailplane equipped with a 210-hp engine and carrying special night sensors.

YOG A U.S. Navy gasoline barge, self-propelled.

YOGN A U.S. Navy gasoline barge, non-self-propelled.

Yokosuka E14Y1 See **Glen.**

YON A U.S. Navy fuel-oil barge, non-self-propelled.

York A British 8,250-ton cruiser completed in 1930. It had a length of 540 ft, a speed of 32 knots, a complement of 600 men, and main armament consisting of six 8-in. and eight 4-in. guns, plus six 21-in. torpedo tubes. It also carried one aircraft.

Yorktown A U.S. aircraft carrier produced in the late 1930s and a sister ship of the **Enterprise,** which see. The *Yorktown* was sunk at the Battle of Midway in June 1942 by a Japanese submarine (I 168).

YOS A U.S. Navy oil storage barge.

YP A U.S. Navy yard patrol craft.

YPD A U.S. Navy floating pile driver.

Yperite See **mustard gas.**

YPK A U.S. Navy pontoon stowage barge.

YR A U.S. Navy floating workshop.

YRB A U.S. Navy repair and berthing barge.

YRBM A U.S. Navy repair, berthing, and messing barge.

YRDH A U.S. Navy floating dry-dock workshop (hull).

YRDM A U.S. Navy floating dry-dock workshop (machinery).

YRL A U.S. Navy covered lighter (repair).

YRR A U.S. Navy radiological repair barge.

YS A U.S. Navy stevedoring barge.

YSD A U.S. Navy seaplane wrecking derrick.

YSP A U.S. Navy stowage pontoon.

YSR A U.S. Navy sludge-removal barge.

YF. (*U.S. Navy.*)

yatagan. (*The Smithsonian Institution, National Museum Collection.*)

Y-gun. (*U.S. Navy.*)

YTB, second from the left. (*U.S. Navy.*)

YT   A U.S. Navy harbor tug.

YTB   A U.S. Navy large harbor tug.

YTBM   A U.S. Navy harbor tug.

YTL   A U.S. Navy small harbor tug.

YTM   A U.S. Navy medium harbor tug.

YTT   A U.S. Navy torpedo-testing barge.

Yu 1001 Class   A class of Japanese 392-ton submarines developed by the Japanese Army to supply their island garrison. They had a length of 160 ft and could carry 40 tons of cargo.

Yugoslav 7.62mm submachine gun M-49   A weapon designed shortly after the close of World War II and adopted by the Yugoslav armed forces in 1949. It is similar in appearance to the Soviet PPSh-41 and has some of its design characteristics. Models of this weapon are chambered for the 7.62mm or 7.63mm Mauser cartridge. It is blowback-operated and has a cyclic rate of fire of about 700 rounds per minute. It has selective full automatic and semiautomatic fire. The length is 34.52 in., with a barrel length of 10.75 in. With a 35-round magazine the weapon weighs 10 lb.

Yugumo   A class of Japanese 2,000-ton destroyers produced in the early 1940s. There were 20 in the class, and all were lost during World War II. They had a speed of 35.5 knots, a complement of 228 men, and armament consisting of six 5-in. and four 25mm guns, eight torpedo tubes, and 36 depth charges.

YV   A U.S. Navy drone aircraft catapult control craft.

YW   A U.S. Navy water barge, self-propelled.

YWN   A U.S. Navy water barge, non-self-propelled.

Z

Z In general U.S. Navy usage, a lighter-than-air craft.

Z 16 torpedo A French torpedo with a length of 24 ft, a diameter of 22 in., a weight of 3,740 lb, a speed of 30 knots, and a range of 10,000 meters. It is presently in service with the French forces.

Z-23 to Z-34 A class of German 2,600-ton destroyers produced in 1940–1942. They had a length of 390 ft, a beam of 40 ft, a speed of 38.5 knots, and a complement of 321 men. Armament consisted of four 5.9-in. guns, plus four 37mm and fourteen 20mm antiaircraft guns. Eight 21-in. torpedo tubes were also carried. Six of the twelve ships in this class were lost to action during World War II.

zaba A seventh-century mail shirt worn by the Goths.

zaghnal A type of East Indian war ax with a steel crowbill. See **crowbill**.

Zambesi A class of British destroyers of 1,710 tons standard displacement completed in 1944. They had a speed of 33 knots, a complement of 186 men, and armament consisting of three to four 4.5-in. guns, six 40mm antiaircraft guns, four depth-charge throwers, and eight 21-in. torpedo tubes.

Zaunkönig (German for "Wren.") A World War II German acoustic torpedo, officially called "T-5," used by submarines against Allied convoys. The British called it "Gnat" (an acronym for "German Naval Acoustic Torpedo").

ZB 7.92mm machine gun Model 50 A Czech recoil-operated air-cooled machine gun with a rate of fire of 550 to 600 rounds per minute. It weighed 34 lb and was fed from a 200-round link belt.

ZB 7.92mm machine gun Model 1926 A Czech gas-operated air-cooled machine gun with a rate of fire of 450 to 500 rounds per minute. It weighed 19.5 lb and was fed from 25- or 40-round magazines.

Z battery A British World War II surface-to-air rocket fired in salvos of 48. Individual rockets had a 9½-lb warhead and reached an altitude of 4 mi.

Z Class A class of large Soviet oceangoing submarines of 1,900 tons standard surface displacement first completed in 1954. They have a length of 295 ft, a beam of 26 ft, a speed of 15 knots submerged, and a complement of 70 to 85 men. Originally armed with eight 21-in. torpedo tubes, a number have been converted to ballistic-missile types with two missile tubes and six 21-in. torpedo tubes.

Zeke The code name for the Mitsubishi Zero-Sen, a single-engine single-seat fighter-interceptor and fighter-bomber devel-

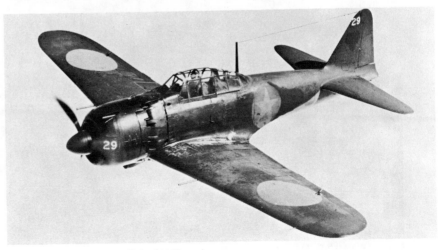

Zeke. (*The Smithsonian Institution, National Air Museum.*)

509

oped for the Japanese Naval Air Force and first flown in April 1939. The Zero was the most famous of the Japanese aircraft of World War II and was the warplane produced in the greatest numbers. Several versions were manufactured, with Mitsubishi having built 3,879 airplanes, and Nakajima another 6,215. Later versions were equipped with 1,560-hp engines and flew at speeds up to 356 mph. Armament consisted of two 20mm cannons and three 13.2mm machine guns. The wingspan was about 36 ft, the length was 29.75 ft, and the height was 9 ft.

ZELL Zero-length launch. A system used by the West Germans which employs a North American Rocketdyne solid rocket motor to boost their Lockheed F-104's from a launch platform without the need of a runway.

Zeppelins Count Ferdinand von Zeppelin, a retired German Army officer, was responsible for the design and construction of numerous large rigid airships prior to World War I. They were quickly pressed into wartime service, and the first raids on England were begun on January 19, 1915. Germany used about 80 airships during World War I, all but seven of which were destroyed. More than 200 bombing flights were made over England (50 of them at night), and some 6,000 bombs were dropped, causing 500 deaths and wounding approximately 1,100. One raid was made on Paris. Zeppelins flew at speeds up to 80 mph at altitudes in excess of 20,000 ft, and could lift fifty tons. They were armed with machine guns in cars and atop the hulls.

The Allies produced no large military airships but did develop a line of blimps for antisubmarine patrol. The largest U.S. Navy blimp of World War I had a speed of 60 mph and a range of 1,800 miles.

Zeppelin (Staaken) R.VI A German four-engine (two pushers, two tractors) bomber with a wingspan of 138 ft, a length of 72 ft, and a speed of about 80 mph. It carried up to eighteen 220-lb bombs internally, and its maximum bombload was 4,409 lb. Delivered in June 1917, these aircraft were used in bombing raids against England and France. Three gunners were carried, and two pilots sat side by side in an enclosed cabin.

Zero The Mitsubishi Zero-Sen fighter. See **Zeke.**

zero deflection The adjustment of a sight exactly parallel to the axis of the bore of the gun to which it is attached.

zero height of burst The condition obtained when rounds fired with the same fuze setting and the same quadrant elevation result in an equal number of airs and grazes.

zero in 1. To adjust the sight setting of a weapon by calibrated results of firings. **2.** To adjust any device to another so that automatic synchronization results.

zero-length launcher A short, mobile launcher designed essentially to hold the object launched in position for launching, not to give it guidance.

zero-length launching A technique in which the first motion of the missile or aircraft removes it from the launcher.

ZI Zone of the interior.

zigzag 1. In naval usage, a series of relatively short straight-line variations from the base course of a vessel; evasive steering. **2.** In fortifications, the windings in trenches to prevent enfilading fire.

ZIL-485 (BAV) A post-World War II Soviet copy of the **DUKW,** which see. It featured a larger cargo space and a tailgate.

zizarme A sort of ancient pike or lance.

ZK 383 9mm Parabellum submachine gun See **Czech 9mm Parabellum submachine gun Model ZK 383.**

zone I (nuclear) A circular area, determined by using minimum safe distance as the radius and the desired ground zero as the center, from which all armed forces are evacuated. If evacuation is not possible or if a commander elects a higher degree of risk, maximum protective measures will be required.

zone II (nuclear) A circular area (less zone I), determined by using minimum safe distance II as the radius and the desired ground zero as the center, in which all personnel require maximum protection. Maximum protection denotes that armed-forces personnel are in "buttoned-up" tanks or crouched in foxholes with improvised overhead shielding.

zone III (nuclear) A circular area (less zones I and II), determined by using minimum safe distance III as the radius and the desired ground zero as the center, in which all personnel require minimum protection. Minimum protection denotes that armed-forces personnel are prone on open ground

Zeppelin (Staaken) R.VI. (*The Imperial War Museum.*)

with all skin areas covered and with an overall thermal protection at least equal to that provided by a two-layer uniform.

zone fire Artillery or mortar fire that is designed to cover an area in which a target is situated.

zone of action A tactical subdivision of a larger area, the responsibility for which is assigned to a tactical unit; generally applied to offensive action.

zone of defense In fortifications, the ground lying in front of the works that falls within the effective range of the defenders' weapons.

zone of dispersion An area over which shots scatter when fired with the same setting.

zone of fire An area within which a designated ground unit or fire-support ship delivers, or is prepared to deliver, fire support. Fire may or may not be observed.

zone of war A theater of war.

Zouave Formerly, a body of French infantry, originally Algerians but later mostly Frenchmen. They were noted for their dash and valor. A number of volunteer regiments

Zuni. (*U.S. Navy.*)

in the U.S. Army during the Civil War adopted the dress and drill of the Zouaves.

ZP (code) The Navy designation for lighter-than-air patrol and escort aircraft. See **z.**

ZPM (code) The Navy designation for a class of patrol airships some 310 ft in length and noted for their flight endurance.

ZPN (code) The Navy designation for a class of airships some 324 ft in length.

ZPU1, ZPU2, and ZPU4 Special mounts

for the **Soviet 14.5mm heavy machine gun KPV,** which see.

zulu time An expression indicating Greenwich mean time.

Zuni A U.S. solid-propellant 5-in. air-to-surface unguided rocket. It can be armed with various types of heads, including flares, fragmentation heads, and armor-piercing heads. It has a range of about 5 mi.

Bibliography

Ashdown, Charles Henry, *European Arms & Armour*, Brussel & Brussel, New York, 1967.

Barlow, J. A., *Small Arms Manual*, John Murray (Publishers), Ltd., London, 1960.

Barrett, William E., *The First War Planes*, Fawcett Publications, Inc., New York, 1960.

Bebie, Jules, *Manual of Explosives, Military Pyrotechnics, and Chemical Warfare Agents*, The Macmillan Company, New York, 1943.

Boothroyd, Geoffrey, *Guns through the Ages*, Bonanza Books, Crown Publishers, Inc., New York, 1961.

Bradford, G., and Morgan, L., *50 Famous Tanks*, Arco Publishing, Inc., New York, 1967.

Brassy's Naval Annual, various editions, The Macmillan Company, New York.

Brodie, Bernard, and Brodie, Fawn, *From Crossbow to H-Bomb*, Dell Publishing Co., Inc., New York, 1962.

Brown, Heyn, Freeman, Bowyer, and Berry, *United States Army and Air Force Fighters: 1916–1961*, Harleyford Publications, Letchworth, England, 1961.

Canby, Courtlandt, *A History of Weaponry*, Leisure Arts, Ltd., London, 1968.

Carman, W. Y., *A History of Firearms*, Routledge & Kegan Paul, Ltd., London, 1963.

Cary, James, *Tanks and Armor in Modern Warfare*, Franklin Watts, Inc., New York, 1966.

Chapelle, Howard I., *The American Sailing Navy*, W. W. Norton & Company, Inc., New York, 1949.

Cooke, David C., *The Aircraft Annual: 1946*, Robert M. McBride Co., Inc., New York, 1946.

Cooney, David M., *A Chronology of the U.S. Navy: 1775–1965*, Franklin Watts, Inc., New York, 1965.

Crew-served Weapons, Military Service Publishing Co., Harrisburg, Pa., 1953.

Deanes' Manual of the History and Science of Fire-Arms, Longman, Brown, Green, Longmans & Roberts, London, 1858.

Dictionary of Acronyms and Project Names, General Dynamics, New York, 1966.

Dictionary of American Naval Fighting Ships, various volumes, Department of the Navy, Washington, 1968.

Dictionary of Technical Terms for Aerospace Use, National Aeronautics and Space Administration, Washington, 1965.

Dictionary of United States Military Terms for Joint Usage, The Joint Chiefs of Staff, Washington, 1968.

Dmitri, Ivan, *Fight to Everywhere*, McGraw-Hill Book Company, New York, 1944.

Dupuy, T. N., *The Almanac of World Military Power*, Dupuy–Stackpole Books, Harrisburg, Pa., 1970.

FM 20-32, Employment of Land Mines, Department of the Army, Washington, 1955.

FM 23-35, Pistols and Revolvers, Department of the Army, Washington, 1953.

FM 23-55, Browning Machine Guns Caliber .30, M1917A1, M1919A4, M1919A4E1, M1919A6, and M36, Department of the Army, Washington, 1955.

Foundations of Air Power, U.S. Air Force, Maxwell Air Force Base, Alabama, 1958.

Fryer, Douglas J., *Antique Weapons, A–Z*, G. Bell & Sons, Ltd., London, 1969.

Gaynor, Frank, *Aerospace Dictionary*, Philosophical Library, Inc., New York, 1960.

Green, C. M., Thomson, H. C., and Roots, P. C., *The Ordnance Department: Planning Munitions for War*, U.S. Army, Washington, 1955.

Green, William, *Famous Bombers of the Second World War*, Hanover House, Doubleday & Company, Inc., Garden City, N.Y., 1959, 2 vols.

———, *War Planes of the Second World War: Fighters*, Hanover

House, Doubleday & Company, Inc., Garden City, N.Y., 1961, 4 vols.

———, *War Planes of the Second World War: Flying Boats*, Doubleday & Company, Inc., Garden City, N.Y., 1962.

———, *War Planes of the Second World War: Floatplanes*, Doubleday & Company, Inc., Garden City, N.Y., 1963.

———, *War Planes of the Second World War: Bombers and Reconnaissance Aircraft*, Doubleday & Company, Inc., Garden City, N.Y., 1967, 4 vols.

———, and Punnett, Dennis, *MacDonald World Air Power Guide*, MacDonald & Co., Publishers, Ltd., London, 1963.

Greener, W. W., *The Gun and Its Development*, Bonanza Books, Crown Publishers, Inc., New York, 1910.

Gurney, Gene, *Rocket and Missile Technology*, Franklin Watts, Inc., New York, 1964.

Hailey, Foster, and Lancelot, Milton, *Clear for Action*, Bonanza Books, Crown Publishers, Inc., New York, 1964.

Hamersly, L. R., *A Naval Encyclopedia*, Philadelphia, 1881.

Hicks, James E., *Notes on U.S. Ordnance: 1776–1941*, Modern Books and Crafts, Green Farms, Conn., 1971.

History of the World War, Doubleday Page, Garden City, N.Y. 1920, 5 vols.

Hogg, Ian V., *The Guns: 1939–45*, Ballantine Books, Inc., New York, 1970.

Holley, Alexander L., *A Treatise on Ordnance and Armor*, D. Van Nostrand Company, Inc., New York, 1865.

"International Aerospace Specification Tables: 1971," *Aviation Week and Space Technology*, March 8, 1971.

Jane's All the World's Aircraft, various editions, McGraw-Hill Book Company, New York.

Jane's Fighting Ships, various editions, McGraw-Hill Book Company, New York.

Jane's Weapons Systems: 1969–1970, McGraw-Hill Book Company, New York, 1970.

Jones, Lloyd S., *U.S. Bombers: B1–B70*, Aero Publishers, Inc., Fallbrook, Calif., 1962.

Killen, John, *A History of the Luftwaffe*, Doubleday & Company, Inc., Garden City, N.Y., 1968.

Kirk, John, and Young, Robert, *Great Weapons of World War II*, Walker Publishing Company, Inc., New York, 1961.

Liddel, Hart, *The Tanks*, Cassell & Co., Ltd., London, 1959.

Macintyre, Donald, and Bathe, Basil W., *Man-of-War: A History of the Combat Vessel*, McGraw-Hill Book Company, New York, 1969.

Manchester, William, *The Arms of Krupp: 1587–1968*, Little, Brown and Company, Boston, 1968.

Manucy, Albert, *Artillery through the Ages*, U.S. Government Printing Office, Washington, 1949.

Military Science & Tactics: Coast Artillery, P. S. Bond Publishing, Washington, 1940.

Mitchel, William A., *Outlines of the World's Military History*, Military Service Publishing Co., Harrisburg, Pa., 1940.

Montross, Lynn, *War through the Ages*, Harper & Brothers, New York, 1946.

Mordal, Jacques, *Twenty-Five Centuries of Sea Warfare*, Clarkson N. Potter, Inc., New York, 1959.

Mueller, Chester, and Olson, John, *Small Arms Lexicon and Concise Encyclopedia*, Shooter's Bible, South Hackensack, N.J., 1968.

Munson, Kenneth, *Bombers 1914–19*, The Macmillan Company, New York, 1968.

———, *Fighters 1914–19*, The Macmillan Company, New York, 1968.

———, *Helicopters*, The Macmillan Company, New York, 1969.

Nelson, Thomas B., *The World's Submachine Guns*, International Small Arms Publishers, Cologne, 1963.

Newlon, Clarke, *The Aerospace Age Dictionary*, Franklin Watts, Inc., New York, 1965.

Noel, John V., *Naval Terms Dictionary*, United States Naval Institute, Annapolis, 1966.

Oman, Charles, *A History of the Art of War in the Middle Ages*, Houghton Mifflin Company, Boston, 1924, 2 vols.

Ordnance Technical Terminology, U.S. Army Ordnance School, Aberdeen Proving Ground, Maryland, 1962.

Parkes, Oscar, *The British Battleship: 1860–1950*, Seelye Services, London, 1958.

Pater, Alan F., *United States Battleships*, Monitor Book Co., Beverly Hills, Calif., 1968.

Perrett, B., *Fighting Vehicles of the Red Army*, Ian Allan, London, 1969.

Peterson, Harold L., *The Treasury of the Gun*, Golden Press, New York, 1962.

———, *Daggers & Fighting Knives of the Western World*, Walker Publishing Company, Inc., New York, 1968.

———, *Round Shot and Rammers*, Stackpole Books, Harrisburg, Pa., 1969.

Polmar, Norman, *Aircraft Carriers*, Doubleday & Company, Inc., Garden City, N.Y., 1969.

Pope, Dudley, *Guns*, Spring Books, London, 1965.

Reynolds, Clark G., *The Fast Carriers*, The Forging of an Air Navy, McGraw-Hill Book Company, New York, 1968.

Rodgers, William L., *Greek and Roman Naval Warfare*, U.S. Naval Institute, Annapolis, 1937.

Ruffner, Frederick G., and Thomas, Robert C. (eds.), *Code Names Dictionary*, Gale Research Company, Detroit, 1963.

Russell, Carl P., *Guns on the Early Frontiers*, Bonanza Books, Crown Publishers, Inc., New York, 1957.

Schofield, William G., *Destroyers: 60 Years*, Bonanza Books, Crown Publishers, Inc., New York, 1962.

Smith, W. H. B., and Smith, Joseph E., *The Book of Rifles*, Stackpole Books, Harrisburg, Pa., 1963.

——— and ———, *Book of Pistols and Revolvers*, Stackpole Books, Harrisburg, Pa., 1968.

——— and ———, *Small Arms of the World*, Stackpole Books, Harrisburg, Pa., 1969.

The Soldier's Manual, Nesmith, Philadelphia, 1824.

SR 320-5-1, Military Terms, Abbreviations and Symbols, Dictionary of U.S. Army Terms, Department of the Army, Washington, 1955.

Stebbins, Henry M., *Pistols: A Modern Encyclopedia*, Stackpole Books, Harrisburg, Pa., 1961.

Stevens, Philip H., *Artillery through the Ages*, Franklin Watts, Inc., New York, 1965.

Stone, George C., *A Glossary of the Construction, Decoration and Use of Arms and Armor in All Countries and in All Times*, Jack Brussel, New York, 1961.

Stout, Wesley W., *Bullets by the Billion*, Chrysler Corporation, Detroit, 1946.

Sunderman, James F., *World War II in the Air: The Pacific*, Bramhall House, Inc., New York, 1962.

———, *World War II in the Air: Europe*, Bramhall House, Inc., New York, 1963.

Tank Data, WE Inc., Old Greenwich, Conn., 1969, 2 vols.

Taylor, J. C., *Japanese Warships of World War II*, Doubleday & Company, Inc., Garden City, N.Y., 1966.

———, *German Warships of World War II*, Doubleday & Company, Inc., Garden City, N.Y., 1967.

Thomas, Bruno, Gamber, Ortwin, and Schedelmann, Hans, *Arms and Armour of the Western World*, McGraw-Hill Book Company, New York, 1964.

TM 3-215, Military Chemistry and Chemical Agents, Department of the Army, Washington, 1963.

TM 3-216, Military Biology and Biological Agents, Department of the Army, Washington, 1964.

TM 3-400, Chemical Bombs and Clusters, Department of the Army, Washington, 1957.

TM 9-1300-203, Artillery Ammunition, Department of the Army, Washington, 1967.

TM 9-1300-214, Military Explosives, Department of the Army, Washington, 1967.

TM 9-1305-200, Small Arms Ammunition, Department of the Army, Washington, 1961.

TM 9-1325-200, Bombs and Bomb Components, Department of the Army, Washington, 1966.

TM 9-1330-200, Grenades, Hand and Rifle, Department of the Army, Washington, 1966.

TM 9-1345-200, Land Mines, Department of the Army, Washington, 1964.

TM 9-1370-200, Military Pyrotechnics, Department of the Army, Washington, 1966.

TM 9-1375-200, Demolition Materials, Department of the Army, Washington, 1964.

TM 9-1900, Ammunition, General, Department of the Army, Washington, 1956.

TM 9-1950, Rockets, Department of the Army, Washington, 1958.

TM 9-2800, Military Vehicles, Department of the Army, Washington, 1947.

TM 9-3305-1, Principles of Artillery: Weapons, Department of the Army, Washington, 1956.

Tompkins, John S. *The Weapons of World War III,* Doubleday & Company, Inc., Garden City, N.Y., 1966.

Turnbull, A. D., and Lord, C. L., *History of United States Naval Aviation,* Yale University Press, New Haven, Conn., 1949.

The United States Air Force Dictionary, Air University Press, Washington, 1956.

United States Naval Aviation: 1910–1960, Department of the Navy, Washington, 1960.

The United States Strategic Bombing Survey: Over-all Report (European War), Washington, 1945.

The United States Strategic Bombing Survey: Summary Report (Pacific War), Washington, 1946.

Vanderveen, Bart H., *The Observer's Fighting Vehicles Directory: World War II,* Frederick Warne & Co., Inc., New York, 1969.

Waitt, Alden H., *Gas Warfare,* Duell, Sloan & Pearce, Inc., New York, 1942.

Watrous, George R., *The History of Winchester Firearms, 1866–1966,* Winchester-Western Press, New Haven, Conn., 1966.

Westrate, J. Lee, *European Military Museums,* The Smithsonian Institution, Washington, 1961.

Wilhelm, Thomas, *A Military Dictionary and Gazetteer,* L. R. Hamersly & Co., Philadelphia, 1881.

Wilson, A. W., *The Story of the Gun,* Royal Artillery School, Woolwich, England, 1944.

Wright, Quincy, *A Study of War,* The University of Chicago Press, Chicago, 1965.

Zim, Gerbert S., *Rockets and Jets,* Harcourt, Brace and Company, Inc., New York, 1945.